MILLENNIUM STAR ATLAS
VOLUME II

MILLENNIUM STAR ATLAS

An All-Sky Atlas Comprising
One Million Stars to Visual Magnitude Eleven
from the Hipparcos and Tycho Catalogues
and Ten Thousand Nonstellar Objects

VOLUME II: 8 TO 16 HOURS

Roger W. Sinnott
Sky & Telescope

Michael A. C. Perryman
EUROPEAN SPACE AGENCY
FOR THE HIPPARCOS PROJECT

1997

SKY PUBLISHING CORPORATION
Cambridge, Massachusetts

EUROPEAN SPACE AGENCY
ESTEC, Noordwijk, The Netherlands

Principal Collaborators

TYCHO CATALOGUE

Erik Høg

Ulrich Bastian	Valeri V. Makarov
Claus Fabricius	Jean-Louis Halbwachs
Volkmar Großmann	Andreas Wicenec

HIPPARCOS CATALOGUE

Hans Schrijver

Michel Grenon	Lennart Lindegren
Jean Kovalevsky	François Mignard
Floor van Leeuwen	Catherine Turon

SKY PUBLISHING CORPORATION

Sally M. MacGillivray

E. Talmadge Mentall	Imelda B. Joson
Richard Tresch Fienberg	Samantha Parker
Gregg Dinderman	Leif J. Robinson

LIBRARY OF CONGRESS CATALOGUING-IN-PUBLICATION DATA

Sinnott, Roger W.
    Millennium Star Atlas: an all-sky atlas comprising one million stars to visual magnitude eleven from the Hipparcos and Tycho Catalogues and ten thousand nonstellar objects / Roger W. Sinnott, Michael A. C. Perryman.
        p.   cm.
    Includes bibliographical references and index.
    Contents: v.1. 0 to 8 hours — v.2. 8 to 16 hours — v.3. 16 to 24 hours.
    ISBN 0-933346-84-0 (3-vol. set: alk. paper).—ISBN 0-933346-81-6 (Vol. I: alk. paper). —ISBN 0-933346-82-4 (Vol. II: alk. paper). —ISBN 0-933346-83-2 (Vol. III: alk. paper).
    1. Stars—Atlases. 2. Astronomy—Charts, diagrams, etc.
I. Perryman, Michael A. C. II. Title.
    QB65.S62   1997   97-2552
                                                    CIP

CONTENTS

HOW TO USE THIS ATLAS

THE *MILLENNIUM STAR ATLAS* contains about 1,058,000 stars, all those observed by the European Space Agency's Hipparcos spacecraft. More than 10,000 nonstellar objects have been included from other sources. The chart arrangement and scale have been chosen to make the atlas practical and efficient to use, considering the wealth of information it contains.

The atlas divides the celestial sphere into three lunes, or gores, each spanning a particular range of right ascension from pole to pole. Volume I covers from 0^h to 8^h, Volume II from 8^h to 16^h, and Volume III from 16^h to 24^h. Often just one of the three, encompassing the sky overhead and along the meridian from north to south, is all that will be needed for an observing session at the telescope. The following table tells which volume is most useful during specific seasons and observing times:

MONTH OF YEAR	TIME OF NIGHT				
	8 pm	10 pm	Midnight	2 am	4 am
January	I	I		II	II
February	I		II	II	II
March		II	II	II	
April	II	II	II		III
May	II	II		III	III
June	II		III	III	III
July		III	III	III	
August	III	III	III		I
September	III	III		I	I
October	III		I	I	I
November		I	I	I	
December	I	I	I		II

CHART SCALE AND GRID LINES

Each chart embraces a very small sky area, roughly that seen with a pair of 7×50 binoculars. North is up. Right ascensions are labeled along the top and bottom of each page, and declinations are printed at 1° intervals along the side of the chart. The grid lines, based on the International Celestial Reference System (ICRS), are consistent with coordinates measured from the 2000.0 equator and equinox.

The chart scale is 100 arcseconds per millimeter throughout. The 1° spacing of the declination grid lines may also be used to estimate angular separations on the sky.

Constellation boundaries are shown as gray lines. The ecliptic, the Sun's apparent path in the course of the year, is a dashed line marked at 1° intervals with ecliptic longitude. Another dashed line traces the galactic equator, the adopted plane of the Milky Way; it is labeled at 1° intervals with galactic longitude.

FINDING A CELESTIAL OBJECT

At the end of each volume, four chart keys show at a glance the region of sky covered. Chart numbers are the large numerals at the lower outside corner of each atlas page. Charts 1 through 516 are found in Volume I, 517 through 1032 in Volume II, and 1033 through 1548 in Volume III. An index lists the charts containing bright or unusual stars and deep-sky objects bearing popular names.

Within each volume, the charts start at the north celestial pole and work southward through consecutive declination bands in 6° steps. The central declination of the band is printed in large numerals at the upper outside corner of each chart.

If you know only the ICRS or 2000.0 coordinates of an object you are seeking, three steps will quickly locate the chart on which it lies: (1) Select the volume covering the general range of right ascension. (2) Flip through the pages to the desired declination band. (3) Turn consecutive pages left or right to locate the right ascension being sought.

Each pair of facing charts forms a continuous stretch of sky with a narrow overlap down the middle. Turning pages from front to back through the volume moves west, toward decreasing right ascension. Turning the pages from back to front moves east, toward increasing right ascension. (These rules apply until a volume boundary is reached at right ascension 0^h, 8^h, or 16^h. While the chart immediately west of chart 763 is 764 in Volume II, that to its east is 1302 in Volume III, as the chart keys in both volumes make clear.)

Centered near the top of each chart is a small up arrow labeled with the chart number(s) immediately to the north. At the bottom of each chart, a down arrow identifies adjacent chart(s) to the south.

THE STARS

In the legend at the bottom of each left-hand page, a tapered scale of black disks shows the range of symbols used for individual stars. The smaller the disk the fainter the star, particular sizes being shown for visual (V) magnitude 2.0 (brightest), 3.0, 4.0, and so on up to 11.0 (faintest). The stars on the charts themselves can have these or any intermediate sizes, so that relative brightnesses are faithfully portrayed. An exception has been made for the four dozen brightest stars of all, listed in Table IV on page XI of Volume I. To avoid excessively large disks, these well-known stars are plotted as if they, too, were of magnitude 2.0.

Only stars brighter than about magnitude 6 are visible to the naked eye. Some of these have popular names, such as Sirius or Polaris, while many more carry a Flamsteed number, a Bayer (Greek-letter) designation, or both.

Finally, every star that was found by Hipparcos to lie within 200 light-years of the Sun is labeled with its measured distance in light-years (ly). The light-year value, divided by 3.26, gives the distance in parsecs.

Variable stars. A black disk surrounded by some type of open circle identifies a variable star listed in the Hipparcos Catalogue. A variable is also identified by its standard designation, either an uppercase Roman letter from R to Z, a two-letter pair such as AX or CQ, or the letter V followed by 334 or a higher number. The constellation is omitted, even though it would always be included when mentioning the star in speech or writing, because a constellation label appears elsewhere on the same chart.

The size of a variable star's central disk corresponds to its median magnitude, as measured by Hipparcos, rather than to its maximum or minimum value. A surrounding dotted circle means that the amplitude of the light fluctuations is less than 0.1 magnitude. A dashed circle means the variation falls in the range of 0.1 to 1.0 magnitude. A solid circle implies the range is 1.0 or greater, and in this case the changes are obvious in a telescope even to the casual observer.

Next to the star or its designation, in parentheses, a lowercase italic letter identifies the broad class to which the variable belongs and a single digit its approximate period (expressed logarithmically), according to the following schemes:

Variability Class		Period in Days
(*e*) Eclipsing	(*s*) Semiregular	(*0*) Less than 1
(*c*) Cepheid	(*i*) Irregular	(*1*) 1 to 9
(*m*) Mira	(*f*) UV Ceti	(*2*) 10 to 99
(*d*) δ Scuti	(*x*) Novalike	(*3*) 100 to 999
(*r*) RR Lyrae	(*v*) Other	(*4*) 1,000 or more

Mnemonically, it may help to note that the period code equals the number of digits used to express the whole number of days in the period.

For example, a star marked "RV (*e1*)" appears on chart 1274 of a region in Ophiuchus. The label tells us the star is RV Ophiuchi, an eclipsing binary with a period between 1 and 9 days. For more about the plotting of variable stars, including the complete correspondence between these variability classes and the standard variable-star types, see page XII of Volume I.

Some well-known variable stars were not observed by Hipparcos, generally because of their faint magnitude at the time of the mission, and they have been added from other sources. For example, locations of historical novae and supernovae are marked with a simple × and the letters N or SN followed by the year of appearance. Mira variables that spend much of the time near or fainter than the cutoff magnitude appear as small open circles. They can be distinguished from face-on galaxies by their designations.

Stars of high proper motion. All stars found in the Hipparcos Catalogue to have a proper motion greater than 0.2 arcsecond per year are plotted with an attached arrow showing the direction of this motion. The arrow's length represents the angular distance the star will move on the sky during one millennium. For example, at the chart scale of 100 arcseconds per millimeter, a 5-mm arrow means the star will move 500 arcseconds in 1,000 years. The length of an arrow should always be measured from just outside the rim of the star's disk (where the shaft begins) to the tip of the arrowhead.

Double and multiple stars. When the components of a double or multiple star are separated by more than 30 arcseconds, they are plotted individually with overlapping disks. But if the separation is less than 30 arcseconds, a single, enlarged disk representing the combined light is plotted at the brightest member's location with a protruding "tick" for each companion. The orientation and length of this tick, derived from Hipparcos measurements, show the state of the system at the catalogue epoch (1991.25). Most double and multiple stars with separations larger than a few tenths of an arcsecond retain nearly the same configuration for many decades.

To express angular separations meaningfully, the lengths of double-star ticks are greatly exaggerated. They are plotted on a logarithmic scale so that the closer, more interesting pairs are better distinguished. Three examples are shown in the legend, but ticks with lengths corresponding to any separation from 0.1 to 30 arcseconds are found throughout the atlas. Each tick begins just outside the rim of the primary star's enlarged disk and extends radially outward in the companion star's direction on the sky. When using the atlas at the telescope, it is important to remember that many optical systems present an inverted or mirror-reversed view.

NONSTELLAR OBJECTS

The legend on the right-hand chart pages explains the symbols used for nebulae, star clusters, galaxies, galaxy clusters, and quasars. Many of the brightest and most striking nonstellar objects are still best known from Charles Messier's observations with small comet-seeking telescopes in the late 18th century; they carry the letter M followed by a number from 1 to 110. Thousands of other objects were enumerated by J. L. E. Dreyer in his famous *New General Catalogue* (1888), or in its two supplements together known as the *Index Catalogue* (1895 and 1908). In this atlas NGC numbers (from 1 to 7840) are printed without any prefix; IC numbers (1 to 5386) are preceded by the letters IC.

Nebulae. Large, bright nebulae are plotted with a continuous, irregular outline that indicates their approximate extent on long-exposure photographs. Those measuring about 10 arcminutes across or smaller are marked with an open square. Similarly, dark nebulae are shown by a dashed outline when large, or by a small dashed square when they span 10 arcminutes or less. Planetary nebulae are usually too small to plot to scale; the symbols in the legend give an idea of their diameter, including any extremely faint outer halo that may be present. When not identified by an NGC or IC number, nebulae carry the designations assigned by the astronomers who discovered or studied them, as explained in the Introduction (Volume I).

Open and globular star clusters. For many clusters the brighter stars are plotted individually. Open clusters are marked by a dashed open circle and globular clusters by a solid open circle and cross. The circle's diameter represents the approximate visual extent of the cluster. A minimal symbol, given in the legend, marks clusters smaller than 5 arcminutes across. When lacking an NGC or IC number, a cluster is designated by the name of an astronomer or observatory and a serial number.

Galaxies. The completeness limit for galaxies is a total visual magnitude brighter than about 13.5, though a number of fainter ones are included as well. All large galaxies are shown by an ellipse whose aspect ratio and orientation correspond to those on time-exposure photographs with large telescopes or CCD images. If a galaxy's major axis is smaller than 2 arcminutes it is plotted as 2 arcminutes, and if the minor axis is smaller than 1 arcminute it is plotted as 1 arcminute. This procedure preserves some idea of the orientation, even for very tiny objects.

Quasars. An open-centered cross is used for objects that are nearly stellar in appearance but well below the atlas's magnitude cutoff for stars. They are included for their astrophysical aura. Extragalactic quasars and their cousins, the BL Lacertae objects, make up the great majority of these, selected to be 16th magnitude or brighter visually. They are identified by such prefixes as PKS for a number in the Parkes radio survey and 3C for a number in the revised third Cambridge radio survey. The same open-cross symbol has been used for a handful of high-energy sources within our own galaxy, even though they are not quasars. These include several pulsars, the Geminga gamma-ray source, and the galactic center itself.

Galaxy clusters. A pentagon symbol marks a rich cluster of galaxies that has at least 10 members of 16th magnitude or brighter. In many cases, along with the pentagon, several of the brightest member galaxies are plotted individually. The prefix A refers to a number from the original northern and southern Abell catalogues; AS denotes a cluster in the southern supplement. The pentagon simply marks the cluster's location without indicating its angular extent. Most galaxy clusters in the atlas are smaller than $\frac{1}{4}°$ across.

CHARTS 517–1032

Right Ascension 8 to 16 Hours

+90°

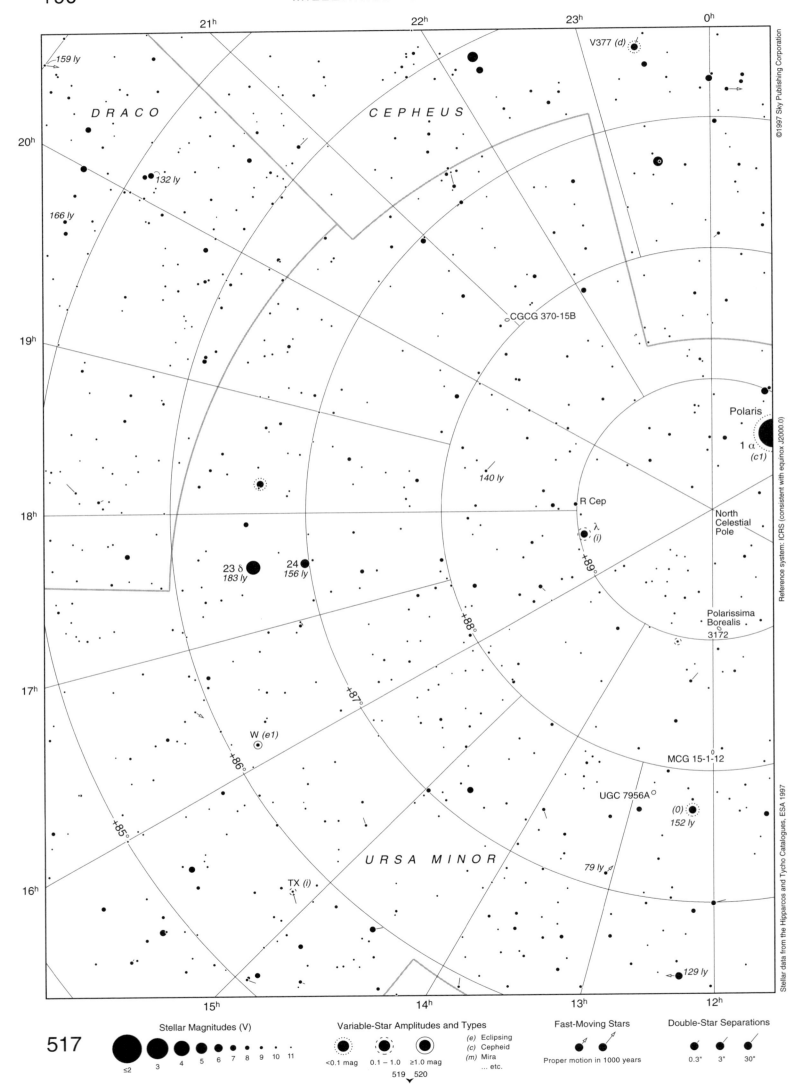

V377 (d)

D R A C O

C E P H E U S

159 ly

132 ly

166 ly

CGCG 370-15B

Polaris

1 α
(c1)

140 ly

R Cep

North
Celestial
Pole

λ
(i)

23 δ
183 ly

24
156 ly

+89°

Polarissima
Borealis
3172

+88°

+87°

MCG 15-1-12

UGC 7956A

(0)
152 ly

+86°

W (e1)

+85°

U R S A   M I N O R

79 ly

TX (i)

129 ly

©1997 Sky Publishing Corporation

Reference system: ICRS (consistent with equinox J2000.0)

Stellar data from the Hipparcos and Tycho Catalogues, ESA 1997

21h

22h

23h

0h

20h

19h

18h

17h

16h

15h

14h

13h

12h

517

Stellar Magnitudes (V)

≤2   3   4   5   6   7 8 9 10 11

Variable-Star Amplitudes and Types

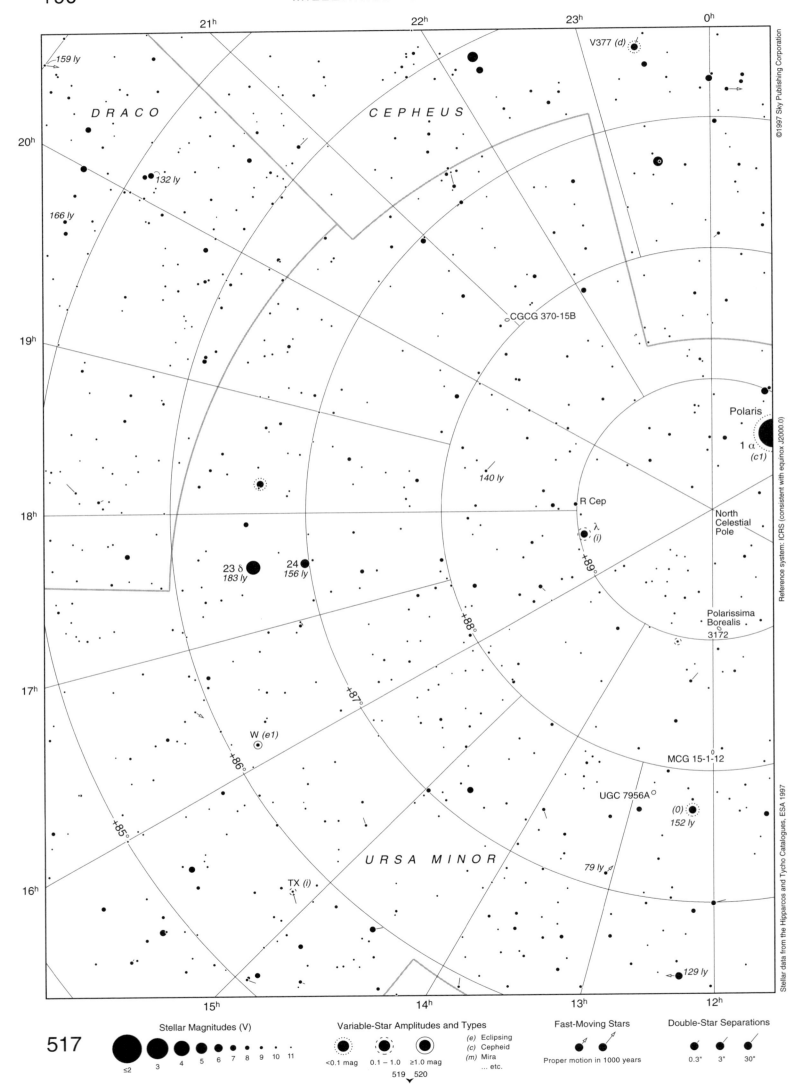

<0.1 mag   0.1 – 1.0   ≥1.0 mag

(e) Eclipsing
(c) Cepheid
(m) Mira
... etc.

Fast-Moving Stars

Proper motion in 1000 years

Double-Star Separations

0.3"   3"   30"

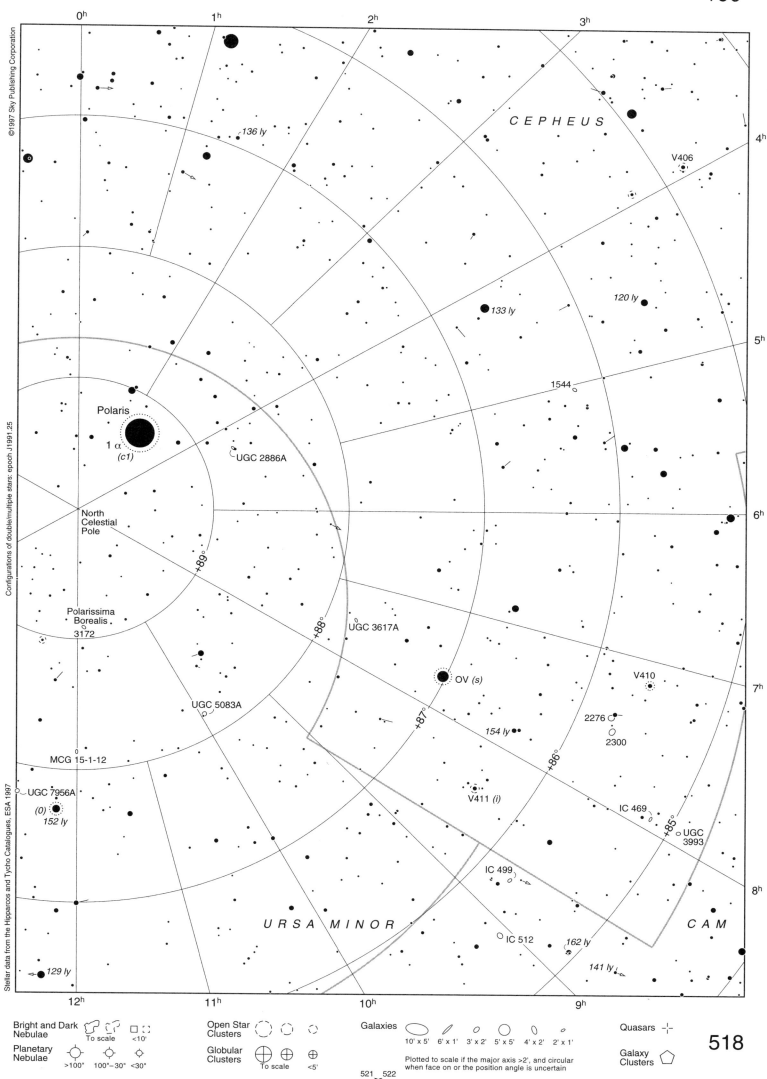

©1997 Sky Publishing Corporation

Configurations of double/multiple stars: epoch J1991.25

Stellar data from the Hipparcos and Tycho Catalogues, ESA 1997

C E P H E U S

V406

136 ly

133 ly

120 ly

1544

Polaris

1 α

(c1)

UGC 2886A

North
Celestial
Pole

+89°

+88°

UGC 3617A

OV *(s)*

V410

Polarissima
Borealis
3172

2276

2300

UGC 5083A

154 ly

+87°

V411 *(i)*

MCG 15-1-12

+86°

IC 469

UGC 7956A

+85° UGC
3993

(0)

152 ly

IC 499

U R S A   M I N O R

C A M

IC 512

162 ly

129 ly

141 ly

Bright and Dark Nebulae				Open Star Clusters			Galaxies							Quasars	-|-
	To scale	<10'					10' x 5'	6' x 1'	3' x 2'	5' x 5'	4' x 2'	2' x 1'			
Planetary Nebulae				Globular Clusters										Galaxy Clusters	
	>100"	100"–30"	<30"		To scale	<5'									

Plotted to scale if the major axis >2', and circular
when face on or the position angle is uncertain

518

521 522

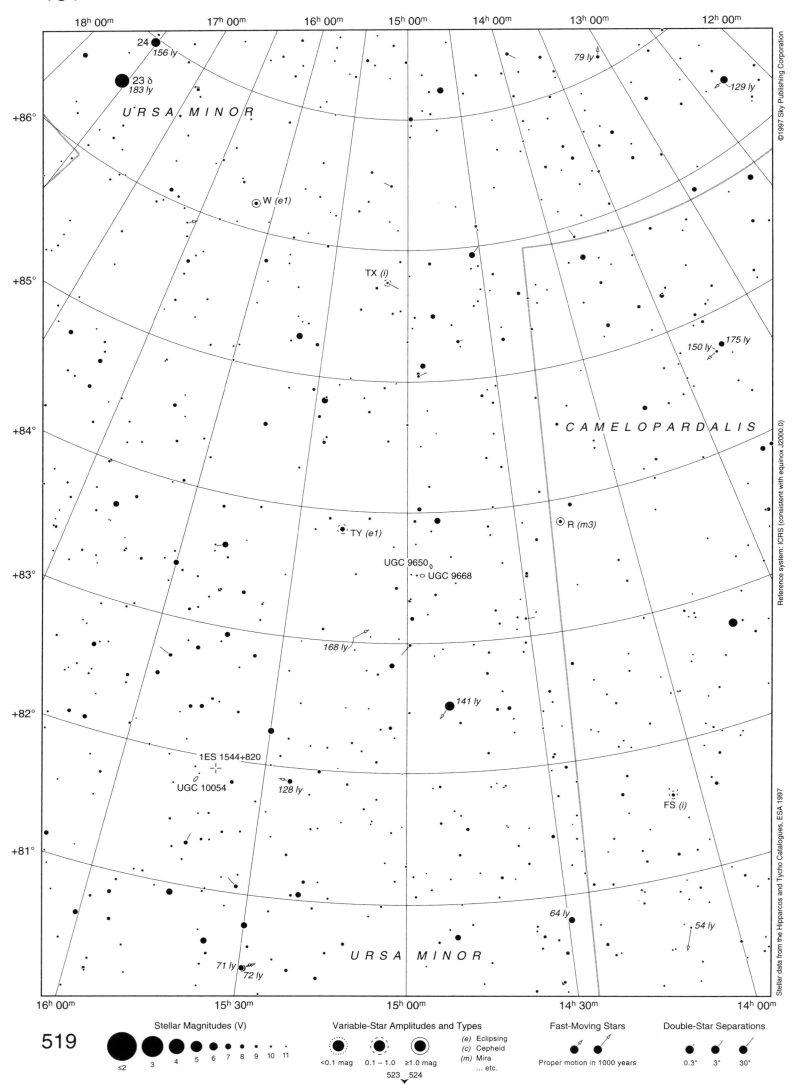

©1997 Sky Publishing Corporation

Reference system: ICRS (consistent with equinox J2000.0)

Stellar data from the Hipparcos and Tycho Catalogues, ESA 1997

18ʰ 00ᵐ   17ʰ 00ᵐ   16ʰ 00ᵐ   15ʰ 00ᵐ   14ʰ 00ᵐ   13ʰ 00ᵐ   12ʰ 00ᵐ

24
156 ly

23 δ
183 ly

79 ly

129 ly

URSA MINOR

+86°

W (e1)

+85°

TX (i)

150 ly   175 ly

+84°

CAMELOPARDALIS

TY (e1)

R (m3)

UGC 9650
UGC 9668

+83°

168 ly

141 ly

+82°

1ES 1544+820

FS (i)

UGC 10054

128 ly

+81°

64 ly

54 ly

URSA MINOR

71 ly
72 ly

16ʰ 00ᵐ   15ʰ 30ᵐ   15ʰ 00ᵐ   14ʰ 30ᵐ   14ʰ 00ᵐ

519

Stellar Magnitudes (V)

≤2   3   4   5   6   7   8   9   10   11

Variable-Star Amplitudes and Types

<0.1 mag   0.1 – 1.0   ≥1.0 mag

(e) Eclipsing
(c) Cepheid
(m) Mira
... etc.

523   524

Fast-Moving Stars

Proper motion in 1000 years

Double-Star Separations

0.3"   3"   30"

MILLENNIUM STAR ATLAS

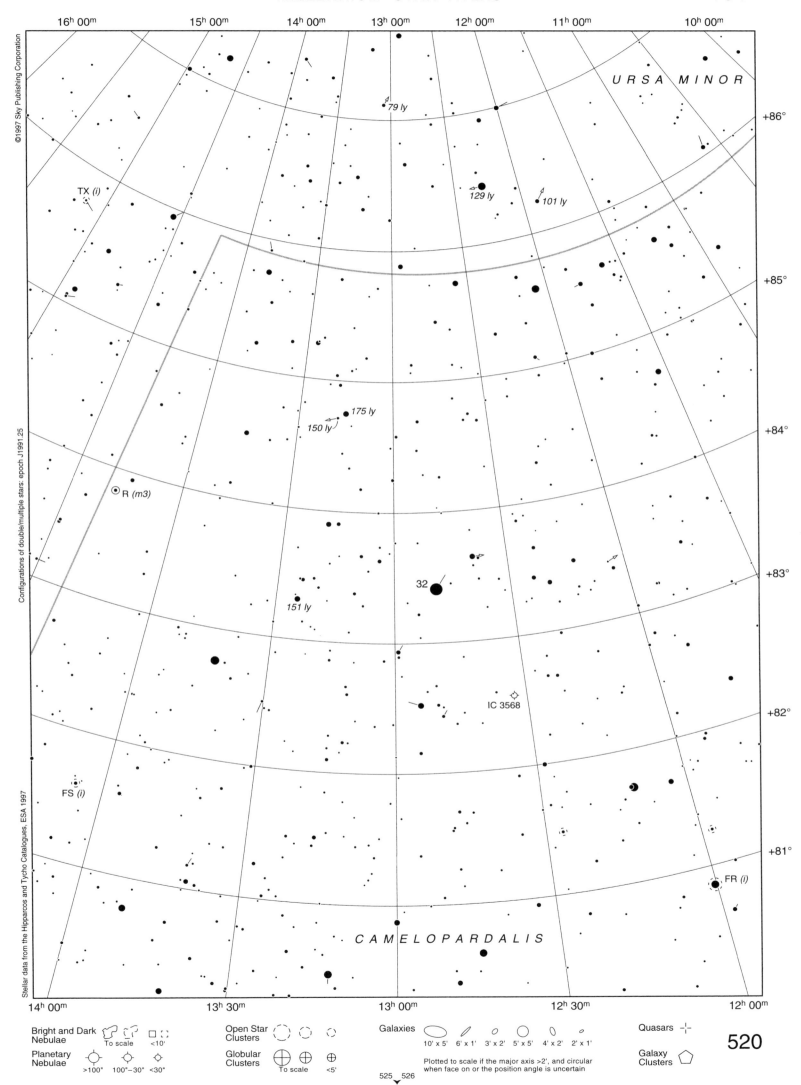

URSA MINOR

TX (i)

79 ly

129 ly

101 ly

175 ly

150 ly

R (m3)

32

151 ly

IC 3568

FS (i)

FR (i)

CAMELOPARDALIS

16h 00m   15h 00m   14h 00m   13h 00m   12h 00m   11h 00m   10h 00m

14h 00m   13h 30m   13h 00m   12h 30m   12h 00m

+86°
+85°
+84°
+83°
+82°
+81°

Bright and Dark Nebulae | To scale | <10'
Planetary Nebulae | >100" | 100"–30" | <30"
Open Star Clusters
Globular Clusters | To scale | <5'
Galaxies | 10' x 5' | 6' x 1' | 3' x 2' | 5' x 5' | 4' x 2' | 2' x 1'
Plotted to scale if the major axis >2', and circular when face on or the position angle is uncertain
Quasars
Galaxy Clusters

520

525 526

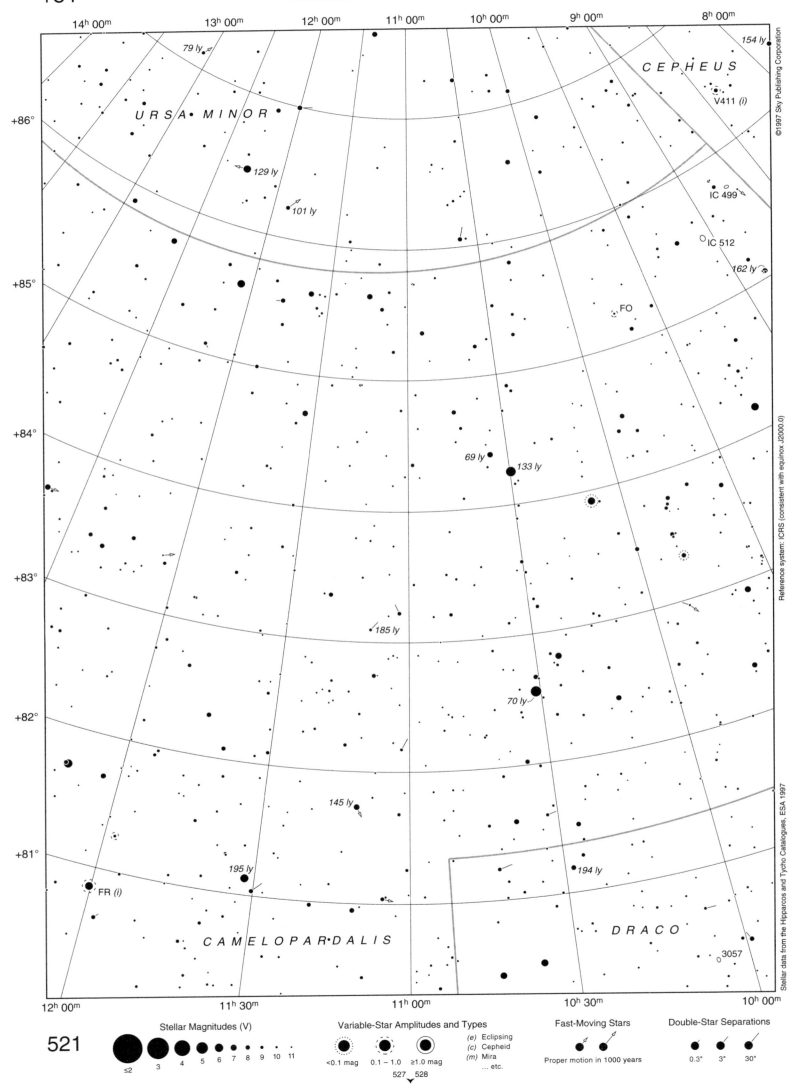

Reference system: ICRS (consistent with equinox J2000.0)

Stellar data from the Hipparcos and Tycho Catalogues, ESA 1997

521

Stellar Magnitudes (V)

≤2 3 4 5 6 7 8 9 10 11

Variable-Star Amplitudes and Types

<0.1 mag   0.1 – 1.0   ≥1.0 mag

527 528

(e) Eclipsing
(c) Cepheid
(m) Mira
... etc.

Fast-Moving Stars

Proper motion in 1000 years

Double-Star Separations

0.3" 3" 30"

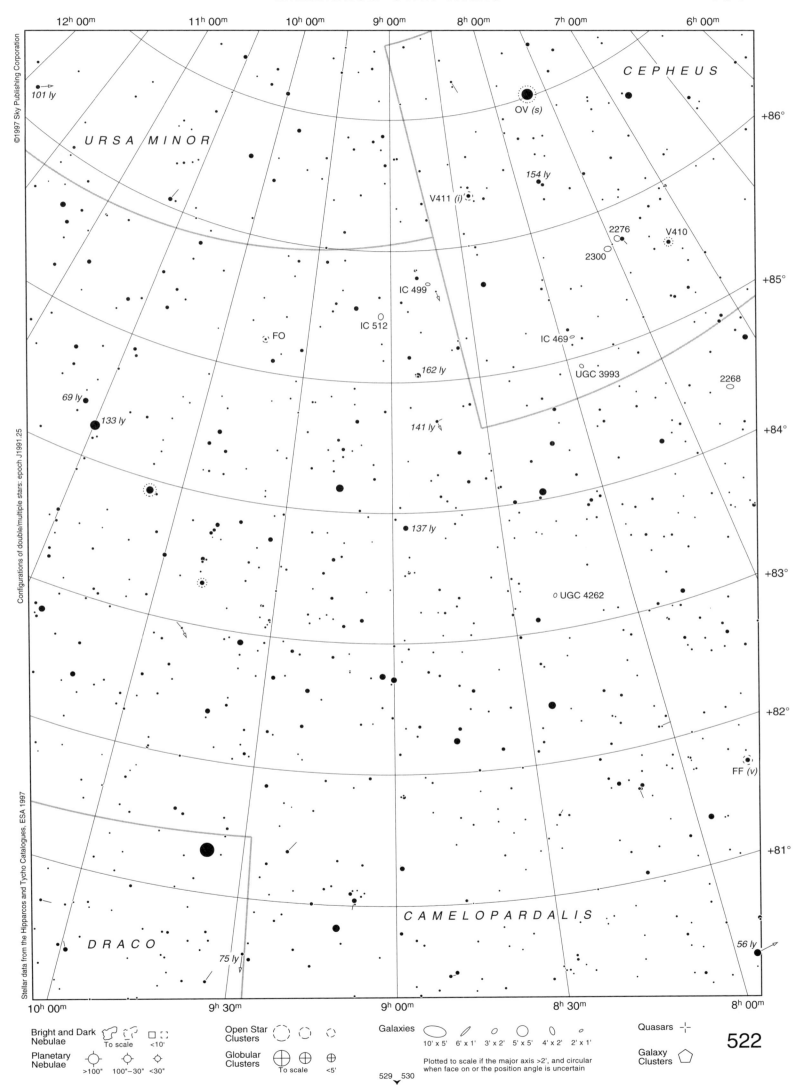

CEPHEUS

URSA MINOR

101 ly

OV (s)

154 ly

V411 (i)

2276
2300
V410

IC 499

IC 512

FO

IC 469

162 ly

UGC 3993

2268

69 ly

133 ly

141 ly

137 ly

UGC 4262

FF (v)

CAMELOPARDALIS

DRACO

56 ly

75 ly

Bright and Dark Nebulae	To scale <10'	Open Star Clusters	Galaxies
Planetary Nebulae	>100" 100"-30" <30"	Globular Clusters	To scale <5'

Galaxies

10' x 5'   6' x 1'   3' x 2'   5' x 5'   4' x 2'   2' x 1'

Plotted to scale if the major axis >2', and circular when face on or the position angle is uncertain

Quasars

Galaxy Clusters

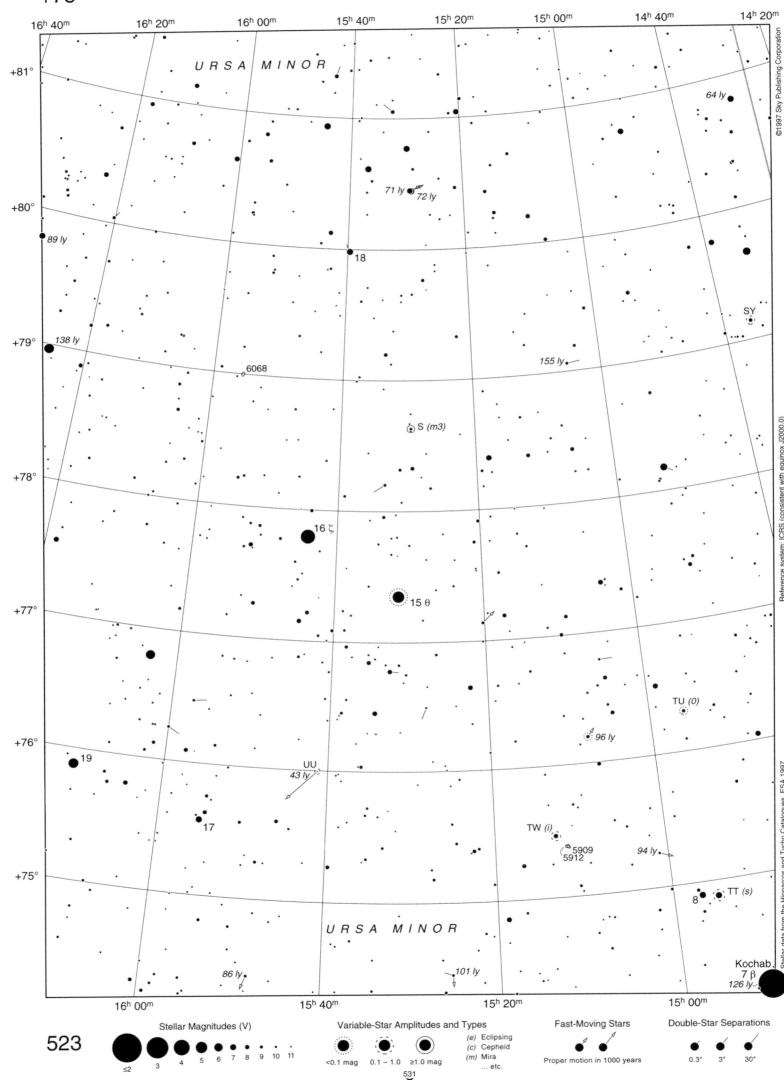

©1997 Sky Publishing Corporation

Reference system: ICRS (consistent with equinox J2000.0)

Stellar data from the Hipparcos and Tycho Catalogues, ESA 1997

URSA MINOR

URSA MINOR

64 ly

89 ly

71 ly   72 ly

18

SY

138 ly

155 ly

6068

S (m3)

16 ζ

15 θ

TU (0)

96 ly

19

UU
43 ly

17

TW (i)

5909
5912

94 ly

8   TT (s)

Kochab
7 β
126 ly

523

Stellar Magnitudes (V)

≤2   3   4   5   6   7   8   9   10   11

Variable-Star Amplitudes and Types

<0.1 mag   0.1 – 1.0   ≥1.0 mag

(e) Eclipsing
(c) Cepheid
(m) Mira
... etc.

Fast-Moving Stars

Proper motion in 1000 years

Double-Star Separations

0.3"   3"   30"

531

MILLENNIUM STAR ATLAS

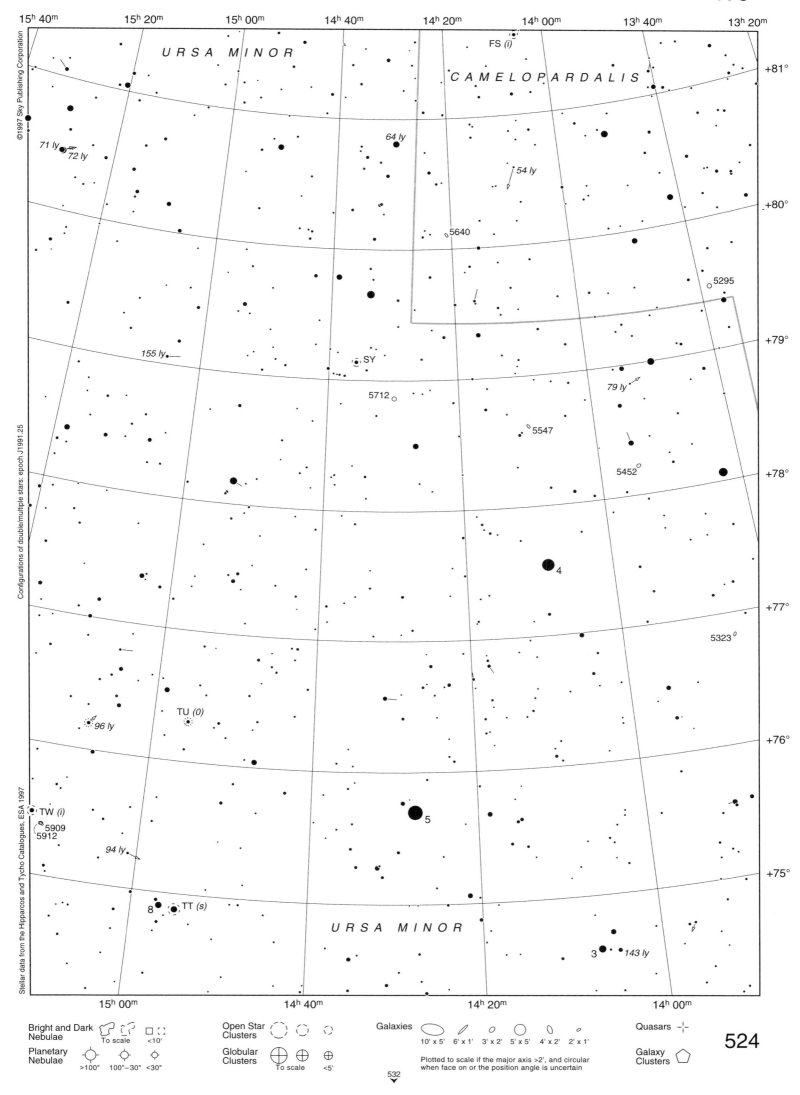

URSA MINOR

CAMELOPARDALIS

FS (i)

64 ly

54 ly

71 ly
72 ly

5640

5295

155 ly

SY

5712

79 ly

5547

5452

+81°

+80°

+79°

+78°

+77°

+76°

+75°

4

5323

TU (0)

96 ly

TW (i)

5909
5912

94 ly

5

3 143 ly

8 TT (s)

URSA MINOR

Configurations of double/multiple stars: epoch J1991.25

Stellar data from the Hipparcos and Tycho Catalogues, ESA 1997

Bright and Dark Nebulae	Open Star Clusters	Galaxies	Quasars

Bright and Dark Nebulae — To scale — <10'

Planetary Nebulae — >100" — 100"–30" — <30"

Open Star Clusters

Globular Clusters — To scale — <5'

Galaxies — 10' x 5' — 6' x 1' — 3' x 2' — 5' x 5' — 4' x 2' — 2' x 1'

Plotted to scale if the major axis >2', and circular when face on or the position angle is uncertain

Quasars

Galaxy Clusters

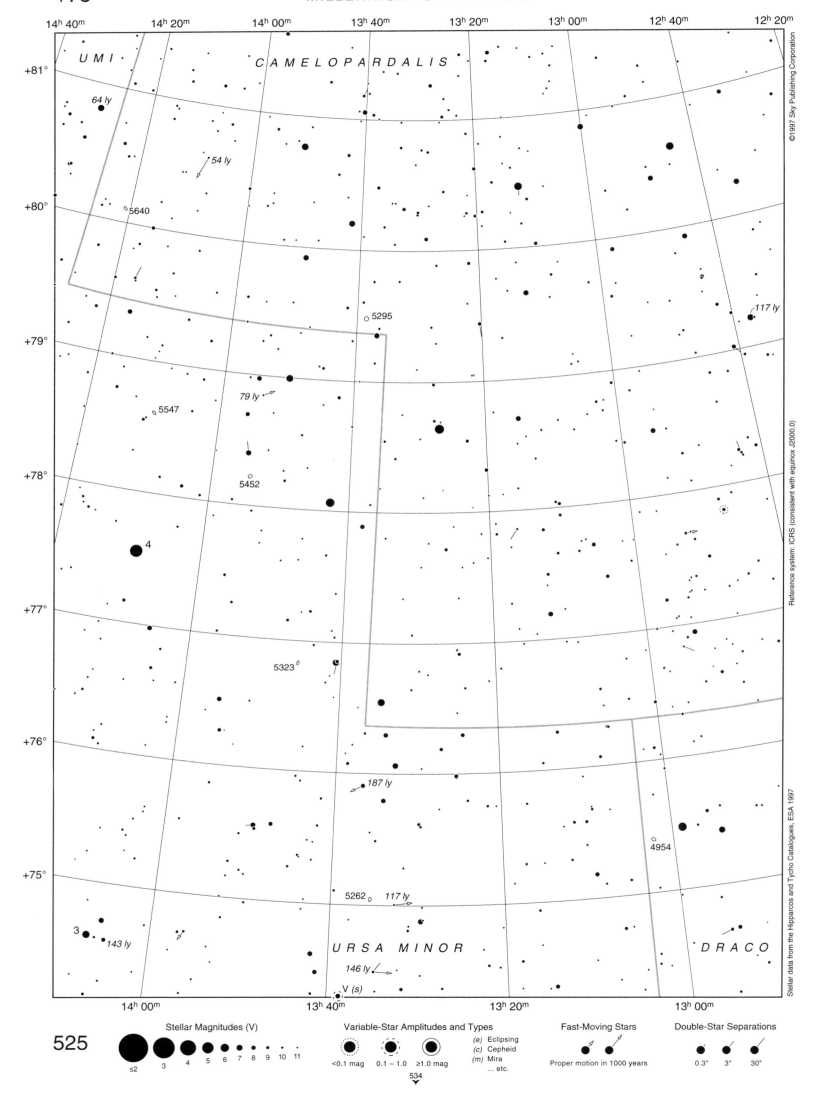

©1997 Sky Publishing Corporation

Reference system: ICRS (consistent with equinox J2000.0)

Stellar data from the Hipparcos and Tycho Catalogues, ESA 1997

U M I

C A M E L O P A R D A L I S

64 ly

54 ly

5640

117 ly

5295

79 ly

5547

5452

4

5323

5452

4954

187 ly

5262   *117 ly*

3

143 ly

U R S A   M I N O R

D R A C O

146 ly

V (s)

525

Stellar Magnitudes (V)	Variable-Star Amplitudes and Types	Fast-Moving Stars	Double-Star Separations

≤2   3   4   5   6   7   8   9 10 11

<0.1 mag   0.1 – 1.0   ≥1.0 mag

(e) Eclipsing
(c) Cepheid
(m) Mira
... etc.

Proper motion in 1000 years

0.3"   3"   30"

534

MILLENNIUM STAR ATLAS

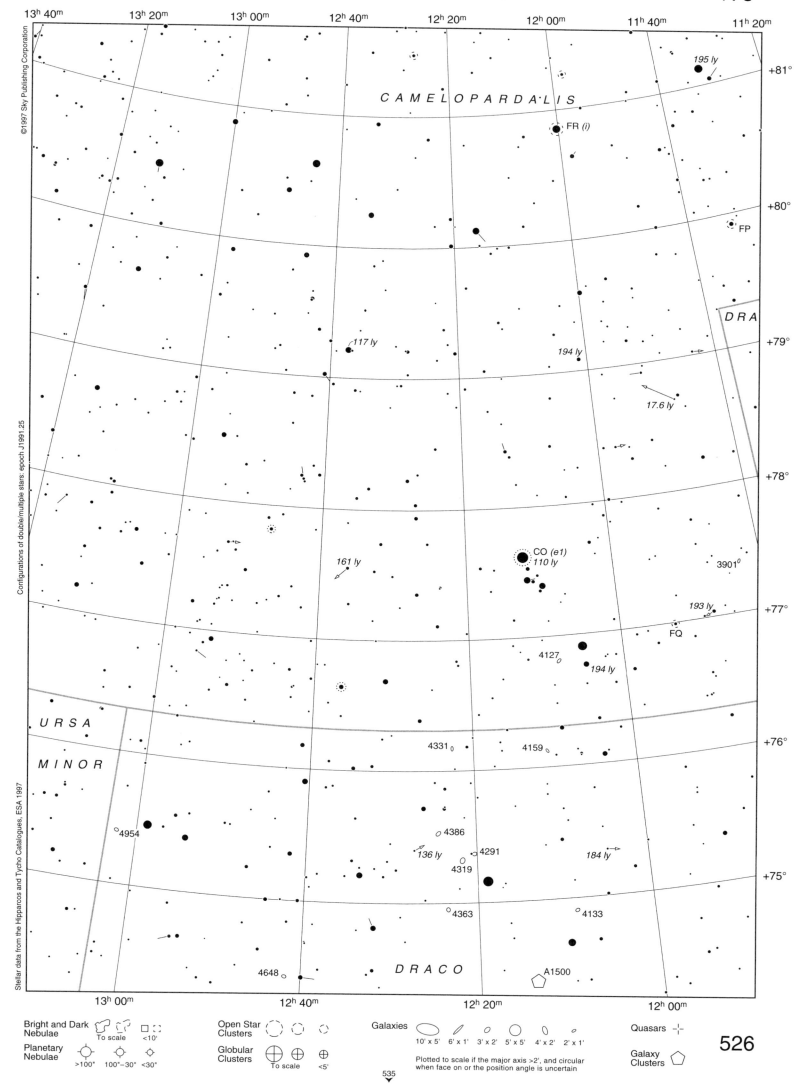

© 1997 Sky Publishing Corporation

Configurations of double/multiple stars: epoch J1991.25

Stellar data from the Hipparcos and Tycho Catalogues, ESA 1997

CAMELOPARDALIS

DRA

URSA

MINOR

DRACO

195 ly

FR (i)

FP

117 ly

194 ly

17.6 ly

161 ly

CO (e1)
110 ly

3901

193 ly

FQ

4127

194 ly

4331

4159

4954

4386

136 ly

4291

4319

184 ly

4363

4133

A1500

4648

13ʰ 40ᵐ 13ʰ 20ᵐ 13ʰ 00ᵐ 12ʰ 40ᵐ 12ʰ 20ᵐ 12ʰ 00ᵐ 11ʰ 40ᵐ 11ʰ 20ᵐ

13ʰ 00ᵐ 12ʰ 40ᵐ 12ʰ 20ᵐ 12ʰ 00ᵐ

+81°
+80°
+79°
+78°
+77°
+76°
+75°

Bright and Dark Nebulae	Open Star Clusters	Galaxies	Quasars

Bright and Dark Nebulae To scale <10'

Planetary Nebulae >100" 100"–30" <30"

Open Star Clusters

Globular Clusters To scale <5'

Galaxies 10' x 5' 6' x 1' 3' x 2' 5' x 5' 4' x 2' 2' x 1'

Plotted to scale if the major axis >2', and circular when face on or the position angle is uncertain

Quasars

Galaxy Clusters

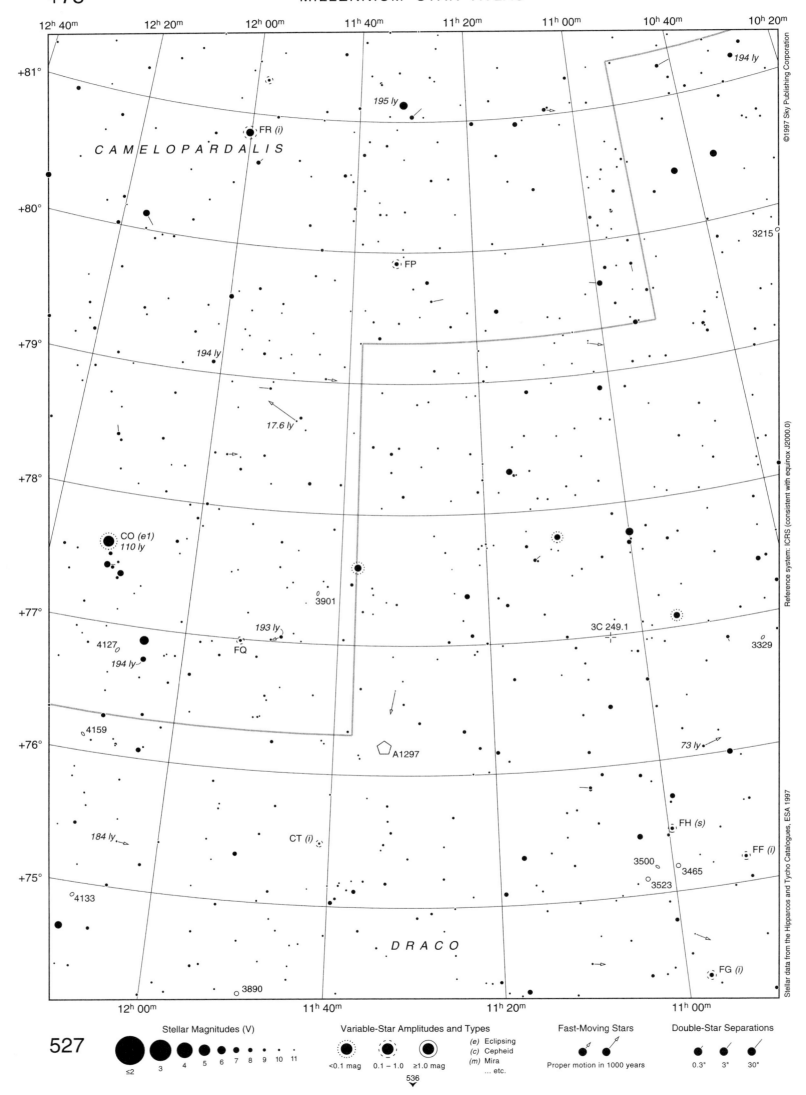

527

Stellar Magnitudes (V)

≤2 3 4 5 6 7 8 9 10 11

Variable-Star Amplitudes and Types

<0.1 mag   0.1 – 1.0   ≥1.0 mag

(e) Eclipsing
(c) Cepheid
(m) Mira
... etc.

Fast-Moving Stars

Proper motion in 1000 years

Double-Star Separations

0.3"   3"   30"

MILLENNIUM STAR ATLAS

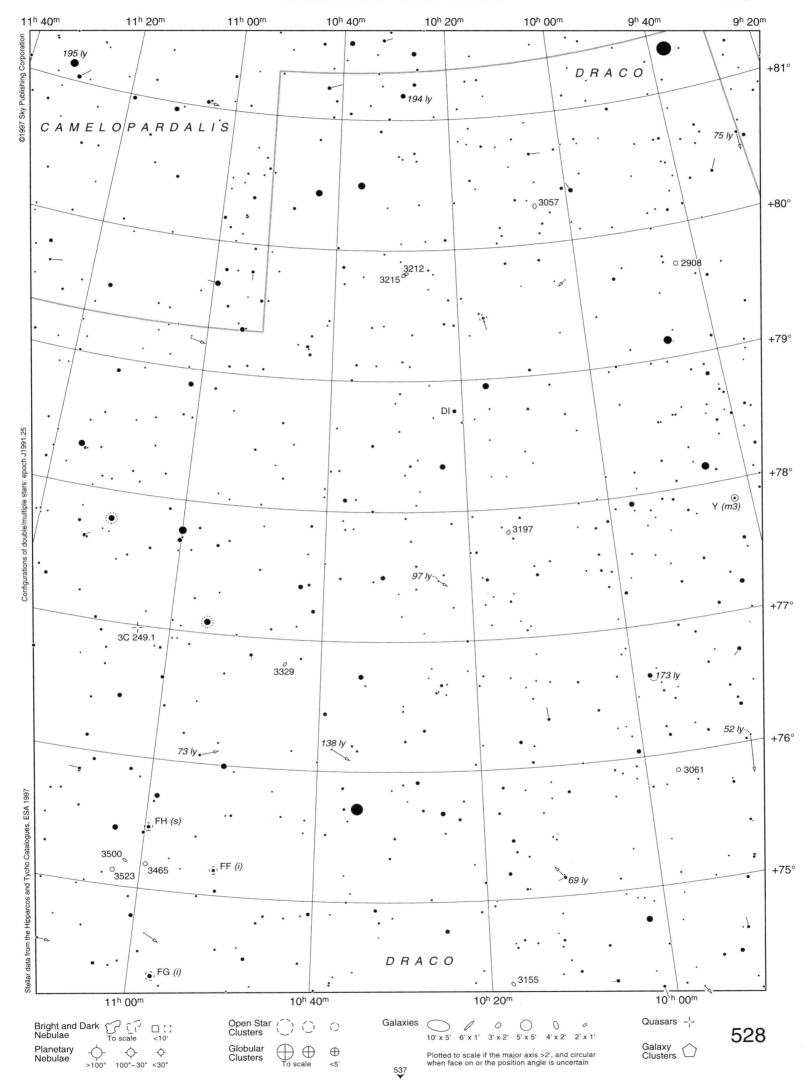

11h 40m 11h 20m 11h 00m 10h 40m 10h 20m 10h 00m 9h 40m 9h 20m

+81°
+80°
+79°
+78°
+77°
+76°
+75°

D R A C O

C A M E L O P A R D A L I S

195 ly
194 ly
75 ly
3057
3212
3215
2908
DI
Y (m3)
3197
97 ly
3C 249.1
3329
173 ly
52 ly
138 ly
73 ly
3061
FH (s)
3500
3523 3465 FF (i)
69 ly
D R A C O
FG (i)
3155

Configurations of double/multiple stars: epoch J1991.25

Stellar data from the Hipparcos and Tycho Catalogues, ESA 1997

11h 00m 10h 40m 10h 20m 10h 00m

| Bright and Dark Nebulae | | | To scale | <10' |
| Planetary Nebulae | >100" | 100"–30" | <30" | |

| Open Star Clusters | | | |
| Globular Clusters | To scale | <5' | |

Galaxies
10' x 5' 6' x 1' 3' x 2' 5' x 5' 4' x 2' 2' x 1'

Plotted to scale if the major axis >2', and circular when face on or the position angle is uncertain

Quasars

Galaxy Clusters

528

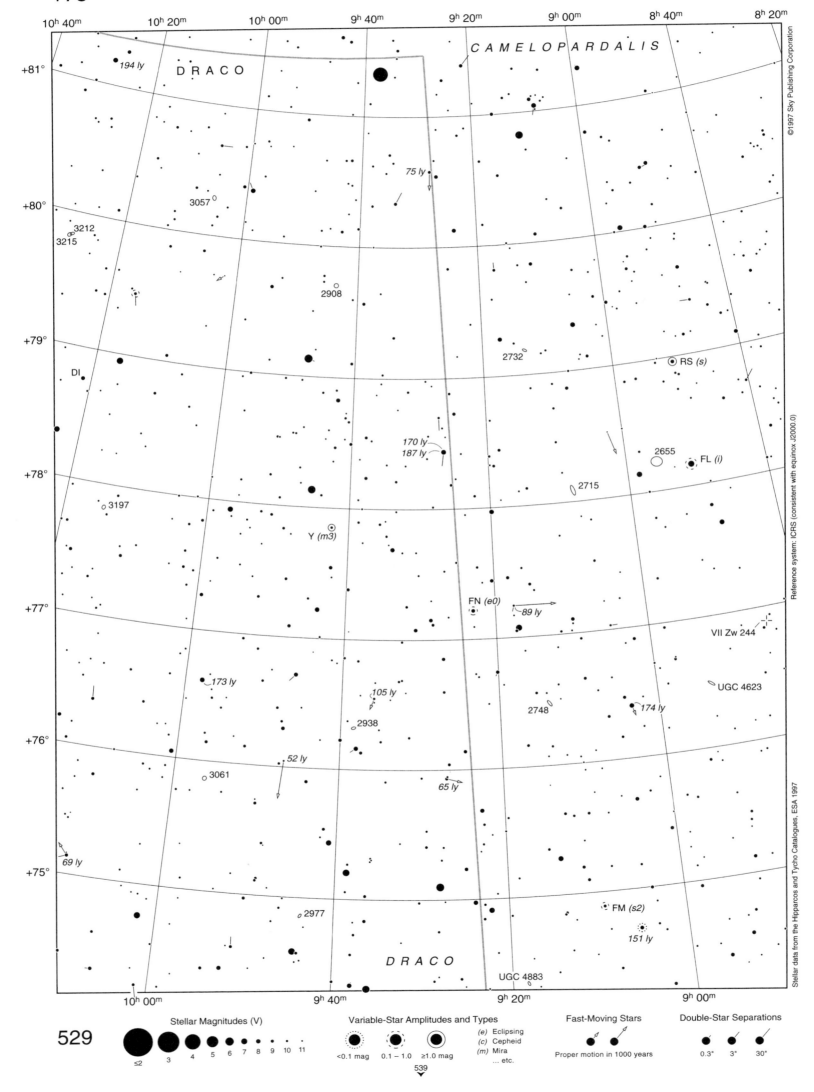

©1997 Sky Publishing Corporation

Reference system: ICRS (consistent with equinox J2000.0)

Stellar data from the Hipparcos and Tycho Catalogues, ESA 1997

10h 40m   10h 20m   10h 00m   9h 40m   9h 20m   9h 00m   8h 40m   8h 20m

CAMELOPARDALIS

DRACO

194 ly

+81°

3057

3212
3215

2908

+80°

DI

+79°

2732

RS (s)

170 ly
187 ly

2655

FL (i)

+78°

3197

2715

Y (m3)

FN (e0)   89 ly

+77°

VII Zw 244

173 ly

105 ly

2748   174 ly   UGC 4623

2938

+76°

52 ly

3061

65 ly

69 ly

+75°

2977

FM (s2)

151 ly

DRACO

UGC 4883

10h 00m   9h 40m   9h 20m   9h 00m

Stellar Magnitudes (V)

≤2   3   4   5   6   7   8   9 10 11

Variable-Star Amplitudes and Types

<0.1 mag   0.1 – 1.0   ≥1.0 mag

(e) Eclipsing
(c) Cepheid
(m) Mira
... etc.

Fast-Moving Stars

Proper motion in 1000 years

Double-Star Separations

0.3"   3"   30"

539

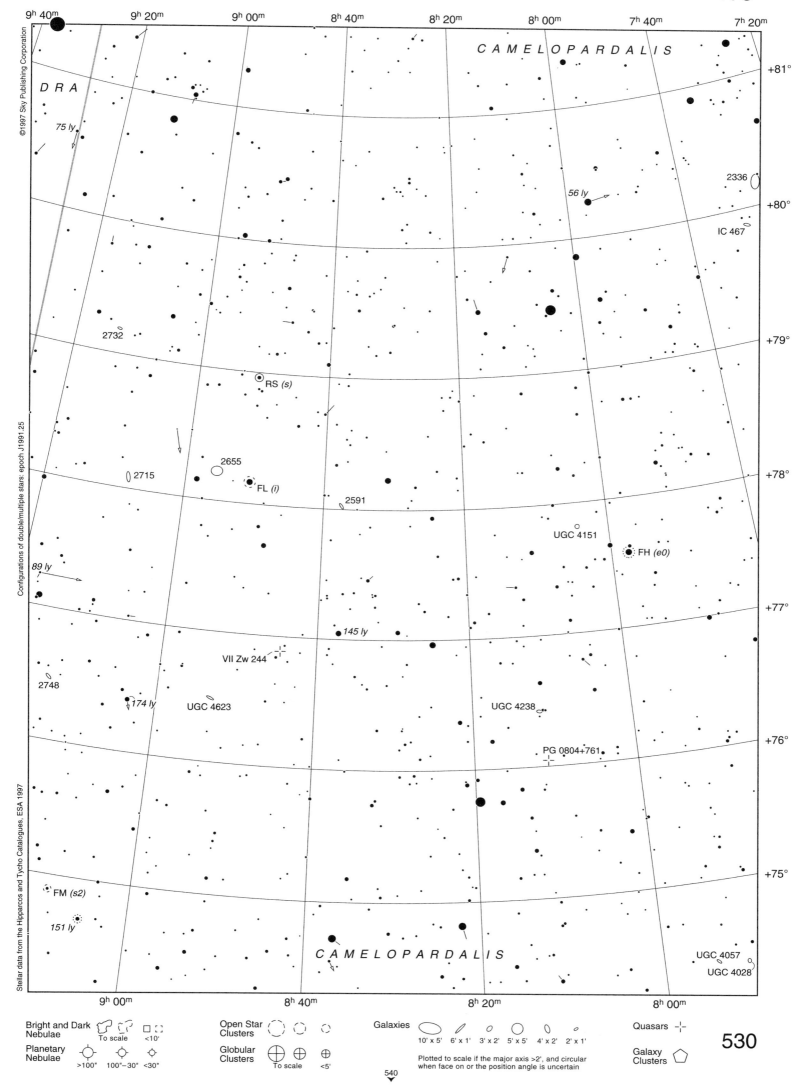

© 1997 Sky Publishing Corporation

Configurations of double/multiple stars: epoch J1991.25

Stellar data from the Hipparcos and Tycho Catalogues, ESA 1997

9h 40m   9h 20m   9h 00m   8h 40m   8h 20m   8h 00m   7h 40m   7h 20m

CAMELOPARDALIS

DRA

75 ly

2336

56 ly

IC 467

+81°

+80°

2732

+79°

RS (s)

2655

2715

FL (i)

2591

UGC 4151

FH (e0)

+78°

89 ly

+77°

145 ly

VII Zw 244

2748

174 ly

UGC 4623

UGC 4238

PG 0804+761

+76°

+75°

FM (s2)

151 ly

CAMELOPARDALIS

UGC 4057

UGC 4028

9h 00m   8h 40m   8h 20m   8h 00m

| Bright and Dark Nebulae | Open Star Clusters | Galaxies | Quasars |

Bright and Dark Nebulae   Open Star Clusters   Galaxies   Quasars
To scale   <10'   10' x 5' 6' x 1' 3' x 2' 5' x 5' 4' x 2' 2' x 1'

Planetary Nebulae   Globular Clusters   Galaxy Clusters
>100" 100"-30" <30"   To scale   <5'

Plotted to scale if the major axis >2', and circular
when face on or the position angle is uncertain

530

540

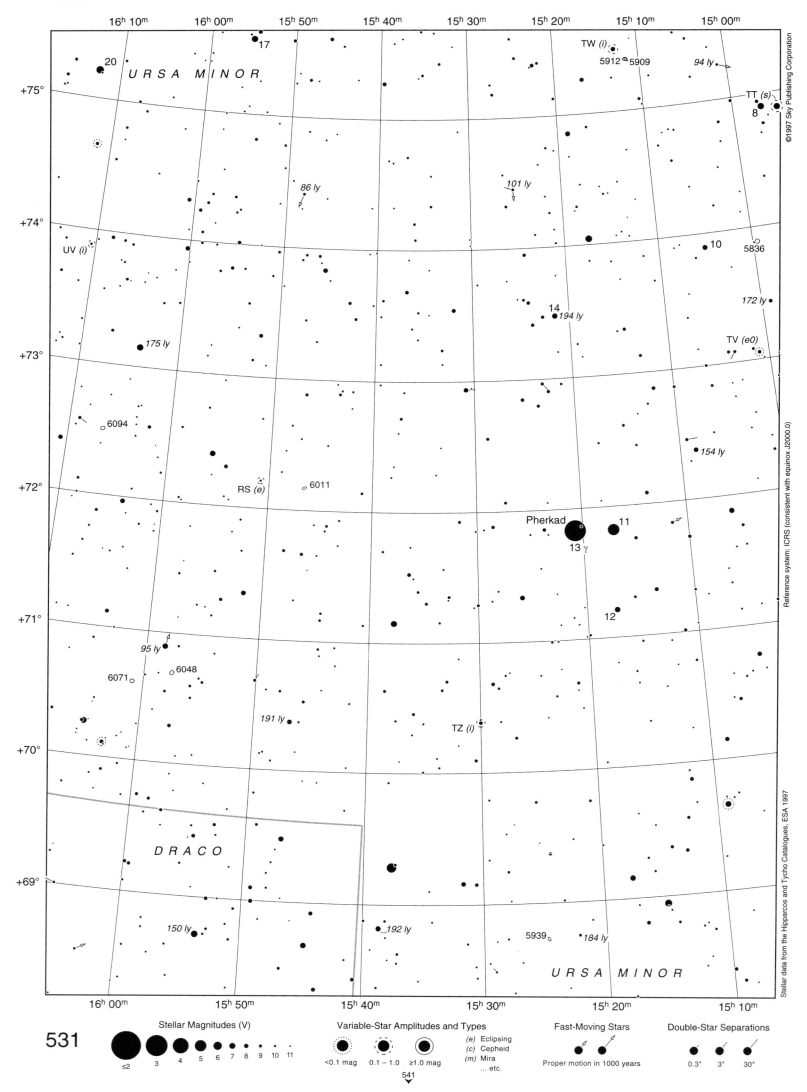

URSA MINOR

20

17

TW *(i)*
5912 5909

94 ly

TT *(s)*
8

+75°

86 ly

101 ly

UV *(i)*

10
5836

+74°

14
194 ly

172 ly

TV *(e0)*

175 ly

+73°

6094

154 ly

+72°

RS *(e)*
6011

Pherkad
11
13 γ

12

+71°

95 ly

6071   6048

191 ly

TZ *(i)*

+70°

DRACO

+69°

150 ly

192 ly

5939   184 ly

URSA MINOR

©1997 Sky Publishing Corporation

Reference system: ICRS (consistent with equinox J2000.0)

Stellar data from the Hipparcos and Tycho Catalogues, ESA 1997

531

Stellar Magnitudes (V)

≤2 3 4 5 6 7 8 9 10 11

Variable-Star Amplitudes and Types

<0.1 mag   0.1 – 1.0   ≥1.0 mag

(e) Eclipsing
(c) Cepheid
(m) Mira
... etc.

Fast-Moving Stars

Proper motion in 1000 years

Double-Star Separations

0.3"   3"   30"

541

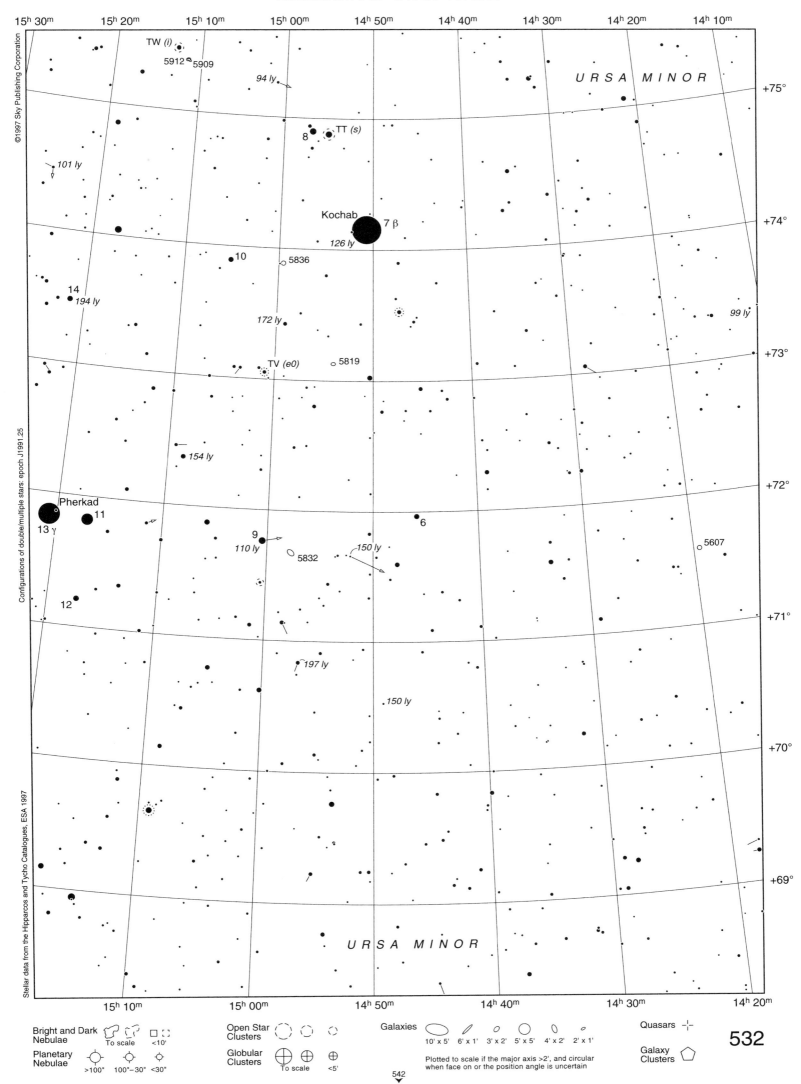

Configurations of double/multiple stars: epoch J1991.25

Stellar data from the Hipparcos and Tycho Catalogues, ESA 1997

URSA MINOR

TW (i)
5912 5909
94 ly
8 TT (s)
101 ly
Kochab
7 β
126 ly
10 5836
14
194 ly
172 ly
99 ly
TV (e0) 5819
154 ly
Pherkad
13 γ 11
6
9 5607
110 ly 5832 150 ly
12
197 ly
150 ly

URSA MINOR

Bright and Dark Nebulae
To scale <10'
Planetary Nebulae
>100" 100"-30" <30"
Open Star Clusters
Globular Clusters
To scale <5'
Galaxies
10' x 5' 6' x 1' 3' x 2' 5' x 5' 4' x 2' 2' x 1'
Plotted to scale if the major axis >2', and circular when face on or the position angle is uncertain
Quasars
Galaxy Clusters

532

542

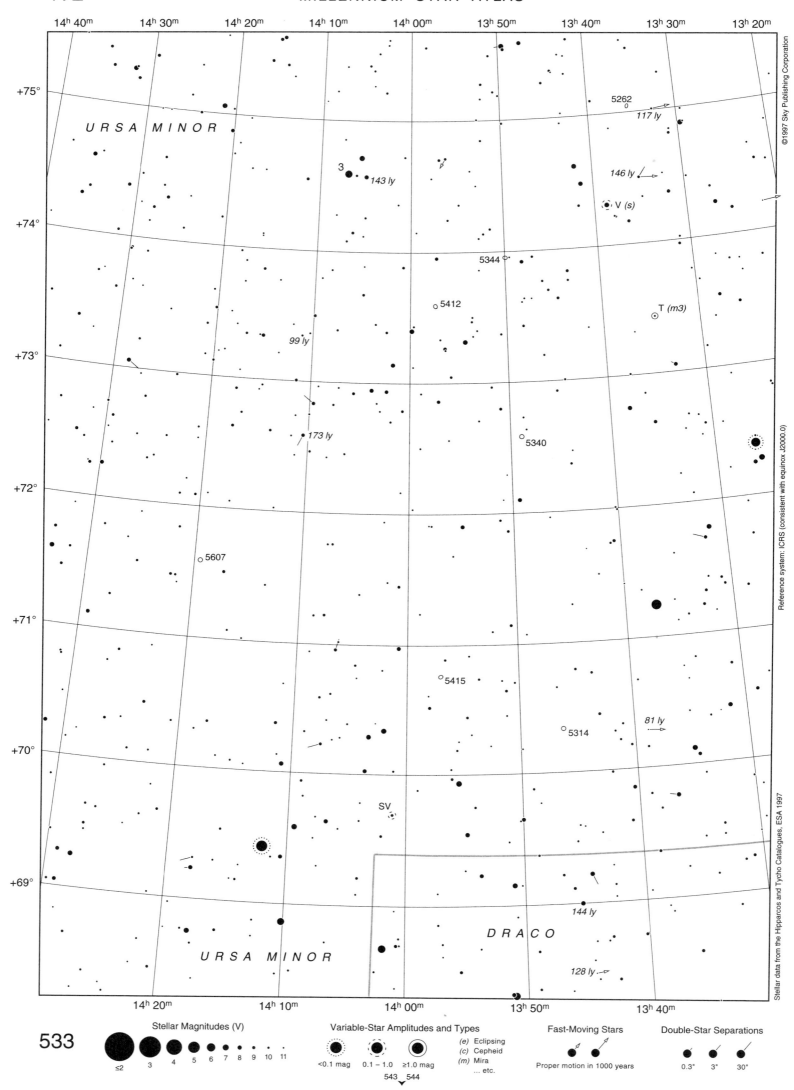

Reference system: ICRS (consistent with equinox J2000.0)

Stellar data from the Hipparcos and Tycho Catalogues, ESA 1997

URSA MINOR

3   143 ly

5262
117 ly

146 ly

V (s)

5344

5412

T (m3)

99 ly

173 ly

5340

5607

5415

81 ly

5314

SV

URSA MINOR

DRACO

144 ly

128 ly

533

Stellar Magnitudes (V)
≤2   3   4   5   6   7   8   9   10   11

Variable-Star Amplitudes and Types
<0.1 mag   0.1 – 1.0   ≥1.0 mag

(e) Eclipsing
(c) Cepheid
(m) Mira
... etc.

Fast-Moving Stars
Proper motion in 1000 years

Double-Star Separations
0.3"   3"   30"

543   544

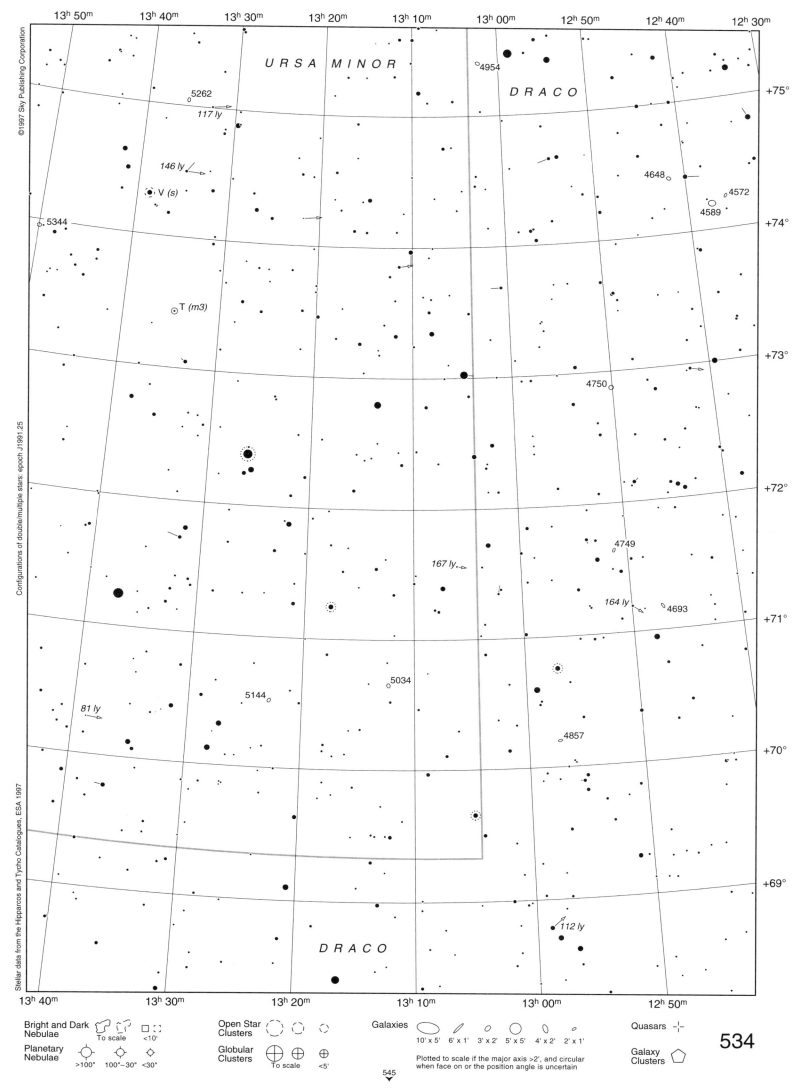

Bright and Dark Nebulae			Open Star Clusters			Galaxies							Quasars	

Bright and Dark Nebulae — To scale — <10'

Planetary Nebulae — >100" — 100"–30" — <30"

Open Star Clusters

Globular Clusters — To scale — <5'

Galaxies — 10' x 5' — 6' x 1' — 3' x 2' — 5' x 5' — 4' x 2' — 2' x 1'

Plotted to scale if the major axis >2', and circular when face on or the position angle is uncertain

Quasars

Galaxy Clusters

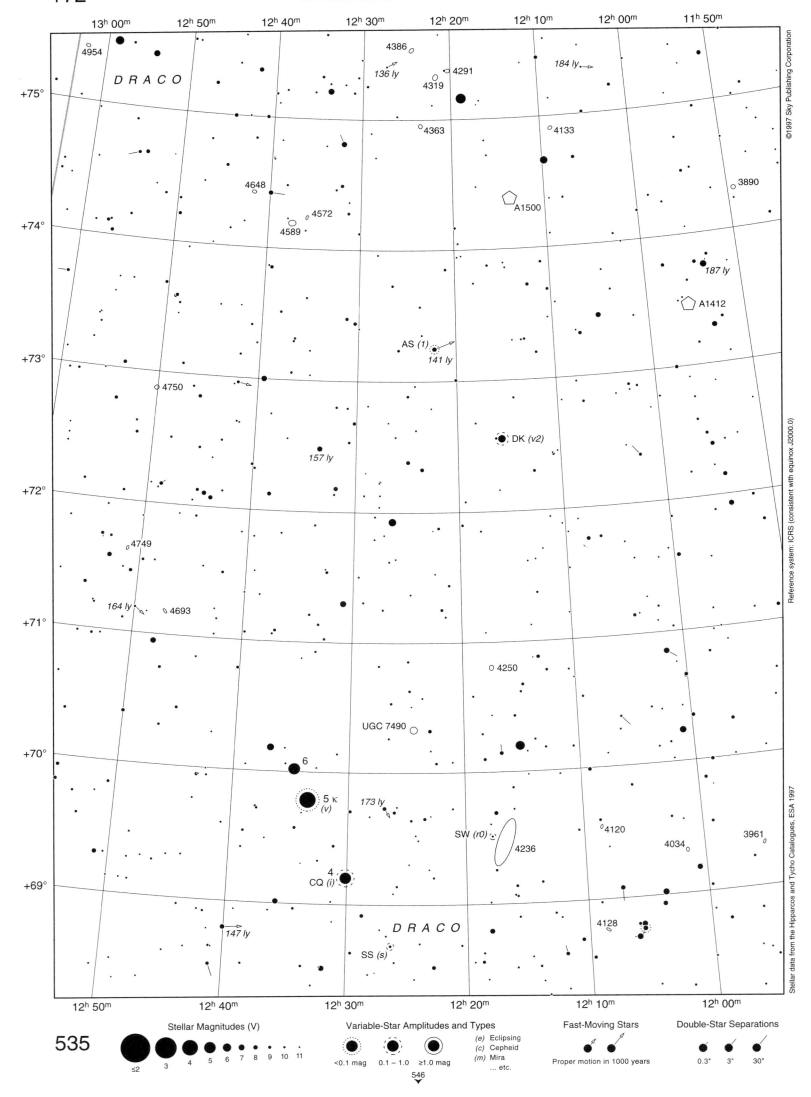

©1997 Sky Publishing Corporation

Reference system: ICRS (consistent with equinox J2000.0)

Stellar data from the Hipparcos and Tycho Catalogues, ESA 1997

DRACO

DRACO

4954
4386
4291
4319
136 ly
184 ly
4363
4133
3890
4648
A1500
4572
4589
187 ly
A1412
AS (1)
141 ly
4750
DK (v2)
157 ly
4749
164 ly
4693
4250
UGC 7490
6
5 κ (v)
173 ly
SW (r0)
4236
4120
4034
3961
4
CQ (i)
4128
147 ly
SS (s)

535

Stellar Magnitudes (V)

≤2 3 4 5 6 7 8 9 10 11

Variable-Star Amplitudes and Types

<0.1 mag   0.1 – 1.0 mag   ≥1.0 mag

(e) Eclipsing
(c) Cepheid
(m) Mira
... etc.

546

Fast-Moving Stars

Proper motion in 1000 years

Double-Star Separations

0.3"   3"   30"

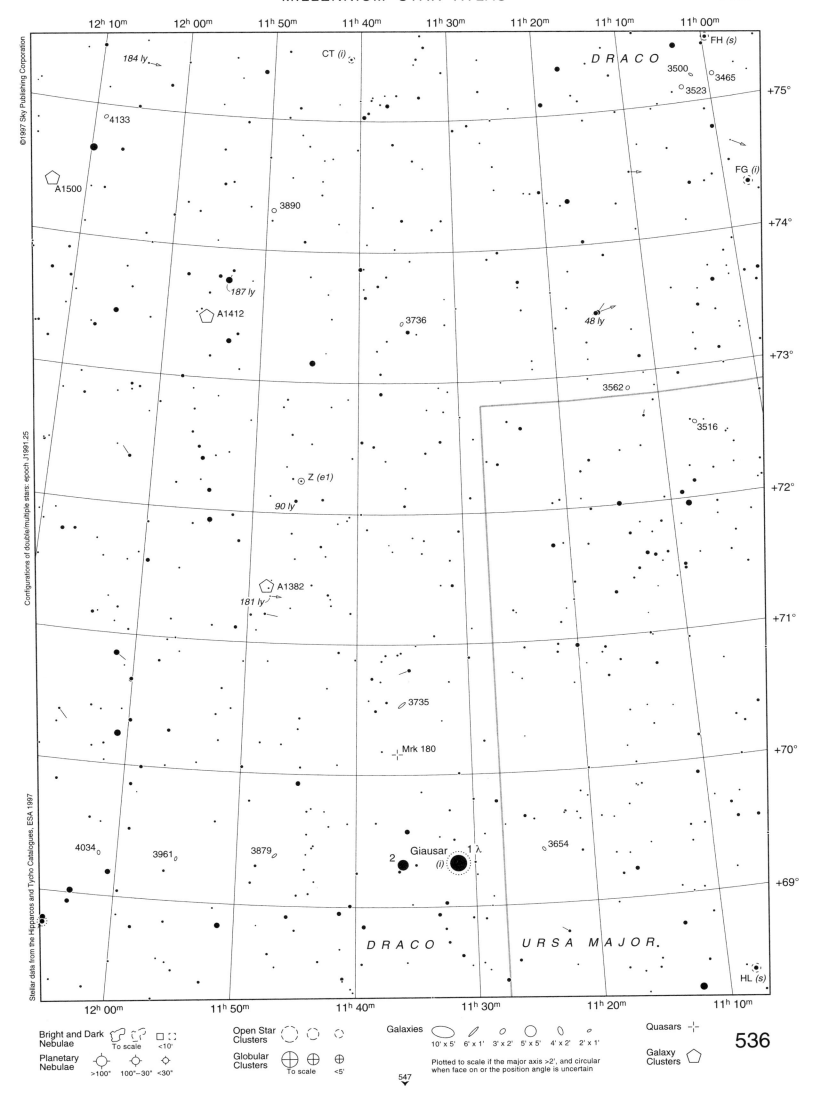

D R A C O

FH (s)

3500
3465
3523

4133

184 ly

A1500

+75°

3890

FG (i)

+74°

187 ly

A1412

3736

48 ly

+73°

3562

3516

Z (e1)

90 ly

+72°

A1382

181 ly

+71°

3735

Mrk 180

+70°

4034   3961   3879   3654

2   Giausar   1 λ
(i)

+69°

D R A C O   U R S A   M A J O R

HL (s)

Bright and Dark Nebulae		To scale	<10'

Planetary Nebulae	>100"	100"–30"	<30"

Open Star Clusters			

Globular Clusters		To scale	<5'

Galaxies

10' x 5'   6' x 1'   3' x 2'   5' x 5'   4' x 2'   2' x 1'

Plotted to scale if the major axis >2', and circular when face on or the position angle is uncertain

Quasars

Galaxy Clusters

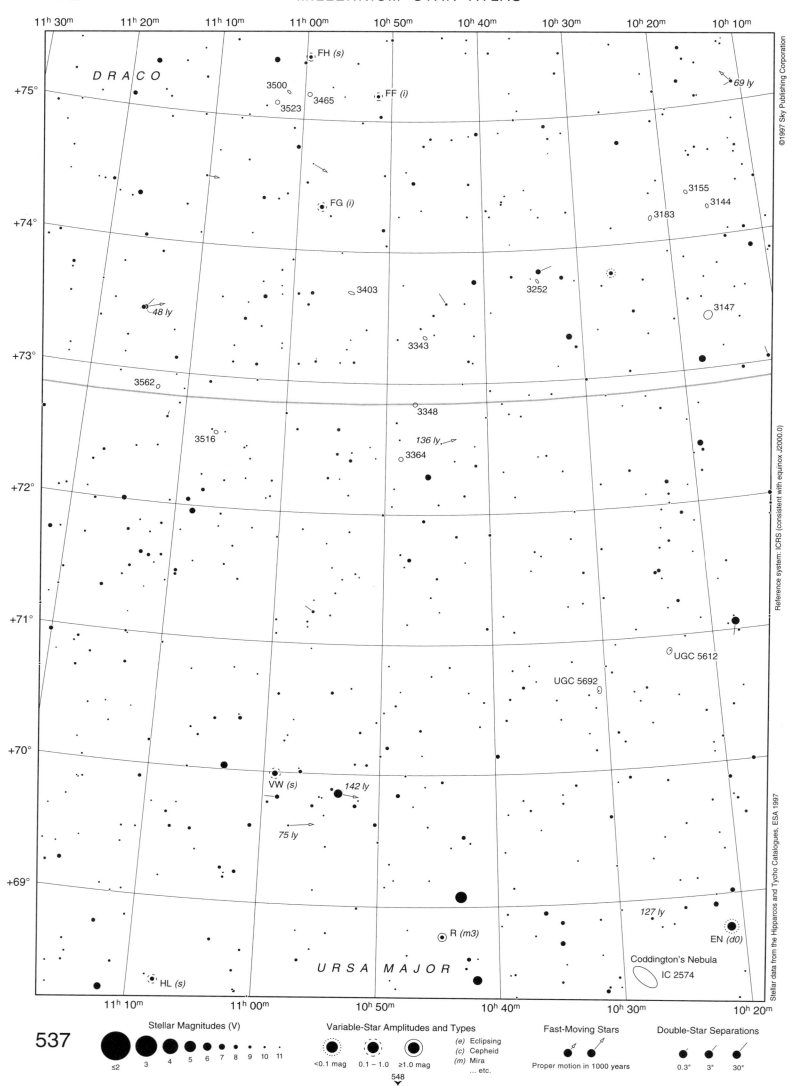

©1997 Sky Publishing Corporation

Reference system: ICRS (consistent with equinox J2000.0)

Stellar data from the Hipparcos and Tycho Catalogues, ESA 1997

DRACO

FH (s)
3500
3523
3465
FF (i)
FG (i)
3155
3144
3183
3403
3252
3147
48 ly
3343
3562
3348
3516
136 ly
3364
UGC 5612
UGC 5692
VW (s)
142 ly
75 ly
127 ly
R (m3)
EN (d0)
URSA MAJOR
Coddington's Nebula
IC 2574
HL (s)
69 ly

Stellar Magnitudes (V)

≤2 3 4 5 6 7 8 9 10 11

Variable-Star Amplitudes and Types

<0.1 mag   0.1 – 1.0   ≥1.0 mag

(e) Eclipsing
(c) Cepheid
(m) Mira
... etc.

Fast-Moving Stars

Proper motion in 1000 years

Double-Star Separations

0.3"   3"   30"

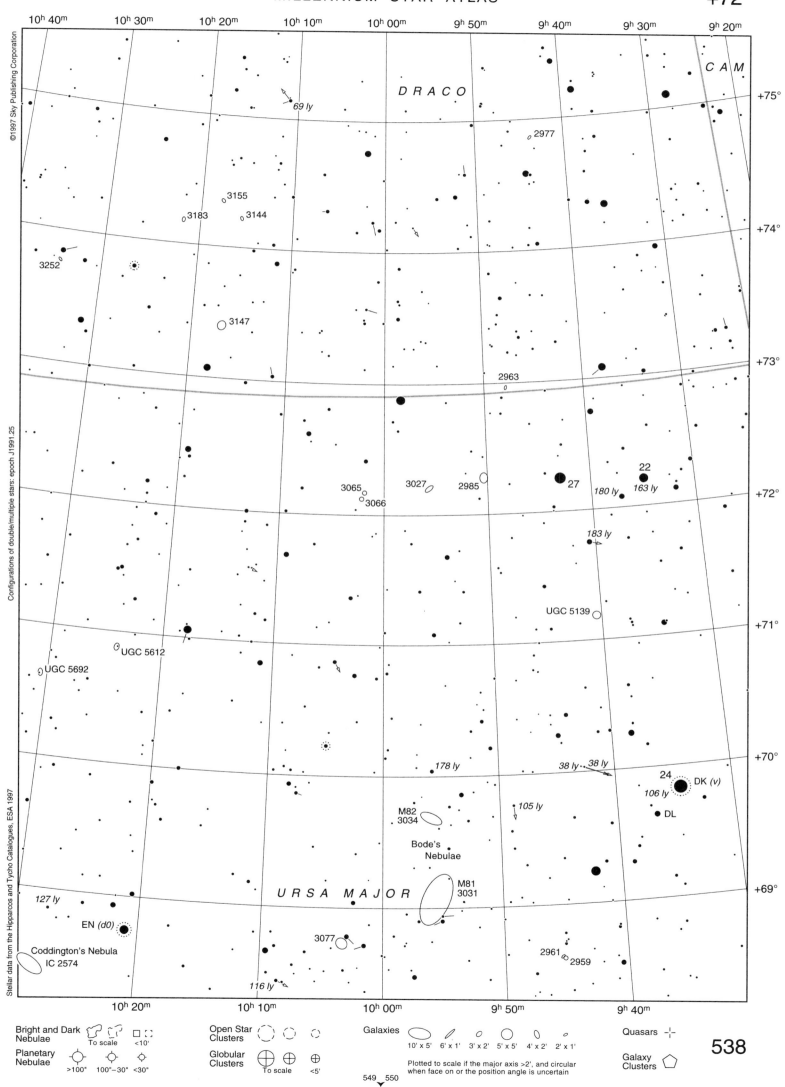

C A M

D R A C O

69 ly

2977

3155
3183   3144

3252

3147

2963

3065   3027   2985   27   180 ly   22
3066   163 ly

183 ly

UGC 5139

UGC 5612

UGC 5692

178 ly   38 ly   38 ly
                                              24
                                              DK (v)
                                    105 ly   106 ly
M82
3034   DL

Bode's
Nebulae

U R S A   M A J O R   M81
                             3031
127 ly

EN (d0)

3077   2961 2959

Coddington's Nebula
IC 2574

116 ly

Bright and Dark Nebulae			Open Star Clusters			Galaxies							Quasars
		To scale <10'				10' x 5' 6' x 1' 3' x 2' 5' x 5' 4' x 2' 2' x 1'						
Planetary Nebulae			Globular Clusters										Galaxy Clusters
>100" 100"-30" <30"			To scale <5'			Plotted to scale if the major axis >2', and circular when face on or the position angle is uncertain						

538

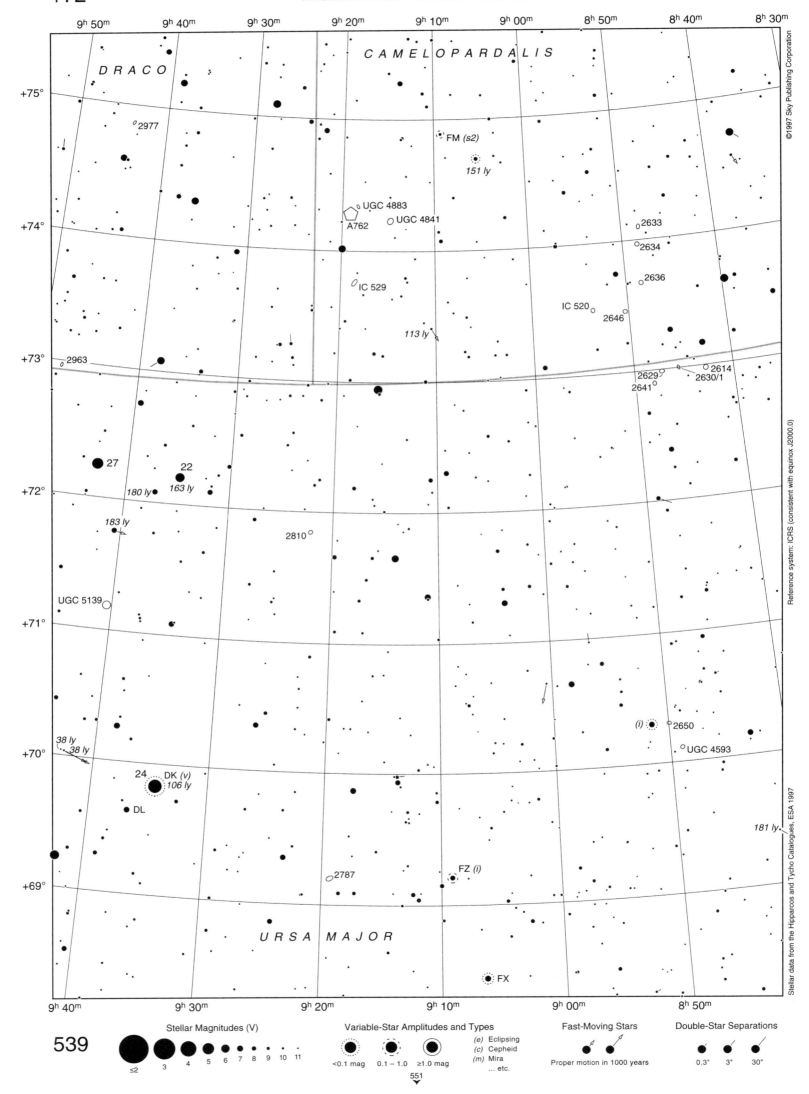

©1997 Sky Publishing Corporation

Reference system: ICRS (consistent with equinox J2000.0)

Stellar data from the Hipparcos and Tycho Catalogues, ESA 1997

539

Stellar Magnitudes (V)

≤2   3   4   5   6   7   8   9   10   11

Variable-Star Amplitudes and Types

<0.1 mag   0.1 – 1.0   ≥1.0 mag

(e) Eclipsing
(c) Cepheid
(m) Mira
... etc.

Fast-Moving Stars

Proper motion in 1000 years

Double-Star Separations

0.3"   3"   30"

MILLENNIUM STAR ATLAS

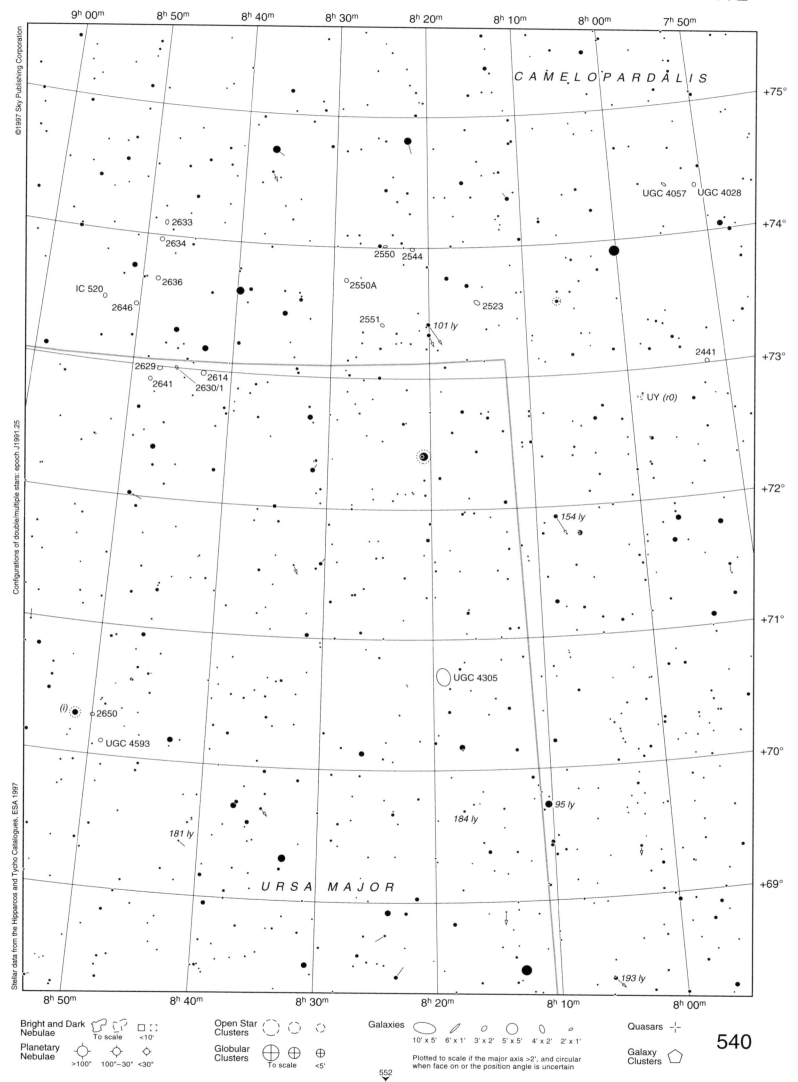

Configurations of double/multiple stars: epoch J1991.25

Stellar data from the Hipparcos and Tycho Catalogues, ESA 1997

CAMELOPARDALIS

URSA MAJOR

UGC 4057   UGC 4028

2633
2634
2636
IC 520
2646
2629
2641   2614
2630/1

2550 2544
2550A
2523
2551   101 ly
2441
UY (r0)

154 ly

UGC 4305

(i) 2650
UGC 4593

95 ly
184 ly
181 ly

193 ly

9h 00m   8h 50m   8h 40m   8h 30m   8h 20m   8h 10m   8h 00m   7h 50m

+75°
+74°
+73°
+72°
+71°
+70°
+69°

8h 50m   8h 40m   8h 30m   8h 20m   8h 10m   8h 00m

Bright and Dark Nebulae			
To scale		<10'	

Planetary Nebulae		
>100"	100"–30"	<30"

Open Star Clusters		

Globular Clusters	
To scale	<5'

Galaxies					
10' x 5'	6' x 1'	3' x 2'	5' x 5'	4' x 2'	2' x 1'

Plotted to scale if the major axis >2', and circular when face on or the position angle is uncertain

Quasars -|-

Galaxy Clusters

552

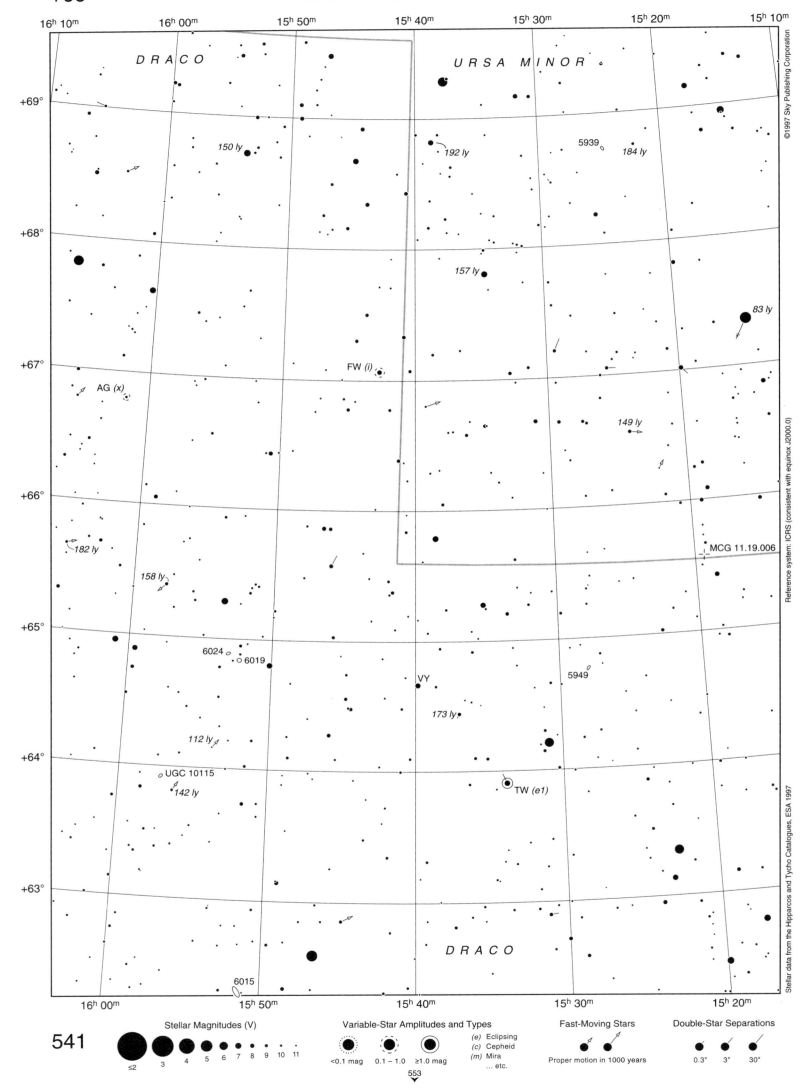

DRACO

URSA MINOR

DRACO

5939

MCG 11.19.006

6024   6019

5949

VY

173 ly

UGC 10115

112 ly

142 ly

TW (e1)

FW (i)

AG (x)

182 ly

158 ly

150 ly

192 ly

157 ly

83 ly

149 ly

184 ly

6015

541

Stellar Magnitudes (V)	Variable-Star Amplitudes and Types	Fast-Moving Stars	Double-Star Separations
≤2 3 4 5 6 7 8 9 10 11	<0.1 mag 0.1 – 1.0 ≥1.0 mag	Proper motion in 1000 years	0.3" 3" 30"

(e) Eclipsing
(c) Cepheid
(m) Mira
... etc.

MILLENNIUM STAR ATLAS

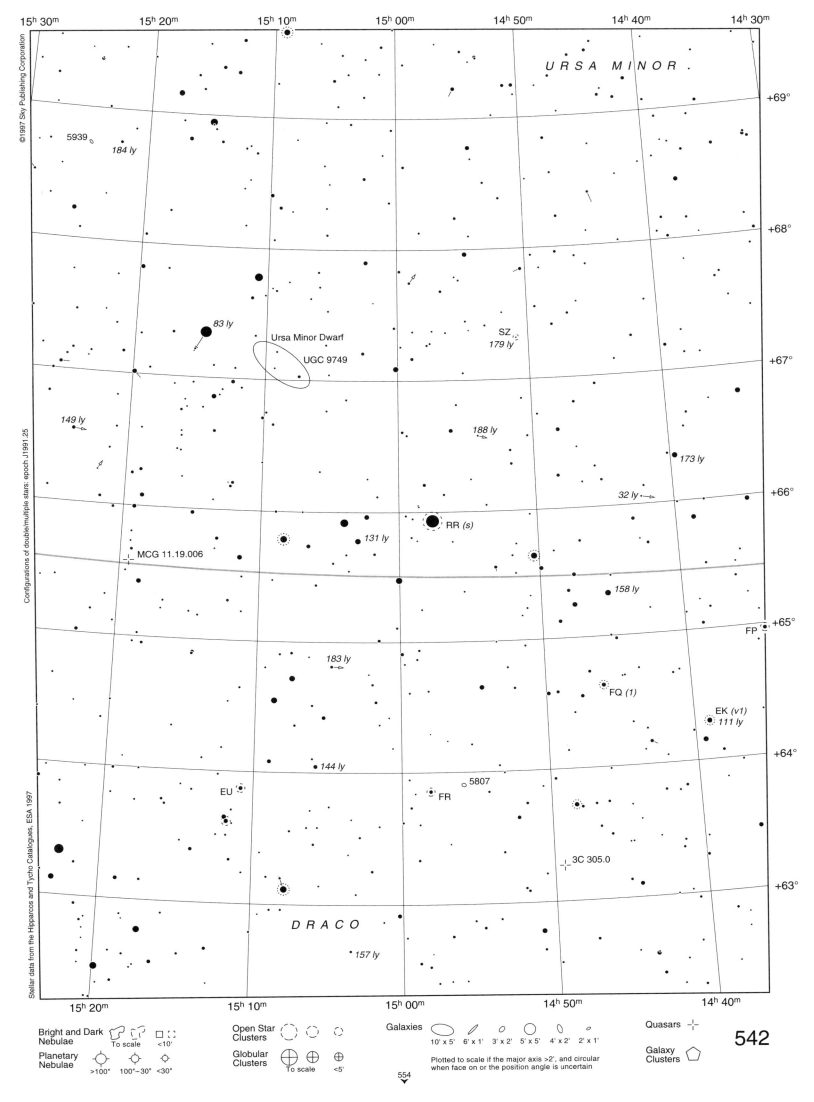

15ʰ30ᵐ 15ʰ20ᵐ 15ʰ10ᵐ 15ʰ00ᵐ 14ʰ50ᵐ 14ʰ40ᵐ 14ʰ30ᵐ

U R S A   M I N O R

+69°

+68°

5939

184 ly

83 ly

Ursa Minor Dwarf

UGC 9749

SZ
179 ly

+67°

149 ly

188 ly

173 ly

32 ly

+66°

MCG 11.19.006

RR *(s)*

131 ly

158 ly

FP +65°

183 ly

FQ *(1)*

EK *(v1)*
111 ly

+64°

144 ly

EU

5807

FR

3C 305.0

+63°

D R A C O

157 ly

15ʰ20ᵐ 15ʰ10ᵐ 15ʰ00ᵐ 14ʰ50ᵐ 14ʰ40ᵐ

Bright and Dark
Nebulae
To scale   <10'

Planetary
Nebulae
>100" 100"–30" <30"

Open Star
Clusters

Globular
Clusters
To scale   <5'

Galaxies
10' x 5' 6' x 1' 3' x 2' 5' x 5' 4' x 2' 2' x 1'

Plotted to scale if the major axis >2', and circular
when face on or the position angle is uncertain

Quasars

Galaxy
Clusters

542

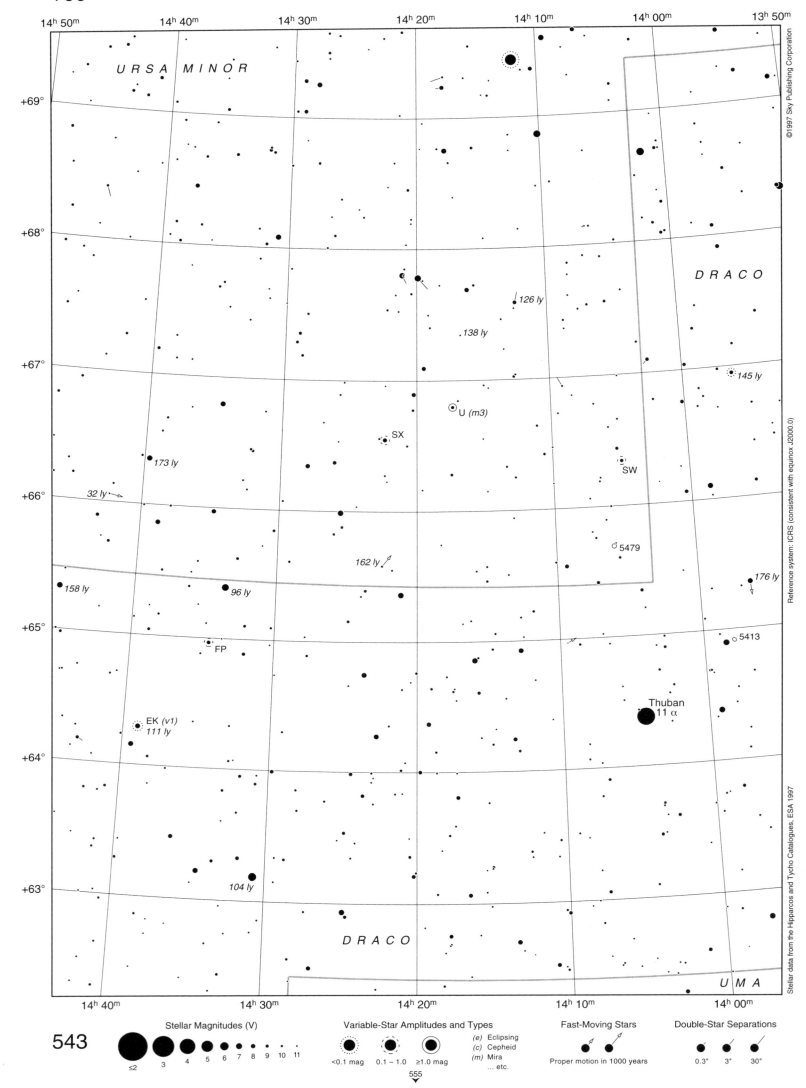

©1997 Sky Publishing Corporation

Reference system: ICRS (consistent with equinox J2000.0)

Stellar data from the Hipparcos and Tycho Catalogues, ESA 1997

U R S A   M I N O R

D R A C O

126 ly

138 ly

145 ly

U (m3)

SX

SW

173 ly

32 ly

♂ 5479

162 ly

176 ly

158 ly

96 ly

○ 5413

FP

Thuban
11 α

EK (v1)
111 ly

104 ly

D R A C O

U M A

543

Stellar Magnitudes (V)

≤2   3   4   5   6   7   8   9 10 11

Variable-Star Amplitudes and Types

<0.1 mag   0.1 – 1.0   ≥1.0 mag

(e) Eclipsing
(c) Cepheid
(m) Mira
... etc.

Fast-Moving Stars

Proper motion in 1000 years

Double-Star Separations

0.3"   3"   30"

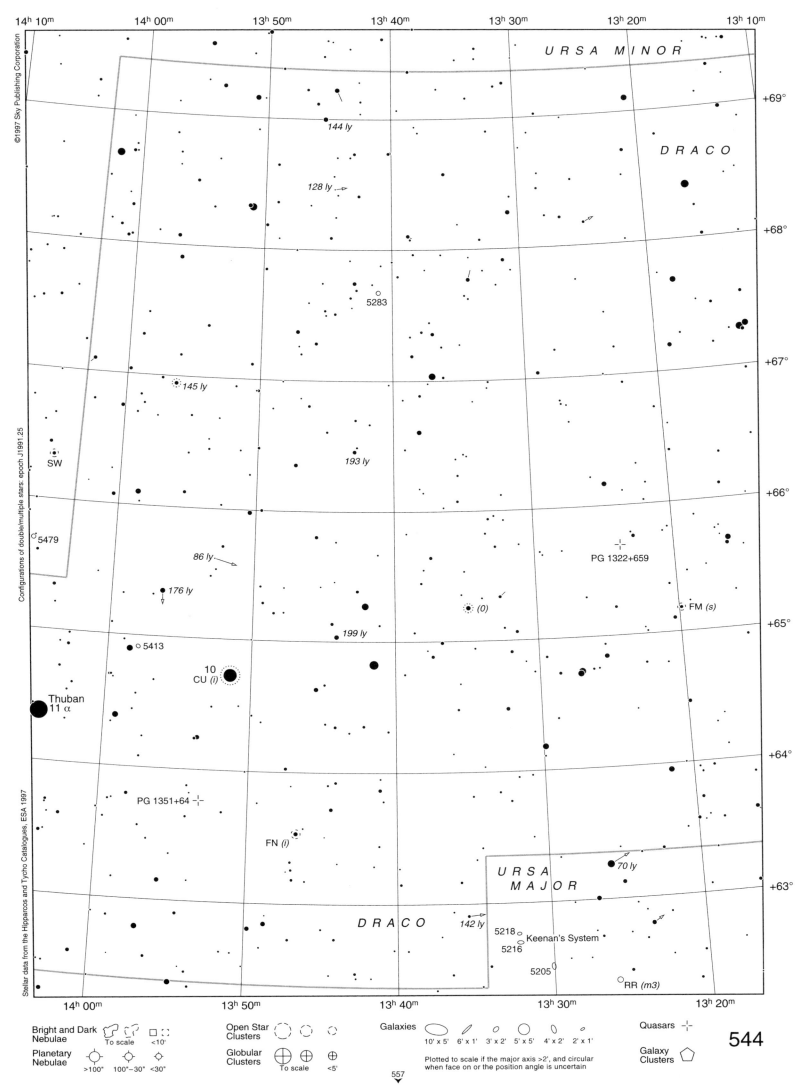

Configurations of double/multiple stars: epoch J1991.25

Stellar data from the Hipparcos and Tycho Catalogues, ESA 1997

URSA MINOR

DRACO

+69°

144 ly

128 ly

+68°

5283

+67°

145 ly

SW

193 ly

+66°

PG 1322+659

5479

86 ly

176 ly

(0)

FM (s)

+65°

199 ly

5413

10
CU (i)

Thuban
11 α

+64°

PG 1351+64

FN (i)

URSA
MAJOR

70 ly

+63°

DRACO

142 ly

5218

Keenan's System

5216

5205

RR (m3)

Bright and Dark Nebulae	To scale <10'	
Planetary Nebulae	>100" 100"–30" <30"	
Open Star Clusters		
Globular Clusters	To scale <5'	
Galaxies	10' x 5' 6' x 1' 3' x 2' 5' x 5' 4' x 2' 2' x 1'	
Quasars		
Galaxy Clusters		

Plotted to scale if the major axis >2', and circular when face on or the position angle is uncertain

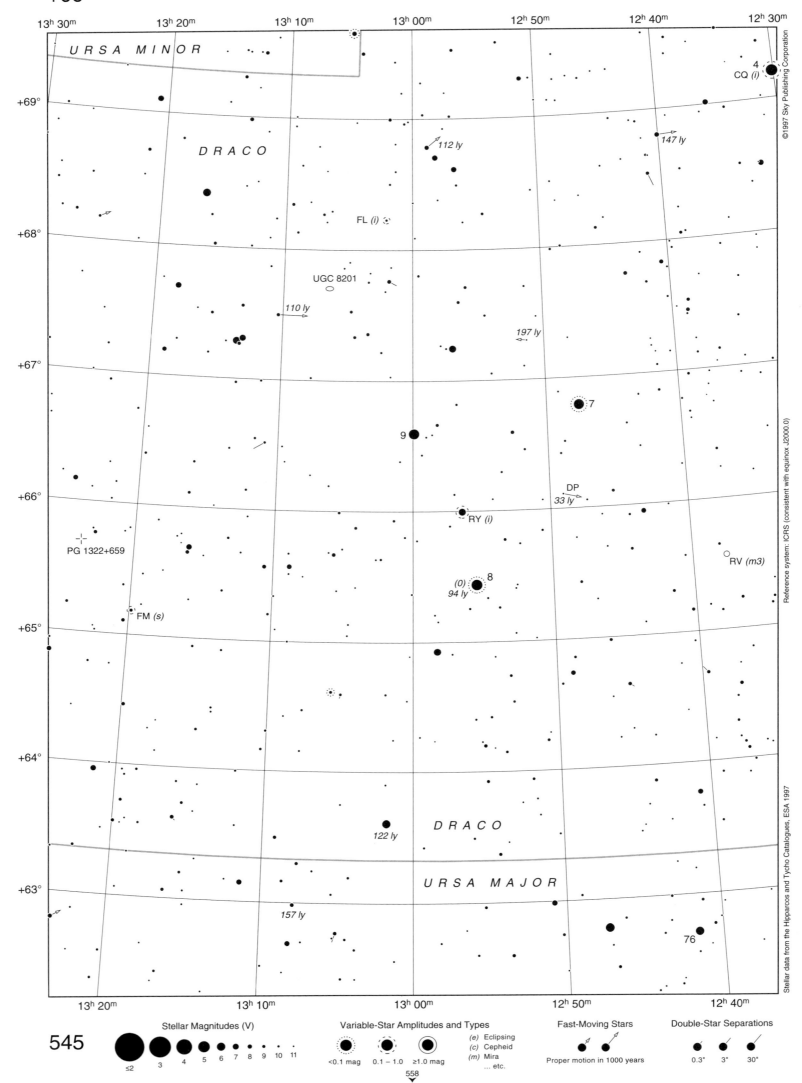

©1997 Sky Publishing Corporation

Reference system: ICRS (consistent with equinox J2000.0)

Stellar data from the Hipparcos and Tycho Catalogues, ESA 1997

URSA MINOR

DRACO

UGC 8201

PG 1322+659

FM (s)

FL (i)

RY (i)

DP
33 ly

(0)
94 ly

8

7

9

RV (m3)

112 ly

147 ly

110 ly

197 ly

4
CQ (i)

122 ly

DRACO

URSA MAJOR

157 ly

76

545

Stellar Magnitudes (V)

≤2 3 4 5 6 7 8 9 10 11

Variable-Star Amplitudes and Types

<0.1 mag   0.1 – 1.0   ≥1.0 mag

(e) Eclipsing
(c) Cepheid
(m) Mira
... etc.

Fast-Moving Stars

Proper motion in 1000 years

Double-Star Separations

0.3"   3"   30"

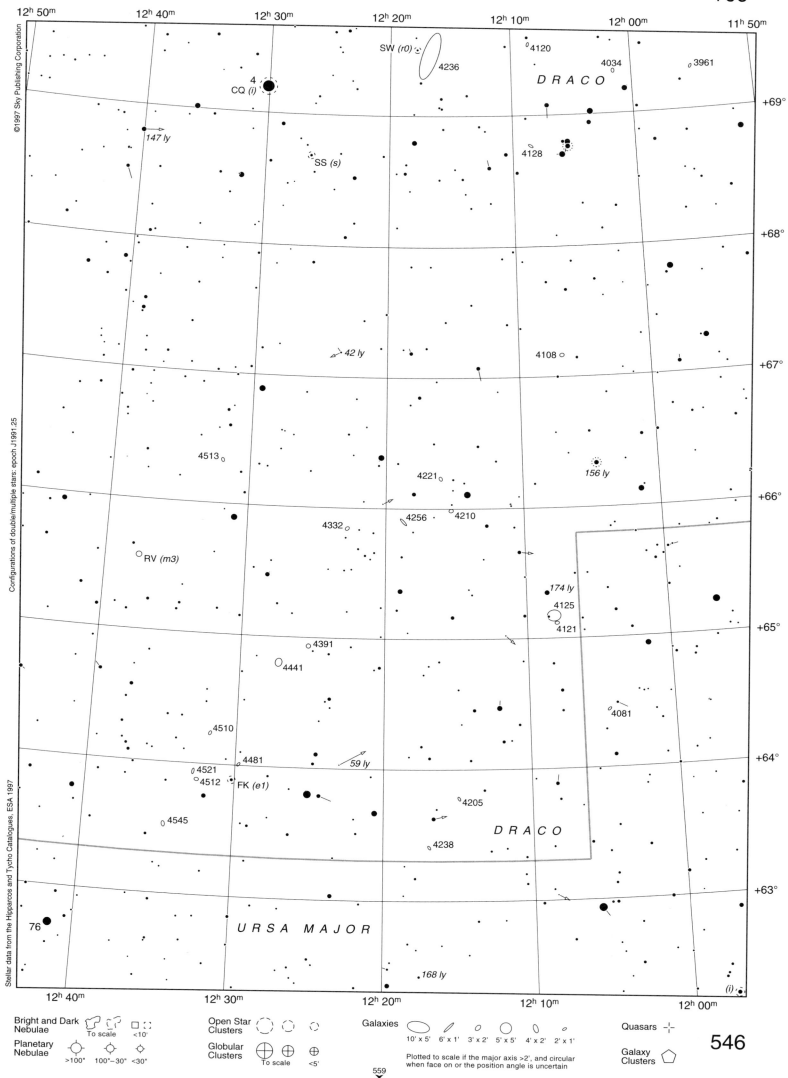

SW *(r0)*

4236

4120

4034

3961

D R A C O

CQ *(i)*   4

147 ly

SS *(s)*

4128

+69°

+68°

42 ly

4108

+67°

4513

4221

156 ly

+66°

4332   4256   4210

RV *(m3)*

174 ly

4125

4121

+65°

4391

4441

4081

4510

4521

4481

59 ly

4512   FK *(e1)*

4205

4545

4238

D R A C O

+64°

76

U R S A   M A J O R

+63°

168 ly

(i)

Bright and Dark Nebulae	To scale	<10'
Planetary Nebulae	>100" 100"–30" <30"	
Open Star Clusters		
Globular Clusters	To scale	<5'
Galaxies	10' x 5' 6' x 1' 3' x 2' 5' x 5' 4' x 2' 2' x 1'	
	Plotted to scale if the major axis >2', and circular when face on or the position angle is uncertain	
Quasars		
Galaxy Clusters		

546

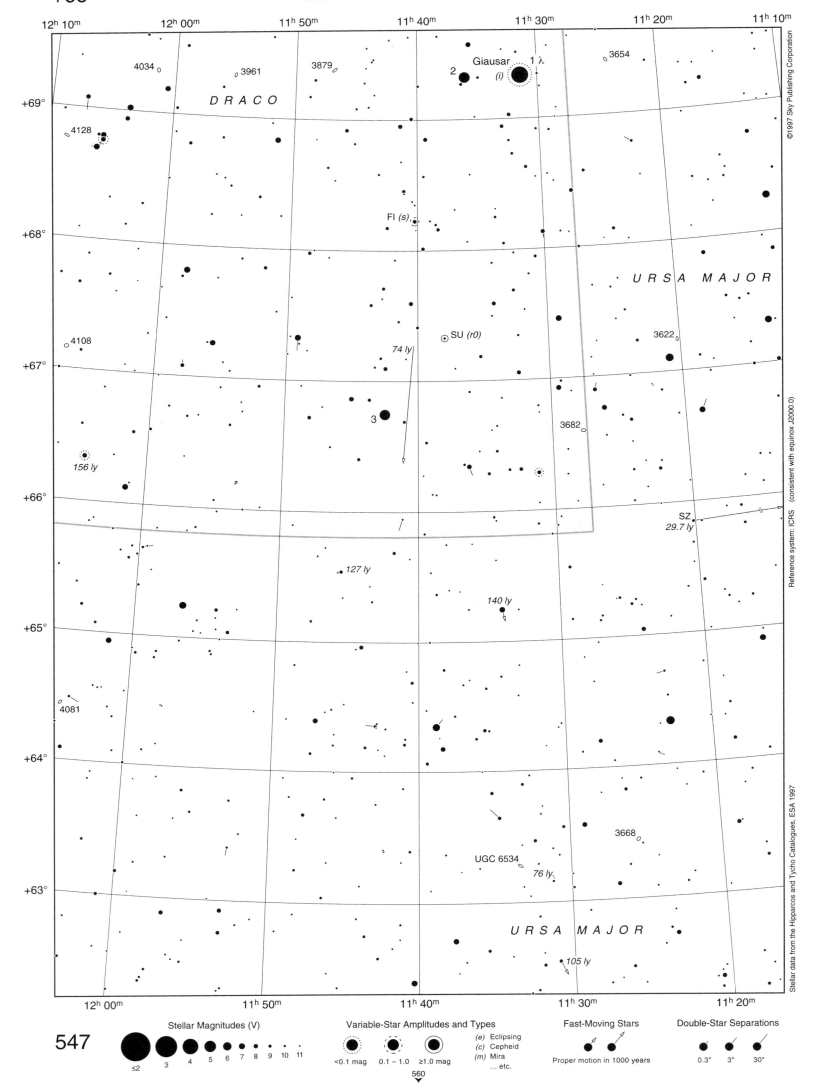

©1997 Sky Publishing Corporation

Reference system: ICRS   (consistent with equinox J2000.0)

Stellar data from the Hipparcos and Tycho Catalogues, ESA 1997

547

Stellar Magnitudes (V)	Variable-Star Amplitudes and Types	Fast-Moving Stars	Double-Star Separations

≤2 3 4 5 6 7 8 9 10 11

<0.1 mag   0.1 – 1.0   ≥1.0 mag

(e) Eclipsing
(c) Cepheid
(m) Mira
... etc.

Proper motion in 1000 years

0.3"   3"   30"

560

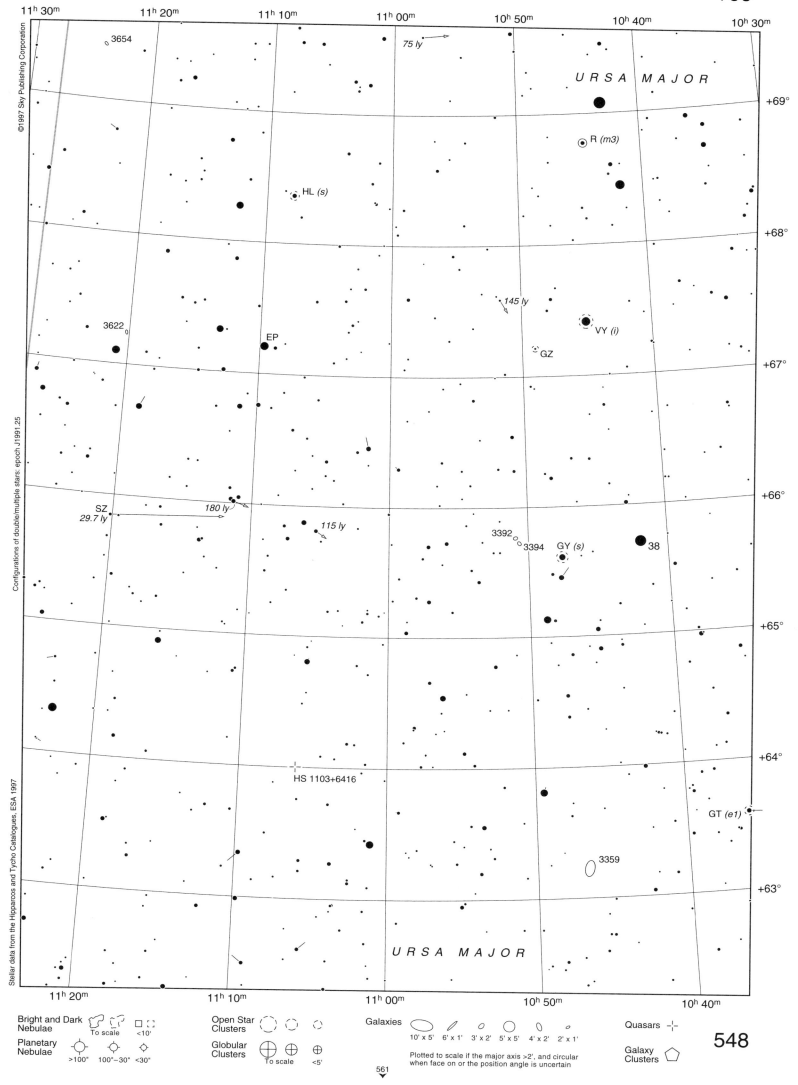

11h 30m 11h 20m 11h 10m 11h 00m 10h 50m 10h 40m 10h 30m

©1997 Sky Publishing Corporation

3654

URSA MAJOR

+69°

R (m3)

HL (s)

+68°

145 ly

VY (i)

GZ

3622

EP

+67°

Configurations of double/multiple stars: epoch J1991.25

SZ
29.7 ly

180 ly

+66°

115 ly

3392
3394

GY (s)

38

+65°

Stellar data from the Hipparcos and Tycho Catalogues, ESA 1997

+64°

HS 1103+6416

GT (e1)

3359

+63°

URSA MAJOR

11h 20m 11h 10m 11h 00m 10h 50m 10h 40m

Bright and Dark Nebulae			Open Star Clusters			Galaxies						Quasars
To scale		<10'				10' x 5'	6' x 1'	3' x 2'	5' x 5'	4' x 2'	2' x 1'	

Planetary Nebulae			Globular Clusters						Galaxy Clusters
>100"	100"–30"	<30"	To scale	<5'					

Plotted to scale if the major axis >2', and circular
when face on or the position angle is uncertain

548

561

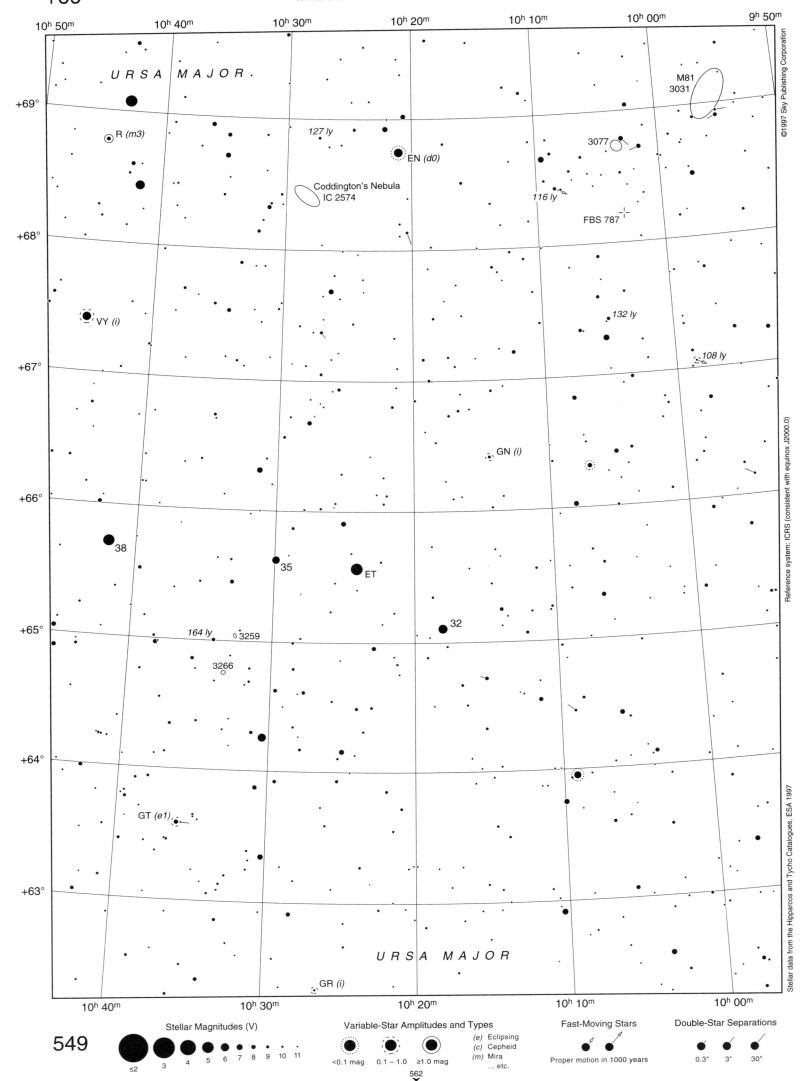

URSA MAJOR

R (m3)

127 ly

EN (d0)

Coddington's Nebula
IC 2574

M81
3031

3077

116 ly

FBS 787

VY (i)

132 ly

108 ly

GN (i)

38

35

ET

32

164 ly

3259

3266

GT (e1)

URSA MAJOR

GR (i)

©1997 Sky Publishing Corporation

Reference system: ICRS (consistent with equinox J2000.0)

Stellar data from the Hipparcos and Tycho Catalogues, ESA 1997

549

Stellar Magnitudes (V)

≤2   3   4   5   6   7   8   9   10   11

Variable-Star Amplitudes and Types

<0.1 mag   0.1 – 1.0   ≥1.0 mag

(e) Eclipsing
(c) Cepheid
(m) Mira
... etc.

Fast-Moving Stars

Proper motion in 1000 years

Double-Star Separations

0.3"   3"   30"

MILLENNIUM STAR ATLAS

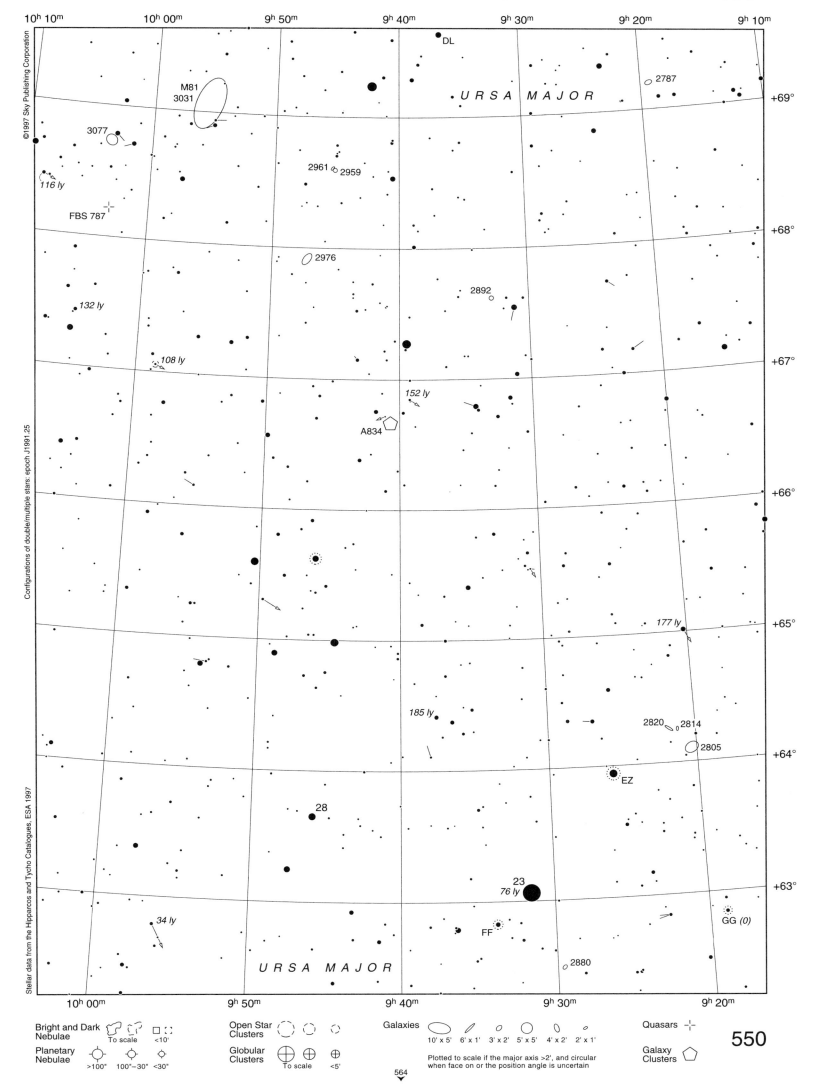

URSA MAJOR

URSA MAJOR

M81
3031

3077

116 ly

FBS 787

132 ly

108 ly

2961 2959

2976

DL

2787

2892

152 ly

A834

177 ly

185 ly

2820 2814

2805

EZ

28

2880

23
76 ly

FF

GG (0)

34 ly

| Bright and Dark Nebulae | | To scale | <10' |
| Planetary Nebulae | >100" | 100"–30" | <30" |

| Open Star Clusters | | |
| Globular Clusters | | To scale | <5' |

| Galaxies | 10' x 5' | 6' x 1' | 3' x 2' | 5' x 5' | 4' x 2' | 2' x 1' |

Plotted to scale if the major axis >2', and circular when face on or the position angle is uncertain

| Quasars | |
| Galaxy Clusters | |

550

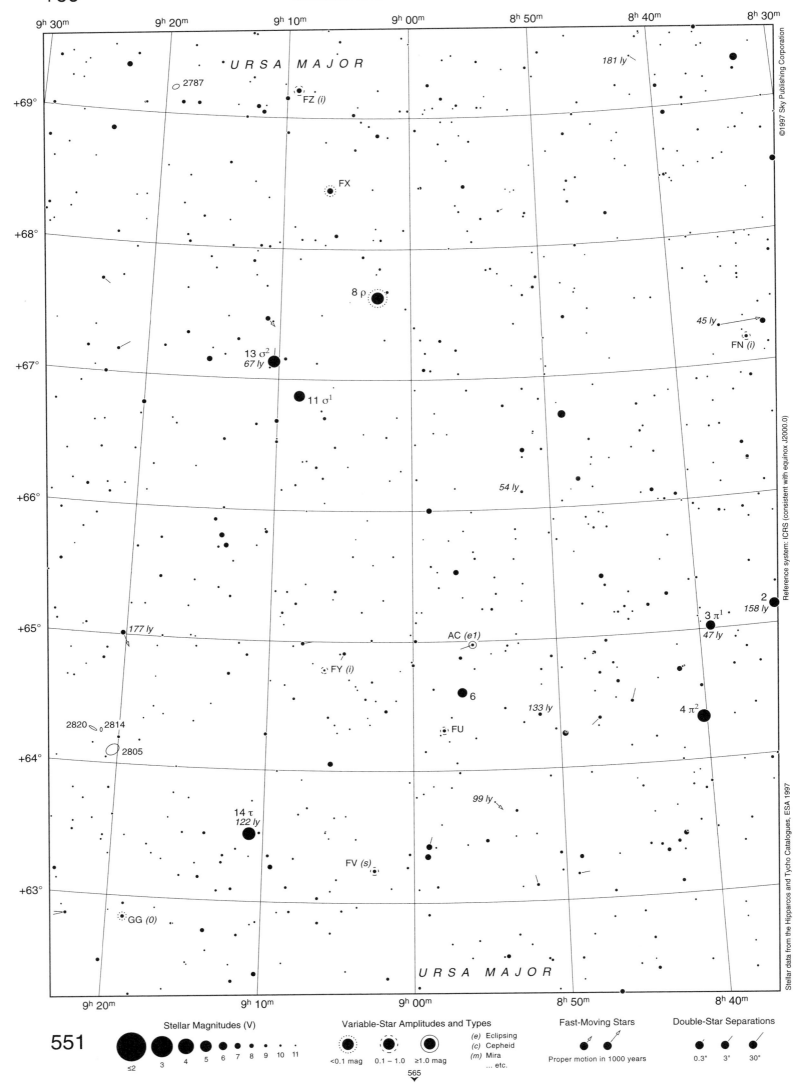

URSA MAJOR

2787

FZ (i)

FX

8 ρ

13 σ² ⌋
67 ly

11 σ¹

181 ly

45 ly

FN (i)

54 ly

2
158 ly

3 π¹
47 ly

177 ly

AC (e1)

FY (i)

6

133 ly

4 π²

FU

2820   2814

2805

14 τ
122 ly

99 ly

FV (s)

GG (0)

URSA MAJOR

©1997 Sky Publishing Corporation

Reference system: ICRS (consistent with equinox J2000.0)

Stellar data from the Hipparcos and Tycho Catalogues, ESA 1997

551

Stellar Magnitudes (V)

≤2   3   4   5   6 7 8 9 10 11

Variable-Star Amplitudes and Types

<0.1 mag   0.1 – 1.0   ≥1.0 mag

(e) Eclipsing
(c) Cepheid
(m) Mira
... etc.

Fast-Moving Stars

Proper motion in 1000 years

Double-Star Separations

0.3"   3"   30"

MILLENNIUM STAR ATLAS

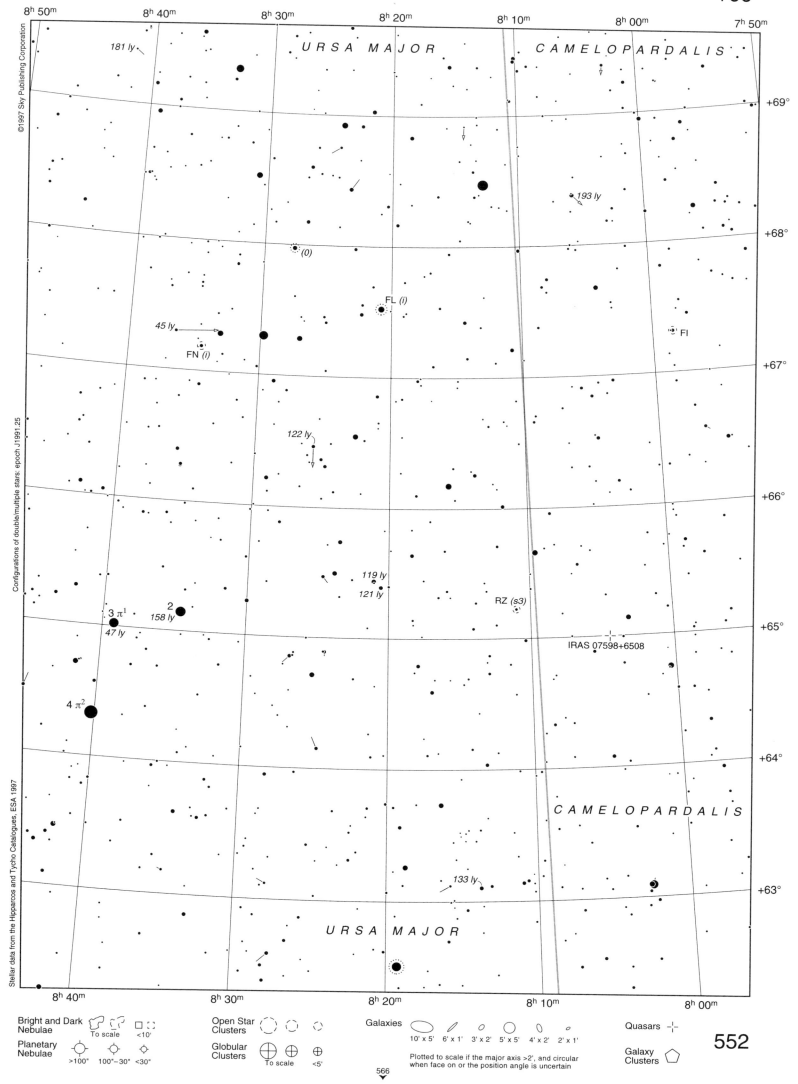

URSA MAJOR   CAMELOPARDALIS

181 ly

+69°

193 ly

+68°

(0)

FL (i)

45 ly

FN (i)

FI

+67°

122 ly

+66°

119 ly

121 ly

RZ (s3)

2

3 π¹   158 ly

47 ly

IRAS 07598+6508

+65°

4 π²

+64°

CAMELOPARDALIS

133 ly

+63°

URSA MAJOR

Bright and Dark Nebulae				Open Star Clusters			Galaxies							Quasars
	To scale	<10'					10' x 5'	6' x 1'	3' x 2'	5' x 5'	4' x 2'	2' x 1'		
Planetary Nebulae				Globular Clusters										Galaxy Clusters
	>100"	100"–30"	<30"		To scale	<5'	Plotted to scale if the major axis >2', and circular when face on or the position angle is uncertain							

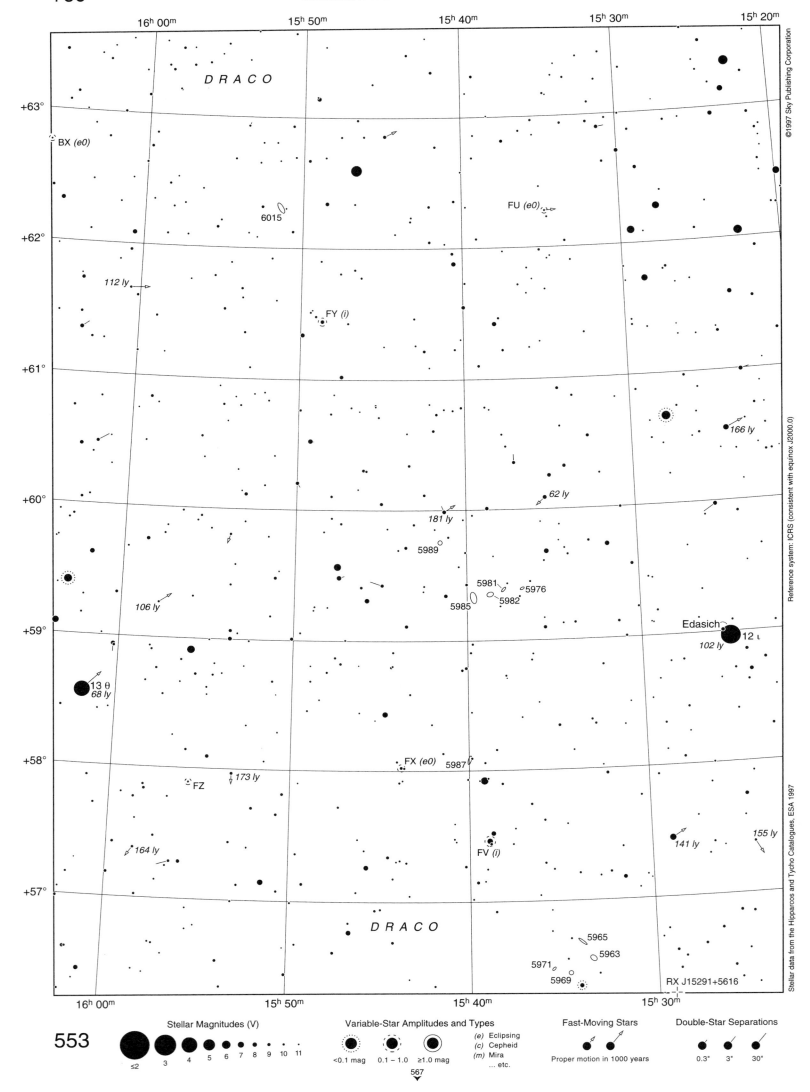

©1997 Sky Publishing Corporation

Reference system: ICRS (consistent with equinox J2000.0)

Stellar data from the Hipparcos and Tycho Catalogues, ESA 1997

553

Stellar Magnitudes (V)

≤2 3 4 5 6 7 8 9 10 11

Variable-Star Amplitudes and Types

<0.1 mag   0.1 – 1.0 mag   ≥1.0 mag

(e) Eclipsing
(c) Cepheid
(m) Mira
... etc.

Fast-Moving Stars

Proper motion in 1000 years

Double-Star Separations

0.3"   3"   30"

MILLENNIUM STAR ATLAS

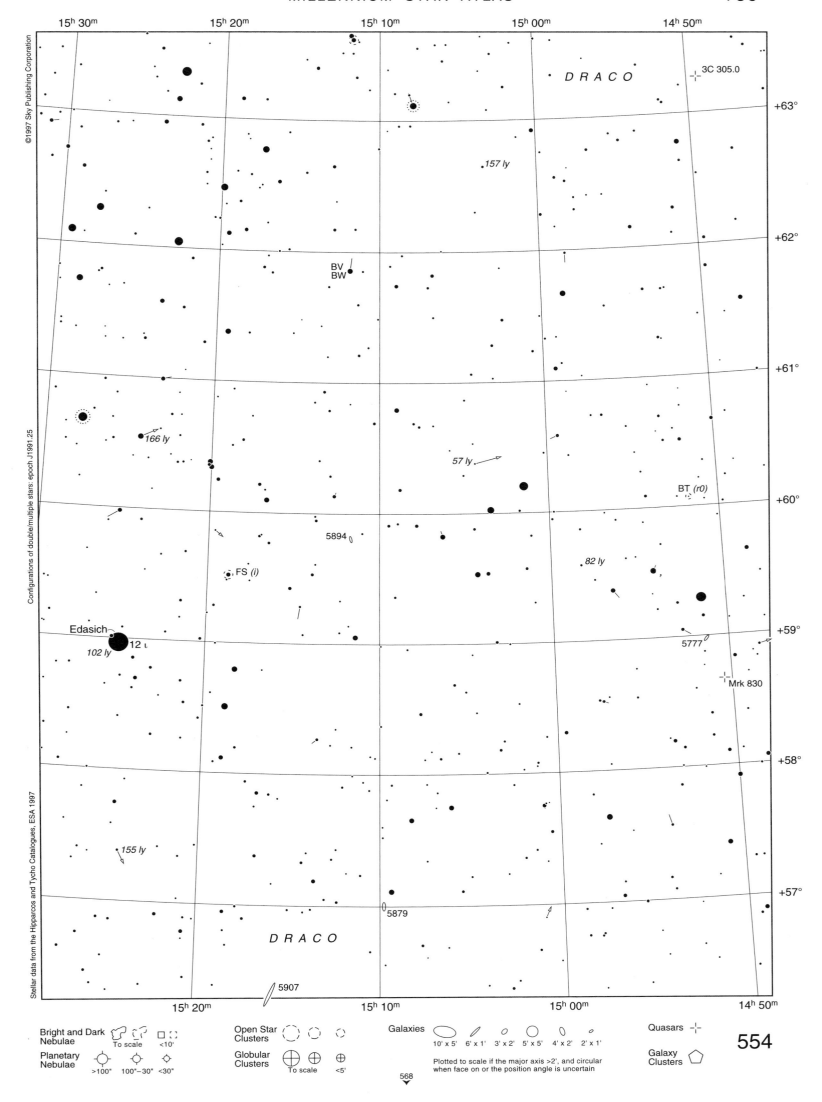

Configurations of double/multiple stars: epoch J1991.25

Stellar data from the Hipparcos and Tycho Catalogues, ESA 1997

15h 30m | 15h 20m | 15h 10m | 15h 00m | 14h 50m

D R A C O

3C 305.0

+63°

157 ly

+62°

BV
BW

+61°

166 ly

57 ly

BT *(r0)*

+60°

5894

82 ly

FS *(i)*

5777

+59°

Edasich
12 ι
102 ly

Mrk 830

+58°

155 ly

+57°

5879

D R A C O

5907

15h 20m | 15h 10m | 15h 00m | 14h 50m

Bright and Dark Nebulae
To scale   <10'

Open Star Clusters

Galaxies
10' x 5'   6' x 1'   3' x 2'   5' x 5'   4' x 2'   2' x 1'

Quasars

554

Planetary Nebulae
>100"   100"–30"   <30"

Globular Clusters
To scale   <5'

Plotted to scale if the major axis >2', and circular when face on or the position angle is uncertain

Galaxy Clusters

568

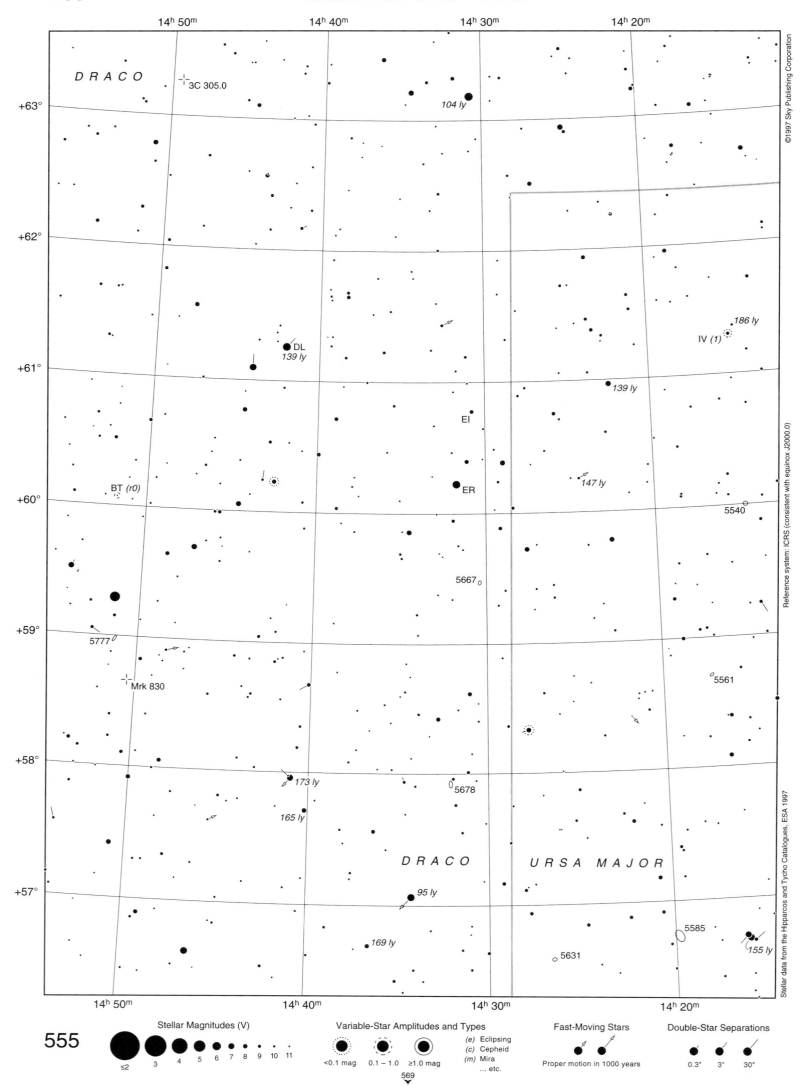

D R A C O

3C 305.0

104 ly

186 ly

IV (1)

DL
139 ly

139 ly

EI

BT (r0)

147 ly

ER

5540

5667

5777

Mrk 830

5561

173 ly

5678

165 ly

D R A C O   U R S A   M A J O R

95 ly

169 ly

5585

5631

155 ly

555

Stellar Magnitudes (V)

≤2   3   4   5   6   7   8   9 10 11

Variable-Star Amplitudes and Types

<0.1 mag   0.1 – 1.0   ≥1.0 mag

(e) Eclipsing
(c) Cepheid
(m) Mira
... etc.

Fast-Moving Stars

Proper motion in 1000 years

Double-Star Separations

0.3"   3"   30"

569

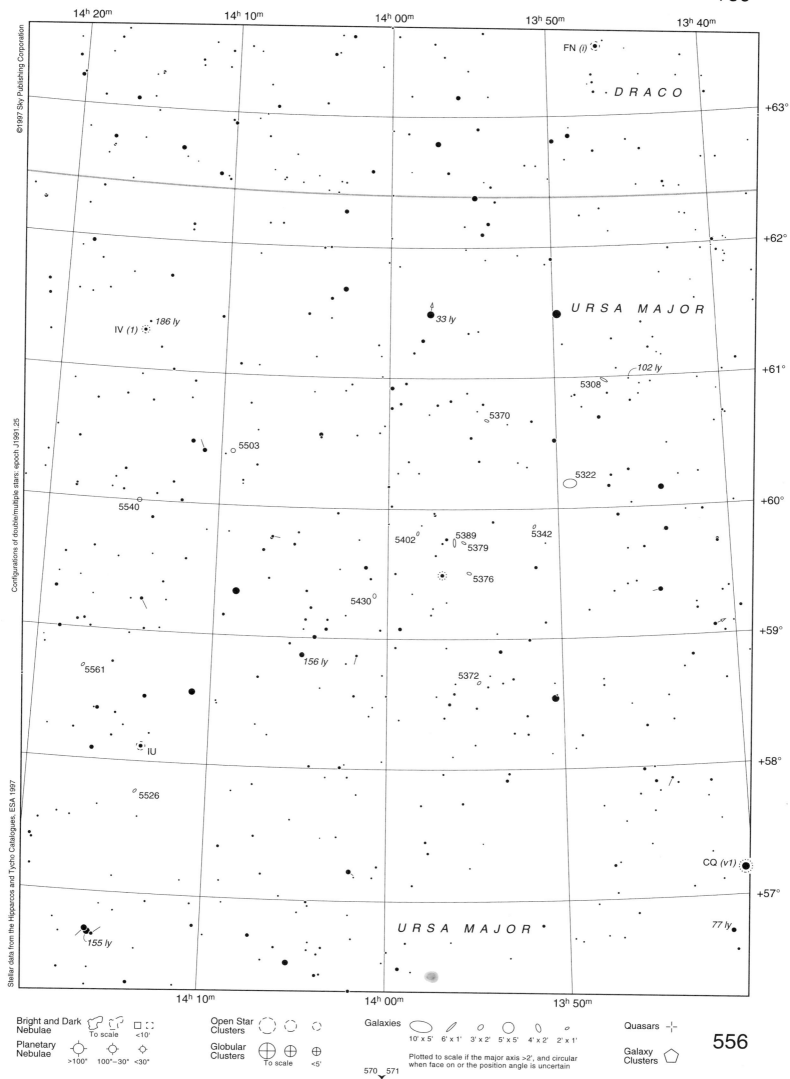

14h 20m   14h 10m   14h 00m   13h 50m   13h 40m

FN *(i)*

D R A C O

+63°

+62°

U R S A   M A J O R

186 ly

IV *(1)*

33 ly

102 ly

+61°

5308

5370

5503

5322

+60°

5540

5402   5389
5379
5342

5430   5376

+59°

5561

156 ly

5372

IU

+58°

5526

CQ *(v1)*

+57°

U R S A   M A J O R

77 ly

155 ly

14h 10m   14h 00m   13h 50m

Bright and Dark Nebulae   To scale   <10'

Planetary Nebulae   >100"   100"–30"   <30"

Open Star Clusters

Globular Clusters   To scale   <5'

Galaxies   10' x 5'   6' x 1'   3' x 2'   5' x 5'   4' x 2'   2' x 1'

Plotted to scale if the major axis >2', and circular when face on or the position angle is uncertain

Quasars

Galaxy Clusters

556

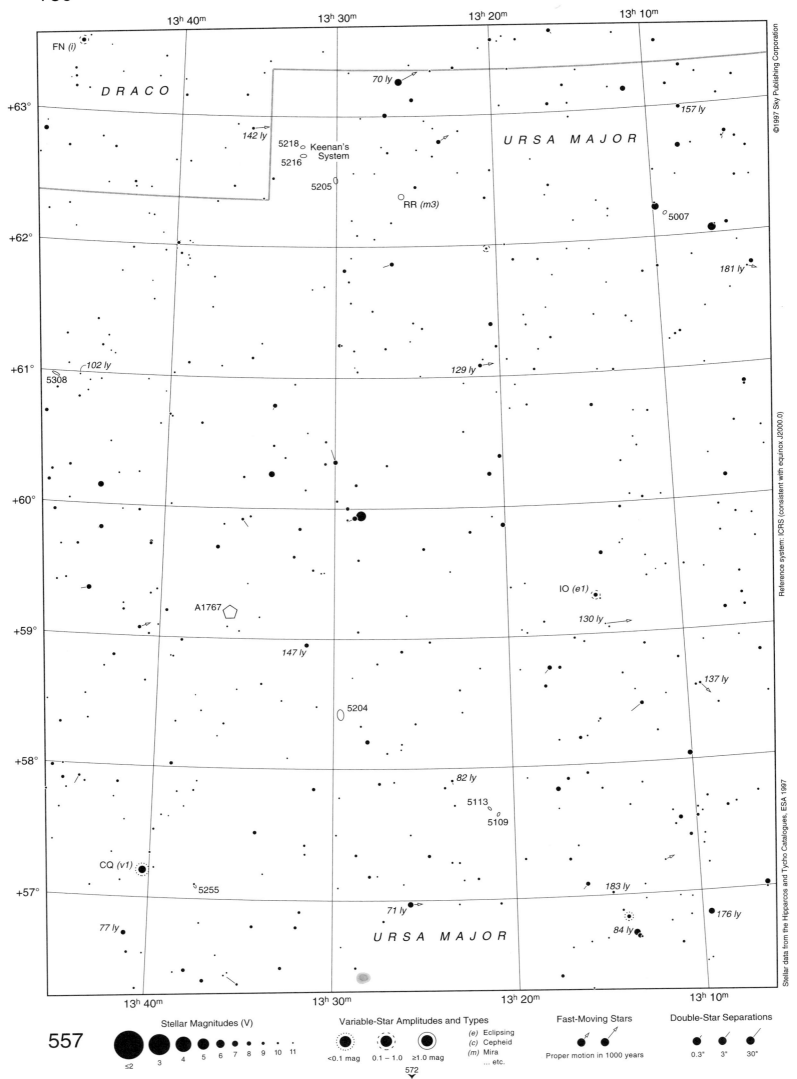

FN *(i)*

D R A C O

70 ly

142 ly

5218
5216

Keenan's
System

5205

RR *(m3)*

U R S A   M A J O R

157 ly

5007

181 ly

102 ly

129 ly

5308

IO *(e1)*

A1767

130 ly

147 ly

137 ly

5204

82 ly

5113
5109

CQ *(v1)*

5255

183 ly

176 ly

71 ly

77 ly

84 ly

U R S A   M A J O R

©1997 Sky Publishing Corporation

Reference system: ICRS (consistent with equinox J2000.0)

Stellar data from the Hipparcos and Tycho Catalogues, ESA 1997

Stellar Magnitudes (V)	Variable-Star Amplitudes and Types	Fast-Moving Stars	Double-Star Separations

Stellar Magnitudes (V)
≤2   3   4   5   6   7   8   9   10   11

Variable-Star Amplitudes and Types
<0.1 mag   0.1 – 1.0   ≥1.0 mag

(e) Eclipsing
(c) Cepheid
(m) Mira
... etc.

Fast-Moving Stars
Proper motion in 1000 years

Double-Star Separations
0.3"   3"   30"

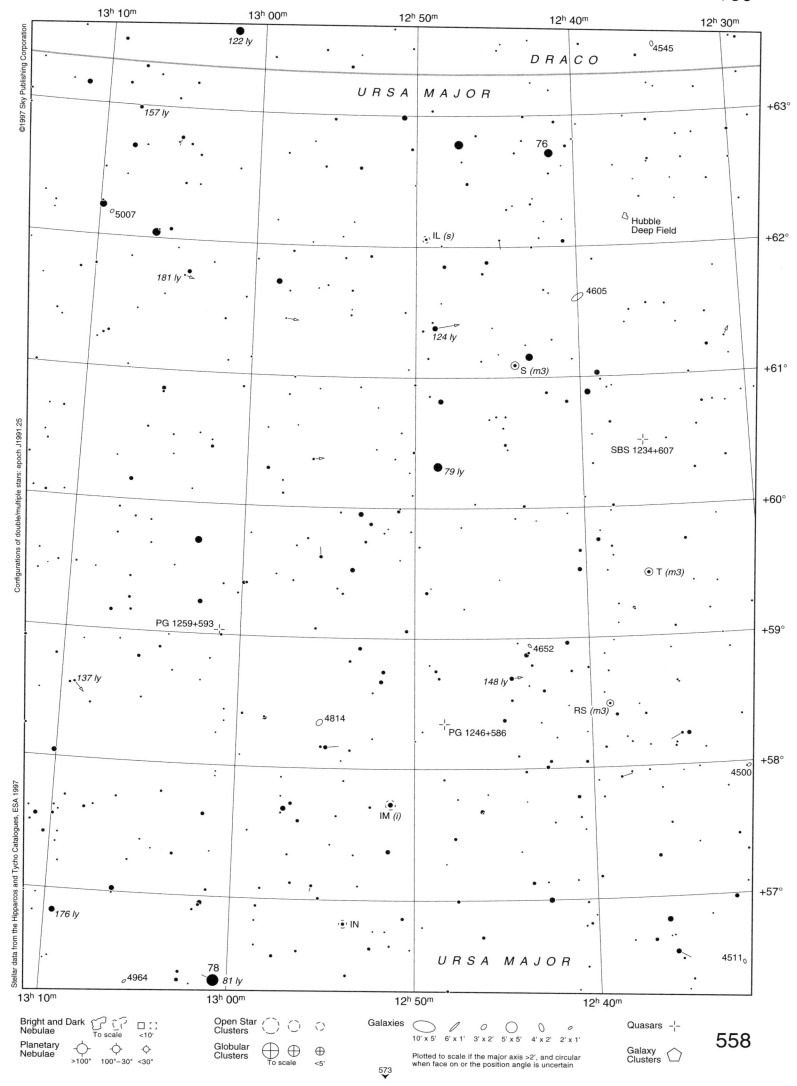

©1997 Sky Publishing Corporation

Configurations of double/multiple stars: epoch J1991.25

Stellar data from the Hipparcos and Tycho Catalogues, ESA 1997

DRACO

URSA MAJOR

122 ly

157 ly

4545

76

5007

IL (s)

181 ly

Hubble
Deep Field

4605

124 ly

S (m3)

SBS 1234+607

79 ly

T (m3)

PG 1259+593

4652

137 ly

148 ly

RS (m3)

4814

PG 1246+586

4500

IM (i)

176 ly

IN

URSA MAJOR

4511

78

4964

81 ly

Bright and Dark Nebulae	Open Star Clusters	Galaxies	Quasars

Bright and Dark Nebulae — To scale — <10'

Planetary Nebulae — >100" — 100"–30" — <30'

Open Star Clusters

Globular Clusters — To scale — <5'

Galaxies — 10' x 5'   6' x 1'   3' x 2'   5' x 5'   4' x 2'   2' x 1'
Plotted to scale if the major axis >2', and circular when face on or the position angle is uncertain

Quasars

Galaxy Clusters

558

573

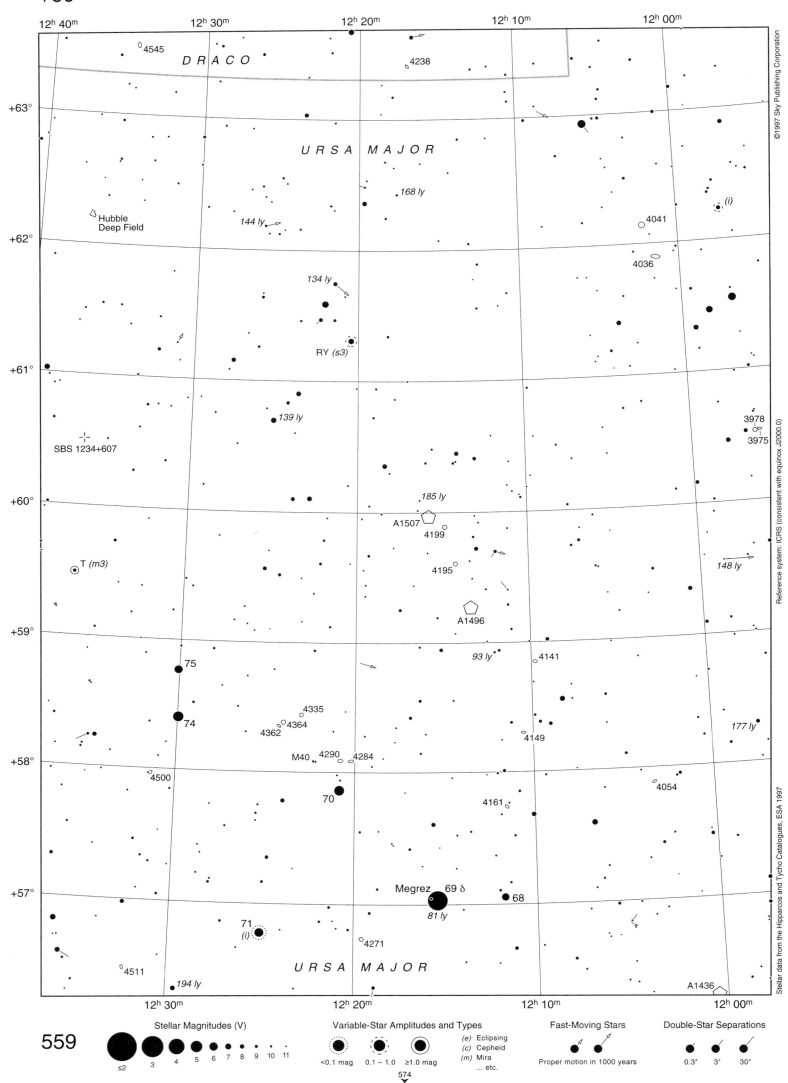

DRACO

4545

URSA MAJOR

4238

168 ly

144 ly

Hubble
Deep Field

134 ly

RY (s3)

(i)

4041

4036

139 ly

3978

3975

SBS 1234+607

185 ly

148 ly

A1507
4199

4195

T (m3)

A1496

93 ly

4141

75

4335

177 ly

74

4364
4362

4149

M40 4290 4284

4500

4054

70

4161

Megrez   69 δ

68

81 ly

71
(i)

4271

4511

URSA MAJOR

194 ly

A1436

Stellar Magnitudes (V)

≤2   3   4   5   6 7 8 9 10 11

Variable-Star Amplitudes and Types

<0.1 mag   0.1 – 1.0   ≥1.0 mag

(e) Eclipsing
(c) Cepheid
(m) Mira
... etc.

Fast-Moving Stars

Proper motion in 1000 years

Double-Star Separations

0.3"   3"   30"

574

©1997 Sky Publishing Corporation

Reference system: ICRS (consistent with equinox J2000.0)

Stellar data from the Hipparcos and Tycho Catalogues, ESA 1997

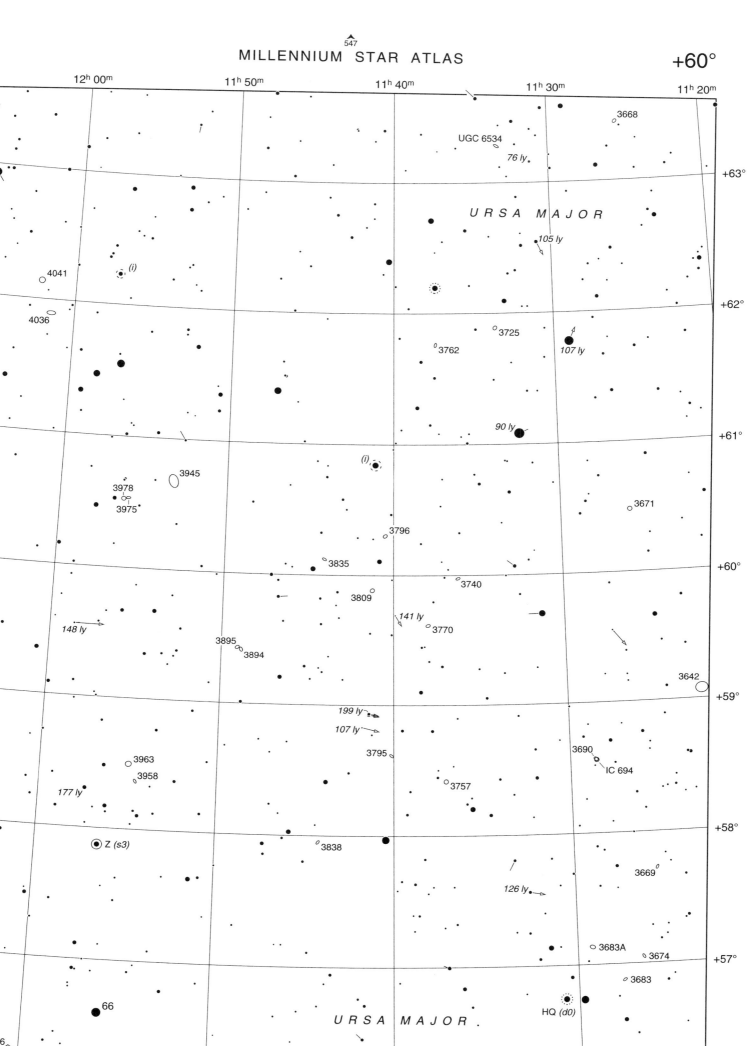

12ʰ 00ᵐ 11ʰ 50ᵐ 11ʰ 40ᵐ 11ʰ 30ᵐ 11ʰ 20ᵐ

3668

UGC 6534

76 ly

URSA MAJOR

+63°

105 ly

4041

(i)

+62°

4036

3725

3762

107 ly

90 ly

+61°

3945

(i)

3978
3975

3671

3796

+60°

3835

3740

3809

141 ly

148 ly

3770

3895
3894

3642

+59°

199 ly

107 ly

3963

3795

3690
IC 694

3958

3757

177 ly

+58°

Z (s3)

3838

3669

126 ly

3683A
3674

+57°

3683

66

HQ (d0)

A1436

URSA MAJOR

12ʰ 00ᵐ 11ʰ 50ᵐ 11ʰ 40ᵐ 11ʰ 30ᵐ

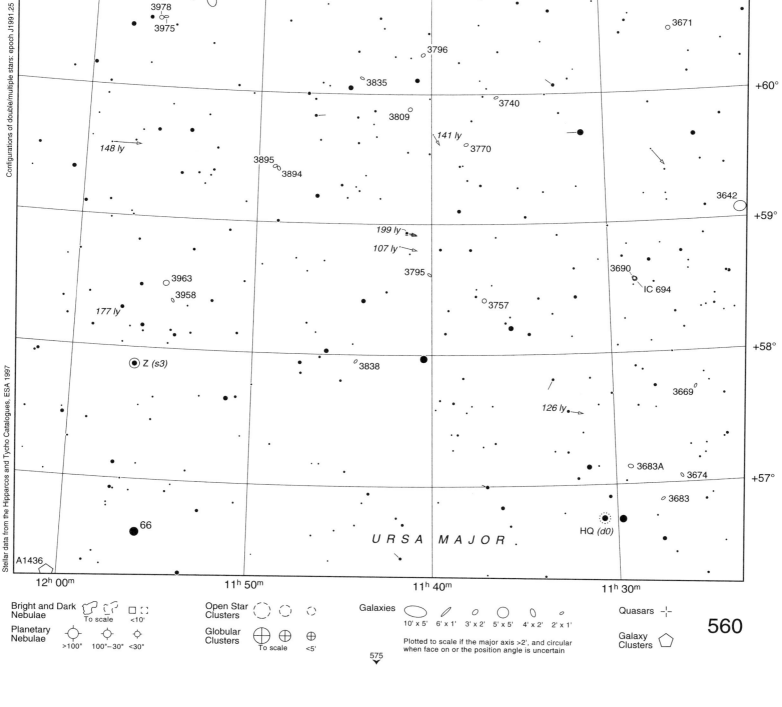

Bright and Dark Nebulae			Open Star Clusters			Galaxies						Quasars
To scale	<10'					10' x 5'	6' x 1'	3' x 2'	5' x 5'	4' x 2'	2' x 1'	
Planetary Nebulae			Globular Clusters									Galaxy Clusters
>100"	100"–30"	<30"	To scale	<5'								

Plotted to scale if the major axis >2', and circular when face on or the position angle is uncertain

575

560

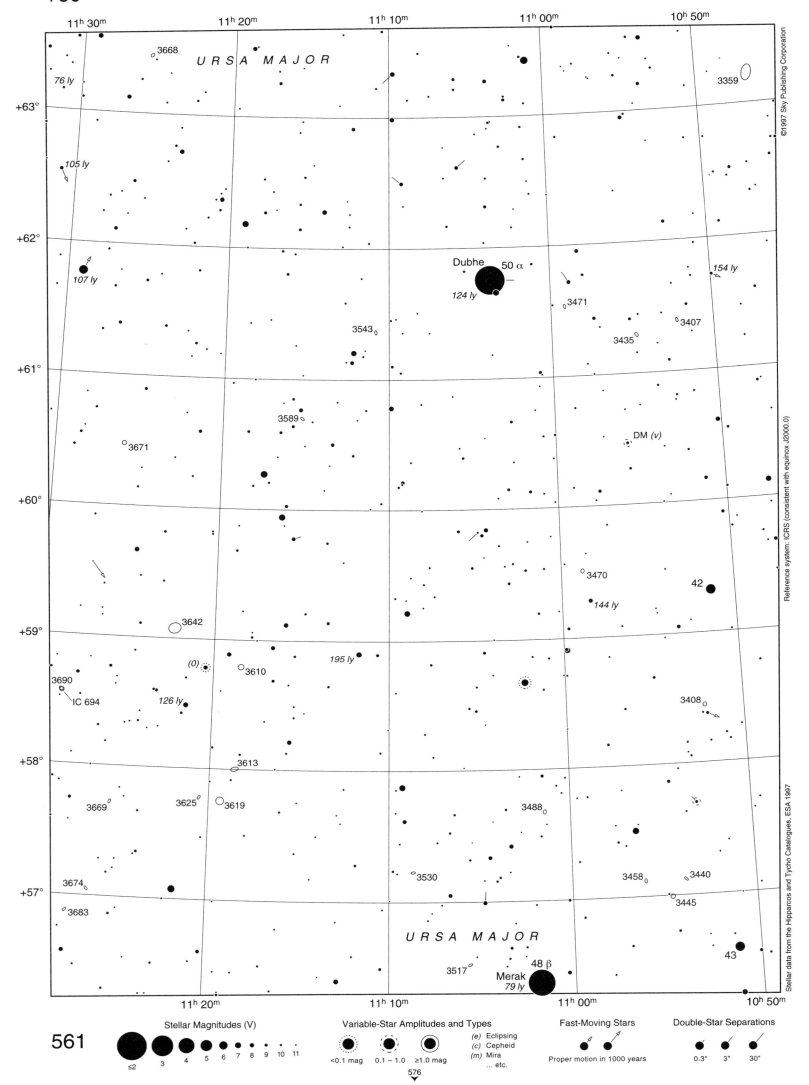

©1997 Sky Publishing Corporation

Reference system: ICRS (consistent with equinox J2000.0)

Stellar data from the Hipparcos and Tycho Catalogues, ESA 1997

URSA MAJOR

3668

76 ly

105 ly

107 ly

Dubhe   50 α
124 ly

154 ly

3543

3471

3407

3435

3589

DM (v)

3671

3470

42
144 ly

3642

(0)

3610

195 ly

3690
IC 694

126 ly

3408

3613

3669   3625   3619

3488

3674   3530

3458   3440

3683

3445

URSA MAJOR

3517

48 β
Merak
79 ly

43

Stellar Magnitudes (V)

≤2   3   4   5   6   7   8   9   10   11

Variable-Star Amplitudes and Types

<0.1 mag   0.1 – 1.0   ≥1.0 mag

(e) Eclipsing
(c) Cepheid
(m) Mira
... etc.

Fast-Moving Stars

Proper motion in 1000 years

Double-Star Separations

0.3"   3"   30"

576

MILLENNIUM STAR ATLAS

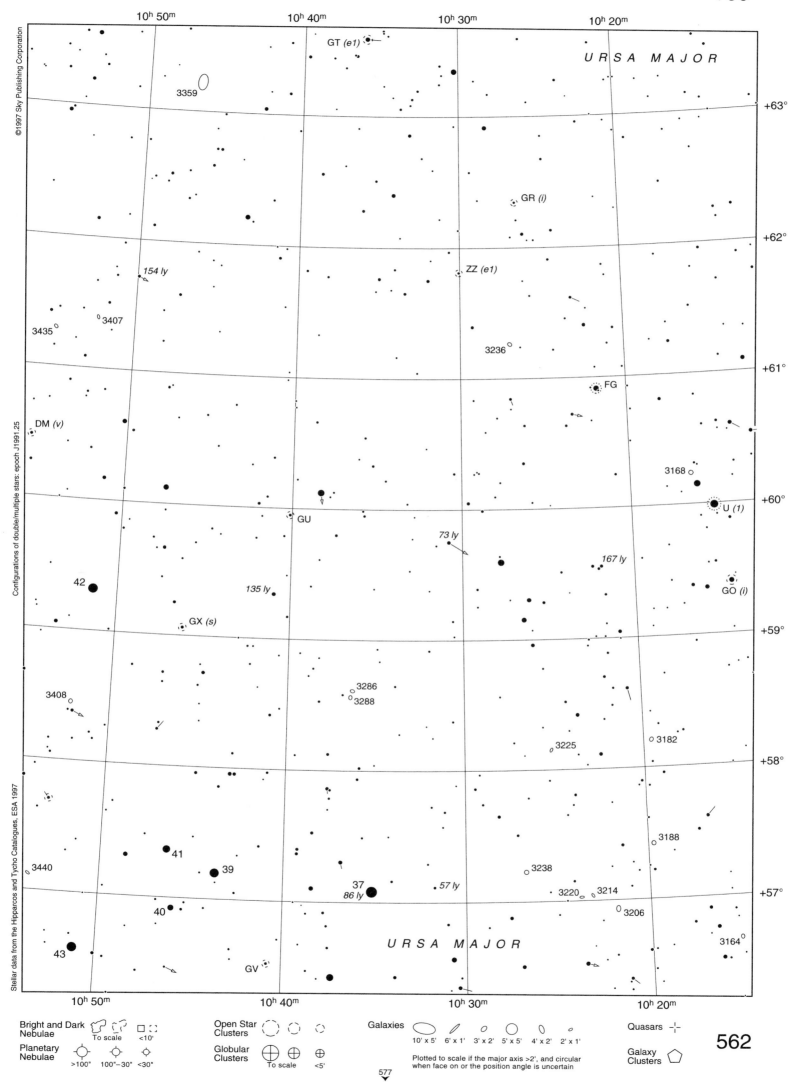

Configurations of double/multiple stars: epoch J1991.25

Stellar data from the Hipparcos and Tycho Catalogues, ESA 1997

10ʰ 50ᵐ   10ʰ 40ᵐ   10ʰ 30ᵐ   10ʰ 20ᵐ

+63°

+62°

+61°

+60°

+59°

+58°

+57°

URSA MAJOR

GT (e1)

GR (i)

ZZ (e1)

3359

154 ly

3407

3435

3236

FG

DM (v)

3168

U (1)

GU

73 ly

167 ly

42

135 ly

GO (i)

GX (s)

3286
3288

3408

3182

3225

3238

3188

41

3440

39

3220   3214

3206

37
86 ly

57 ly

40

3164

43

GV

URSA MAJOR

10ʰ 50ᵐ   10ʰ 40ᵐ   10ʰ 30ᵐ   10ʰ 20ᵐ

Bright and Dark Nebulae — To scale — <10'
Planetary Nebulae — >100" — 100"–30" — <30"
Open Star Clusters — To scale
Globular Clusters — To scale — <5'
Galaxies — 10' x 5' — 6' x 1' — 3' x 2' — 5' x 5' — 4' x 2' — 2' x 1'
Plotted to scale if the major axis >2', and circular when face on or the position angle is uncertain
Quasars
Galaxy Clusters

562

MILLENNIUM STAR ATLAS

+60°

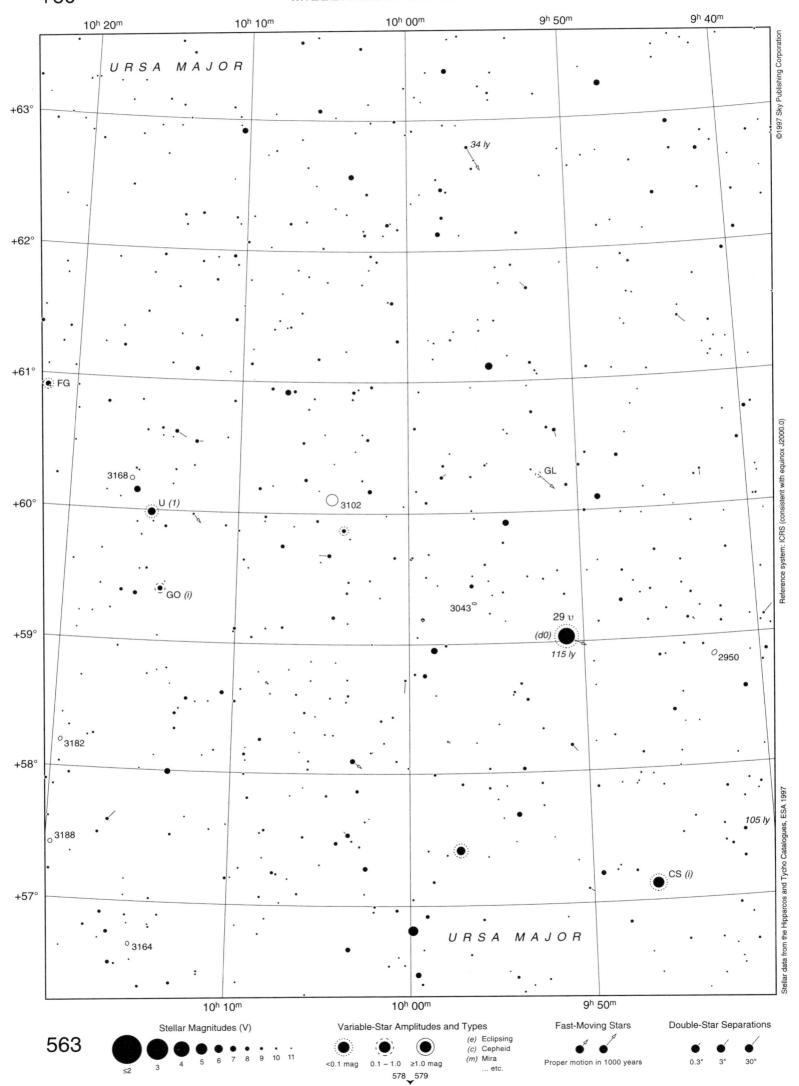

URSA MAJOR

34 ly

FG

3168

U (1)

3102

GL

GO (i)

3043

29 υ

(d0)

115 ly

2950

3182

105 ly

3188

CS (i)

3164

URSA MAJOR

563

Stellar Magnitudes (V)

≤2 3 4 5 6 7 8 9 10 11

Variable-Star Amplitudes and Types

<0.1 mag   0.1 – 1.0   ≥1.0 mag

(e) Eclipsing
(c) Cepheid
(m) Mira
... etc.

Fast-Moving Stars

Proper motion in 1000 years

Double-Star Separations

0.3"   3"   30"

578 579

©1997 Sky Publishing Corporation

Reference system: ICRS (consistent with equinox J2000.0)

Stellar data from the Hipparcos and Tycho Catalogues, ESA 1997

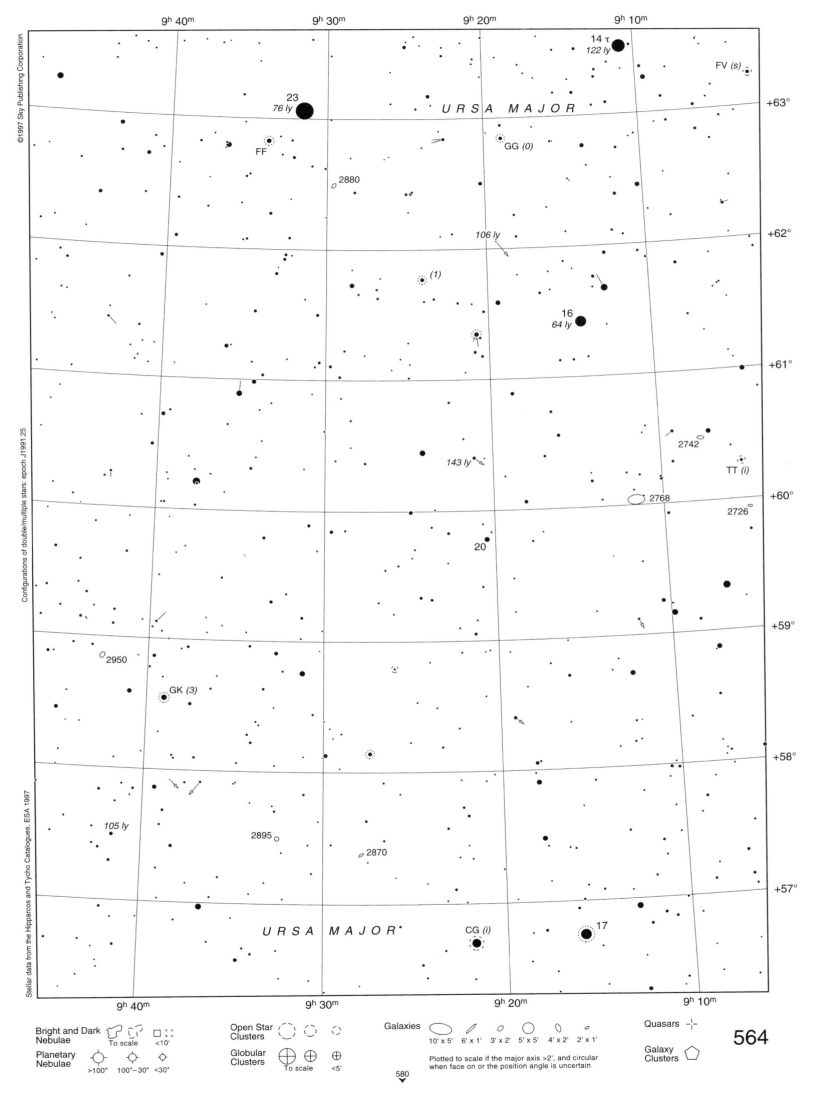

550

14 τ
122 ly

FV (s)

23
76 ly

URSA MAJOR

FF

GG (0)

2880

106 ly

(1)

16
64 ly

2742

TT (i)

143 ly

2768

2726

20

2950

GK (3)

2895

2870

105 ly

URSA MAJOR

CG (i)

17

Bright and Dark Nebulae   To scale   <10'

Planetary Nebulae   >100"   100"–30"   <30'

Open Star Clusters

Globular Clusters   To scale   <5'

Galaxies   10' x 5'   6' x 1'   3' x 2'   5' x 5'   4' x 2'   2' x 1'

Plotted to scale if the major axis >2', and circular when face on or the position angle is uncertain

Quasars

Galaxy Clusters

564

580

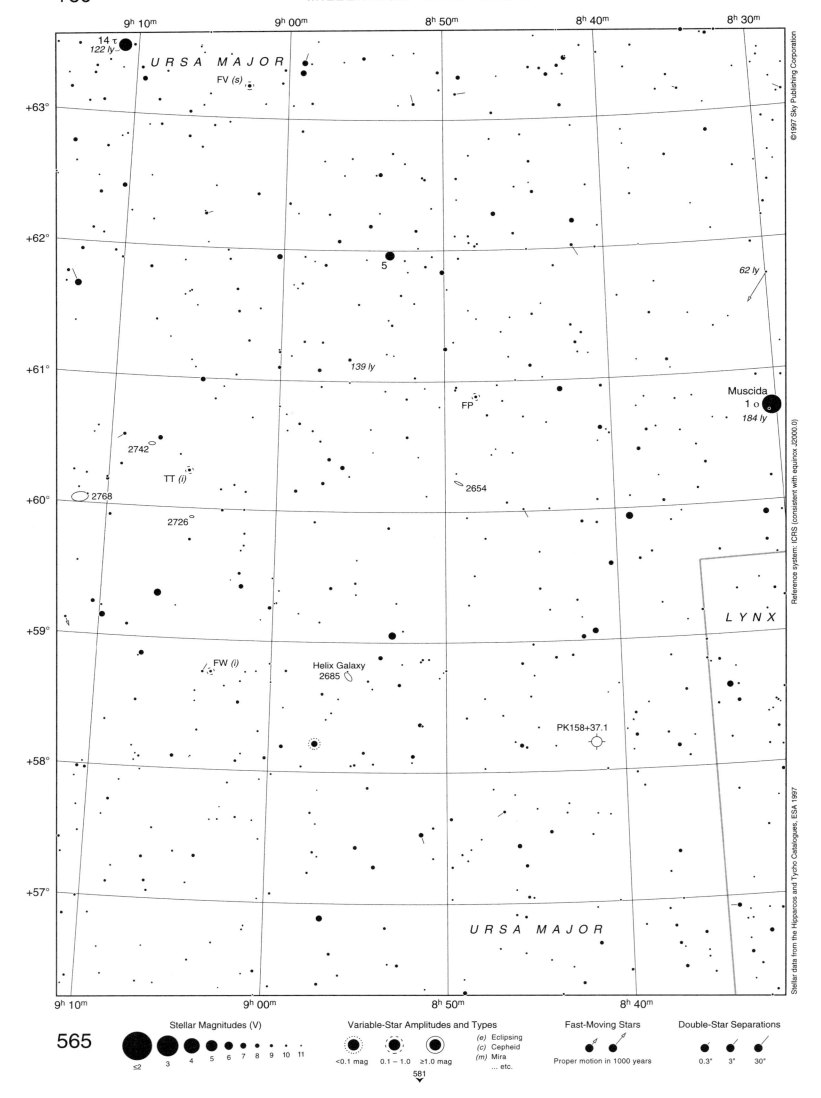

©1997 Sky Publishing Corporation

Reference system: ICRS (consistent with equinox J2000.0)

Stellar data from the Hipparcos and Tycho Catalogues, ESA 1997

565

Stellar Magnitudes (V)

≤2   3   4   5   6   7   8   9   10   11

Variable-Star Amplitudes and Types

<0.1 mag   0.1 – 1.0   ≥1.0 mag

(e) Eclipsing
(c) Cepheid
(m) Mira
... etc.

Fast-Moving Stars

Proper motion in 1000 years

Double-Star Separations

0.3"   3"   30"

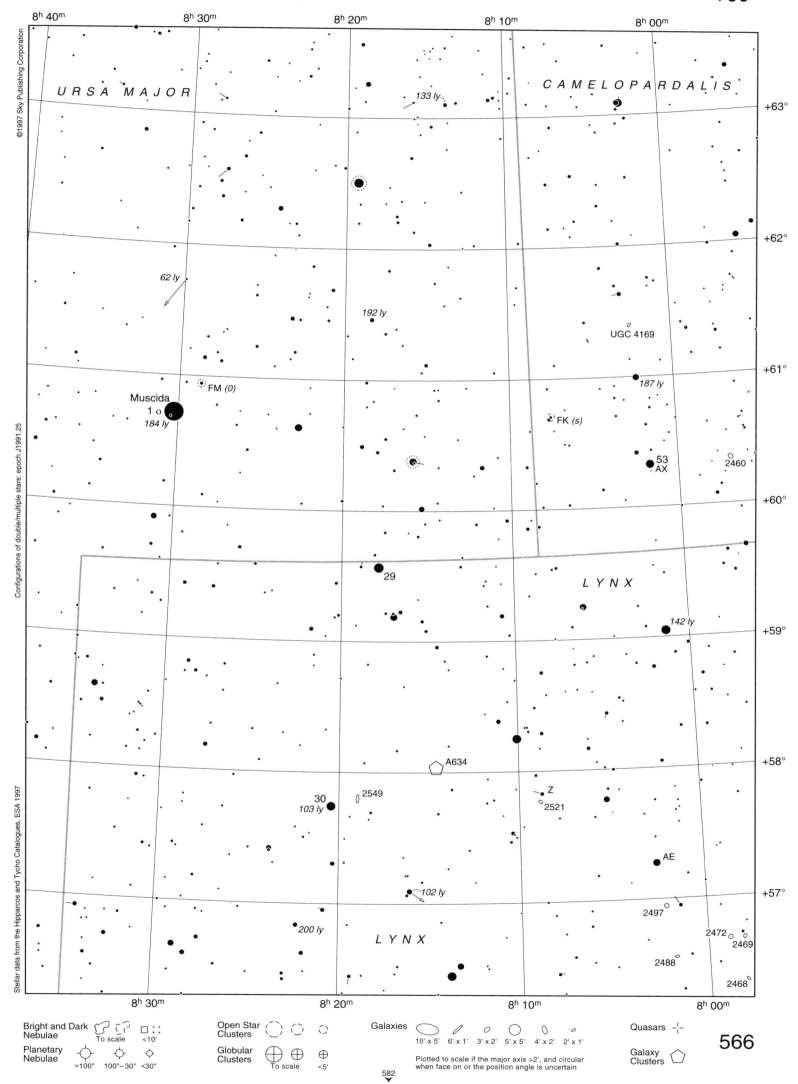

8ʰ 40ᵐ   8ʰ 30ᵐ   8ʰ 20ᵐ   8ʰ 10ᵐ   8ʰ 00ᵐ

U R S A   M A J O R

C A M E L O P A R D A L I S

+63°

133 ly

62 ly

192 ly

UGC 4169

+62°

+61°

FM (0)

Muscida
1 o
184 ly

187 ly

FK (s)

53
AX

2460

+60°

29

L Y N X

142 ly

+59°

A634

+58°

Z

2521

30
103 ly

2549

AE

102 ly

2497

+57°

200 ly

L Y N X

2472   2469

2488

2468

8ʰ 30ᵐ   8ʰ 20ᵐ   8ʰ 10ᵐ   8ʰ 00ᵐ

Bright and Dark
Nebulae
To scale   <10'

Planetary
Nebulae
>100" 100"–30" <30"

Open Star
Clusters

Globular
Clusters
To scale   <5'

Galaxies
10' x 5' 6' x 1' 3' x 2' 5' x 5' 4' x 2' 2' x 1'

Plotted to scale if the major axis >2', and circular
when face on or the position angle is uncertain

Quasars

Galaxy
Clusters

566

582

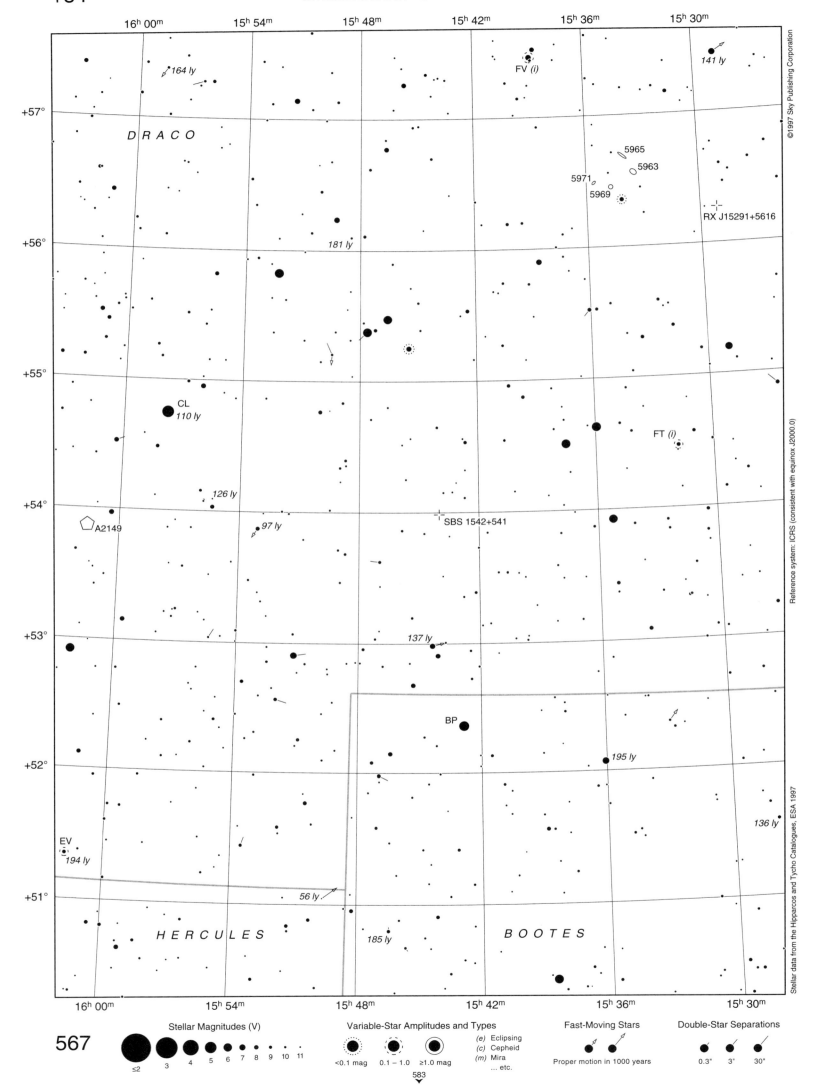

DRACO

HERCULES

BOOTES

164 ly

FV (i)

141 ly

5965

5963

5971

5969

RX J15291+5616

181 ly

CL
110 ly

FT (i)

126 ly

A2149

97 ly

SBS 1542+541

137 ly

BP

195 ly

EV

194 ly

136 ly

56 ly

185 ly

Stellar Magnitudes (V)

≤2 3 4 5 6 7 8 9 10 11

Variable-Star Amplitudes and Types

<0.1 mag   0.1 – 1.0   ≥1.0 mag

(e) Eclipsing
(c) Cepheid
(m) Mira
... etc.

Fast-Moving Stars

Proper motion in 1000 years

Double-Star Separations

0.3"   3"   30"

583

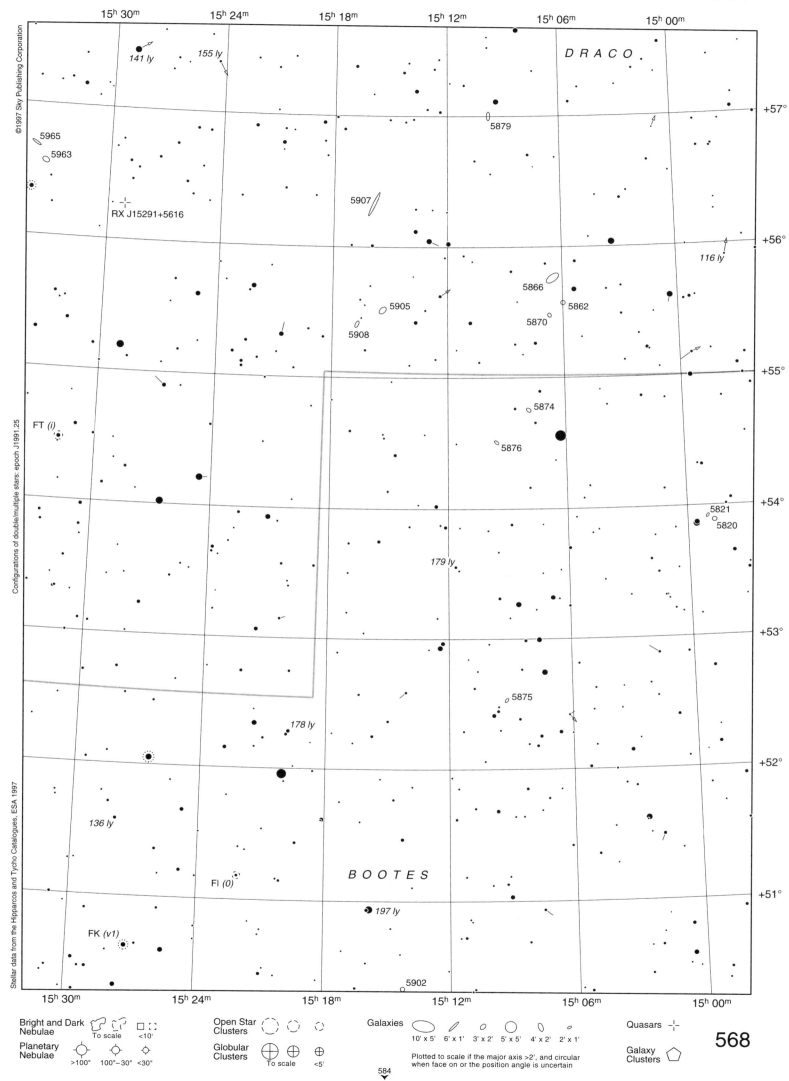

Configurations of double/multiple stars: epoch J1991.25

Stellar data from the Hipparcos and Tycho Catalogues, ESA 1997

D R A C O

B O O T E S

141 ly
155 ly
5965
5963
RX J15291+5616
5879
116 ly
5907
5866
5905
5862
5908
5870
FT (i)
5874
5876
5821
5820
179 ly
5875
178 ly
136 ly
FI (0)
197 ly
FK (v1)
5902

15h 30m   15h 24m   15h 18m   15h 12m   15h 06m   15h 00m

+57°
+56°
+55°
+54°
+53°
+52°
+51°

Bright and Dark Nebulae
To scale   <10'

Planetary Nebulae
>100"   100"–30"   <30"

Open Star Clusters

Globular Clusters
To scale   <5'

Galaxies
10' x 5'   6' x 1'   3' x 2'   5' x 5'   4' x 2'   2' x 1'

Plotted to scale if the major axis >2', and circular when face on or the position angle is uncertain

Quasars

Galaxy Clusters

568

584

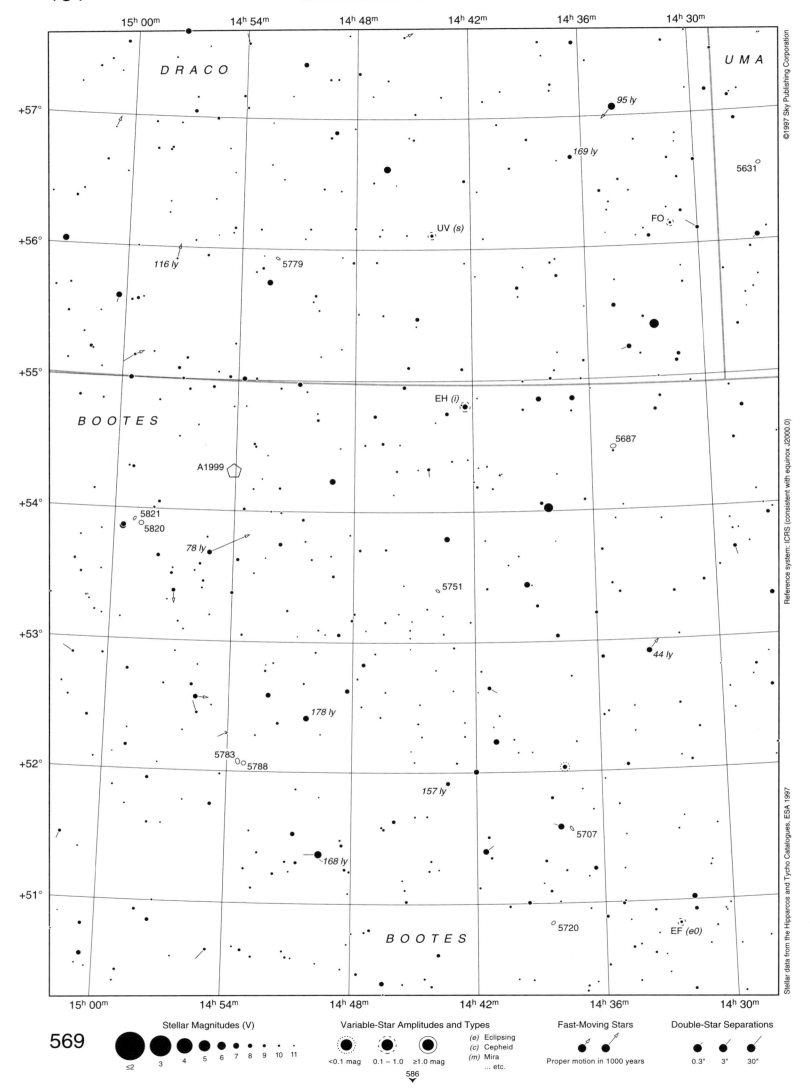

©1997 Sky Publishing Corporation

Reference system: ICRS (consistent with equinox J2000.0)

Stellar data from the Hipparcos and Tycho Catalogues, ESA 1997

DRACO

UMA

95 ly

169 ly

5631

UV (s)

FO

116 ly

5779

BOOTES

EH (i)

5687

A1999

5821
5820

78 ly

5751

44 ly

178 ly

5783
5788

157 ly

5707

168 ly

BOOTES

5720

EF (e0)

Stellar Magnitudes (V)

≤2   3   4   5   6   7   8   9   10   11

Variable-Star Amplitudes and Types

<0.1 mag   0.1 – 1.0   ≥1.0 mag

(e) Eclipsing
(c) Cepheid
(m) Mira
... etc.

Fast-Moving Stars

Proper motion in 1000 years

Double-Star Separations

0.3"   3"   30"

+54°

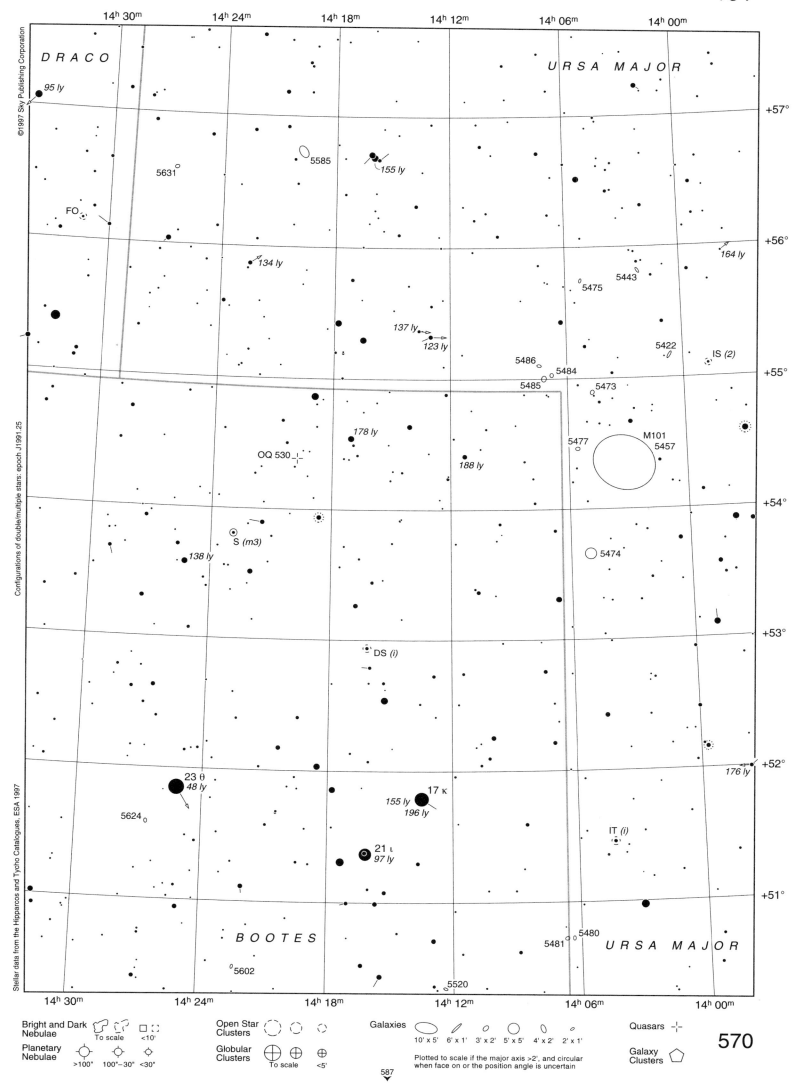

Configurations of double/multiple stars: epoch J1991.25

Stellar data from the Hipparcos and Tycho Catalogues, ESA 1997

D R A C O

U R S A   M A J O R

95 ly

5631

5585

155 ly

FO

134 ly

164 ly

5443

5475

137 ly

123 ly

5422

IS (2)

5486

5484

5485

5473

178 ly

M101

OQ 530

5477

5457

188 ly

S (m3)

5474

138 ly

DS (i)

23 θ
48 ly

17 κ

5624

155 ly

196 ly

IT (i)

21 ι
97 ly

B O O T E S

5602

5480

5481

U R S A   M A J O R

5520

14ʰ 30ᵐ   14ʰ 24ᵐ   14ʰ 18ᵐ   14ʰ 12ᵐ   14ʰ 06ᵐ   14ʰ 00ᵐ

+57°

+56°

+55°

+54°

+53°

+52°

+51°

Bright and Dark Nebulae	Open Star Clusters	Galaxies

Bright and Dark Nebulae
To scale   <10'

Planetary Nebulae
>100"   100"−30"   <30"

Open Star Clusters

Globular Clusters
To scale   <5'

Galaxies
10' x 5'   6' x 1'   3' x 2'   5' x 5'   4' x 2'   2' x 1'

Plotted to scale if the major axis >2', and circular when face on or the position angle is uncertain

Quasars

Galaxy Clusters

570

587

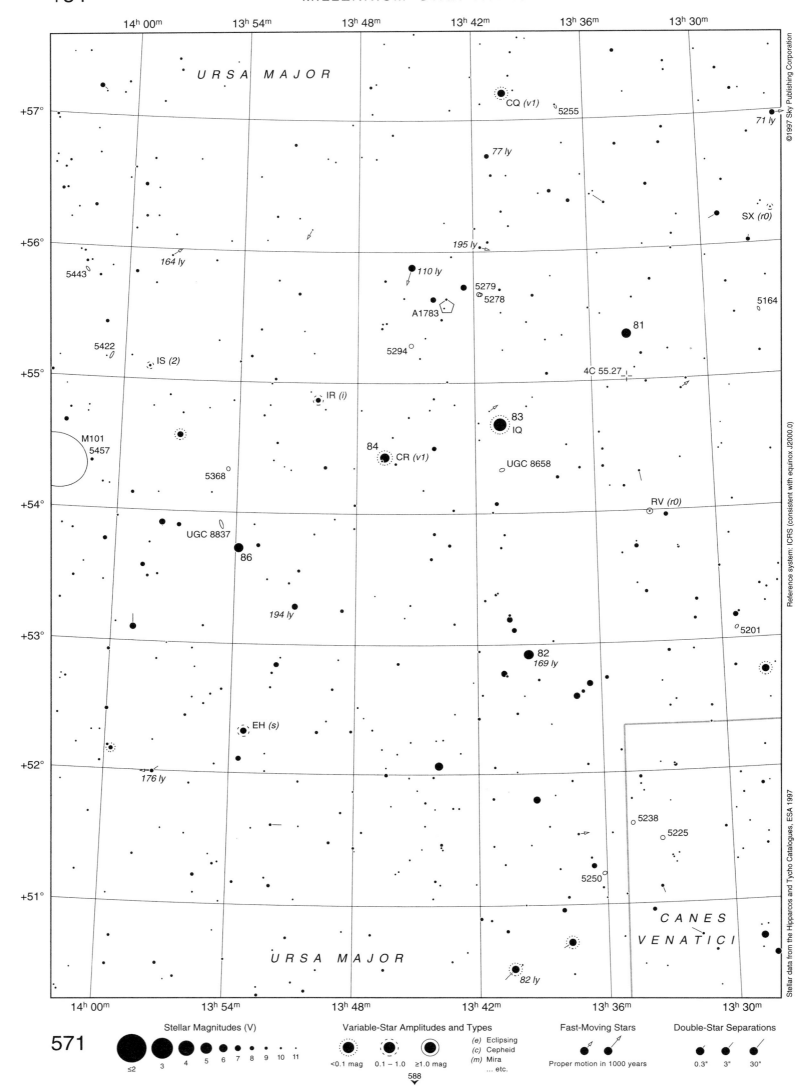

571

Stellar Magnitudes (V)

≤2   3   4   5   6   7   8   9   10   11

Variable-Star Amplitudes and Types

<0.1 mag   0.1 – 1.0   ≥1.0 mag

(e) Eclipsing
(c) Cepheid
(m) Mira
... etc.

Fast-Moving Stars

Proper motion in 1000 years

Double-Star Separations

0.3"   3"   30"

588

MILLENNIUM STAR ATLAS

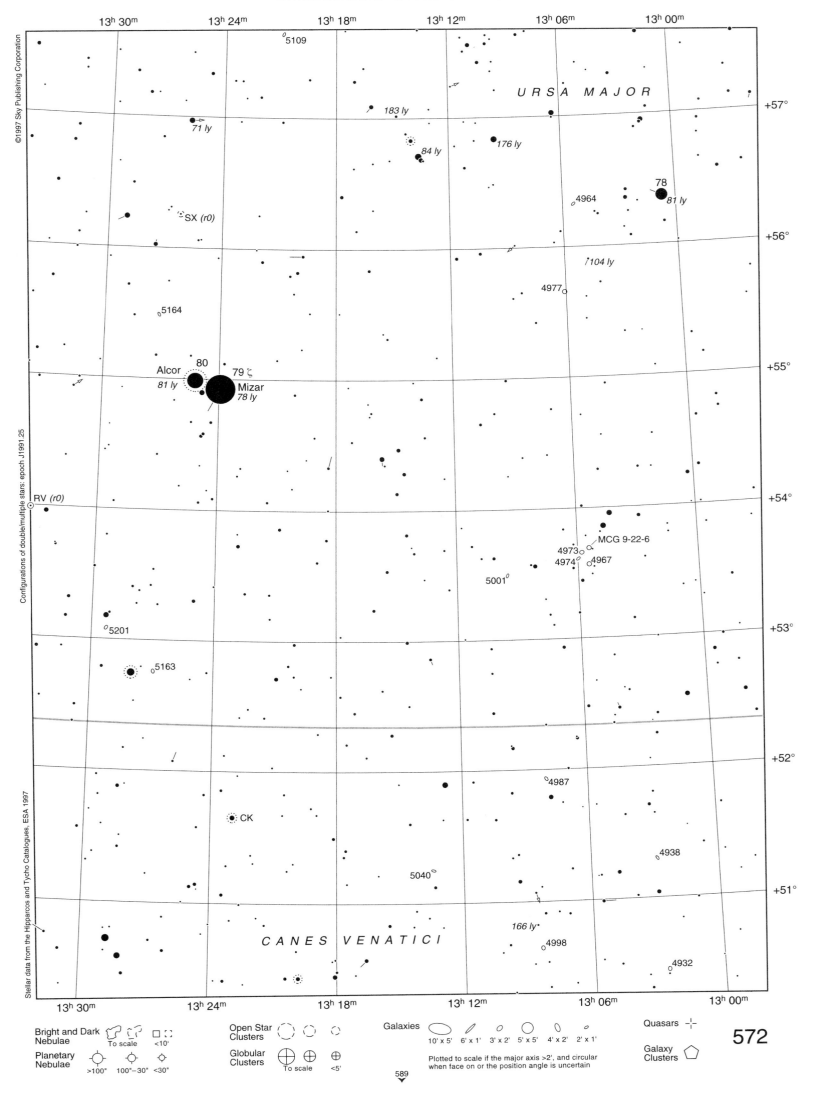

©1997 Sky Publishing Corporation

Configurations of double/multiple stars: epoch J1991.25

Stellar data from the Hipparcos and Tycho Catalogues, ESA 1997

URSA MAJOR

CANES VENATICI

Bright and Dark Nebulae
To scale <10'

Planetary Nebulae
>100" 100"–30" <30"

Open Star Clusters

Globular Clusters
To scale <5'

Galaxies
10' x 5' 6' x 1' 3' x 2' 5' x 5' 4' x 2' 2' x 1'

Plotted to scale if the major axis >2', and circular when face on or the position angle is uncertain

Quasars

Galaxy Clusters

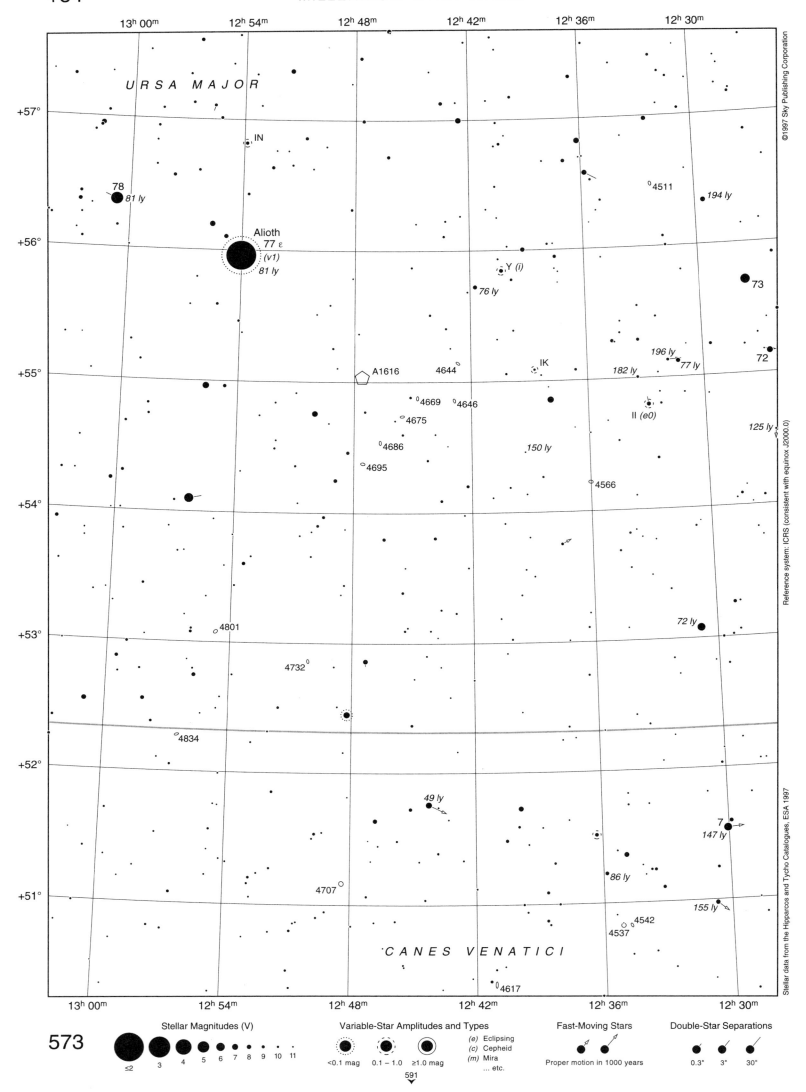

©1997 Sky Publishing Corporation

U R S A   M A J O R

IN

78
81 ly

Alioth
77 ε
(v1)
81 ly

0 4511
194 ly

Y (i)
76 ly

73

72

A1616   4644
4669   4646
4675
4686
4695

IK

150 ly

II (e0)

182 ly

196 ly
77 ly

125 ly

4566

4801

4732 0

4834

72 ly

49 ly

7
147 ly

86 ly

155 ly

4707

4542
4537

C A N E S   V E N A T I C I

0 4617

Reference system: ICRS (consistent with equinox J2000.0)

Stellar data from the Hipparcos and Tycho Catalogues, ESA 1997

573

Stellar Magnitudes (V)
≤2   3   4   5   6   7   8   9 10 11

Variable-Star Amplitudes and Types
<0.1 mag   0.1 – 1.0   ≥1.0 mag

(e) Eclipsing
(c) Cepheid
(m) Mira
... etc.

Fast-Moving Stars
Proper motion in 1000 years

Double-Star Separations
0.3"   3"   30"

591

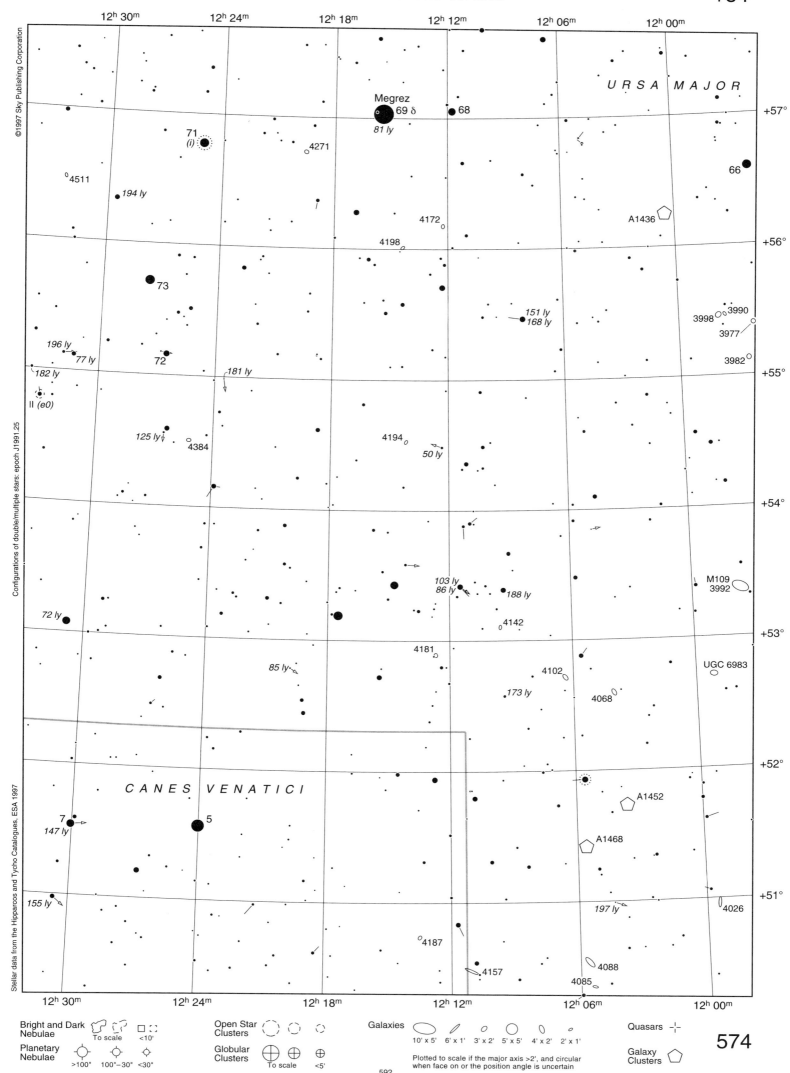

URSA MAJOR

Megrez
69 δ
68
81 ly

71
(i)
4271

4511
194 ly
4172
4198
66
A1436
73
151 ly
168 ly
3998 3990
3977
196 ly
77 ly
72
3982
182 ly
181 ly
II (e0)
125 ly
4384
4194
50 ly
103 ly
86 ly
188 ly
M109
3992
72 ly
4142
4181
UGC 6983
85 ly
4102
173 ly
4068
CANES VENATICI
A1452
7
5
A1468
147 ly
155 ly
197 ly
4026
4187
4088
4157
4085

©1997 Sky Publishing Corporation
Configurations of double/multiple stars: epoch J1991.25
Stellar data from the Hipparcos and Tycho Catalogues, ESA 1997

Bright and Dark Nebulae	Open Star Clusters	Galaxies	Quasars

To scale   <10'

Planetary Nebulae
>100" 100"-30" <30'

Globular Clusters
To scale <5'

Galaxies
10' x 5' 6' x 1' 3' x 2' 5' x 5' 4' x 2' 2' x 1'

Plotted to scale if the major axis >2', and circular when face on or the position angle is uncertain

Quasars

Galaxy Clusters

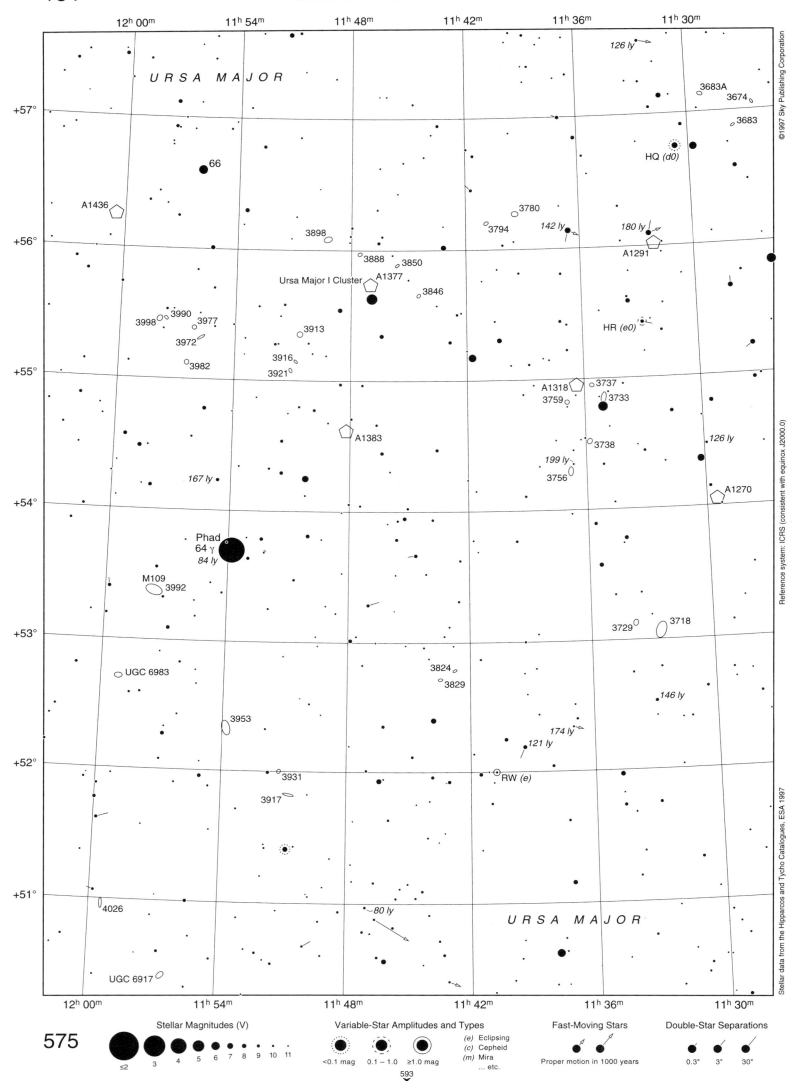

©1997 Sky Publishing Corporation

Reference system: ICRS (consistent with equinox J2000.0)

Stellar data from the Hipparcos and Tycho Catalogues, ESA 1997

575

Stellar Magnitudes (V)

≤2 3 4 5 6 7 8 9 10 11

Variable-Star Amplitudes and Types

<0.1 mag   0.1 – 1.0   ≥1.0 mag

(e) Eclipsing
(c) Cepheid
(m) Mira
... etc.

Fast-Moving Stars

Proper motion in 1000 years

Double-Star Separations

0.3"   3"   30"

593

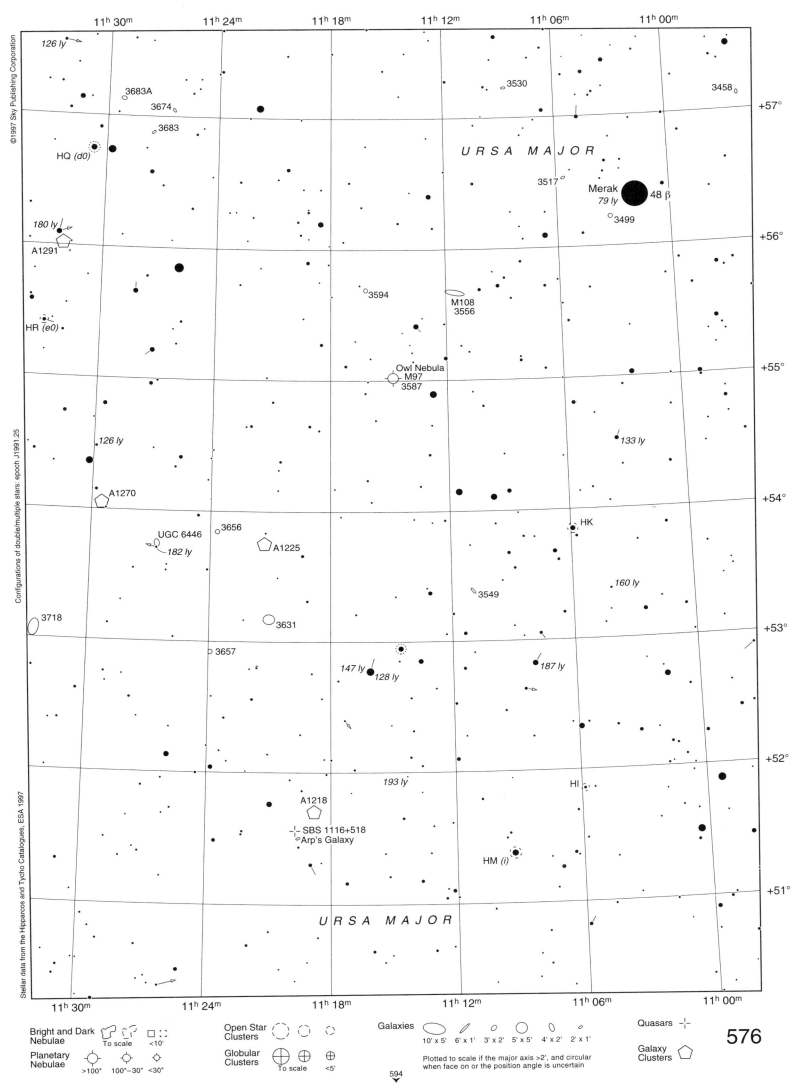

126 ly

3683A

3674

3683

HQ (d0)

180 ly

A1291

HR (e0)

126 ly

A1270

UGC 6446

182 ly

3718

3656

A1225

3631

3657

147 ly

128 ly

A1218

SBS 1116+518

Arp's Galaxy

193 ly

HM (i)

HI

HK

160 ly

187 ly

133 ly

3549

3530

3458 0

URSA MAJOR

3517

Merak

79 ly

48 β

3499

3594

M108

3556

Owl Nebula

M97

3587

URSA MAJOR

+57°

+56°

+55°

+54°

+53°

+52°

+51°

11h 30m   11h 24m   11h 18m   11h 12m   11h 06m   11h 00m

Bright and Dark Nebulae
To scale   <10'

Planetary Nebulae
>100"   100"–30"   <30"

Open Star Clusters

Globular Clusters
To scale   <5'

Galaxies
10' x 5'   6' x 1'   3' x 2'   5' x 5'   4' x 2'   2' x 1'

Plotted to scale if the major axis >2', and circular
when face on or the position angle is uncertain

Quasars

Galaxy Clusters

576

594

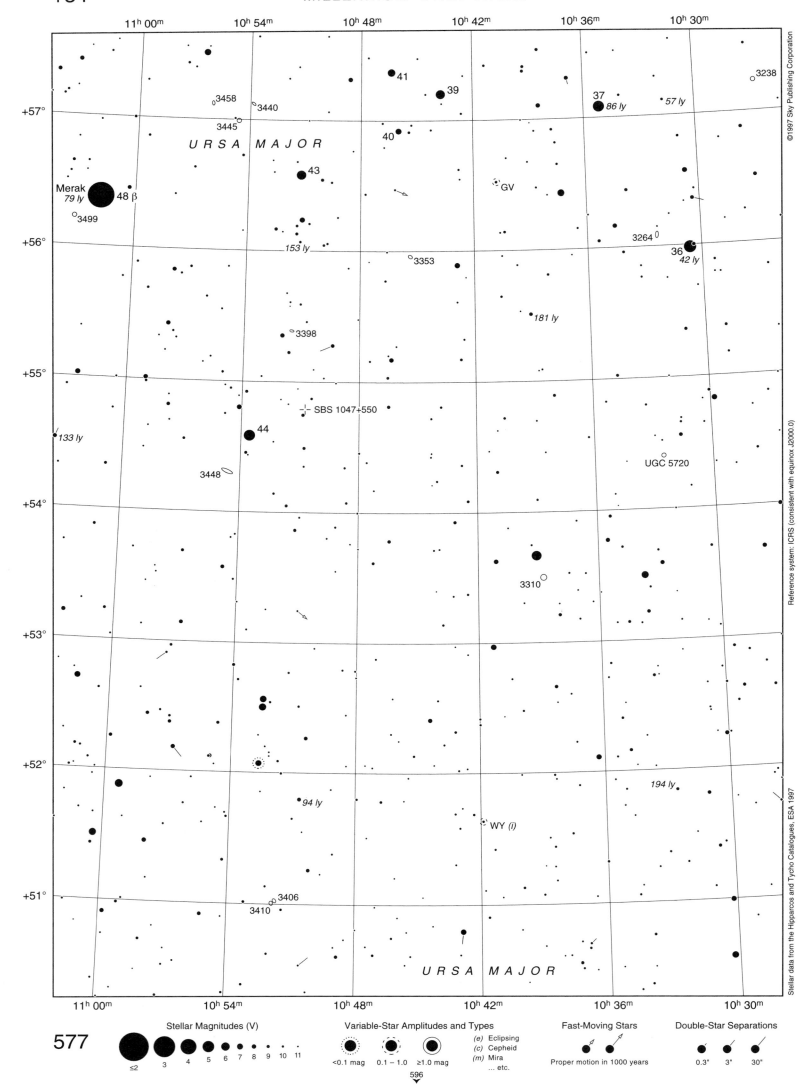

©1997 Sky Publishing Corporation

Reference system: ICRS (consistent with equinox J2000.0)

Stellar data from the Hipparcos and Tycho Catalogues, ESA 1997

577

Stellar Magnitudes (V)

≤2 3 4 5 6 7 8 9 10 11

Variable-Star Amplitudes and Types

<0.1 mag   0.1 – 1.0   ≥1.0 mag

(e) Eclipsing
(c) Cepheid
(m) Mira
... etc.

Fast-Moving Stars

Proper motion in 1000 years

Double-Star Separations

0.3"   3"   30"

596

MILLENNIUM STAR ATLAS

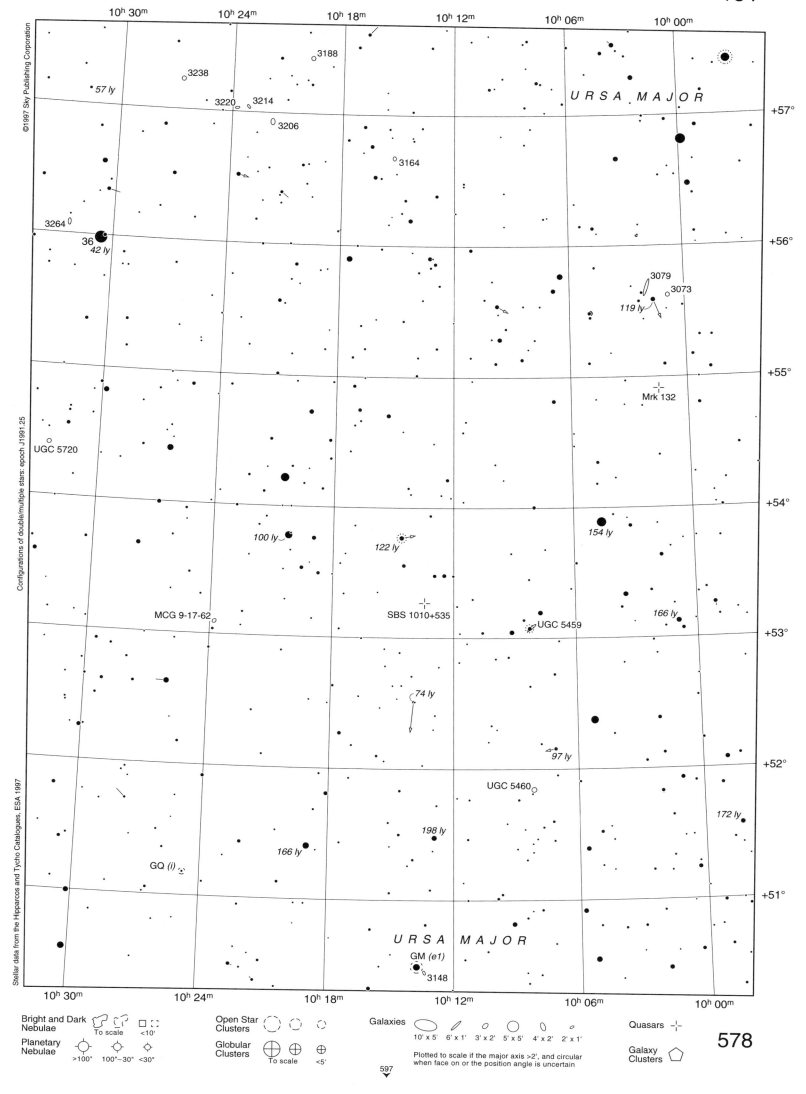

©1997 Sky Publishing Corporation

Configurations of double/multiple stars: epoch J1991.25

Stellar data from the Hipparcos and Tycho Catalogues, ESA 1997

URSA MAJOR

3188
3238
57 ly
3220 3214
3206
3164
3264
36
42 ly

3079
3073
119 ly

Mrk 132

UGC 5720

100 ly
122 ly
154 ly

SBS 1010+535
166 ly
MCG 9-17-62
UGC 5459

74 ly

97 ly
UGC 5460

172 ly
198 ly
166 ly
GQ (i)

URSA MAJOR

GM (e1)
3148

Bright and Dark Nebulae			Open Star Clusters			Galaxies						Quasars
	To scale	<10'				10' x 5'	6' x 1'	3' x 2'	5' x 5'	4' x 2'	2' x 1'	
Planetary Nebulae			Globular Clusters									Galaxy Clusters
>100"	100"–30"	<30"	To scale	<5'		Plotted to scale if the major axis >2', and circular when face on or the position angle is uncertain						

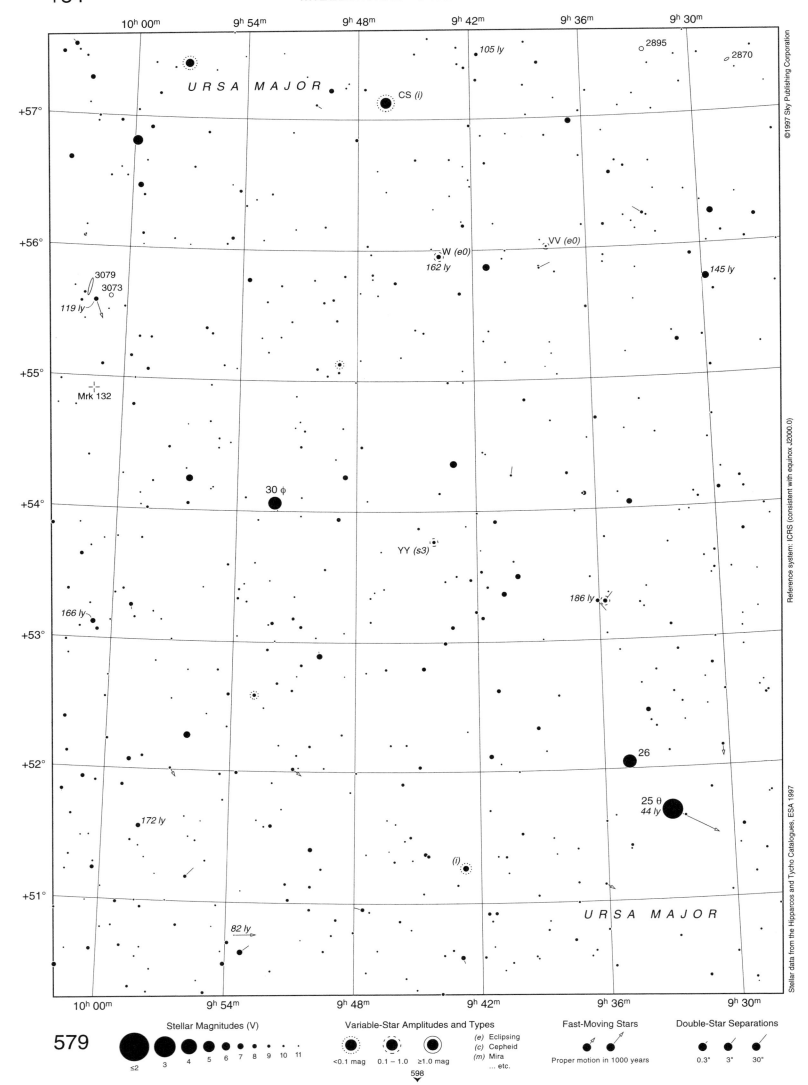

MILLENNIUM STAR ATLAS

563

URSA MAJOR

CS (i)

105 ly

2895

2870

VV (e0)

W (e0)
162 ly

145 ly

3079
3073
119 ly

Mrk 132

30 φ

YY (s3)

186 ly

166 ly

26

25 θ
44 ly

172 ly

(i)

URSA MAJOR

82 ly

579

©1997 Sky Publishing Corporation

Reference system: ICRS (consistent with equinox J2000.0)

Stellar data from the Hipparcos and Tycho Catalogues, ESA 1997

Stellar Magnitudes (V)

≤2 3 4 5 6 7 8 9 10 11

Variable-Star Amplitudes and Types

<0.1 mag   0.1 – 1.0   ≥1.0 mag

(e) Eclipsing
(c) Cepheid
(m) Mira
... etc.

598

Fast-Moving Stars

Proper motion in 1000 years

Double-Star Separations

0.3"   3"   30"

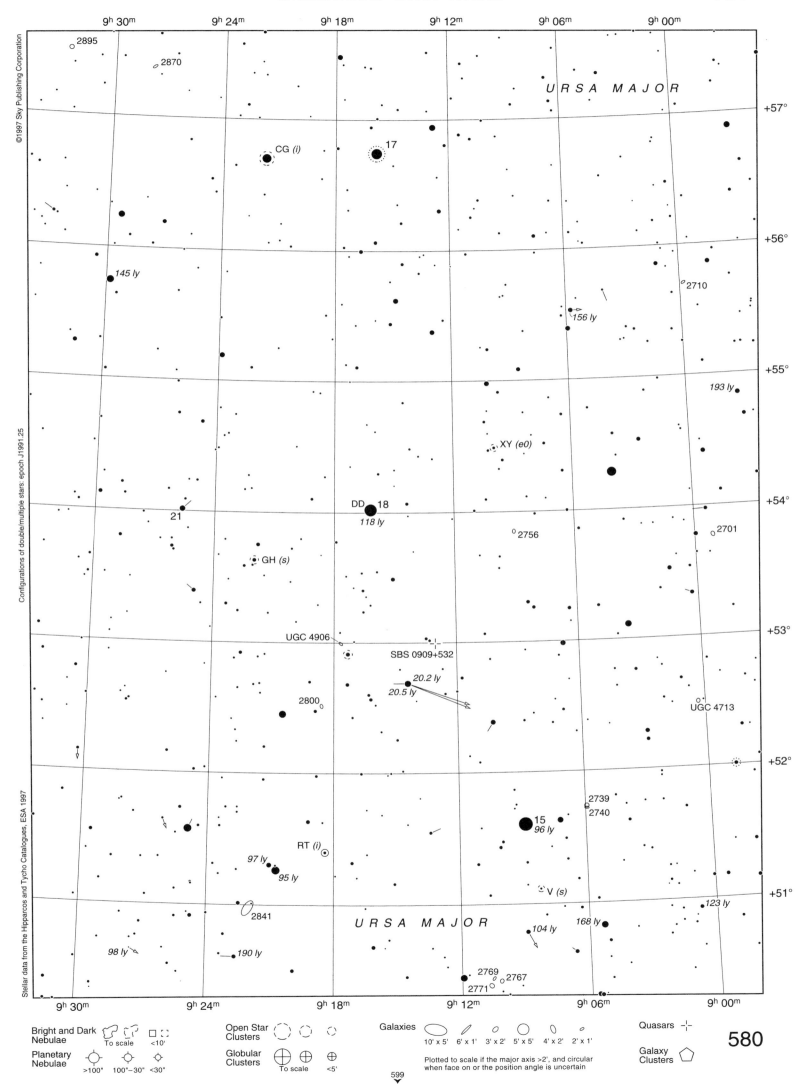

URSA MAJOR

URSA MAJOR

580

Bright and Dark Nebulae — To scale — <10'

Planetary Nebulae — >100" — 100"–30" — <30"

Open Star Clusters

Globular Clusters — To scale — <5'

Galaxies — 10' x 5' — 6' x 1' — 3' x 2' — 5' x 5' — 4' x 2' — 2' x 1'

Plotted to scale if the major axis >2', and circular when face on or the position angle is uncertain

Quasars

Galaxy Clusters

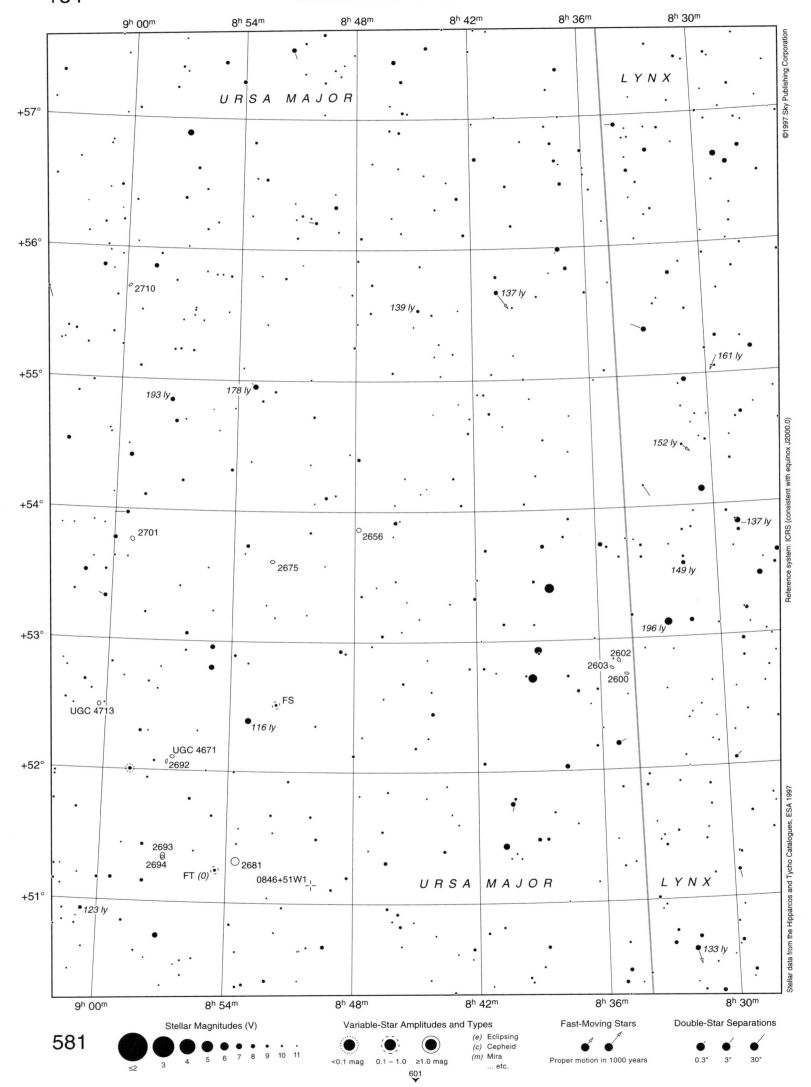

©1997 Sky Publishing Corporation

Reference system: ICRS (consistent with equinox J2000.0)

Stellar data from the Hipparcos and Tycho Catalogues, ESA 1997

LYNX

URSA MAJOR

2710

137 ly

139 ly

161 ly

193 ly   178 ly

152 ly

137 ly

2701

2656

149 ly

2675

196 ly

2602
2603
2600

UGC 4713

FS

116 ly

UGC 4671
2692

2693
2694

FT (0)   2681

0846+51W1

URSA MAJOR

LYNX

123 ly

133 ly

Stellar Magnitudes (V)

≤2   3   4   5   6   7   8   9 10 11

Variable-Star Amplitudes and Types

<0.1 mag   0.1 – 1.0   ≥1.0 mag

(e) Eclipsing
(c) Cepheid
(m) Mira
... etc.

Fast-Moving Stars

Proper motion in 1000 years

Double-Star Separations

0.3"   3"   30"

601

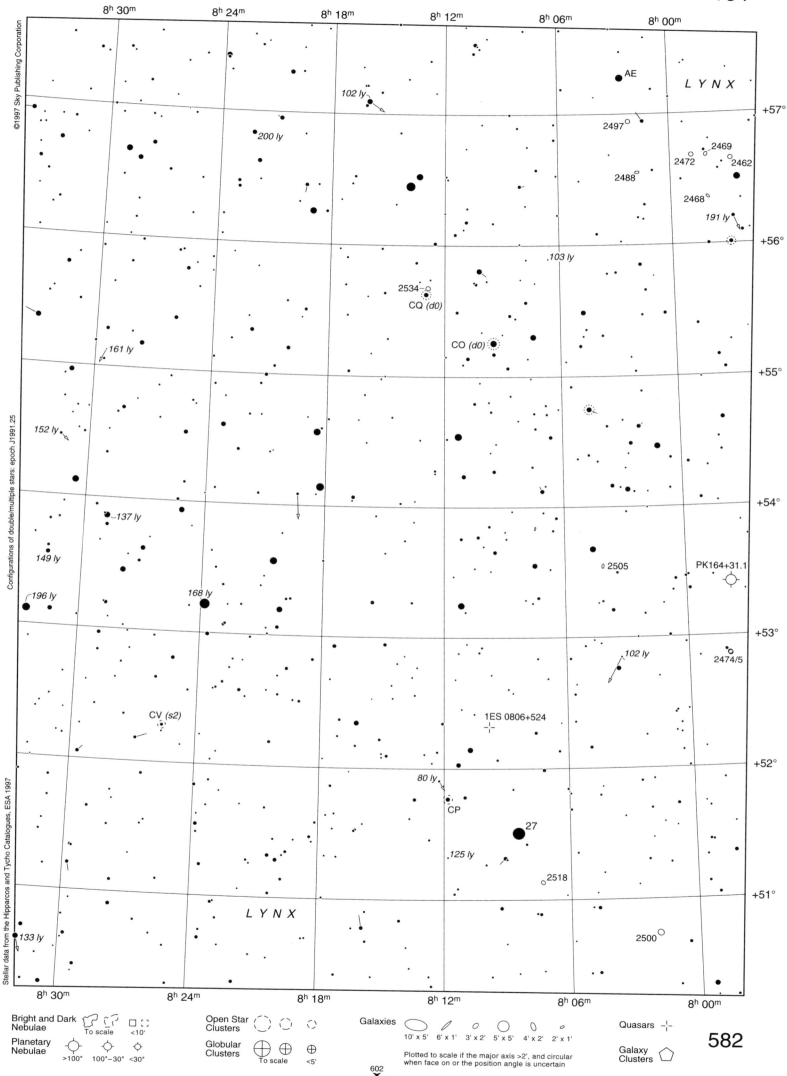

Configurations of double/multiple stars: epoch J1991.25

Stellar data from the Hipparcos and Tycho Catalogues, ESA 1997

LYNX

AE

2497

2469
2472   2462
2488

2468

191 ly

102 ly

200 ly

.103 ly

2534
CQ (d0)

CO (d0)

161 ly

152 ly

137 ly

149 ly

196 ly

168 ly

0 2505

PK164+31.1

102 ly

2474/5

CV (s2)

1ES 0806+524

80 ly

CP

27

125 ly

2518

LYNX

133 ly

2500

+57°
+56°
+55°
+54°
+53°
+52°
+51°

8h 30m   8h 24m   8h 18m   8h 12m   8h 06m   8h 00m

Bright and Dark
Nebulae
To scale   <10'

Planetary
Nebulae
>100" 100"–30" <30"

Open Star
Clusters
To scale   <5'

Globular
Clusters
To scale   <5'

Galaxies
10' x 5'   6' x 1'   3' x 2'   5' x 5'   4' x 2'   2' x 1'

Plotted to scale if the major axis >2', and circular
when face on or the position angle is uncertain

Quasars

Galaxy
Clusters

582

602

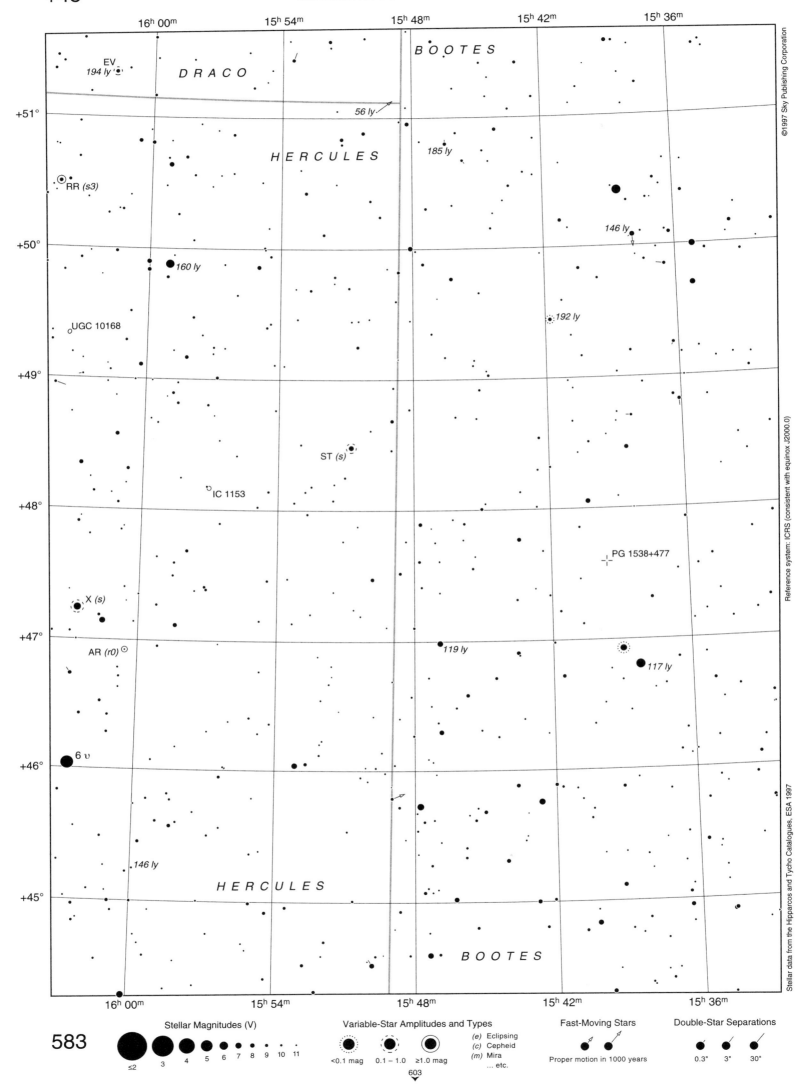

©1997 Sky Publishing Corporation

Reference system: ICRS (consistent with equinox J2000.0)

Stellar data from the Hipparcos and Tycho Catalogues, ESA 1997

BOOTES

DRACO

EV
194 ly

56 ly

HERCULES

185 ly

RR (s3)

146 ly

160 ly

192 ly

UGC 10168

ST (s)

IC 1153

PG 1538+477

X (s)

119 ly

117 ly

AR (r0)

6 υ

146 ly

HERCULES

BOOTES

583

Stellar Magnitudes (V)
≤2 3 4 5 6 7 8 9 10 11

Variable-Star Amplitudes and Types
<0.1 mag   0.1 – 1.0   ≥1.0 mag

(e) Eclipsing
(c) Cepheid
(m) Mira
... etc.

Fast-Moving Stars
Proper motion in 1000 years

Double-Star Separations
0.3"   3"   30"

MILLENNIUM STAR ATLAS

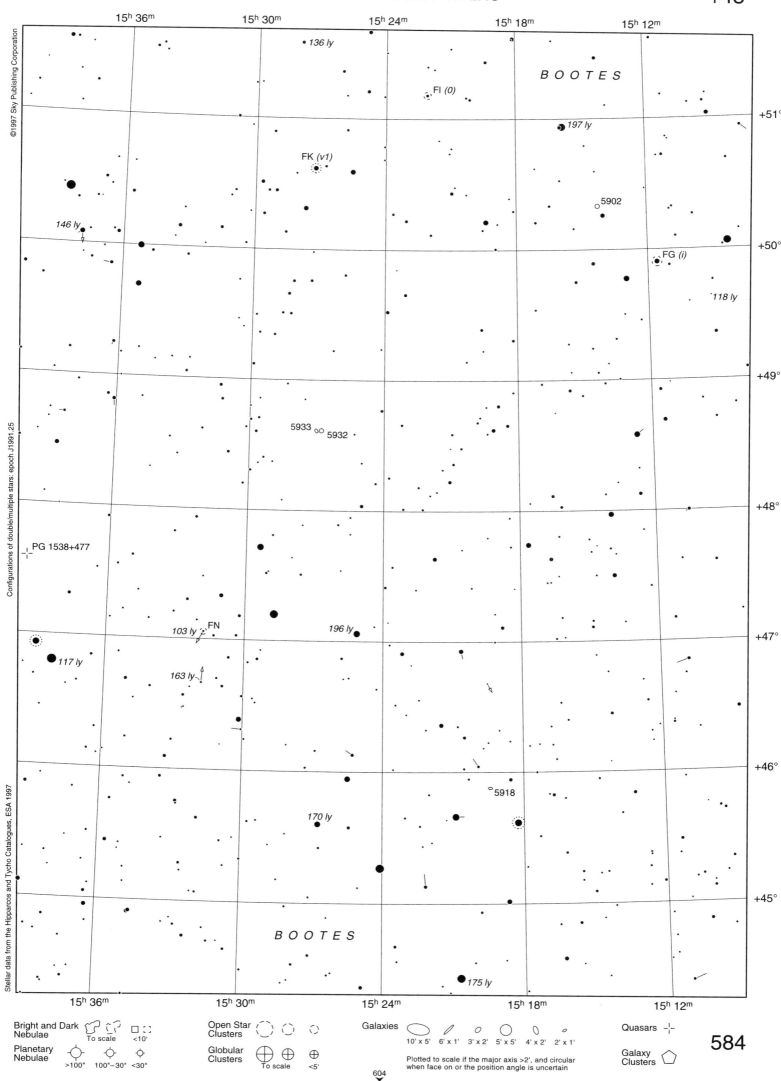

136 ly

B O O T E S

FI *(0)*

+51°

197 ly

FK *(v1)*

5902

146 ly

+50°

FG *(i)*

118 ly

+49°

5933 ○○ 5932

+48°

PG 1538+477

FN

103 ly

196 ly

+47°

117 ly

163 ly

+46°

5918

170 ly

+45°

175 ly

B O O T E S

15h 36m   15h 30m   15h 24m   15h 18m   15h 12m

Bright and Dark Nebulae — To scale, <10'	
Planetary Nebulae — >100", 100"–30", <30"	
Open Star Clusters — To scale, <5'	
Globular Clusters — To scale, <5'	
Galaxies — 10' x 5', 6' x 1', 3' x 2', 5' x 5', 4' x 2', 2' x 1'	
Quasars	
Galaxy Clusters	

Plotted to scale if the major axis >2', and circular when face on or the position angle is uncertain

+48°

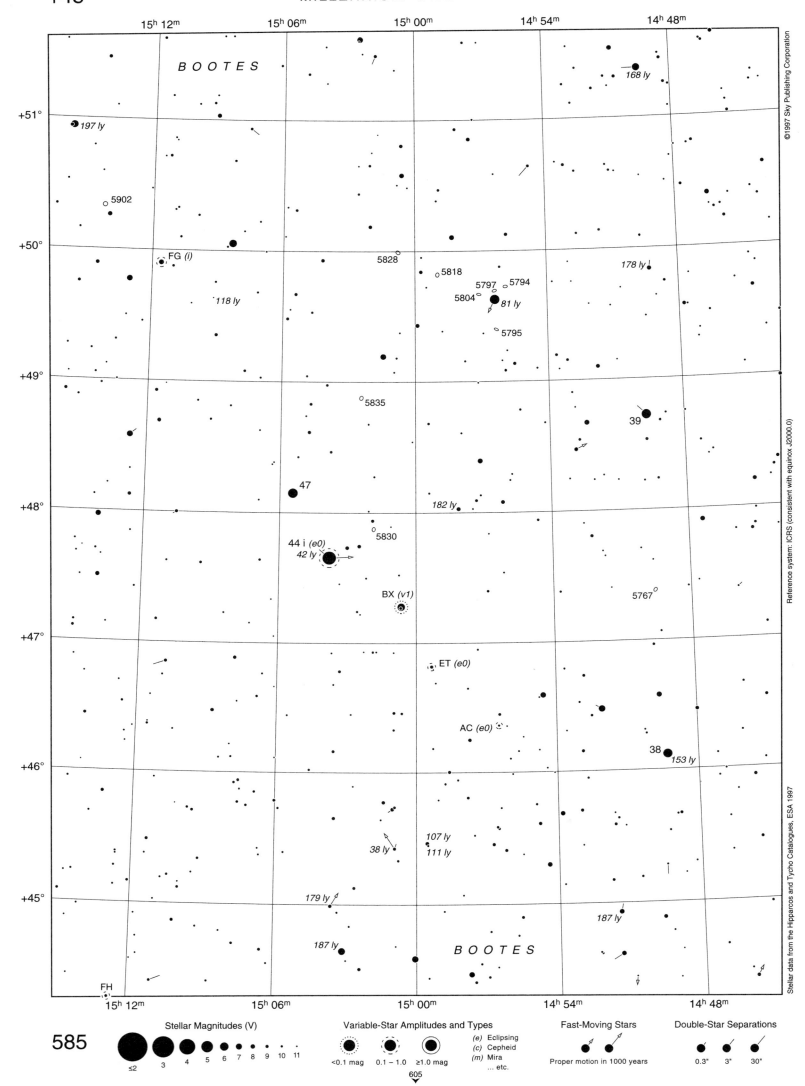

BOOTES

15h 12m   15h 06m   15h 00m   14h 54m   14h 48m

168 ly

+51°

197 ly

5902

+50°

FG (i)

5828

5818

5797   5794
5804   81 ly

118 ly

178 ly

5795

+49°

5835

39

47

+48°

182 ly

5830

44 i (e0)
42 ly

BX (v1)

5767

+47°

ET (e0)

AC (e0)

38
153 ly

+46°

107 ly
111 ly

38 ly

+45°

179 ly

187 ly

BOOTES

187 ly

FH

15h 12m   15h 06m   15h 00m   14h 54m   14h 48m

©1997 Sky Publishing Corporation

Reference system: ICRS (consistent with equinox J2000.0)

Stellar data from the Hipparcos and Tycho Catalogues, ESA 1997

585

Stellar Magnitudes (V)

≤2   3   4   5   6   7   8   9   10   11

Variable-Star Amplitudes and Types

<0.1 mag   0.1 – 1.0   ≥1.0 mag

(e) Eclipsing
(c) Cepheid
(m) Mira
... etc.

Fast-Moving Stars

Proper motion in 1000 years

Double-Star Separations

0.3"   3"   30"

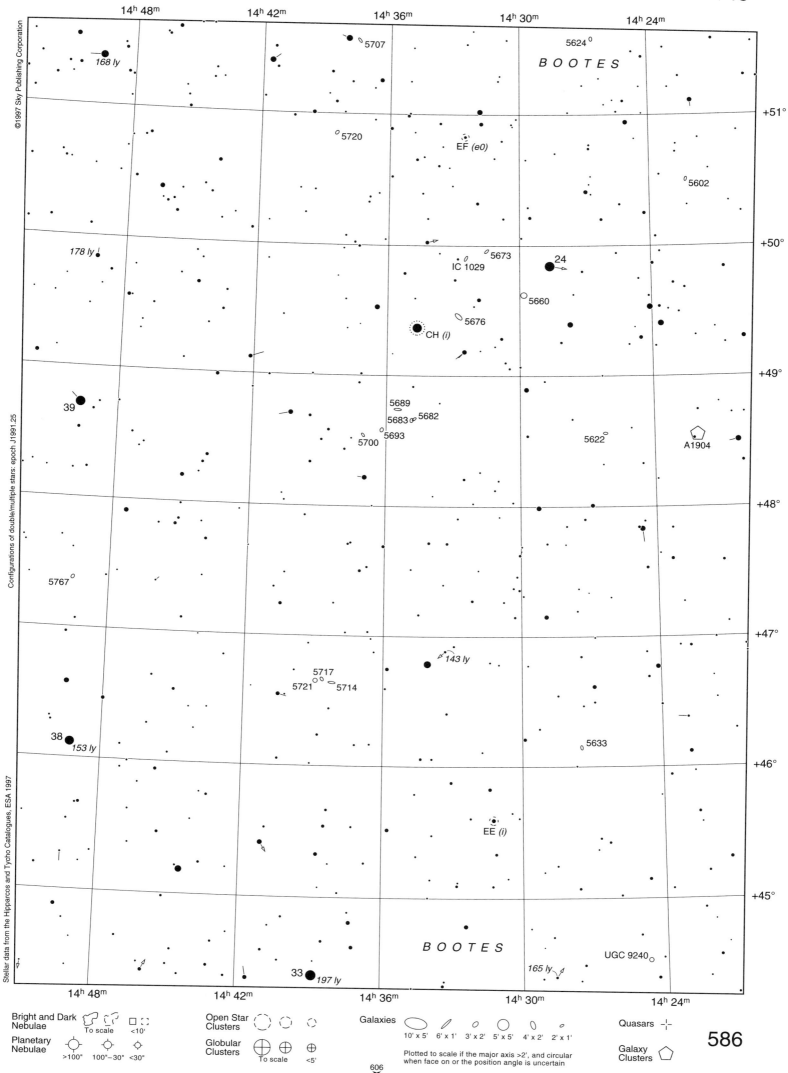

14h 48m   14h 42m   14h 36m   14h 30m   14h 24m

B O O T E S

5624

5707

168 ly

5720

5602

EF (e0)

+51°

178 ly

5673
IC 1029   24
5660
5676
CH (i)   5682

+50°

39

5689
5683   5682
5693
5700

5622

A1904

+49°

5767

+48°

5717
5721   5714

143 ly

+47°

38
153 ly

5633

EE (i)

+46°

+45°

B O O T E S

UGC 9240

33   197 ly   165 ly

14h 48m   14h 42m   14h 36m   14h 30m   14h 24m

Bright and Dark Nebulae
To scale   <10'

Planetary Nebulae
>100"   100"–30"   <30"

Open Star Clusters

Globular Clusters
To scale   <5'

Galaxies
10' x 5'   6' x 1'   3' x 2'   5' x 5'   4' x 2'   2' x 1'

Plotted to scale if the major axis >2', and circular when face on or the position angle is uncertain

Quasars

Galaxy Clusters

586

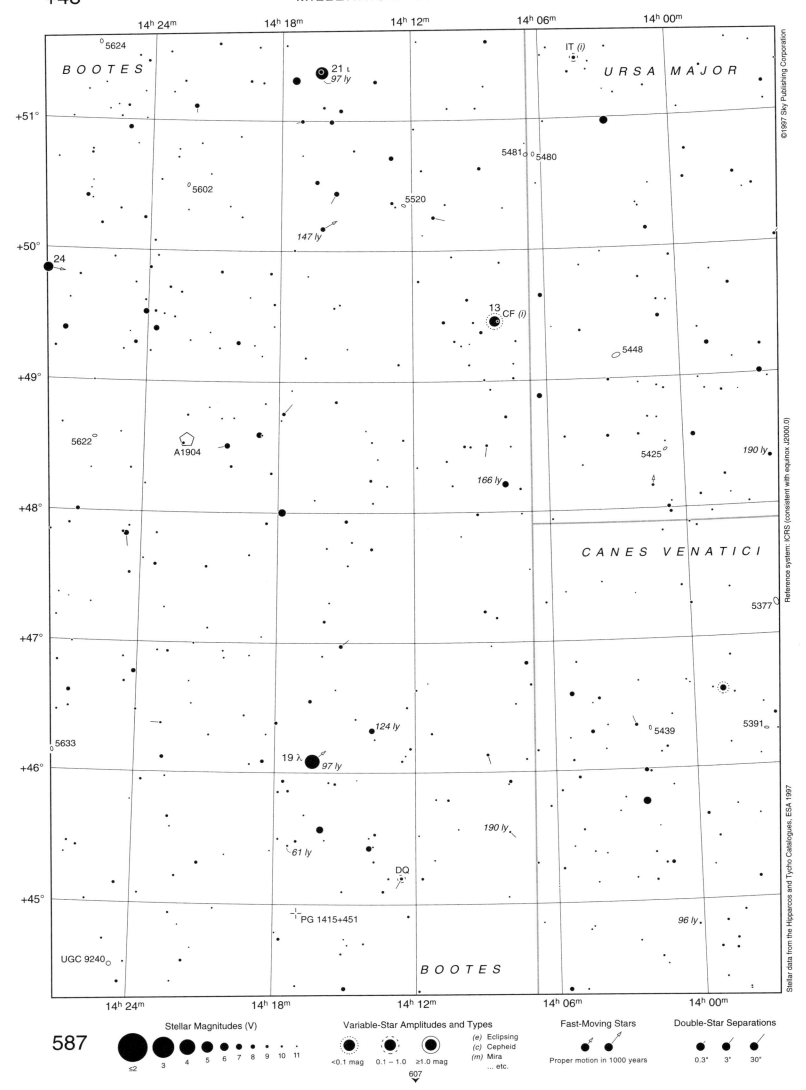

©1997 Sky Publishing Corporation

Reference system: ICRS (consistent with equinox J2000.0)

Stellar data from the Hipparcos and Tycho Catalogues, ESA 1997

B O O T E S

U R S A   M A J O R

IT (i)

21 ι
97 ly

5624

5602

5481   5480

5520

147 ly

24

13 CF (i)

5448

5622
A1904

5425

190 ly

166 ly

C A N E S   V E N A T I C I

5377

124 ly

5439   5391

5633

19 λ
97 ly

190 ly

61 ly

DQ

PG 1415+451

96 ly

UGC 9240

B O O T E S

587

Stellar Magnitudes (V)

≤2   3   4   5   6   7   8   9   10   11

Variable-Star Amplitudes and Types

<0.1 mag   0.1 − 1.0   ≥1.0 mag

(e) Eclipsing
(c) Cepheid
(m) Mira
... etc.

Fast-Moving Stars

Proper motion in 1000 years

Double-Star Separations

0.3"   3"   30"

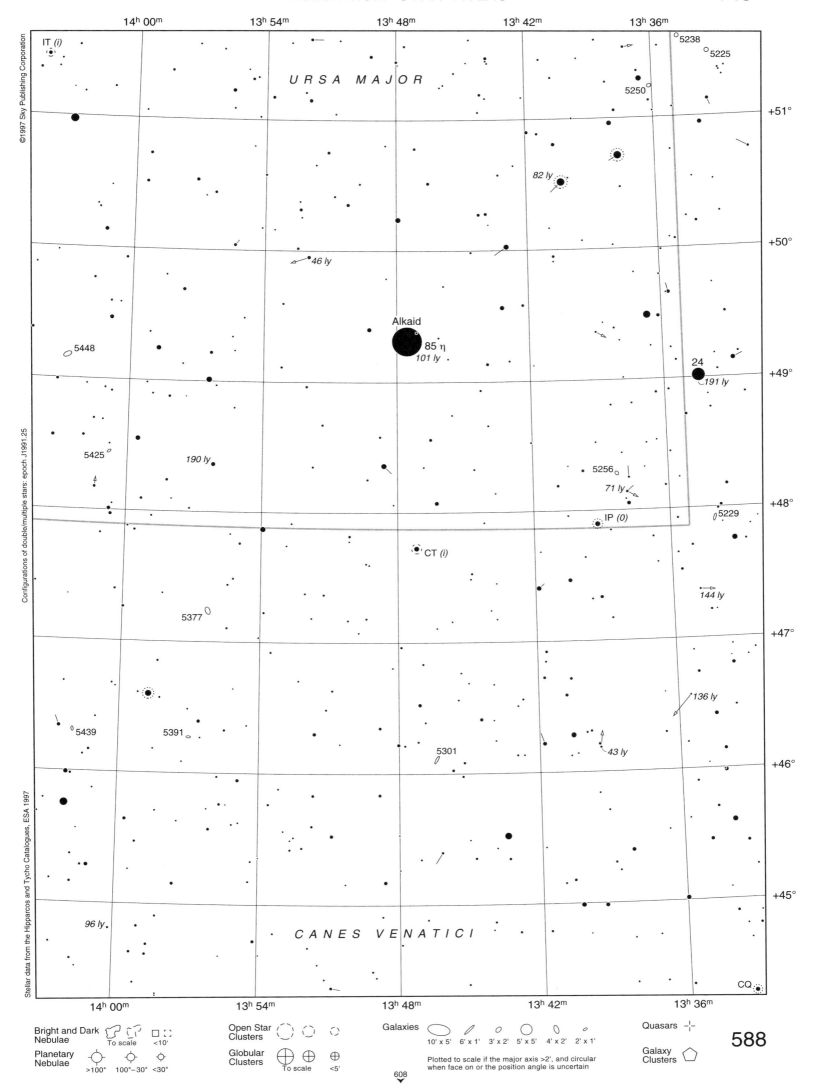

IT *(i)*

U R S A   M A J O R

○5238
○5225

5250

82 ly

+51°

46 ly

+50°

Alkaid
85 η
101 ly

24
191 ly

+49°

5448

5425

190 ly

5256
71 ly

IP *(0)*

5229

+48°

CT *(i)*

144 ly

5377

+47°

136 ly

5439

5391

5301

43 ly

+46°

+45°

96 ly

C A N E S   V E N A T I C I

CQ

14h 00m   13h 54m   13h 48m   13h 42m   13h 36m

©1997 Sky Publishing Corporation

Configurations of double/multiple stars: epoch J1991.25

Stellar data from the Hipparcos and Tycho Catalogues, ESA 1997

Bright and Dark
Nebulae
To scale   <10'

Planetary
Nebulae
>100"   100"–30"   <30"

Open Star
Clusters

Globular
Clusters
To scale   <5'

Galaxies
10' x 5'   6' x 1'   3' x 2'   5' x 5'   4' x 2'   2' x 1'

Plotted to scale if the major axis >2', and circular
when face on or the position angle is uncertain

Quasars

Galaxy
Clusters

588

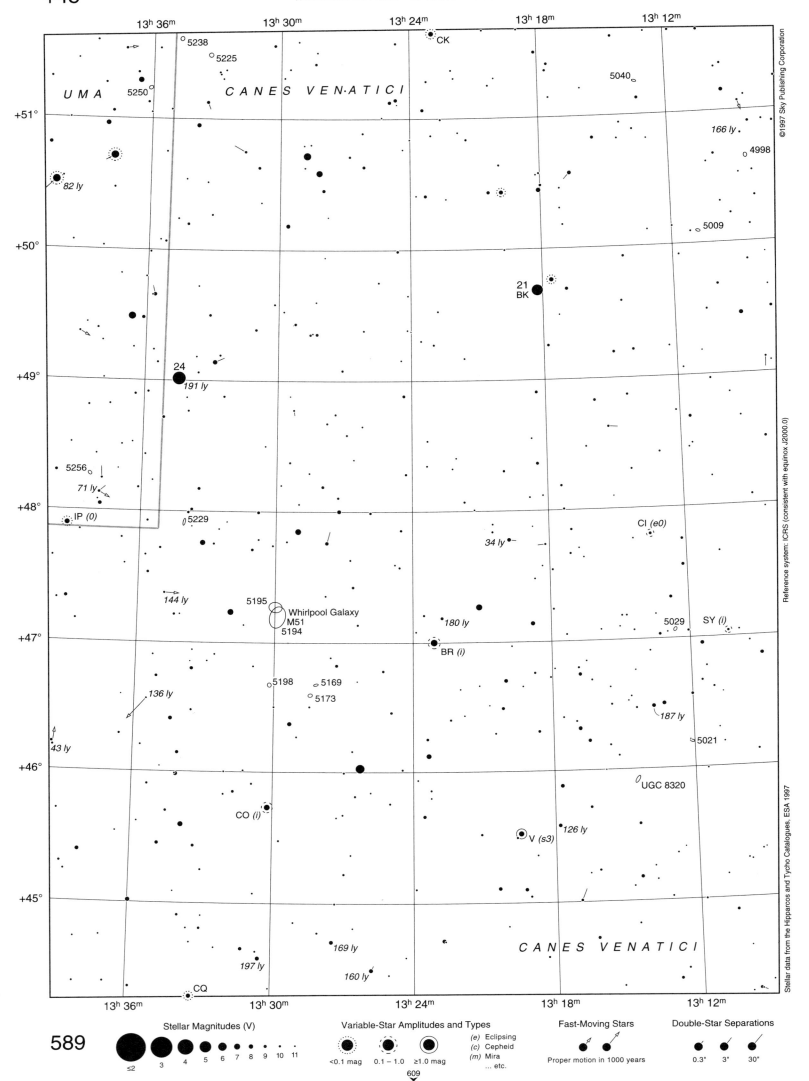

©1997 Sky Publishing Corporation

Reference system: ICRS (consistent with equinox J2000.0)

Stellar data from the Hipparcos and Tycho Catalogues, ESA 1997

Stellar Magnitudes (V)

≤2 3 4 5 6 7 8 9 10 11

Variable-Star Amplitudes and Types

<0.1 mag   0.1 – 1.0   ≥1.0 mag

(e) Eclipsing
(c) Cepheid
(m) Mira
... etc.

Fast-Moving Stars

Proper motion in 1000 years

Double-Star Separations

0.3" 3" 30"

589

MILLENNIUM STAR ATLAS

+48°

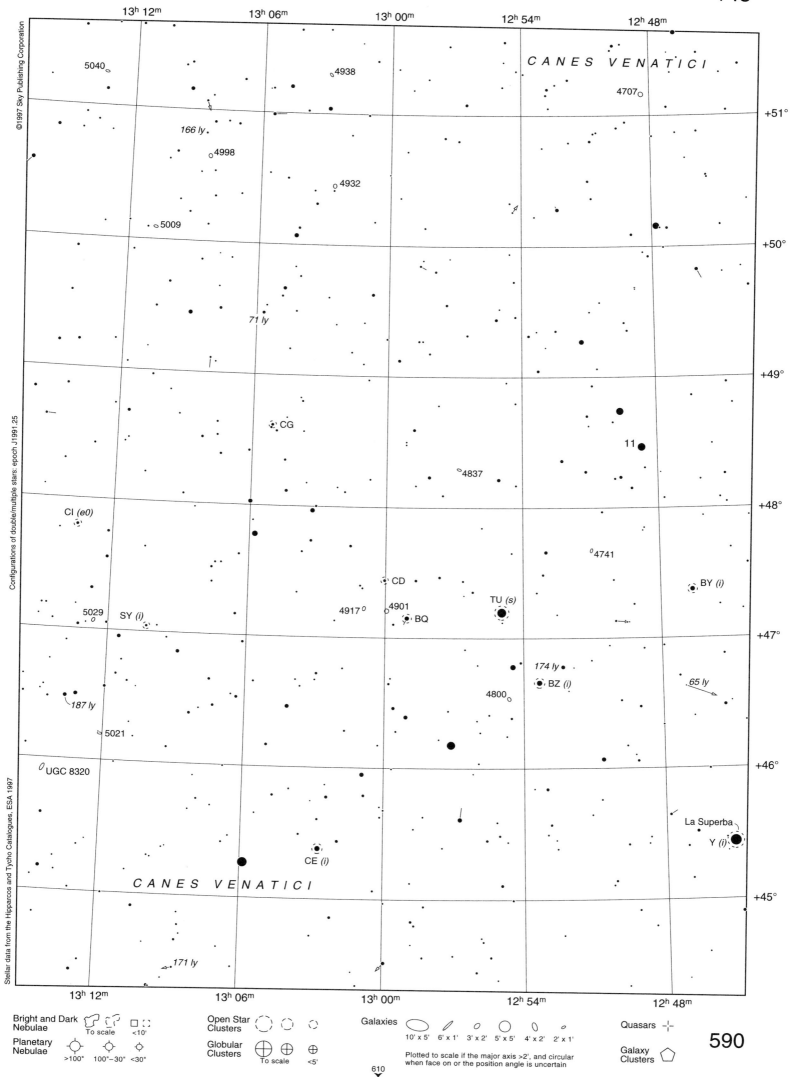

©1997 Sky Publishing Corporation

Configurations of double/multiple stars: epoch J1991.25

Stellar data from the Hipparcos and Tycho Catalogues, ESA 1997

13h 12m   13h 06m   13h 00m   12h 54m   12h 48m

CANES VENATICI

5040

4938

4707

166 ly

4998

4932

5009

+51°

+50°

71 ly

+49°

CG

11

4837

+48°

CI (e0)

4741

CD

BY (i)

5029

SY (i)

4917

4901

BQ

TU (s)

+47°

174 ly

187 ly

BZ (i)

65 ly

5021

4800

UGC 8320

+46°

La Superba

CE (i)

Y (i)

CANES VENATICI

+45°

171 ly

13h 12m   13h 06m   13h 00m   12h 54m   12h 48m

Bright and Dark Nebulae	To scale <10'	**Open Star Clusters**	**Galaxies**
Planetary Nebulae	>100" 100"–30" <30"	**Globular Clusters** To scale <5'	10' x 5' 6' x 1' 3' x 2' 5' x 5' 4' x 2' 2' x 1'

Quasars

Plotted to scale if the major axis >2', and circular when face on or the position angle is uncertain

Galaxy Clusters

590

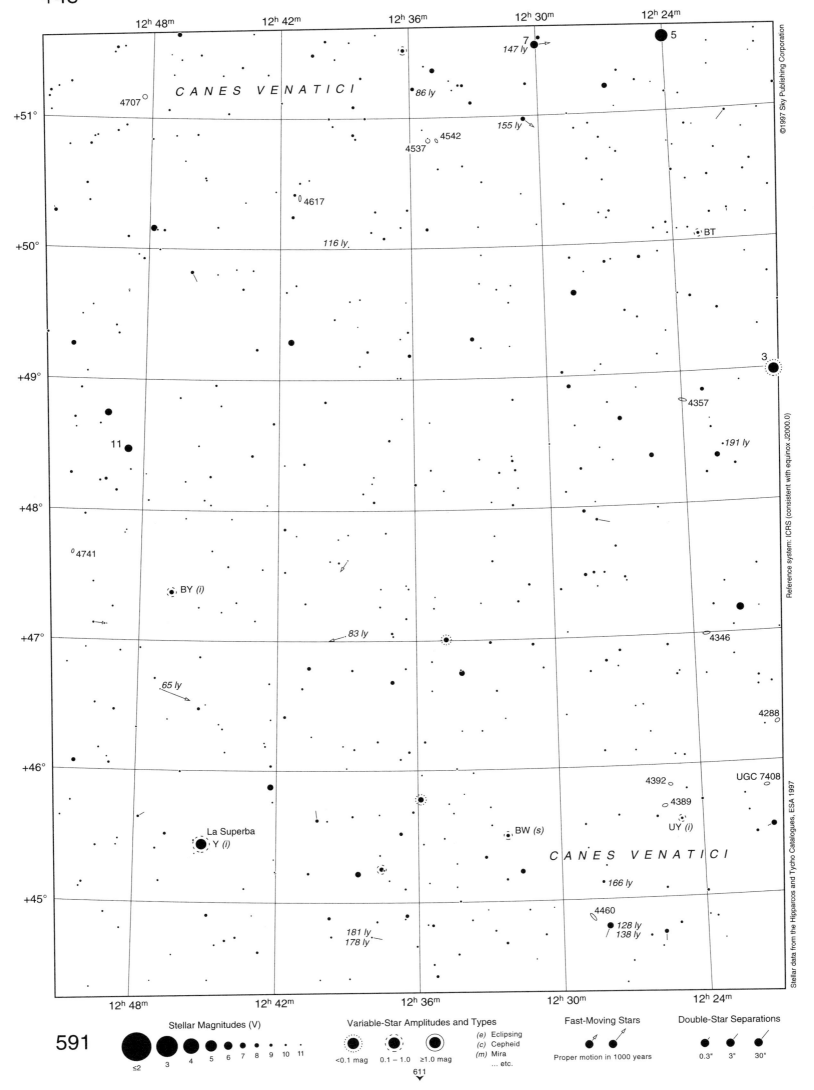

©1997 Sky Publishing Corporation

Reference system: ICRS (consistent with equinox J2000.0)

Stellar data from the Hipparcos and Tycho Catalogues, ESA 1997

CANES VENATICI

CANES VENATICI

4707

86 ly

147 ly

155 ly

4542
4537

4617

116 ly

BT

3

4357

191 ly

11

4741

BY (i)

4346

83 ly

65 ly

4288

4392
4389
UGC 7408

BW (s)

UY (i)

La Superba
Y (i)

166 ly

4460
128 ly
138 ly

181 ly
178 ly

591

Stellar Magnitudes (V)

≤2 3 4 5 6 7 8 9 10 11

Variable-Star Amplitudes and Types

<0.1 mag   0.1 – 1.0   ≥1.0 mag

(e) Eclipsing
(c) Cepheid
(m) Mira
... etc.

Fast-Moving Stars

Proper motion in 1000 years

Double-Star Separations

0.3"   3"   30"

611

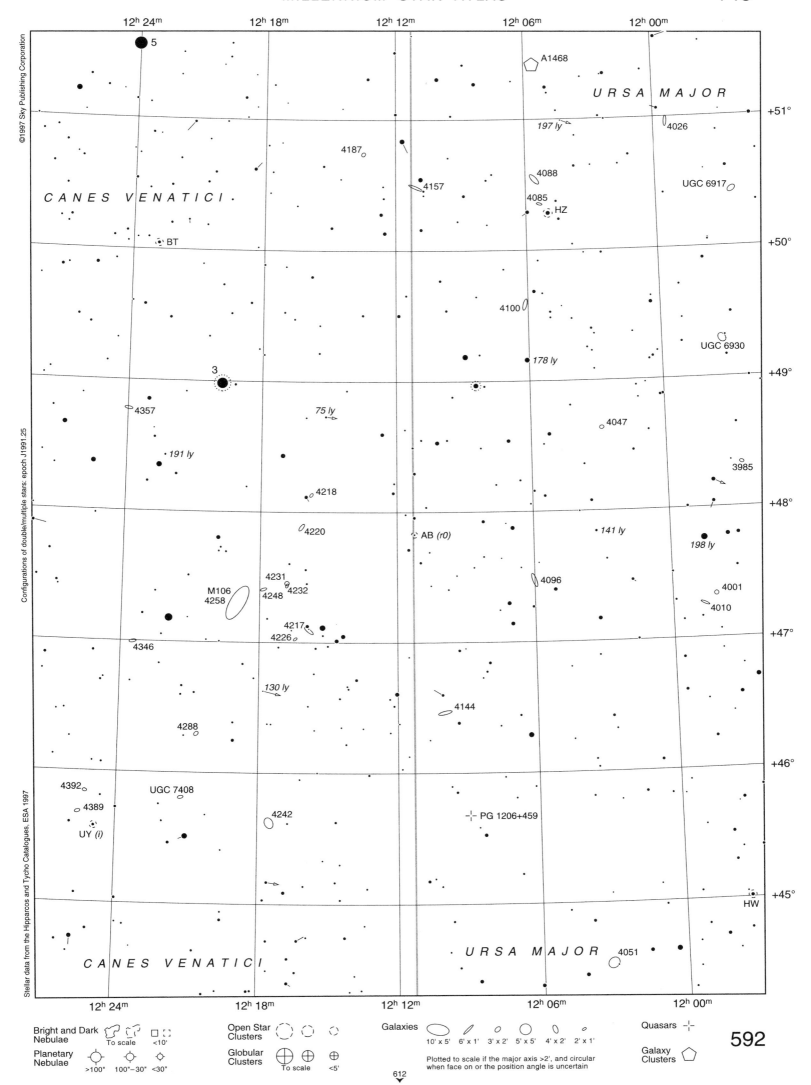

12ʰ 24ᵐ 12ʰ 18ᵐ 12ʰ 12ᵐ 12ʰ 06ᵐ 12ʰ 00ᵐ

5

A1468

URSA MAJOR

+51°

197 ly

4026

4187

4157

4088

UGC 6917

4085

HZ

CANES VENATICI

BT

+50°

4100

178 ly

UGC 6930

3

+49°

4357

75 ly

4047

191 ly

3985

4218

+48°

4220

AB (r0)

141 ly

198 ly

4096

4231

4001

4232

M106
4258

4248

4010

4217

4226

+47°

4346

130 ly

4144

4288

+46°

4392

UGC 7408

4389

4242

PG 1206+459

UY (i)

+45°

HW

CANES VENATICI

URSA MAJOR

4051

12ʰ 24ᵐ 12ʰ 18ᵐ 12ʰ 12ᵐ 12ʰ 06ᵐ 12ʰ 00ᵐ

Bright and Dark
Nebulae

To scale   <10'

Open Star
Clusters

Globular
Clusters

To scale   <5'

Galaxies

10' x 5'   6' x 1'   3' x 2'   5' x 5'   4' x 2'   2' x 1'

Quasars

Galaxy
Clusters

Planetary
Nebulae

>100"   100"–30"   <30"

Plotted to scale if the major axis >2', and circular
when face on or the position angle is uncertain

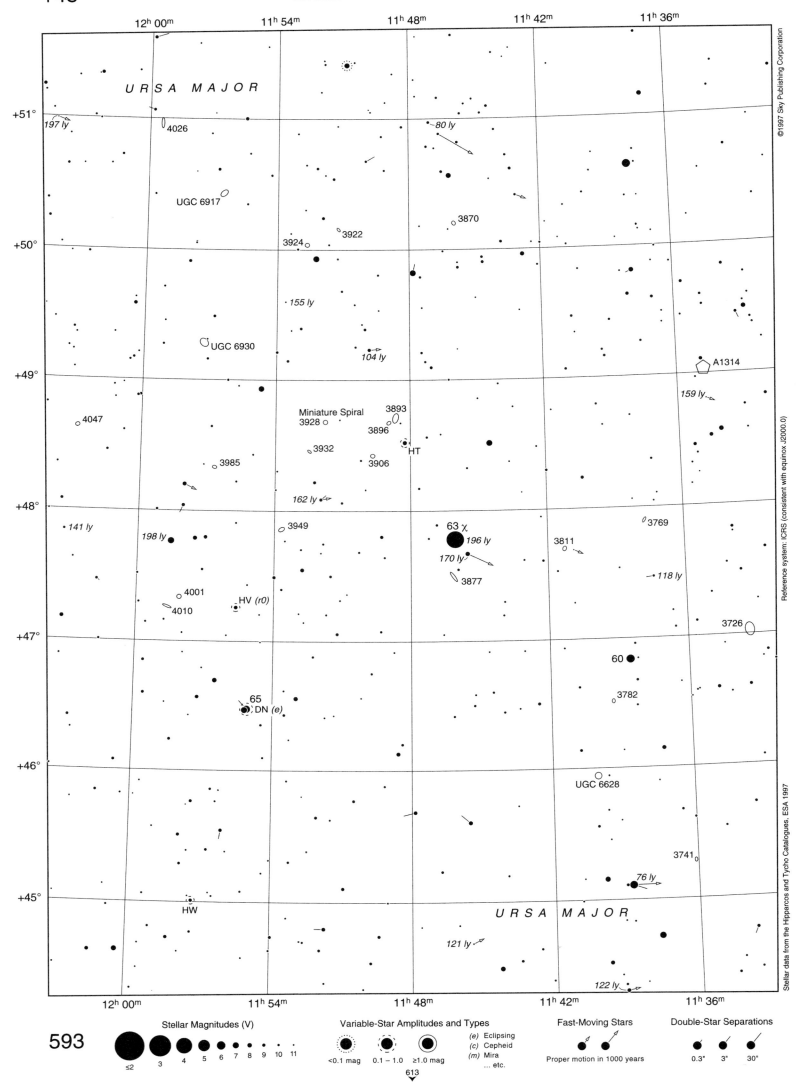

Stellar Magnitudes (V)

≤2 3 4 5 6 7 8 9 10 11

Variable-Star Amplitudes and Types

<0.1 mag   0.1 – 1.0   ≥1.0 mag

(e) Eclipsing
(c) Cepheid
(m) Mira
... etc.

Fast-Moving Stars

Proper motion in 1000 years

Double-Star Separations

0.3"   3"   30"

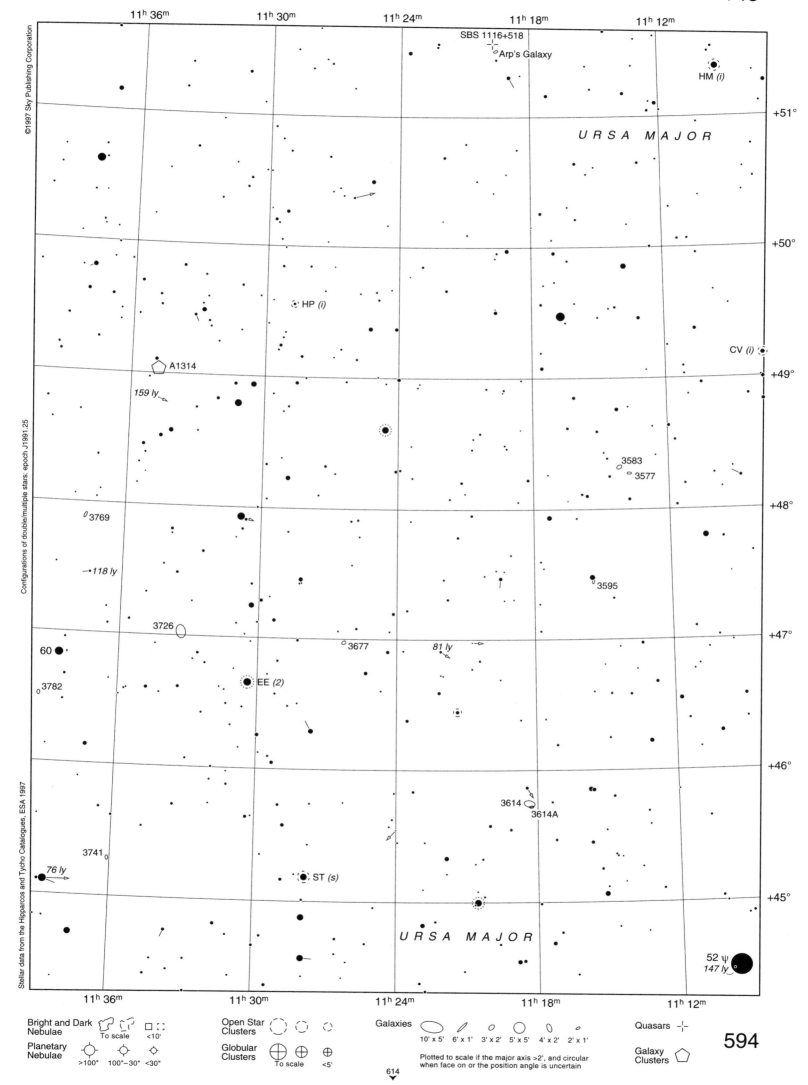

11ʰ 36ᵐ 11ʰ 30ᵐ 11ʰ 24ᵐ 11ʰ 18ᵐ 11ʰ 12ᵐ

SBS 1116+518

Arp's Galaxy

HM *(i)*

URSA MAJOR

+51°

+50°

HP *(i)*

CV *(i)*

+49°

A1314

159 ly

3583
3577

+48°

⁰ 3769

118 ly

3595

3726

+47°

60

⁰ 3677

81 ly

⁰ 3782

EE *(2)*

3614
3614A

3741₀

76 ly

ST *(s)*

+46°

+45°

URSA MAJOR

52 ψ
147 ly

Bright and Dark Nebulae				Open Star Clusters			Galaxies						Quasars
	To scale		<10'				10' x 5'	6' x 1'	3' x 2'	5' x 5'	4' x 2'	2' x 1'	
Planetary Nebulae				Globular Clusters									Galaxy Clusters
	>100"	100"–30"	<30"		To scale	<5'							

Plotted to scale if the major axis >2', and circular
when face on or the position angle is uncertain

+48°

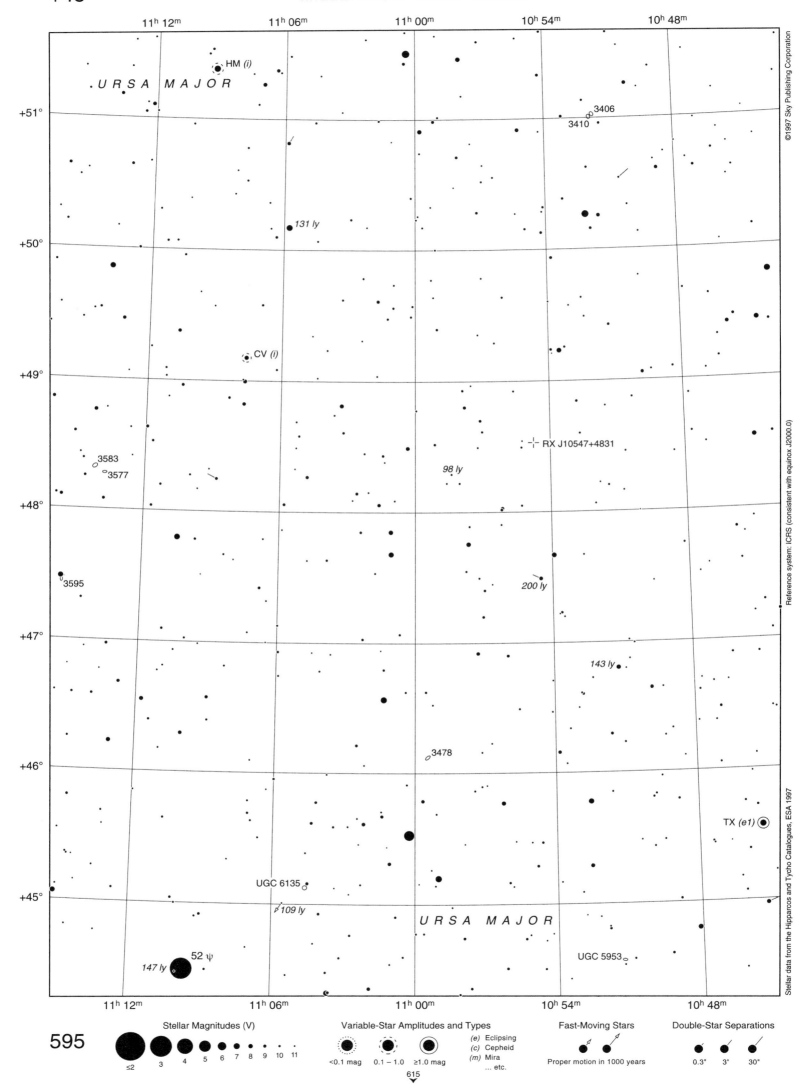

URSA MAJOR

HM (i)

3406
3410

+51°

131 ly

+50°

CV (i)

+49°

3583
3577

RX J10547+4831

98 ly

+48°

υ 3595

200 ly

+47°

143 ly

3478

+46°

TX (e1)

+45°

UGC 6135

109 ly

URSA MAJOR

UGC 5953

52 ψ

147 ly

11ʰ 12ᵐ   11ʰ 06ᵐ   11ʰ 00ᵐ   10ʰ 54ᵐ   10ʰ 48ᵐ

595

Stellar Magnitudes (V)
≤2   3   4   5   6   7   8   9   10   11

Variable-Star Amplitudes and Types
<0.1 mag   0.1 – 1.0   ≥1.0 mag
(e) Eclipsing
(c) Cepheid
(m) Mira
... etc.

Fast-Moving Stars
Proper motion in 1000 years

Double-Star Separations
0.3"   3"   30"

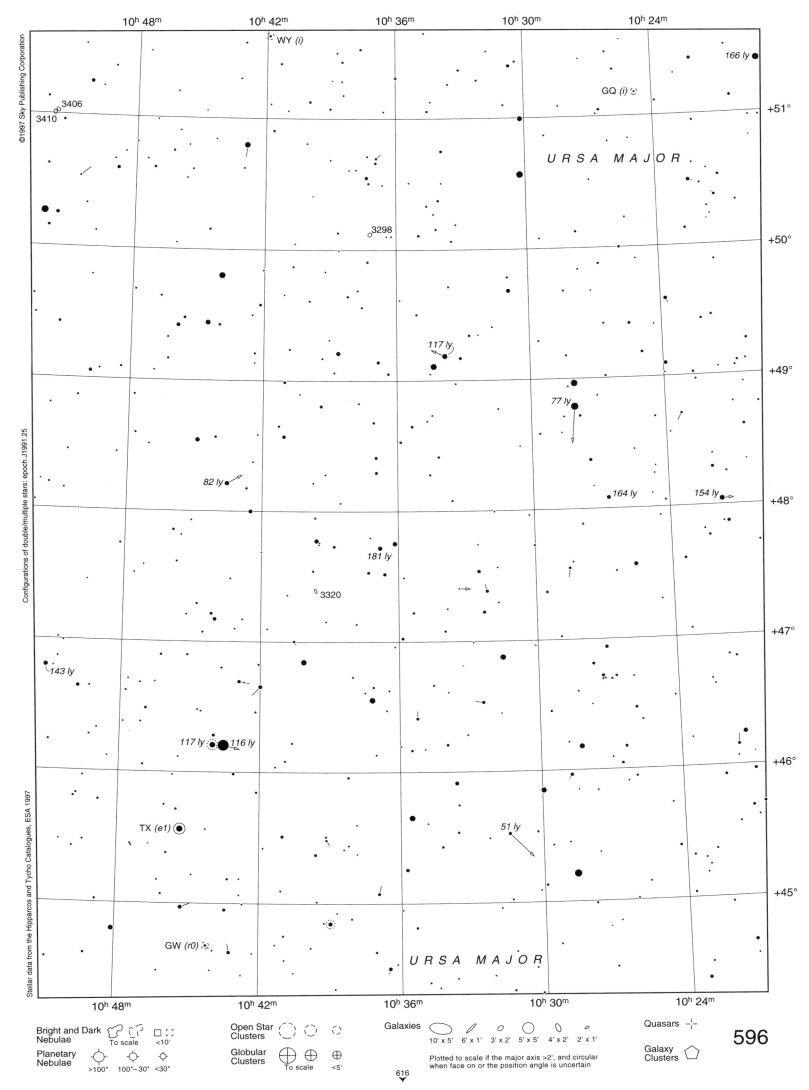

3406
3410

WY *(i)*

GQ *(i)*

166 ly

U R S A   M A J O R

3298

117 ly

77 ly

82 ly

164 ly   154 ly

181 ly

3320

143 ly

117 ly • 116 ly

TX *(e1)*

51 ly

GW *(r0)*

U R S A   M A J O R

Bright and Dark Nebulae
To scale   <10'

Planetary Nebulae
>100"   100"–30"   <30"

Open Star Clusters

Globular Clusters
To scale   <5'

Galaxies
10' x 5'   6' x 1'   3' x 2'   5' x 5'   4' x 2'   2' x 1'

Plotted to scale if the major axis >2', and circular when face on or the position angle is uncertain

Quasars

Galaxy Clusters

596

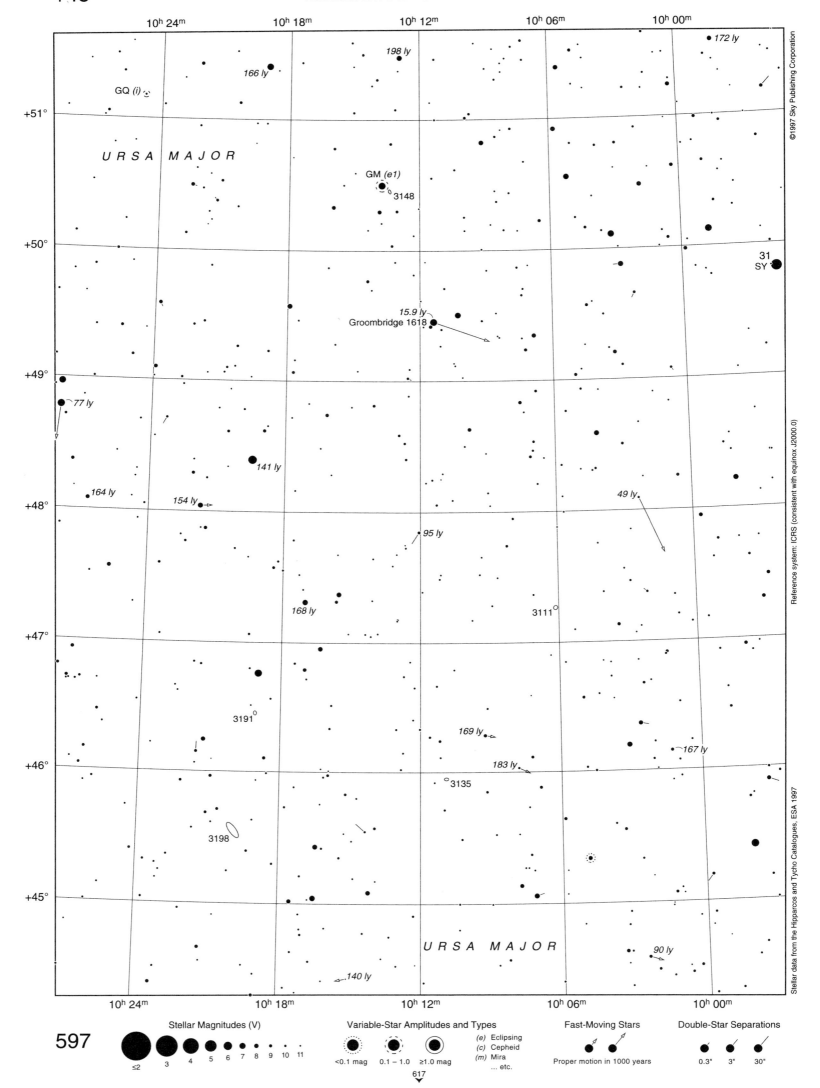

©1997 Sky Publishing Corporation

Reference system: ICRS (consistent with equinox J2000.0)

Stellar data from the Hipparcos and Tycho Catalogues, ESA 1997

597

Stellar Magnitudes (V)

≤2 3 4 5 6 7 8 9 10 11

Variable-Star Amplitudes and Types

<0.1 mag   0.1 – 1.0   ≥1.0 mag

(e) Eclipsing
(c) Cepheid
(m) Mira
... etc.

Fast-Moving Stars

Proper motion in 1000 years

Double-Star Separations

0.3"   3"   30"

617

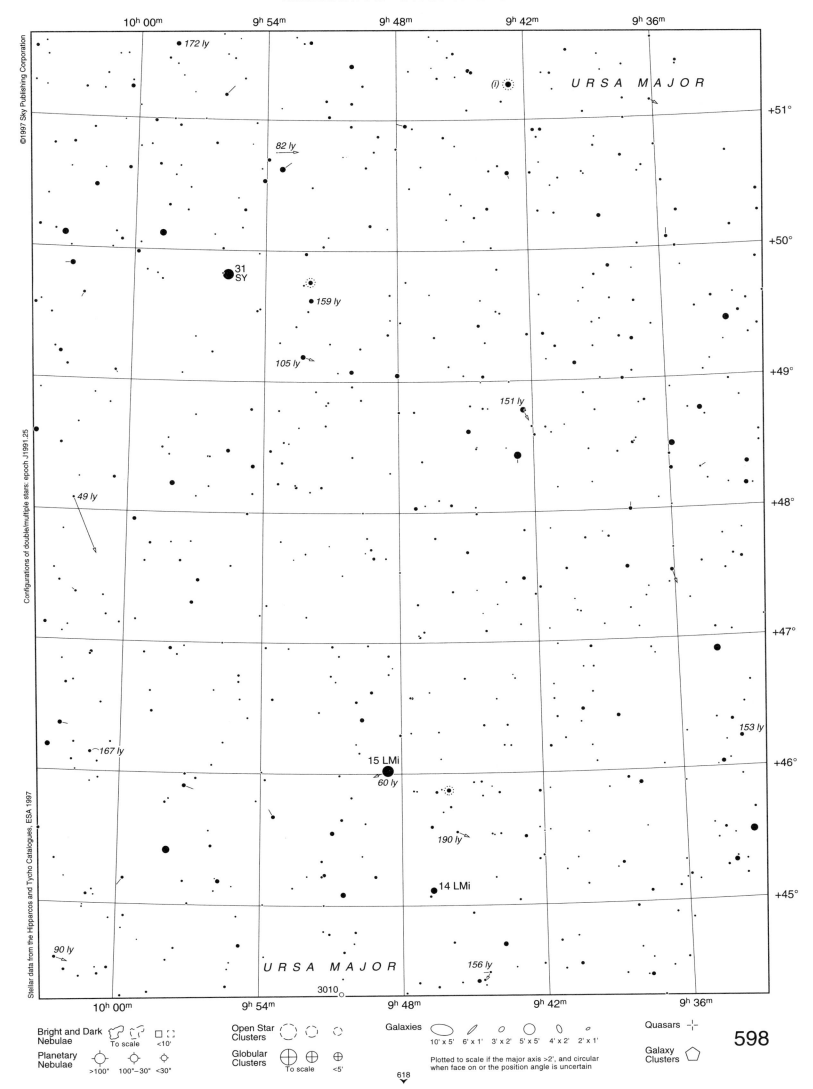

172 ly

U R S A   M A J O R

(i)

+51°

82 ly

+50°

31
SY

159 ly

105 ly

+49°

151 ly

49 ly

+48°

+47°

153 ly

167 ly

15 LMi
60 ly

+46°

190 ly

14 LMi

+45°

90 ly

U R S A   M A J O R

156 ly

3010

10ʰ 00ᵐ   9ʰ 54ᵐ   9ʰ 48ᵐ   9ʰ 42ᵐ   9ʰ 36ᵐ

Bright and Dark
Nebulae
To scale   <10'

Planetary
Nebulae
>100"   100"–30"   <30"

Open Star
Clusters

Globular
Clusters
To scale   <5'

Galaxies
10' x 5'   6' x 1'   3' x 2'   5' x 5'   4' x 2'   2' x 1'

Plotted to scale if the major axis >2', and circular
when face on or the position angle is uncertain

Quasars

Galaxy
Clusters

598

618

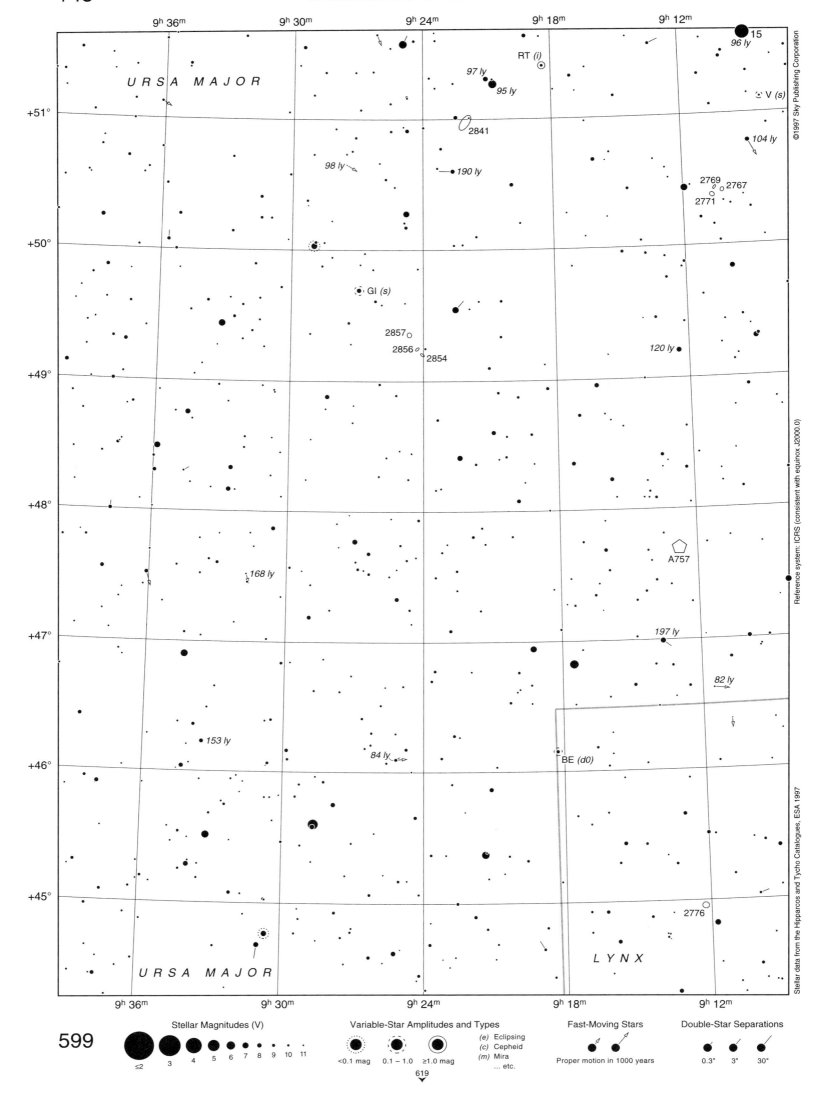

URSA MAJOR

LYNX

RT (i)

97 ly
95 ly

2841

98 ly

190 ly

Gl (s)

2857
2856
2854

15
96 ly

V (s)

104 ly

2769 2767
2771

120 ly

A757

197 ly

82 ly

BE (d0)

168 ly

153 ly

84 ly

2776

URSA MAJOR

599

Stellar Magnitudes (V)
≤2 3 4 5 6 7 8 9 10 11

Variable-Star Amplitudes and Types
<0.1 mag   0.1 – 1.0   ≥1.0 mag

(e) Eclipsing
(c) Cepheid
(m) Mira
... etc.

Fast-Moving Stars
Proper motion in 1000 years

Double-Star Separations
0.3" 3" 30"

619

MILLENNIUM STAR ATLAS

+48°

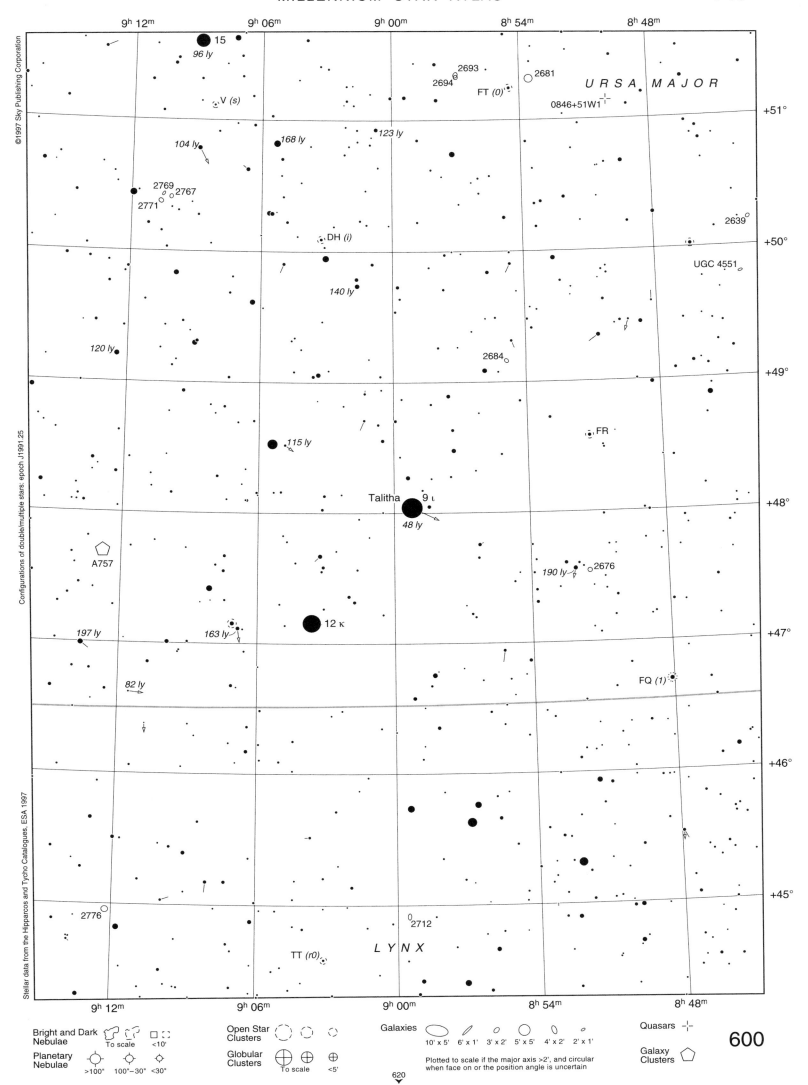

9h 12m 9h 06m 9h 00m 8h 54m 8h 48m

15
96 ly

2693
2694
2681
FT (0)
0846+51W1
URSA MAJOR

V (s)

104 ly
168 ly
123 ly

2769 2767
2771

2639

DH (i)

UGC 4551

140 ly

120 ly

2684

115 ly

FR

Talitha 9 ι
48 ly

A757

190 ly 2676

197 ly
163 ly
12 κ

82 ly

FQ (1)

+51°
+50°
+49°
+48°
+47°
+46°
+45°

2776
2712
TT (r0)
LYNX

9h 12m 9h 06m 9h 00m 8h 54m 8h 48m

Bright and Dark Nebulae	Open Star Clusters	Galaxies	Quasars

To scale <10'

Planetary Nebulae
>100" 100"–30" <30"

Globular Clusters
To scale <5'

10' x 5' 6' x 1' 3' x 2' 5' x 5' 4' x 2' 2' x 1'

Plotted to scale if the major axis >2', and circular when face on or the position angle is uncertain

Galaxy Clusters

600

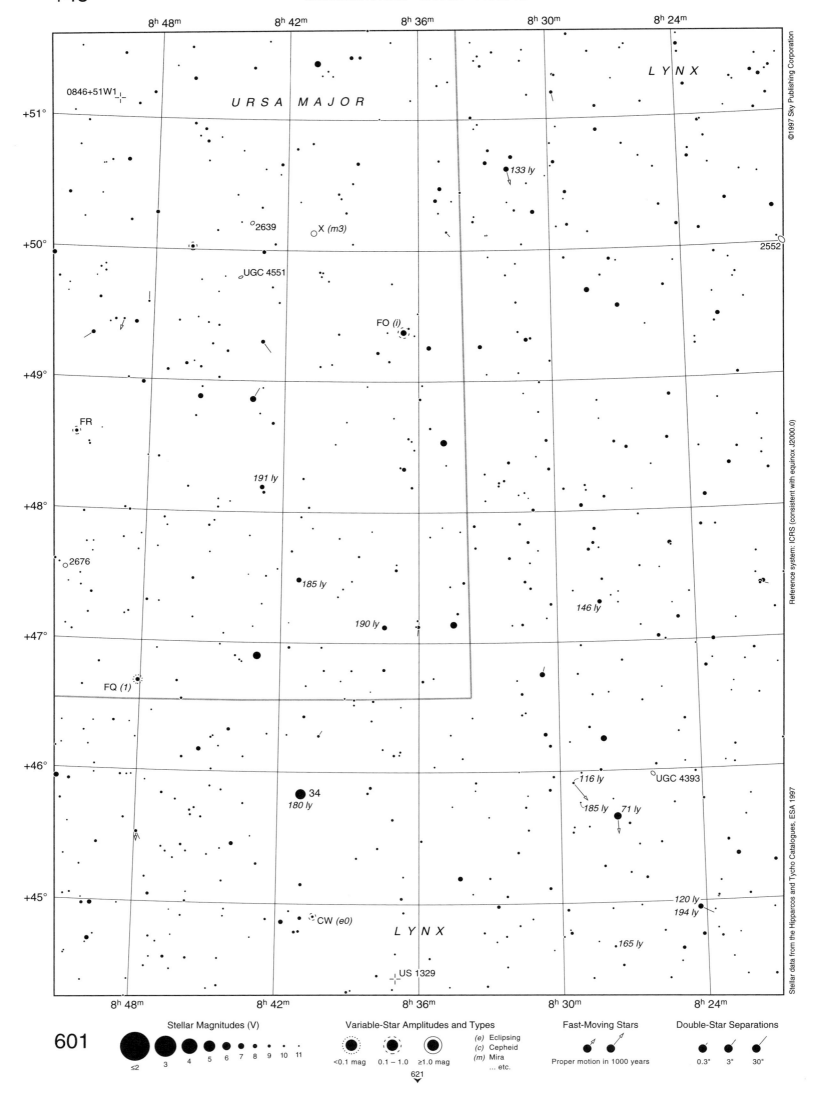

©1997 Sky Publishing Corporation

Reference system: ICRS (consistent with equinox J2000.0)

Stellar data from the Hipparcos and Tycho Catalogues, ESA 1997

0846+51W1

U R S A   M A J O R

L Y N X

133 ly

2639
X (m3)

UGC 4551

2552

FO (i)

FR

191 ly

146 ly

2676

185 ly

190 ly

FQ (1)

116 ly
UGC 4393

34
180 ly

185 ly
71 ly

120 ly
194 ly

CW (e0)

L Y N X

165 ly

US 1329

Stellar Magnitudes (V)

≤2   3   4   5   6   7   8   9   10   11

Variable-Star Amplitudes and Types

<0.1 mag   0.1 – 1.0   ≥1.0 mag

(e) Eclipsing
(c) Cepheid
(m) Mira
... etc.

Fast-Moving Stars

Proper motion in 1000 years

Double-Star Separations

0.3"   3"   30"

621

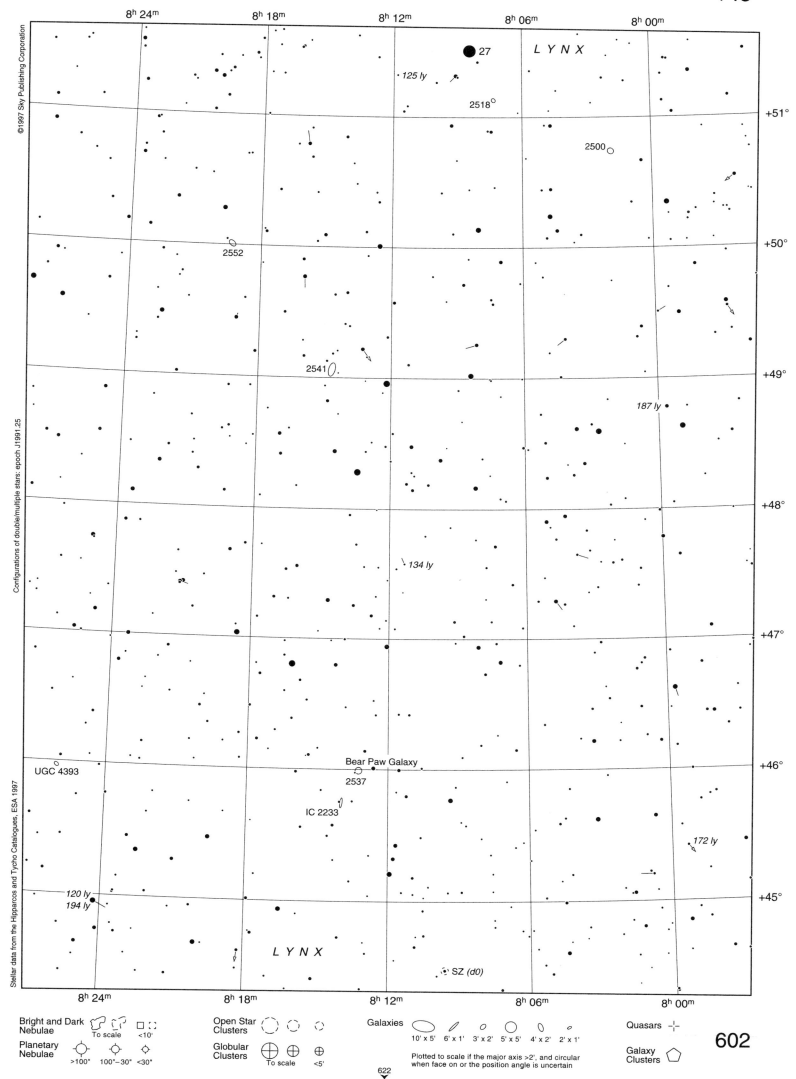

8ʰ 24ᵐ   8ʰ 18ᵐ   8ʰ 12ᵐ   8ʰ 06ᵐ   8ʰ 00ᵐ

27

L Y N X

125 ly

2518

+51°

2500

2552

+50°

2541

+49°

187 ly

+48°

134 ly

+47°

Bear Paw Galaxy

+46°

UGC 4393

2537

IC 2233

172 ly

120 ly
194 ly

+45°

L Y N X

SZ (d0)

8ʰ 24ᵐ   8ʰ 18ᵐ   8ʰ 12ᵐ   8ʰ 06ᵐ   8ʰ 00ᵐ

Bright and Dark Nebulae
To scale   <10'
Planetary Nebulae
>100"   100"–30"   <30"

Open Star Clusters

Globular Clusters
To scale   <5'

Galaxies
10' x 5'   6' x 1'   3' x 2'   5' x 5'   4' x 2'   2' x 1'

Plotted to scale if the major axis >2', and circular when face on or the position angle is uncertain

Quasars

Galaxy Clusters

602

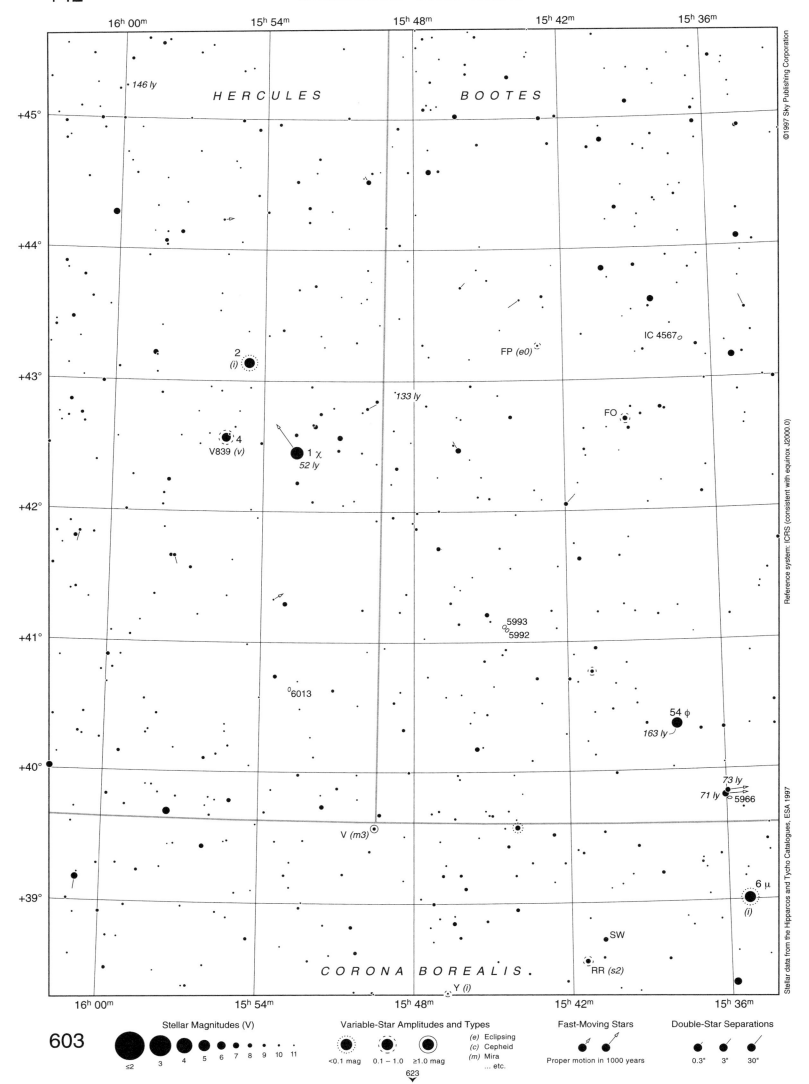

146 ly

H E R C U L E S

B O O T E S

IC 4567

FP (e0)

2
(i)

133 ly

FO

4
V839 (v)

1 χ
52 ly

5993
5992

6013

54 φ
163 ly

73 ly
71 ly 5966

V (m3)

6 μ
(i)

SW

C O R O N A   B O R E A L I S

RR (s2)

Y (i)

©1997 Sky Publishing Corporation

Reference system: ICRS (consistent with equinox J2000.0)

Stellar data from the Hipparcos and Tycho Catalogues, ESA 1997

603

Stellar Magnitudes (V)

≤2   3   4   5 6 7 8 9 10 11

Variable-Star Amplitudes and Types

<0.1 mag   0.1 – 1.0   ≥1.0 mag

(e) Eclipsing
(c) Cepheid
(m) Mira
... etc.

Fast-Moving Stars

Proper motion in 1000 years

Double-Star Separations

0.3"   3"   30"

623

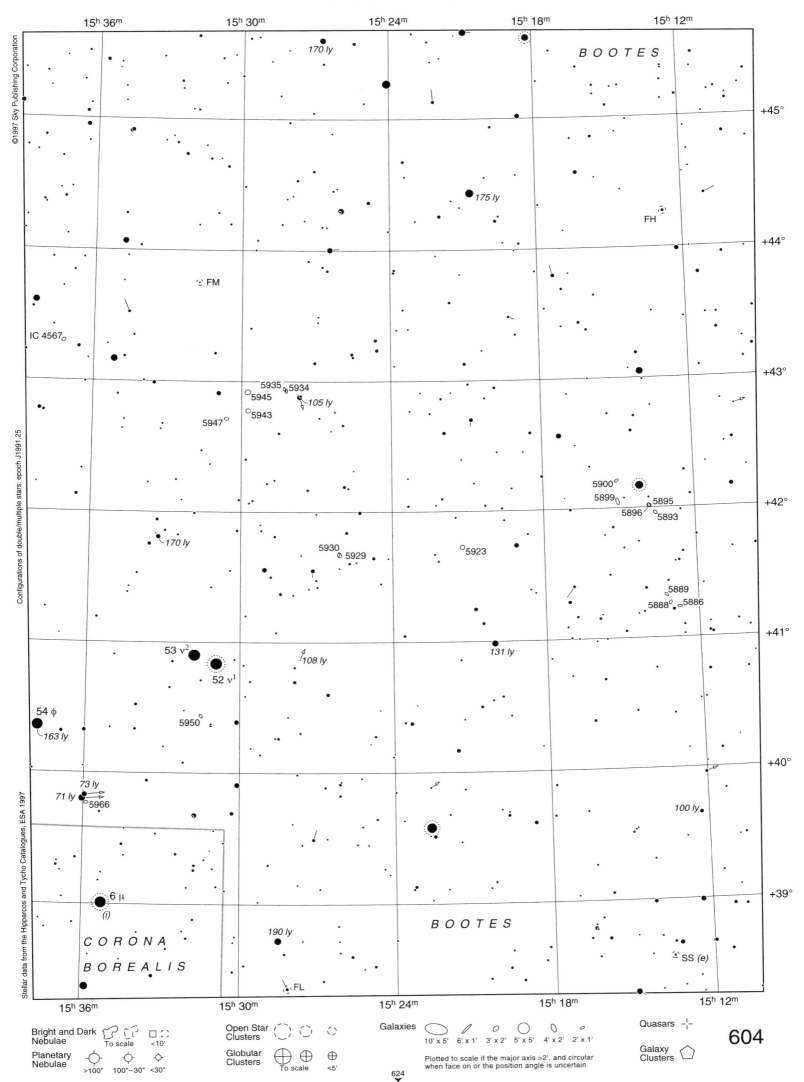

BOOTES

170 ly

175 ly

FH

FM

IC 4567

5935 5934
5945
5947   5943   105 ly

5900
5899   5895
5896   5893

170 ly

5930 5929   5923

5889
5888 5886

53 ν²
52 ν¹   108 ly   131 ly

54 φ
5950
163 ly

73 ly
71 ly
5966

100 ly

6 μ
(i)

CORONA
BOREALIS

190 ly

BOOTES

SS (e)

FL

Bright and Dark Nebulae	Open Star Clusters	Galaxies	Quasars
To scale <10'	To scale <10'	10' x 5' 6' x 1' 3' x 2' 5' x 5' 4' x 2' 2' x 1'	
Planetary Nebulae	Globular Clusters	Plotted to scale if the major axis >2', and circular when face on or the position angle is uncertain	Galaxy Clusters
>100" 100"–30" <30"	To scale <5'		

624

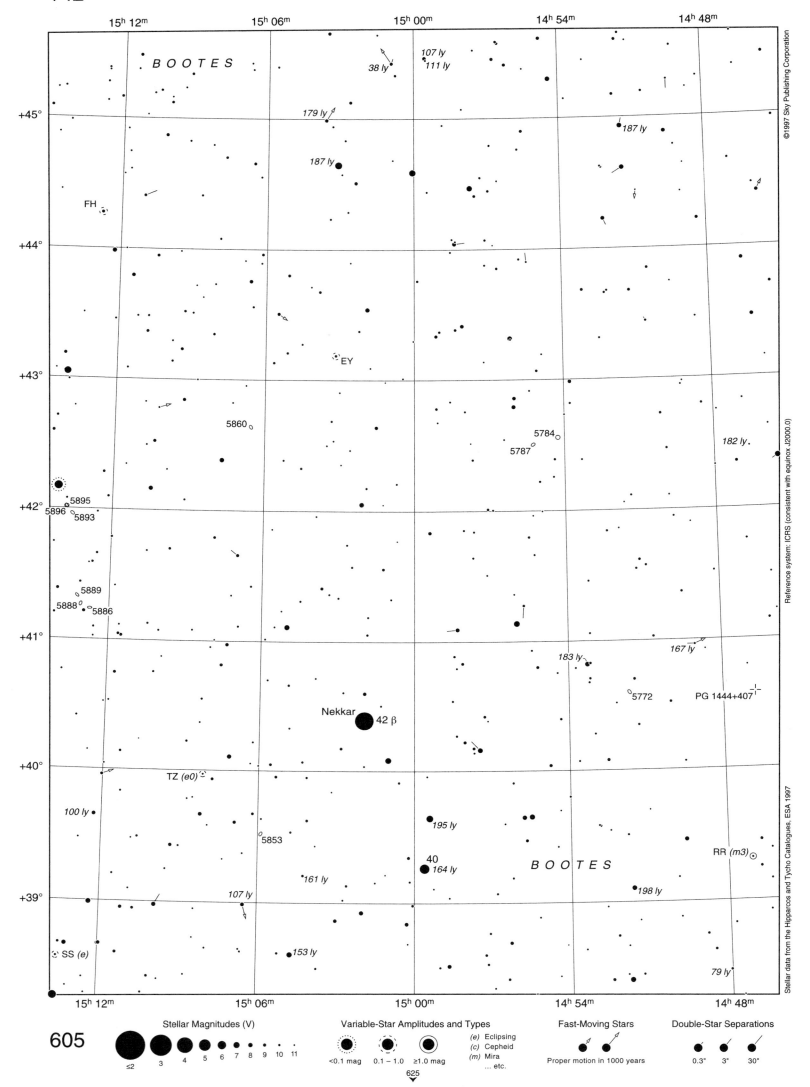

©1997 Sky Publishing Corporation

Reference system: ICRS (consistent with equinox J2000.0)

Stellar data from the Hipparcos and Tycho Catalogues, ESA 1997

15h 12m   15h 06m   15h 00m   14h 54m   14h 48m

BOOTES

107 ly
38 ly   111 ly

179 ly

187 ly

187 ly

FH

EY

5860

5784
5787

182 ly

5895
5896   5893

5889
5888   5886

167 ly

183 ly
5772   PG 1444+407

Nekkar   42 β

TZ (e0)

100 ly

5853

RR (m3)

161 ly

40
164 ly

BOOTES

198 ly

195 ly

SS (e)

153 ly

79 ly

15h 12m   15h 06m   15h 00m   14h 54m   14h 48m

605

Stellar Magnitudes (V)
≤2   3   4   5   6   7   8   9 10 11

Variable-Star Amplitudes and Types
<0.1 mag   0.1 – 1.0   ≥1.0 mag

(e) Eclipsing
(c) Cepheid
(m) Mira
... etc.

Fast-Moving Stars
Proper motion in 1000 years

Double-Star Separations
0.3"   3"   30"

625

MILLENNIUM STAR ATLAS

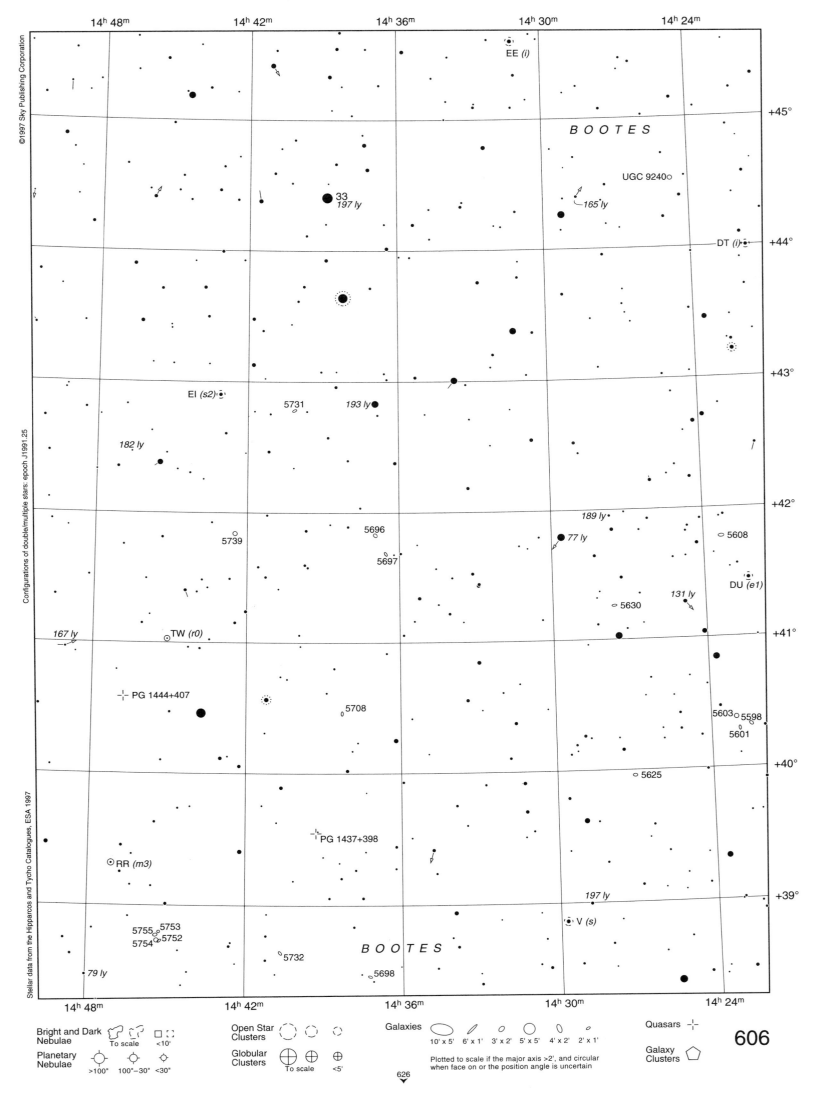

Configurations of double/multiple stars: epoch J1991.25

Stellar data from the Hipparcos and Tycho Catalogues, ESA 1997

14ʰ 48ᵐ   14ʰ 42ᵐ   14ʰ 36ᵐ   14ʰ 30ᵐ   14ʰ 24ᵐ

EE (i)

BOOTES

+45°

UGC 9240

33
197 ly

165 ly

DT (i)   +44°

+43°

El (s2)

5731   193 ly

182 ly

+42°

189 ly

5696   77 ly   5608

5739

5697

DU (e1)

131 ly

5630

167 ly

TW (r0)   +41°

5603 5598

PG 1444+407   5601

5708

+40°

5625

PG 1437+398

197 ly

RR (m3)   +39°

V (s)

5755 5753
5754 5752

BOOTES

79 ly   5732

5698

14ʰ 48ᵐ   14ʰ 42ᵐ   14ʰ 36ᵐ   14ʰ 30ᵐ   14ʰ 24ᵐ

Bright and Dark Nebulae — To scale — <10'
Planetary Nebulae — >100" — 100"–30" — <30"

Open Star Clusters
Globular Clusters — To scale — <5'

Galaxies — 10' x 5' 6' x 1' 3' x 2' 5' x 5' 4' x 2' 2' x 1'

Plotted to scale if the major axis >2', and circular when face on or the position angle is uncertain

Quasars

Galaxy Clusters

606

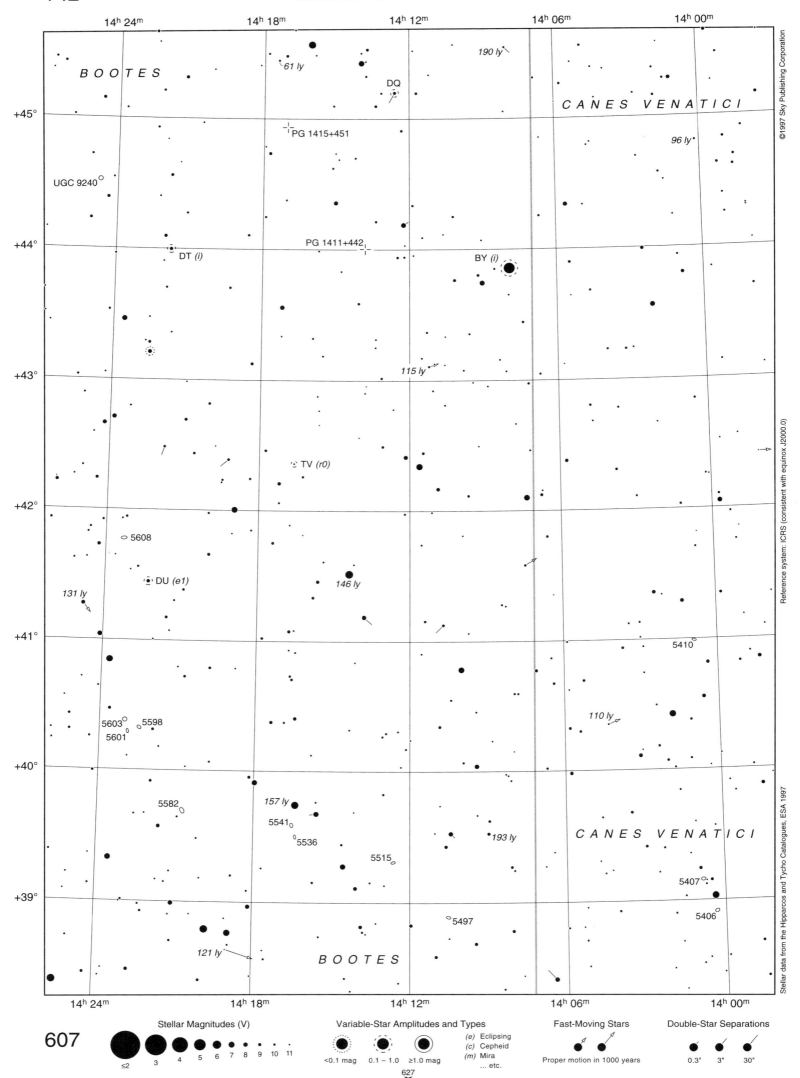

©1997 Sky Publishing Corporation

Reference system: ICRS (consistent with equinox J2000.0)

Stellar data from the Hipparcos and Tycho Catalogues, ESA 1997

607

Stellar Magnitudes (V)

≤2   3   4   5   6   7   8   9   10   11

Variable-Star Amplitudes and Types

<0.1 mag   0.1 – 1.0   ≥1.0 mag

(e) Eclipsing
(c) Cepheid
(m) Mira
... etc.

Fast-Moving Stars

Proper motion in 1000 years

Double-Star Separations

0.3"   3"   30"

MILLENNIUM STAR ATLAS

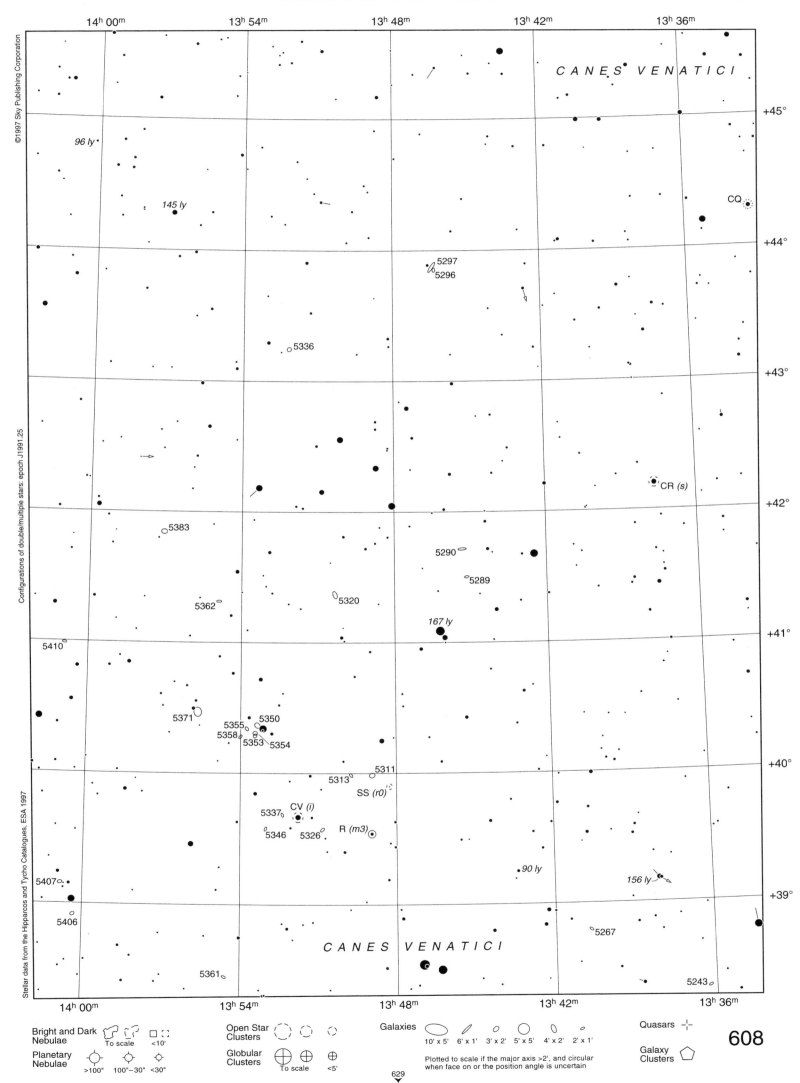

14h 00m   13h 54m   13h 48m   13h 42m   13h 36m

C A N E S   V E N A T I C I

+45°

96 ly

145 ly

CQ

+44°

5297
5296

5336

+43°

CR *(s)*

+42°

5383

5290

5289

5362   5320

167 ly

+41°

5410

5371

5350
5355
5358   5353   5354

+40°

5311
5313

SS *(r0)*

CV *(i)*

5337
5346   5326   R *(m3)*

90 ly   *156 ly*

5407

+39°

5406

5267

C A N E S   V E N A T I C I

5361   5243

14h 00m   13h 54m   13h 48m   13h 42m   13h 36m

Bright and Dark Nebulae   To scale   <10'

Open Star Clusters

Galaxies   10' x 5'   6' x 1'   3' x 2'   5' x 5'   4' x 2'   2' x 1'

Quasars

608

Planetary Nebulae   >100"   100"–30"   <30"

Globular Clusters   To scale   <5'

Plotted to scale if the major axis >2', and circular when face on or the position angle is uncertain

Galaxy Clusters

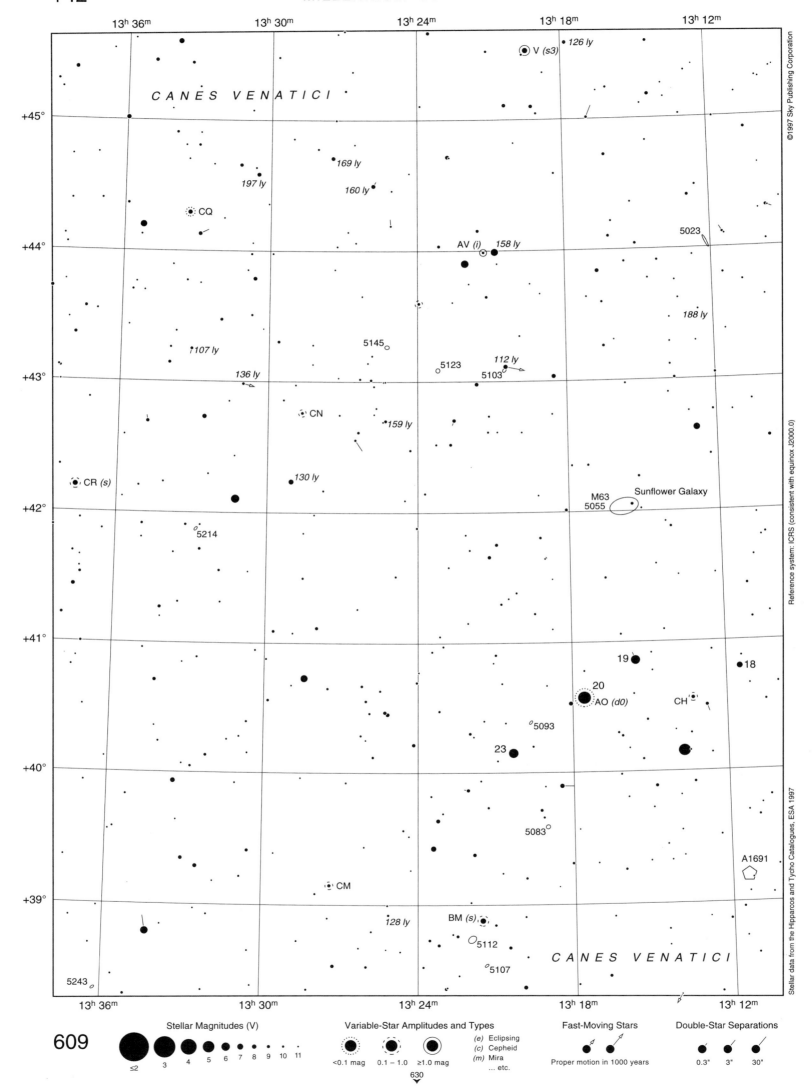

©1997 Sky Publishing Corporation

Reference system: ICRS (consistent with equinox J2000.0)

Stellar data from the Hipparcos and Tycho Catalogues, ESA 1997

CANES VENATICI

CANES VENATICI

V (s3)
126 ly
169 ly
197 ly
CQ
160 ly
AV (i) 158 ly
5023
188 ly
107 ly
5145
5123 112 ly
136 ly 5103
CN
159 ly
130 ly
CR (s)
M63 Sunflower Galaxy
5055
5214
19
18
20
AO (d0)
CH
5093
23
5083
A1691
CM
BM (s)
128 ly
5112
5107
5243

609

Stellar Magnitudes (V)

≤2 3 4 5 6 7 8 9 10 11

Variable-Star Amplitudes and Types

<0.1 mag   0.1 – 1.0   ≥1.0 mag

(e) Eclipsing
(c) Cepheid
(m) Mira
... etc.

Fast-Moving Stars

Proper motion in 1000 years

Double-Star Separations

0.3"   3"   30"

MILLENNIUM STAR ATLAS

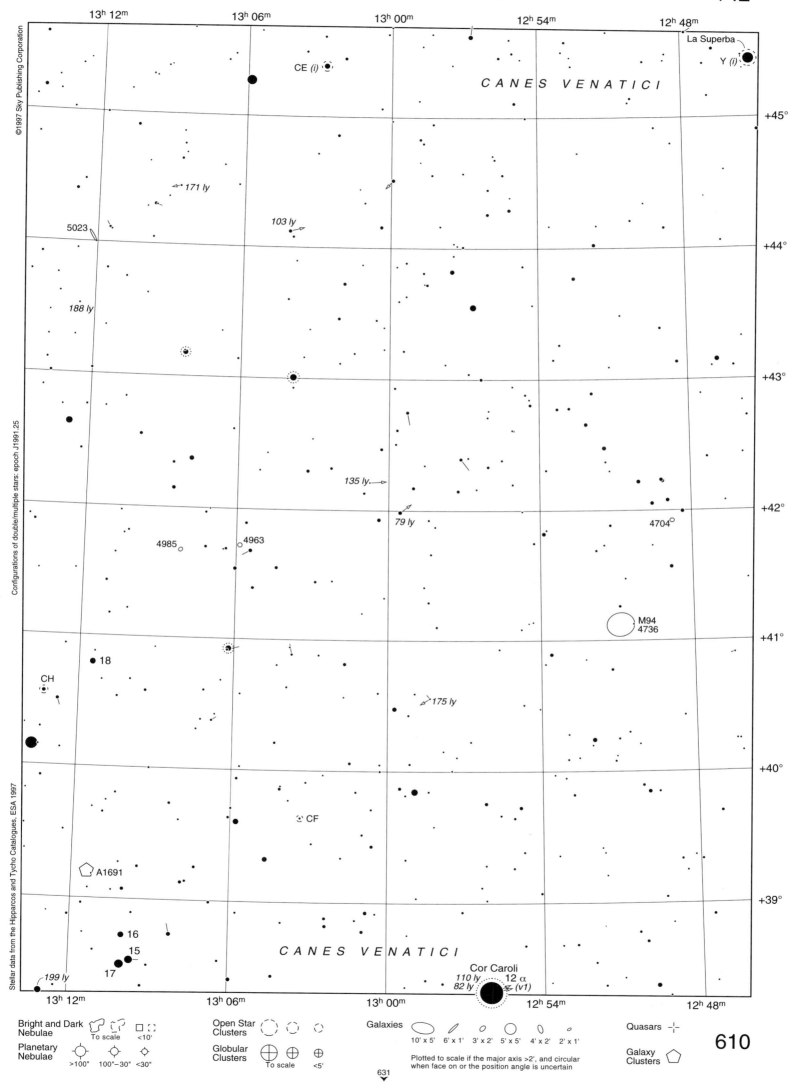

La Superba
Y *(i)*

C A N E S   V E N A T I C I

CE *(i)*

+45°

171 ly

103 ly

+44°

5023

188 ly

+43°

135 ly

+42°

79 ly

4704

4985   4963

M94
4736

+41°

18

CH

175 ly

+40°

CF

A1691

+39°

16

15

C A N E S   V E N A T I C I

17

Cor Caroli
110 ly   12 α
82 ly   *(v1)*

199 ly

13ʰ 12ᵐ   13ʰ 06ᵐ   13ʰ 00ᵐ   12ʰ 54ᵐ   12ʰ 48ᵐ

©1997 Sky Publishing Corporation

Configurations of double/multiple stars: epoch J1991.25

Stellar data from the Hipparcos and Tycho Catalogues, ESA 1997

Bright and Dark Nebulae	To scale <10'
Planetary Nebulae	>100" 100"–30" <30"
Open Star Clusters	
Globular Clusters	To scale <5'

Galaxies
10' x 5'   6' x 1'   3' x 2'   5' x 5'   4' x 2'   2' x 1'

Plotted to scale if the major axis >2', and circular
when face on or the position angle is uncertain

Quasars

Galaxy Clusters

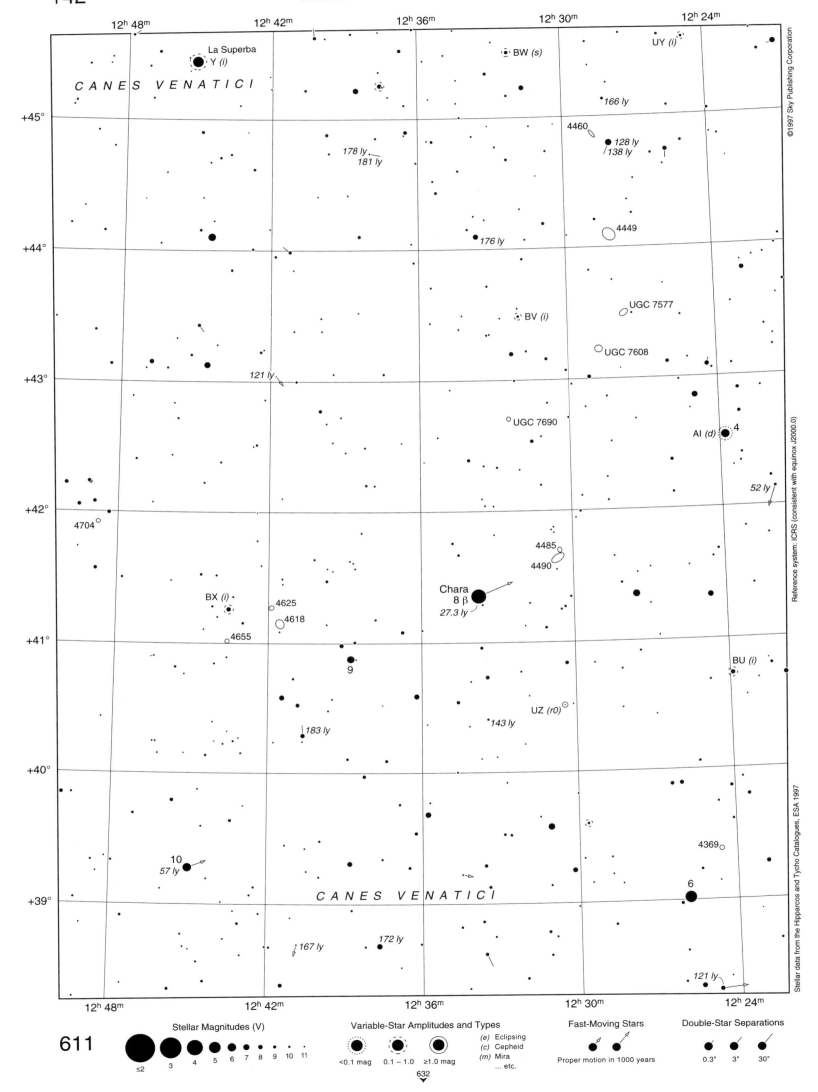

©1997 Sky Publishing Corporation

Reference system: ICRS (consistent with equinox J2000.0)

Stellar data from the Hipparcos and Tycho Catalogues, ESA 1997

CANES VENATICI

La Superba
Y (i)

BW (s)

UY (i)

166 ly

178 ly
181 ly

4460
128 ly
138 ly

176 ly

4449

BV (i)

UGC 7577

UGC 7608

121 ly

UGC 7690

AI (d)   4

52 ly

4704

4485
4490

Chara
8 β
27.3 ly

BX (i)
4625
4618
4655

9

BU (i)

UZ (r0)

143 ly

183 ly

CANES VENATICI

10
57 ly

4369

6

167 ly

172 ly

121 ly

611

Stellar Magnitudes (V)
≤2   3   4   5   6   7   8   9   10   11

Variable-Star Amplitudes and Types
<0.1 mag   0.1 – 1.0   ≥1.0 mag

(e) Eclipsing
(c) Cepheid
(m) Mira
... etc.

Fast-Moving Stars
Proper motion in 1000 years

Double-Star Separations
0.3"   3"   30"

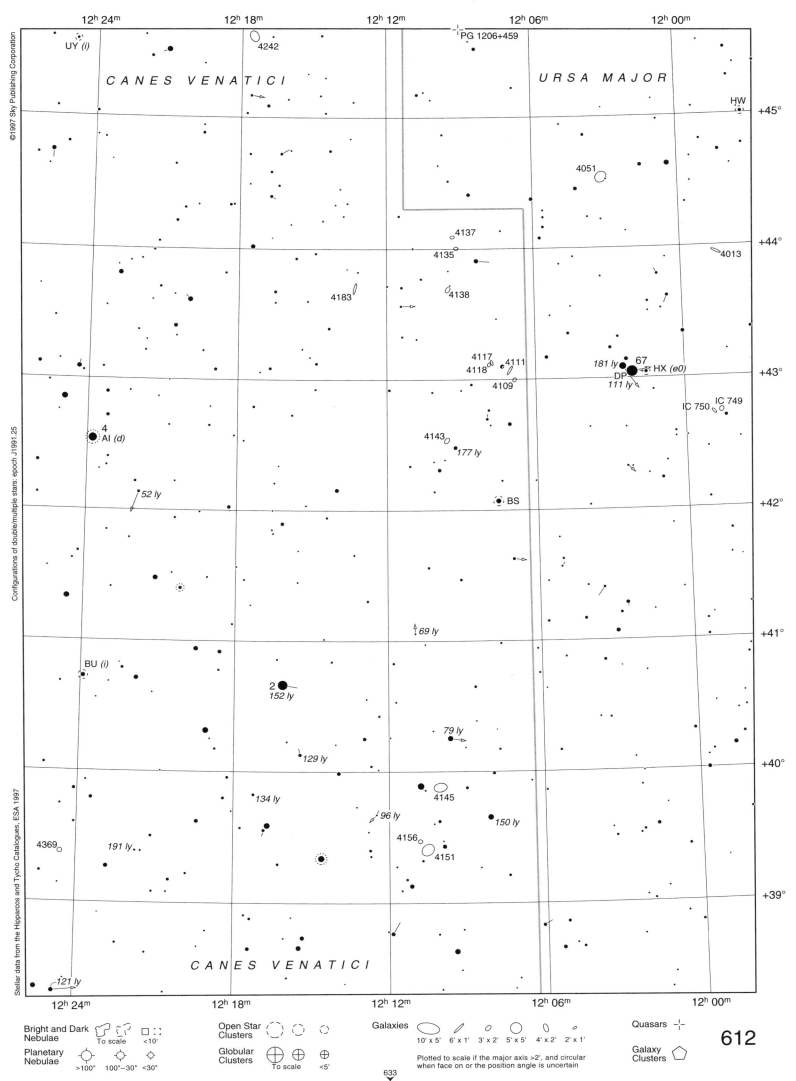

CANES VENATICI

URSA MAJOR

UY *(i)*

4242

PG 1206+459

HW

4051

4137

4135

4013

4183

4138

4117
4118

4111

181 ly

67

HX *(e0)*

4109

DP

111 ly

IC 750

IC 749

4
AI *(d)*

4143

177 ly

52 ly

BS

69 ly

BU *(i)*

2
152 ly

79 ly

129 ly

134 ly

4145

96 ly

150 ly

4156

4369

191 ly

4151

CANES VENATICI

121 ly

Bright and Dark Nebulae	Open Star Clusters	Galaxies	Quasars

Bright and Dark
Nebulae   To scale   <10'

Open Star
Clusters

Globular
Clusters   To scale   <5'

Galaxies
10' x 5'   6' x 1'   3' x 2'   5' x 5'   4' x 2'   2' x 1'

Planetary
Nebulae
>100"   100"–30"   <30"

Plotted to scale if the major axis >2', and circular
when face on or the position angle is uncertain

Quasars

Galaxy
Clusters

612

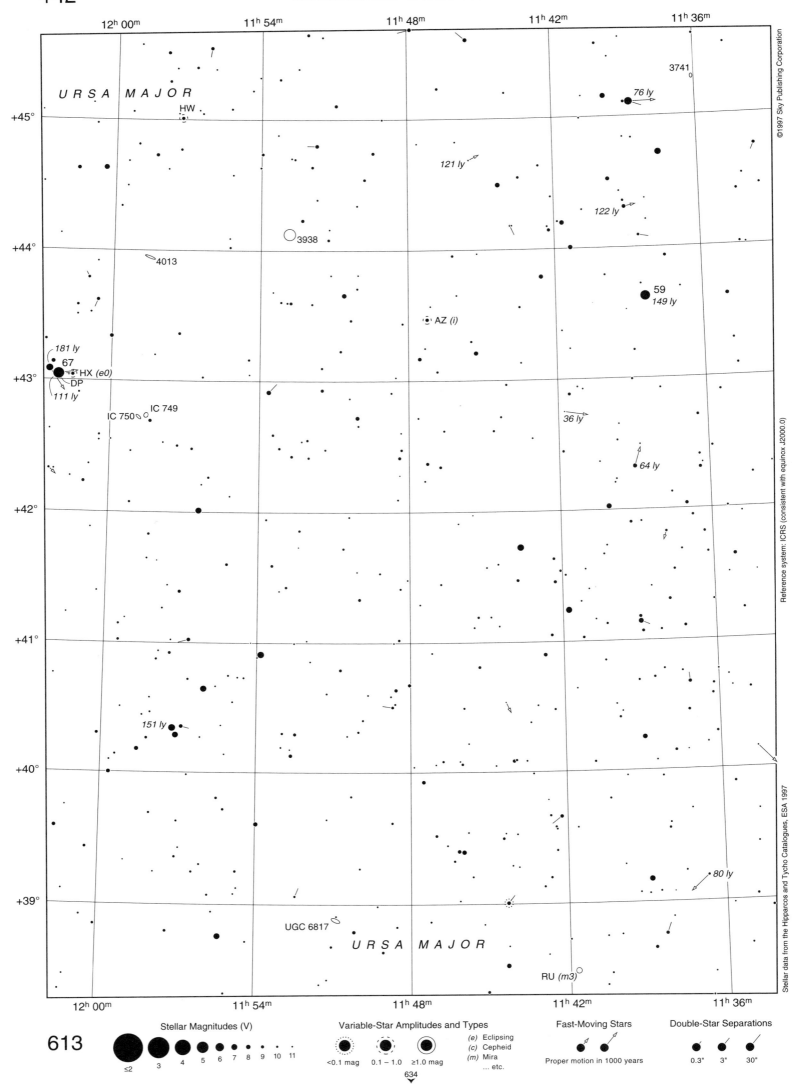

URSA MAJOR

HW

121 ly

3938

4013

181 ly
67
HX (e0)
DP
111 ly

IC 750 IC 749

3741

76 ly

122 ly

59
149 ly

AZ (i)

36 ly

64 ly

151 ly

80 ly

UGC 6817

URSA MAJOR

RU (m3)

©1997 Sky Publishing Corporation

Reference system: ICRS (consistent with equinox J2000.0)

Stellar data from the Hipparcos and Tycho Catalogues, ESA 1997

613

Stellar Magnitudes (V)	Variable-Star Amplitudes and Types	Fast-Moving Stars	Double-Star Separations

Stellar Magnitudes (V)
≤2   3   4   5   6   7   8   9   10   11

Variable-Star Amplitudes and Types
<0.1 mag   0.1 – 1.0   ≥1.0 mag

(e) Eclipsing
(c) Cepheid
(m) Mira
... etc.

Fast-Moving Stars
Proper motion in 1000 years

Double-Star Separations
0.3"   3"   30"

634

MILLENNIUM STAR ATLAS

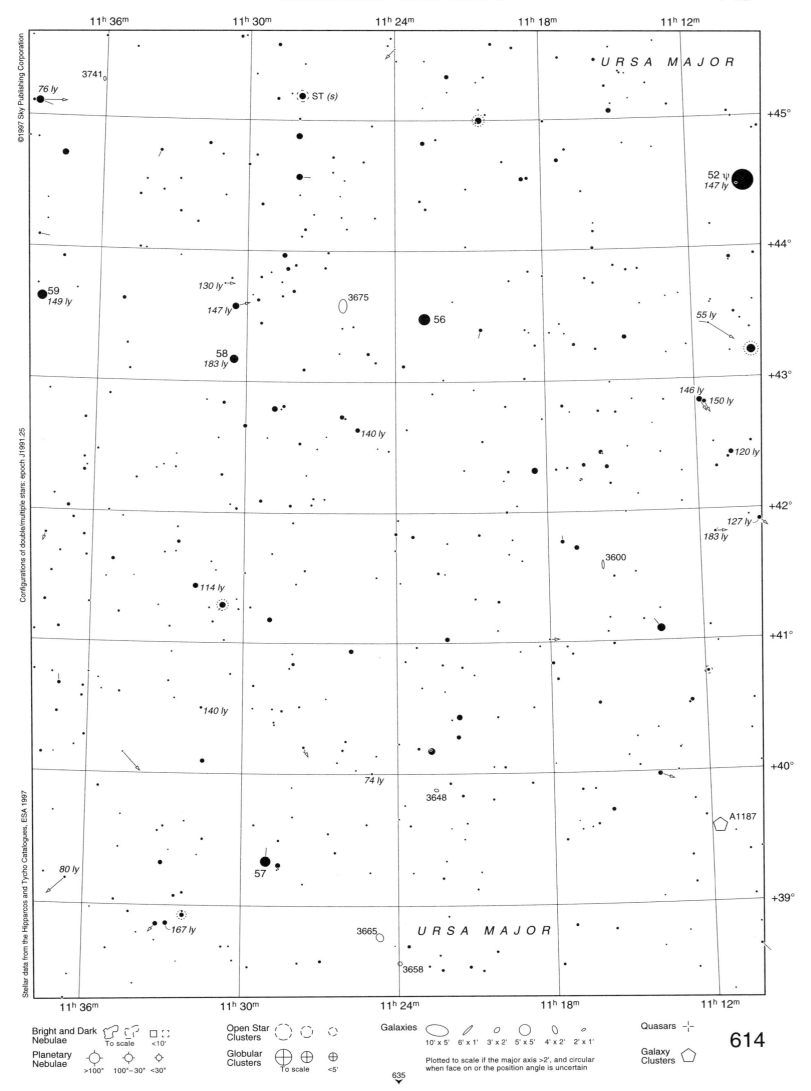

©1997 Sky Publishing Corporation

Configurations of double/multiple stars: epoch J1991.25

Stellar data from the Hipparcos and Tycho Catalogues, ESA 1997

11ʰ 36ᵐ   11ʰ 30ᵐ   11ʰ 24ᵐ   11ʰ 18ᵐ   11ʰ 12ᵐ

U R S A   M A J O R

3741

76 ly

ST (s)

+45°

52 ψ
147 ly

+44°

59
149 ly

130 ly

147 ly

3675

56

55 ly

58
183 ly

+43°

146 ly   150 ly

140 ly

120 ly

+42°

127 ly

183 ly

114 ly

3600

+41°

140 ly

+40°

74 ly

3648

A1187

57

+39°

80 ly

167 ly

3665   *U R S A   M A J O R*

3658

11ʰ 36ᵐ   11ʰ 30ᵐ   11ʰ 24ᵐ   11ʰ 18ᵐ   11ʰ 12ᵐ

Bright and Dark Nebulae		Open Star Clusters	Galaxies		Quasars

Bright and Dark Nebulae   To scale   <10'

Open Star Clusters

Galaxies
10' x 5'   6' x 1'   3' x 2'   5' x 5'   4' x 2'   2' x 1'

Quasars

Planetary Nebulae
>100"   100"–30"   <30"

Globular Clusters
To scale   <5'

Plotted to scale if the major axis >2', and circular
when face on or the position angle is uncertain

Galaxy Clusters

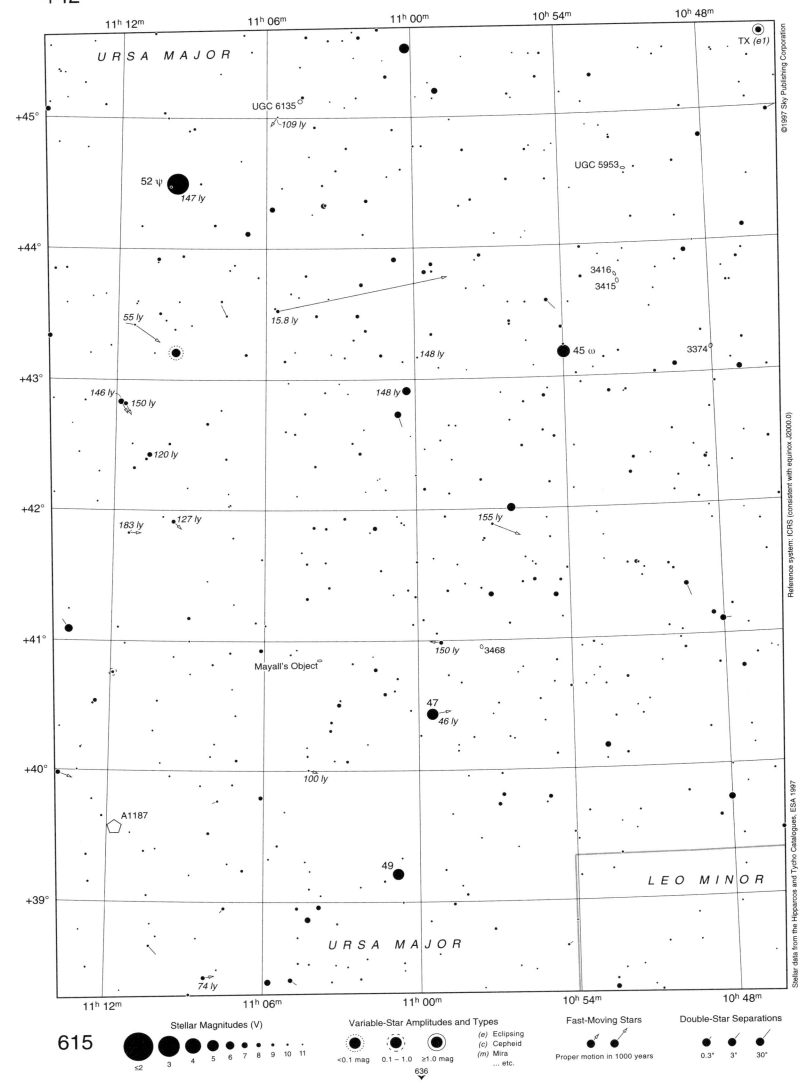

TX *(e1)*

URSA MAJOR

UGC 6135

109 ly

52 ψ
147 ly

UGC 5953

15.8 ly

3416
3415

55 ly

45 ω
3374

148 ly

146 ly
150 ly

148 ly

120 ly

127 ly
183 ly

155 ly

150 ly
°3468

Mayall's Object

47
46 ly

100 ly

A1187

LEO MINOR

49

URSA MAJOR

74 ly

©1997 Sky Publishing Corporation

Reference system: ICRS (consistent with equinox J2000.0)

Stellar data from the Hipparcos and Tycho Catalogues, ESA 1997

615

Stellar Magnitudes (V)
≤2 3 4 5 6 7 8 9 10 11

Variable-Star Amplitudes and Types
<0.1 mag   0.1 – 1.0   ≥1.0 mag

(e) Eclipsing
(c) Cepheid
(m) Mira
… etc.

Fast-Moving Stars
Proper motion in 1000 years

Double-Star Separations
0.3"   3"   30"

636

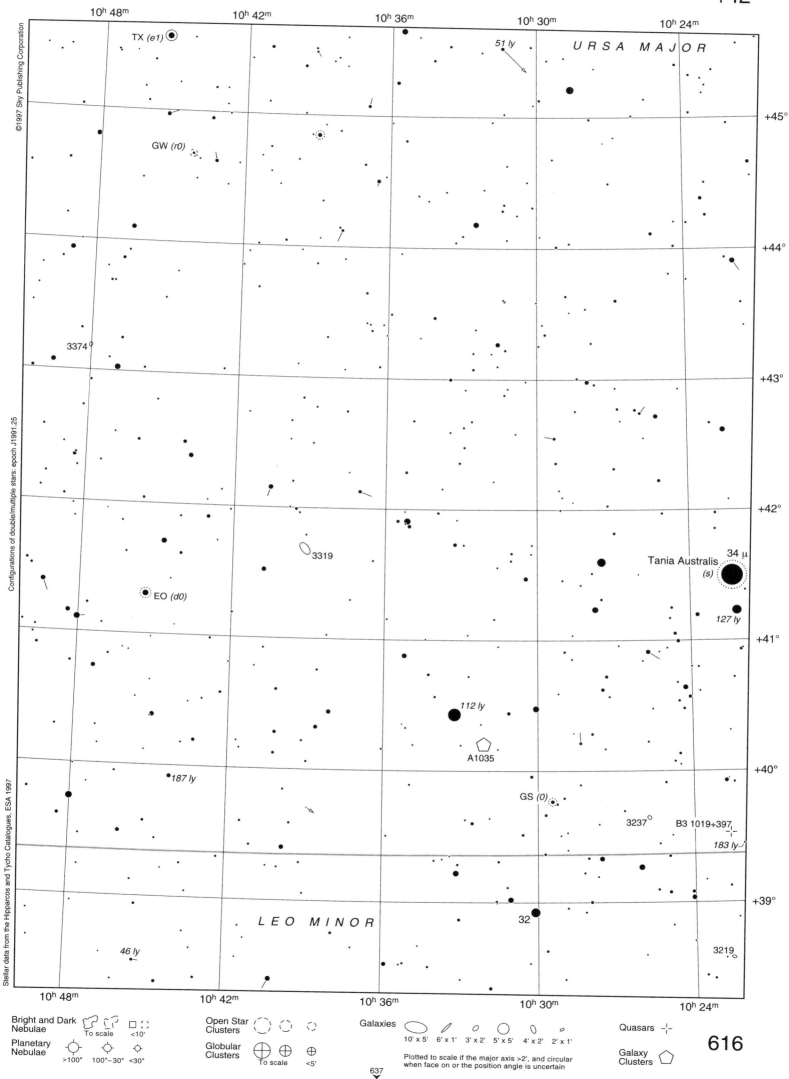

Configurations of double/multiple stars: epoch J1991.25

Stellar data from the Hipparcos and Tycho Catalogues, ESA 1997

10h 48m   10h 42m   10h 36m   10h 30m   10h 24m

TX (e1)

51 ly   *URSA MAJOR**

+45°

GW (r0)

+44°

3374

+43°

+42°

3319

Tania Australis
(s)   34 μ

EO (d0)

127 ly

+41°

112 ly

A1035

+40°

187 ly

GS (0)

3237   B3 1019+397

183 ly

+39°

32

LEO MINOR

46 ly   3219

10h 48m   10h 42m   10h 36m   10h 30m   10h 24m

Bright and Dark Nebulae
To scale   <10'

Open Star Clusters

Galaxies

Quasars

Planetary Nebulae
>100"   100"–30"   <30"

Globular Clusters
To scale   <5'

10' x 5'   6' x 1'   3' x 2'   5' x 5'   4' x 2'   2' x 1'

Plotted to scale if the major axis >2', and circular
when face on or the position angle is uncertain

Galaxy Clusters

616

637

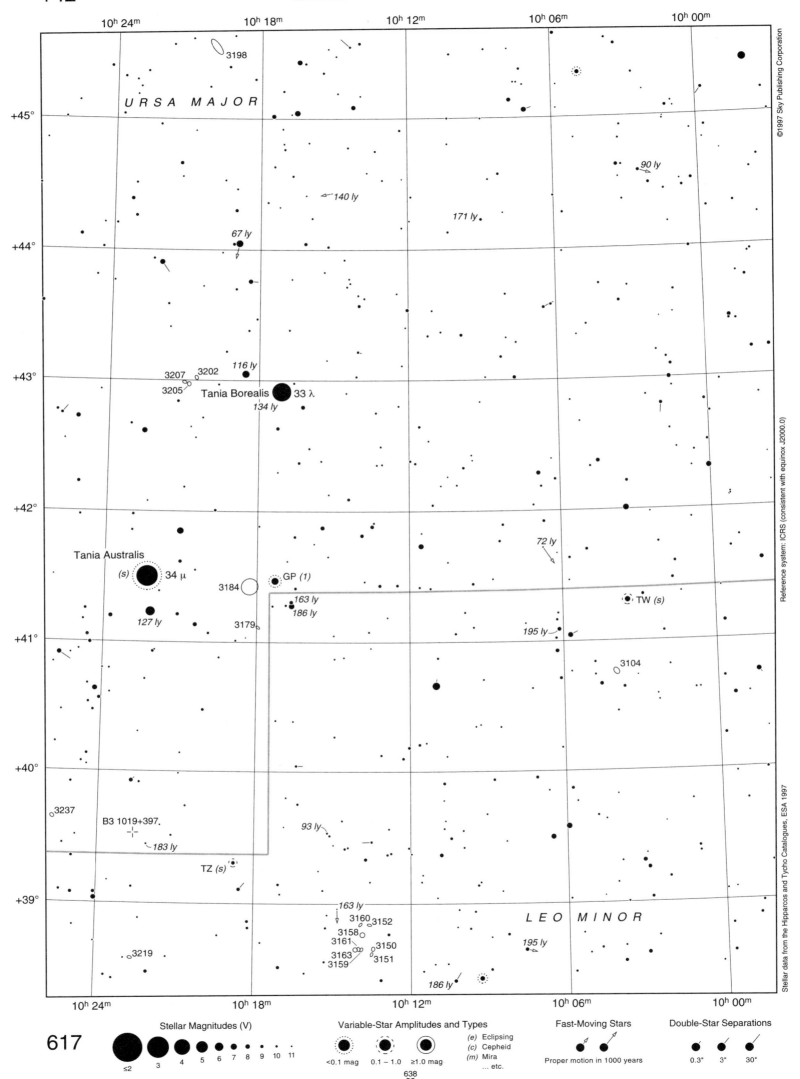

©1997 Sky Publishing Corporation

Reference system: ICRS (consistent with equinox J2000.0)

Stellar data from the Hipparcos and Tycho Catalogues, ESA 1997

URSA MAJOR

3198

90 ly

140 ly

171 ly

67 ly

116 ly

3207 3202
3205
Tania Borealis 33 λ
134 ly

72 ly

Tania Australis

(s) 34 μ

3184 GP (1)

TW (s)

163 ly
186 ly

195 ly

127 ly

3179

3104

3237

B3 1019+397

93 ly

183 ly

TZ (s)

LEO MINOR

163 ly

3160 3152
3158
3161 3150
3163 3151
3159

195 ly

3219

186 ly

617

Stellar Magnitudes (V)

≤2 3 4 5 6 7 8 9 10 11

Variable-Star Amplitudes and Types

<0.1 mag 0.1 − 1.0 ≥1.0 mag

(e) Eclipsing
(c) Cepheid
(m) Mira
... etc.

Fast-Moving Stars

Proper motion in 1000 years

Double-Star Separations

0.3" 3" 30"

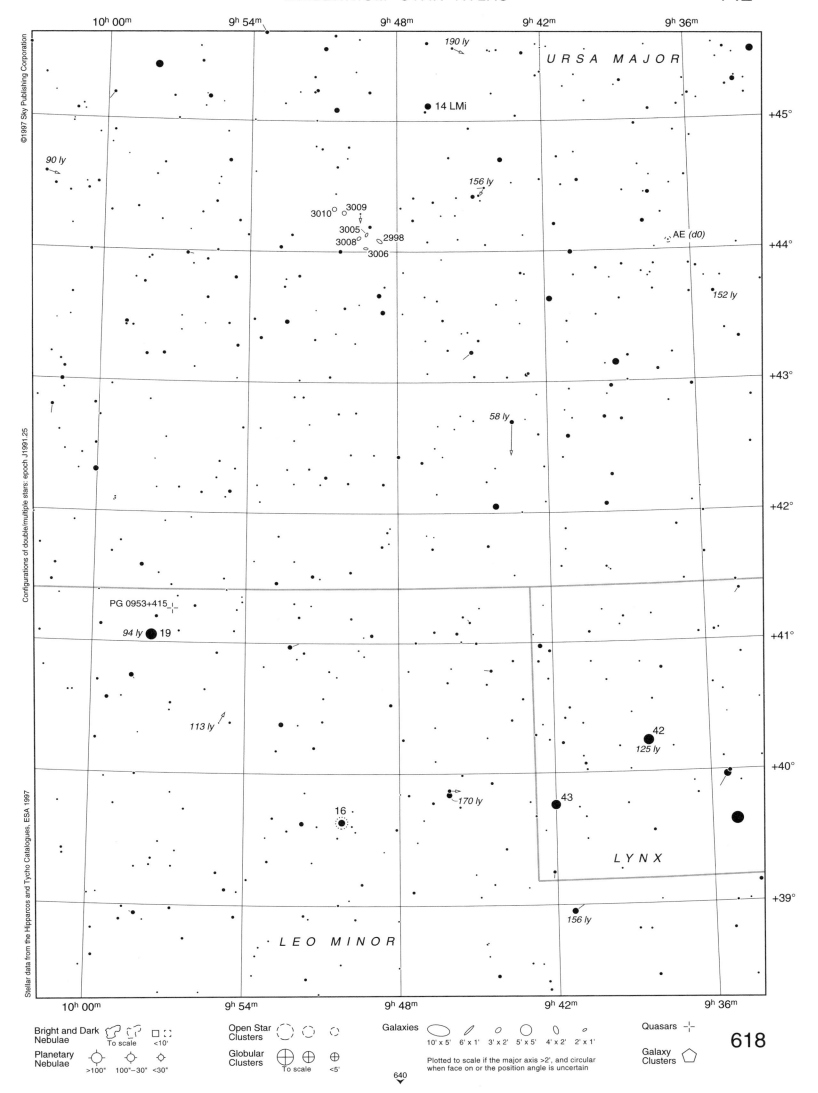

MILLENNIUM STAR ATLAS

+42°

10h 00m · 9h 54m · 9h 48m · 9h 42m · 9h 36m

URSA MAJOR

190 ly

14 LMi

+45°

90 ly

156 ly

3010° °3009
3005 °
3008° °2998
3006

AE (d0)

+44°

152 ly

+43°

58 ly

+42°

PG 0953+415

+41°

94 ly 19

113 ly

42
125 ly

+40°

16

170 ly

43

LYNX

+39°

156 ly

LEO MINOR

10h 00m · 9h 54m · 9h 48m · 9h 42m · 9h 36m

Bright and Dark Nebulae	Open Star Clusters	Galaxies	Quasars

To scale   <10'

Open Star Clusters
To scale

Galaxies
10' x 5' 6' x 1' 3' x 2' 5' x 5' 4' x 2' 2' x 1'

Quasars

618

Planetary Nebulae
>100" 100"–30" <30"

Globular Clusters
To scale <5'

Plotted to scale if the major axis >2', and circular when face on or the position angle is uncertain

Galaxy Clusters

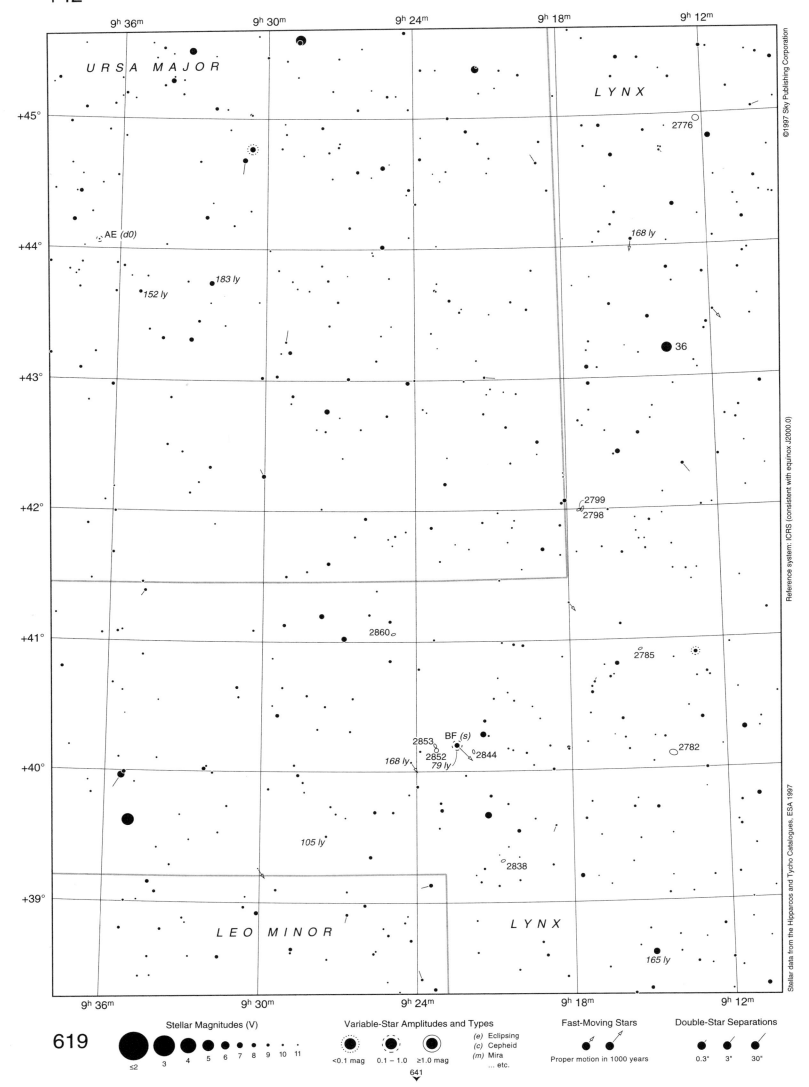

©1997 Sky Publishing Corporation

Reference system: ICRS (consistent with equinox J2000.0)

Stellar data from the Hipparcos and Tycho Catalogues, ESA 1997

Stellar Magnitudes (V)

619

≤2 3 4 5 6 7 8 9 10 11

Variable-Star Amplitudes and Types

<0.1 mag   0.1 – 1.0   ≥1.0 mag

(e) Eclipsing
(c) Cepheid
(m) Mira
... etc.

Fast-Moving Stars

Proper motion in 1000 years

Double-Star Separations

0.3"   3"   30"

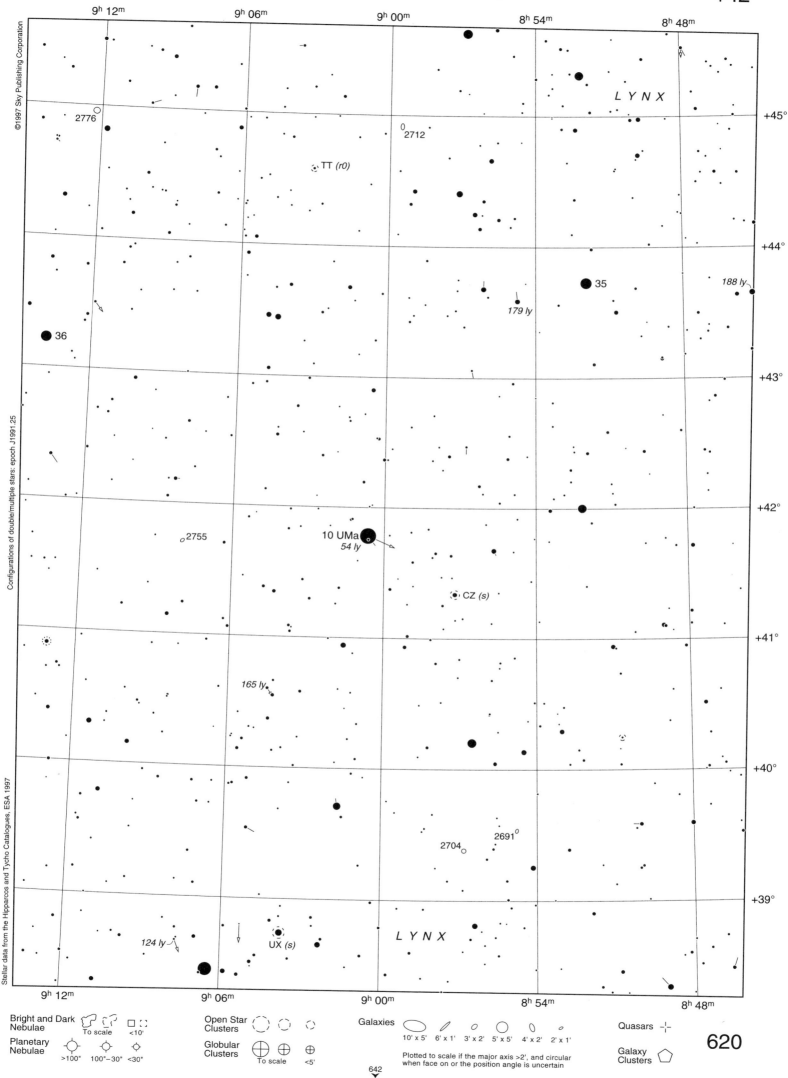

©1997 Sky Publishing Corporation

Configurations of double/multiple stars: epoch J1991.25

Stellar data from the Hipparcos and Tycho Catalogues, ESA 1997

L Y N X

2776

2712

TT (r0)

35

179 ly

188 ly

36

2755

10 UMa

54 ly

CZ (s)

165 ly

2691

2704

L Y N X

124 ly

UX (s)

Bright and Dark Nebulae

To scale   <10'

Planetary Nebulae

>100"   100"–30"   <30"

Open Star Clusters

Globular Clusters

To scale   <5'

Galaxies

10' x 5'   6' x 1'   3' x 2'   5' x 5'   4' x 2'   2' x 1'

Plotted to scale if the major axis >2', and circular when face on or the position angle is uncertain

Quasars

Galaxy Clusters

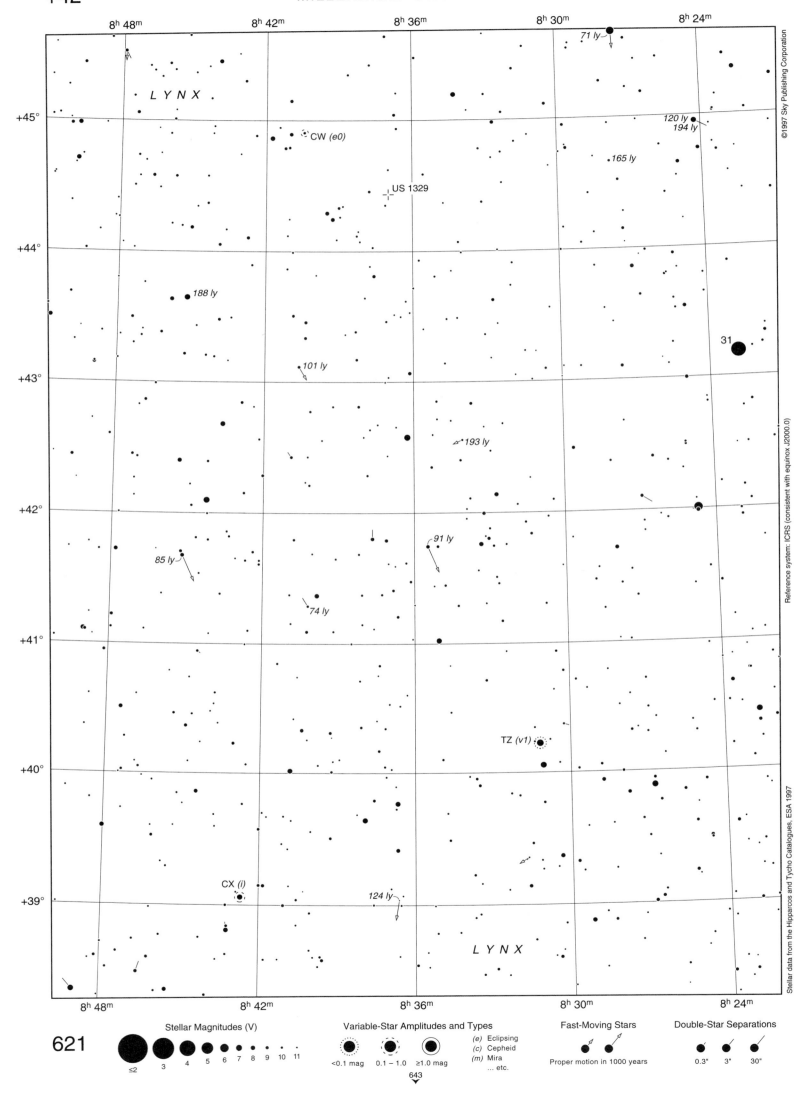

©1997 Sky Publishing Corporation

Reference system: ICRS (consistent with equinox J2000.0)

Stellar data from the Hipparcos and Tycho Catalogues, ESA 1997

Stellar Magnitudes (V)

≤2 3 4 5 6 7 8 9 10 11

Variable-Star Amplitudes and Types

<0.1 mag   0.1 – 1.0   ≥1.0 mag

(e) Eclipsing
(c) Cepheid
(m) Mira
... etc.

Fast-Moving Stars

Proper motion in 1000 years

Double-Star Separations

0.3"   3"   30"

621

643

MILLENNIUM STAR ATLAS

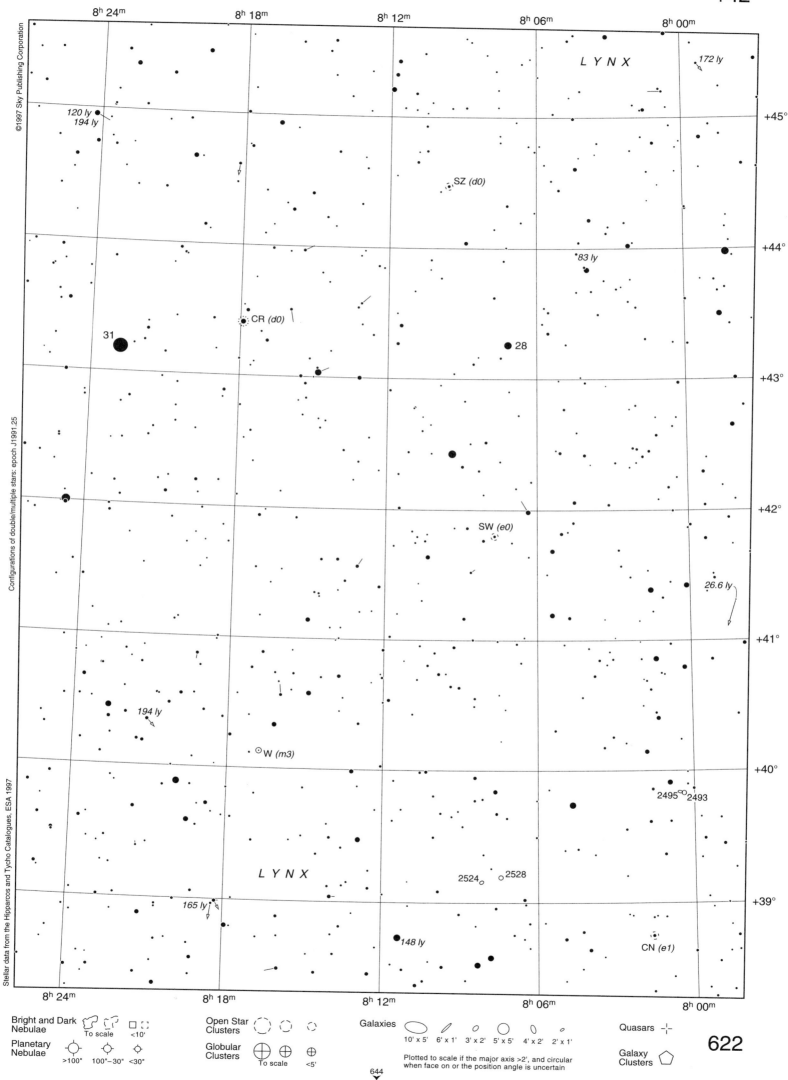

Configurations of double/multiple stars: epoch J1991.25

Stellar data from the Hipparcos and Tycho Catalogues, ESA 1997

8h 24m   8h 18m   8h 12m   8h 06m   8h 00m

L Y N X

172 ly

+45°

120 ly
194 ly

SZ *(d0)*

+44°

83 ly

CR *(d0)*

31

28

+43°

SW *(e0)*

+42°

26.6 ly

+41°

194 ly

W *(m3)*

+40°

2495 ∞ 2493

L Y N X

2524 ∘   ∘ 2528

+39°

165 ly

148 ly

CN *(e1)*

8h 24m   8h 18m   8h 12m   8h 06m   8h 00m

Bright and Dark Nebulae			Open Star Clusters			Galaxies						Quasars	
To scale		<10'				10' x 5'	6' x 1'	3' x 2'	5' x 5'	4' x 2'	2' x 1'		

Planetary Nebulae   >100" 100"–30" <30"

Globular Clusters   To scale <5'

Plotted to scale if the major axis >2', and circular when face on or the position angle is uncertain

Galaxy Clusters

622

644

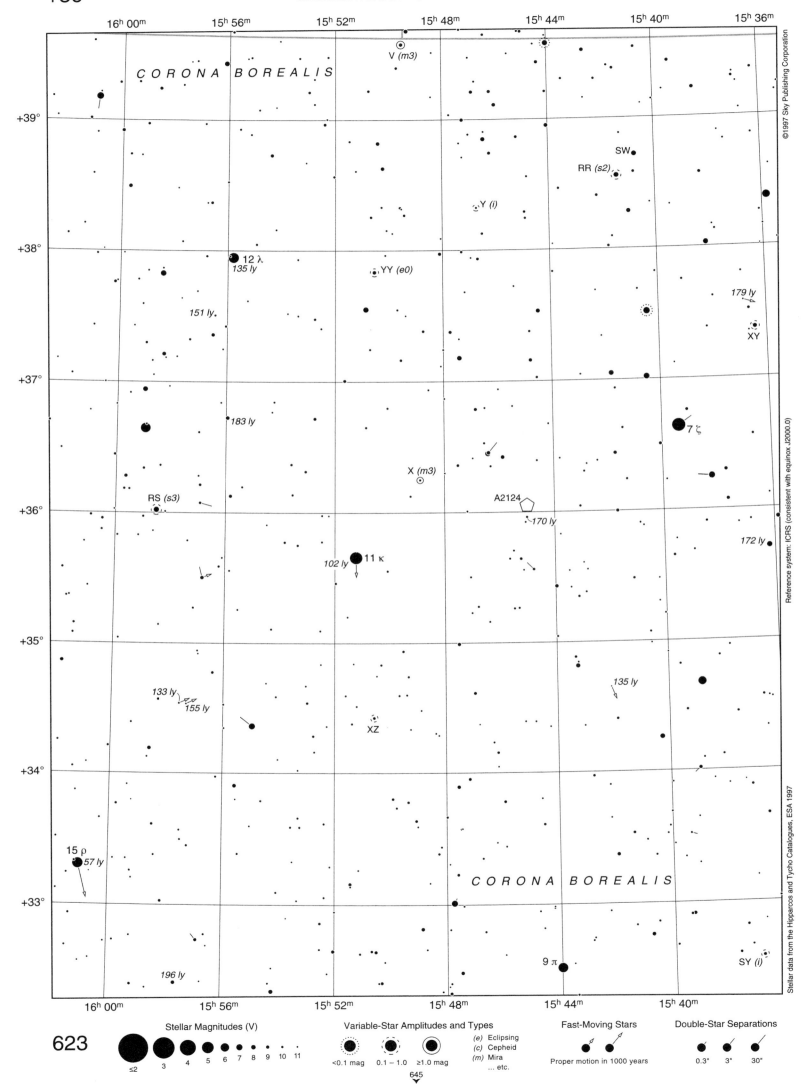

©1997 Sky Publishing Corporation

Reference system: ICRS (consistent with equinox J2000.0)

Stellar data from the Hipparcos and Tycho Catalogues, ESA 1997

CORONA BOREALIS

V (m3)

SW

RR (s2)

Y (i)

12 λ
135 ly

179 ly

YY (e0)

XY

151 ly

7 ζ

183 ly

X (m3)

A2124

RS (s3)

170 ly

172 ly

11 κ
102 ly

133 ly
155 ly

135 ly

XZ

15 ρ
57 ly

CORONA BOREALIS

9 π

SY (i)

196 ly

623

Stellar Magnitudes (V)

≤2 3 4 5 6 7 8 9 10 11

Variable-Star Amplitudes and Types

<0.1 mag   0.1 – 1.0   ≥1.0 mag

(e) Eclipsing
(c) Cepheid
(m) Mira
... etc.

Fast-Moving Stars

Proper motion in 1000 years

Double-Star Separations

0.3"   3"   30"

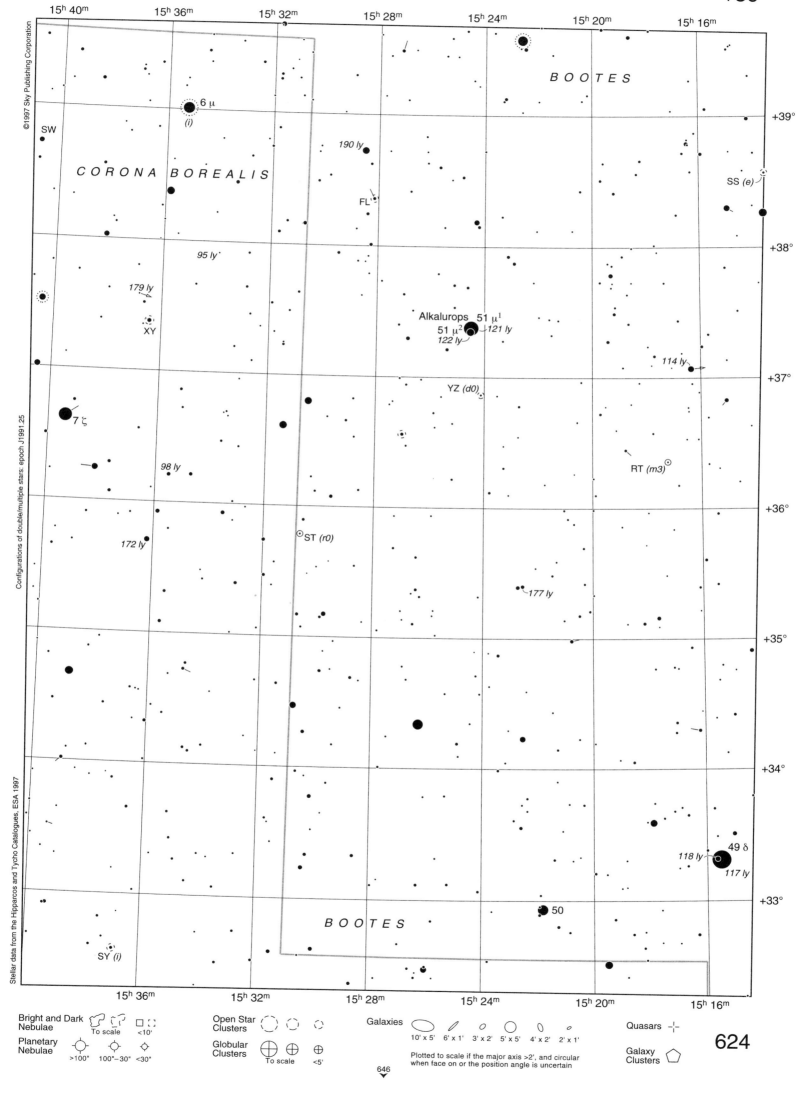

©1997 Sky Publishing Corporation

Configurations of double/multiple stars: epoch J1991.25

Stellar data from the Hipparcos and Tycho Catalogues, ESA 1997

B O O T E S

C O R O N A B O R E A L I S

SW

6 μ
(i)

190 ly

FL

SS (e)

95 ly

179 ly

XY

Alkalurops 51 μ¹
51 μ² 121 ly
122 ly

114 ly

7 ζ

YZ (d0)

RT (m3)

98 ly

172 ly

ST (r0)

177 ly

49 δ
118 ly
117 ly

50

B O O T E S

SY (i)

+39°
+38°
+37°
+36°
+35°
+34°
+33°

15ʰ 40ᵐ 15ʰ 36ᵐ 15ʰ 32ᵐ 15ʰ 28ᵐ 15ʰ 24ᵐ 15ʰ 20ᵐ 15ʰ 16ᵐ
15ʰ 36ᵐ 15ʰ 32ᵐ 15ʰ 28ᵐ 15ʰ 24ᵐ 15ʰ 20ᵐ 15ʰ 16ᵐ

Bright and Dark Nebulae   To scale   <10'
Planetary Nebulae   >100" 100"–30" <30"
Open Star Clusters   To scale   <5'
Globular Clusters   To scale   <5'
Galaxies   10' x 5' 6' x 1' 3' x 2' 5' x 5' 4' x 2' 2' x 1'
Plotted to scale if the major axis >2', and circular when face on or the position angle is uncertain
Quasars
Galaxy Clusters

624

646

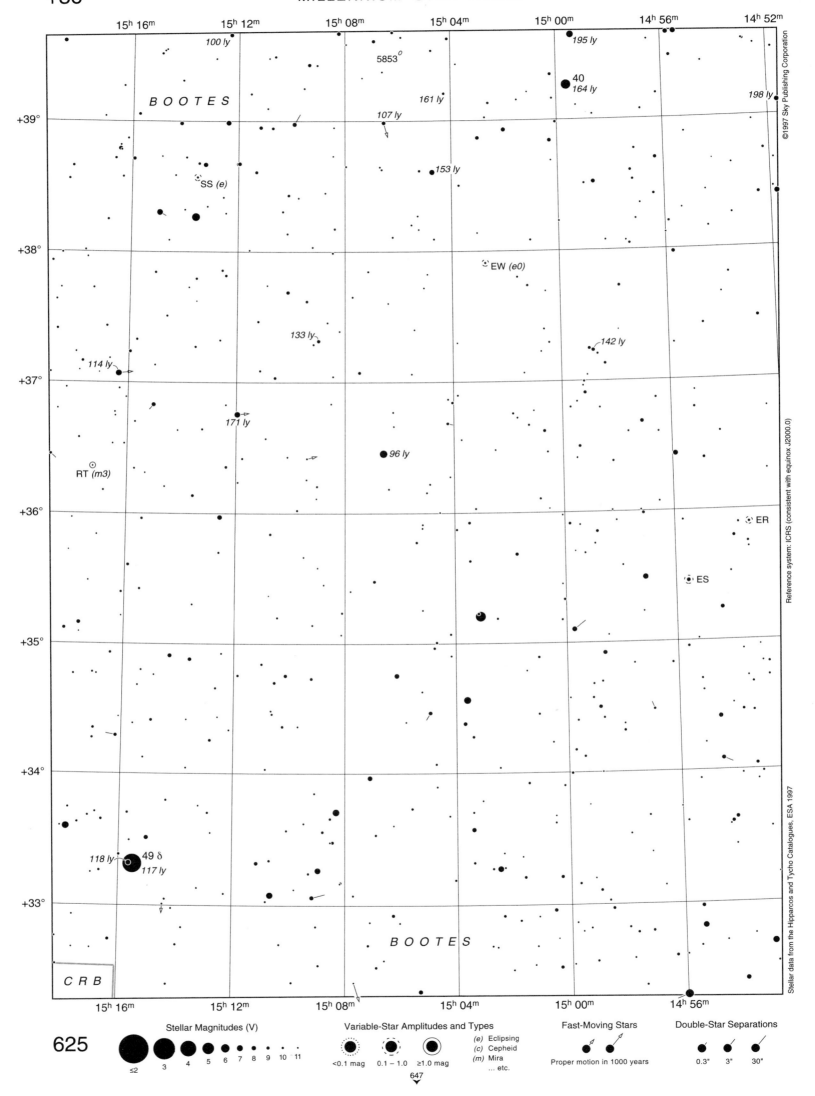

B O O T E S

100 ly

5853

195 ly

40
164 ly

161 ly

198 ly

107 ly

SS (e)

153 ly

EW (e0)

133 ly

142 ly

114 ly

171 ly

96 ly

RT (m3)

ER

ES

49 δ

118 ly
117 ly

B O O T E S

C R B

625

Stellar Magnitudes (V)

≤2   3   4   5   6   7   8   9   10   11

Variable-Star Amplitudes and Types

<0.1 mag   0.1 – 1.0   ≥1.0 mag

(e) Eclipsing
(c) Cepheid
(m) Mira
... etc.

Fast-Moving Stars

Proper motion in 1000 years

Double-Star Separations

0.3"   3"   30"

647

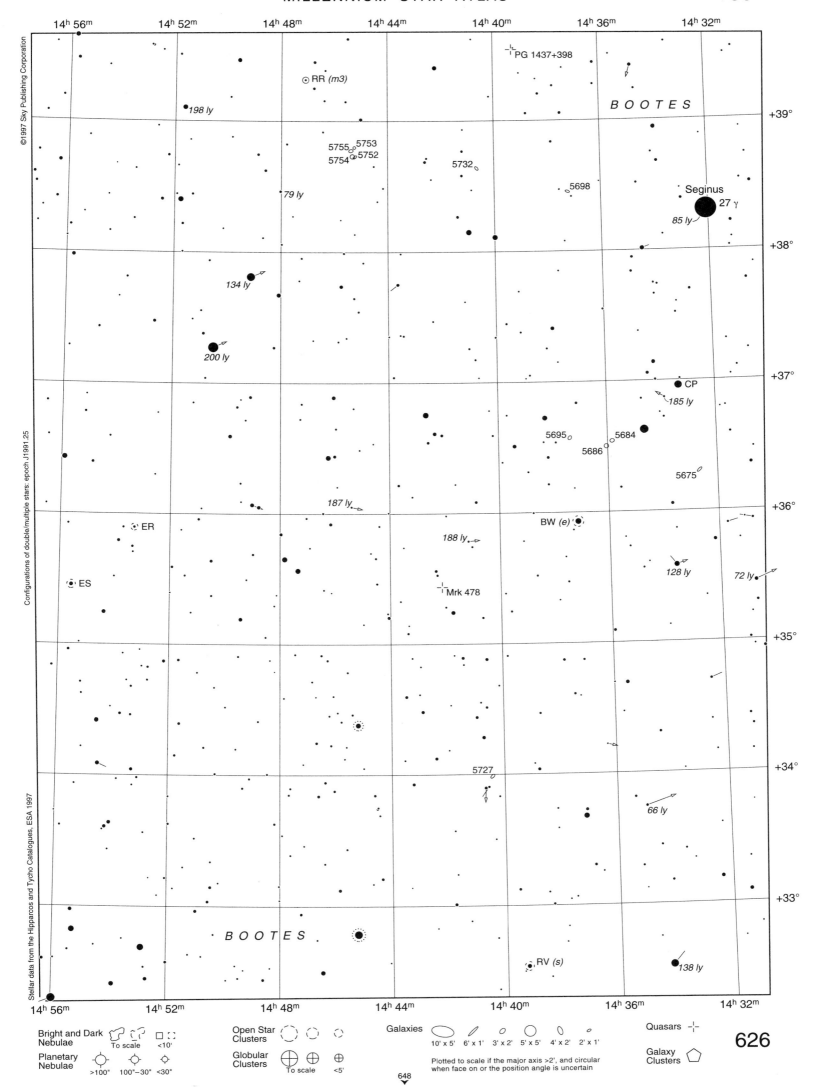

BOOTES

PG 1437+398

RR *(m3)*

198 *ly*

5755 5753
5754 5752

5732

5698

Seginus

27 γ

85 *ly*

79 *ly*

134 *ly*

200 *ly*

CP

185 *ly*

5695

5686

5684

5675

187 *ly*

ER

BW *(e)*

188 *ly*

128 *ly*

72 *ly*

ES

Mrk 478

5727

66 *ly*

BOOTES

RV *(s)*

138 *ly*

Bright and Dark Nebulae
To scale   <10'

Planetary Nebulae
>100"   100"–30"   <30"

Open Star Clusters

Globular Clusters
To scale   <5'

Galaxies
10' x 5'   6' x 1'   3' x 2'   5' x 5'   4' x 2'   2' x 1'

Plotted to scale if the major axis >2', and circular when face on or the position angle is uncertain

Quasars

Galaxy Clusters

648

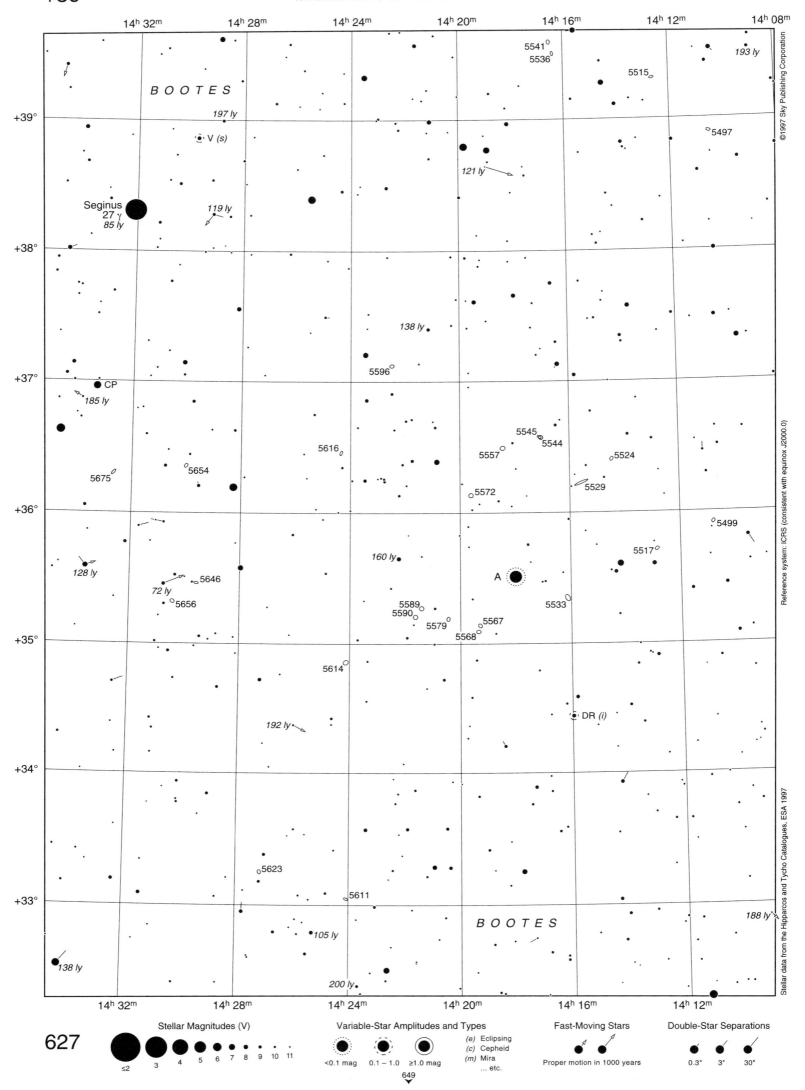

627

Stellar Magnitudes (V)

≤2   3   4   5   6   7   8   9 10 11

Variable-Star Amplitudes and Types

<0.1 mag   0.1 – 1.0   ≥1.0 mag

(e) Eclipsing
(c) Cepheid
(m) Mira
... etc.

Fast-Moving Stars

Proper motion in 1000 years

Double-Star Separations

0.3"   3"   30"

649

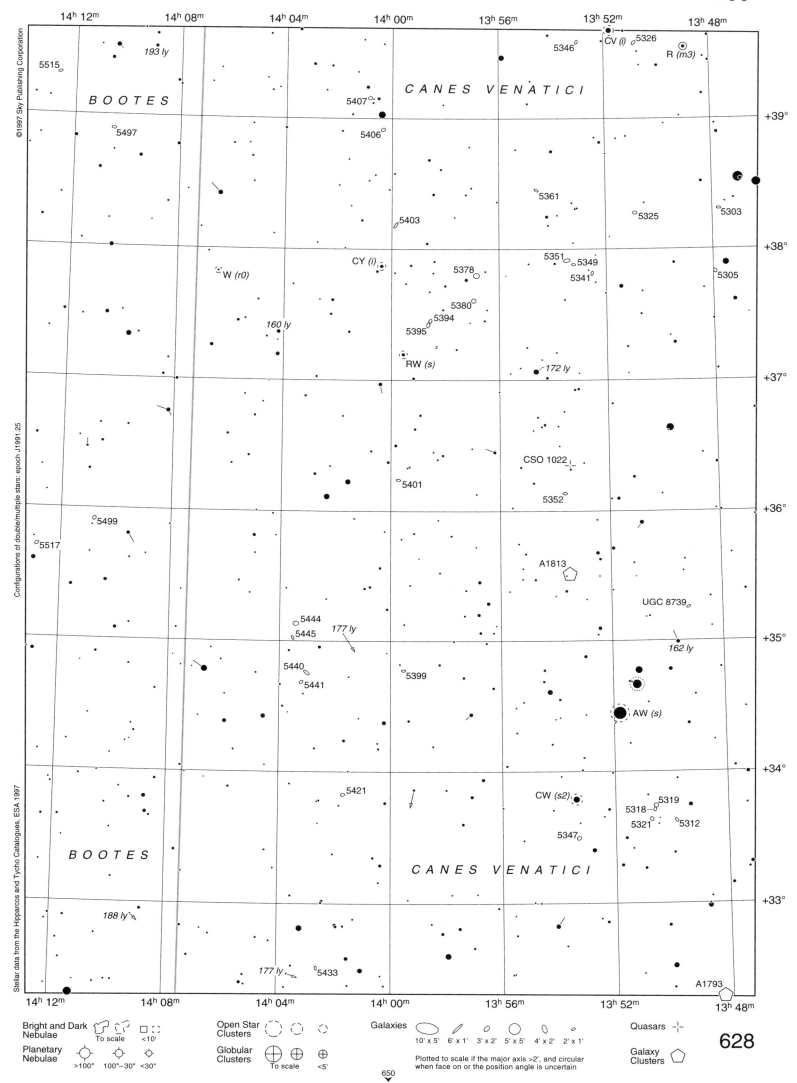

CANES VENATICI

BOOTES

5515

193 ly

5497

5407

5406

CV (i) 5326

5346

R (m3)

5361

5303

5325

5403

CY (i)

W (r0)

5378

5351 5349

5341

5305

5380

5394

5395

160 ly

RW (s)

172 ly

CSO 1022

5401

5352

5499

A1813

5517

UGC 8739

5444

5445

177 ly

162 ly

5440

5441

5399

AW (s)

5421

CW (s2)

5319

5318

5312

5321

5347

188 ly

BOOTES

CANES VENATICI

177 ly

5433

A1793

+39°

+38°

+37°

+36°

+35°

+34°

+33°

Bright and Dark Nebulae	Open Star Clusters	Galaxies	Quasars

To scale   <10'

Open Star Clusters

To scale   <10'

Galaxies

10' x 5'   6' x 1'   3' x 2'   5' x 5'   4' x 2'   2' x 1'

Quasars

Planetary Nebulae

>100"   100"–30"   <30"

Globular Clusters

To scale   <5'

Plotted to scale if the major axis >2', and circular when face on or the position angle is uncertain

Galaxy Clusters

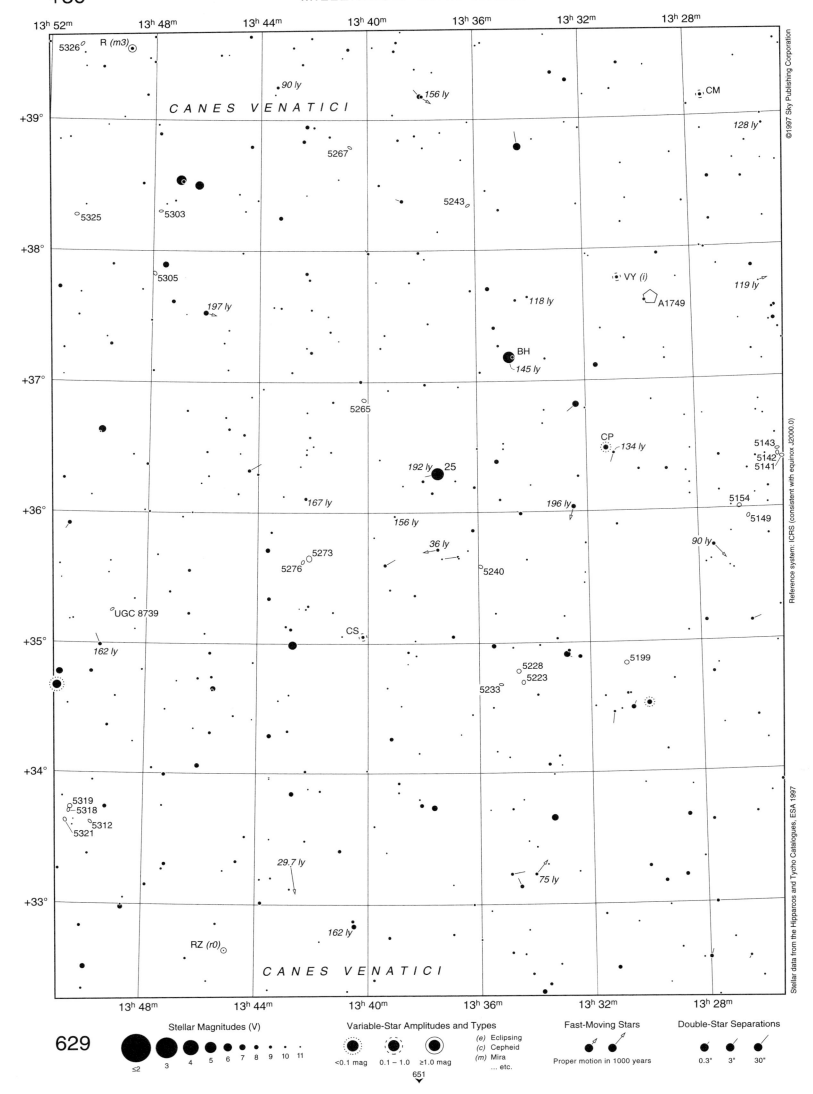

©1997 Sky Publishing Corporation

Reference system: ICRS (consistent with equinox J2000.0)

Stellar data from the Hipparcos and Tycho Catalogues, ESA 1997

629

Stellar Magnitudes (V)

≤2   3   4   5   6   7   8   9   10   11

Variable-Star Amplitudes and Types

<0.1 mag   0.1 – 1.0 mag   ≥1.0 mag

(e) Eclipsing
(c) Cepheid
(m) Mira
... etc.

Fast-Moving Stars

Proper motion in 1000 years

Double-Star Separations

0.3"   3"   30"

651

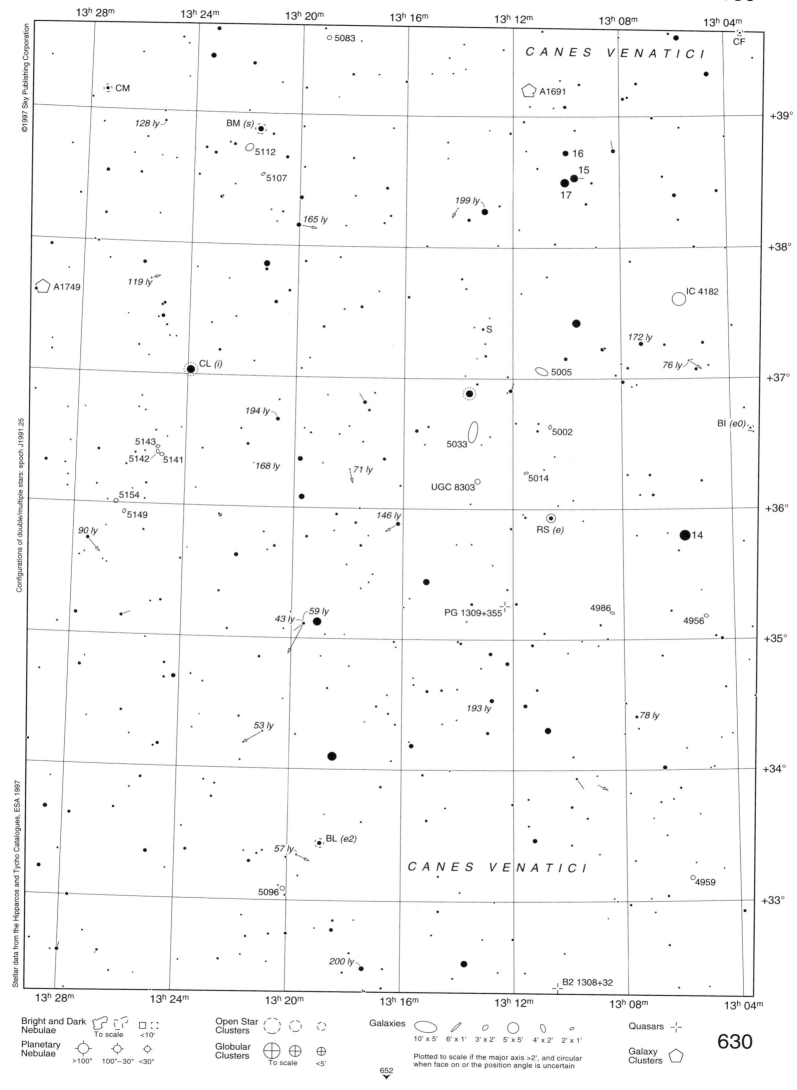

©1997 Sky Publishing Corporation

13h 28m   13h 24m   13h 20m   13h 16m   13h 12m   13h 08m   13h 04m

CANES VENATICI

CF

○ 5083

CM

A1691

+39°

128 ly
BM (s)
○ 5112
16
○ 5107
15
17

199 ly

165 ly

+38°

A1749
119 ly
IC 4182
S
172 ly

CL (i)
5005
76 ly

+37°

194 ly

BI (e0)

5143
5142 5141
5033
○ 5002

168 ly
71 ly
UGC 8303 ○
5014

5154
○ 5149
146 ly
RS (e)

+36°

90 ly
14

43 ly 59 ly
PG 1309+355
4986 ○
4956 ○

+35°

53 ly
193 ly
78 ly

+34°

Configurations of double/multiple stars: epoch J1991.25

BL (e2)
57 ly
CANES VENATICI
4959 ○

5096 ○

+33°

200 ly

B2 1308+32

Stellar data from the Hipparcos and Tycho Catalogues, ESA 1997

13h 28m   13h 24m   13h 20m   13h 16m   13h 12m   13h 08m   13h 04m

Bright and Dark Nebulae
To scale   <10'

Open Star Clusters

Galaxies
10' x 5'   6' x 1'   3' x 2'   5' x 5'   4' x 2'   2' x 1'

Quasars

Planetary Nebulae
>100"   100"–30"   <30"

Globular Clusters
To scale   <5'

Plotted to scale if the major axis >2', and circular when face on or the position angle is uncertain

Galaxy Clusters

630

652

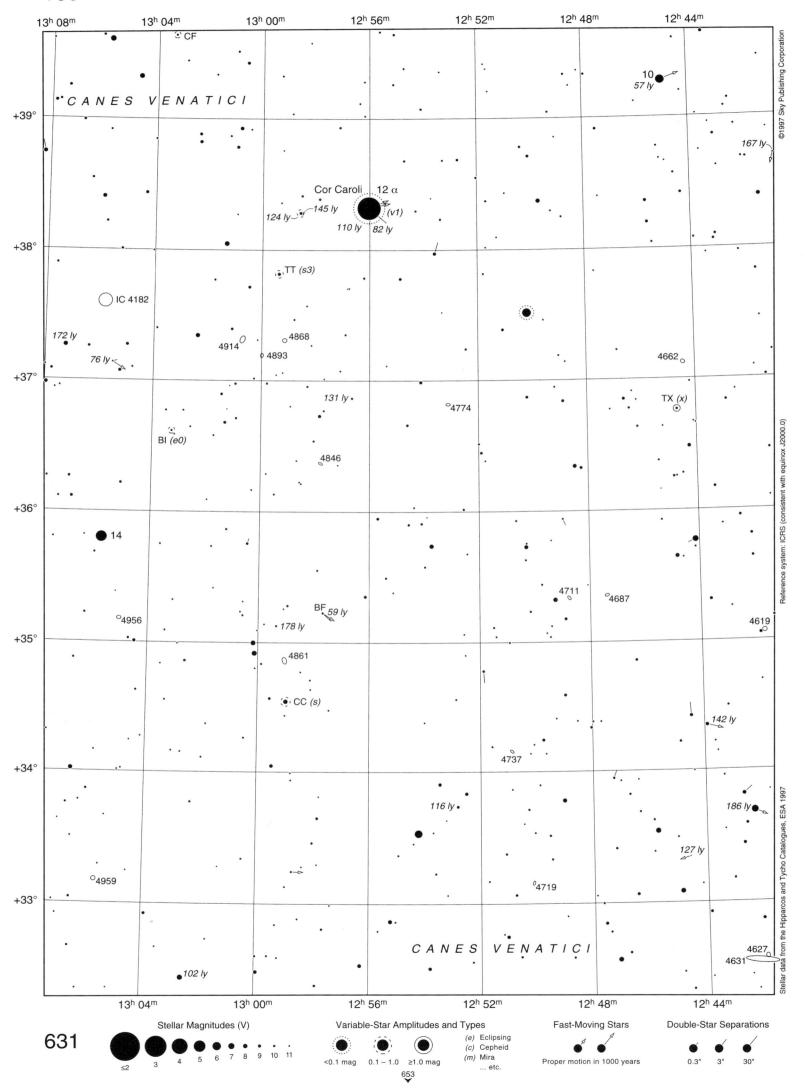

©1997 Sky Publishing Corporation

Reference system: ICRS (consistent with equinox J2000.0)

Stellar data from the Hipparcos and Tycho Catalogues, ESA 1997

C A N E S   V E N A T I C I

Cor Caroli   12 α

124 ly — 145 ly   (v1)
110 ly   82 ly

10
57 ly
167 ly

TT (s3)

IC 4182

172 ly
76 ly

4914   4868
4893

4662

131 ly
4774   TX (x)

BI (e0)

4846

14

4711   4687

4956
178 ly   BF 59 ly   4619

4861

CC (s)
142 ly

4737
116 ly

4719   127 ly

4959
186 ly

C A N E S   V E N A T I C I

102 ly   4627
4631

631

Stellar Magnitudes (V)

≤2   3   4   5   6   7   8   9   10   11

Variable-Star Amplitudes and Types

<0.1 mag   0.1 – 1.0   ≥1.0 mag

(e) Eclipsing
(c) Cepheid
(m) Mira
... etc.

Fast-Moving Stars

Proper motion in 1000 years

Double-Star Separations

0.3"   3"   30"

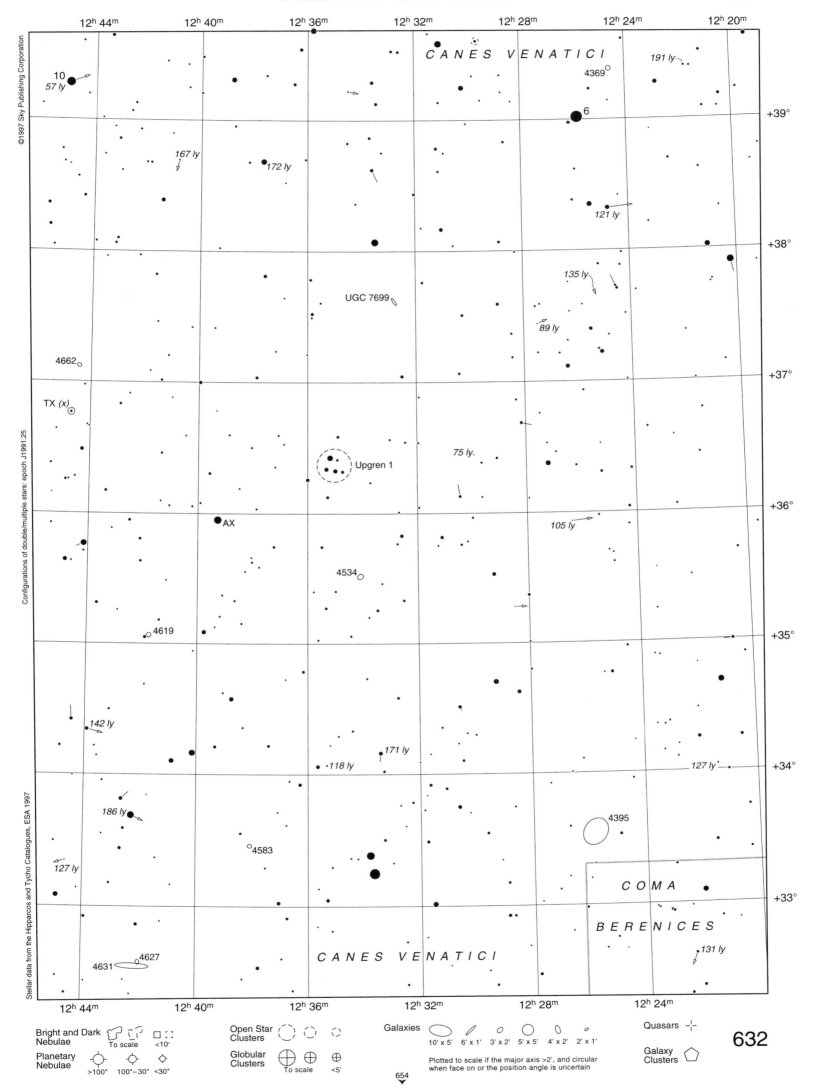

CANES VENATICI

191 ly

4369

10
57 ly

6

167 ly

172 ly

121 ly

135 ly

89 ly

UGC 7699

4662

TX (x)

75 ly.

Upgren 1

105 ly

AX

4534

4619

142 ly

171 ly

118 ly

127 ly

186 ly

4395

4583

COMA

127 ly

BERENICES

131 ly

CANES VENATICI

4627
4631

Bright and Dark Nebulae
To scale   <10'

Open Star Clusters

Galaxies
10' x 5'   6' x 1'   3' x 2'   5' x 5'   4' x 2'   2' x 1'

Quasars

Planetary Nebulae
>100"   100"–30"   <30"

Globular Clusters
To scale   <5'

Plotted to scale if the major axis >2', and circular when face on or the position angle is uncertain

Galaxy Clusters

632

654

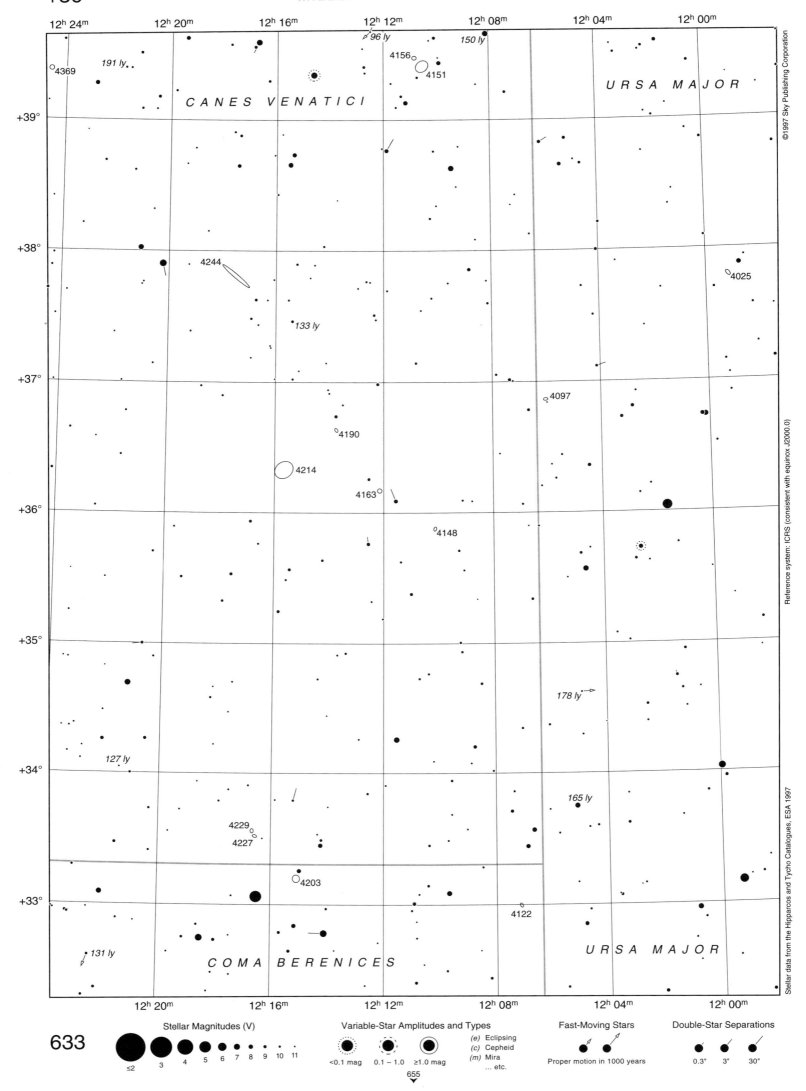

©1997 Sky Publishing Corporation

Reference system: ICRS (consistent with equinox J2000.0)

Stellar data from the Hipparcos and Tycho Catalogues, ESA 1997

CANES VENATICI

URSA MAJOR

URSA MAJOR

COMA BERENICES

191 ly

96 ly

150 ly

4369

4156

4151

4244

133 ly

4025

4097

4190

4214

4163

4148

178 ly

127 ly

165 ly

4229

4227

4203

4122

131 ly

655

633

Stellar Magnitudes (V)

≤2   3   4   5   6   7   8   9   10   11

Variable-Star Amplitudes and Types

<0.1 mag   0.1 – 1.0   ≥1.0 mag

(e) Eclipsing
(c) Cepheid
(m) Mira
... etc.

Fast-Moving Stars

Proper motion in 1000 years

Double-Star Separations

0.3"   3"   30"

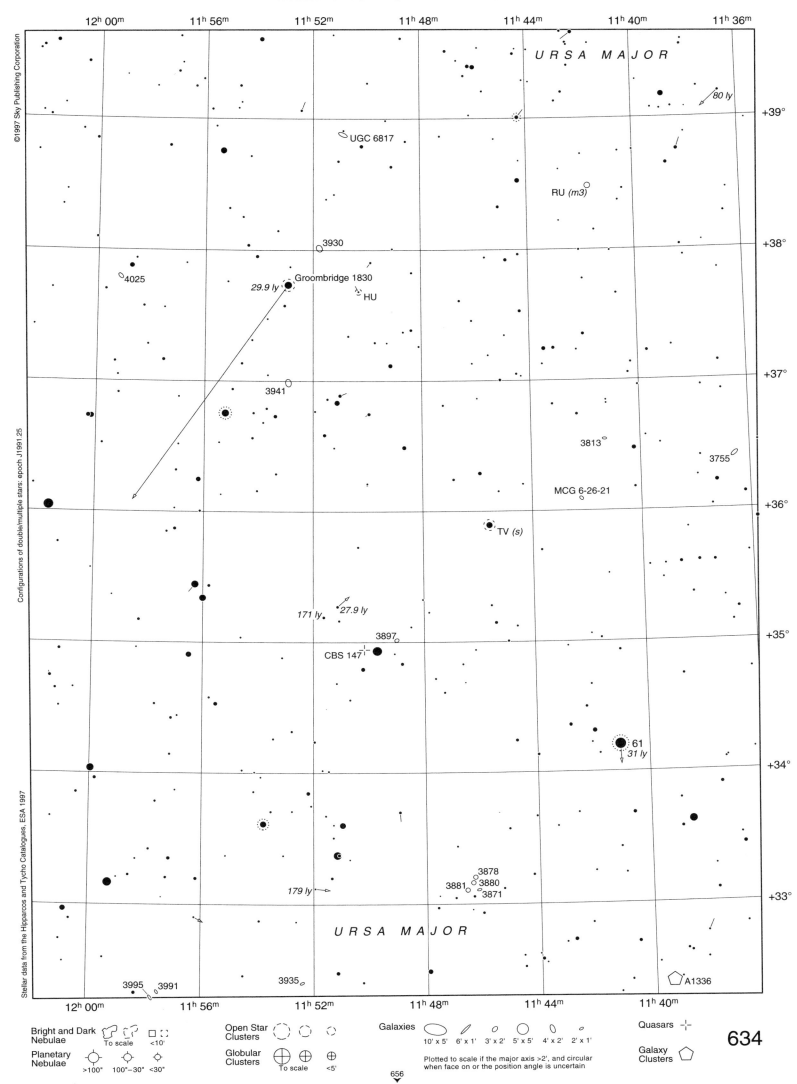

©1997 Sky Publishing Corporation

Configurations of double/multiple stars: epoch J1991.25

Stellar data from the Hipparcos and Tycho Catalogues, ESA 1997

12ʰ 00ᵐ   11ʰ 56ᵐ   11ʰ 52ᵐ   11ʰ 48ᵐ   11ʰ 44ᵐ   11ʰ 40ᵐ   11ʰ 36ᵐ

U R S A   M A J O R

80 ly

+39°

UGC 6817

RU *(m3)*

+38°

3930

4025

Groombridge 1830

29.9 ly

HU

+37°

3941

3813

3755

MCG 6-26-21

+36°

TV *(s)*

171 ly   27.9 ly

+35°

3897

CBS 147

61
31 ly

+34°

3878
3881 3880
3871

+33°

179 ly

U R S A   M A J O R

3935

3995   3991

A1336

12ʰ 00ᵐ   11ʰ 56ᵐ   11ʰ 52ᵐ   11ʰ 48ᵐ   11ʰ 44ᵐ   11ʰ 40ᵐ

Bright and Dark Nebulae	Open Star Clusters	Galaxies	Quasars

To scale   <10'

Planetary Nebulae
>100"   100"–30"   <30"

Globular Clusters
To scale   <5'

10' x 5'   6' x 1'   3' x 2'   5' x 5'   4' x 2'   2' x 1'

Galaxy Clusters

Plotted to scale if the major axis >2', and circular when face on or the position angle is uncertain

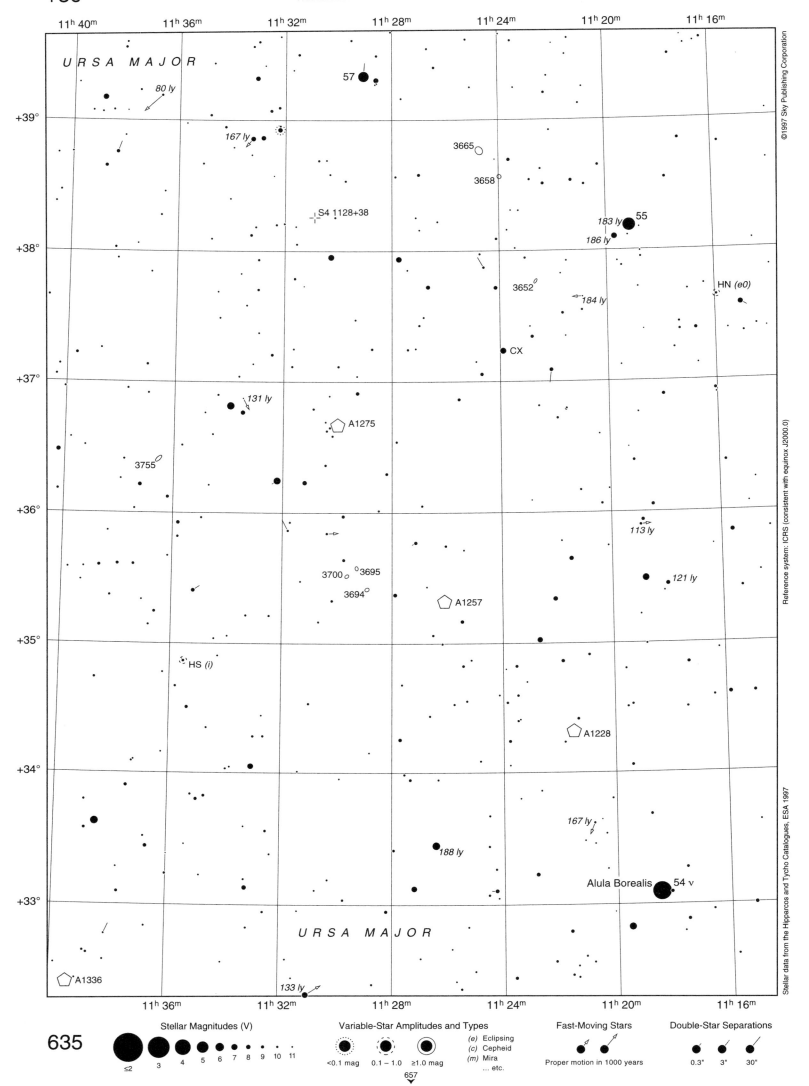

URSA MAJOR

80 ly

57

167 ly

3665

3658

S4 1128+38

183 ly   55
186 ly

3652

HN (e0)

184 ly

CX

131 ly

A1275

3755

113 ly

121 ly

3700   3695

3694

A1257

HS (i)

A1228

167 ly

188 ly

Alula Borealis   54 ν

URSA MAJOR

A1336

133 ly

Stellar Magnitudes (V)

≤2   3   4   5   6   7   8   9   10   11

Variable-Star Amplitudes and Types

<0.1 mag   0.1 – 1.0   ≥1.0 mag

(e) Eclipsing
(c) Cepheid
(m) Mira
... etc.

Fast-Moving Stars

Proper motion in 1000 years

Double-Star Separations

0.3"   3"   30"

657

©1997 Sky Publishing Corporation

Reference system: ICRS (consistent with equinox J2000.0)

Stellar data from the Hipparcos and Tycho Catalogues, ESA 1997

MILLENNIUM STAR ATLAS

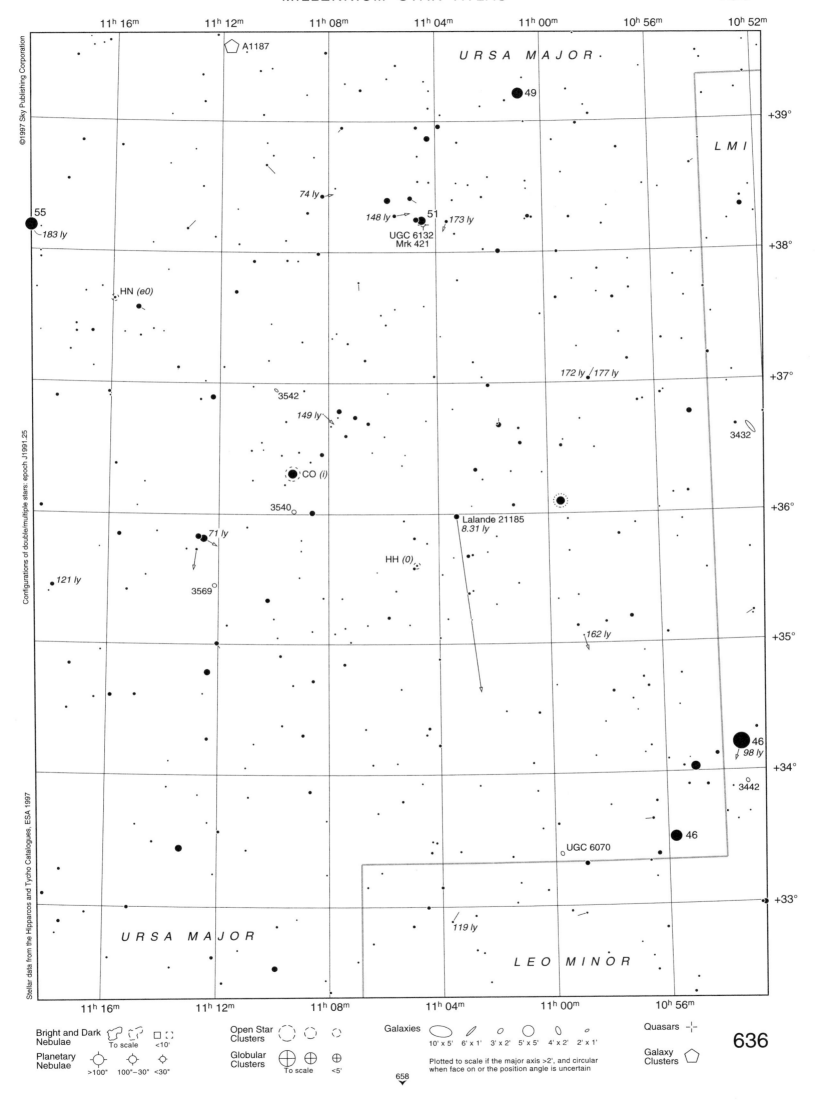

URSA MAJOR

LMI

A1187

49

74 ly

148 ly   51
          173 ly
55
183 ly   UGC 6132
           Mrk 421

HN (e0)

172 ly 177 ly

3542

149 ly   3432

CO (i)

3540

Lalande 21185
8.31 ly

71 ly   HH (0)

121 ly

3569

162 ly

46
98 ly

3442

46

UGC 6070

URSA MAJOR

119 ly

LEO MINOR

Bright and Dark Nebulae			Open Star Clusters			Galaxies						Quasars
To scale		<10'				10' x 5'	6' x 1'	3' x 2'	5' x 5'	4' x 2'	2' x 1'	
Planetary Nebulae			Globular Clusters									Galaxy Clusters
>100"	100"–30"	<30"	To scale		<5'	Plotted to scale if the major axis >2', and circular when face on or the position angle is uncertain						

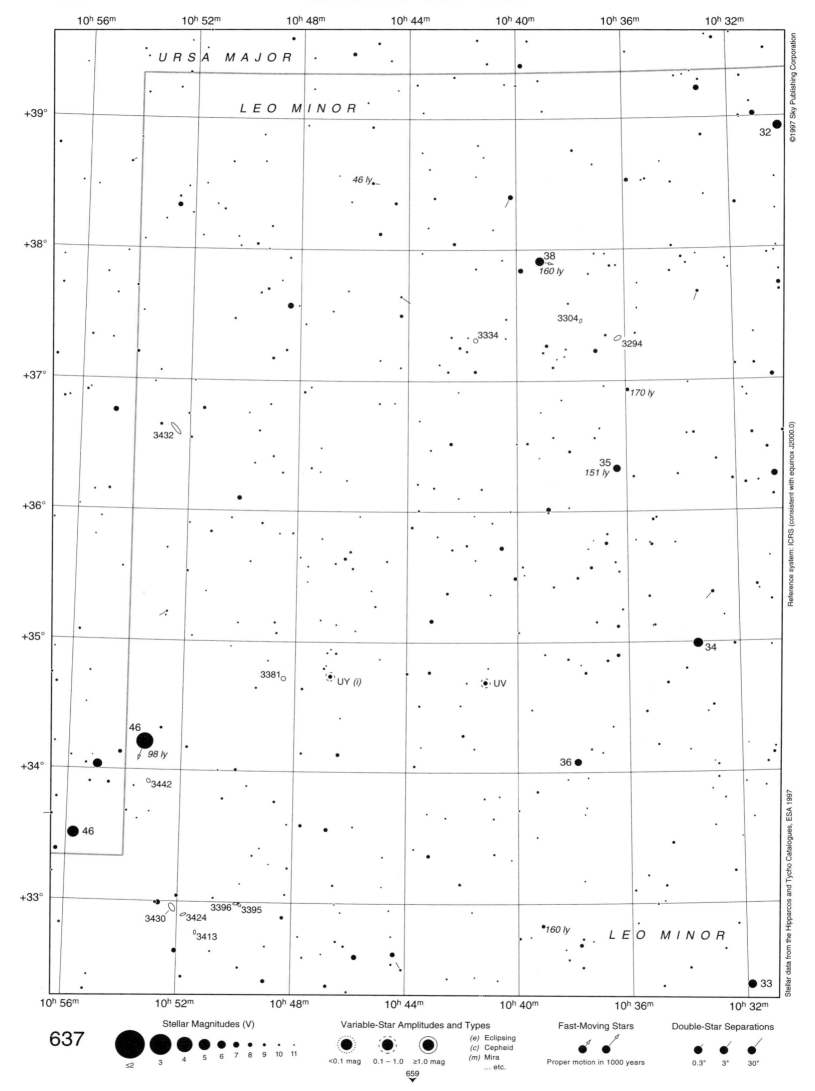

©1997 Sky Publishing Corporation

Reference system: ICRS (consistent with equinox J2000.0)

Stellar data from the Hipparcos and Tycho Catalogues, ESA 1997

URSA MAJOR

LEO MINOR

46 ly

38
160 ly

3304₀

3334

3294

170 ly

3432

35
151 ly

34

3381₀   UY (i)   UV

46
98 ly

36

3442

46

3430 3424   3396 3395

3413

160 ly

LEO MINOR

33

637

Stellar Magnitudes (V)

≤2   3   4   5   6   7   8   9 10 11

Variable-Star Amplitudes and Types

<0.1 mag   0.1 – 1.0   ≥1.0 mag

(e) Eclipsing
(c) Cepheid
(m) Mira
... etc.

Fast-Moving Stars

Proper motion in 1000 years

Double-Star Separations

0.3"   3"   30"

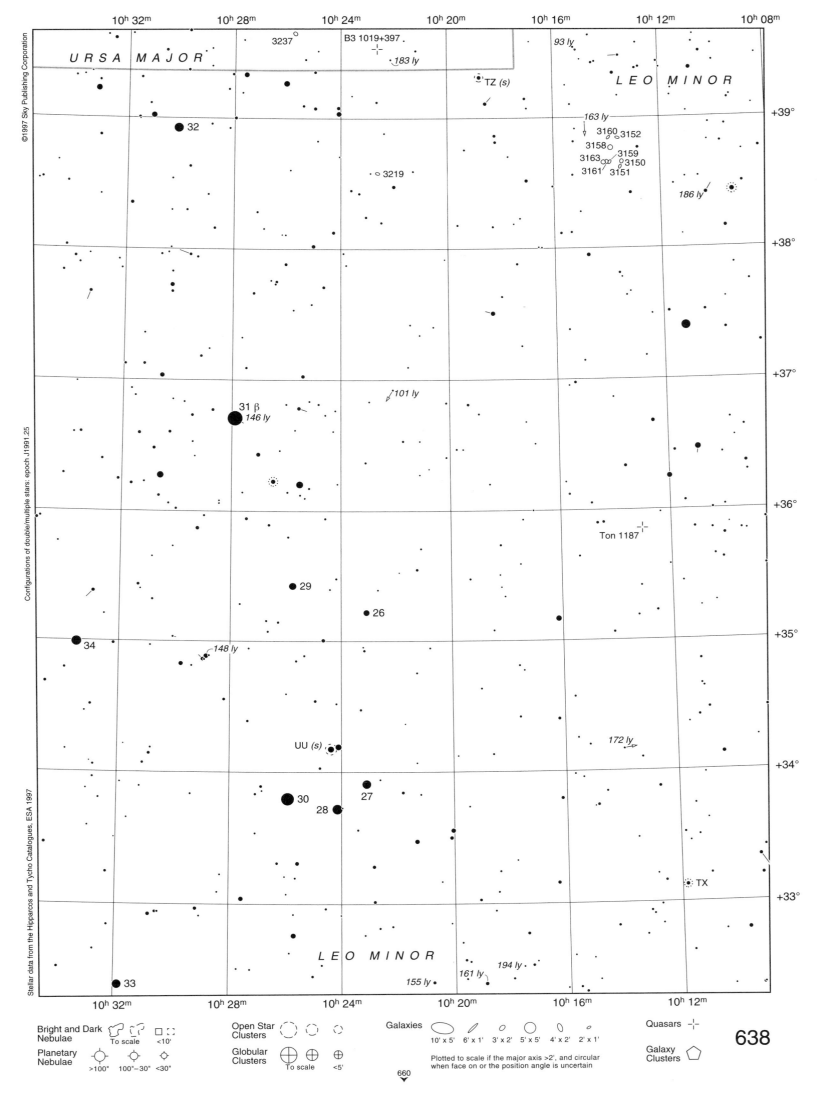

U R S A   M A J O R

3237
B3 1019+397
183 ly
93 ly
TZ (s)

L E O   M I N O R

163 ly
3160 3152
3158
3163 3159
3150
3161 3151
186 ly

3219

32

101 ly

31 β
146 ly

Ton 1187

29

26

34

148 ly

172 ly

UU (s)

30
27
28

TX

L E O   M I N O R

194 ly
161 ly
155 ly

33

Bright and Dark Nebulae	Open Star Clusters	Galaxies	Quasars
To scale <10'	To scale	10' x 5' 6' x 1' 3' x 2' 5' x 5' 4' x 2' 2' x 1'	
Planetary Nebulae	Globular Clusters		Galaxy Clusters
>100" 100"–30" <30"	To scale <5'	Plotted to scale if the major axis >2', and circular when face on or the position angle is uncertain	

+36°

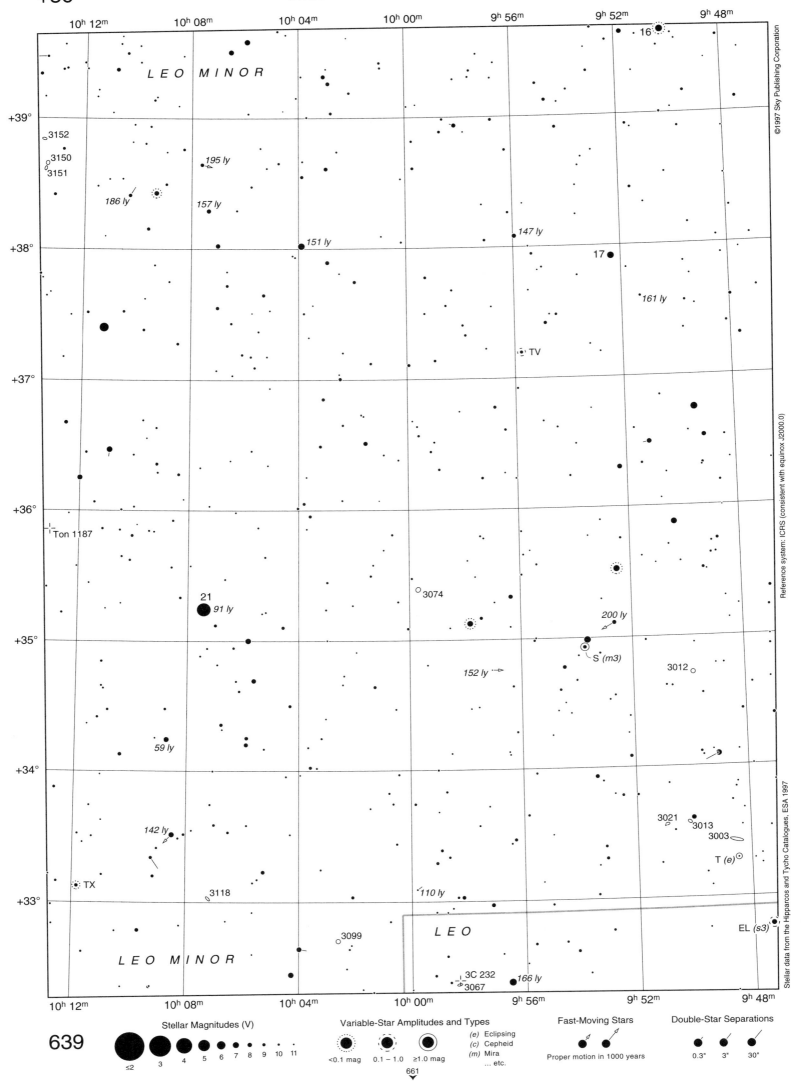

LEO MINOR

16

3152
3150
3151

195 ly

186 ly

157 ly

147 ly

151 ly

17

161 ly

TV

Ton 1187

21
91 ly

3074

200 ly

152 ly

S (m3)

3012

59 ly

3021
3013
3003

142 ly

T (e)

TX

3118

110 ly

EL (s3)

3099

LEO

LEO MINOR

3C 232
3067

166 ly

639

Stellar Magnitudes (V)
≤2 3 4 5 6 7 8 9 10 11

Variable-Star Amplitudes and Types
<0.1 mag   0.1 – 1.0   ≥1.0 mag

(e) Eclipsing
(c) Cepheid
(m) Mira
... etc.

Fast-Moving Stars
Proper motion in 1000 years

Double-Star Separations
0.3"   3"   30"

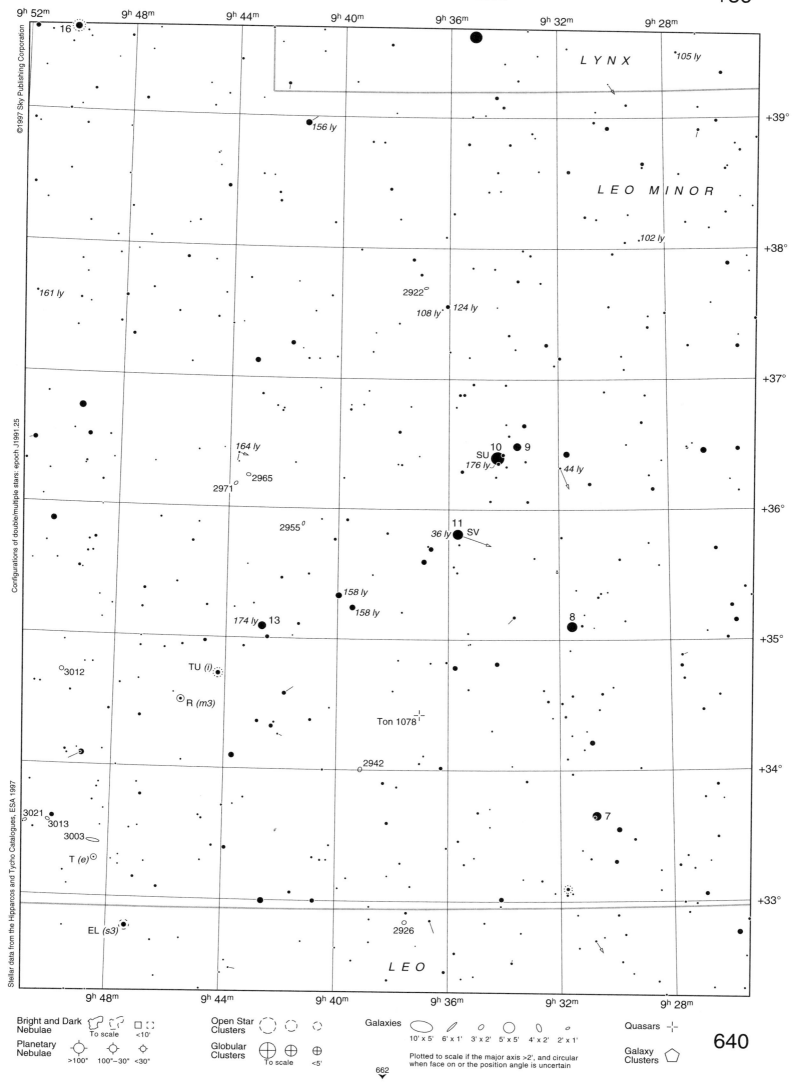

©1997 Sky Publishing Corporation

Configurations of double/multiple stars: epoch J1991.25

Stellar data from the Hipparcos and Tycho Catalogues, ESA 1997

LYNX

LEO MINOR

LEO

16
105 ly
156 ly
161 ly
102 ly
2922
108 ly 124 ly
164 ly
2965
2971
10 9
SU
176 ly
44 ly
2955
11
36 ly SV
158 ly
158 ly
174 ly 13
8
3012
TU (i)
R (m3)
Ton 1078
2942
3021
3013 7
3003
T (e)
EL (s3)
2926

+39°
+38°
+37°
+36°
+35°
+34°
+33°

9h 52m
9h 48m
9h 44m
9h 40m
9h 36m
9h 32m
9h 28m

9h 48m
9h 44m
9h 40m
9h 36m
9h 32m
9h 28m

Bright and Dark
Nebulae
To scale <10'

Planetary
Nebulae
>100" 100"–30" <30"

Open Star
Clusters

Globular
Clusters
To scale <5'

Galaxies
10' x 5' 6' x 1' 3' x 2' 5' x 5' 4' x 2' 2' x 1'

Plotted to scale if the major axis >2', and circular
when face on or the position angle is uncertain

Quasars

Galaxy
Clusters

640

662

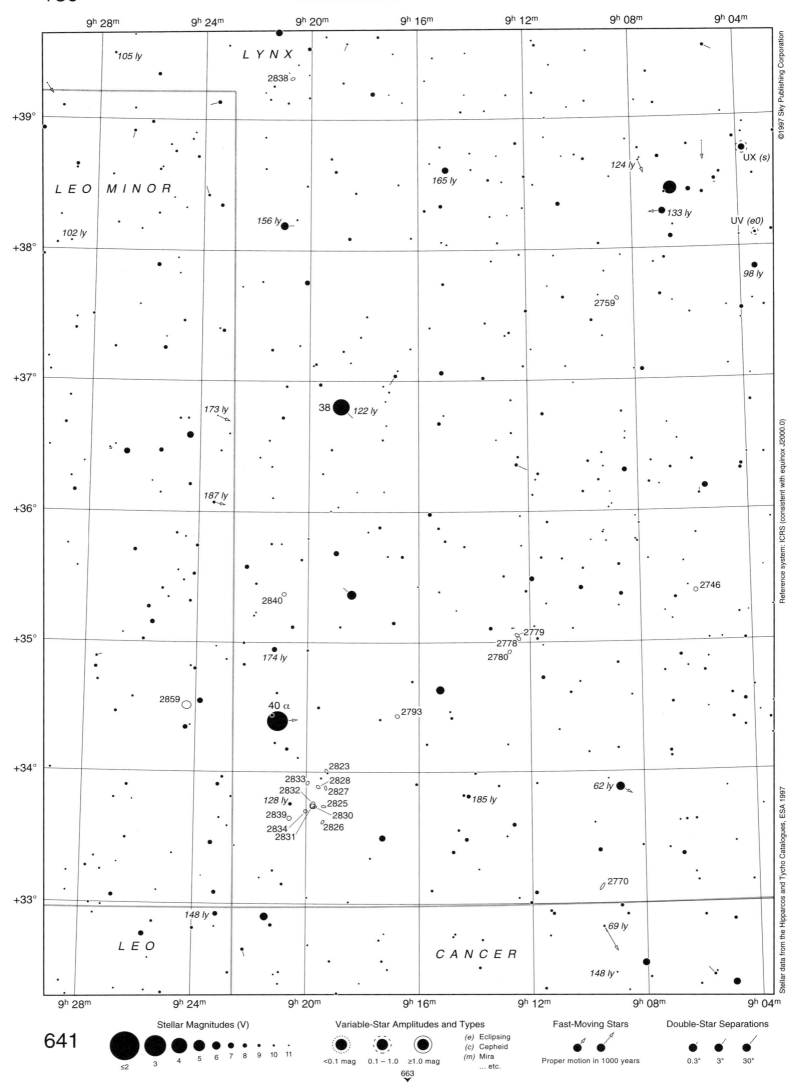

LYNX

LEO MINOR

105 ly

2838

102 ly

156 ly

124 ly

UX (s)

133 ly

UV (e0)

165 ly

2759

98 ly

173 ly

38   122 ly

187 ly

2746

2840

2779
2778
2780

174 ly

2859

40 α

2793

2823
2833   2828
2832   2827
128 ly   2825
2839   2830
2834   2826
2831

185 ly

62 ly

2770

148 ly

69 ly

LEO

CANCER

148 ly

©1997 Sky Publishing Corporation

Reference system: ICRS (consistent with equinox J2000.0)

Stellar data from the Hipparcos and Tycho Catalogues, ESA 1997

641

Stellar Magnitudes (V)

≤2   3   4   5   6   7   8   9   10   11

Variable-Star Amplitudes and Types

<0.1 mag   0.1 – 1.0   ≥1.0 mag

663

(e) Eclipsing
(c) Cepheid
(m) Mira
... etc.

Fast-Moving Stars

Proper motion in 1000 years

Double-Star Separations

0.3"   3"   30"

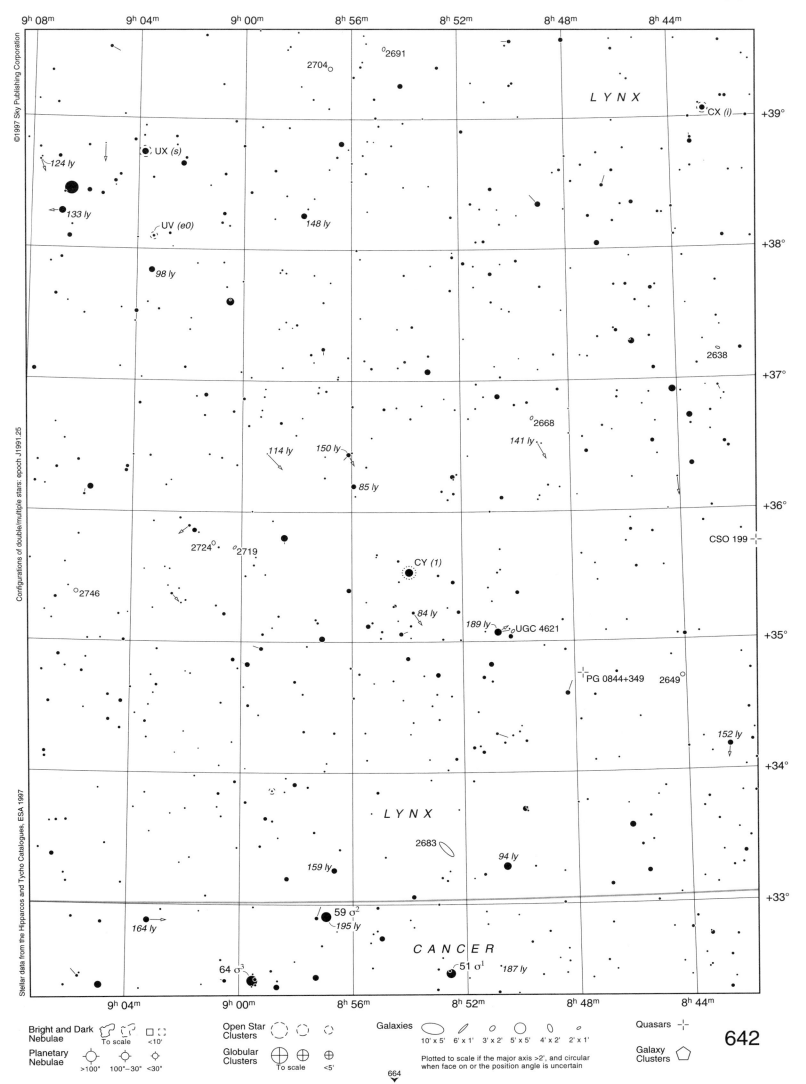

Bright and Dark Nebulae
To scale   <10'

Planetary Nebulae
>100"   100"–30"   <30"

Open Star Clusters
To scale

Globular Clusters
To scale   <5'

Galaxies
10' x 5'   6' x 1'   3' x 2'   5' x 5'   4' x 2'   2' x 1'

Plotted to scale if the major axis >2', and circular when face on or the position angle is uncertain

Quasars

Galaxy Clusters

642

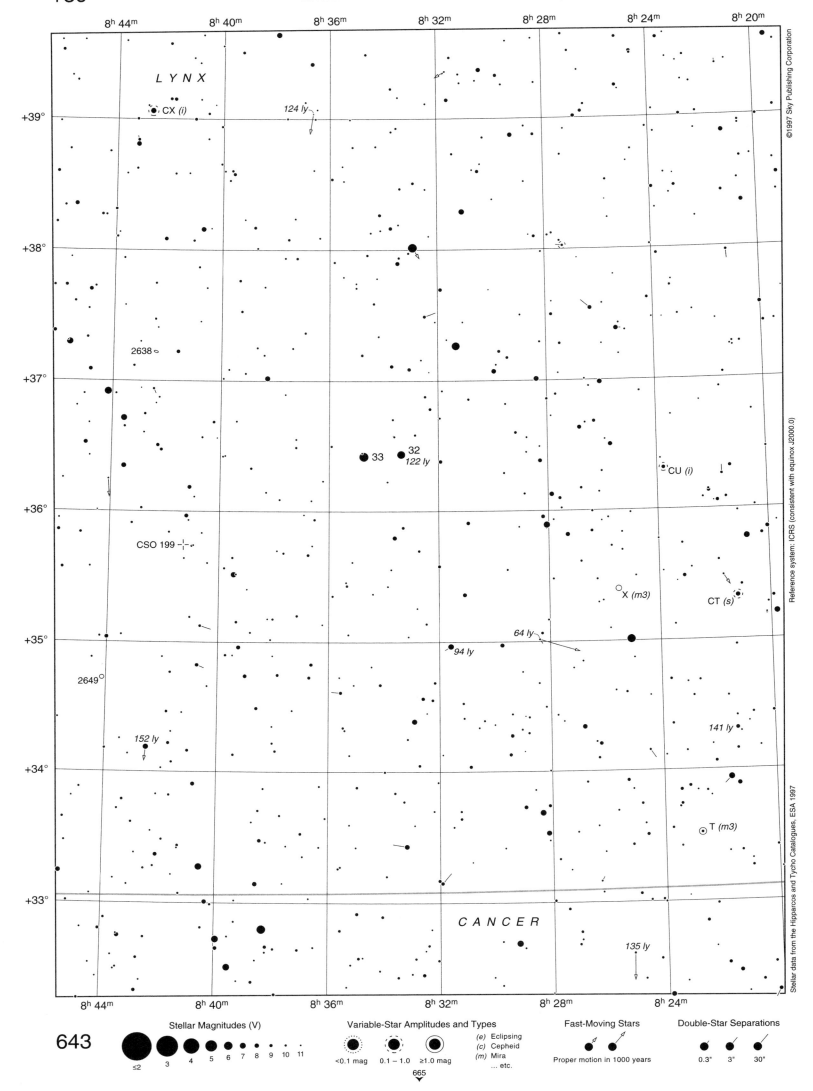

Stellar Magnitudes (V)

≤2   3   4   5   6 7 8 9 10 11

Variable-Star Amplitudes and Types

<0.1 mag   0.1 – 1.0   ≥1.0 mag

(e) Eclipsing
(c) Cepheid
(m) Mira
... etc.

Fast-Moving Stars

Proper motion in 1000 years

Double-Star Separations

0.3"   3"   30"

643

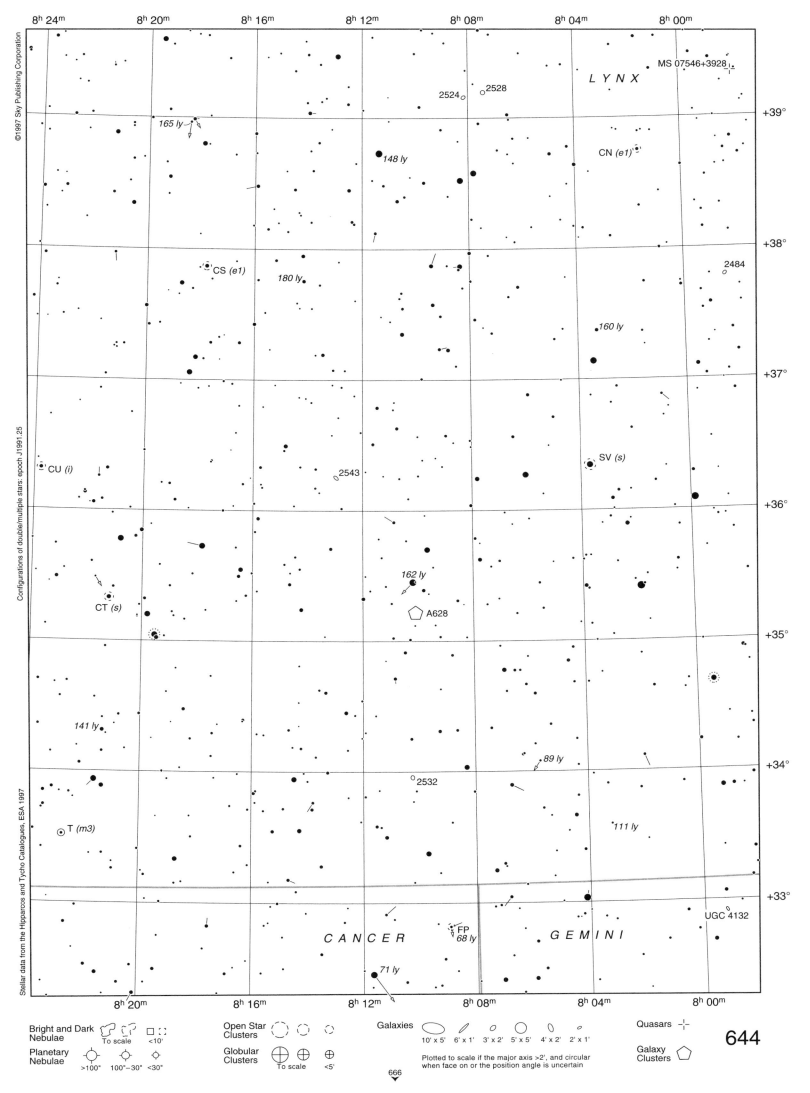

Bright and Dark Nebulae	To scale	<10'		
Planetary Nebulae	>100"	100"–30"	<30"	
Open Star Clusters				
Globular Clusters	To scale	<5'		
Galaxies	10' x 5'	6' x 1'	3' x 2'	5' x 5'	4' x 2'	2' x 1'
	Plotted to scale if the major axis >2', and circular when face on or the position angle is uncertain			
Quasars				
Galaxy Clusters				

644

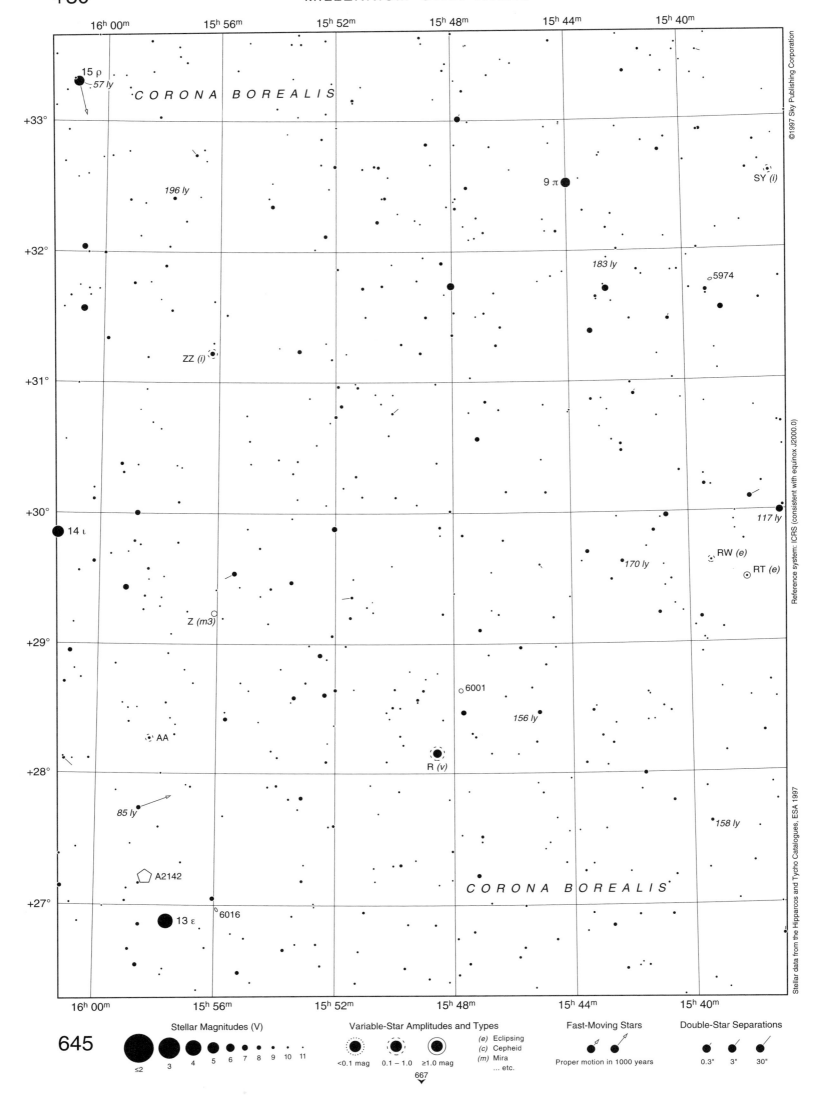

©1997 Sky Publishing Corporation

Reference system: ICRS (consistent with equinox J2000.0)

Stellar data from the Hipparcos and Tycho Catalogues, ESA 1997

CORONA BOREALIS

15 ρ
57 ly

196 ly

9 π

SY (i)

183 ly

5974

ZZ (i)

14 ι

117 ly

RW (e)

170 ly

RT (e)

Z (m3)

6001

156 ly

AA

R (v)

85 ly

158 ly

A2142

CORONA BOREALIS

6016

13 ε

Stellar Magnitudes (V)

≤2   3   4   5   6   7   8   9   10   11

Variable-Star Amplitudes and Types

<0.1 mag   0.1 – 1.0   ≥1.0 mag

(e) Eclipsing
(c) Cepheid
(m) Mira
... etc.

Fast-Moving Stars

Proper motion in 1000 years

Double-Star Separations

0.3"   3"   30"

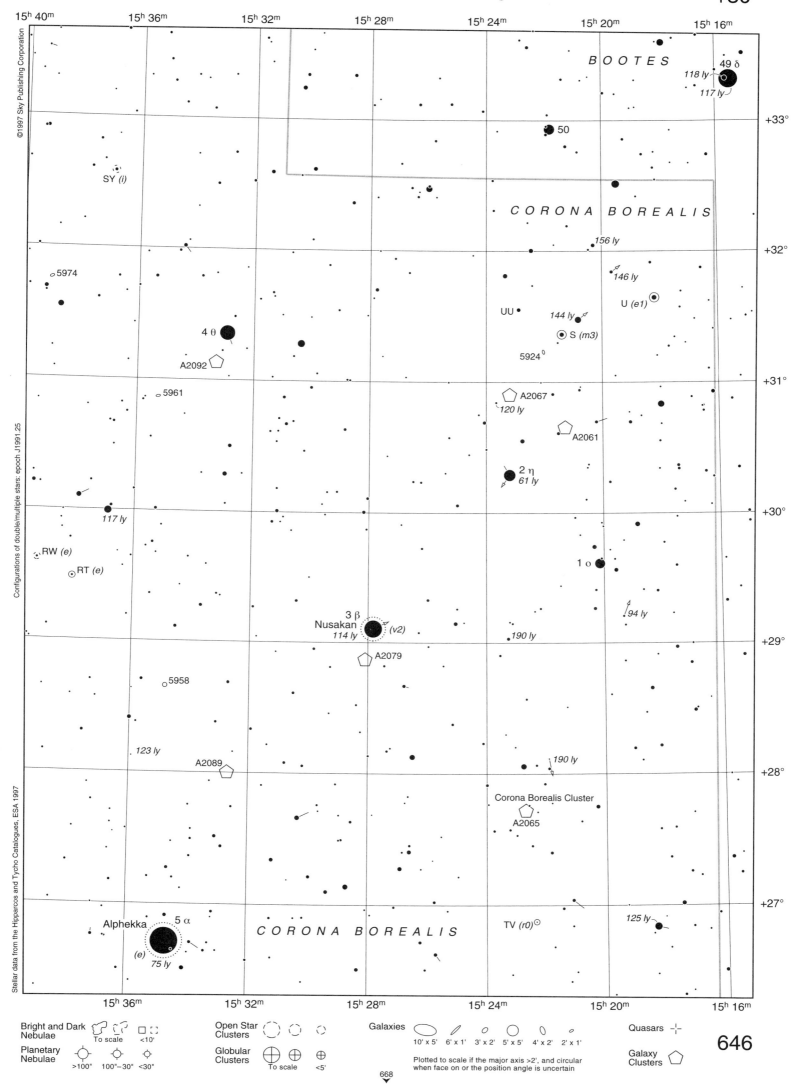

Configurations of double/multiple stars: epoch J1991.25

Stellar data from the Hipparcos and Tycho Catalogues, ESA 1997

B O O T E S

49 δ
118 ly
117 ly

50

C O R O N A   B O R E A L I S

SY (i)

156 ly

5974

146 ly

U (e1)

4 θ

UU

144 ly

S (m3)

A2092

5924

5961

A2067
120 ly

A2061

2 η
61 ly

117 ly

1 o

RW (e)

RT (e)

94 ly

3 β
Nusakan   (v2)
114 ly

190 ly

A2079

5958

123 ly

190 ly

A2089

Corona Borealis Cluster

A2065

Alphekka   5 α

C O R O N A   B O R E A L I S

TV (r0)

125 ly

(e)
75 ly

+33°

+32°

+31°

+30°

+29°

+28°

+27°

15h 40m   15h 36m   15h 32m   15h 28m   15h 24m   15h 20m   15h 16m

15h 36m   15h 32m   15h 28m   15h 24m   15h 20m   15h 16m

Bright and Dark Nebulae	Open Star Clusters	Galaxies	Quasars

Bright and Dark
Nebulae
To scale   <10'

Planetary
Nebulae
>100"   100"–30"   <30'

Open Star
Clusters

Globular
Clusters
To scale   <5'

Galaxies
10' x 5'   6' x 1'   3' x 2'   5' x 5'   4' x 2'   2' x 1'

Plotted to scale if the major axis >2', and circular
when face on or the position angle is uncertain

Quasars

Galaxy
Clusters

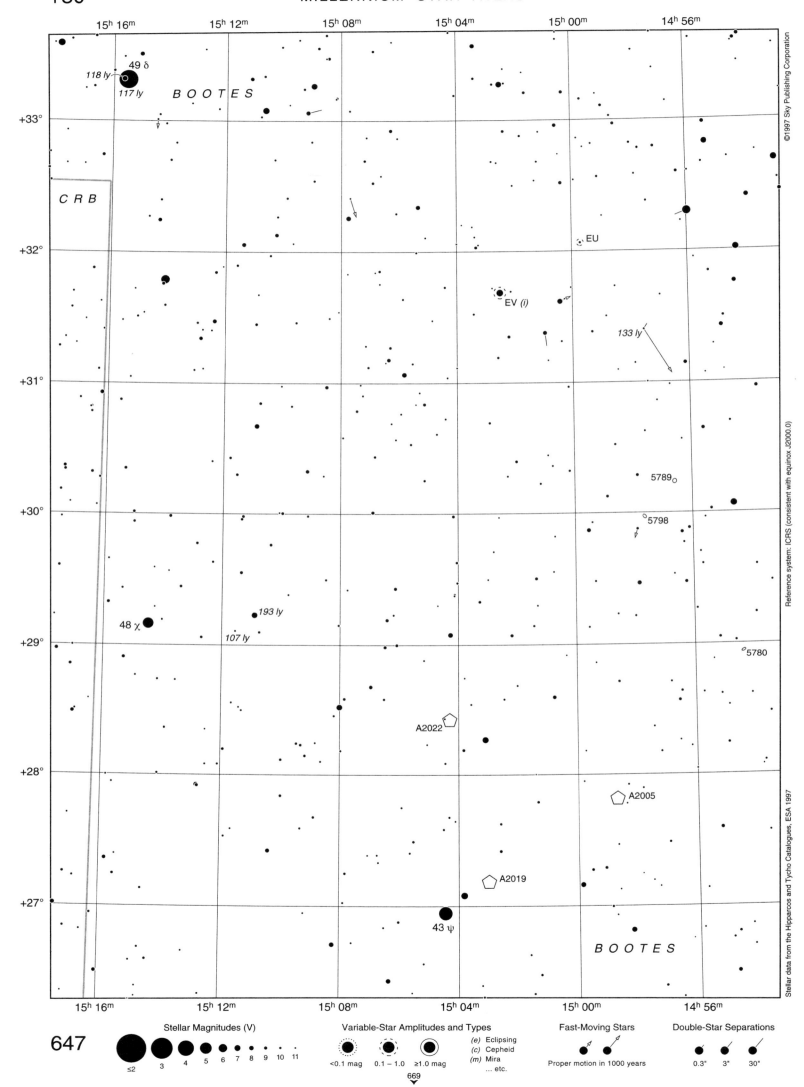

©1997 Sky Publishing Corporation

Reference system: ICRS (consistent with equinox J2000.0)

Stellar data from the Hipparcos and Tycho Catalogues, ESA 1997

B O O T E S

C R B

49 δ
118 ly
117 ly

EU

EV *(i)*

133 ly

5789

5798

48 χ
193 ly
107 ly

5780

A2022

A2005

A2019

A2005

43 ψ

B O O T E S

647

Stellar Magnitudes (V)
≤2   3   4   5   6   7   8   9   10   11

Variable-Star Amplitudes and Types
<0.1 mag   0.1 − 1.0   ≥1.0 mag

(e) Eclipsing
(c) Cepheid
(m) Mira
... etc.

Fast-Moving Stars
Proper motion in 1000 years

Double-Star Separations
0.3"   3"   30"

669

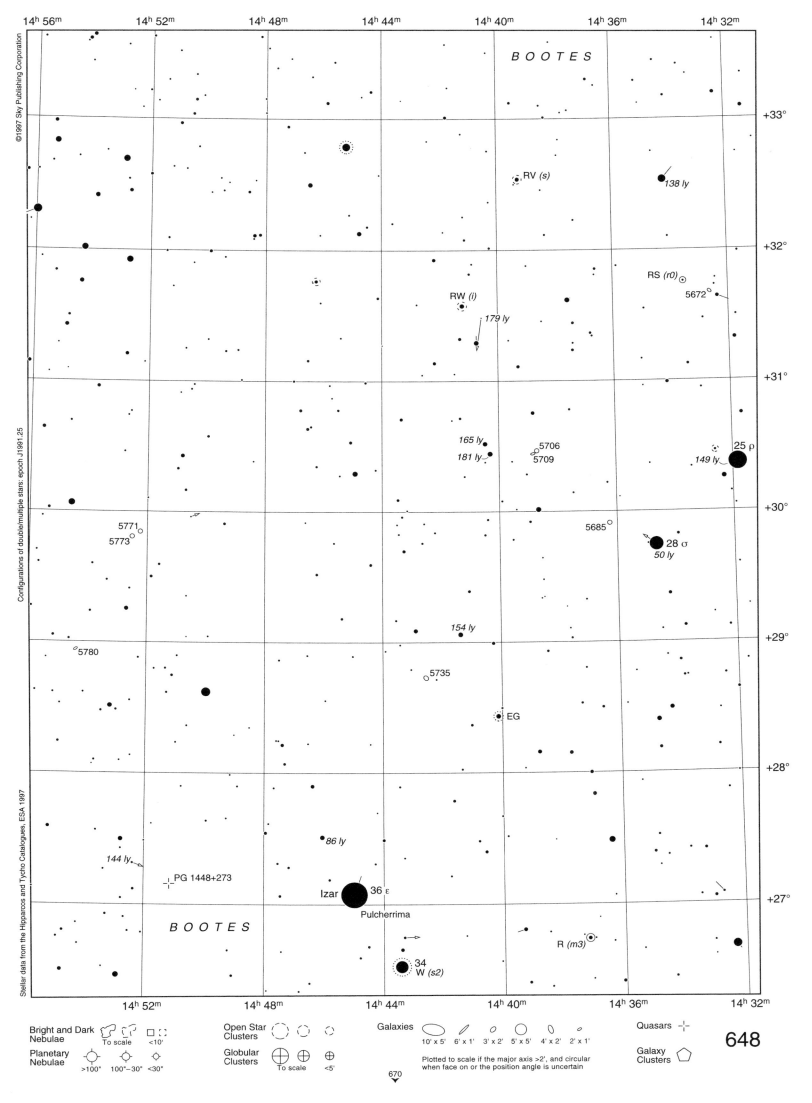

B O O T E S

RV (s)

138 ly

RS (r0)
5672

RW (i)

179 ly

165 ly
181 ly

5706
5709

25 ρ
149 ly

5771
5773

5685

28 σ
50 ly

154 ly

5780

5735

EG

86 ly

144 ly

PG 1448+273

Izar   36 ε
Pulcherrima

B O O T E S

R (m3)

34
W (s2)

©1997 Sky Publishing Corporation

Configurations of double/multiple stars: epoch J1991.25

Stellar data from the Hipparcos and Tycho Catalogues, ESA 1997

Bright and Dark Nebulae
To scale   <10'

Planetary Nebulae
>100"   100"–30"   <30"

Open Star Clusters

Globular Clusters
To scale   <5'

Galaxies
10' x 5'   6' x 1'   3' x 2'   5' x 5'   4' x 2'   2' x 1'

Plotted to scale if the major axis >2', and circular when face on or the position angle is uncertain

Quasars

Galaxy Clusters

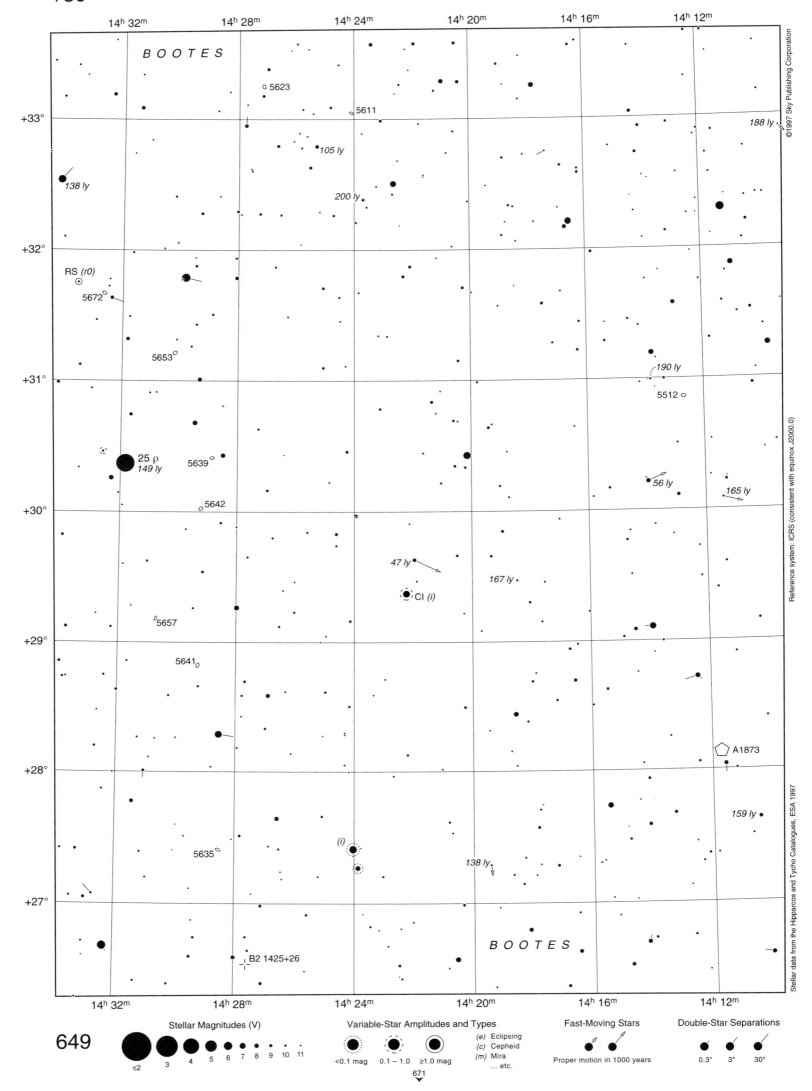

BOOTES

o 5623

o 5611

105 ly

200 ly

138 ly

RS (r0)
⊙
5672 o

5653 o

25 ρ
149 ly

5639 o

5642 o

5657 o

5641 o

5635 o

190 ly

5512 o

56 ly

165 ly

188 ly

47 ly

167 ly

Cl (i)

A1873

159 ly

(i)

138 ly

BOOTES

B2 1425+26

Stellar Magnitudes (V)

≤2 3 4 5 6 7 8 9 10 11

Variable-Star Amplitudes and Types

<0.1 mag   0.1 – 1.0   ≥1.0 mag

(e) Eclipsing
(c) Cepheid
(m) Mira
... etc.

Fast-Moving Stars

Proper motion in 1000 years

Double-Star Separations

0.3"   3"   30"

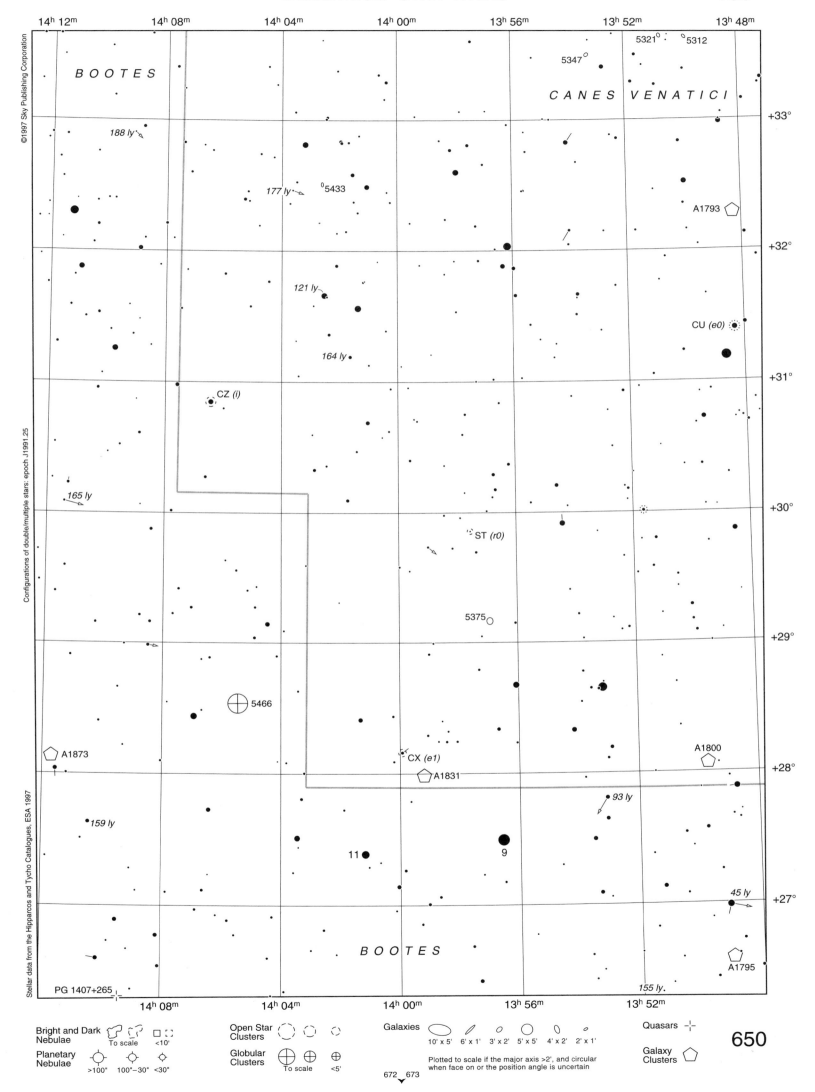

Configurations of double/multiple stars: epoch J1991.25

Stellar data from the Hipparcos and Tycho Catalogues, ESA 1997

BOOTES

CANES VENATICI

188 ly

177 ly

5347
5321   5312

5433

A1793

121 ly

CU (e0)

164 ly

CZ (i)

165 ly

ST (r0)

5375

5466

A1873

CX (e1)

A1800

A1831

93 ly

159 ly

11   9

45 ly

BOOTES

A1795

PG 1407+265   155 ly.

Bright and Dark Nebulae	Open Star Clusters	Galaxies	Quasars
To scale <10'		10' x 5' 6' x 1' 3' x 2' 5' x 5' 4' x 2' 2' x 1'	
Planetary Nebulae	Globular Clusters		Galaxy Clusters
>100' 100"–30" <30"	To scale <5'	Plotted to scale if the major axis >2', and circular when face on or the position angle is uncertain	

650

672 673

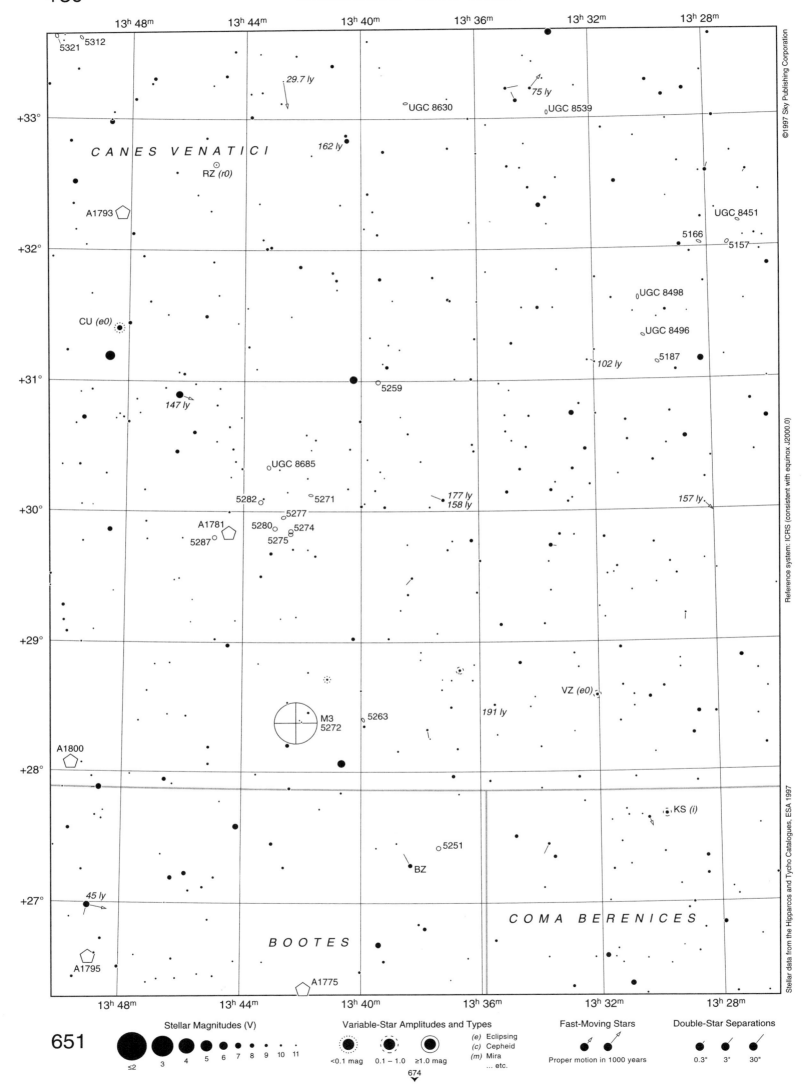

©1997 Sky Publishing Corporation

Reference system: ICRS (consistent with equinox J2000.0)

Stellar data from the Hipparcos and Tycho Catalogues, ESA 1997

CANES VENATICI

29.7 ly

UGC 8630

75 ly

UGC 8539

162 ly

RZ (r0)

A1793

UGC 8451

5166

5157

UGC 8498

CU (e0)

UGC 8496

5187

102 ly

5259

147 ly

UGC 8685

177 ly
158 ly

157 ly

5282   5271

A1781   5277

5280   5274

5287   5275

VZ (e0)

191 ly

M3
5272

5263

A1800

KS (i)

5251

BZ

45 ly

COMA BERENICES

A1795

BOOTES

A1775

Stellar Magnitudes (V)

≤2 3 4 5 6 7 8 9 10 11

Variable-Star Amplitudes and Types

<0.1 mag   0.1 – 1.0   ≥1.0 mag

(e) Eclipsing
(c) Cepheid
(m) Mira
... etc.

Fast-Moving Stars

Proper motion in 1000 years

Double-Star Separations

0.3" 3" 30"

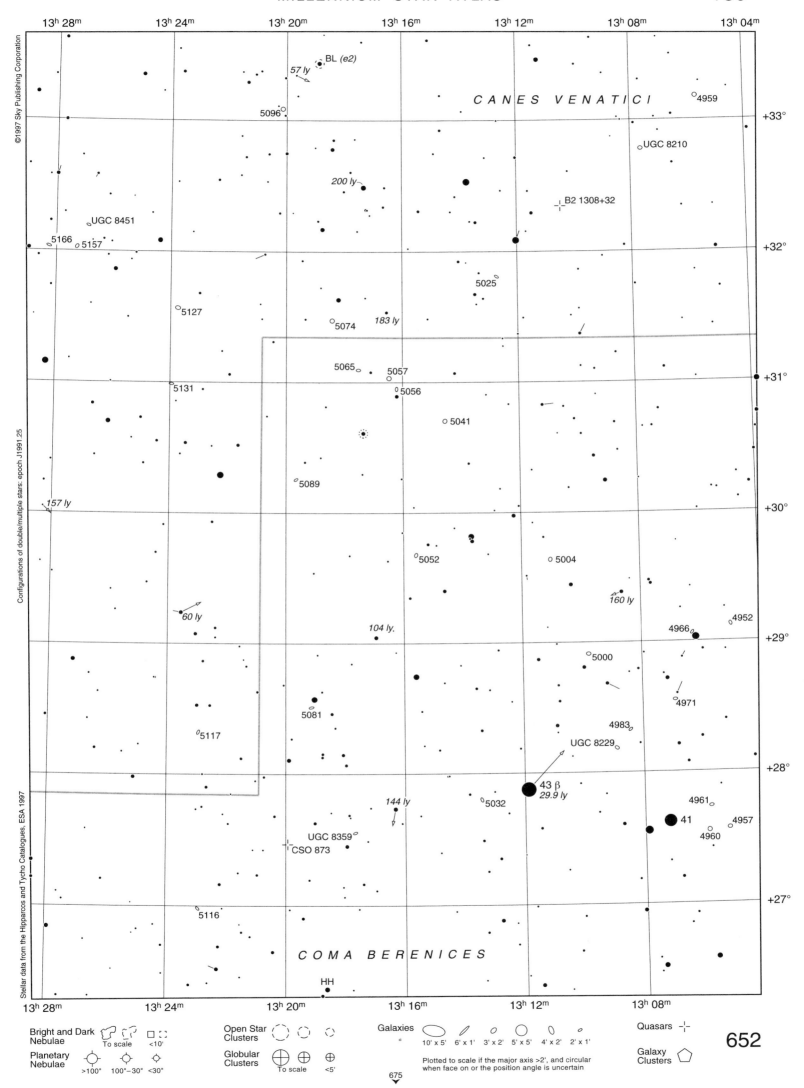

13h 28m 13h 24m 13h 20m 13h 16m 13h 12m 13h 08m 13h 04m

BL (e2)

57 ly

5096

C A N E S   V E N A T I C I

4959

+33°

UGC 8210

200 ly

B2 1308+32

UGC 8451

5025

+32°

5166 5157

5127

5074   183 ly

+31°

5065   5057

5131   5056

5041

5089

157 ly

+30°

5052   5004

160 ly

60 ly

104 ly.

4952

4966

+29°

5000

4971

5081

4983

5117

UGC 8229

+28°

43 β
29.9 ly

5032   4961

144 ly

41   4957

UGC 8359

4960

CSO 873

+27°

5116

C O M A   B E R E N I C E S

HH

13h 28m 13h 24m 13h 20m 13h 16m 13h 12m 13h 08m

Bright and Dark
Nebulae   To scale   <10'

Planetary
Nebulae
>100" 100"–30" <30'

Open Star
Clusters

Globular
Clusters
To scale   <5'

Galaxies
10' x 5' 6' x 1' 3' x 2' 5' x 5' 4' x 2' 2' x 1'

Plotted to scale if the major axis >2', and circular
when face on or the position angle is uncertain

Quasars

Galaxy
Clusters

675

+30°

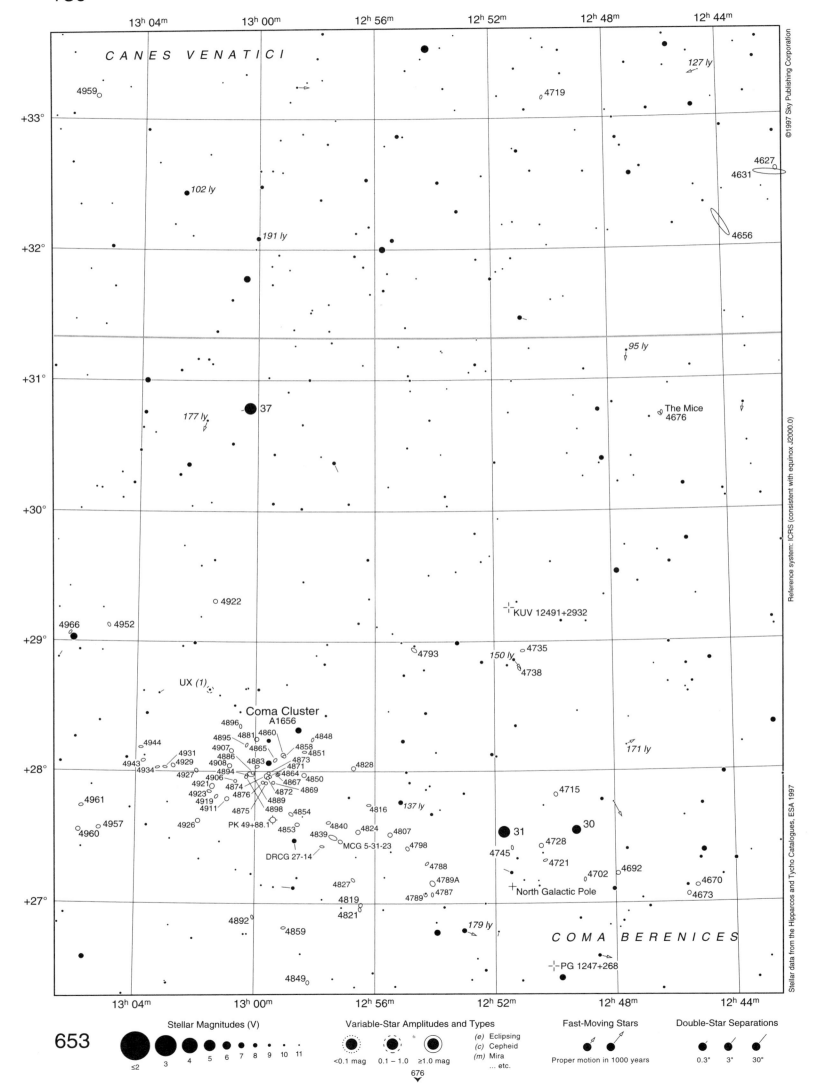

Reference system: ICRS (consistent with equinox J2000.0)

Stellar data from the Hipparcos and Tycho Catalogues, ESA 1997

C A N E S   V E N A T I C I

4959

127 ly

4719

4627
4631

4656

102 ly

191 ly

95 ly

The Mice
4676

37

177 ly

4922

KUV 12491+2932

4966   4952

4793

4735

150 ly   4738

171 ly

UX (1)

Coma Cluster
A1656

4896
4881   4860
4895   4858   4848
4944   4851
4907   4865
4931   4886   4873
4929   4908   4883   4871
4943   4828
4934   4894   4715
4927   4906   4864
4921   4874   4867   4850
4923   4872   4869
4919   4876   4889
4911   4875   4898   4854
4816   137 ly

31   30

4926   PK 49+88.1   4728
4961   4853   4745   4721
4957   4840   4824
4960   4839   4807   4702   4692
MCG 5-31-23   4798
DRCG 27-14   North Galactic Pole   4670
4788   4673
4827   4789A
4789   4787
4819
4821   179 ly
4892
4859   C O M A   B E R E N I C E S
4849   PG 1247+268

MILLENNIUM STAR ATLAS

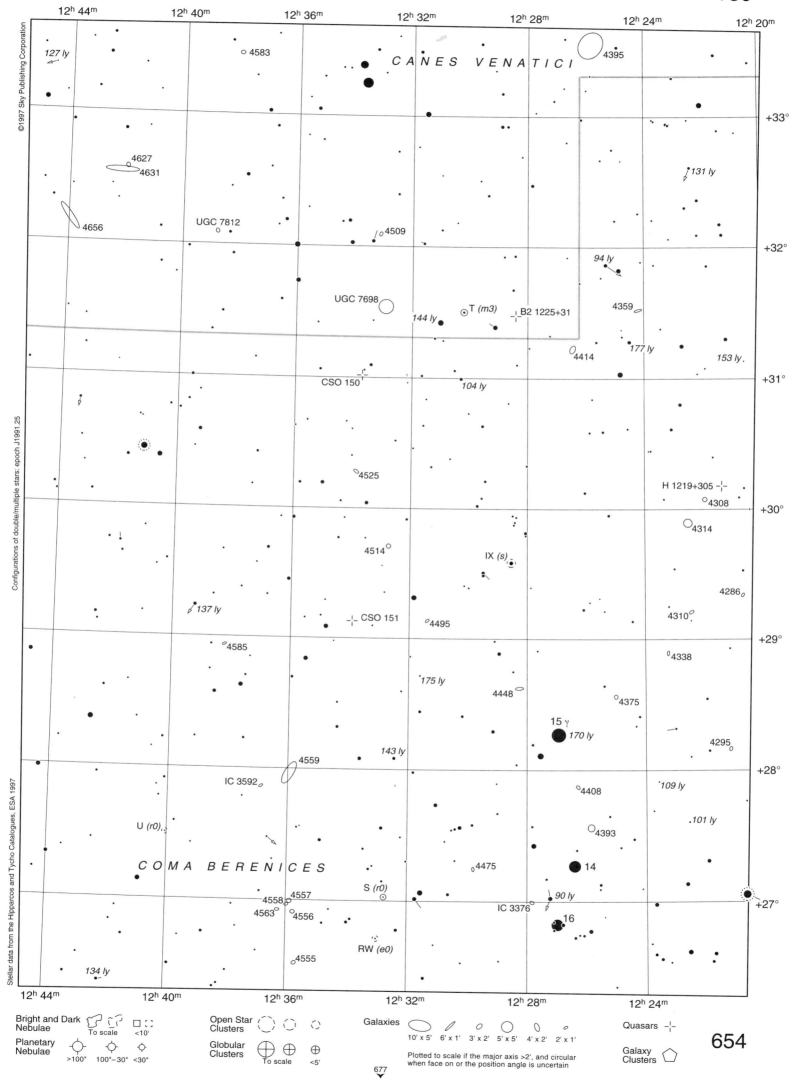

Configurations of double/multiple stars: epoch J1991.25

Stellar data from the Hipparcos and Tycho Catalogues, ESA 1997

12ʰ 44ᵐ	12ʰ 40ᵐ	12ʰ 36ᵐ	12ʰ 32ᵐ	12ʰ 28ᵐ	12ʰ 24ᵐ	12ʰ 20ᵐ

127 ly

4583

4395

CANES VENATICI

+33°

4627
4631

131 ly

4656

UGC 7812

4509

+32°

94 ly

UGC 7698

T (m3)

B2 1225+31

4359

144 ly

4414

177 ly

153 ly

CSO 150

104 ly

+31°

4525

H 1219+305

4308

+30°

4314

4514

IX (s)

4286

4310

137 ly

CSO 151

4495

+29°

4585

4338

175 ly

4448

4375

15 γ

170 ly

4295

143 ly

+28°

4559

4408

109 ly

IC 3592

101 ly

U (r0)

4393

COMA BERENICES

4475

14

S (r0)

90 ly

IC 3376

+27°

4558 4557

16

4563 4556

4555

RW (e0)

134 ly

12ʰ 44ᵐ	12ʰ 40ᵐ	12ʰ 36ᵐ	12ʰ 32ᵐ	12ʰ 28ᵐ	12ʰ 24ᵐ

Bright and Dark Nebulae   To scale   <10'

Planetary Nebulae   >100"   100"–30"   <30"

Open Star Clusters

Globular Clusters   To scale   <5'

Galaxies   10' x 5'   6' x 1'   3' x 2'   5' x 5'   4' x 2'   2' x 1'

Plotted to scale if the major axis >2', and circular when face on or the position angle is uncertain

Quasars

Galaxy Clusters

654

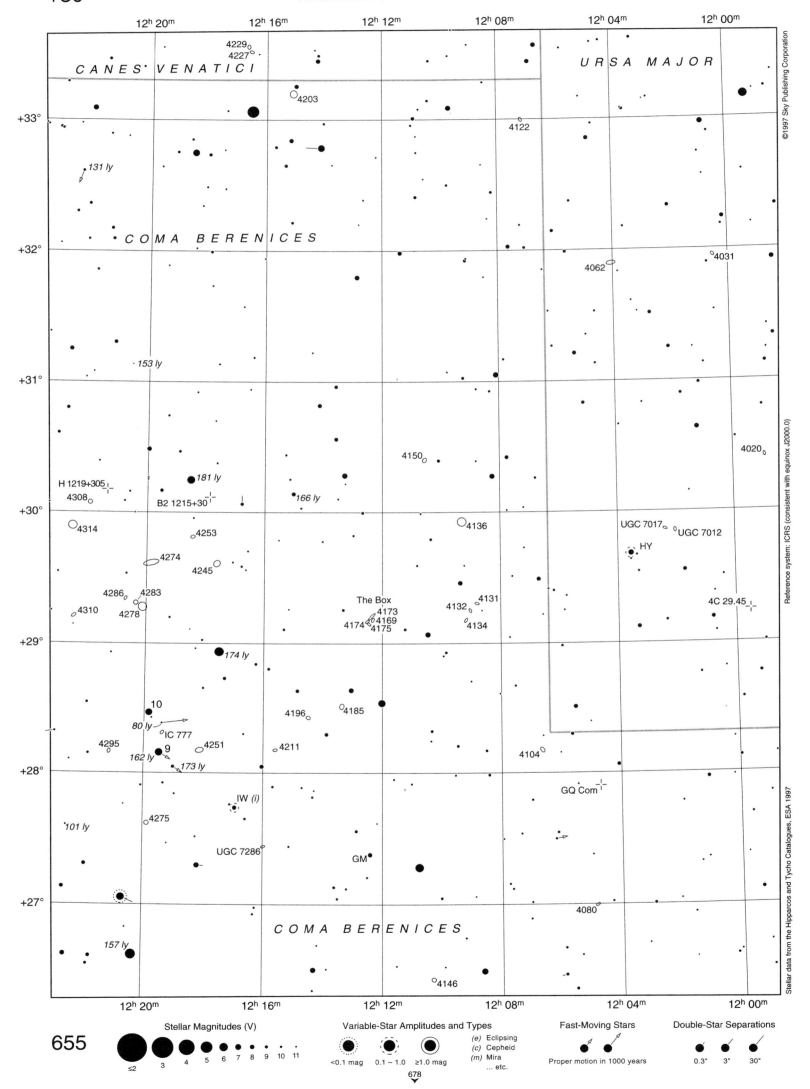

MILLENNIUM STAR ATLAS

633

CANES VENATICI

URSA MAJOR

COMA BERENICES

4229
4227

4203

4122

131 ly

153 ly

4062

4031

4150

4020

H 1219+305
4308

181 ly

B2 1215+30

166 ly

4136

UGC 7017   UGC 7012

4314

4253

HY

4274

4245

4C 29.45

4286   4283

The Box

4132   4131

4310   4278

4173
4169
4174   4175

4134

174 ly

10

4196   4185

80 ly

IC 777

4295   9

4251   4211

4104

162 ly

173 ly

GQ Com

IW (i)

4275

101 ly

UGC 7286

GM

157 ly

4080

COMA BERENICES

4146

Reference system: ICRS (consistent with equinox J2000.0)

Stellar data from the Hipparcos and Tycho Catalogues, ESA 1997

655

Stellar Magnitudes (V)

≤2   3   4   5   6   7   8   9   10   11

Variable-Star Amplitudes and Types

<0.1 mag   0.1 – 1.0   ≥1.0 mag

(e) Eclipsing
(c) Cepheid
(m) Mira
... etc.

Fast-Moving Stars

Proper motion in 1000 years

Double-Star Separations

0.3"   3"   30"

678

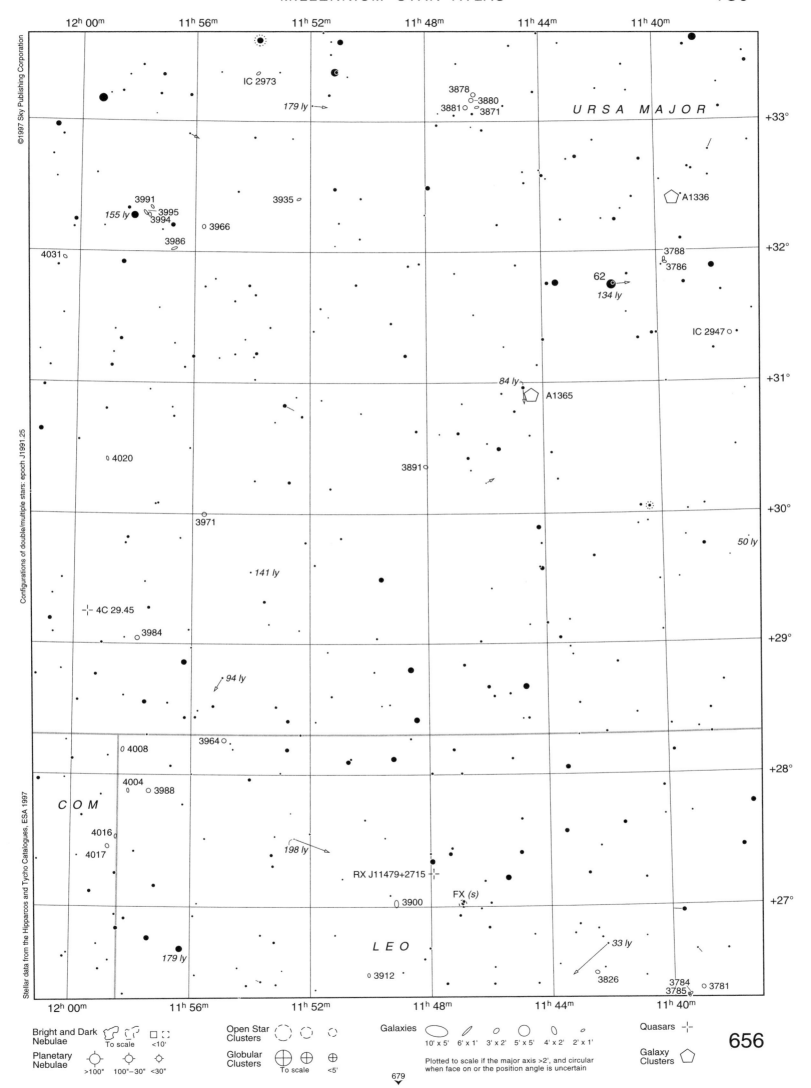

IC 2973

179 ly →

3878
3880
3881   3871

U R S A   M A J O R

3991
155 ly   3995
3994
3986

3935

○ 3966

A1336

4031 ○

3788
3786

62
134 ly →

IC 2947 ○

84 ly
A1365

○ 4020

3891 ○

+33°
+32°
+31°
+30°

3971

50 ly

141 ly

⊣⊢ 4C 29.45

○ 3984

94 ly

+29°

3964 ○

0 4008

4004
0   ○ 3988

4016 ○
• 4017

198 ly

RX J11479+2715 ⊣⊢

FX *(s)*

○ 3900

+28°

+27°

C O M

L E O

179 ly

○ 3912

33 ly

3826 ○

3784
3785   ○ 3781

12ʰ 00ᵐ   11ʰ 56ᵐ   11ʰ 52ᵐ   11ʰ 48ᵐ   11ʰ 44ᵐ   11ʰ 40ᵐ

Bright and Dark Nebulae   To scale   <10'

Planetary Nebulae   >100"   100"–30"   <30"

Open Star Clusters

Globular Clusters   To scale   <5'

Galaxies   10' x 5'   6' x 1'   3' x 2'   5' x 5'   4' x 2'   2' x 1'

Plotted to scale if the major axis >2', and circular when face on or the position angle is uncertain

Quasars   ⊣⊢

Galaxy Clusters

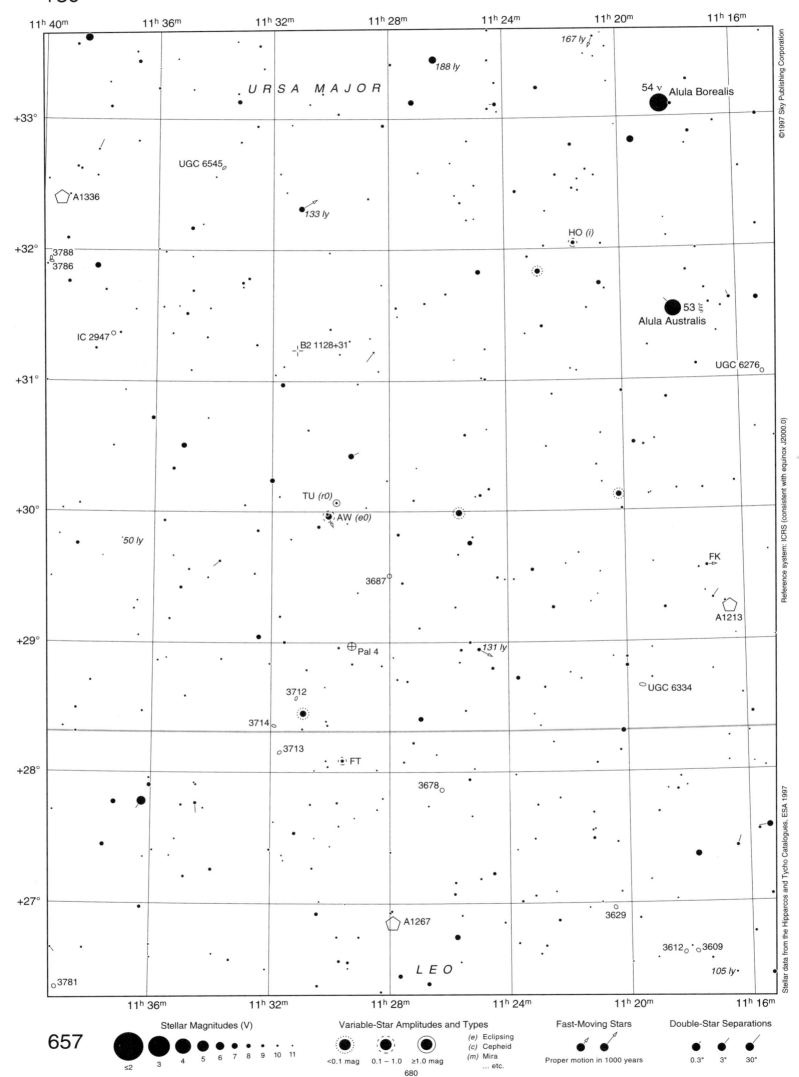

U R S A   M A J O R

167 ly

188 ly

54 ν Alula Borealis

UGC 6545

A1336

133 ly

HO (i)

3788
3786

53 ξ
Alula Australis

IC 2947

UGC 6276

B2 1128+31

TU (r0)

AW (e0)

FK

50 ly

3687

A1213

Pal 4

131 ly

UGC 6334

3712

3714

3678

3713

FT

A1267

3629

3612 3609

L E O

105 ly

3781

©1997 Sky Publishing Corporation

Reference system: ICRS (consistent with equinox J2000.0)

Stellar data from the Hipparcos and Tycho Catalogues, ESA 1997

657

Stellar Magnitudes (V)

≤2   3   4   5   6   7   8   9   10   11

Variable-Star Amplitudes and Types

<0.1 mag   0.1 – 1.0   ≥1.0 mag

(e) Eclipsing
(c) Cepheid
(m) Mira
... etc.

Fast-Moving Stars

Proper motion in 1000 years

Double-Star Separations

0.3"   3"   30"

680

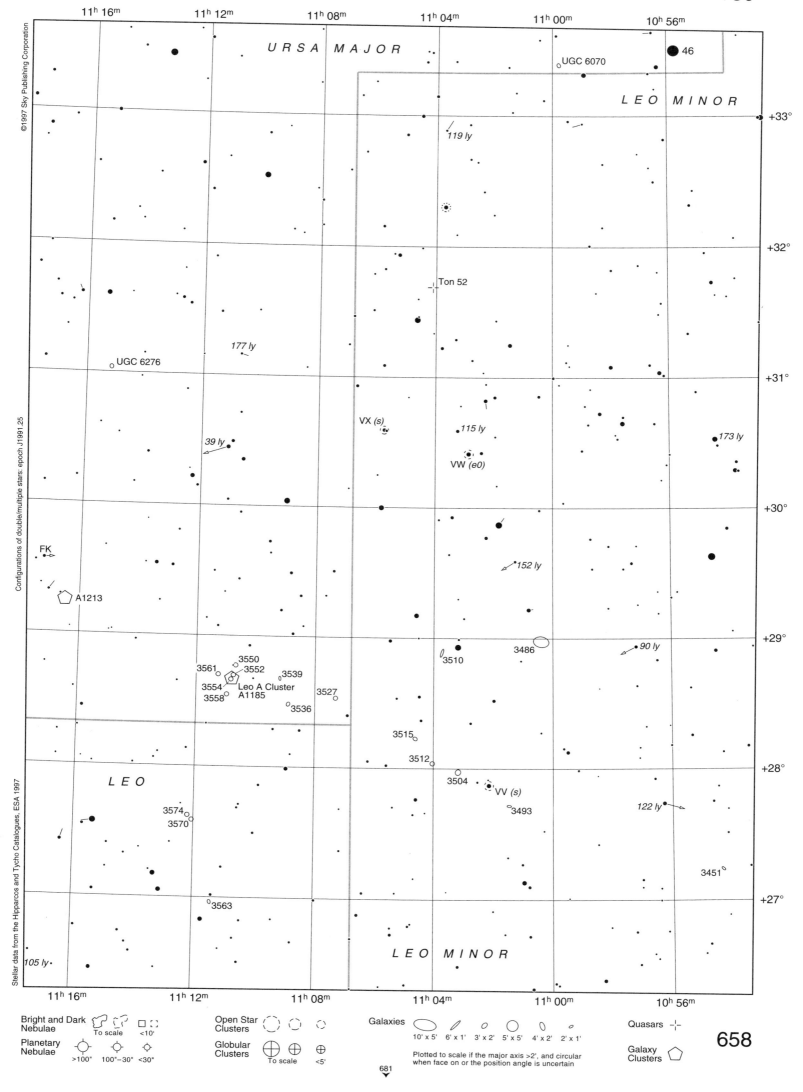

URSA MAJOR

UGC 6070

46

LEO MINOR

+33°

119 ly

+32°

Ton 52

177 ly

UGC 6276

+31°

VX (s)

115 ly

173 ly

39 ly

VW (e0)

+30°

FK

152 ly

A1213

+29°

3486

90 ly

3550
3561   3552
3554   Leo A Cluster   3539
3558   A1185
3527
3536

3510

3515

3512

LEO

3504
VV (s)

3574
3570

3493

122 ly

3451

3563

LEO MINOR

105 ly

©1997 Sky Publishing Corporation

Configurations of double/multiple stars: epoch J1991.25

Stellar data from the Hipparcos and Tycho Catalogues, ESA 1997

Bright and Dark Nebulae   To scale   <10'

Planetary Nebulae   >100"   100"–30"   <30'

Open Star Clusters

Globular Clusters   To scale   <5'

Galaxies   10' x 5'   6' x 1'   3' x 2'   5' x 5'   4' x 2'   2' x 1'

Quasars

Galaxy Clusters

Plotted to scale if the major axis >2', and circular when face on or the position angle is uncertain

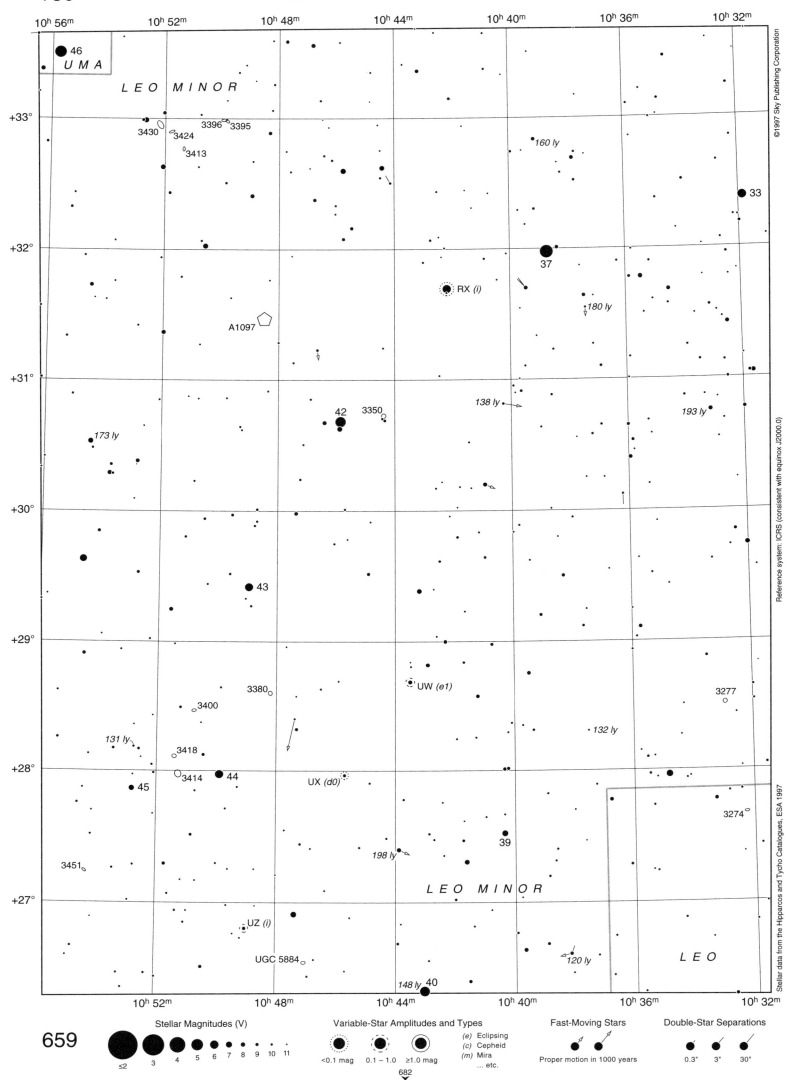

659

Stellar Magnitudes (V)

≤2 3 4 5 6 7 8 9 10 11

Variable-Star Amplitudes and Types

<0.1 mag   0.1 – 1.0   ≥1.0 mag

(e) Eclipsing
(c) Cepheid
(m) Mira
... etc.

Fast-Moving Stars

Proper motion in 1000 years

Double-Star Separations

0.3"   3"   30"

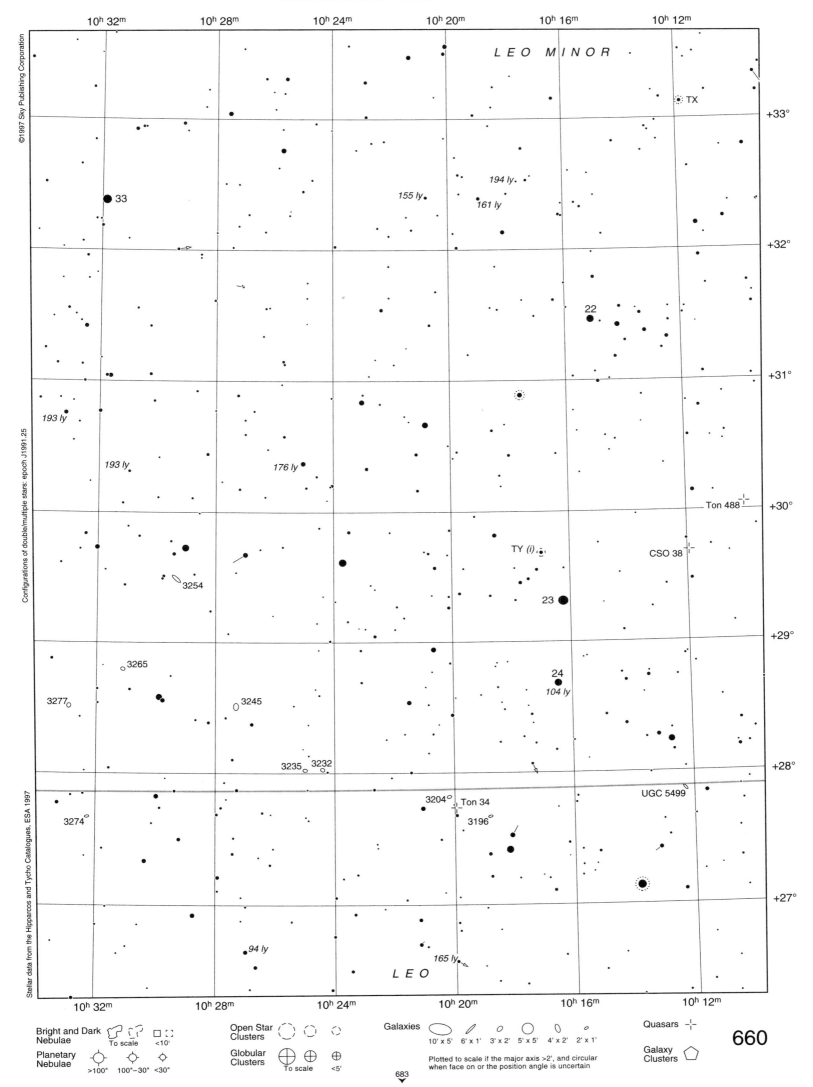

©1997 Sky Publishing Corporation

Configurations of double/multiple stars: epoch J1991.25

Stellar data from the Hipparcos and Tycho Catalogues, ESA 1997

LEO MINOR

10h 32m   10h 28m   10h 24m   10h 20m   10h 16m   10h 12m

TX

+33°

194 ly
155 ly   161 ly

33

+32°

22

+31°

193 ly

193 ly   176 ly

Ton 488   +30°

TY (i)

CSO 38

3254

23

+29°

3265

24
104 ly

3277

3245

3235   3232

+28°

3274

3204   Ton 34

UGC 5499

3196

+27°

94 ly

165 ly

LEO

10h 32m   10h 28m   10h 24m   10h 20m   10h 16m   10h 12m

Bright and Dark
Nebulae
To scale   <10'

Planetary
Nebulae
>100"   100"–30"   <30"

Open Star
Clusters

Globular
Clusters
To scale   <5'

Galaxies

10' x 5'   6' x 1'   3' x 2'   5' x 5'   4' x 2'   2' x 1'

Plotted to scale if the major axis >2', and circular
when face on or the position angle is uncertain

Quasars

Galaxy
Clusters

660

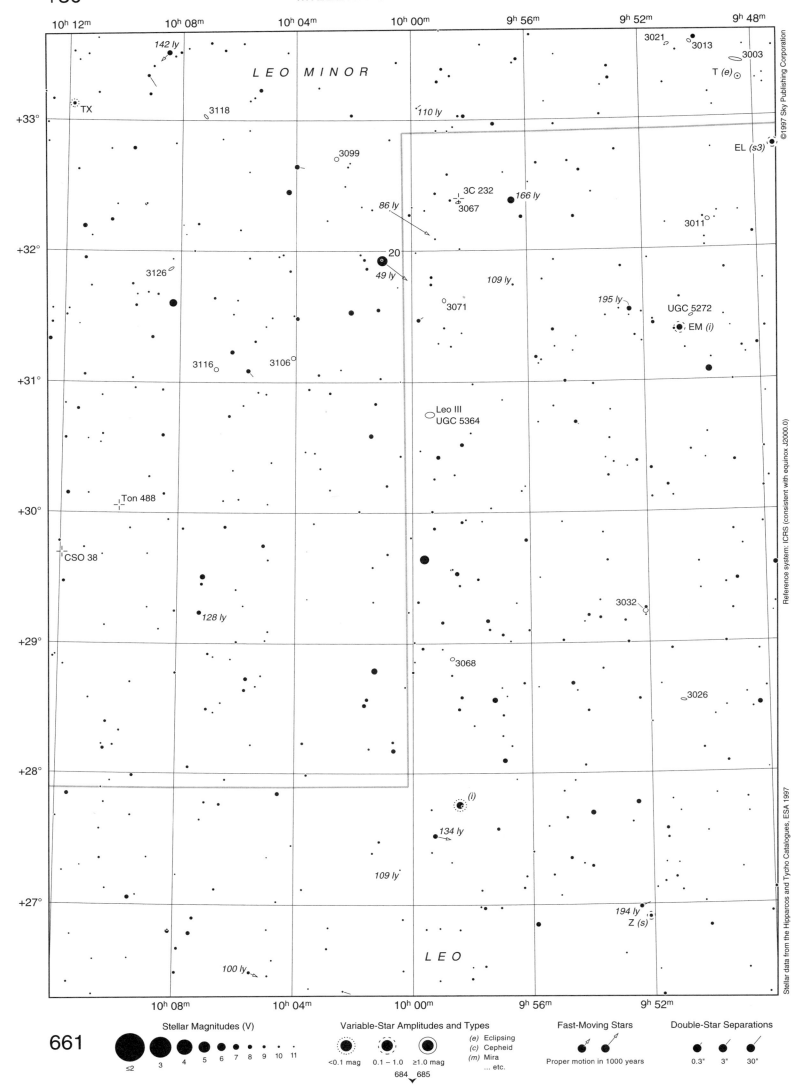

661

Stellar Magnitudes (V)

≤2 3 4 5 6 7 8 9 10 11

Variable-Star Amplitudes and Types

<0.1 mag   0.1 – 1.0   ≥1.0 mag

(e) Eclipsing
(c) Cepheid
(m) Mira
... etc.

684 685

Fast-Moving Stars

Proper motion in 1000 years

Double-Star Separations

0.3"   3"   30"

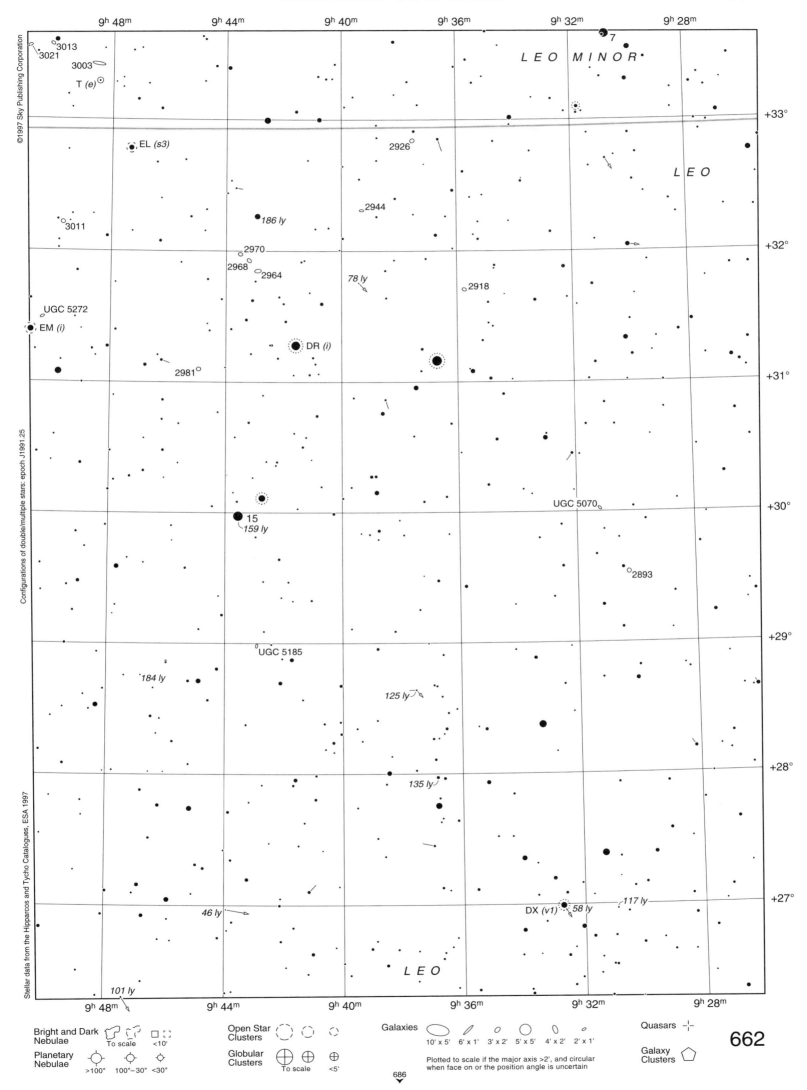

LEO MINOR

7

LEO

2926

2944

186 ly

2970

2968

2964

78 ly

2918

UGC 5272

EM (i)

DR (i)

2981

15

159 ly

UGC 5070

2893

UGC 5185

184 ly

125 ly

135 ly

DX (v1)   58 ly   117 ly

46 ly

LEO

101 ly

3013

3021

3003

T (e)

EL (s3)

3011

©1997 Sky Publishing Corporation

Configurations of double/multiple stars: epoch J1991.25

Stellar data from the Hipparcos and Tycho Catalogues, ESA 1997

Bright and Dark Nebulae
To scale   <10'

Planetary Nebulae
>100"   100"–30"   <30"

Open Star Clusters

Globular Clusters
To scale   <5'

Galaxies
10' x 5'   6' x 1'   3' x 2'   5' x 5'   4' x 2'   2' x 1'

Plotted to scale if the major axis >2', and circular when face on or the position angle is uncertain

Quasars

Galaxy Clusters

686

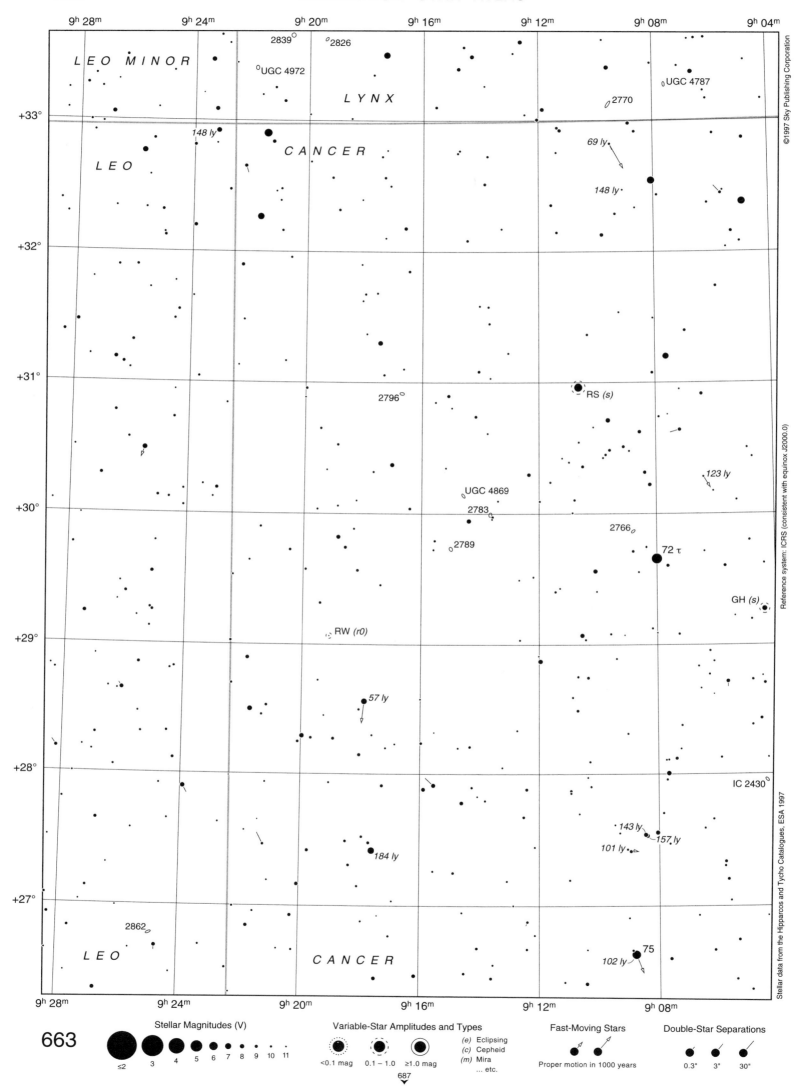

©1997 Sky Publishing Corporation

Reference system: ICRS (consistent with equinox J2000.0)

Stellar data from the Hipparcos and Tycho Catalogues, ESA 1997

LEO MINOR

2839 ○   ○ 2826
○ UGC 4972

L Y N X   ○ UGC 4787
○ 2770

+33°
148 ly

LEO   C A N C E R   69 ly

148 ly

+32°

+31°
2796 ○   RS (s)

123 ly

UGC 4869 ○
2783 ○
2766 ○
○ 2789   72 τ

GH (s)

+29°   ○ RW (r0)

57 ly

+28°   IC 2430 ○

143 ly
157 ly
101 ly

+27°
2862 ○

L E O   C A N C E R   75
102 ly

9ʰ 28ᵐ   9ʰ 24ᵐ   9ʰ 20ᵐ   9ʰ 16ᵐ   9ʰ 12ᵐ   9ʰ 08ᵐ   9ʰ 04ᵐ

663

Stellar Magnitudes (V)
≤2   3   4   5   6   7   8   9   10   11

Variable-Star Amplitudes and Types
<0.1 mag   0.1 – 1.0   ≥1.0 mag

(e) Eclipsing
(c) Cepheid
(m) Mira
... etc.

Fast-Moving Stars
Proper motion in 1000 years

Double-Star Separations
0.3"   3"   30"

687

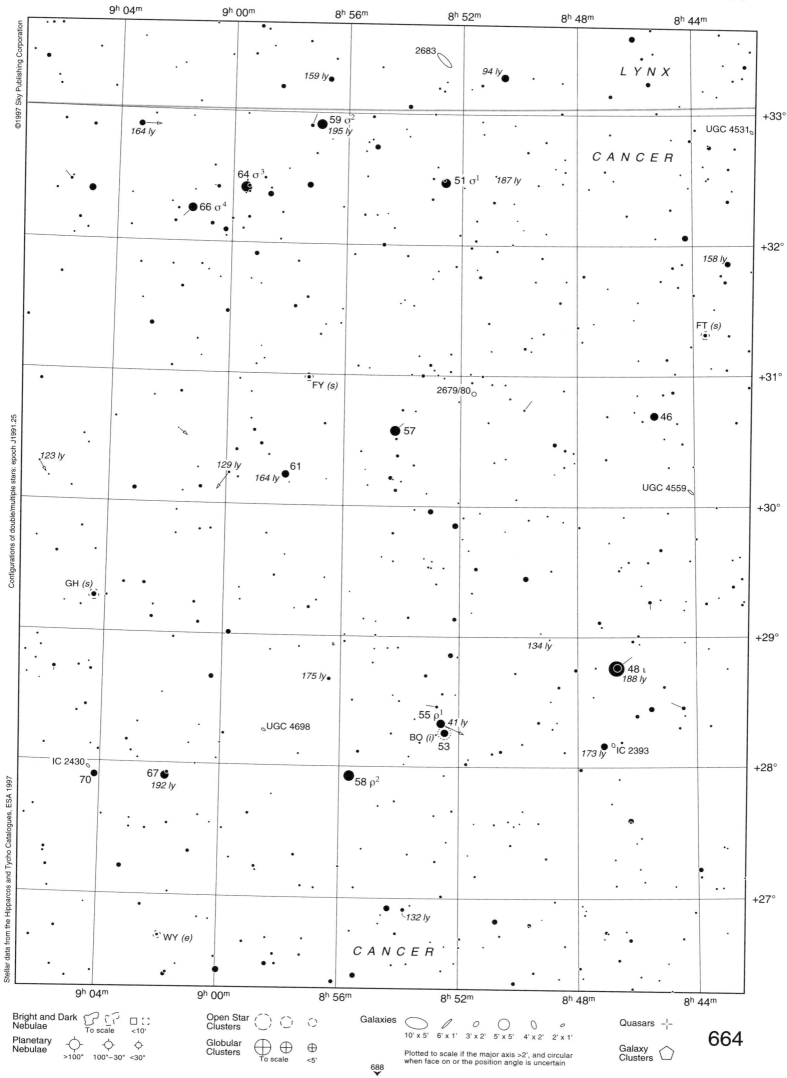

9h 04m   9h 00m   8h 56m   8h 52m   8h 48m   8h 44m

L Y N X

2683

94 ly

159 ly

164 ly

59 σ²
195 ly

CANCER

UGC 4531

+33°

64 σ³

51 σ¹   187 ly

66 σ⁴

158 ly   +32°

FT (s)

FY (s)   +31°

2679/80

123 ly

57

129 ly

61
164 ly

46

UGC 4559   +30°

GH (s)

134 ly   +29°

175 ly

48 ι
188 ly

55 ρ¹
41 ly

UGC 4698

BQ (i)
53

173 ly   ° IC 2393

IC 2430
70

67

+28°

58 ρ²

192 ly

+27°

132 ly

WY (e)

C A N C E R

9h 04m   9h 00m   8h 56m   8h 52m   8h 48m   8h 44m

Bright and Dark
Nebulae   To scale   <10'

Open Star
Clusters

Galaxies

10' x 5'   6' x 1'   3' x 2'   5' x 5'   4' x 2'   2' x 1'

Quasars

Planetary
Nebulae
>100"   100"–30"   <30'

Globular
Clusters
To scale   <5'

Plotted to scale if the major axis >2', and circular
when face on or the position angle is uncertain

Galaxy
Clusters

664

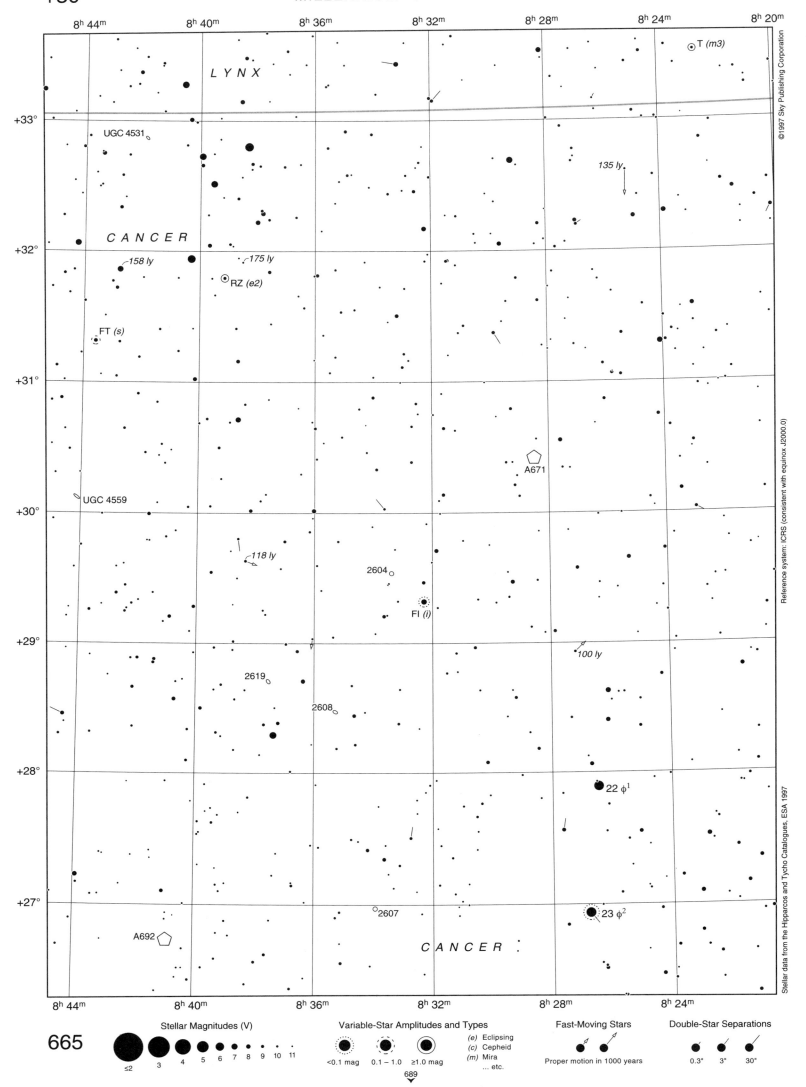

LYNX

CANCER

UGC 4531

158 ly

175 ly

RZ (e2)

FT (s)

UGC 4559

A671

118 ly

2604

FI (i)

100 ly

2619

2608

22 φ¹

T (m3)

135 ly

2607

A692

23 φ²

CANCER

Stellar Magnitudes (V)

≤2   3   4   5   6   7   8   9   10   11

Variable-Star Amplitudes and Types

<0.1 mag   0.1 – 1.0   ≥1.0 mag

(e) Eclipsing
(c) Cepheid
(m) Mira
... etc.

Fast-Moving Stars

Proper motion in 1000 years

Double-Star Separations

0.3"   3"   30"

689

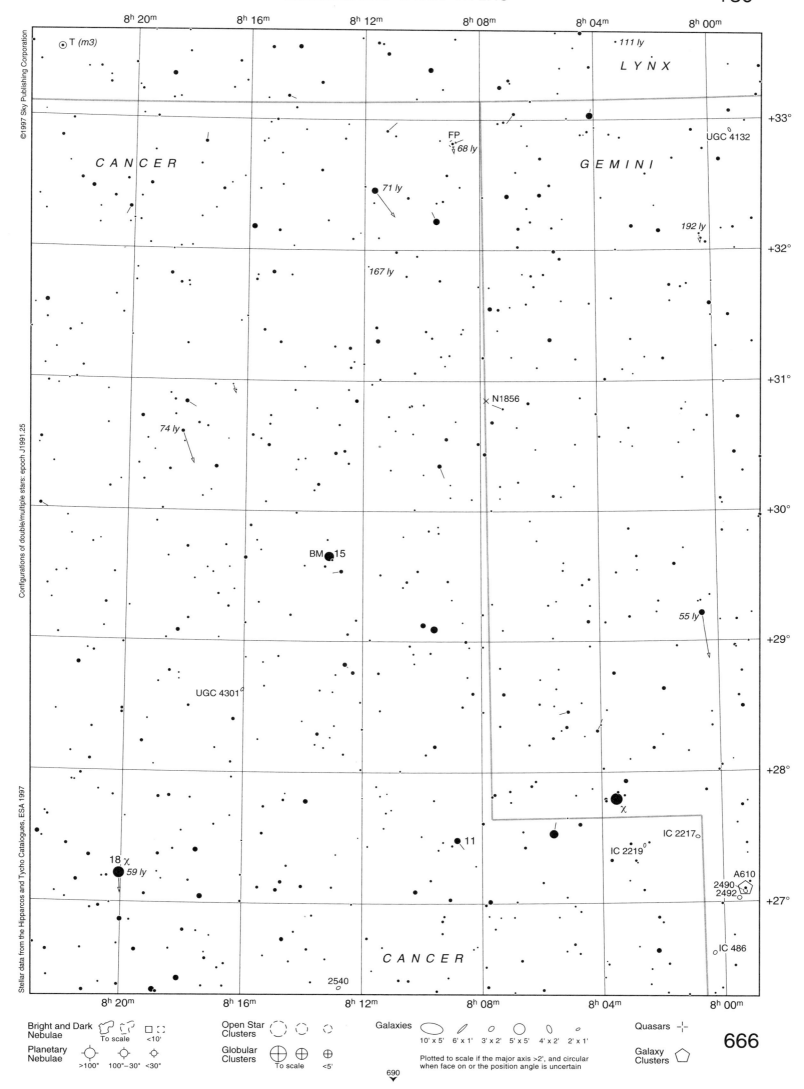

©1997 Sky Publishing Corporation

Configurations of double/multiple stars: epoch J1991.25

Stellar data from the Hipparcos and Tycho Catalogues, ESA 1997

T (m3)

8ʰ 20ᵐ   8ʰ 16ᵐ   8ʰ 12ᵐ   8ʰ 08ᵐ   8ʰ 04ᵐ   8ʰ 00ᵐ

111 ly

L Y N X

+33°

FP
68 ly

UGC 4132

C A N C E R

71 ly

G E M I N I

192 ly

+32°

167 ly

74 ly

N1856

+31°

55 ly

+30°

BM 15

UGC 4301

+29°

18 χ
59 ly

11

χ

IC 2217
IC 2219

A610
2490
2492

+28°

+27°

C A N C E R

2540

IC 486

8ʰ 20ᵐ   8ʰ 16ᵐ   8ʰ 12ᵐ   8ʰ 08ᵐ   8ʰ 04ᵐ   8ʰ 00ᵐ

Bright and Dark Nebulae
To scale   <10'

Open Star Clusters

Galaxies
10' x 5'   6' x 1'   3' x 2'   5' x 5'   4' x 2'   2' x 1'

Quasars

Planetary Nebulae
>100"   100"–30"   <30"

Globular Clusters
To scale   <5'

Plotted to scale if the major axis >2', and circular when face on or the position angle is uncertain

Galaxy Clusters

MILLENNIUM STAR ATLAS

+24°

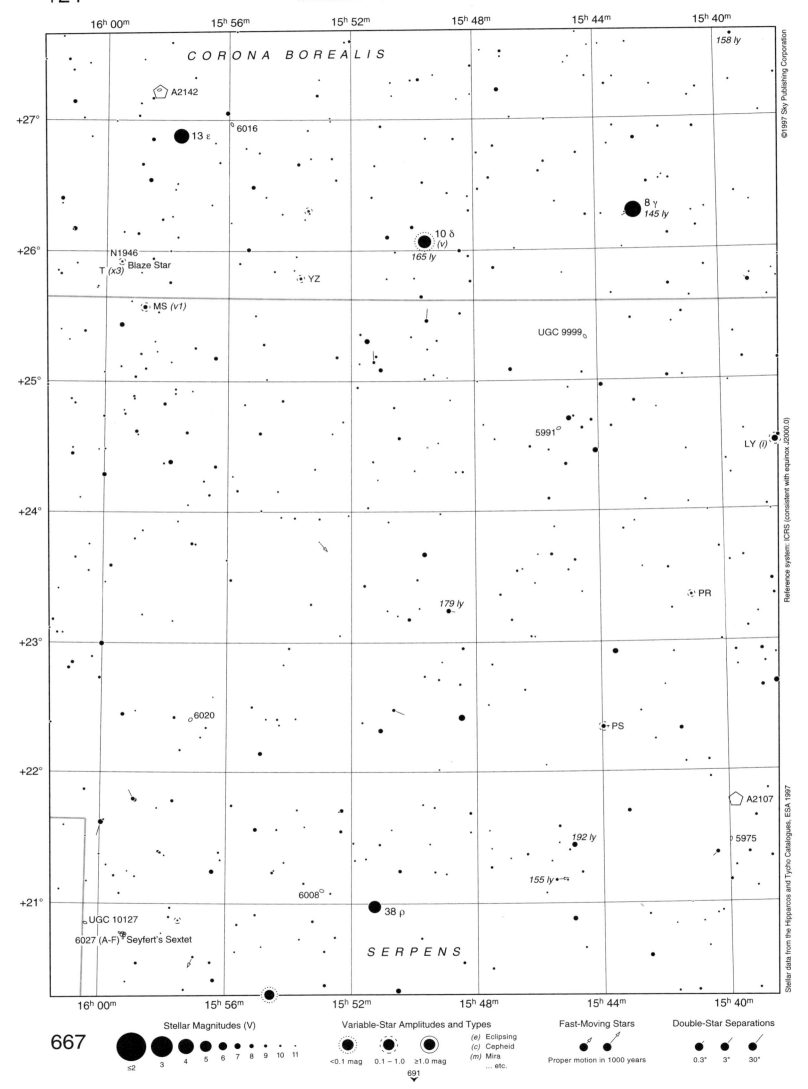

CORONA BOREALIS

A2142

6016

13 ε

8 γ
145 ly

10 δ
(v)
165 ly

N1946
T (x3) Blaze Star

YZ

MS (v1)

UGC 9999

5991

LY (i)

179 ly

PR

6020

PS

A2107

192 ly

5975

155 ly

6008

38 ρ

SERPENS

UGC 10127

6027 (A-F) Seyfert's Sextet

©1997 Sky Publishing Corporation

Reference system: ICRS (consistent with equinox J2000.0)

Stellar data from the Hipparcos and Tycho Catalogues, ESA 1997

667

Stellar Magnitudes (V)

≤2   3   4   5   6   7   8   9   10   11

Variable-Star Amplitudes and Types

<0.1 mag   0.1 – 1.0   ≥1.0 mag

(e) Eclipsing
(c) Cepheid
(m) Mira
... etc.

Fast-Moving Stars

Proper motion in 1000 years

Double-Star Separations

0.3"   3"   30"

+24°

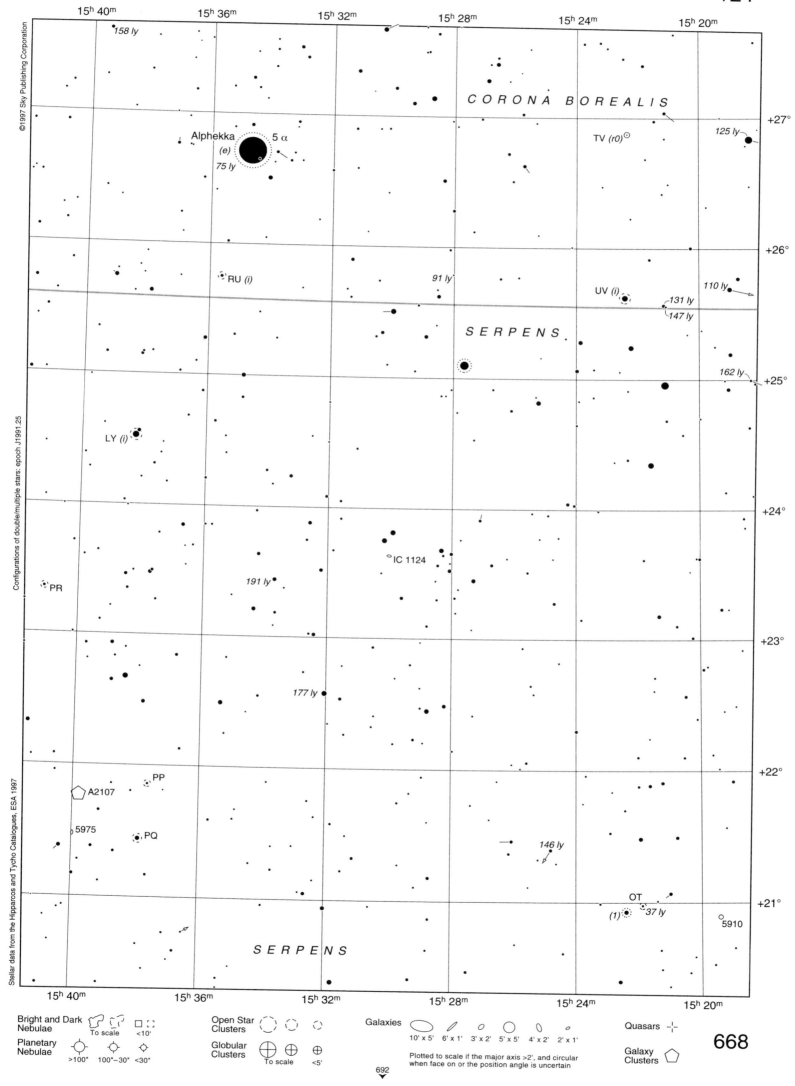

©1997 Sky Publishing Corporation

Configurations of double/multiple stars: epoch J1991.25

Stellar data from the Hipparcos and Tycho Catalogues, ESA 1997

15h 40m 15h 36m 15h 32m 15h 28m 15h 24m 15h 20m

158 ly

CORONA BOREALIS

+27°

Alphekka 5 α
(e)
75 ly

TV *(r0)*⊙

125 ly

+26°

RU *(i)*

91 ly

UV *(i)*

131 ly
147 ly

110 ly

SERPENS

162 ly +25°

LY *(i)*

PR

IC 1124

191 ly

+24°

+23°

177 ly

PP

A2107

146 ly

+22°

5975

PQ

OT

+21°

(1) *37 ly*

5910

SERPENS

15h 40m 15h 36m 15h 32m 15h 28m 15h 24m 15h 20m

Bright and Dark Nebulae   To scale   <10'
Planetary Nebulae   >100"   100"–30"   <30'

Open Star Clusters
Globular Clusters   To scale   <5'

Galaxies   10' x 5'   6' x 1'   3' x 2'   5' x 5'   4' x 2'   2' x 1'
Plotted to scale if the major axis >2', and circular when face on or the position angle is uncertain

Quasars

Galaxy Clusters

668

692

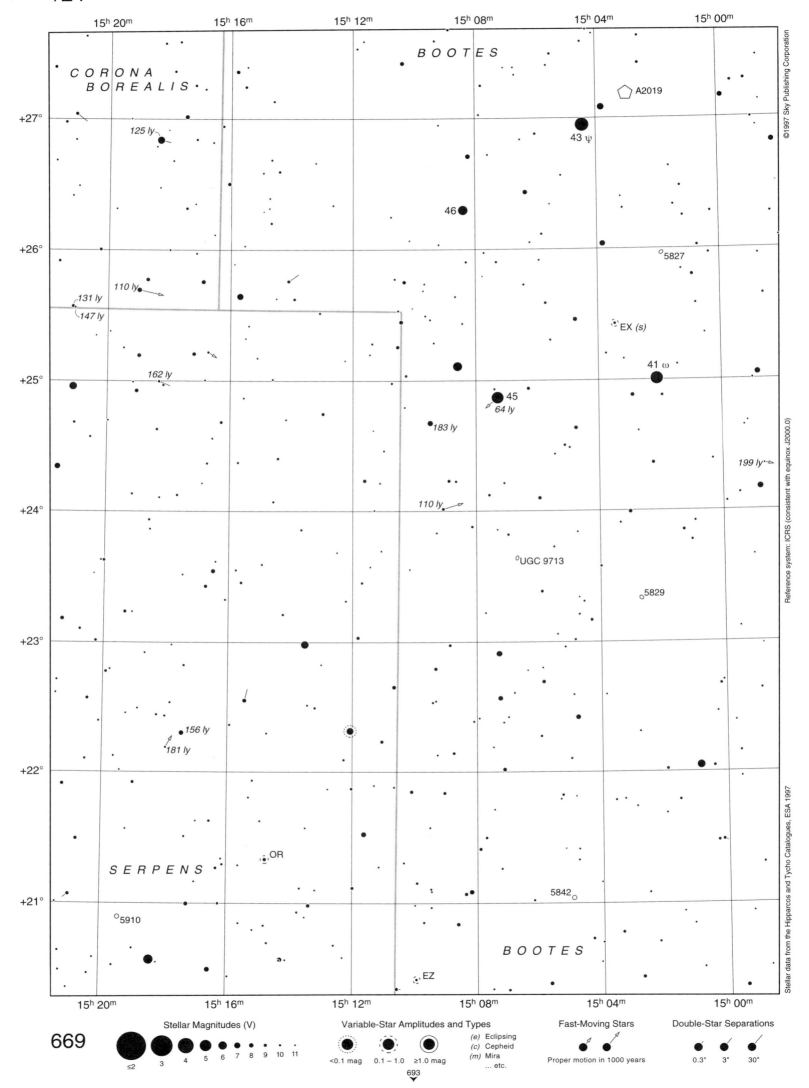

©1997 Sky Publishing Corporation

Reference system: ICRS (consistent with equinox J2000.0)

Stellar data from the Hipparcos and Tycho Catalogues, ESA 1997

CORONA BOREALIS

BOOTES

A2019

43 ψ

46

5827

EX (s)

125 ly

110 ly

131 ly

147 ly

162 ly

41 ω

45

64 ly

183 ly

199 ly

110 ly

UGC 9713

5829

156 ly

181 ly

OR

5842

SERPENS

5910

BOOTES

EZ

Stellar Magnitudes (V)

≤2   3   4   5   6   7   8   9   10   11

Variable-Star Amplitudes and Types

<0.1 mag   0.1 – 1.0   ≥1.0 mag

(e) Eclipsing
(c) Cepheid
(m) Mira
... etc.

Fast-Moving Stars

Proper motion in 1000 years

Double-Star Separations

0.3"   3"   30"

693

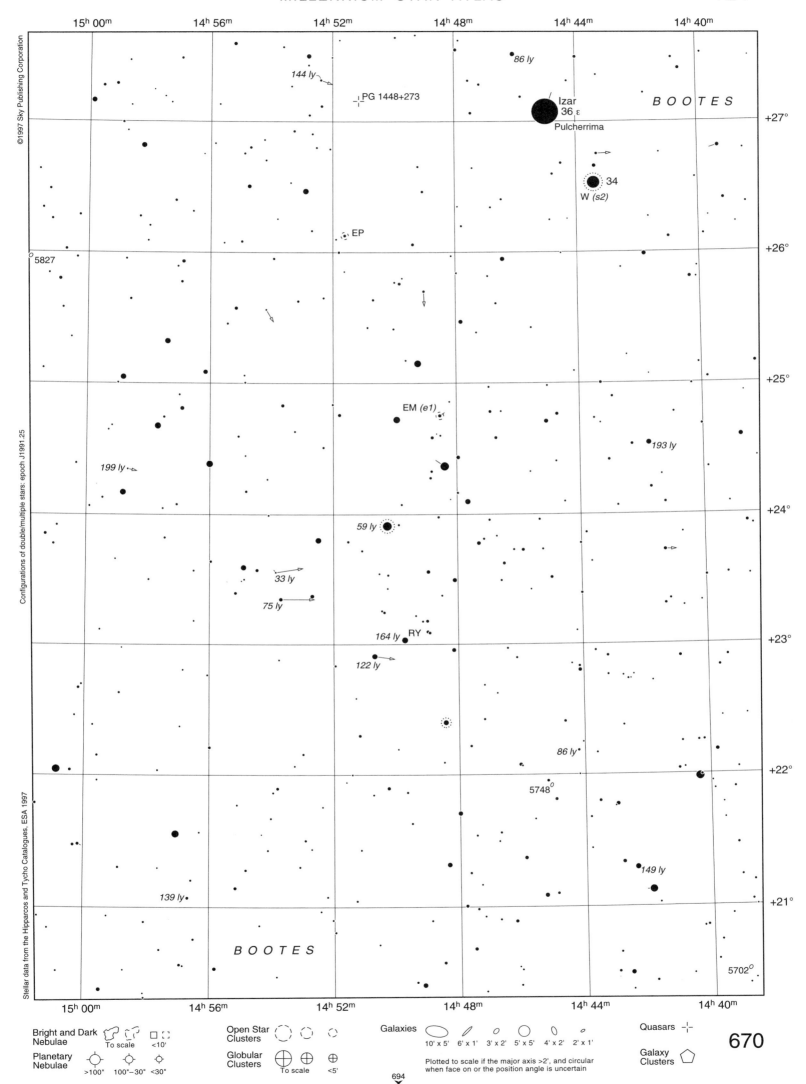

BOOTES

Izar
36 ε
Pulcherrima

86 ly

144 ly

PG 1448+273

34
W (s2)

EP

5827

EM (e1)

193 ly

199 ly

59 ly

33 ly

75 ly

164 ly RY

122 ly

86 ly

5748

149 ly

139 ly

BOOTES

5702

Bright and Dark Nebulae
To scale   <10'

Planetary Nebulae
>100" 100"–30" <30"

Open Star Clusters

Globular Clusters
To scale   <5'

Galaxies
10' x 5'   6' x 1'   3' x 2'   5' x 5'   4' x 2'   2' x 1'

Plotted to scale if the major axis >2', and circular when face on or the position angle is uncertain

Quasars

Galaxy Clusters

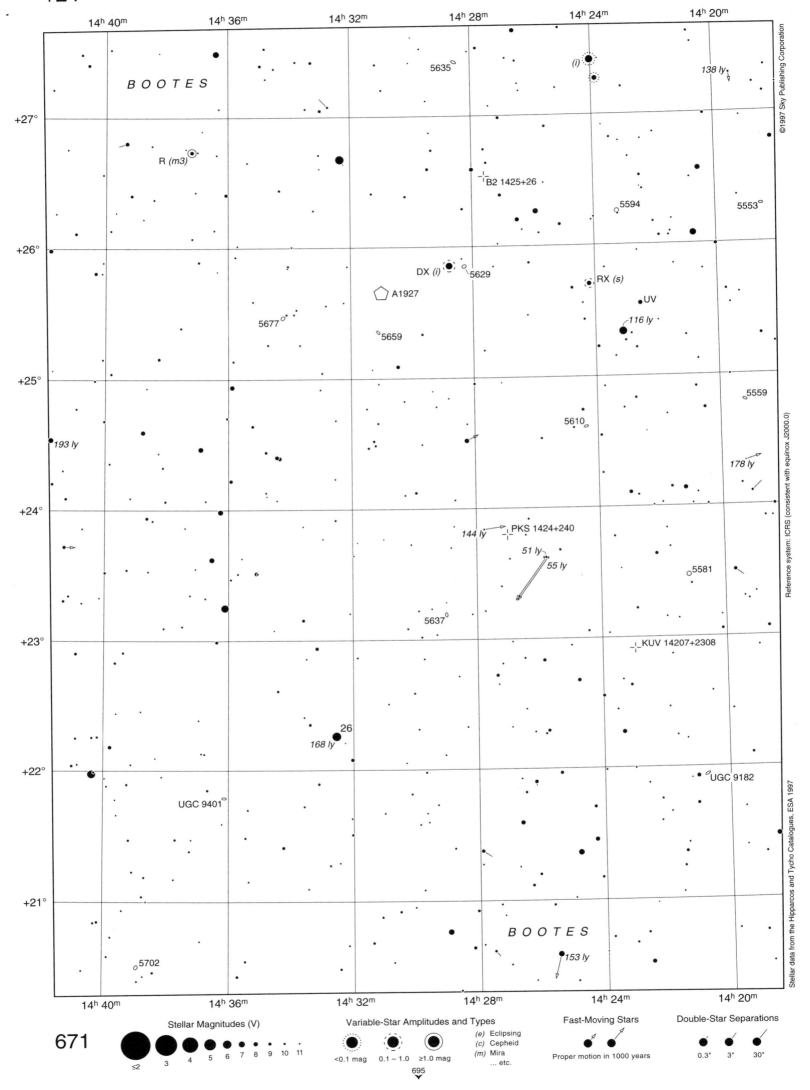

BOOTES

5635

(i)

138 ly

R *(m3)*

B2 1425+26

5594

5553

DX *(i)*   5629

RX *(s)*

A1927

UV

5677

116 ly

5659

5559

193 ly

5610

178 ly

144 ly   PKS 1424+240

51 ly

55 ly

5581

KUV 14207+2308

5637

26

168 ly

UGC 9182

UGC 9401

BOOTES

5702

153 ly

©1997 Sky Publishing Corporation

Reference system: ICRS (consistent with equinox J2000.0)

Stellar data from the Hipparcos and Tycho Catalogues, ESA 1997

671

Stellar Magnitudes (V)

≤2   3   4   5   6   7   8   9   10   11

Variable-Star Amplitudes and Types

<0.1 mag   0.1 – 1.0   ≥1.0 mag

(e) Eclipsing
(c) Cepheid
(m) Mira
... etc.

Fast-Moving Stars

Proper motion in 1000 years

Double-Star Separations

0.3"   3"   30"

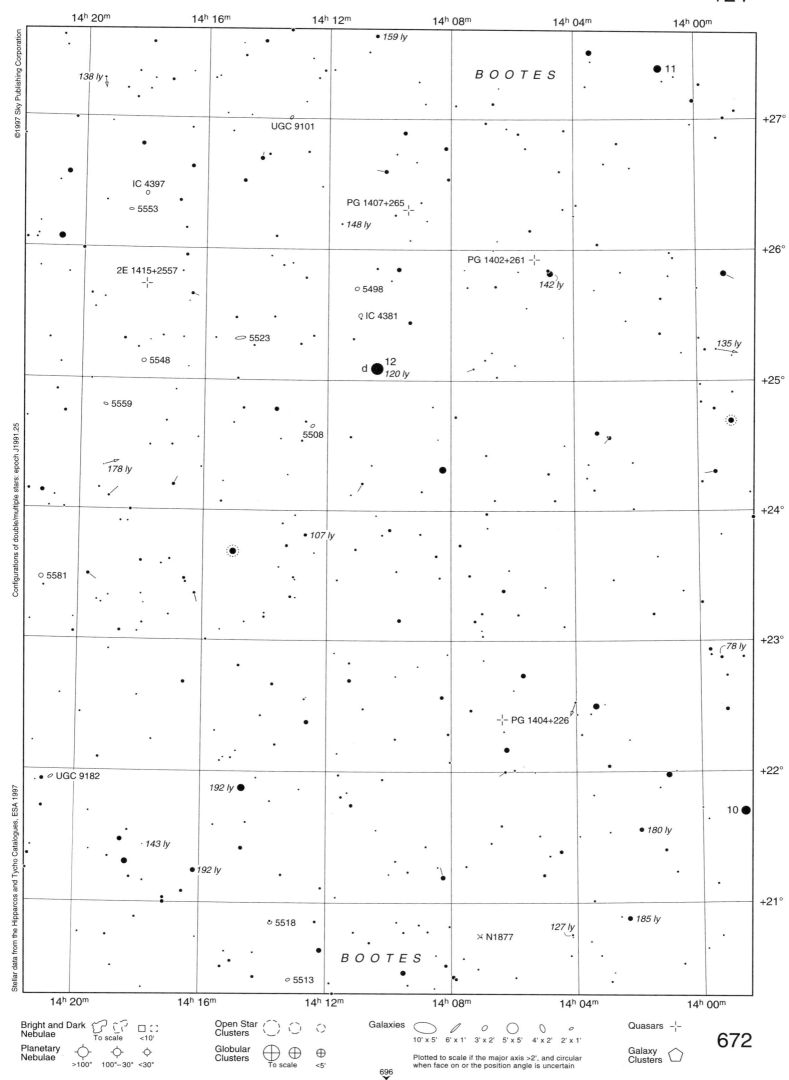

©1997 Sky Publishing Corporation

Configurations of double/multiple stars: epoch J1991.25

Stellar data from the Hipparcos and Tycho Catalogues, ESA 1997

14h 20m   14h 16m   14h 12m   14h 08m   14h 04m   14h 00m

159 ly

B O O T E S

● 11

138 ly

+27°

UGC 9101

IC 4397

○ 5553

PG 1407+265

148 ly

2E 1415+2557

+26°

PG 1402+261

○ 5498

142 ly

♀ IC 4381

○ 5523

135 ly

○ 5548

d ● 12

120 ly

+25°

○ 5559

○ 5508

178 ly

+24°

107 ly

○ 5581

+23°

78 ly

PG 1404+226

○ UGC 9182

+22°

192 ly ●

10 ●

143 ly

180 ly

● *192 ly*

+21°

♄ 5518

185 ly ●

⋇ N1877

127 ly

B O O T E S

○ 5513

14h 20m   14h 16m   14h 12m   14h 08m   14h 04m   14h 00m

Bright and Dark Nebulae	Open Star Clusters	Galaxies	Quasars

Bright and Dark Nebulae — To scale — <10'

Planetary Nebulae — >100" — 100"-30" — <30'

Open Star Clusters

Globular Clusters — To scale — <5'

Galaxies — 10' x 5' — 6' x 1' — 3' x 2' — 5' x 5' — 4' x 2' — 2' x 1'

Plotted to scale if the major axis >2', and circular when face on or the position angle is uncertain

Quasars

Galaxy Clusters

672

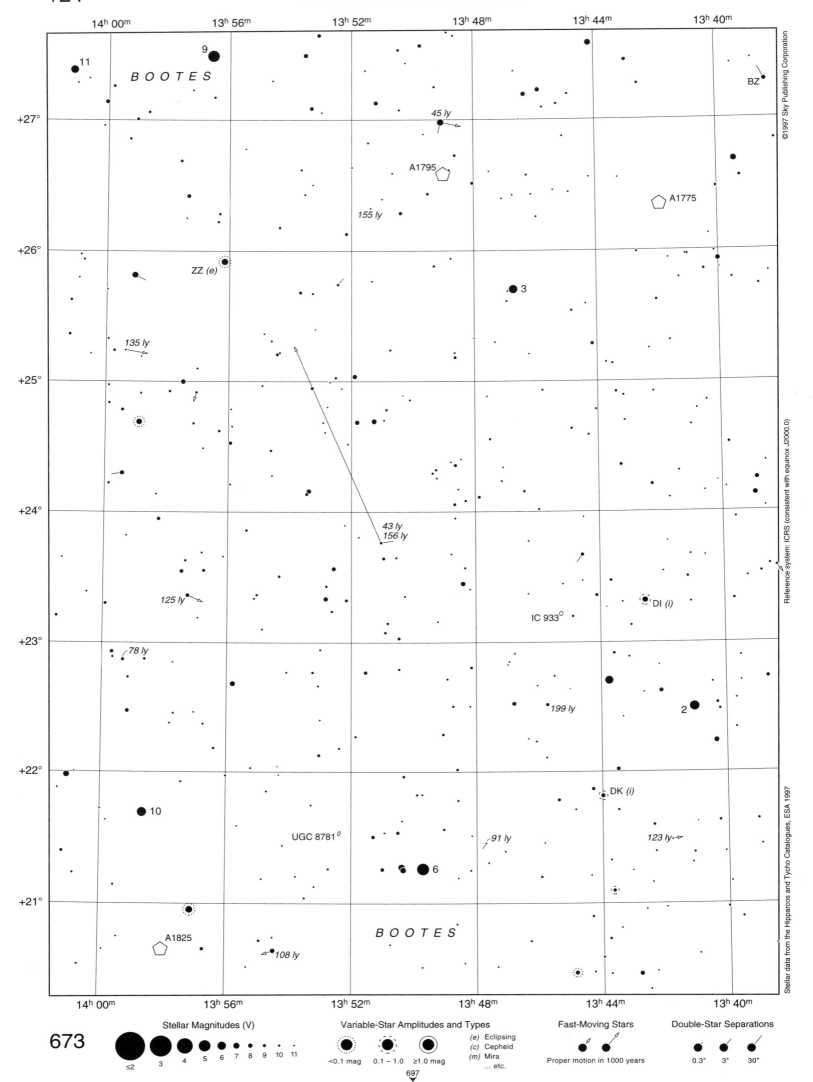

14h 00m   13h 56m   13h 52m   13h 48m   13h 44m   13h 40m

11

BOOTES

9

BZ

+27°

45 ly

A1795

A1775

155 ly

+26°

ZZ *(e)*

3

135 ly

+25°

125 ly

43 ly
156 ly

DI *(i)*

IC 933 °

+23°

78 ly

199 ly

2

+22°

DK *(i)*

10

123 ly

UGC 8781 °

91 ly

6

+21°

A1825

BOOTES

108 ly

14h 00m   13h 56m   13h 52m   13h 48m   13h 44m   13h 40m

©1997 Sky Publishing Corporation

Reference system: ICRS (consistent with equinox J2000.0)

Stellar data from the Hipparcos and Tycho Catalogues, ESA 1997

673

Stellar Magnitudes (V)

≤2   3   4   5   6   7   8   9   10   11

Variable-Star Amplitudes and Types

<0.1 mag   0.1 – 1.0   ≥1.0 mag

(e) Eclipsing
(c) Cepheid
(m) Mira
... etc.

Fast-Moving Stars

Proper motion in 1000 years

Double-Star Separations

0.3"   3"   30"

697

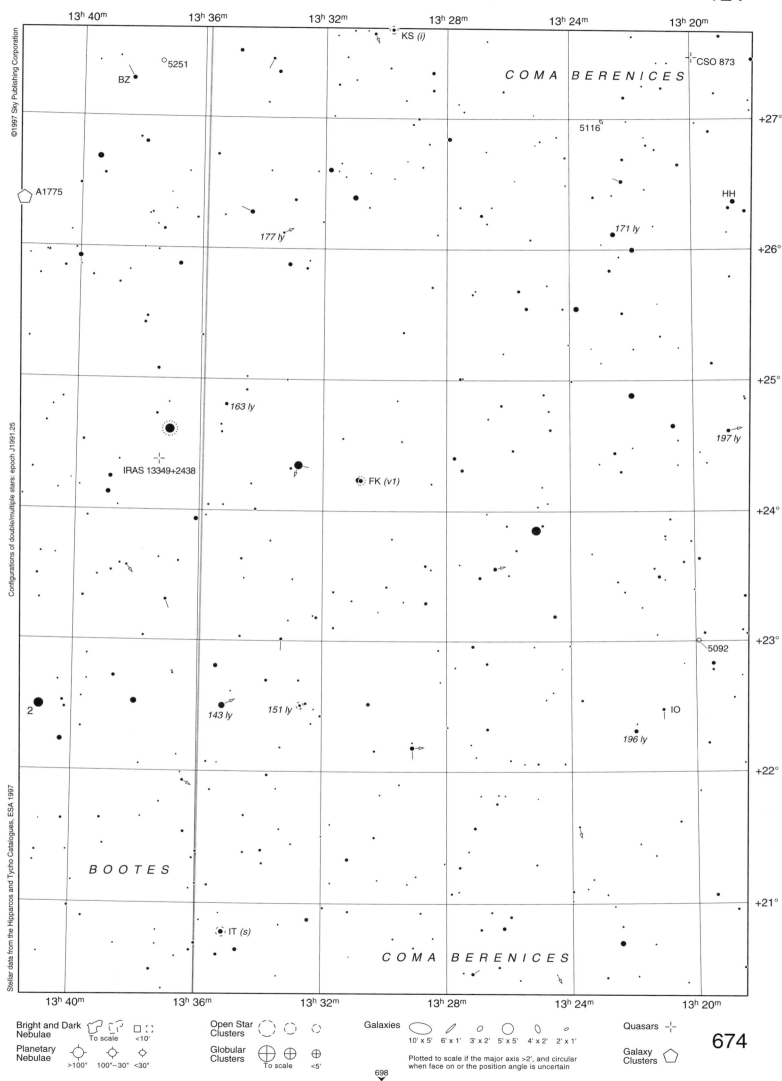

Configurations of double/multiple stars: epoch J1991.25

Stellar data from the Hipparcos and Tycho Catalogues, ESA 1997

COMA BERENICES

BOOTES

COMA BERENICES

KS (i)
CSO 873
5251
BZ
5116
A1775
HH
177 ly
171 ly
163 ly
197 ly
IRAS 13349+2438
FK (v1)
5092
2
IO
143 ly
151 ly
196 ly
IT (s)

Bright and Dark Nebulae	Open Star Clusters	Galaxies	Quasars
To scale <10'		10' x 5' 6' x 1' 3' x 2' 5' x 5' 4' x 2' 2' x 1'	
Planetary Nebulae	Globular Clusters		Galaxy Clusters
>100" 100"–30" <30"	To scale <5'	Plotted to scale if the major axis >2', and circular when face on or the position angle is uncertain	

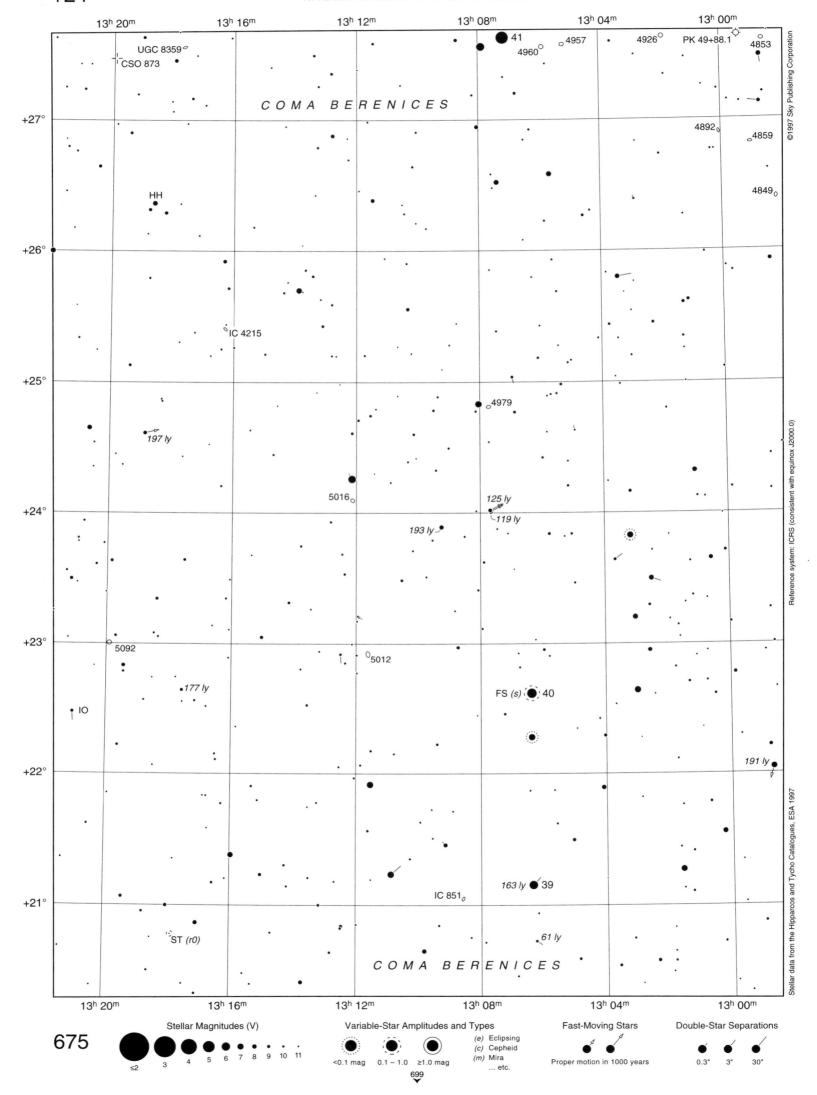

COMA BERENICES

COMA BERENICES

UGC 8359
CSO 873
HH
IC 4215
197 ly
5016
4979
125 ly
119 ly
193 ly
5092
5012
177 ly
IO
FS (s) 40
191 ly
39
163 ly
IC 851
ST (r0)
61 ly

41
4960
4957
4926
PK 49+88.1
4853
4892
4859
4849

675

Stellar Magnitudes (V)

≤2 3 4 5 6 7 8 9 10 11

Variable-Star Amplitudes and Types

<0.1 mag   0.1 – 1.0   ≥1.0 mag

(e) Eclipsing
(c) Cepheid
(m) Mira
... etc.

Fast-Moving Stars

Proper motion in 1000 years

Double-Star Separations

0.3"   3"   30"

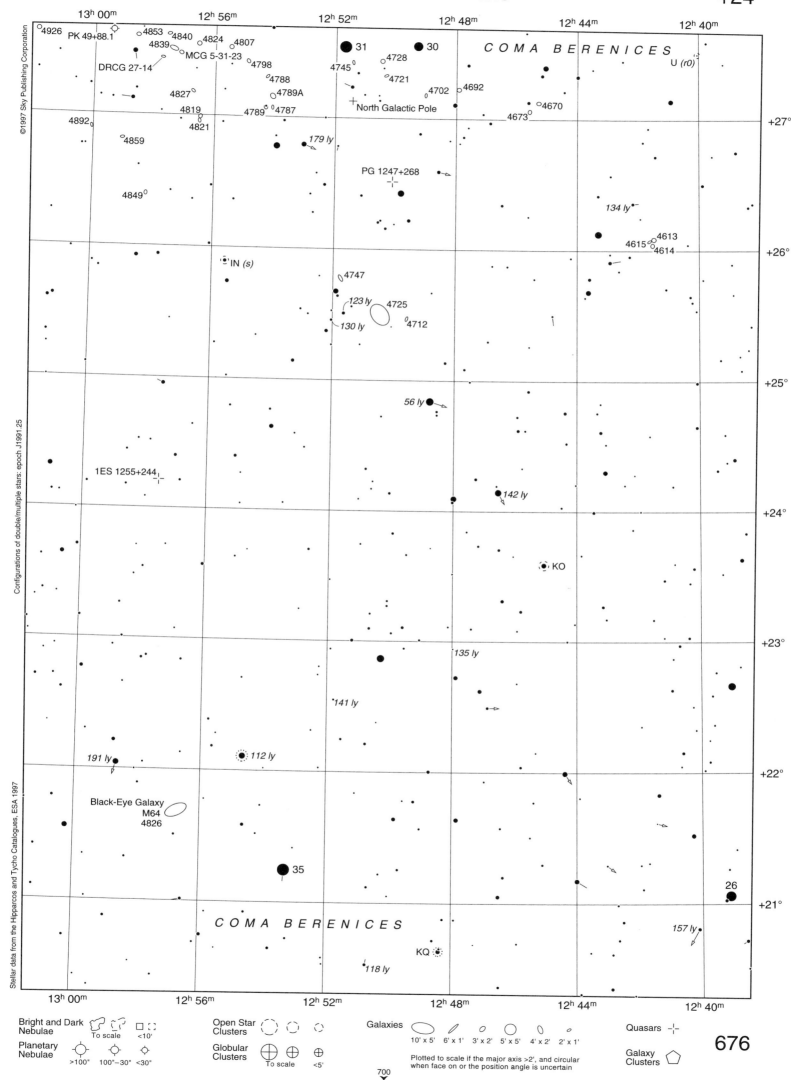

COMA BERENICES

North Galactic Pole

PK 49+88.1
DRCG 27-14
MCG 5-31-23

U (r0)

IN (s)

PG 1247+268

179 ly
134 ly

123 ly
130 ly

4747
4725
4712

56 ly

1ES 1255+244

142 ly

KO

135 ly

141 ly

191 ly
112 ly

Black-Eye Galaxy
M64
4826

35

26

157 ly

COMA BERENICES

KQ

118 ly

676

Bright and Dark Nebulae
To scale   <10'

Planetary Nebulae
>100"   100"-30"   <30"

Open Star Clusters

Globular Clusters
To scale   <5'

Galaxies
10' x 5'   6' x 1'   3' x 2'   5' x 5'   4' x 2'   2' x 1'

Plotted to scale if the major axis >2', and circular
when face on or the position angle is uncertain

Quasars

Galaxy Clusters

700

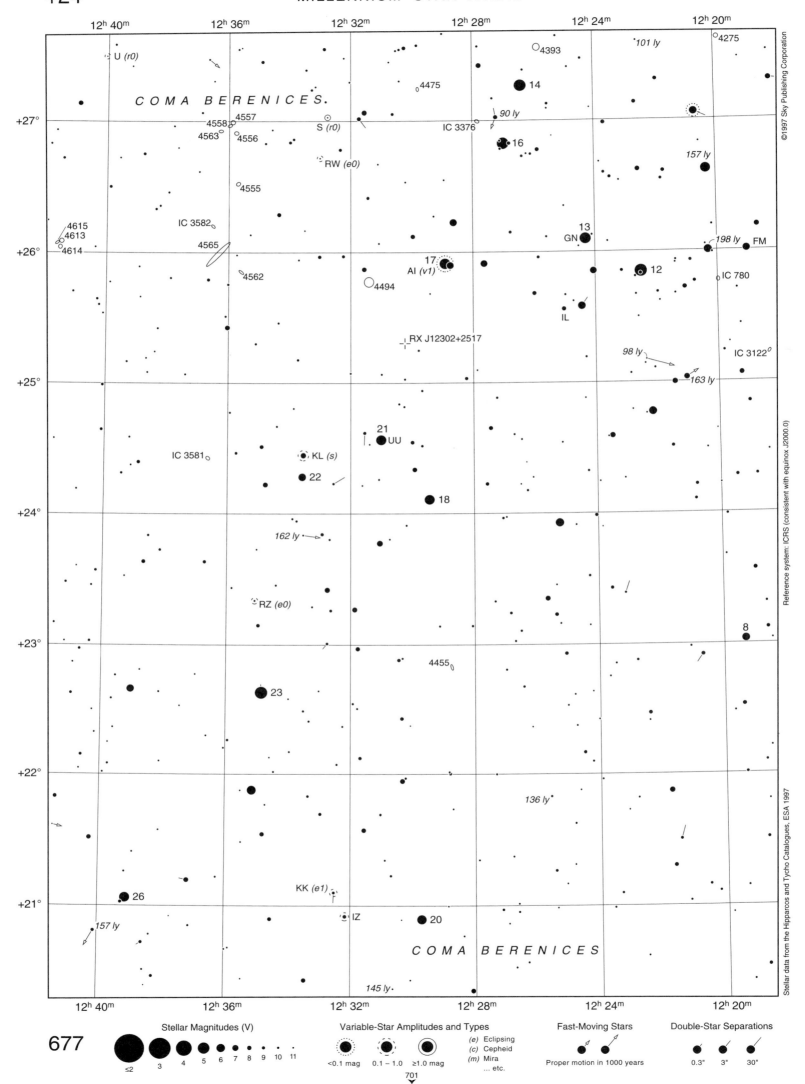

COMA BERENICES.

+27°

+26°

+25°

+24°

+23°

+22°

+21°

COMA BERENICES

12ʰ 40ᵐ   12ʰ 36ᵐ   12ʰ 32ᵐ   12ʰ 28ᵐ   12ʰ 24ᵐ   12ʰ 20ᵐ

U (r0)
4558 4557
4563 4556
4555
S (r0)
RW (e0)
IC 3582
4615
4613
4614
4565
4562
4494
AI (v1)
RX J12302+2517
IC 3581
21
UU
KL (s)
22
18
162 ly
RZ (e0)
4455
23
KK (e1)
IZ
20
26
157 ly
145 ly
4393
14
90 ly
IC 3376
16
GN
13
17
IL
12
IC 780
4475
101 ly
4275
157 ly
198 ly FM
IC 3122
98 ly
163 ly
8
136 ly

©1997 Sky Publishing Corporation

Reference system: ICRS (consistent with equinox J2000.0)

Stellar data from the Hipparcos and Tycho Catalogues, ESA 1997

677

Stellar Magnitudes (V)
≤2 3 4 5 6 7 8 9 10 11

Variable-Star Amplitudes and Types
<0.1 mag   0.1 – 1.0   ≥1.0 mag

(e) Eclipsing
(c) Cepheid
(m) Mira
... etc.

Fast-Moving Stars
Proper motion in 1000 years

Double-Star Separations
0.3"   3"   30"

MILLENNIUM STAR ATLAS

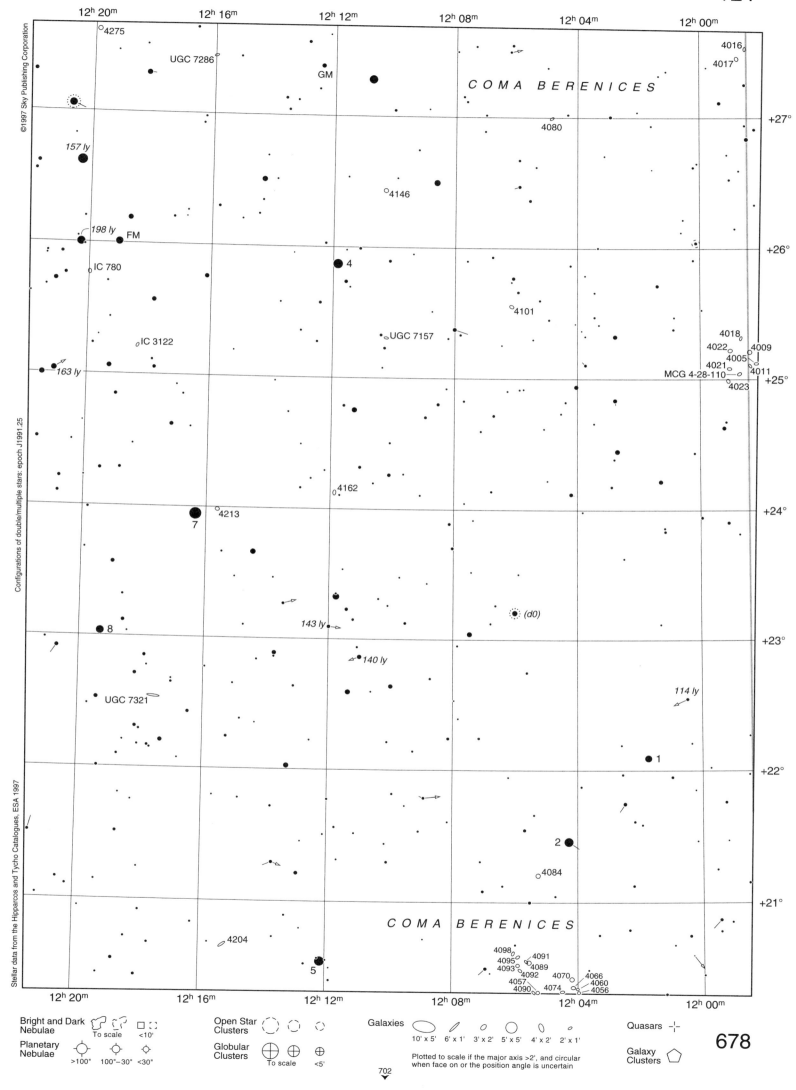

©1997 Sky Publishing Corporation

Configurations of double/multiple stars: epoch J1991.25

Stellar data from the Hipparcos and Tycho Catalogues, ESA 1997

12h 20m   12h 16m   12h 12m   12h 08m   12h 04m   12h 00m

4275

UGC 7286

GM

COMA BERENICES

4016
4017

+27°

157 ly

4080

4146

198 ly   FM

IC 780

4   4101

IC 3122

UGC 7157

4018
4022   4009
4005
4021   4011
MCG 4-28-110
4023

+26°

+25°

163 ly

4162

4213

7

+24°

143 ly

(d0)

140 ly

8

114 ly

UGC 7321

1

+23°

+22°

2

4084

COMA BERENICES

+21°

4204

5

4098
4095   4091
4093   4089
4092
4057   4090   4074   4070   4066
4060
4056

12h 20m   12h 16m   12h 12m   12h 08m   12h 04m   12h 00m

Bright and Dark Nebulae				Open Star Clusters			Galaxies							Quasars	
	To scale	<10'					10' x 5'	6' x 1'	3' x 2'	5' x 5'	4' x 2'	2' x 1'		

Planetary Nebulae >100" 100"-30" <30"

Globular Clusters To scale <5'

Galaxy Clusters

Plotted to scale if the major axis >2', and circular when face on or the position angle is uncertain

678

702

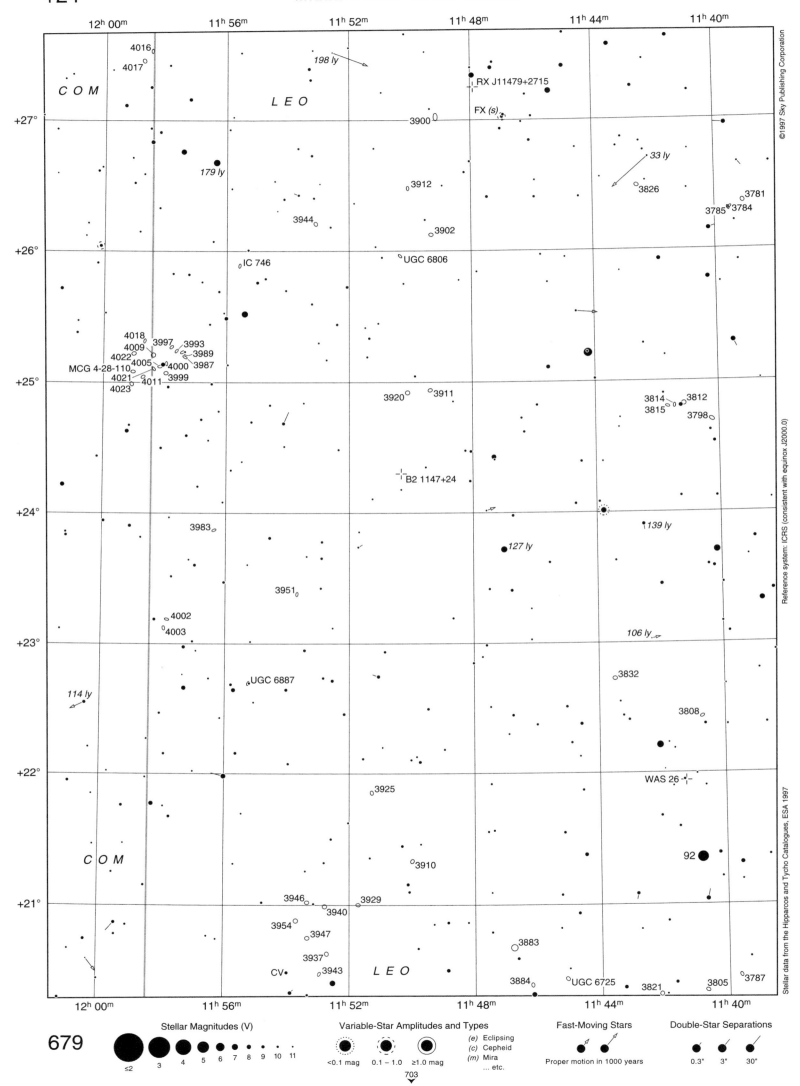

12h 00m   11h 56m   11h 52m   11h 48m   11h 44m   11h 40m

+27°

+26°

+25°

+24°

+23°

+22°

+21°

COM

LEO

198 ly

4016
4017

RX J11479+2715

FX (s)

3900

179 ly

33 ly

3826

3781
3785 3784

3912

3944

3902

IC 746

UGC 6806

4018
4009   3997   3993
4022   3989
4005   3987
MCG 4-28-110   4000
4021   3999
4023   4011

3920   3911

3814   3812
3815
3798

B2 1147+24

139 ly

3983

127 ly

106 ly

3951

3832

4002
4003

3808

114 ly

UGC 6887

WAS 26

92

COM

3925

3910

3946
3940

3929

3954

3947

3883

3937

CV

3943

LEO

3884

UGC 6725

3821

3805

3787

679

Stellar Magnitudes (V)

≤2 3 4 5 6 7 8 9 10 11

Variable-Star Amplitudes and Types

<0.1 mag   0.1 – 1.0   ≥1.0 mag

(e) Eclipsing
(c) Cepheid
(m) Mira
... etc.

Fast-Moving Stars

Proper motion in 1000 years

Double-Star Separations

0.3"   3"   30"

703

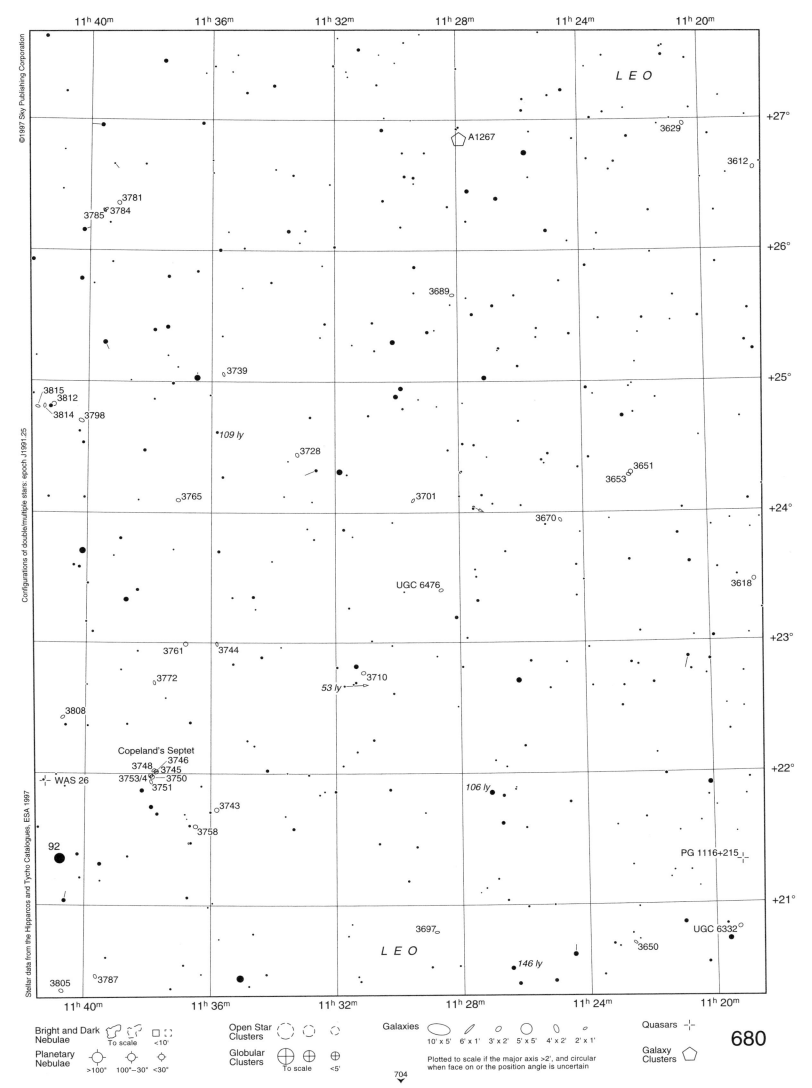

Bright and Dark
Nebulae

To scale   <10'

Planetary
Nebulae

>100"   100"–30"   <30"

Open Star
Clusters

Globular
Clusters

To scale   <5'

Galaxies

10' x 5'   6' x 1'   3' x 2'   5' x 5'   4' x 2'   2' x 1'

Plotted to scale if the major axis >2', and circular
when face on or the position angle is uncertain

Quasars

Galaxy
Clusters

704

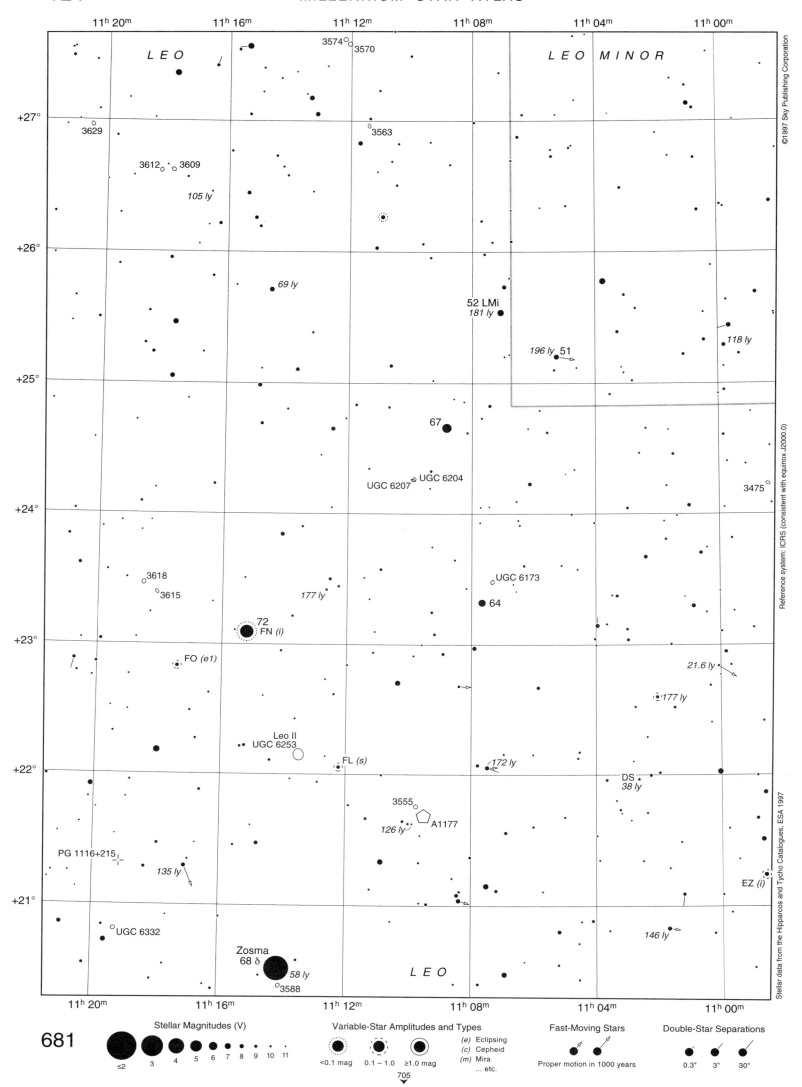

658

LEO

LEO MINOR

11h 20m   11h 16m   11h 12m   11h 08m   11h 04m   11h 00m

+27°

+26°

+25°

+24°

+23°

+22°

+21°

3574 3570

3629

3612 3609

105 ly

3563

69 ly

52 LMi
181 ly

196 ly 51

118 ly

67

UGC 6207 UGC 6204

3475

3618

3615

UGC 6173

64

177 ly

72
FN (i)

21.6 ly

FO (e1)

177 ly

Leo II
UGC 6253

FL (s)

172 ly

DS
38 ly

3555
A1177

126 ly

PG 1116+215

EZ (i)

135 ly

146 ly

UGC 6332

Zosma
68 δ
58 ly

LEO

3588

©1997 Sky Publishing Corporation

Reference system: ICRS (consistent with equinox J2000.0)

Stellar data from the Hipparcos and Tycho Catalogues, ESA 1997

681

Stellar Magnitudes (V)

≤2   3   4   5   6   7   8   9 10 11

Variable-Star Amplitudes and Types

<0.1 mag   0.1 – 1.0   ≥1.0 mag

(e) Eclipsing
(c) Cepheid
(m) Mira
... etc.

Fast-Moving Stars

Proper motion in 1000 years

Double-Star Separations

0.3"   3"   30"

705

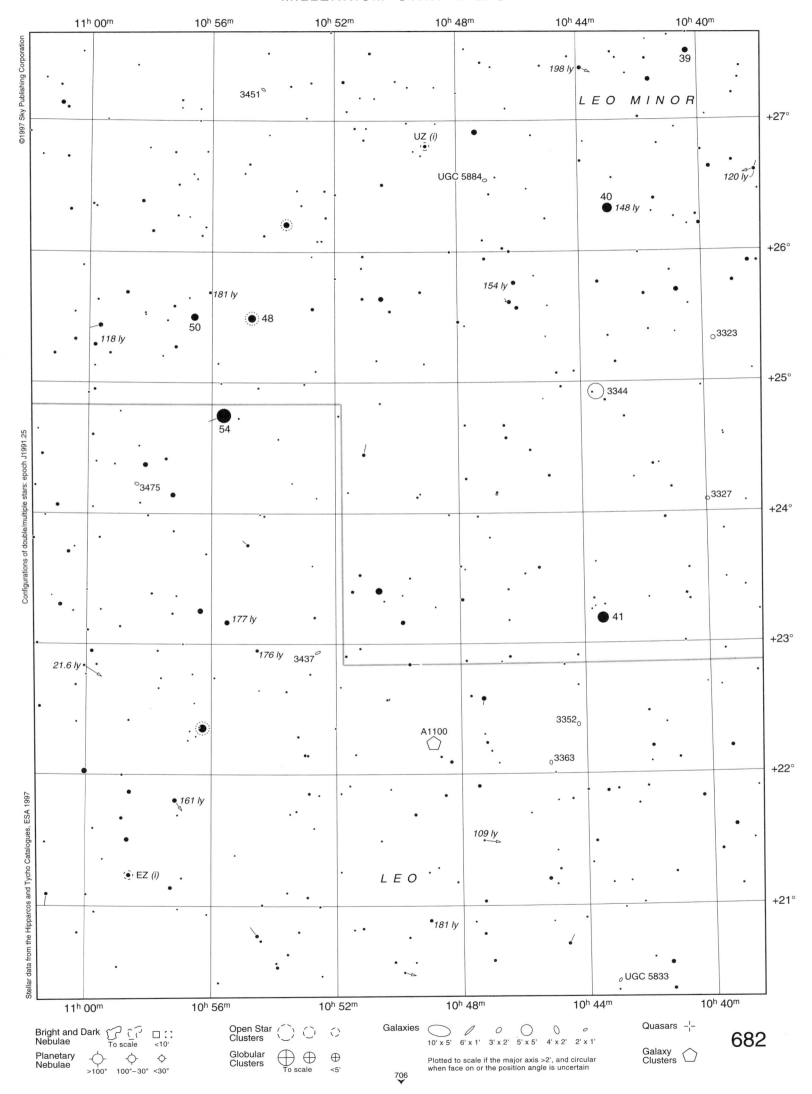

©1997 Sky Publishing Corporation

Configurations of double/multiple stars: epoch J1991.25

Stellar data from the Hipparcos and Tycho Catalogues, ESA 1997

LEO MINOR

39

198 ly

120 ly

UZ *(i)*

UGC 5884

40
148 ly

3451

154 ly

3323

181 ly

50

48

118 ly

3344

54

3475

3327

177 ly

41

176 ly   3437

21.6 ly

3352

A1100

3363

161 ly

109 ly

EZ *(i)*

LEO

181 ly

UGC 5833

Bright and Dark Nebulae			Open Star Clusters			Galaxies						Quasars
To scale		<10'				10' x 5'	6' x 1'	3' x 2'	5' x 5'	4' x 2'	2' x 1'	
Planetary Nebulae			Globular Clusters									Galaxy Clusters
>100"	100"−30"	<30"	To scale		<5'	Plotted to scale if the major axis >2', and circular when face on or the position angle is uncertain						

682

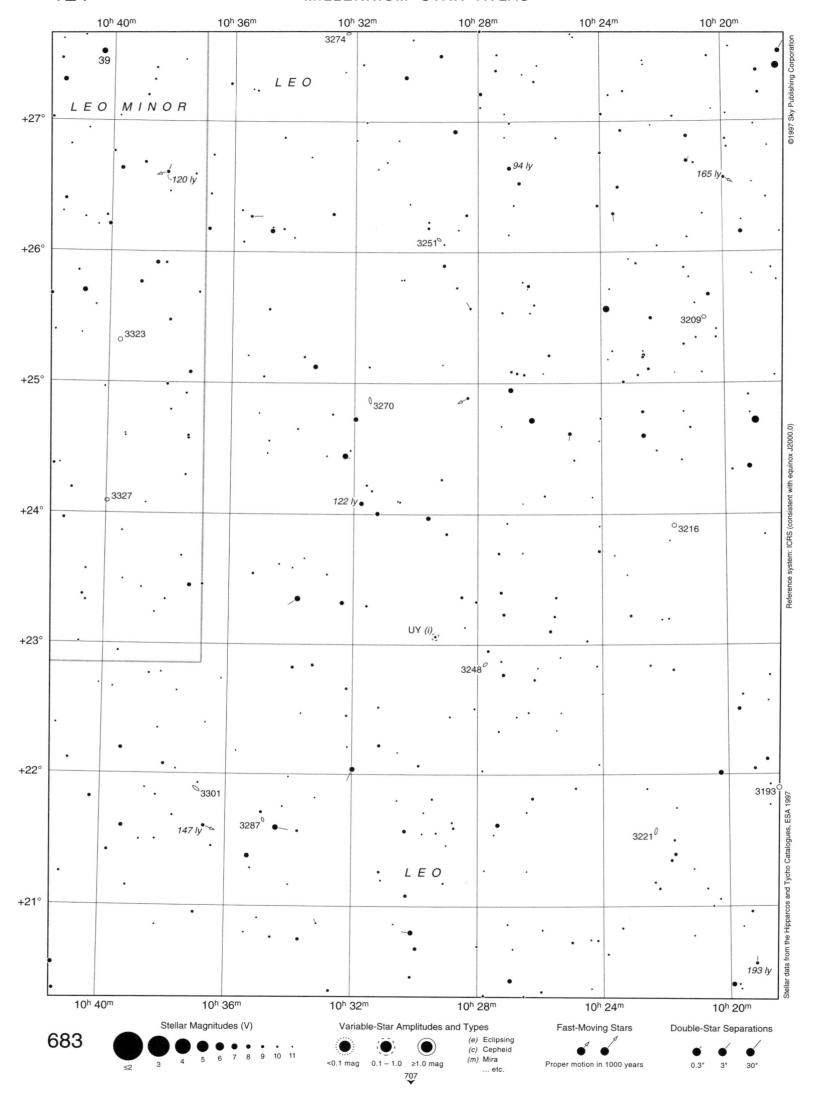

©1997 Sky Publishing Corporation

Reference system: ICRS (consistent with equinox J2000.0)

Stellar data from the Hipparcos and Tycho Catalogues, ESA 1997

LEO MINOR

LEO

39

120 ly

94 ly

165 ly

3323

3209

3327

3270

122 ly

3216

UY (i)

3248

3301

3193

3287

147 ly

3221

LEO

193 ly

3251

3274

683

Stellar Magnitudes (V)

≤2 3 4 5 6 7 8 9 10 11

Variable-Star Amplitudes and Types

<0.1 mag   0.1 – 1.0   ≥1.0 mag

(e) Eclipsing
(c) Cepheid
(m) Mira
... etc.

Fast-Moving Stars

Proper motion in 1000 years

Double-Star Separations

0.3"   3"   30"

MILLENNIUM STAR ATLAS

+24°

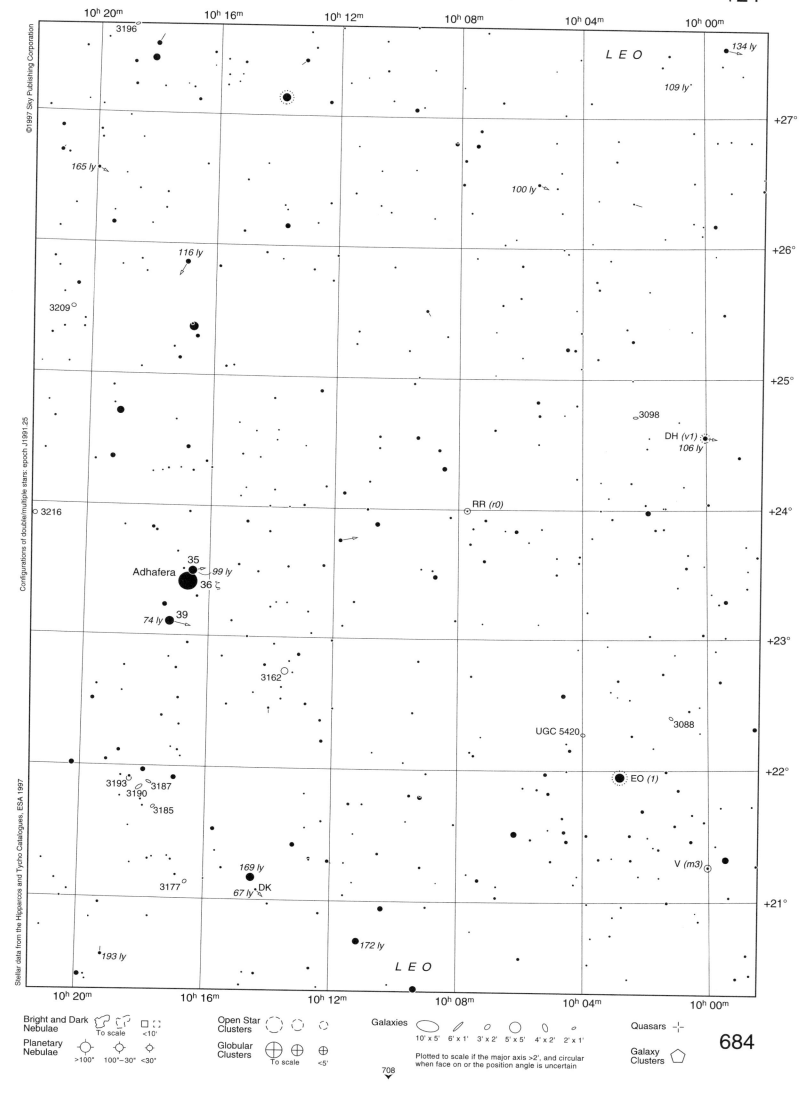

Configurations of double/multiple stars: epoch J1991.25

Stellar data from the Hipparcos and Tycho Catalogues, ESA 1997

10h 20m   10h 16m   10h 12m   10h 08m   10h 04m   10h 00m

LEO

134 ly

109 ly

+27°

165 ly

100 ly

+26°

116 ly

3209

3098

DH (v1)

106 ly

+25°

3216

RR (r0)

+24°

35
Adhafera   99 ly
36 ζ

74 ly   39

+23°

3162

UGC 5420

3088

3193   3187
3190
3185

EO (1)

+22°

169 ly
3177   DK
67 ly

V (m3)

172 ly

193 ly

LEO

+21°

10h 20m   10h 16m   10h 12m   10h 08m   10h 04m   10h 00m

3196

Bright and Dark Nebulae
To scale   <10'

Planetary Nebulae
>100"   100"–30"   <30'

Open Star Clusters
To scale

Globular Clusters
To scale   <5'

Galaxies
10' x 5'   6' x 1'   3' x 2'   5' x 5'   4' x 2'   2' x 1'

Plotted to scale if the major axis >2', and circular when face on or the position angle is uncertain

Quasars

Galaxy Clusters

684

708

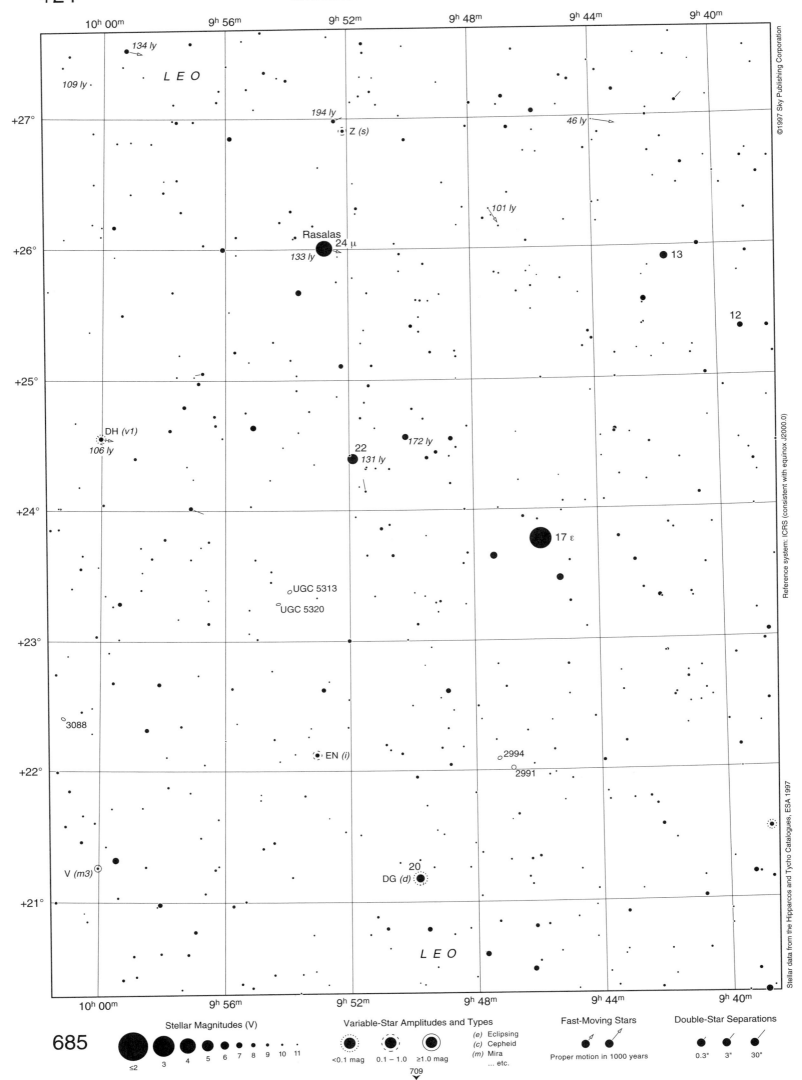

685

Stellar Magnitudes (V)

≤2 3 4 5 6 7 8 9 10 11

Variable-Star Amplitudes and Types

<0.1 mag   0.1 – 1.0   ≥1.0 mag

(e) Eclipsing
(c) Cepheid
(m) Mira
... etc.

Fast-Moving Stars

Proper motion in 1000 years

Double-Star Separations

0.3" 3" 30"

709

MILLENNIUM STAR ATLAS

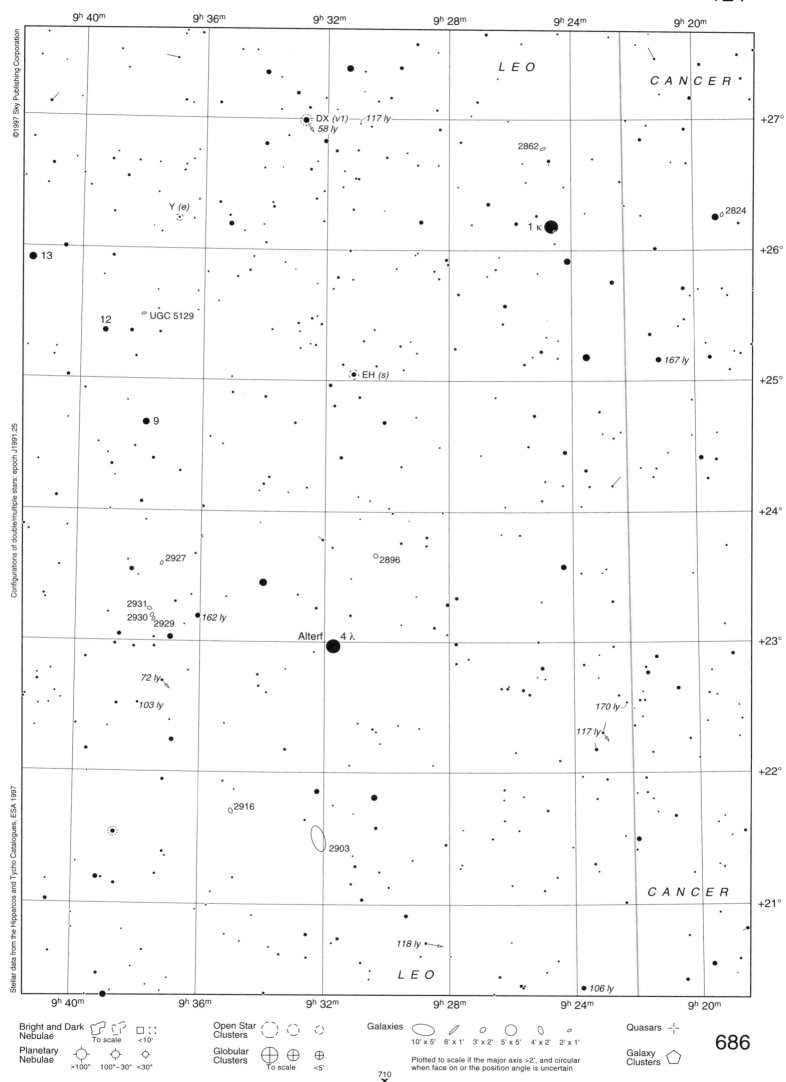

©1997 Sky Publishing Corporation

Configurations of double/multiple stars: epoch J1991.25

Stellar data from the Hipparcos and Tycho Catalogues, ESA 1997

9ʰ 40ᵐ   9ʰ 36ᵐ   9ʰ 32ᵐ   9ʰ 28ᵐ   9ʰ 24ᵐ   9ʰ 20ᵐ

L E O

C A N C E R

DX (v1) ⌐ 117 ly
58 ly

2862

1 κ

2824

13

+27°

+26°

Y (e)

12   UGC 5129

167 ly

EH (s)

+25°

9

+24°

2927

2896

2931
2930   2929   162 ly

Alterf   4 λ

+23°

72 ly

103 ly

170 ly

117 ly

+22°

2916

2903

C A N C E R

+21°

118 ly

L E O

106 ly

9ʰ 40ᵐ   9ʰ 36ᵐ   9ʰ 32ᵐ   9ʰ 28ᵐ   9ʰ 24ᵐ   9ʰ 20ᵐ

Bright and Dark Nebulae	To scale	<10'
Planetary Nebulae	>100" 100"–30" <30"	

Open Star Clusters		
Globular Clusters	To scale	<5'

Galaxies

10' x 5'   6' x 1'   3' x 2'   5' x 5'   4' x 2'   2' x 1'

Plotted to scale if the major axis >2', and circular when face on or the position angle is uncertain

Quasars

Galaxy Clusters

686

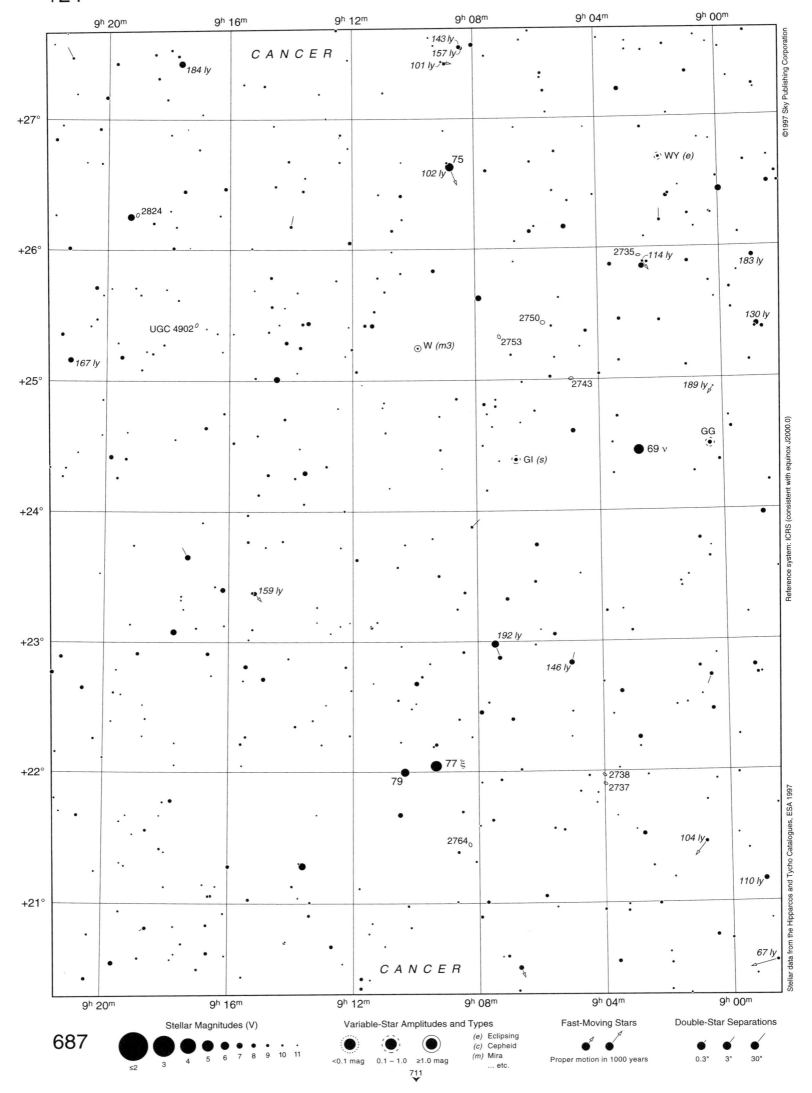

CANCER

143 ly
157 ly
101 ly

75
102 ly

WY (e)

2824

2735 114 ly
183 ly

130 ly

UGC 4902

2750
2753

W (m3)

167 ly

2743
189 ly

GG

GI (s)
69 ν

159 ly

192 ly
146 ly

77 ξ
79

2738
2737

2764

104 ly

110 ly

CANCER

67 ly

687

Stellar Magnitudes (V)

≤2 3 4 5 6 7 8 9 10 11

Variable-Star Amplitudes and Types

<0.1 mag   0.1 – 1.0   ≥1.0 mag

(e) Eclipsing
(c) Cepheid
(m) Mira
... etc.

Fast-Moving Stars

Proper motion in 1000 years

Double-Star Separations

0.3"   3"   30"

©1997 Sky Publishing Corporation

Reference system: ICRS (consistent with equinox J2000.0)

Stellar data from the Hipparcos and Tycho Catalogues, ESA 1997

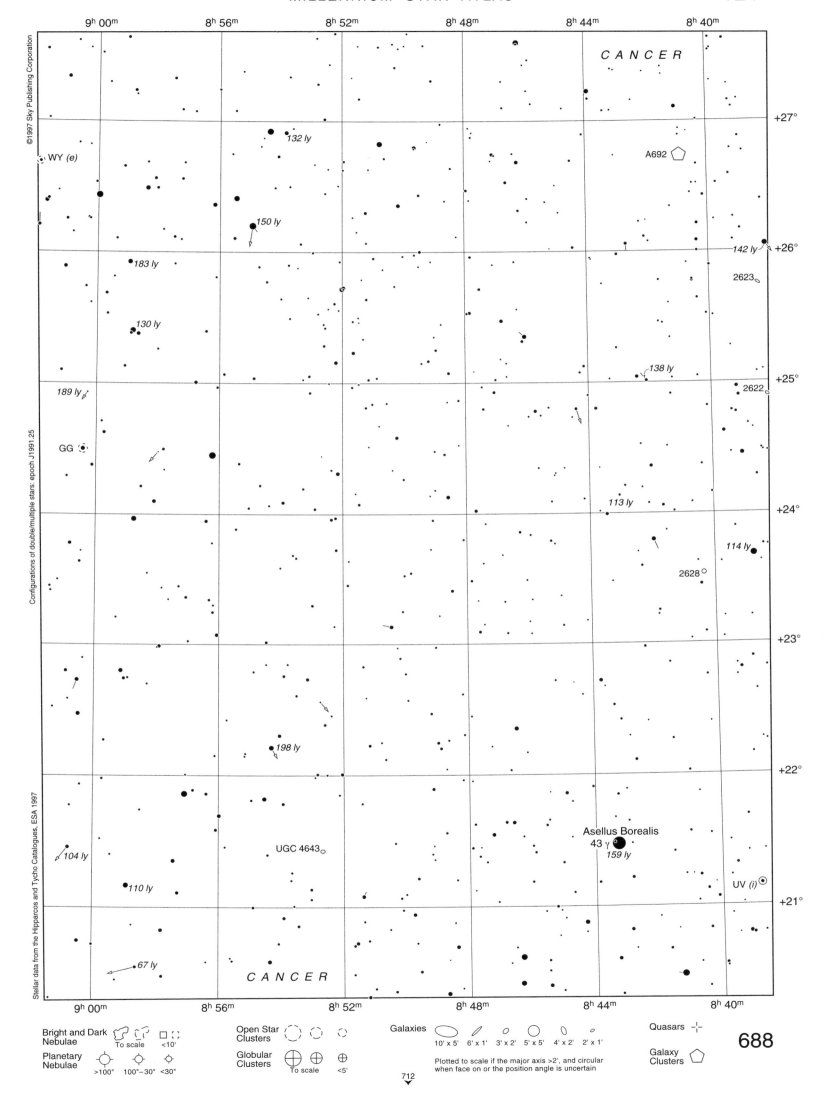

CANCER

©1997 Sky Publishing Corporation

Configurations of double/multiple stars: epoch J1991.25

Stellar data from the Hipparcos and Tycho Catalogues, ESA 1997

WY (e)

132 ly

150 ly

183 ly

130 ly

189 ly

GG

198 ly

104 ly

110 ly

67 ly

A692

142 ly
2623

138 ly
2622

113 ly

114 ly
2628

Asellus Borealis
43 γ
159 ly

UV (i)

UGC 4643

CANCER

+27°
+26°
+25°
+24°
+23°
+22°
+21°

9h 00m   8h 56m   8h 52m   8h 48m   8h 44m   8h 40m

Bright and Dark Nebulae	Open Star Clusters	Galaxies	Quasars

Bright and Dark Nebulae
To scale   <10'

Planetary Nebulae
>100"   100"–30"   <30"

Open Star Clusters

Globular Clusters
To scale   <5'

Galaxies
10' x 5'   6' x 1'   3' x 2'   5' x 5'   4' x 2'   2' x 1'

Plotted to scale if the major axis >2', and circular when face on or the position angle is uncertain

Quasars

Galaxy Clusters

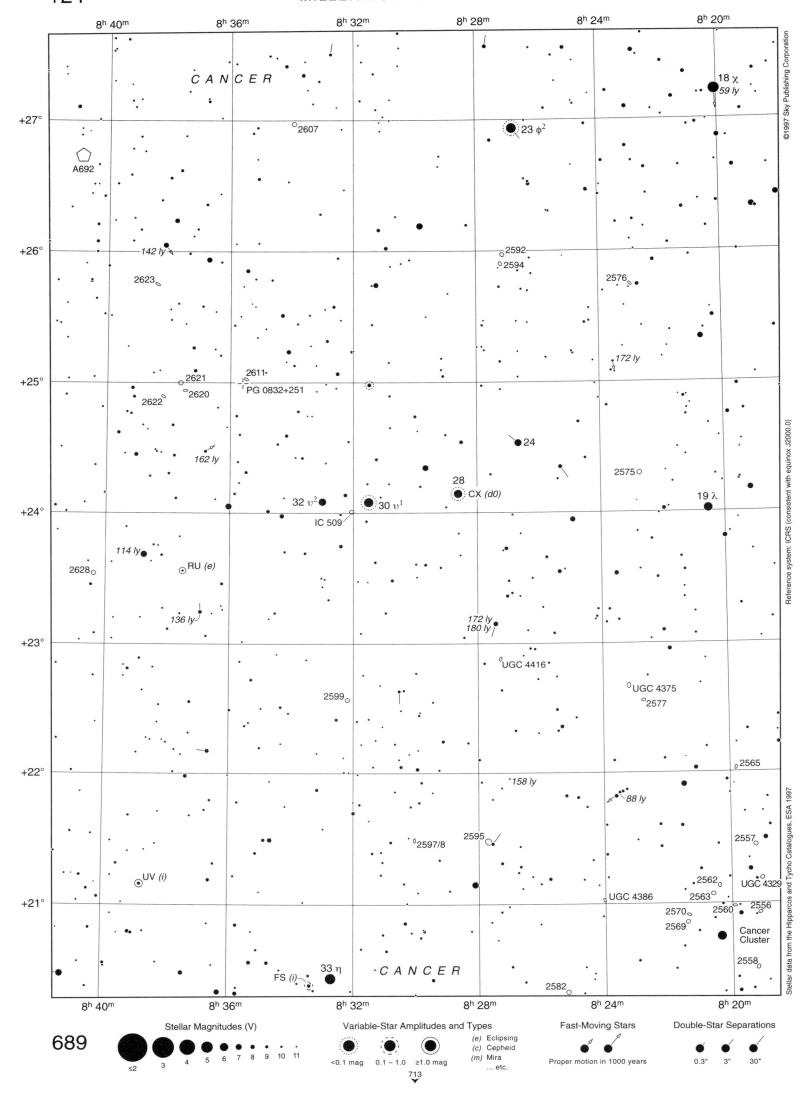

©1997 Sky Publishing Corporation

Reference system: ICRS (consistent with equinox J2000.0)

Stellar data from the Hipparcos and Tycho Catalogues, ESA 1997

CANCER

18 χ
59 ly

2607

A692

142 ly

2623

2592
2594

2576

172 ly

2621
2622   2620
2611
PG 0832+251

162 ly

24

28
CX (d0)   2575

32 υ²   30 υ¹   19 λ
IC 509

114 ly

2628   RU (e)

136 ly   *172 ly*
180 ly

UGC 4416

2599   UGC 4375
2577

2565

158 ly
88 ly

2597/8   2595

UV (i)   2557

2562   UGC 4329
UGC 4386   2563
2570   2560   2556
2569

Cancer
Cluster

2558

FS (i)   33 η   CANCER

2582

Stellar Magnitudes (V)

≤2 3 4 5 6 7 8 9 10 11

Variable-Star Amplitudes and Types

<0.1 mag   0.1 – 1.0   ≥1.0 mag

(e) Eclipsing
(c) Cepheid
(m) Mira
... etc.

Fast-Moving Stars

Proper motion in 1000 years

Double-Star Separations

0.3"   3"   30"

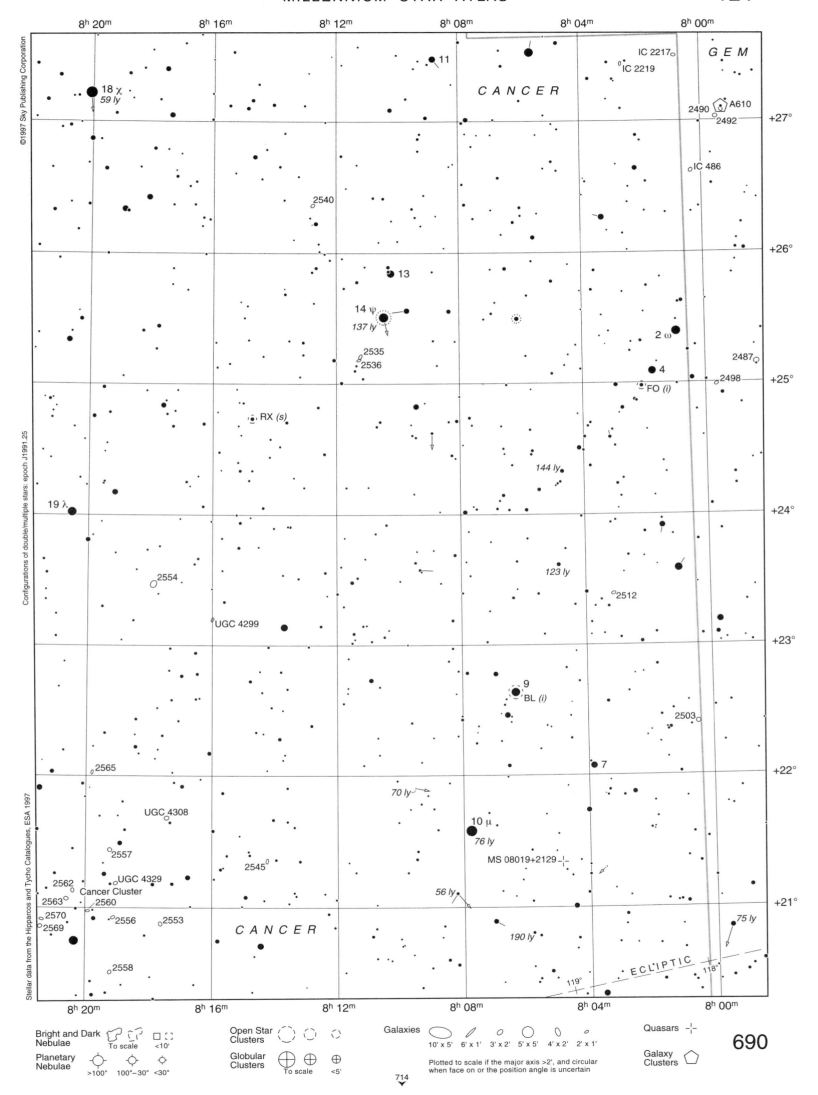

8h 20m   8h 16m   8h 12m   8h 08m   8h 04m   8h 00m

GEM

CANCER

IC 2217
IC 2219

18 χ
59 ly

11

2490   A610
2492

+27°

IC 486

2540

+26°

13

14 ψ
137 ly

2 ω

2535
2536

4
FO (i)

2487
2498

+25°

RX (s)

144 ly

19 λ

+24°

123 ly

2554

2512

UGC 4299

+23°

9
BL (i)

2503

2565

7

+22°

UGC 4308

70 ly

2557

10 μ
76 ly

2545

MS 08019+2129

2562
UGC 4329
Cancer Cluster
2563   2560

56 ly

+21°

2570
2569   2556   2553

CANCER

190 ly

75 ly

2558

ECLIPTIC

119°   118°

8h 20m   8h 16m   8h 12m   8h 08m   8h 04m   8h 00m

Bright and Dark Nebulae   To scale   <10'
Planetary Nebulae   >100"   100"–30"   <30"

Open Star Clusters
Globular Clusters   To scale   <5'

Galaxies   10' x 5'   6' x 1'   3' x 2'   5' x 5'   4' x 2'   2' x 1'
Plotted to scale if the major axis >2', and circular when face on or the position angle is uncertain

Quasars

Galaxy Clusters

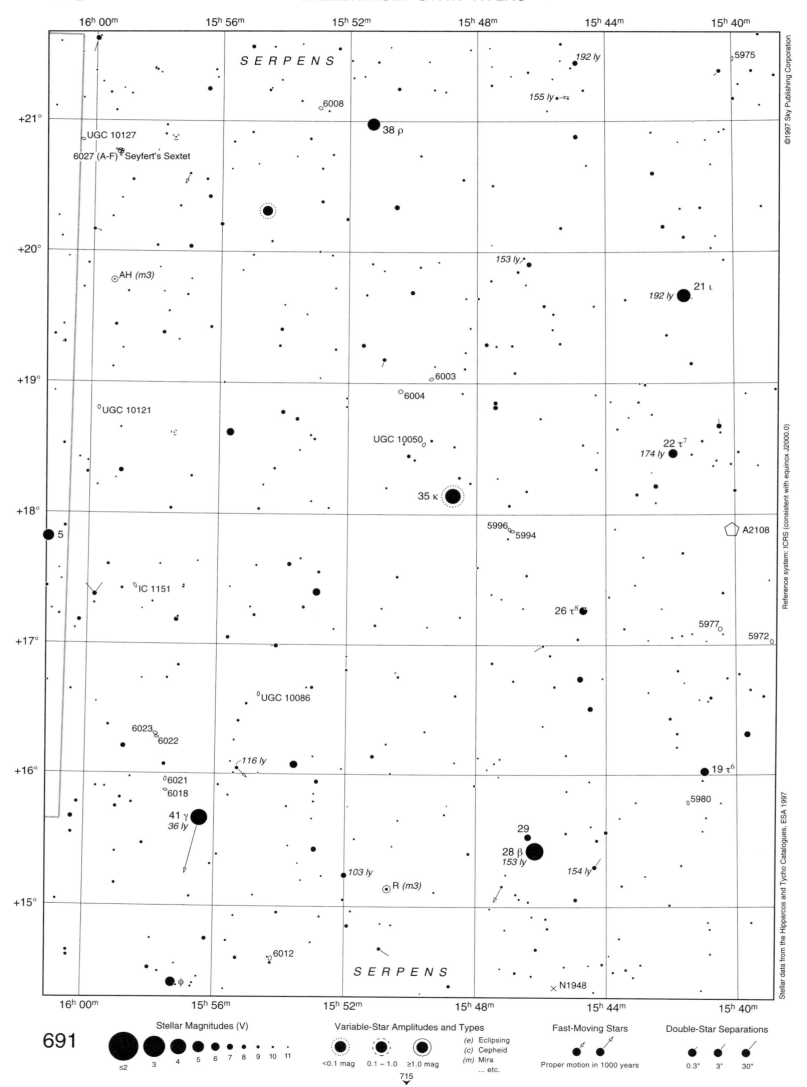

©1997 Sky Publishing Corporation

Reference system: ICRS (consistent with equinox J2000.0)

Stellar data from the Hipparcos and Tycho Catalogues, ESA 1997

691

Stellar Magnitudes (V)

≤2 3 4 5 6 7 8 9 10 11

Variable-Star Amplitudes and Types

<0.1 mag   0.1 – 1.0   ≥1.0 mag

(e) Eclipsing
(c) Cepheid
(m) Mira
... etc.

Fast-Moving Stars

Proper motion in 1000 years

Double-Star Separations

0.3"   3"   30"

715

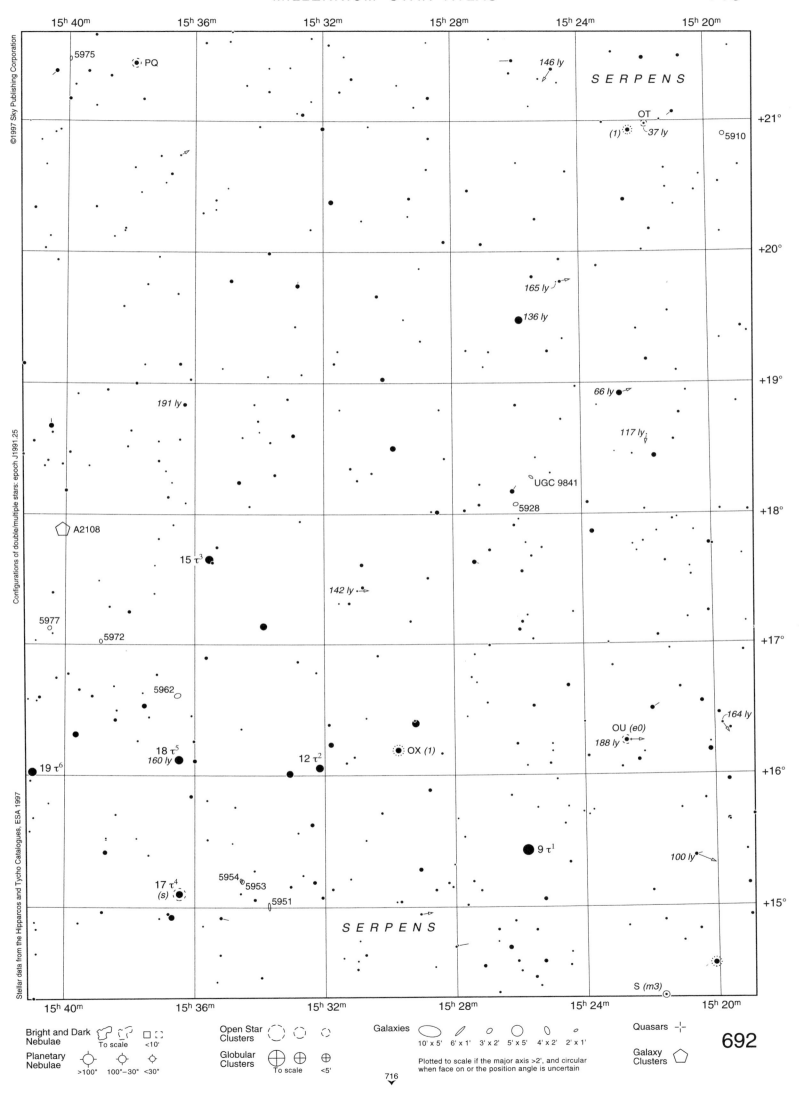

©1997 Sky Publishing Corporation

Configurations of double/multiple stars: epoch J1991.25

Stellar data from the Hipparcos and Tycho Catalogues, ESA 1997

SERPENS

5975
PQ
146 ly
OT
(1)   37 ly
5910

165 ly
136 ly

191 ly
66 ly
117 ly
UGC 9841
5928

A2108
15 τ³
142 ly

5977
5972

5962
164 ly
OU (e0)
188 ly
18 τ⁵
160 ly
12 τ²
OX (1)
19 τ⁶

9 τ¹
100 ly

17 τ⁴
5954 5953
(s)
5951

SERPENS

S (m3)

Bright and Dark Nebulae
To scale   <10'

Planetary Nebulae
>100"   100"–30"   <30"

Open Star Clusters

Globular Clusters
To scale   <5'

Galaxies
10' x 5'   6' x 1'   3' x 2'   5' x 5'   4' x 2'   2' x 1'
Plotted to scale if the major axis >2', and circular when face on or the position angle is uncertain

Quasars

Galaxy Clusters

692

716

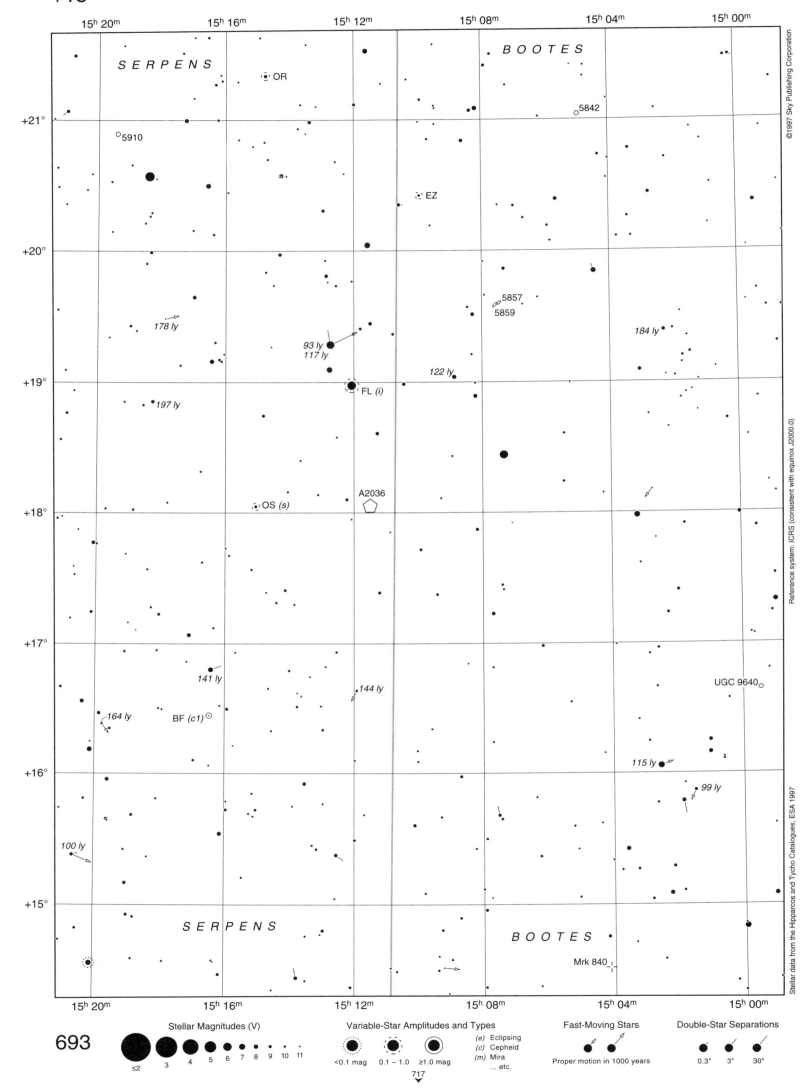

©1997 Sky Publishing Corporation

Reference system: ICRS (consistent with equinox J2000.0)

Stellar data from the Hipparcos and Tycho Catalogues, ESA 1997

SERPENS

BOOTES

OR

EZ

5842

5910

5857
5859

178 ly

93 ly
117 ly

122 ly

184 ly

FL (i)

197 ly

A2036

OS (s)

141 ly

144 ly

UGC 9640

164 ly

BF (c1)

115 ly

99 ly

100 ly

SERPENS

BOOTES

Mrk 840

693

Stellar Magnitudes (V)

≤2   3   4   5   6   7   8   9 10 11

Variable-Star Amplitudes and Types

<0.1 mag   0.1 – 1.0   ≥1.0 mag

(e) Eclipsing
(c) Cepheid
(m) Mira
... etc.

Fast-Moving Stars

Proper motion in 1000 years

Double-Star Separations

0.3"   3"   30"

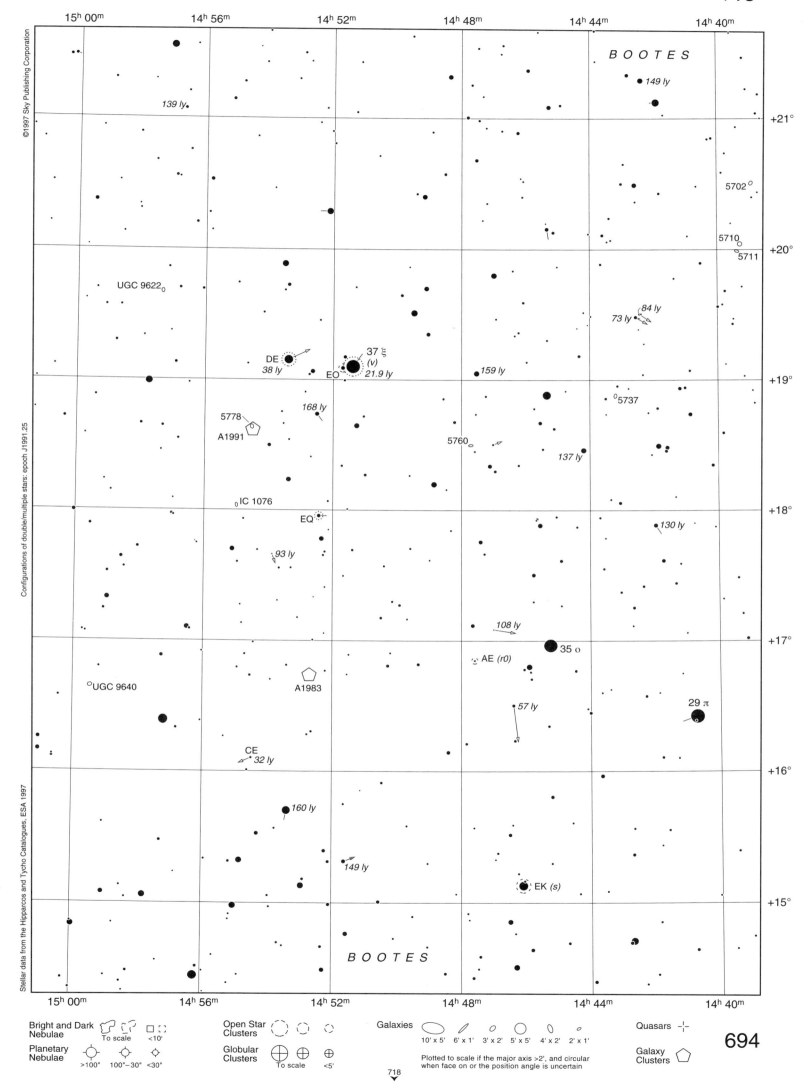

BOOTES

149 ly

5702

5710
5711

139 ly

UGC 9622

84 ly
73 ly

DE
38 ly

37 ξ
(v)
EO   21.9 ly

159 ly

5737

168 ly

5778
A1991

5760

137 ly

IC 1076

EQ

130 ly

93 ly

108 ly

35 o

AE (r0)

UGC 9640

A1983

57 ly

29 π

CE
32 ly

160 ly

149 ly

EK (s)

BOOTES

+21°

+20°

+19°

+18°

+17°

+16°

+15°

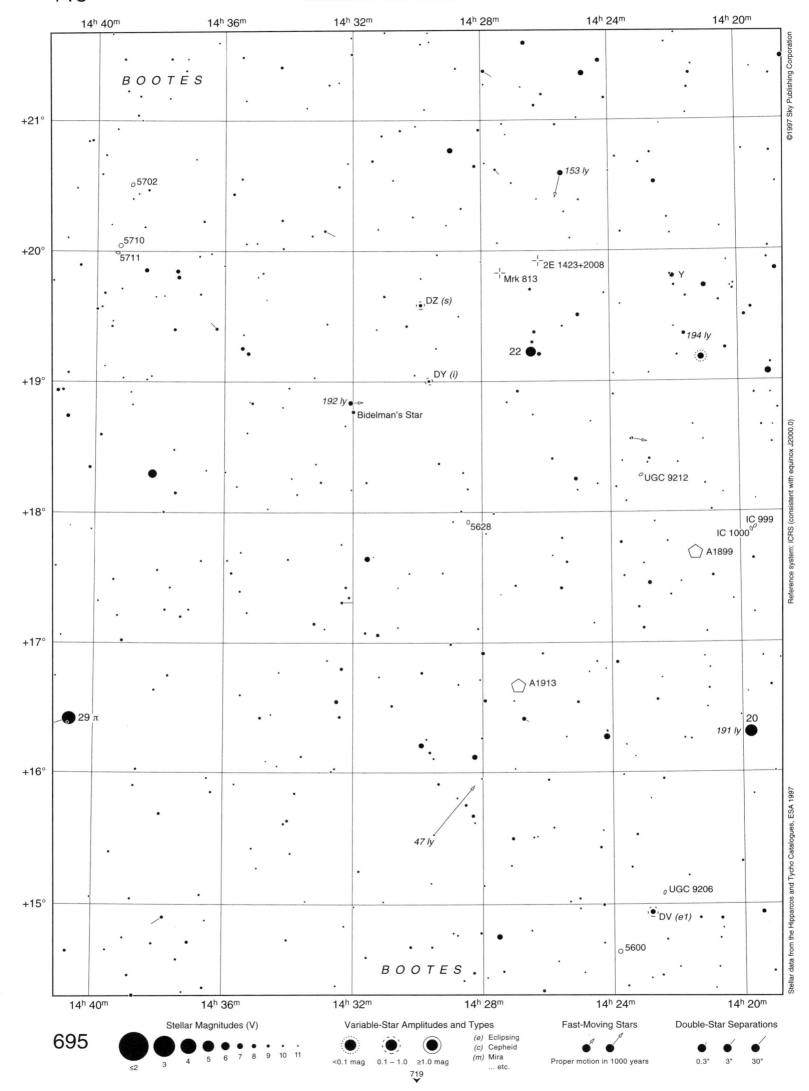

©1997 Sky Publishing Corporation

Reference system: ICRS (consistent with equinox J2000.0)

Stellar data from the Hipparcos and Tycho Catalogues, ESA 1997

BOOTES

5702

5710
5711

153 ly

2E 1423+2008
Mrk 813

DZ (s)

Y

194 ly

22

DY (i)

192 ly
Bidelman's Star

UGC 9212

5628

IC 999
IC 1000
A1899

A1913

29 π

20
191 ly

47 ly

UGC 9206

DV (e1)

5600

BOOTES

695

Stellar Magnitudes (V)

≤2 3 4 5 6 7 8 9 10 11

Variable-Star Amplitudes and Types

<0.1 mag   0.1 – 1.0   ≥1.0 mag

(e) Eclipsing
(c) Cepheid
(m) Mira
... etc.

719

Fast-Moving Stars

Proper motion in 1000 years

Double-Star Separations

0.3"   3"   30"

MILLENNIUM STAR ATLAS

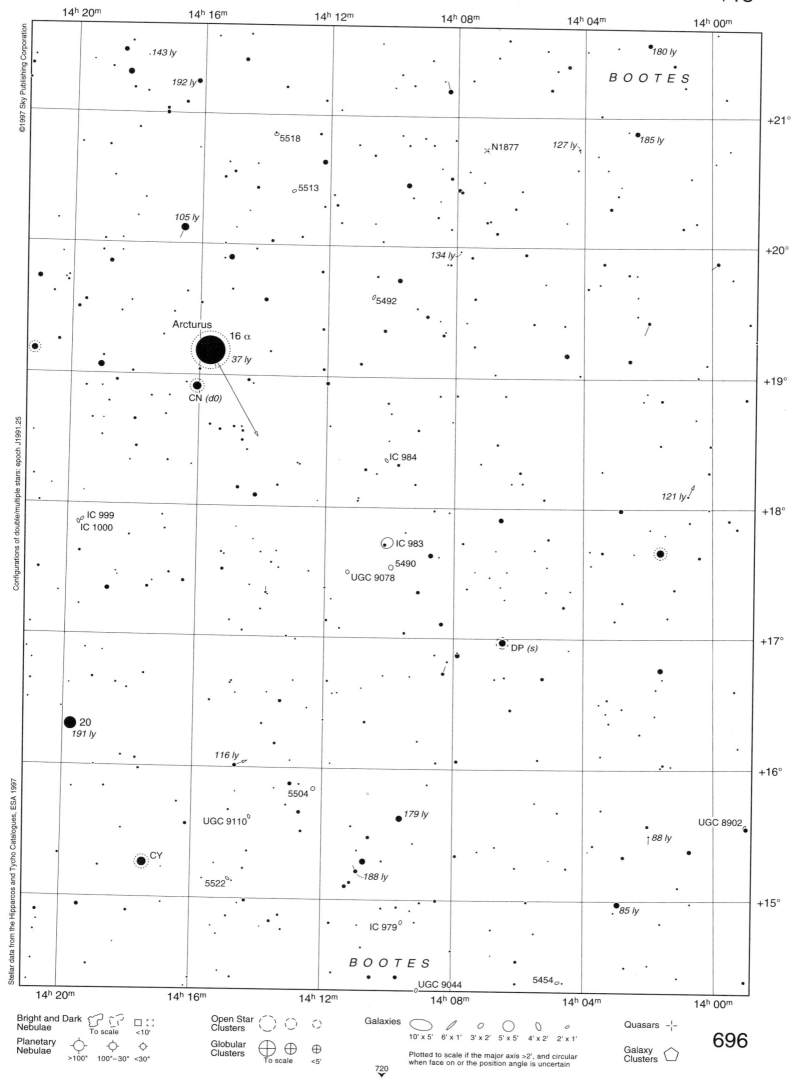

Configurations of double/multiple stars: epoch J1991.25

Stellar data from the Hipparcos and Tycho Catalogues, ESA 1997

B O O T E S

180 ly

+21°

.143 ly

192 ly

5518

N1877   127 ly

185 ly

105 ly

+20°

134 ly

₀5492

Arcturus   16 α

37 ly

+19°

CN (d0)

IC 984

121 ly

IC 999   +18°
IC 1000

IC 983

5490

UGC 9078

DP (s)   +17°

20
191 ly

116 ly   +16°

5504

UGC 9110⁰   179 ly   UGC 8902

88 ly

CY

5522₀   188 ly

85 ly   +15°

IC 979⁰

B O O T E S

UGC 9044   5454

Bright and Dark
Nebulae
To scale   <10'

Planetary
Nebulae
>100"   100"–30"   <30"

Open Star
Clusters

Globular
Clusters
To scale   <5'

Galaxies

10' x 5'   6' x 1'   3' x 2'   5' x 5'   4' x 2'   2' x 1'

Plotted to scale if the major axis >2', and circular
when face on or the position angle is uncertain

Quasars

Galaxy
Clusters

696

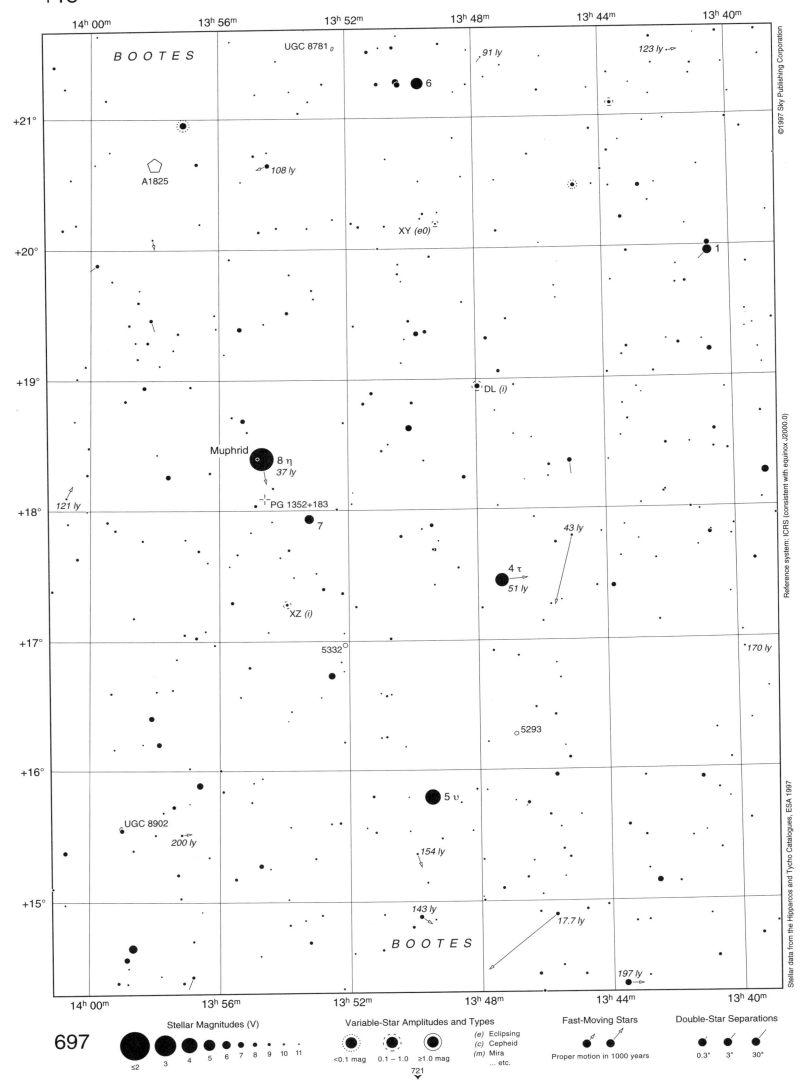

©1997 Sky Publishing Corporation

Reference system: ICRS (consistent with equinox J2000.0)

Stellar data from the Hipparcos and Tycho Catalogues, ESA 1997

B O O T E S

UGC 8781₀

6

91 ly

123 ly

+21°

A1825

108 ly

XY (e0)

+20°

1

+19°

DL (i)

Muphrid

8 η
37 ly

PG 1352+183

121 ly

7

43 ly

4 τ
51 ly

XZ (i)

+17°

5332

170 ly

5293

+16°

5 υ

UGC 8902

200 ly

154 ly

+15°

143 ly

17.7 ly

B O O T E S

197 ly

697

Stellar Magnitudes (V)

≤2   3   4   5   6   7   8   9 10 11

Variable-Star Amplitudes and Types

<0.1 mag   0.1 – 1.0   ≥1.0 mag

(e) Eclipsing
(c) Cepheid
(m) Mira
... etc.

Fast-Moving Stars

Proper motion in 1000 years

Double-Star Separations

0.3"   3"   30"

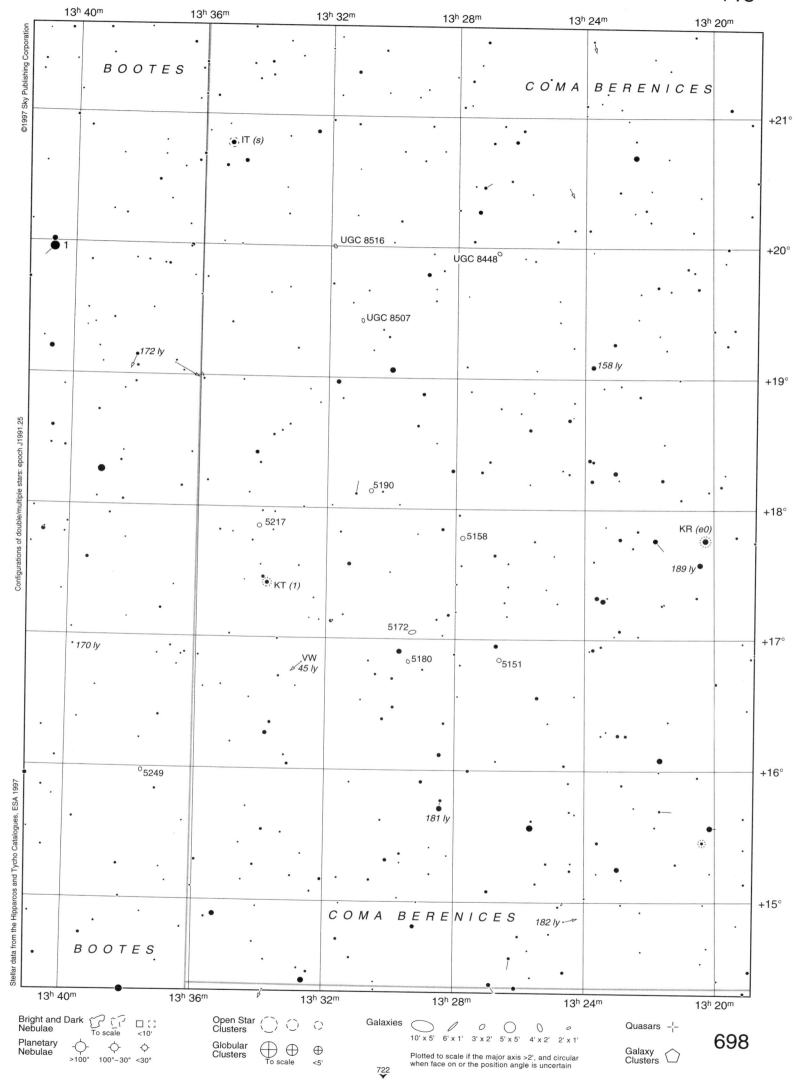

©1997 Sky Publishing Corporation

Configurations of double/multiple stars: epoch J1991.25

Stellar data from the Hipparcos and Tycho Catalogues, ESA 1997

13ʰ 40ᵐ   13ʰ 36ᵐ   13ʰ 32ᵐ   13ʰ 28ᵐ   13ʰ 24ᵐ   13ʰ 20ᵐ

B O O T E S

C O M A   B E R E N I C E S

+21°

IT (s)

+20°
UGC 8516
UGC 8448

UGC 8507

172 ly   158 ly

+19°

5190

+18°
5217   5158   KR (e0)

KT (1)   189 ly

5172

170 ly   +17°
VW
45 ly   5180   5151

5249   +16°

181 ly

+15°
C O M A   B E R E N I C E S
182 ly

B O O T E S

13ʰ 40ᵐ   13ʰ 36ᵐ   13ʰ 32ᵐ   13ʰ 28ᵐ   13ʰ 24ᵐ   13ʰ 20ᵐ

Bright and Dark
Nebulae   To scale   <10'

Planetary
Nebulae   >100" 100"–30" <30"

Open Star
Clusters

Globular
Clusters   To scale   <5'

Galaxies

10' x 5'   6' x 1'   3' x 2'   5' x 5'   4' x 2'   2' x 1'

Plotted to scale if the major axis >2', and circular
when face on or the position angle is uncertain

Quasars

Galaxy
Clusters

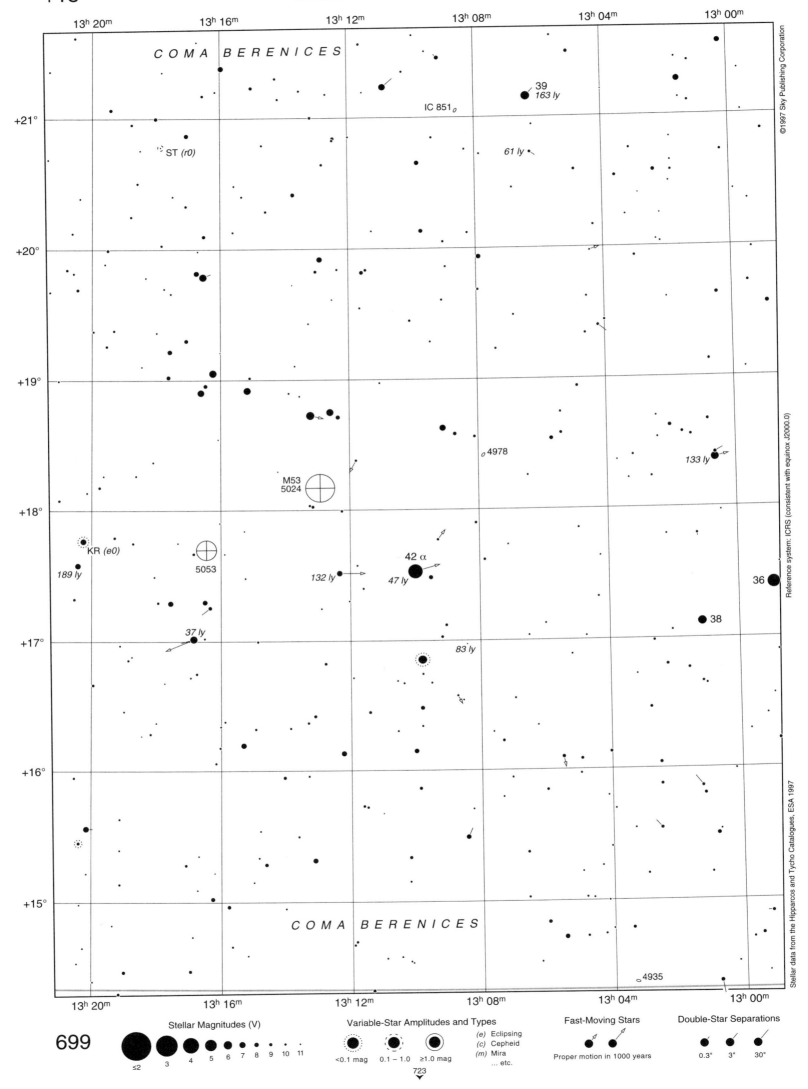

©1997 Sky Publishing Corporation

Reference system: ICRS (consistent with equinox J2000.0)

Stellar data from the Hipparcos and Tycho Catalogues, ESA 1997

COMA BERENICES

39
163 ly

IC 851

ST (r0)

61 ly

M53
5024

4978

133 ly

KR (e0)

5053

42 α

189 ly

132 ly

47 ly

36

38

37 ly

83 ly

COMA BERENICES

4935

Stellar Magnitudes (V)

≤2   3   4   5   6 7 8 9 10 11

Variable-Star Amplitudes and Types

<0.1 mag   0.1 – 1.0   ≥1.0 mag

(e) Eclipsing
(c) Cepheid
(m) Mira
... etc.

Fast-Moving Stars

Proper motion in 1000 years

Double-Star Separations

0.3"   3"   30"

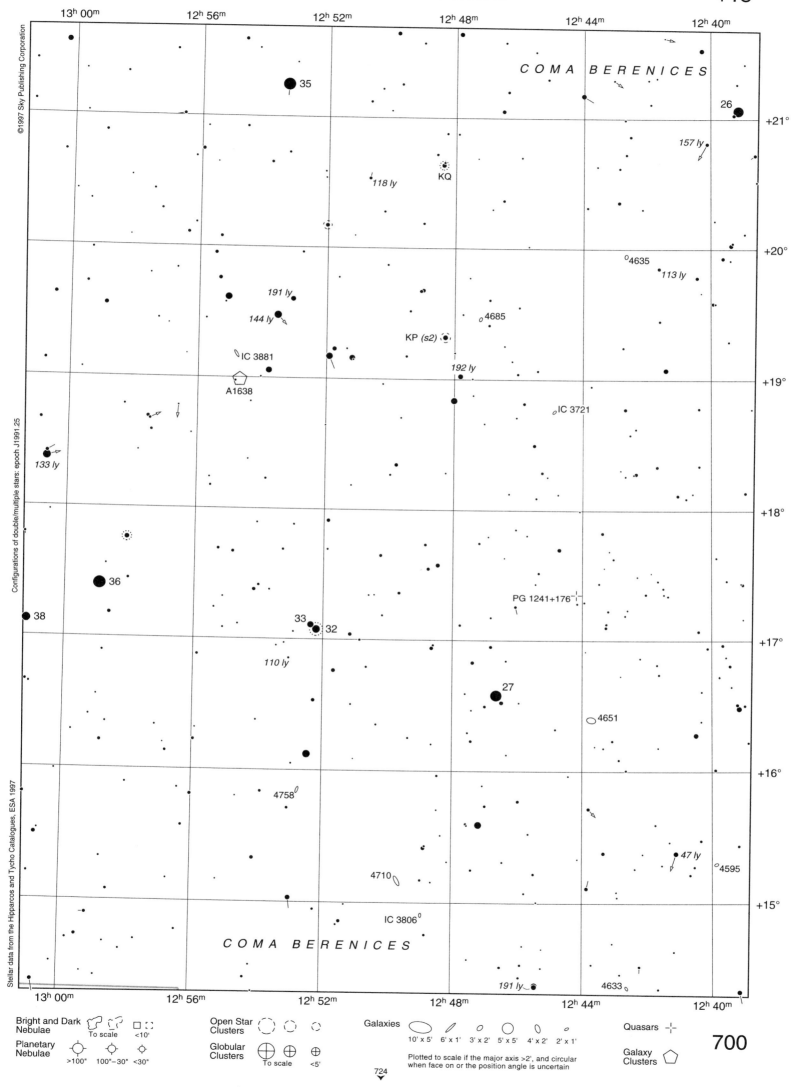

COMA BERENICES

35

26

157 ly

118 ly

KQ

+21°

4635

113 ly

+20°

191 ly

144 ly

4685

KP (s2)

IC 3881

192 ly

A1638

+19°

IC 3721

133 ly

+18°

36

PG 1241+176

38

33

32

+17°

110 ly

27

4651

+16°

4758

4710

47 ly

4595

IC 3806

+15°

COMA BERENICES

191 ly

4633

13h 00m   12h 56m   12h 52m   12h 48m   12h 44m   12h 40m

Bright and Dark
Nebulae
To scale   <10'

Open Star
Clusters

Globular
Clusters
To scale   <5'

Galaxies
10' x 5' 6' x 1' 3' x 2' 5' x 5' 4' x 2' 2' x 1'

Quasars

Galaxy
Clusters

Planetary
Nebulae
>100"   100"−30"   <30"

Plotted to scale if the major axis >2', and circular
when face on or the position angle is uncertain

700

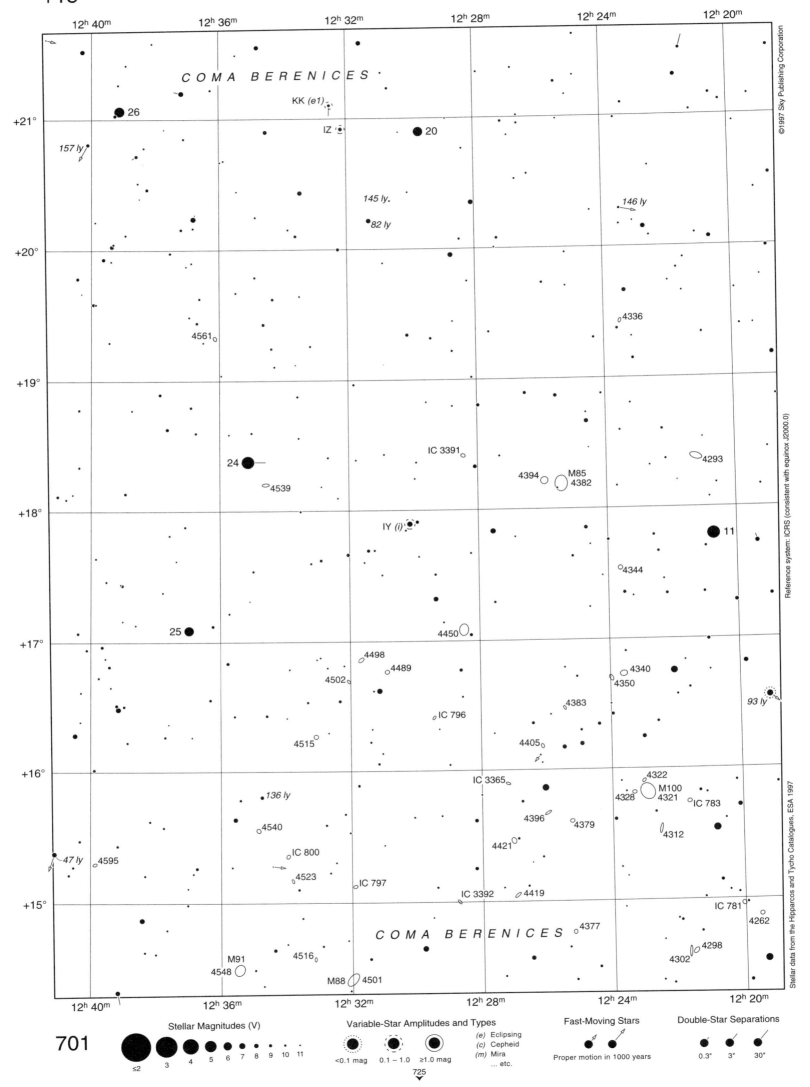

COMA BERENICES

KK (e1)
IZ
20
26
157 ly
145 ly.
82 ly
146 ly
4561
4336
24
4539
IC 3391
4394 M85
4382
4293
IY (i)
11
4344
25
4450
4498
4489
4340
4502
4350
IC 796
93 ly
4515
4383
4405
IC 3365
4322
M100
4328 4321
IC 783
136 ly
4396 4379
4312
4421
4540
IC 800
47 ly
4595
4523
IC 797
IC 3392 4419
IC 781
4262
COMA BERENICES 4377
4298
M91
4302
4548
4516
M88 4501

701

Stellar Magnitudes (V)
≤2 3 4 5 6 7 8 9 10 11

Variable-Star Amplitudes and Types
<0.1 mag   0.1 – 1.0   ≥1.0 mag
(e) Eclipsing
(c) Cepheid
(m) Mira
... etc.

Fast-Moving Stars
Proper motion in 1000 years

Double-Star Separations
0.3" 3" 30"

725

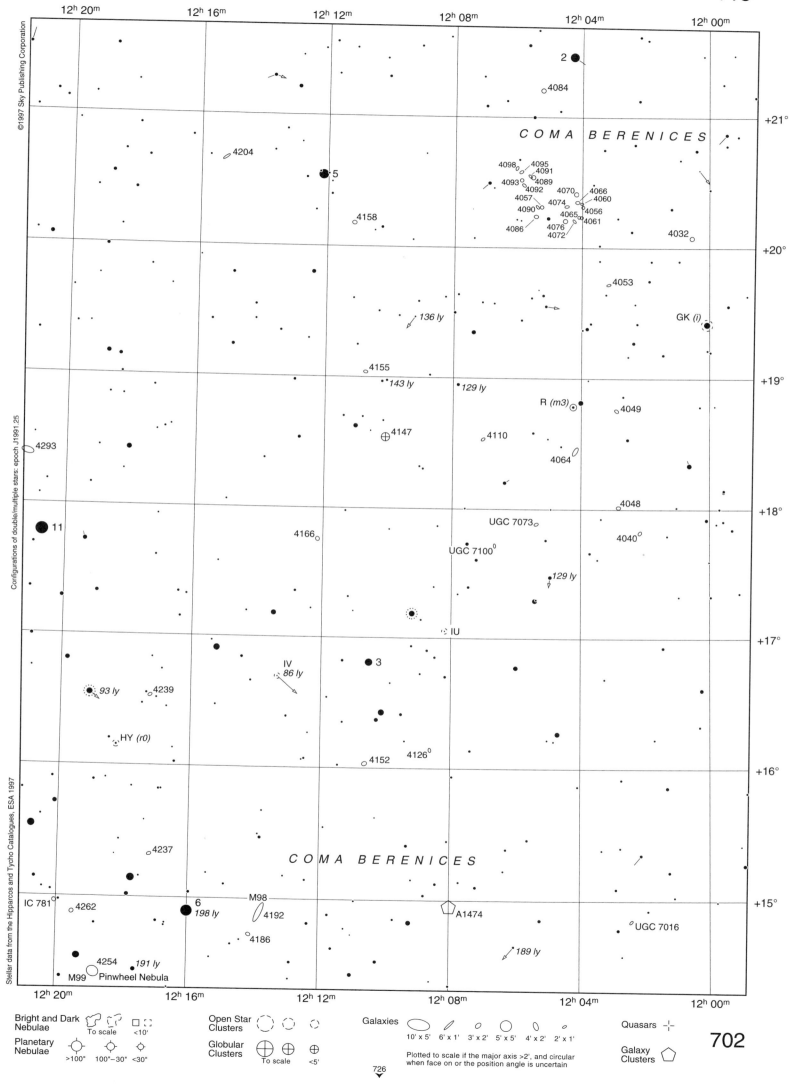

12ʰ 20ᵐ   12ʰ 16ᵐ   12ʰ 12ᵐ   12ʰ 08ᵐ   12ʰ 04ᵐ   12ʰ 00ᵐ

+21°
+20°
+19°
+18°
+17°
+16°
+15°

2
4084

C O M A   B E R E N I C E S

4204
5
4158

4098 4095
4091
4093 4089
4092   4070   4066
4057   4074   4060
4090   4065 4056
4086   4076 4061
4072
4032

4053

136 ly
GK (i)

4155
143 ly   129 ly
R (m3)   4049
4147   4110
4064
4293
4048
11
UGC 7073
4166   UGC 7100   4040
129 ly

IU
IV   3
86 ly
93 ly   4239
HY (r0)
4126
4152

C O M A   B E R E N I C E S

4237

IC 781   M98
4262   6   A1474
198 ly   4192   UGC 7016
4186
189 ly
4254   191 ly
M99   Pinwheel Nebula

12ʰ 20ᵐ   12ʰ 16ᵐ   12ʰ 12ᵐ   12ʰ 08ᵐ   12ʰ 04ᵐ   12ʰ 00ᵐ

Bright and Dark Nebulae   Open Star Clusters   Galaxies   Quasars
To scale <10'   10' x 5' 6' x 1' 3' x 2' 5' x 5' 4' x 2' 2' x 1'

Planetary Nebulae   Globular Clusters
>100" 100"–30" <30"   To scale <5'   Plotted to scale if the major axis >2', and circular
                                                      when face on or the position angle is uncertain

Galaxy Clusters

702

726

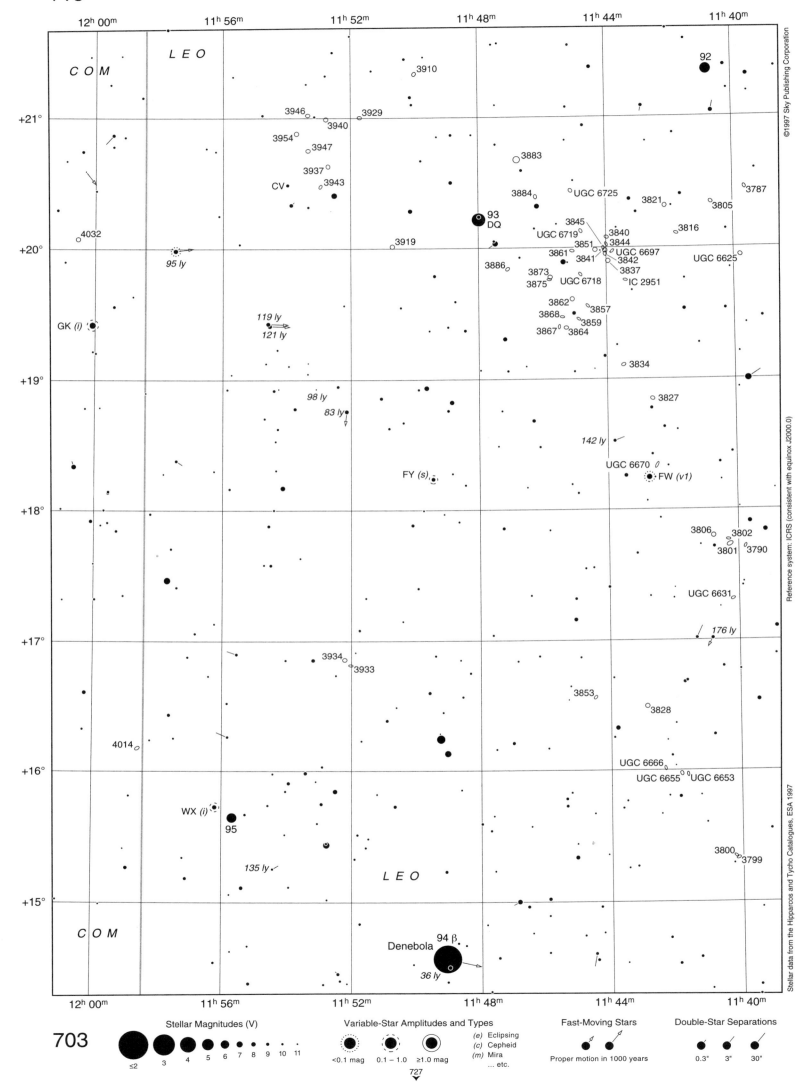

Stellar Magnitudes (V)

≤2 3 4 5 6 7 8 9 10 11

Variable-Star Amplitudes and Types

<0.1 mag   0.1 – 1.0   ≥1.0 mag

(e) Eclipsing
(c) Cepheid
(m) Mira
... etc.

Fast-Moving Stars

Proper motion in 1000 years

Double-Star Separations

0.3"   3"   30"

727

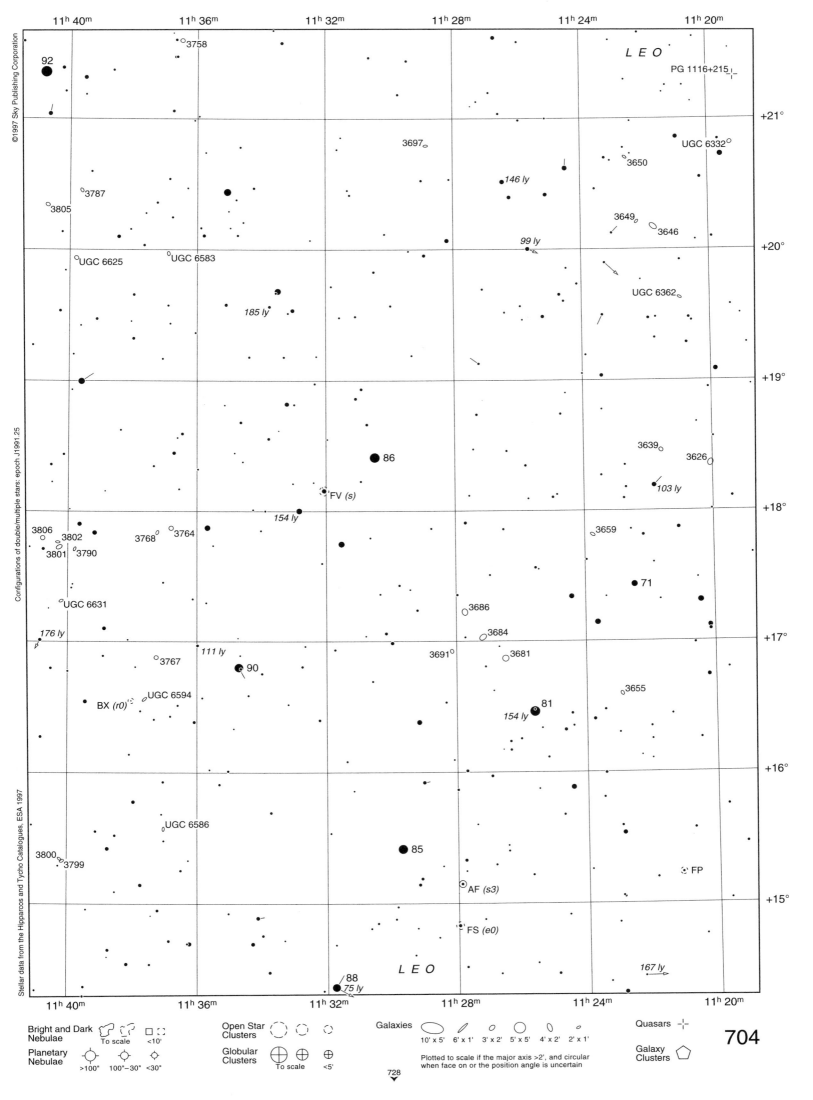

Configurations of double/multiple stars: epoch J1991.25

Stellar data from the Hipparcos and Tycho Catalogues, ESA 1997

LEO

PG 1116+215

92

3758

3787

3805

UGC 6625   UGC 6583

3697

146 ly

99 ly

UGC 6332
3650

3649   3646

UGC 6362

185 ly

86

FV (s)

154 ly

3639   3626

103 ly

3806   3802
3801   3790
3768   3764

UGC 6631

176 ly

3767

111 ly

90

BX (r0)   UGC 6594

3659

71

3686

3684

3691   3681

3655

81

154 ly

UGC 6586

3800
3799

85

AF (s3)

FP

FS (e0)

LEO

167 ly

88
75 ly

+21°

+20°

+19°

+18°

+17°

+16°

+15°

11ʰ 40ᵐ   11ʰ 36ᵐ   11ʰ 32ᵐ   11ʰ 28ᵐ   11ʰ 24ᵐ   11ʰ 20ᵐ

Bright and Dark
Nebulae   To scale   <10'
Planetary
Nebulae   >100" 100"–30" <30'

Open Star
Clusters
Globular
Clusters   To scale   <5'

Galaxies
10' x 5' 6' x 1' 3' x 2' 5' x 5' 4' x 2' 2' x 1'

Plotted to scale if the major axis >2', and circular
when face on or the position angle is uncertain

Quasars

Galaxy
Clusters

704

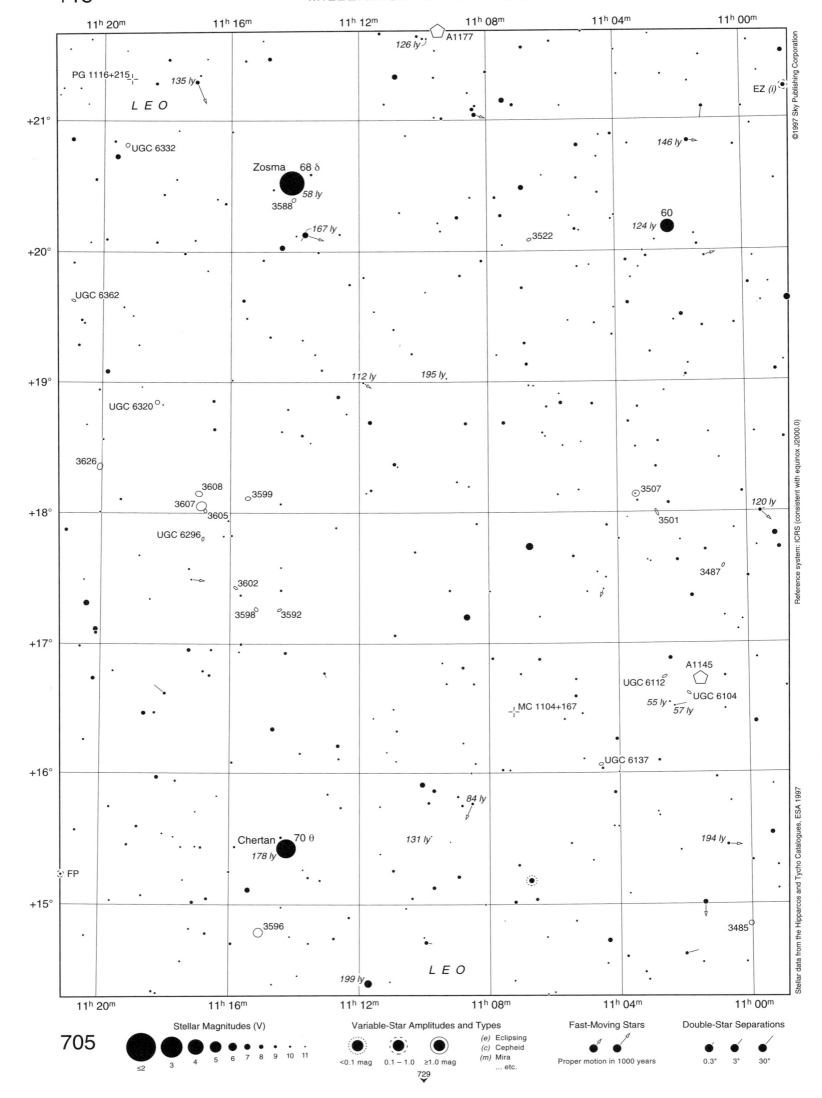

©1997 Sky Publishing Corporation

Reference system: ICRS (consistent with equinox J2000.0)

Stellar data from the Hipparcos and Tycho Catalogues, ESA 1997

LEO

PG 1116+215
135 ly
UGC 6332
Zosma 68 δ
3588
58 ly
167 ly
UGC 6362
112 ly
195 ly
UGC 6320
3626
3608
3607 3605
3599
UGC 6296
3602
3598 3592
Chertan 70 θ
178 ly
3596
FP
199 ly
LEO

A1177
126 ly
EZ (i)
146 ly
60
124 ly
3522
3507
3501
120 ly
3487
A1145
UGC 6112
UGC 6104
55 ly
57 ly
MC 1104+167
UGC 6137
84 ly
131 ly
194 ly
3485

Stellar Magnitudes (V)
≤2   3   4   5   6   7 8 9 10 11

Variable-Star Amplitudes and Types
<0.1 mag   0.1 – 1.0   ≥1.0 mag
(e) Eclipsing
(c) Cepheid
(m) Mira
... etc.

Fast-Moving Stars
Proper motion in 1000 years

Double-Star Separations
0.3"   3"   30"

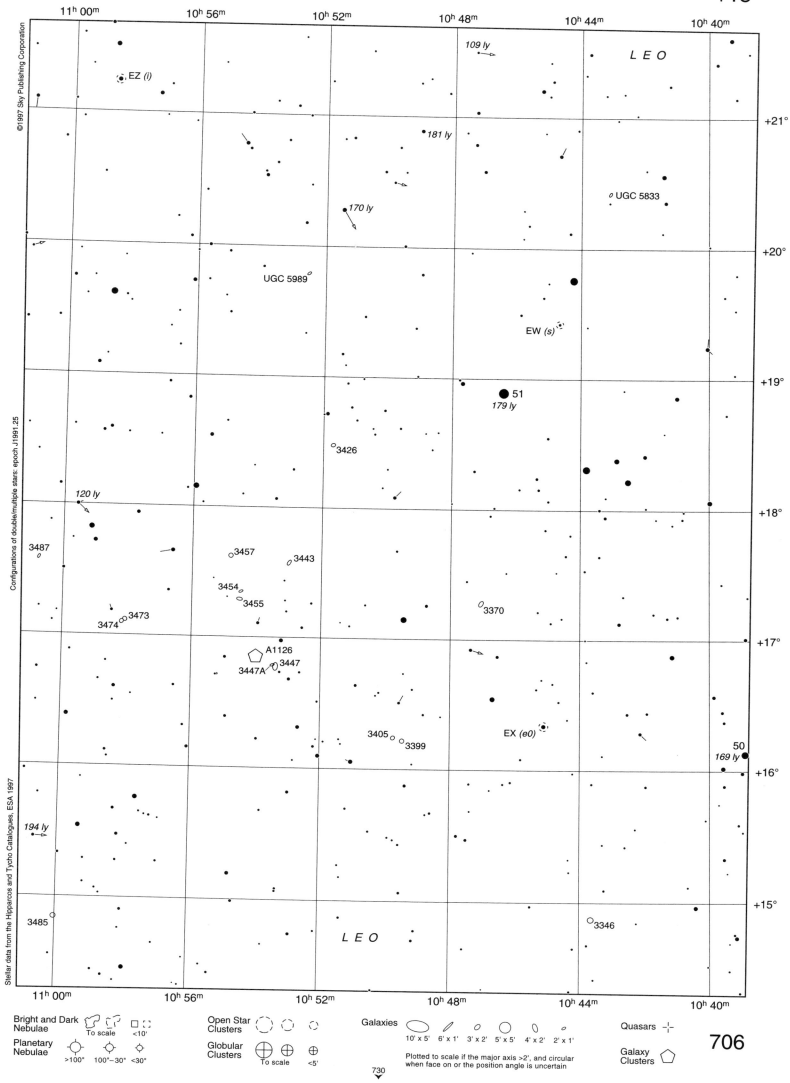

LEO

EZ (i)

109 ly

181 ly

UGC 5833

170 ly

UGC 5989

EW (s)

51
179 ly

3426

120 ly

3487

3457   3443

3454
3455   3370

3474 3473

A1126
3447A   3447

3405 3399   EX (e0)

50
169 ly

194 ly

3485   3346

LEO

Bright and Dark Nebulae
To scale   <10'

Planetary Nebulae
>100"   100"-30"   <30"

Open Star Clusters

Globular Clusters
To scale   <5'

Galaxies
10' x 5'   6' x 1'   3' x 2'   5' x 5'   4' x 2'   2' x 1'

Plotted to scale if the major axis >2', and circular when face on or the position angle is uncertain

Quasars

Galaxy Clusters

706

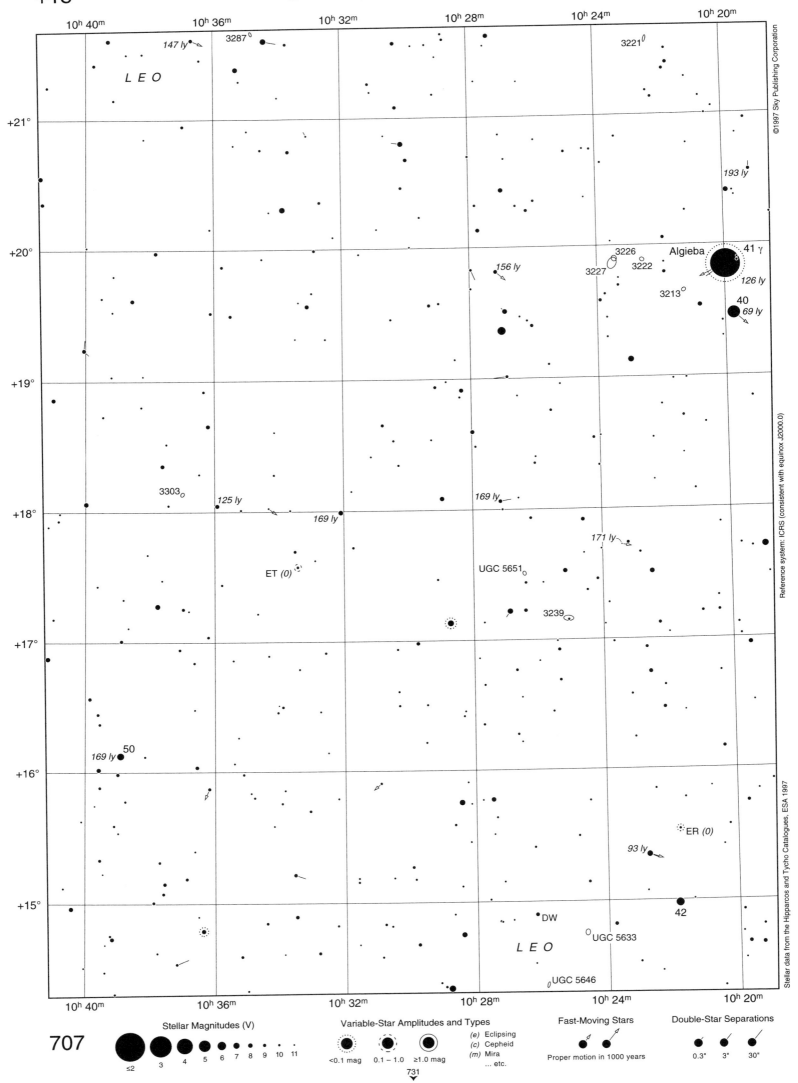

©1997 Sky Publishing Corporation

Reference system: ICRS (consistent with equinox J2000.0)

Stellar data from the Hipparcos and Tycho Catalogues, ESA 1997

LEO

147 ly
3287

3221

193 ly

Algieba   41 γ
3226
3227   3222
3213
126 ly
156 ly

40
69 ly

3303
125 ly
169 ly
169 ly
171 ly

ET (0)
UGC 5651
3239

50
169 ly

ER (0)
93 ly

42
DW
UGC 5633
LEO
UGC 5646

707

Stellar Magnitudes (V)

≤2   3   4   5   6 7 8 9 10 11

Variable-Star Amplitudes and Types

<0.1 mag   0.1 – 1.0   ≥1.0 mag

(e) Eclipsing
(c) Cepheid
(m) Mira
... etc.

Fast-Moving Stars

Proper motion in 1000 years

Double-Star Separations

0.3"   3"   30"

684

+18°

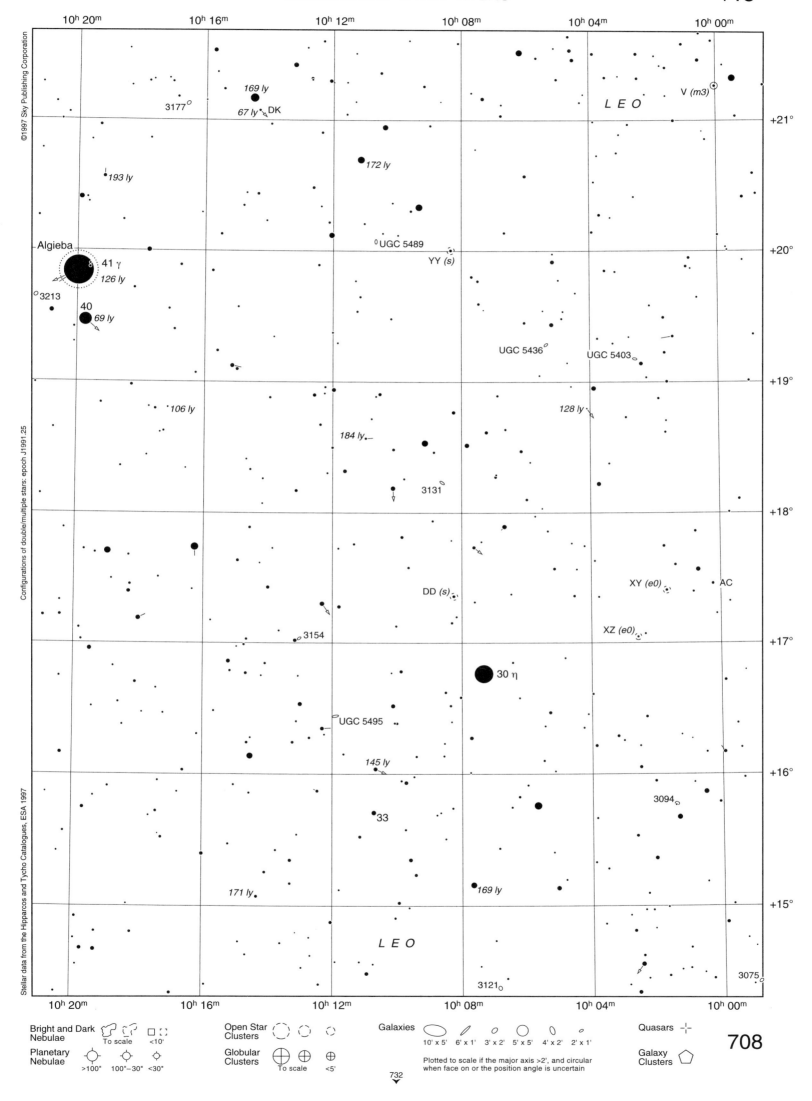

©1997 Sky Publishing Corporation

Configurations of double/multiple stars: epoch J1991.25

Stellar data from the Hipparcos and Tycho Catalogues, ESA 1997

10ʰ 20ᵐ 10ʰ 16ᵐ 10ʰ 12ᵐ 10ʰ 08ᵐ 10ʰ 04ᵐ 10ʰ 00ᵐ

+21°
+20°
+19°
+18°
+17°
+16°
+15°

LEO

V (m3)

169 ly
3177
67 ly · DK

193 ly

172 ly

Algieba
41 γ
126 ly
3213
40
69 ly

UGC 5489
YY (s)

UGC 5436
UGC 5403

106 ly
128 ly

184 ly
3131

DD (s)
XY (e0)   AC
XZ (e0)
30 η

3154

UGC 5495
145 ly
3094
33
171 ly   169 ly
LEO
3121
3075
708

Bright and Dark Nebulae   To scale   <10'
Planetary Nebulae   >100" 100"–30" <30"
Open Star Clusters
Globular Clusters   To scale   <5'
Galaxies   10' x 5' 6' x 1' 3' x 2' 5' x 5' 4' x 2' 2' x 1'
Plotted to scale if the major axis >2', and circular when face on or the position angle is uncertain
Quasars
Galaxy Clusters

732

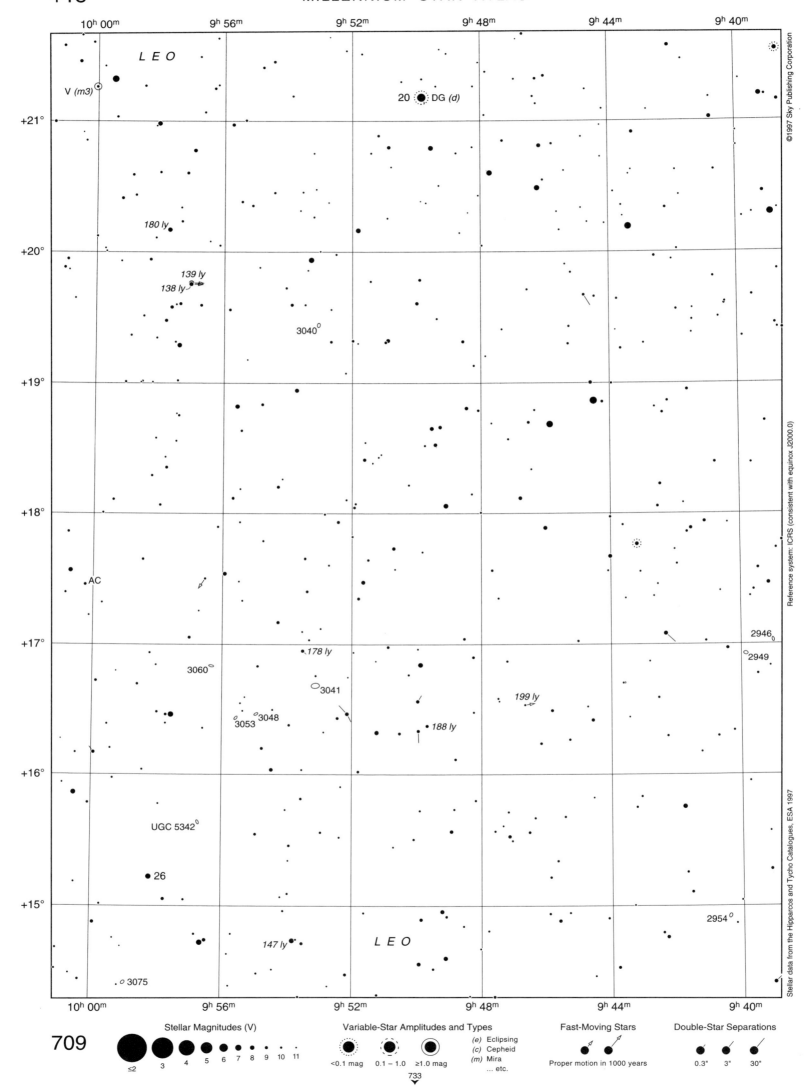

©1997 Sky Publishing Corporation

Reference system: ICRS (consistent with equinox J2000.0)

Stellar data from the Hipparcos and Tycho Catalogues, ESA 1997

LEO

V (m3)

20 DG (d)

180 ly

139 ly
138 ly

3040°

+21°
+20°
+19°
+18°
+17°
+16°
+15°

AC

2946₀

2949

3060°

178 ly

3041

3053 3048

199 ly

188 ly

UGC 5342°

26

2954°

LEO

147 ly

3075

2954°

709

Stellar Magnitudes (V)

≤2   3   4   5   6   7   8   9   10   11

Variable-Star Amplitudes and Types

<0.1 mag   0.1 – 1.0   ≥1.0 mag

(e) Eclipsing
(c) Cepheid
(m) Mira
... etc.

Fast-Moving Stars

Proper motion in 1000 years

Double-Star Separations

0.3"   3"   30"

733

MILLENNIUM STAR ATLAS

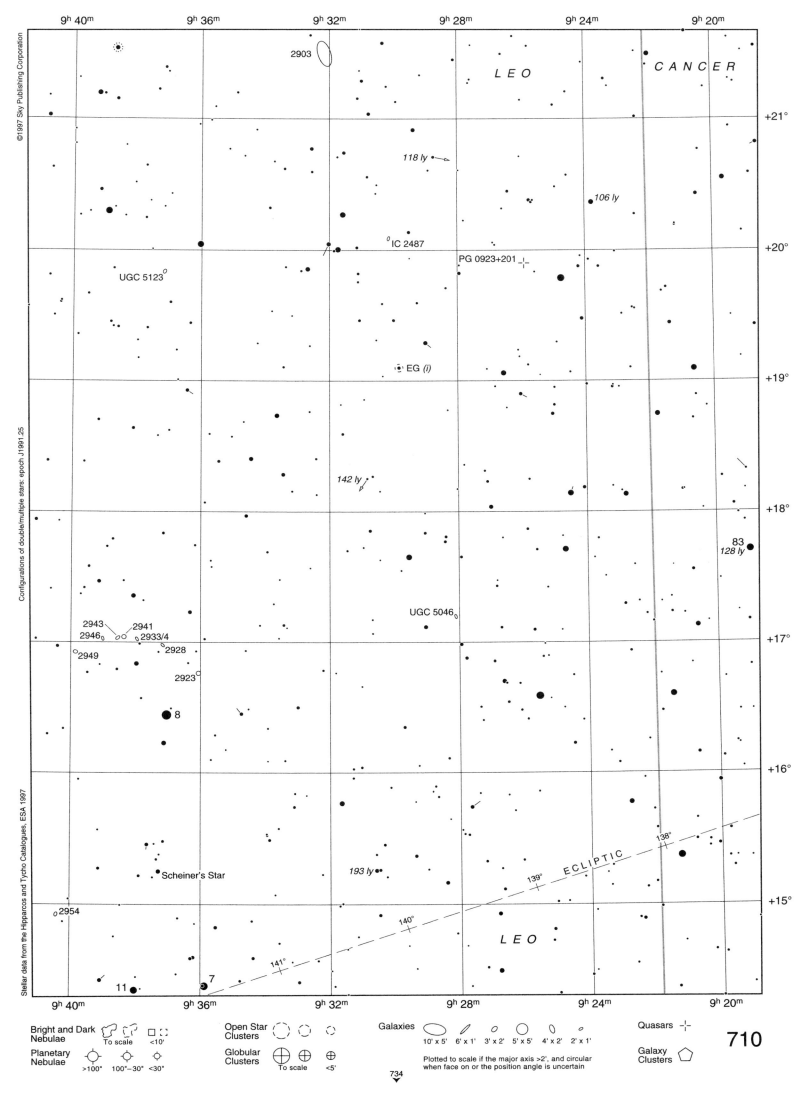

LEO   CANCER

2903

118 ly

106 ly

IC 2487

PG 0923+201

UGC 5123

EG (i)

142 ly

83
128 ly

UGC 5046

2943   2941
2946   2933/4
       2928
2949
2923

8

Scheiner's Star

193 ly

138°

ECLIPTIC

139°

140°

LEO

2954

141°

11   7

Bright and Dark Nebulae	Open Star Clusters	Galaxies	Quasars
To scale <10'		10' x 5' 6' x 1' 3' x 2' 5' x 5' 4' x 2' 2' x 1'	
Planetary Nebulae	Globular Clusters		Galaxy Clusters
>100" 100"–30" <30"	To scale <5'	Plotted to scale if the major axis >2', and circular when face on or the position angle is uncertain	

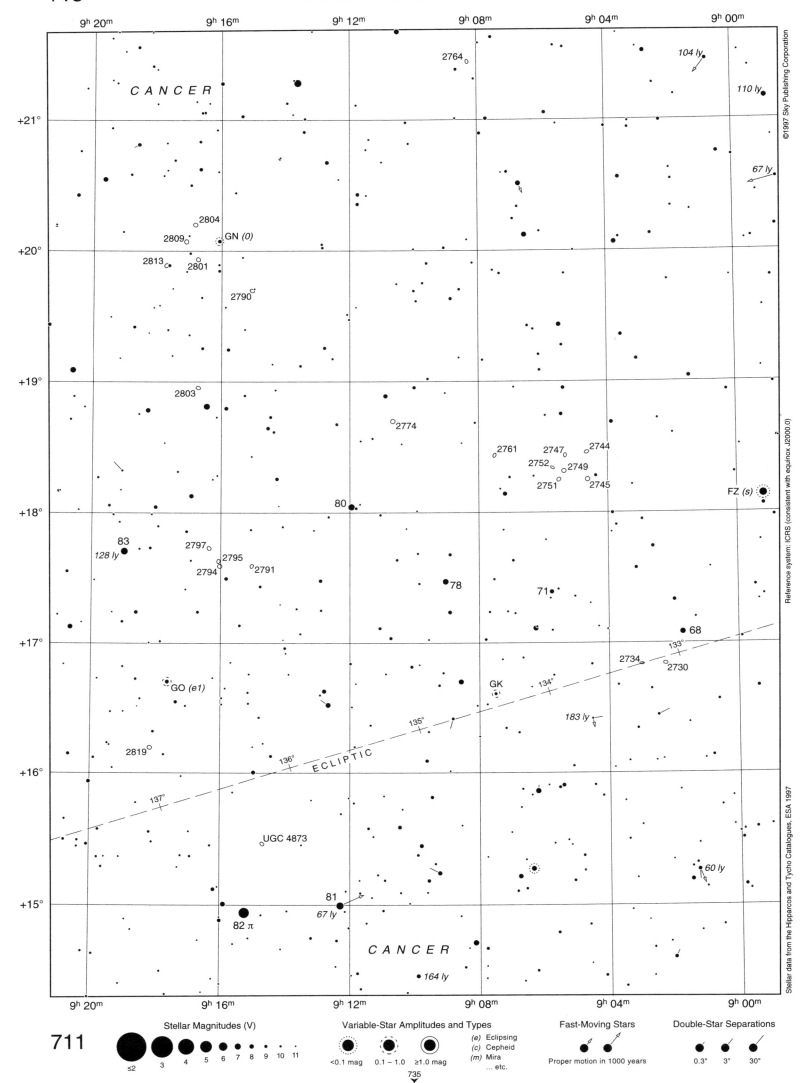

©1997 Sky Publishing Corporation

Reference system: ICRS (consistent with equinox J2000.0)

Stellar data from the Hipparcos and Tycho Catalogues, ESA 1997

CANCER

2764

104 ly

110 ly

67 ly

2804
2809
GN (0)
2813
2801
2790
2803
2774
2761
2747
2744
2752
2749
2751
2745
FZ (s)
80
83
128 ly
2797
2795
2794
2791
78
71
68
GO (e1)
133°
2734
2730
GK
134°
183 ly
135°
2819
ECLIPTIC
136°
137°
UGC 4873
60 ly
81
82 π
67 ly
CANCER
164 ly

711

Stellar Magnitudes (V)

≤2 3 4 5 6 7 8 9 10 11

Variable-Star Amplitudes and Types

<0.1 mag   0.1 – 1.0   ≥1.0 mag

(e) Eclipsing
(c) Cepheid
(m) Mira
... etc.

Fast-Moving Stars

Proper motion in 1000 years

Double-Star Separations

0.3"   3"   30"

735

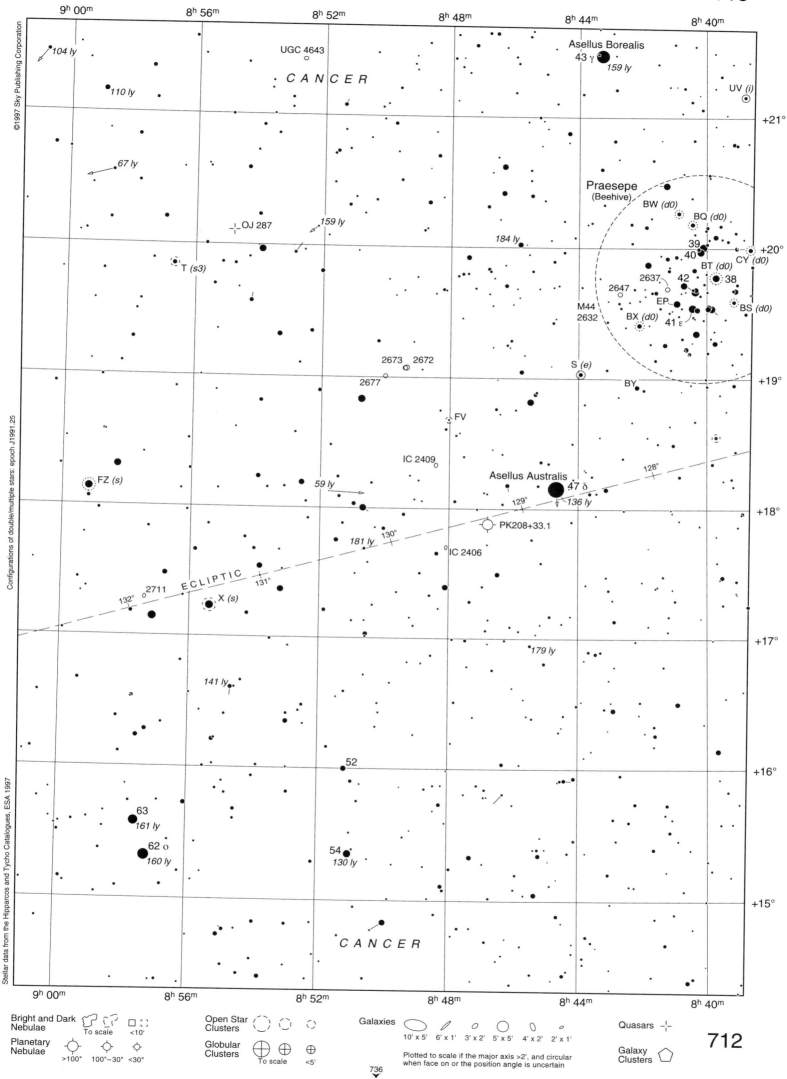

Bright and Dark Nebulae
To scale <10'

Planetary Nebulae
>100" 100"–30" <30"

Open Star Clusters

Globular Clusters
To scale <5'

Galaxies
10' x 5' 6' x 1' 3' x 2' 5' x 5' 4' x 2' 2' x 1'

Plotted to scale if the major axis >2', and circular when face on or the position angle is uncertain

Quasars

Galaxy Clusters

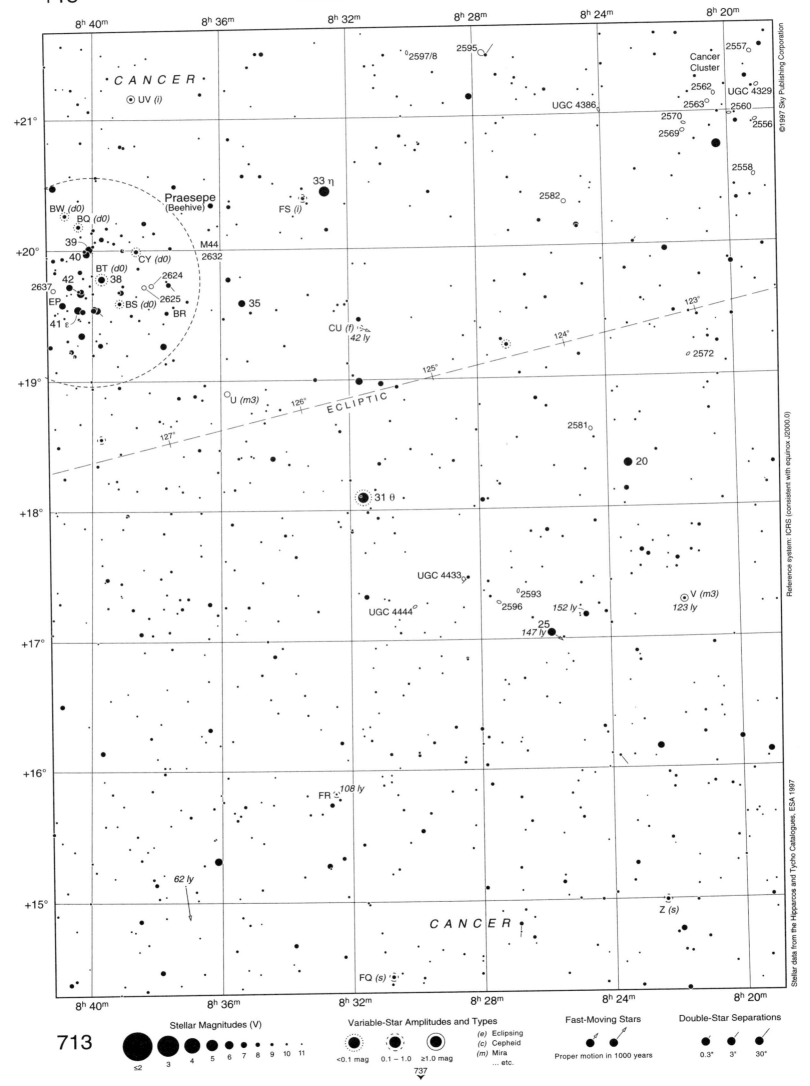

713

Stellar Magnitudes (V)

≤2   3   4   5   6   7   8   9 10 11

Variable-Star Amplitudes and Types

<0.1 mag   0.1 – 1.0   ≥1.0 mag

(e) Eclipsing
(c) Cepheid
(m) Mira
… etc.

Fast-Moving Stars

Proper motion in 1000 years

Double-Star Separations

0.3"   3"   30"

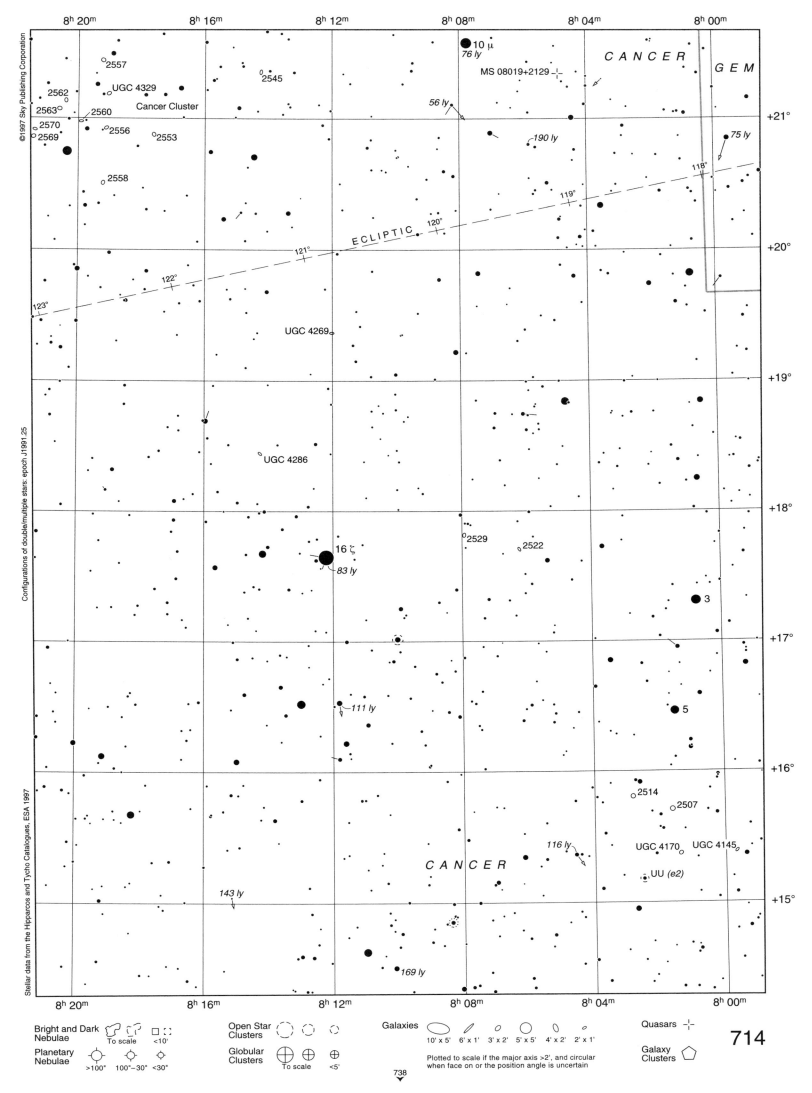

Configurations of double/multiple stars: epoch J1991.25

Stellar data from the Hipparcos and Tycho Catalogues, ESA 1997

8h 20m   8h 16m   8h 12m   8h 08m   8h 04m   8h 00m

10 μ
76 ly

CANCER   GEM

2557
UGC 4329
2562   Cancer Cluster
2563
2570   2560
2569   2556   2553

2558

MS 08019+2129

56 ly

190 ly

118°

75 ly

119°

120°

ECLIPTIC

121°

122°

123°

UGC 4269

UGC 4286

16 ζ
83 ly

2529   2522

3

111 ly

5

116 ly

2514
2507

UGC 4170   UGC 4145

CANCER

UU (e2)

143 ly

169 ly

+21°

+20°

+19°

+18°

+17°

+16°

+15°

8h 20m   8h 16m   8h 12m   8h 08m   8h 04m   8h 00m

Bright and Dark
Nebulae   To scale   <10'

Planetary
Nebulae   >100" 100"−30" <30'

Open Star
Clusters

Globular
Clusters   To scale   <5'

Galaxies

10' x 5'   6' x 1'   3' x 2'   5' x 5'   4' x 2'   2' x 1'

Plotted to scale if the major axis >2', and circular
when face on or the position angle is uncertain

Quasars

Galaxy
Clusters

714

738

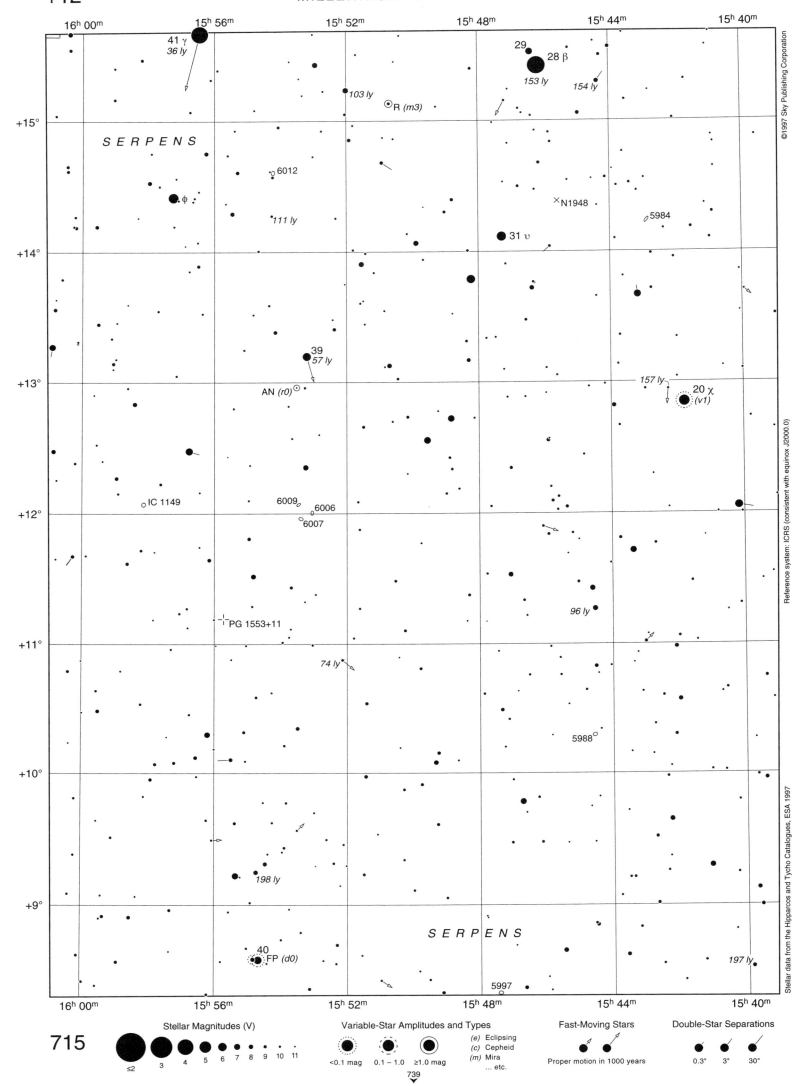

715

Stellar Magnitudes (V)

≤2 3 4 5 6 7 8 9 10 11

Variable-Star Amplitudes and Types

<0.1 mag   0.1 – 1.0   ≥1.0 mag

(e) Eclipsing
(c) Cepheid
(m) Mira
... etc.

Fast-Moving Stars

Proper motion in 1000 years

Double-Star Separations

0.3"   3"   30"

739

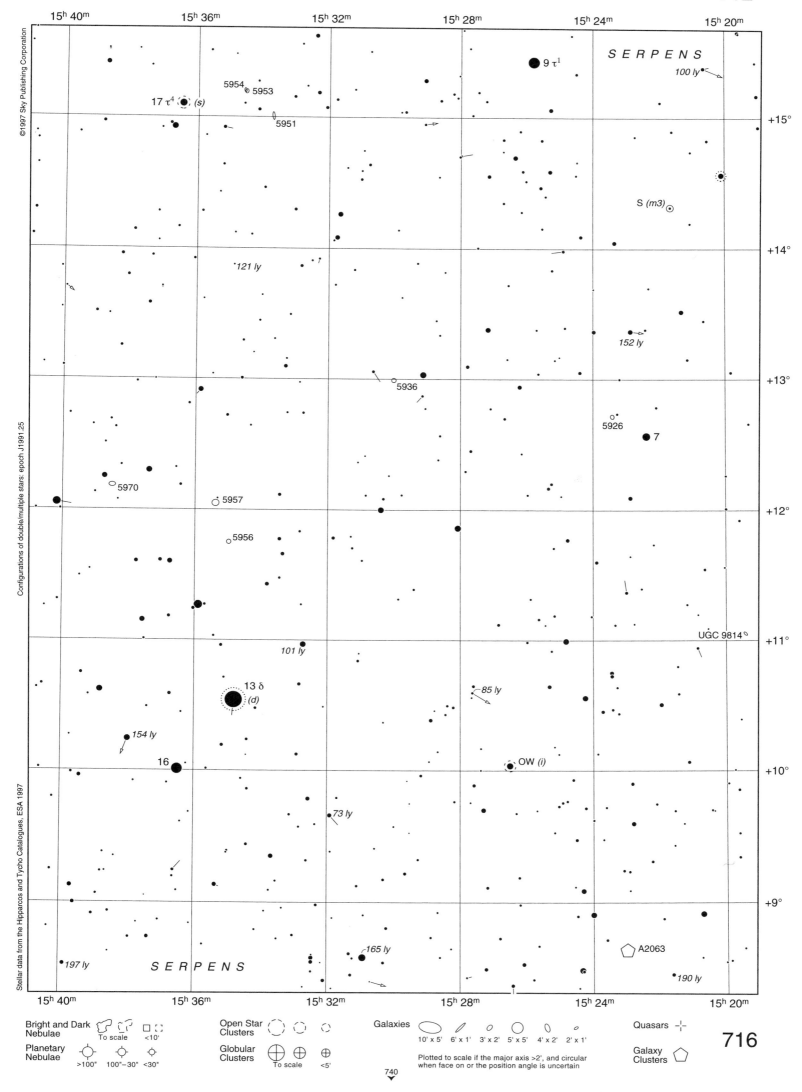

©1997 Sky Publishing Corporation

Configurations of double/multiple stars: epoch J1991.25

Stellar data from the Hipparcos and Tycho Catalogues, ESA 1997

SERPENS

9 τ¹

100 ly

5954   5953

17 τ⁴   (s)

5951

+15°

S (m3)

121 ly

+14°

152 ly

5936

+13°

5926

7

5970

5957

+12°

5956

UGC 9814

+11°

101 ly

13 δ
(d)

85 ly

154 ly

16

OW (i)

+10°

73 ly

+9°

A2063

165 ly

SERPENS

197 ly

190 ly

15ʰ 40ᵐ   15ʰ 36ᵐ   15ʰ 32ᵐ   15ʰ 28ᵐ   15ʰ 24ᵐ   15ʰ 20ᵐ

Bright and Dark Nebulae		Open Star Clusters			Galaxies						Quasars
To scale	<10'				10' x 5'	6' x 1'	3' x 2'	5' x 5'	4' x 2'	2' x 1'	

Planetary Nebulae			Globular Clusters						Galaxy Clusters
>100"	100"–30"	<30"	To scale	<5'					

Plotted to scale if the major axis >2', and circular
when face on or the position angle is uncertain

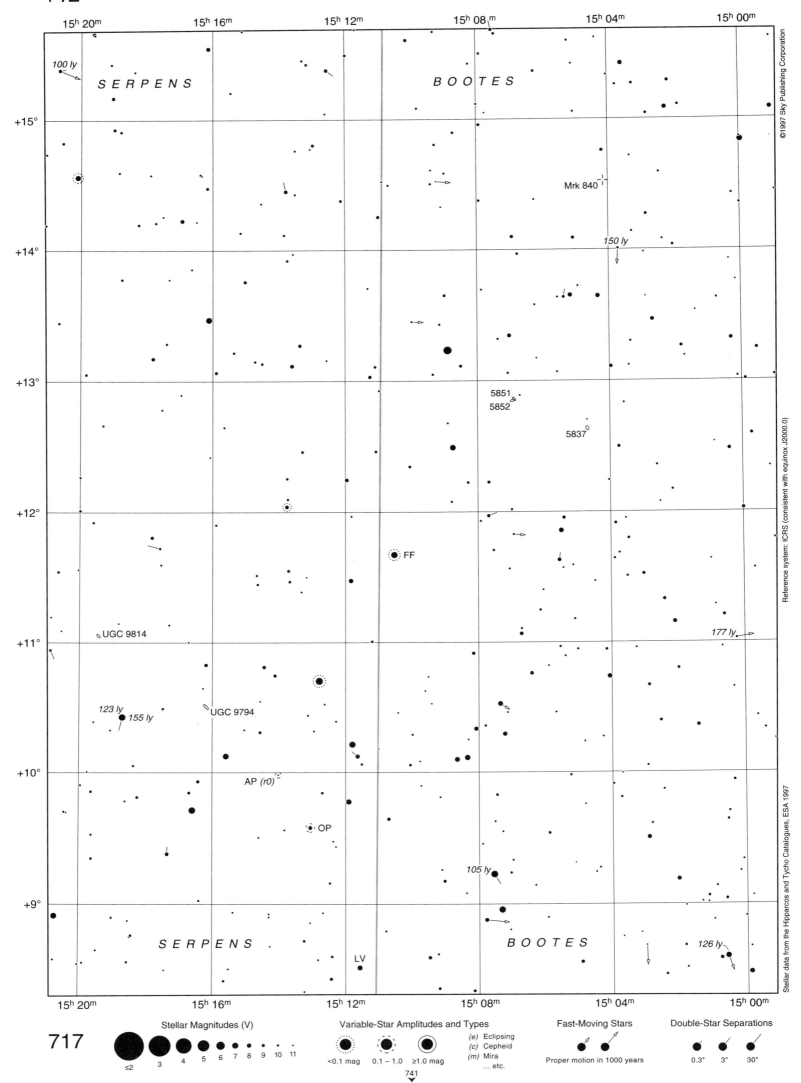

©1997 Sky Publishing Corporation

Reference system: ICRS (consistent with equinox J2000.0)

Stellar data from the Hipparcos and Tycho Catalogues, ESA 1997

717

Stellar Magnitudes (V)

≤2   3   4   5   6   7   8   9   10   11

Variable-Star Amplitudes and Types

<0.1 mag   0.1 – 1.0   ≥1.0 mag

(e) Eclipsing
(c) Cepheid
(m) Mira
... etc.

Fast-Moving Stars

Proper motion in 1000 years

Double-Star Separations

0.3"   3"   30"

MILLENNIUM STAR ATLAS

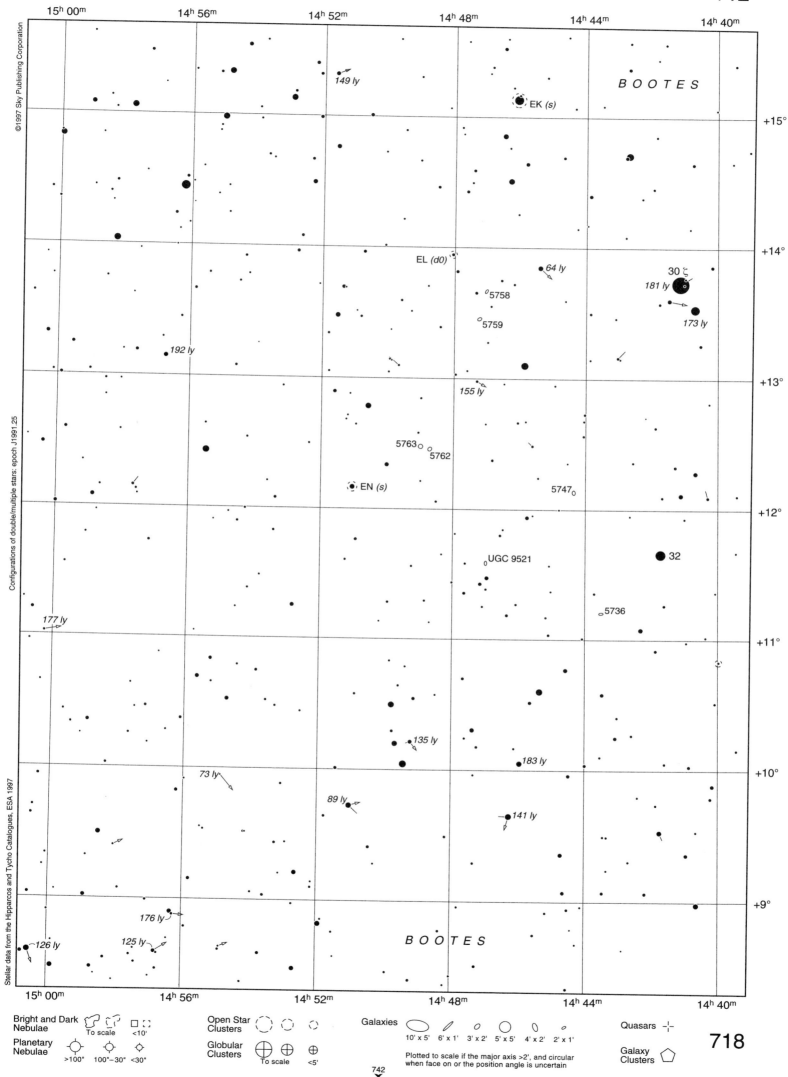

15h 00m   14h 56m   14h 52m   14h 48m   14h 44m   14h 40m

B O O T E S

149 ly

EK (s)

+15°

EL (d0)

64 ly

30 ζ

181 ly

5758

173 ly

192 ly

5759

155 ly

+14°

+13°

5763 ○   ○ 5762

EN (s)

5747 ○

+12°

UGC 9521

32

177 ly

5736

+11°

135 ly

183 ly

73 ly

+10°

89 ly

141 ly

176 ly

+9°

125 ly

126 ly

B O O T E S

15h 00m   14h 56m   14h 52m   14h 48m   14h 44m   14h 40m

Configurations of double/multiple stars: epoch J1991.25

Stellar data from the Hipparcos and Tycho Catalogues, ESA 1997

Bright and Dark Nebulae	To scale	<10'	**Open Star Clusters**		**Galaxies**	**Quasars**
Planetary Nebulae	>100" 100"–30" <30"		**Globular Clusters**	To scale <5'	10' x 5' 6' x 1' 3' x 2' 5' x 5' 4' x 2' 2' x 1'	**Galaxy Clusters**

Plotted to scale if the major axis >2', and circular when face on or the position angle is uncertain

718

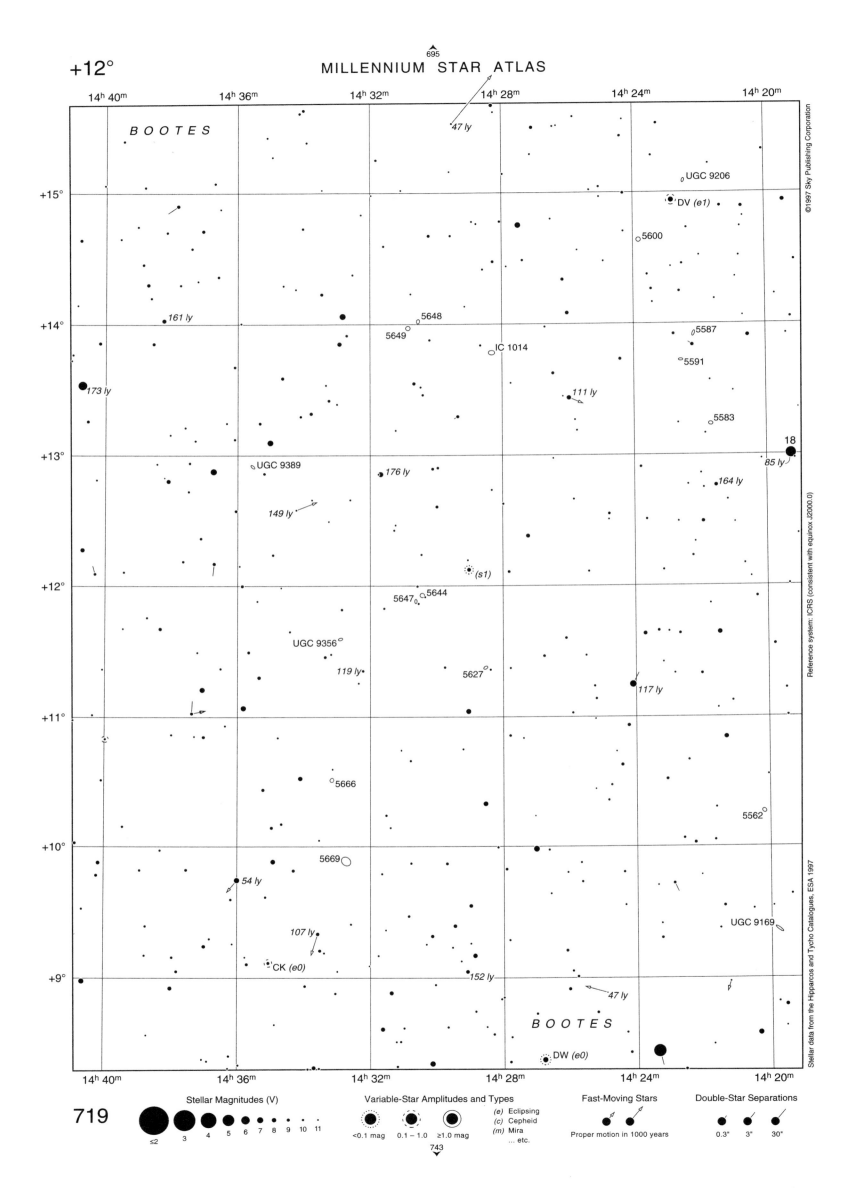

BOOTES

47 ly

UGC 9206

DV (e1)

5600

161 ly

5648

5649

IC 1014

5587

5591

173 ly

111 ly

5583

18

85 ly

UGC 9389

176 ly

164 ly

149 ly

(s1)

5647   5644

UGC 9356

5627

119 ly

117 ly

5666

5562

5669

54 ly

UGC 9169

107 ly

CK (e0)

152 ly

47 ly

BOOTES

DW (e0)

719

Stellar Magnitudes (V)

≤2   3   4   5   6 7 8 9 10 11

Variable-Star Amplitudes and Types

<0.1 mag   0.1 – 1.0   ≥1.0 mag

(e) Eclipsing
(c) Cepheid
(m) Mira
... etc.

Fast-Moving Stars

Proper motion in 1000 years

Double-Star Separations

0.3"   3"   30"

MILLENNIUM STAR ATLAS

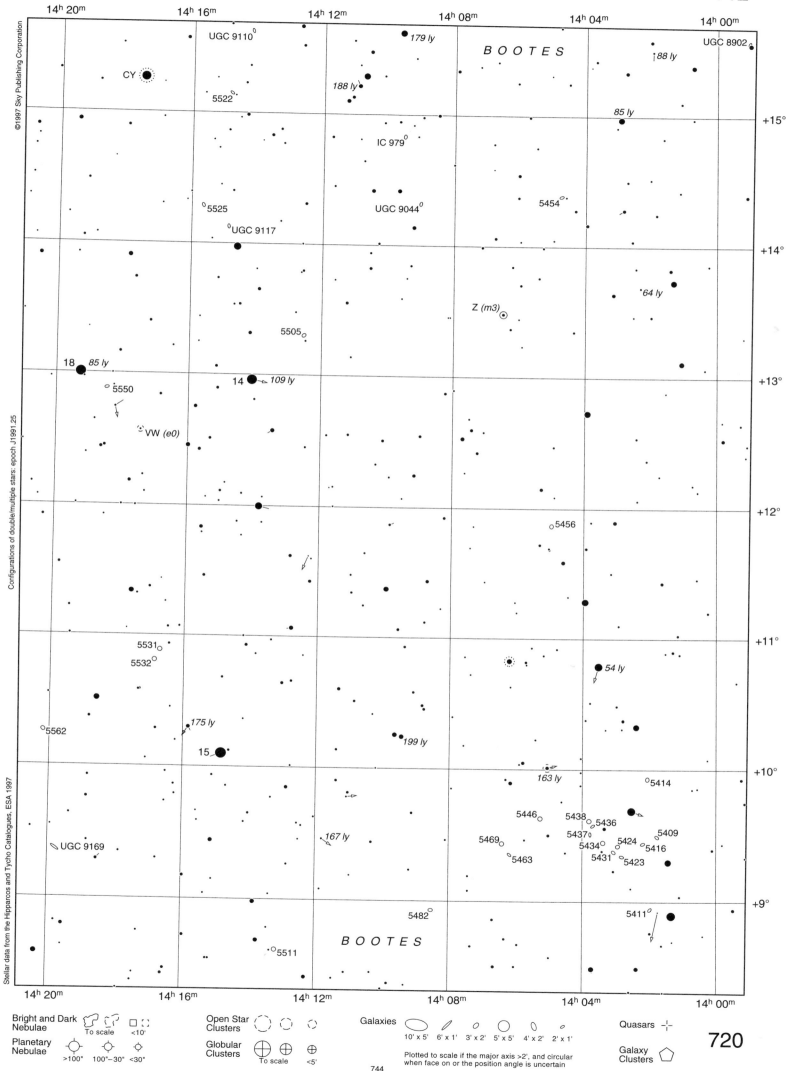

©1997 Sky Publishing Corporation

14h 20m · 14h 16m · 14h 12m · 14h 08m · 14h 04m · 14h 00m

UGC 9110

CY

5522

179 ly

BOOTES

UGC 8902

188 ly

88 ly

85 ly

+15°

IC 979

5454

5525

UGC 9044

UGC 9117

+14°

64 ly

Z (m3)

5505

18 85 ly

5550

14 109 ly

+13°

VW (e0)

+12°

5456

+11°

5531

5532

54 ly

5562

175 ly

15

199 ly

163 ly

5414

+10°

167 ly

5446

5438 5436

5409

5469

5437

5424

5416

UGC 9169

5434

5431

5423

5463

5482

5411

+9°

BOOTES

5511

14h 20m · 14h 16m · 14h 12m · 14h 08m · 14h 04m · 14h 00m

Configurations of double/multiple stars: epoch J1991.25

Stellar data from the Hipparcos and Tycho Catalogues, ESA 1997

Bright and Dark Nebulae
To scale   <10'

Planetary Nebulae
>100"   100"–30"   <30"

Open Star Clusters

Globular Clusters
To scale   <5'

Galaxies
10' x 5'   6' x 1'   3' x 2'   5' x 5'   4' x 2'   2' x 1'

Plotted to scale if the major axis >2', and circular when face on or the position angle is uncertain

Quasars

Galaxy Clusters

744

720

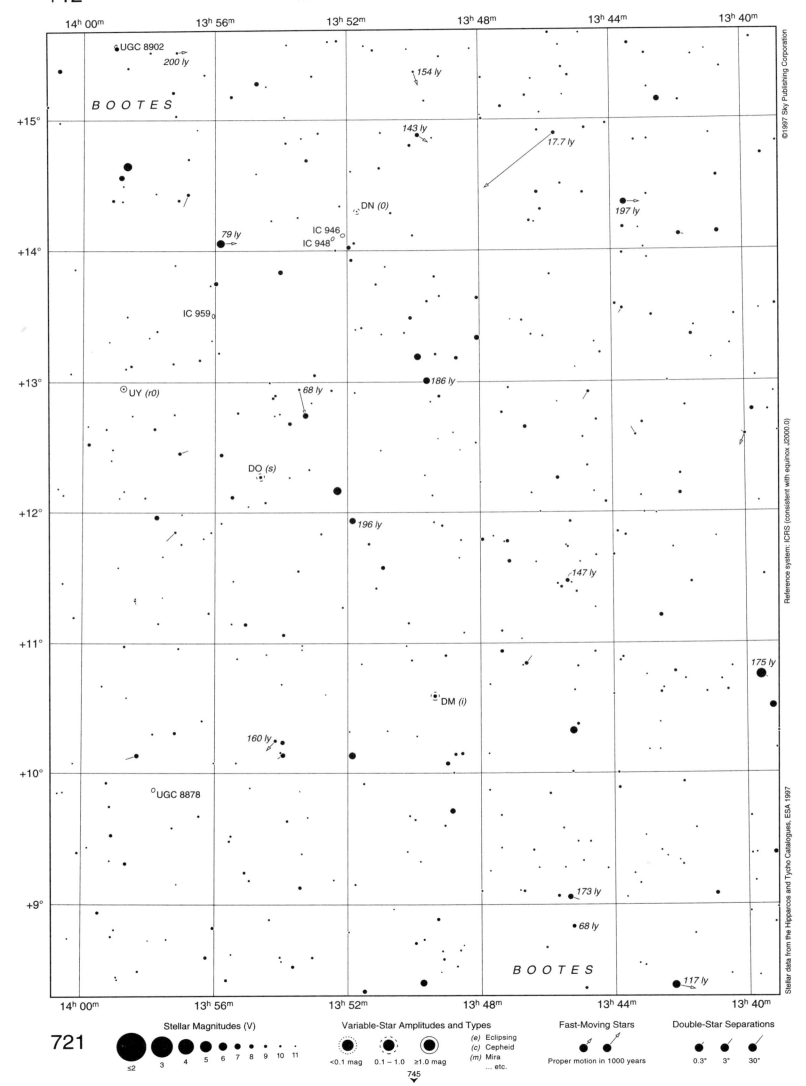

14ʰ 00ᵐ   13ʰ 56ᵐ   13ʰ 52ᵐ   13ʰ 48ᵐ   13ʰ 44ᵐ   13ʰ 40ᵐ

UGC 8902
200 ly
154 ly
B O O T E S
+15°
143 ly
17.7 ly
DN (0)
197 ly
79 ly
IC 946
IC 948
+14°
IC 959
186 ly
UY (r0)
68 ly
DO (s)
+12°
196 ly
147 ly
+11°
175 ly
DM (i)
160 ly
UGC 8878
+10°
173 ly
+9°
68 ly
B O O T E S
117 ly

14ʰ 00ᵐ   13ʰ 56ᵐ   13ʰ 52ᵐ   13ʰ 48ᵐ   13ʰ 44ᵐ   13ʰ 40ᵐ

©1997 Sky Publishing Corporation

Reference system: ICRS (consistent with equinox J2000.0)

Stellar data from the Hipparcos and Tycho Catalogues, ESA 1997

721

Stellar Magnitudes (V)
≤2 3 4 5 6 7 8 9 10 11

Variable-Star Amplitudes and Types
<0.1 mag   0.1 – 1.0   ≥1.0 mag
(e) Eclipsing
(c) Cepheid
(m) Mira
... etc.

Fast-Moving Stars
Proper motion in 1000 years

Double-Star Separations
0.3" 3" 30"

745

MILLENNIUM STAR ATLAS

Configurations of double/multiple stars: epoch J1991.25

Stellar data from the Hipparcos and Tycho Catalogues, ESA 1997

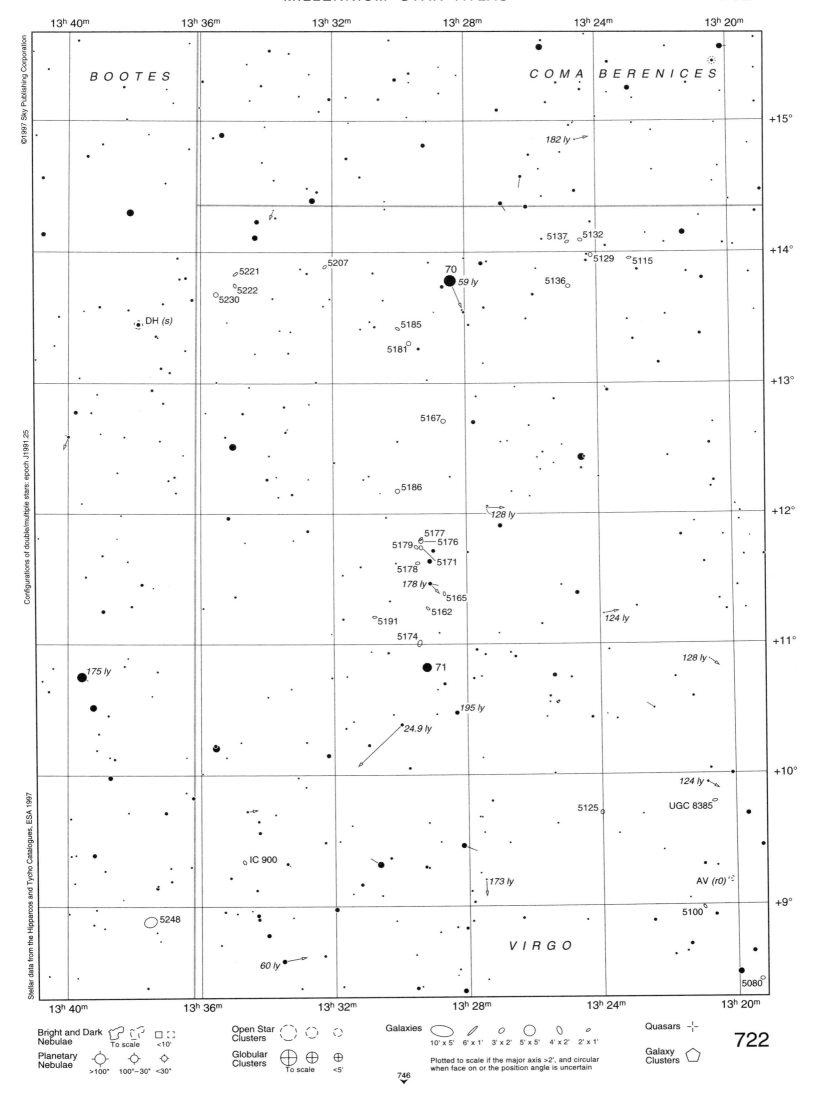

B O O T E S

C O M A   B E R E N I C E S

182 ly

5137 5132

5221

5207

5129 5115

5222

5230

70

5136

DH (s)

59 ly

5185

5181

5167

5186

128 ly

5177

5179 5176

5171

5178

178 ly

5165

5162

5191

124 ly

5174

71

128 ly

175 ly

195 ly

24.9 ly

IC 900

124 ly

5125

UGC 8385

173 ly

AV (r0)

5100

5248

V I R G O

60 ly

5080

Bright and Dark Nebulae To scale <10'

Open Star Clusters

Galaxies 10' x 5' 6' x 1' 3' x 2' 5' x 5' 4' x 2' 2' x 1'

Quasars

722

Planetary Nebulae >100" 100"-30" <30"

Globular Clusters To scale <5'

Plotted to scale if the major axis >2', and circular when face on or the position angle is uncertain

Galaxy Clusters

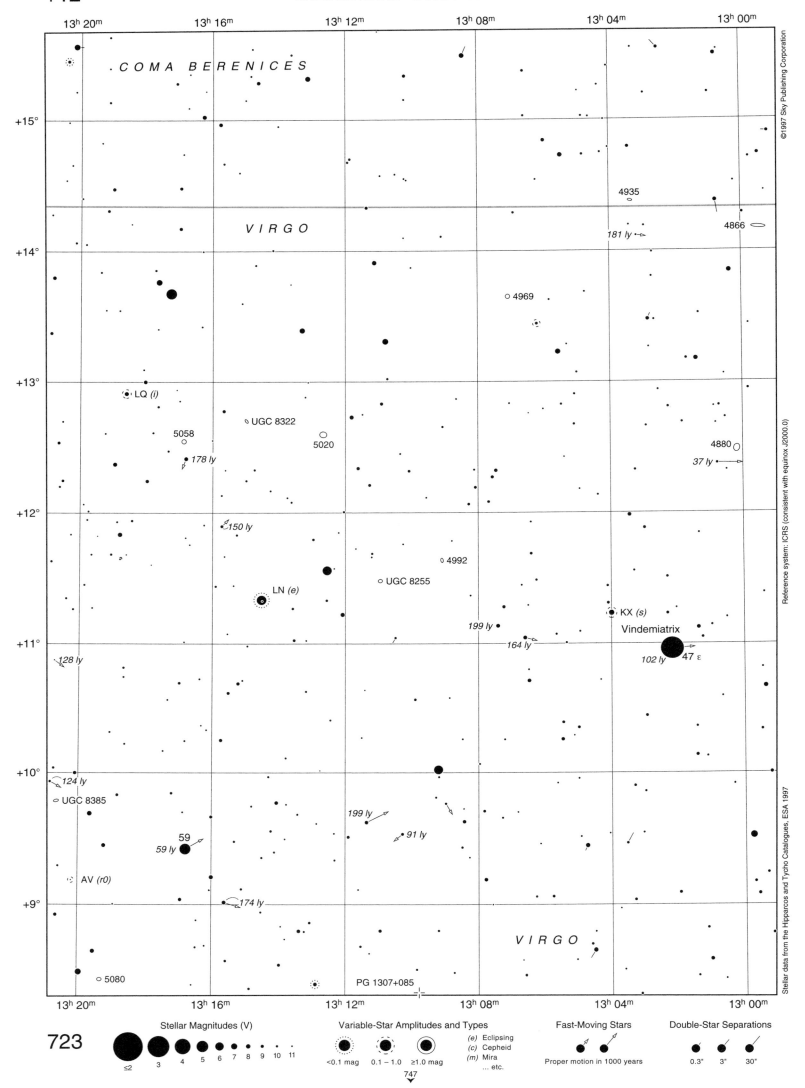

723

Stellar Magnitudes (V)

≤2   3   4   5   6   7   8   9 10 11

Variable-Star Amplitudes and Types

<0.1 mag   0.1 – 1.0   ≥1.0 mag

(e) Eclipsing
(c) Cepheid
(m) Mira
... etc.

Fast-Moving Stars

Proper motion in 1000 years

Double-Star Separations

0.3"   3"   30"

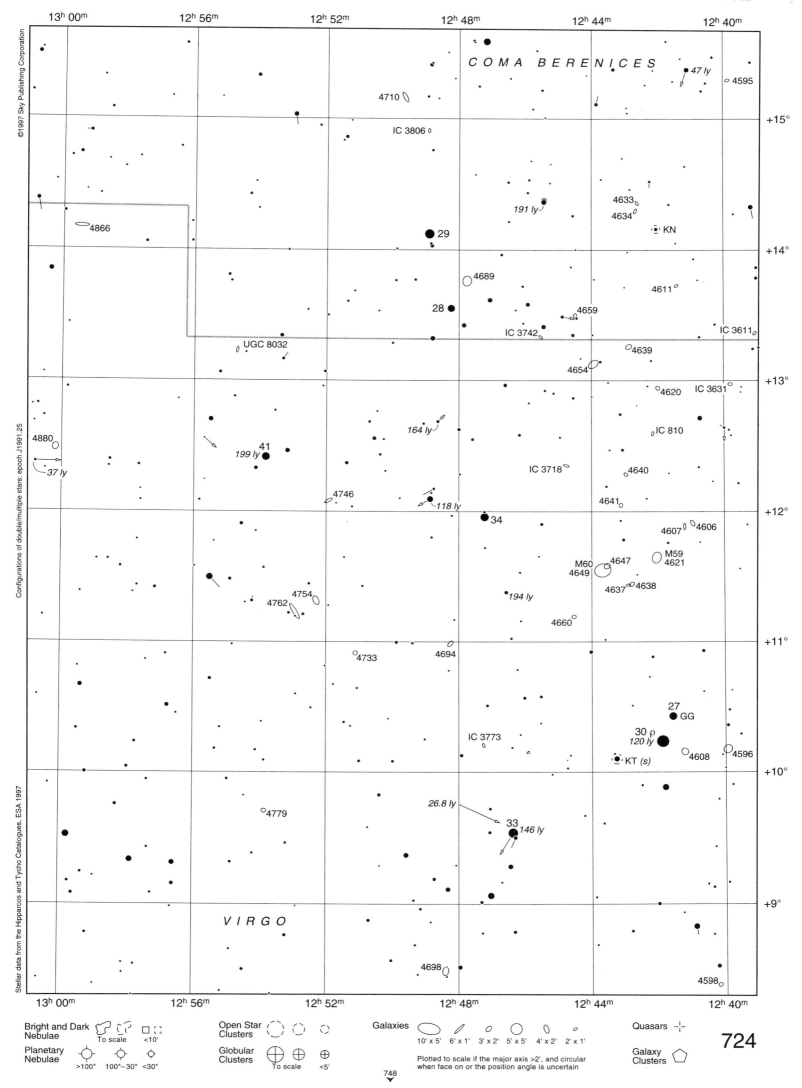

©1997 Sky Publishing Corporation

Configurations of double/multiple stars: epoch J1991.25

Stellar data from the Hipparcos and Tycho Catalogues, ESA 1997

13h 00m   12h 56m   12h 52m   12h 48m   12h 44m   12h 40m

C O M A   B E R E N I C E S

47 ly

4595

4710

IC 3806

+15°

4633
4634

191 ly

KN

29

4866

+14°

4689

4611

28

4659

IC 3742

IC 3611

UGC 8032

4639

4654

+13°

4620   IC 3631

4880

IC 810

164 ly

41
199 ly

IC 3718

4640

37 ly

4746

4641

+12°

118 ly

34

4607 4606

4607 M59
4621

M60
4649   4647

4754

4637 4638

4762

194 ly

4660

+11°

4733   4694

27
GG

30 ρ
120 ly

IC 3773

4608   4596

KT (s)

+10°

4779

26.8 ly

33 146 ly

+9°

V I R G O

4698

4598

13h 00m   12h 56m   12h 52m   12h 48m   12h 44m   12h 40m

Bright and Dark Nebulae
To scale   <10'

Open Star Clusters

Galaxies
10' x 5'   6' x 1'   3' x 2'   5' x 5'   4' x 2'   2' x 1'

Quasars

724

Planetary Nebulae
>100"   100"–30"   <30"

Globular Clusters
To scale   <5'

Plotted to scale if the major axis >2', and circular when face on or the position angle is uncertain

Galaxy Clusters

748

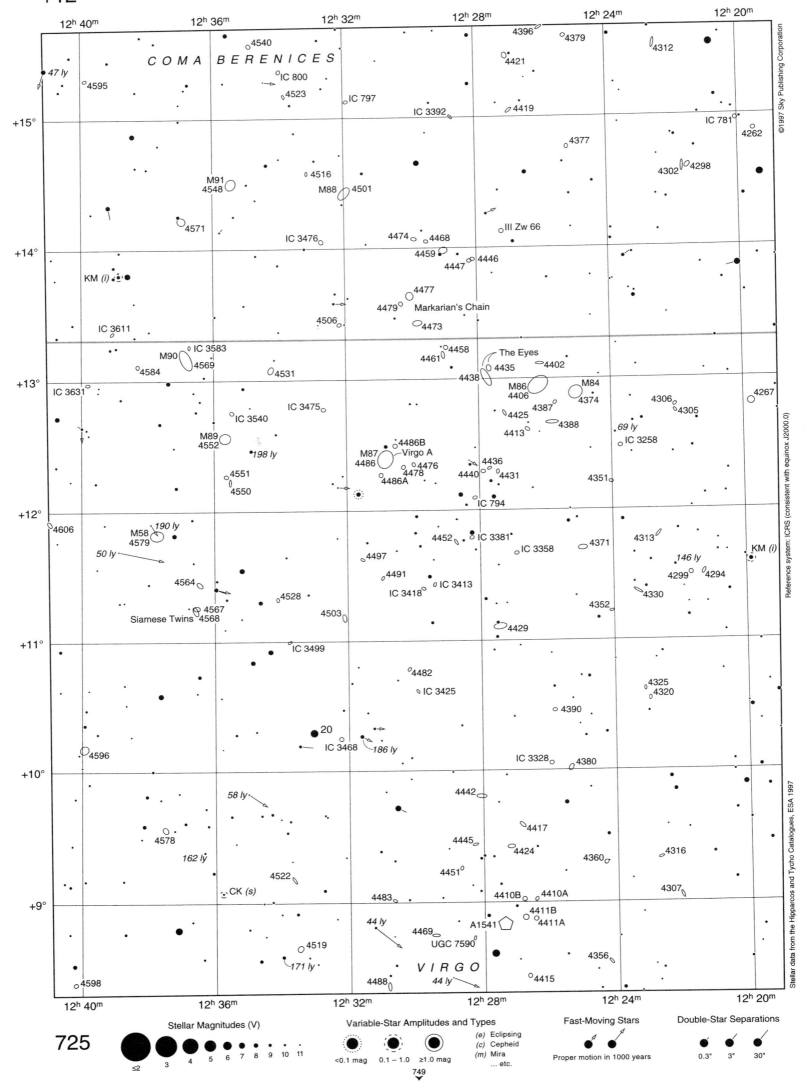

COMA BERENICES

VIRGO

Markarian's Chain

The Eyes

Siamese Twins

Virgo A

	Stellar Magnitudes (V)	Variable-Star Amplitudes and Types	Fast-Moving Stars	Double-Star Separations

725

Stellar Magnitudes (V)
≤2 3 4 5 6 7 8 9 10 11

Variable-Star Amplitudes and Types
<0.1 mag   0.1 – 1.0   ≥1.0 mag
(e) Eclipsing
(c) Cepheid
(m) Mira
... etc.

Fast-Moving Stars
Proper motion in 1000 years

Double-Star Separations
0.3"   3"   30"

749

©1997 Sky Publishing Corporation

Reference system: ICRS (consistent with equinox J2000.0)

Stellar data from the Hipparcos and Tycho Catalogues, ESA 1997

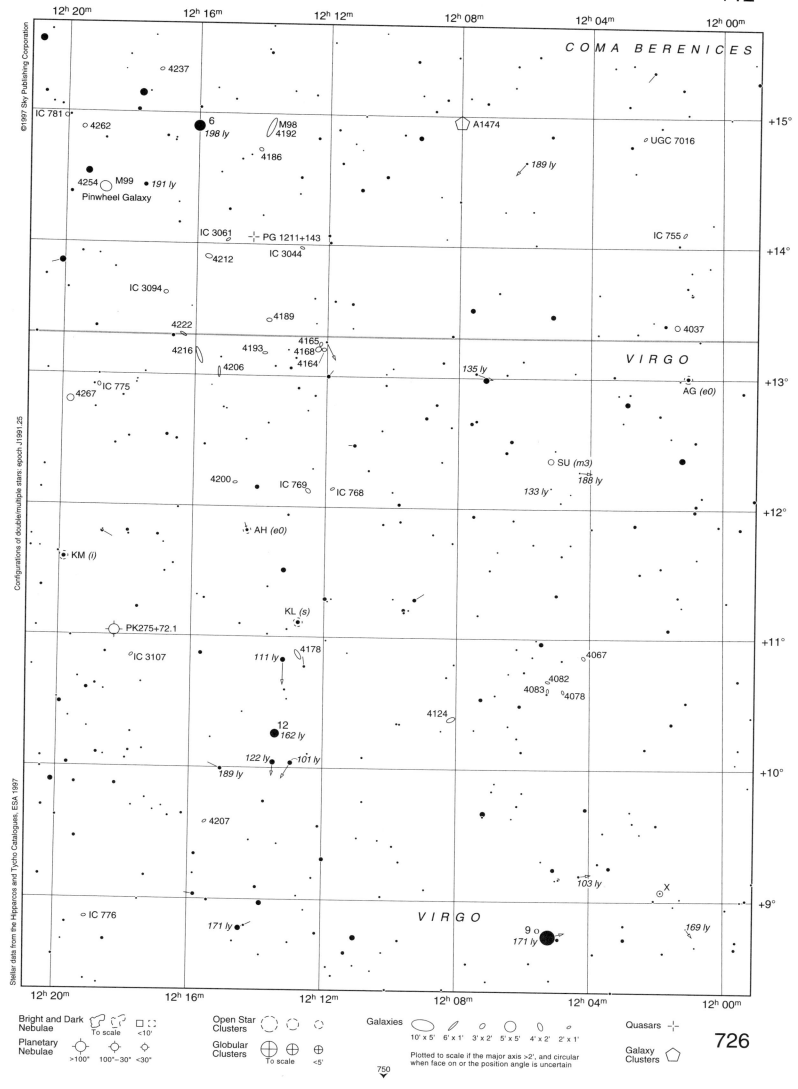

©1997 Sky Publishing Corporation

Configurations of double/multiple stars: epoch J1991.25

Stellar data from the Hipparcos and Tycho Catalogues, ESA 1997

12ʰ 20ᵐ   12ʰ 16ᵐ   12ʰ 12ᵐ   12ʰ 08ᵐ   12ʰ 04ᵐ   12ʰ 00ᵐ

COMA BERENICES

4237

IC 781 o   o 4262   6   M98   A1474   UGC 7016
                                  198 ly   4192
                                          4186   189 ly
4254   M99   • 191 ly   IC 755 o
Pinwheel Galaxy

IC 3061   PG 1211+143   +14°
                    o 4212   IC 3044
IC 3094 o   o 4037
4222   o 4189
4216   4193 o   4165   VIRGO
4206   4168   135 ly   AG (e0)   +13°
o IC 775   4164
o 4267   o SU (m3)
                                                          188 ly
4200 o   IC 769 o   o IC 768   133 ly   +12°
                    AH (e0)
KM (i)
                    KL (s)
PK275+72.1   +11°
o IC 3107   4178   o 4067
                    111 ly   4082
                              4083 o o 4078
                    12   4124
                    162 ly   +10°
         122 ly o---o 101 ly
189 ly   o 103 ly
                                                          X   +9°
o IC 776   VIRGO
         171 ly   9 o
                              171 ly   169 ly

12ʰ 20ᵐ   12ʰ 16ᵐ   12ʰ 12ᵐ   12ʰ 08ᵐ   12ʰ 04ᵐ   12ʰ 00ᵐ

Bright and Dark Nebulae   Open Star Clusters   Galaxies   Quasars
To scale   <10'   10' x 5' 6' x 1' 3' x 2' 5' x 5' 4' x 2' 2' x 1'
Planetary Nebulae   Globular Clusters   Galaxy Clusters
>100" 100"–30" <30"   To scale   <5'   Plotted to scale if the major axis >2', and circular
                                                    when face on or the position angle is uncertain

726

MILLENNIUM STAR ATLAS

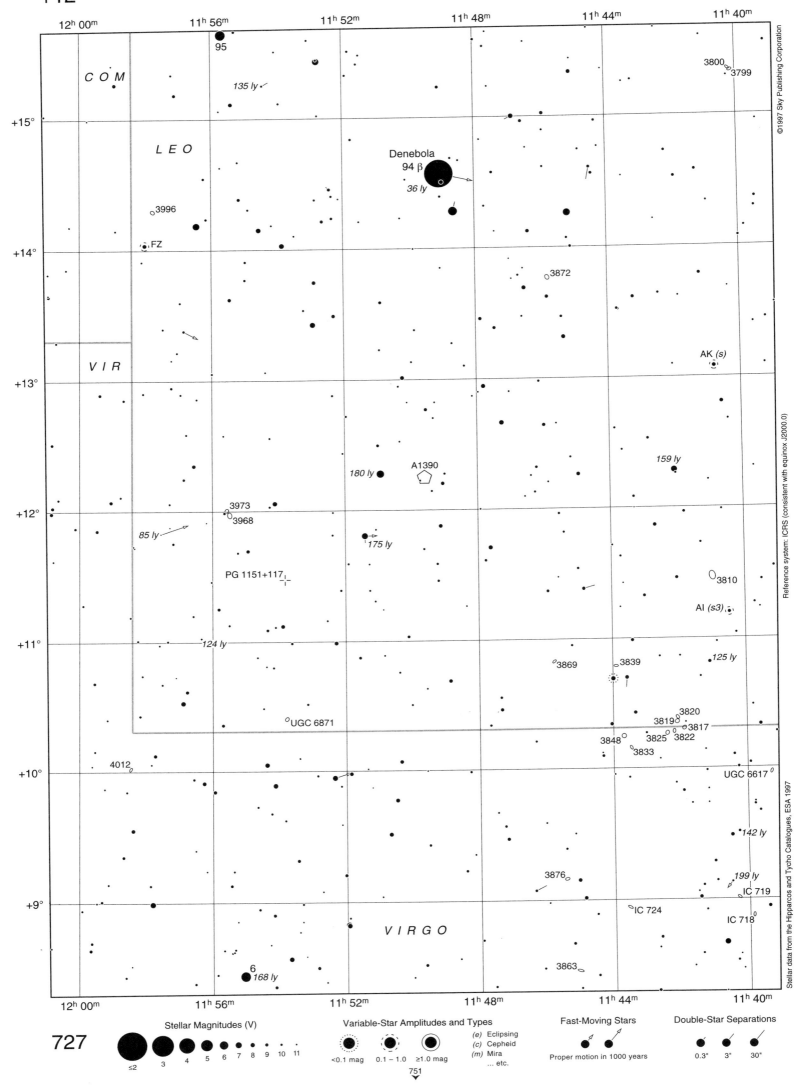

©1997 Sky Publishing Corporation

Reference system: ICRS (consistent with equinox J2000.0)

Stellar data from the Hipparcos and Tycho Catalogues, ESA 1997

727

Stellar Magnitudes (V)

≤2 3 4 5 6 7 8 9 10 11

Variable-Star Amplitudes and Types

<0.1 mag   0.1 – 1.0   ≥1.0 mag

(e) Eclipsing
(c) Cepheid
(m) Mira
... etc.

Fast-Moving Stars

Proper motion in 1000 years

Double-Star Separations

0.3"   3"   30"

751

704

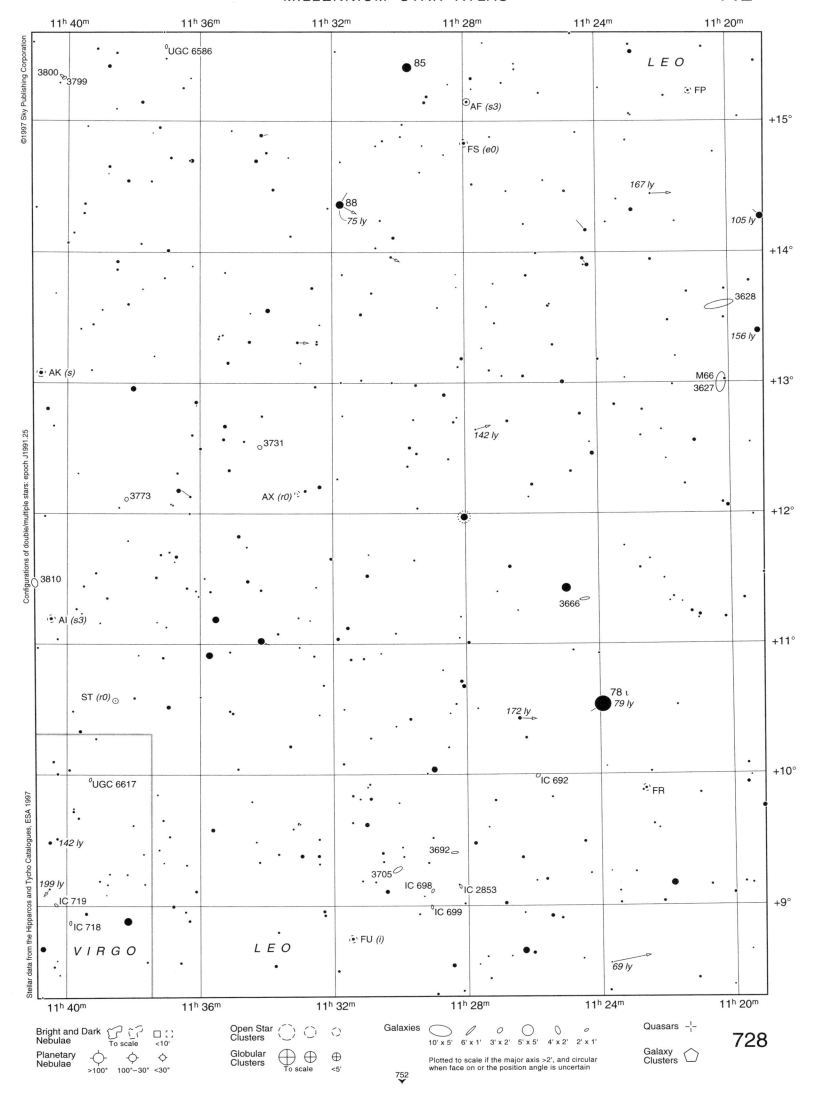

LEO

©1997 Sky Publishing Corporation

⁰UGC 6586

3800 ᵒ 3799

85

AF (s3)

FS (e0)

FP

167 ly

105 ly

88

75 ly

3628

156 ly

AK (s)

M66
3627

142 ly

Configurations of double/multiple stars: epoch J1991.25

ᵒ3731

3773

AX (r0)

3810

3666

AI (s3)

ST (r0)

78 ι
79 ly

172 ly

Stellar data from the Hipparcos and Tycho Catalogues, ESA 1997

⁰UGC 6617

IC 692

FR

142 ly

3692

199 ly

3705

IC 719

IC 698

IC 2853

⁰IC 718

IC 699

VIRGO

LEO

FU (i)

69 ly

+15°

+14°

+13°

+12°

+11°

+10°

+9°

11ʰ 40ᵐ   11ʰ 36ᵐ   11ʰ 32ᵐ   11ʰ 28ᵐ   11ʰ 24ᵐ   11ʰ 20ᵐ

| Bright and Dark Nebulae | Open Star Clusters | Galaxies | | | | | | | Quasars |
| Planetary Nebulae | Globular Clusters | | | | | | | | Galaxy Clusters |

To scale   <10'
>100"   100"–30"   <30"
To scale   <5'
10' x 5'   6' x 1'   3' x 2'   5' x 5'   4' x 2'   2' x 1'

Plotted to scale if the major axis >2', and circular
when face on or the position angle is uncertain

728

752

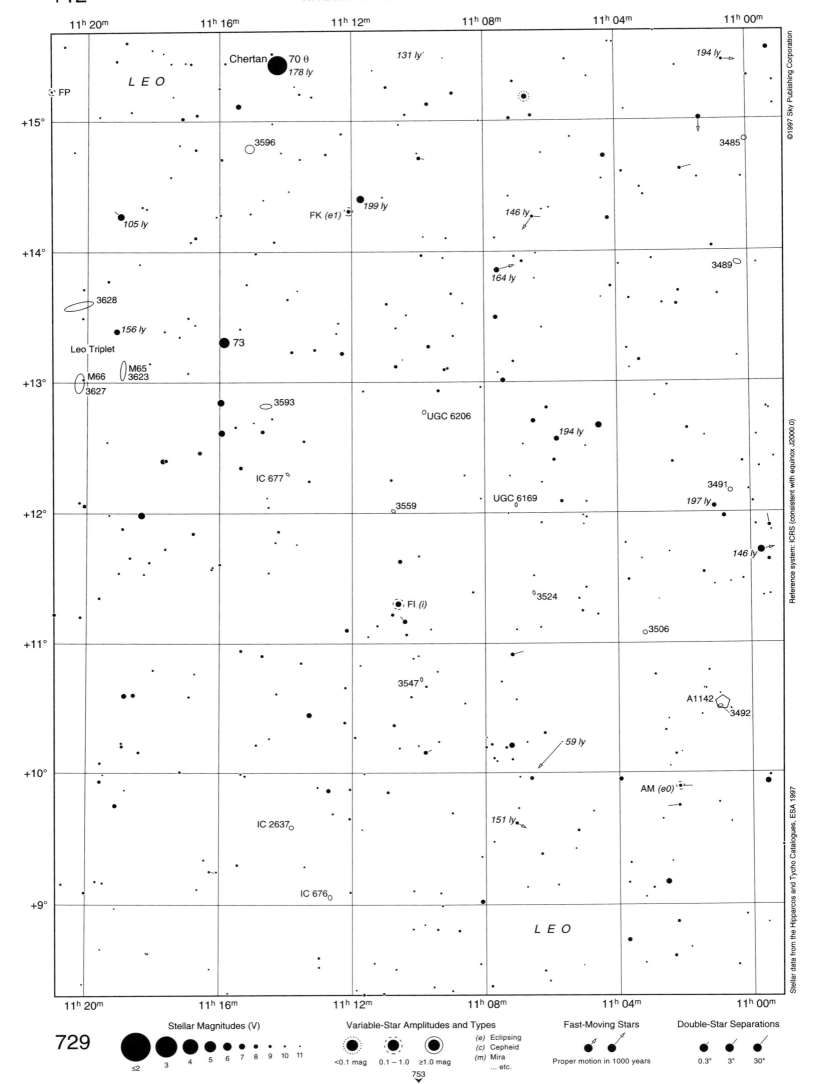

©1997 Sky Publishing Corporation

Reference system: ICRS (consistent with equinox J2000.0)

Stellar data from the Hipparcos and Tycho Catalogues, ESA 1997

Chertan   70 θ
178 ly
131 ly
194 ly
LEO
FP
3485
3596
3489
FK (e1)   199 ly
146 ly
105 ly
164 ly
3628
156 ly
Leo Triplet
73
M65
3623
194 ly
M66
3627
3593
UGC 6206
3491
IC 677
197 ly
3559
UGC 6169
146 ly
3524
3506
FI (i)
3547
A1142
3492
59 ly
AM (e0)
IC 2637
151 ly
IC 676
LEO

Stellar Magnitudes (V)
≤2 3 4 5 6 7 8 9 10 11

Variable-Star Amplitudes and Types
<0.1 mag   0.1 – 1.0   ≥1.0 mag

(e) Eclipsing
(c) Cepheid
(m) Mira
... etc.

Fast-Moving Stars
Proper motion in 1000 years

Double-Star Separations
0.3"   3"   30"

753

MILLENNIUM STAR ATLAS

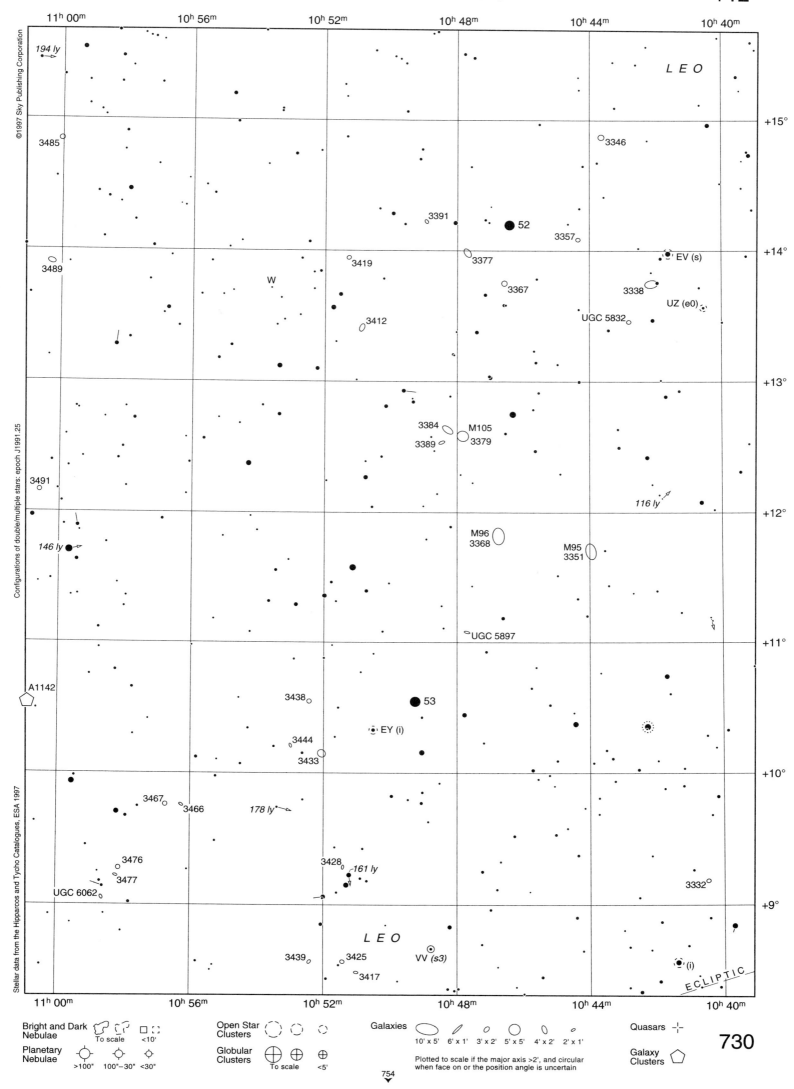

©1997 Sky Publishing Corporation

Configurations of double/multiple stars: epoch J1991.25

Stellar data from the Hipparcos and Tycho Catalogues, ESA 1997

194 ly

L E O

3485

3346

3391
52
3357

3489
3419
EV (s)

W
3367
3338
UZ (e0)
UGC 5832

3412

3384   M105
3389   3379

3491
116 ly

146 ly
M96
3368
M95
3351

UGC 5897

A1142
3438
53

EY (i)

3444
3433

3467   3466
178 ly

3476
3428   161 ly
3332
3477

UGC 6062

L E O
3439   3425
VV (s3)
(i)
3417

ECLIPTIC

Bright and Dark Nebulae		Open Star Clusters		Galaxies						Quasars
To scale	<10'			10' x 5'	6' x 1'	3' x 2'	5' x 5'	4' x 2'	2' x 1'	
Planetary Nebulae		**Globular Clusters**								**Galaxy Clusters**
>100"	100"–30"	<30"	To scale	<5'		Plotted to scale if the major axis >2', and circular when face on or the position angle is uncertain				

730

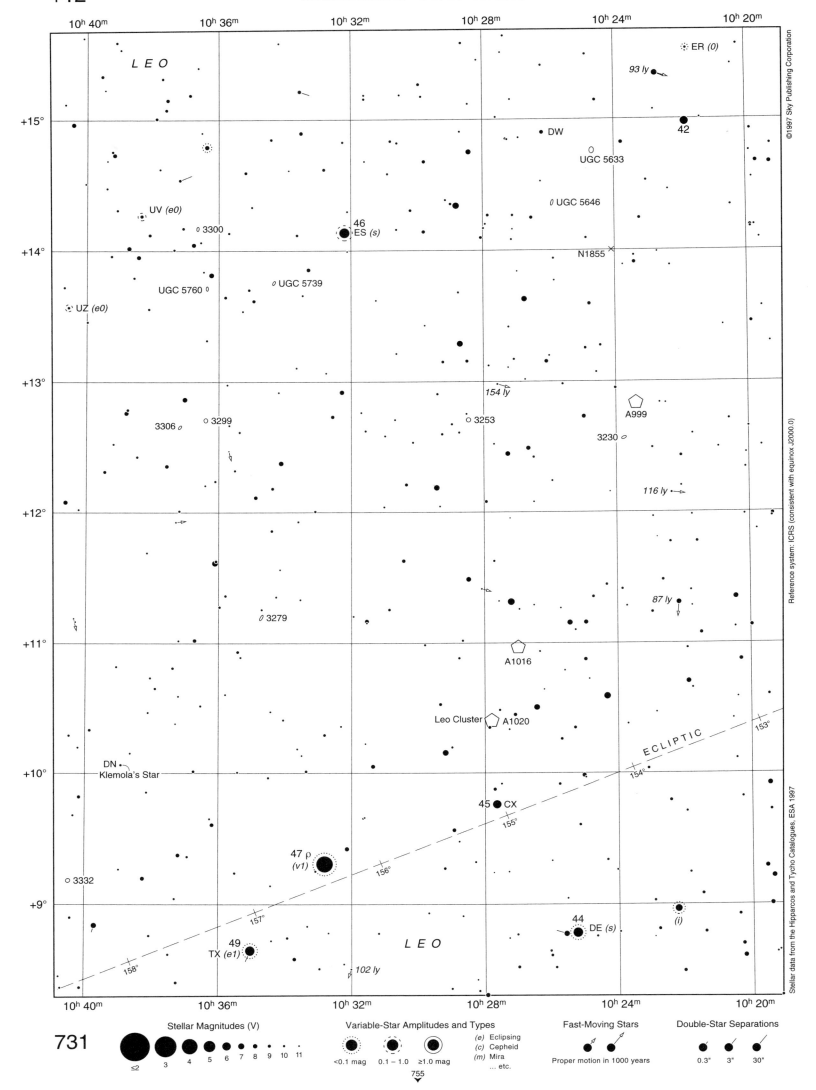

©1997 Sky Publishing Corporation

Reference system: ICRS (consistent with equinox J2000.0)

Stellar data from the Hipparcos and Tycho Catalogues, ESA 1997

LEO

ER (0)

93 ly

DW

42

UGC 5633

UGC 5646

UV (e0)

0 3300

46
ES (s)

N1855

UGC 5760 0

0 UGC 5739

UZ (e0)

154 ly

A999

3306 0   0 3299

0 3253

3230 0

116 ly

0 3279

87 ly

A1016

Leo Cluster   A1020

ECLIPTIC   153°

DN
Klemola's Star

154°

45 ● CX

155°

0 3332

47 ρ
(v1)

156°

44
DE (s)

(i)

157°

49
TX (e1)

LEO

158°   102 ly

731

Stellar Magnitudes (V)

≤2   3   4   5   6   7 8 9 10 11

Variable-Star Amplitudes and Types

<0.1 mag   0.1 – 1.0   ≥1.0 mag

(e) Eclipsing
(c) Cepheid
(m) Mira
... etc.

755

Fast-Moving Stars

Proper motion in 1000 years

Double-Star Separations

0.3"   3"   30"

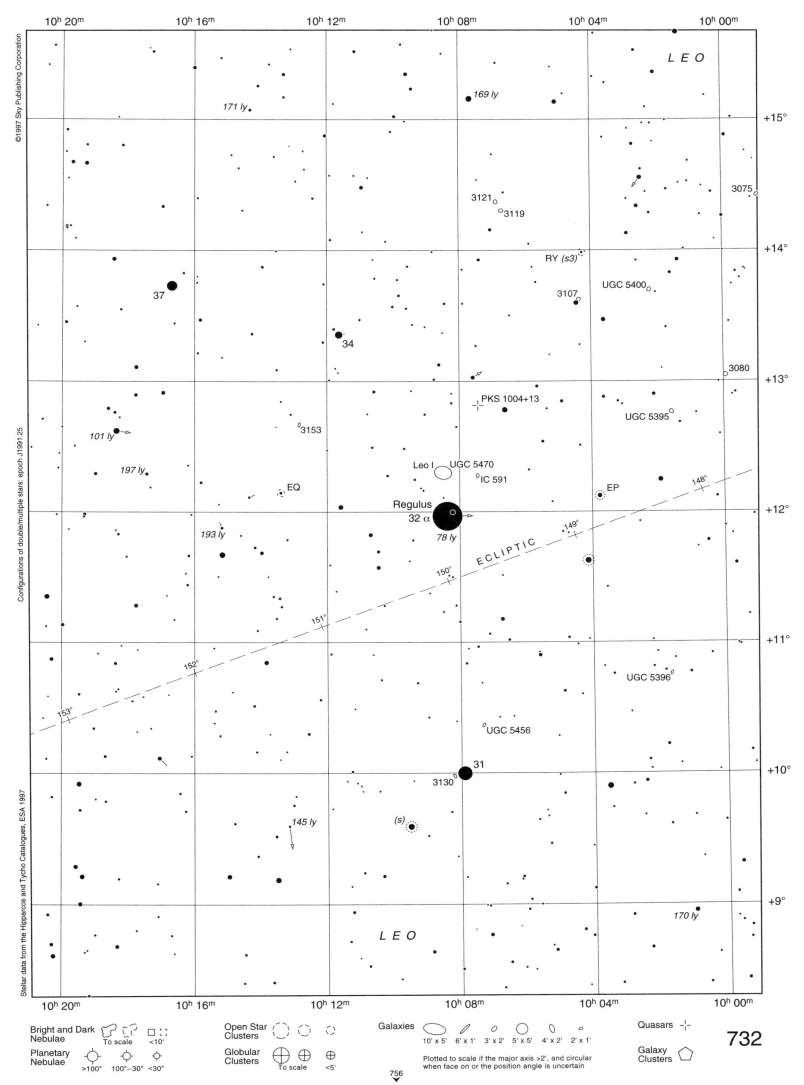

L E O

171 ly

169 ly

3121 3119

3075

37

RY (s3)

3107 UGC 5400

34

3080

101 ly

PKS 1004+13

UGC 5395

3153

197 ly

Leo I   UGC 5470

IC 591

EP   148°

EQ

Regulus
32 α

149°

78 ly

193 ly

ECLIPTIC

150°

151°

152°

UGC 5396

153°

UGC 5456

31

3130

(s)

145 ly

L E O

170 ly

Bright and Dark Nebulae   To scale   <10'

Open Star Clusters

Galaxies   10' x 5'   6' x 1'   3' x 2'   5' x 5'   4' x 2'   2' x 1'

Quasars

Planetary Nebulae   >100"   100"–30"   <30"

Globular Clusters   To scale   <5'

Plotted to scale if the major axis >2', and circular when face on or the position angle is uncertain

Galaxy Clusters

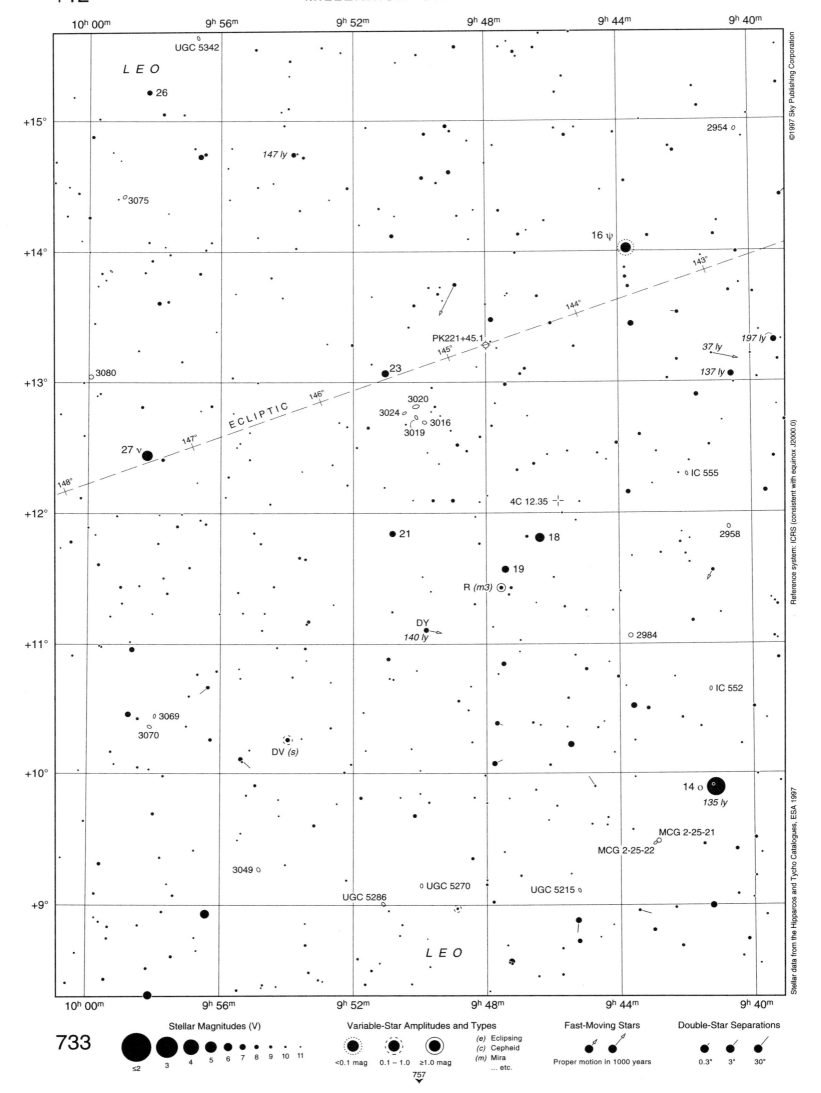

©1997 Sky Publishing Corporation

Reference system: ICRS (consistent with equinox J2000.0)

Stellar data from the Hipparcos and Tycho Catalogues, ESA 1997

LEO

UGC 5342

26

147 ly

3075

2954 o

16 ψ

143°

144°

PK221+45.1

145°

197 ly

37 ly

23

137 ly

3080

3020

3024 o   o 3016

3019

146°

ECLIPTIC

IC 555

147°

27 ν

4C 12.35

148°

2958

21   18

19

R (m3)

DY   2984

140 ly

IC 552

3069

3070

DV (s)

14 o

135 ly

MCG 2-25-21

MCG 2-25-22

3049 o

o UGC 5270

UGC 5215 o

UGC 5286

LEO

733

Stellar Magnitudes (V)

≤2   3   4   5   6 7 8 9 10 11

Variable-Star Amplitudes and Types

<0.1 mag   0.1 – 1.0   ≥1.0 mag

(e) Eclipsing
(c) Cepheid
(m) Mira
... etc.

Fast-Moving Stars

Proper motion in 1000 years

Double-Star Separations

0.3"   3"   30"

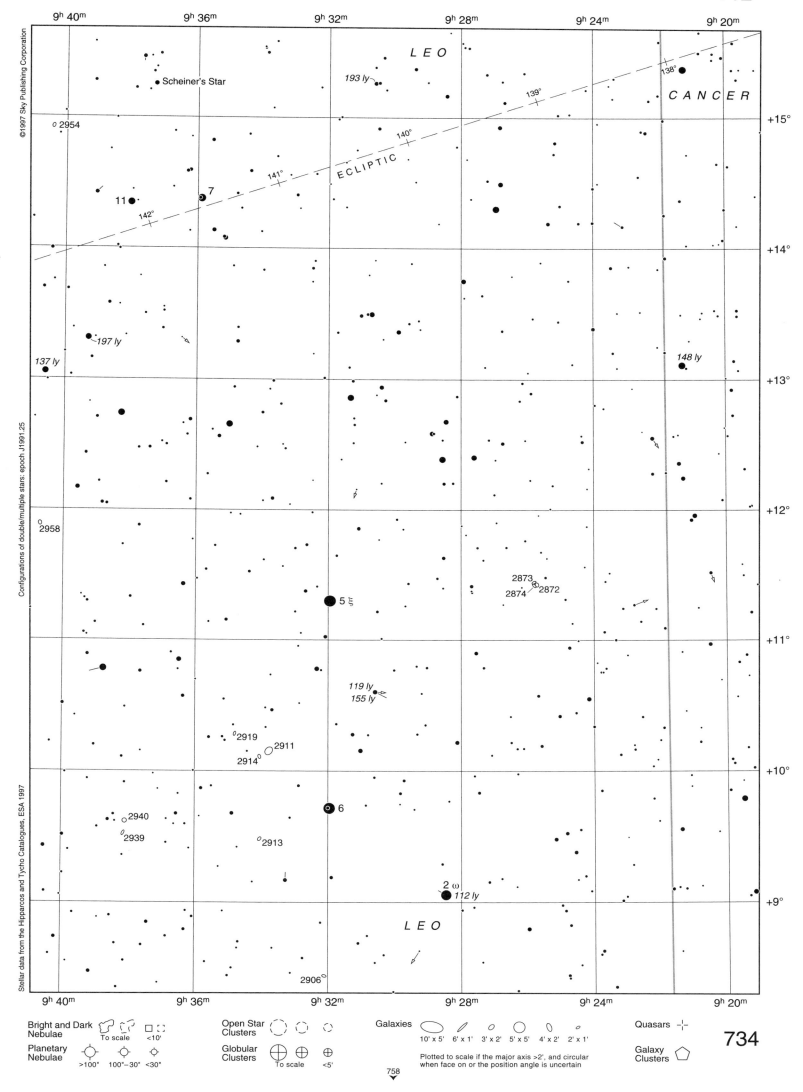

Configurations of double/multiple stars: epoch J1991.25

Stellar data from the Hipparcos and Tycho Catalogues, ESA 1997

LEO

CANCER

Scheiner's Star

193 ly

139°

138°

o 2954

+15°

140°

ECLIPTIC

141°

7

11

142°

+14°

197 ly

148 ly

137 ly

+13°

+12°

o 2958

2873
2874 2872

5 ξ

+11°

119 ly
155 ly

o 2919
2914 o ◯ 2911

+10°

o 2940
o 2939

6

o 2913

2 ω
112 ly

+9°

LEO

2906 o

Bright and Dark Nebulae   To scale   <10'
Planetary Nebulae   >100"   100"–30"   <30'
Open Star Clusters
Globular Clusters   To scale   <5'
Galaxies   10' x 5'   6' x 1'   3' x 2'   5' x 5'   4' x 2'   2' x 1'
Plotted to scale if the major axis >2', and circular when face on or the position angle is uncertain
Quasars
Galaxy Clusters

734

MILLENNIUM STAR ATLAS

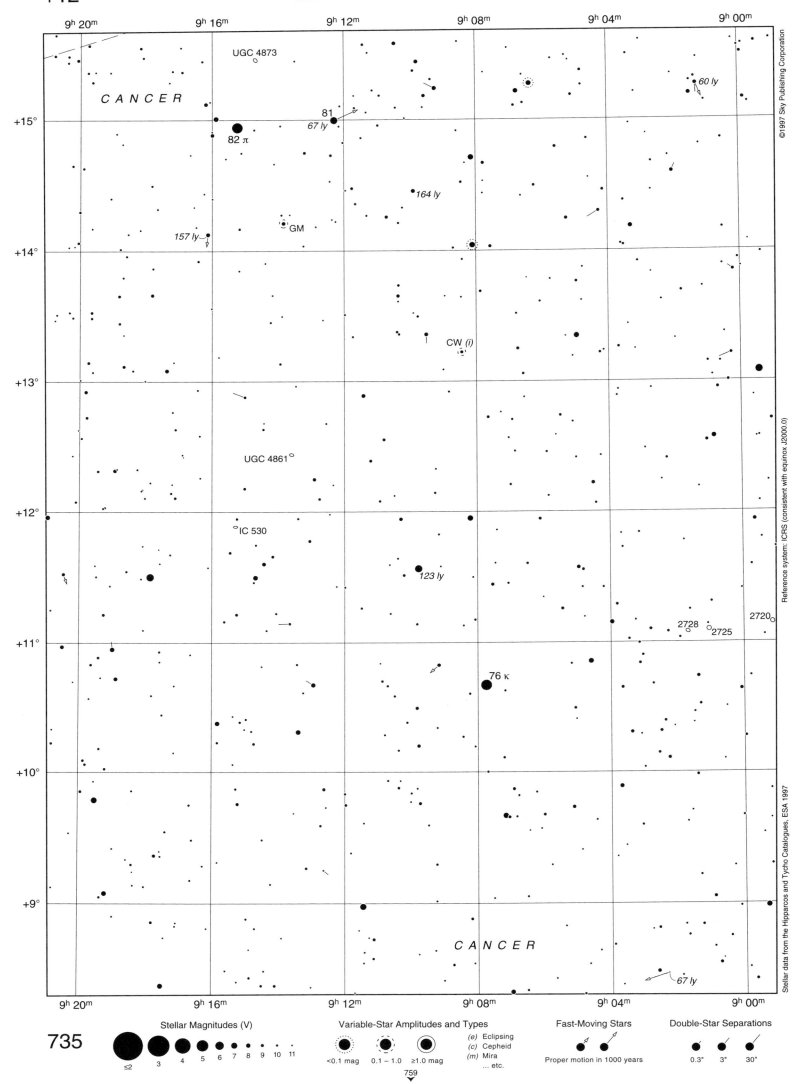

©1997 Sky Publishing Corporation

Reference system: ICRS (consistent with equinox J2000.0)

Stellar data from the Hipparcos and Tycho Catalogues, ESA 1997

UGC 4873

CANCER

81
67 ly

82 π

164 ly

157 ly

GM

CW (i)

UGC 4861

IC 530

123 ly

76 κ

2728

2725

2720

60 ly

CANCER

67 ly

735

Stellar Magnitudes (V)

≤2 3 4 5 6 7 8 9 10 11

Variable-Star Amplitudes and Types

<0.1 mag   0.1 – 1.0   ≥1.0 mag

(e) Eclipsing
(c) Cepheid
(m) Mira
... etc.

Fast-Moving Stars

Proper motion in 1000 years

Double-Star Separations

0.3"   3"   30"

MILLENNIUM STAR ATLAS

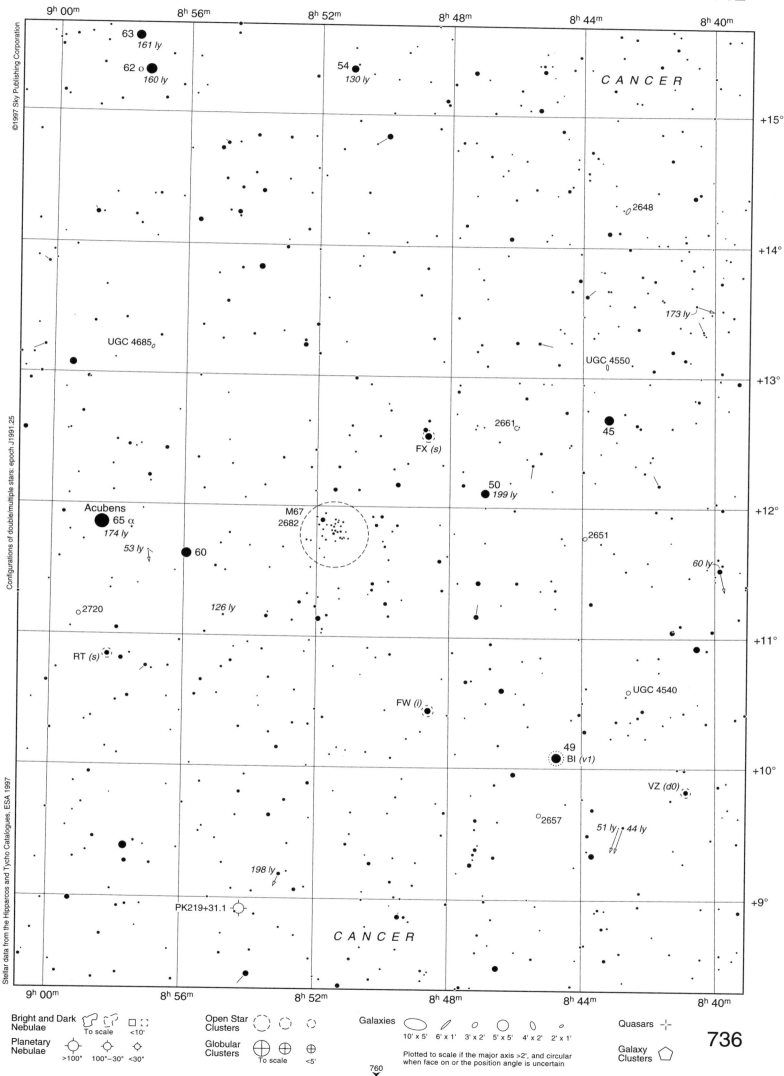

Configurations of double/multiple stars: epoch J1991.25

Stellar data from the Hipparcos and Tycho Catalogues, ESA 1997

9h 00m   8h 56m   8h 52m   8h 48m   8h 44m   8h 40m

+15°
+14°
+13°
+12°
+11°
+10°
+9°

63
161 ly

62 o
160 ly

54
130 ly

CANCER

2648

173 ly

UGC 4685

UGC 4550

2661

45

FX (s)

50
199 ly

Acubens
65 α
174 ly

53 ly

60

M67
2682

2651

60 ly

2720

126 ly

RT (s)

FW (i)

UGC 4540

49
BI (v1)

VZ (d0)

2657

51 ly   44 ly

198 ly

PK219+31.1

CANCER

Bright and Dark Nebulae				
To scale				<10'

Planetary Nebulae
>100"   100"–30"   <30"

Open Star Clusters

Globular Clusters
To scale   <5'

Galaxies
10' x 5'   6' x 1'   3' x 2'   5' x 5'   4' x 2'   2' x 1'

Plotted to scale if the major axis >2', and circular when face on or the position angle is uncertain

Quasars

Galaxy Clusters

736

760

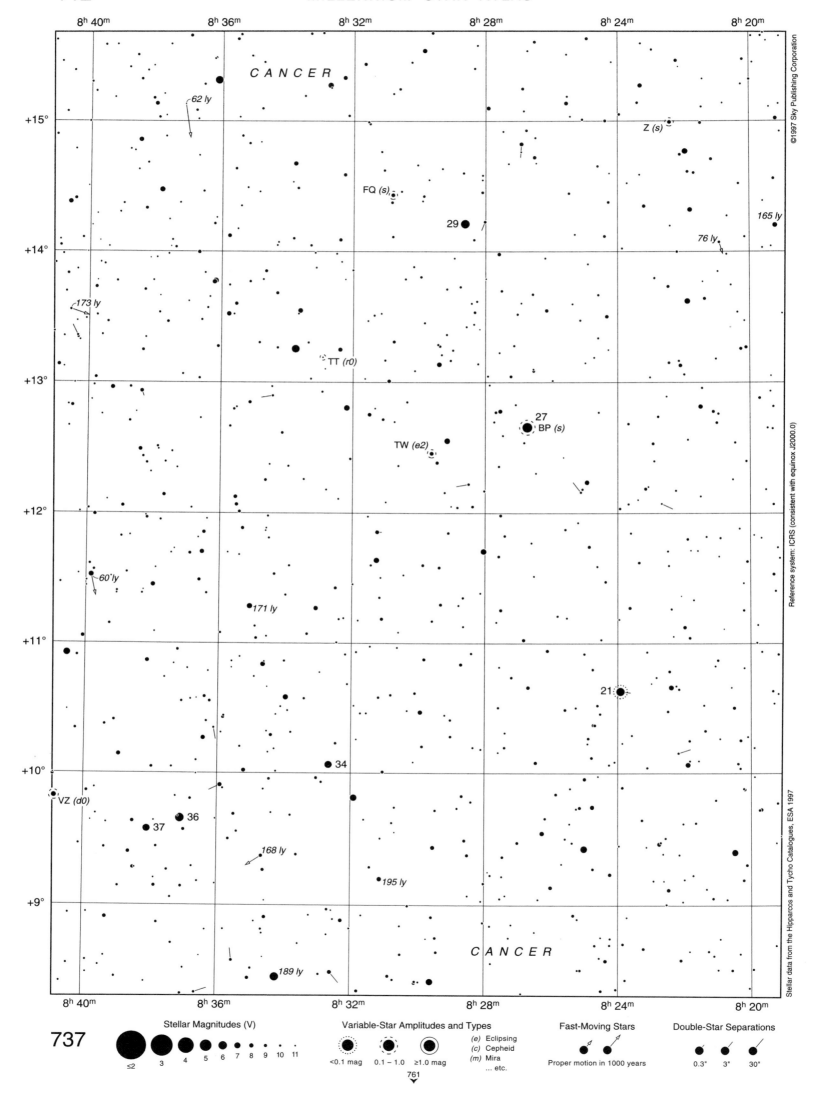

CANCER

62 ly

Z (s)

FQ (s)

29

165 ly

76 ly

173 ly

TT (r0)

27
BP (s)

TW (e2)

60 ly

171 ly

21

34

VZ (d0)

36
37

168 ly

195 ly

CANCER

189 ly

©1997 Sky Publishing Corporation

Reference system: ICRS (consistent with equinox J2000.0)

Stellar data from the Hipparcos and Tycho Catalogues, ESA 1997

737

Stellar Magnitudes (V)

≤2   3   4   5   6   7   8   9   10   11

Variable-Star Amplitudes and Types

<0.1 mag   0.1 – 1.0   ≥1.0 mag

(e) Eclipsing
(c) Cepheid
(m) Mira
... etc.

Fast-Moving Stars

Proper motion in 1000 years

Double-Star Separations

0.3"   3"   30"

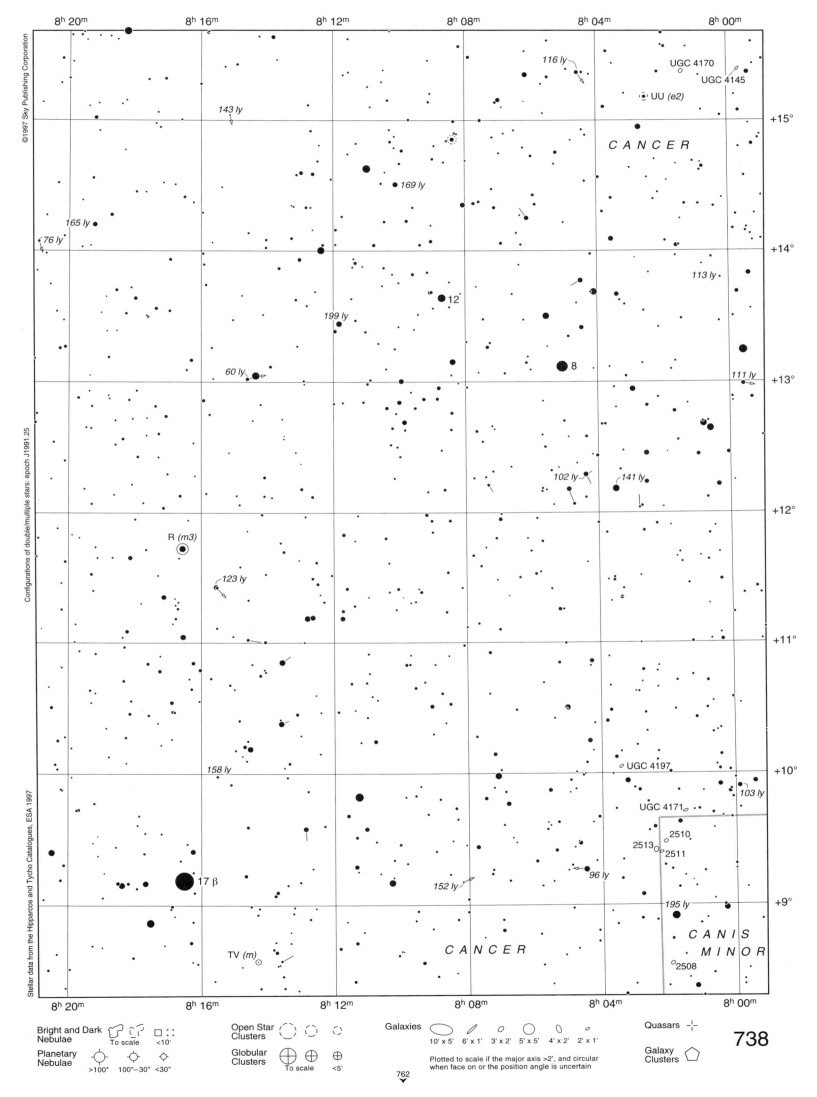

8h 20m   8h 16m   8h 12m   8h 08m   8h 04m   8h 00m

116 ly

UGC 4170
UGC 4145

UU (e2)

+15°

CANCER

143 ly

169 ly

165 ly

76 ly

+14°

113 ly

12

199 ly

8

60 ly

111 ly

+13°

102 ly   141 ly

+12°

R (m3)

123 ly

+11°

UGC 4197   +10°

158 ly

103 ly

UGC 4171

2510

2513   2511

17 β

96 ly

152 ly

195 ly   +9°

CANIS
MINOR

TV (m)

CANCER   2508

Bright and Dark
Nebulae   To scale   <10'

Open Star
Clusters

Galaxies

10' x 5' 6' x 1' 3' x 2' 5' x 5' 4' x 2' 2' x 1'

Quasars

Planetary
Nebulae

>100" 100"–30" <30"

Globular
Clusters

To scale   <5'

Galaxy
Clusters

Plotted to scale if the major axis >2', and circular
when face on or the position angle is uncertain

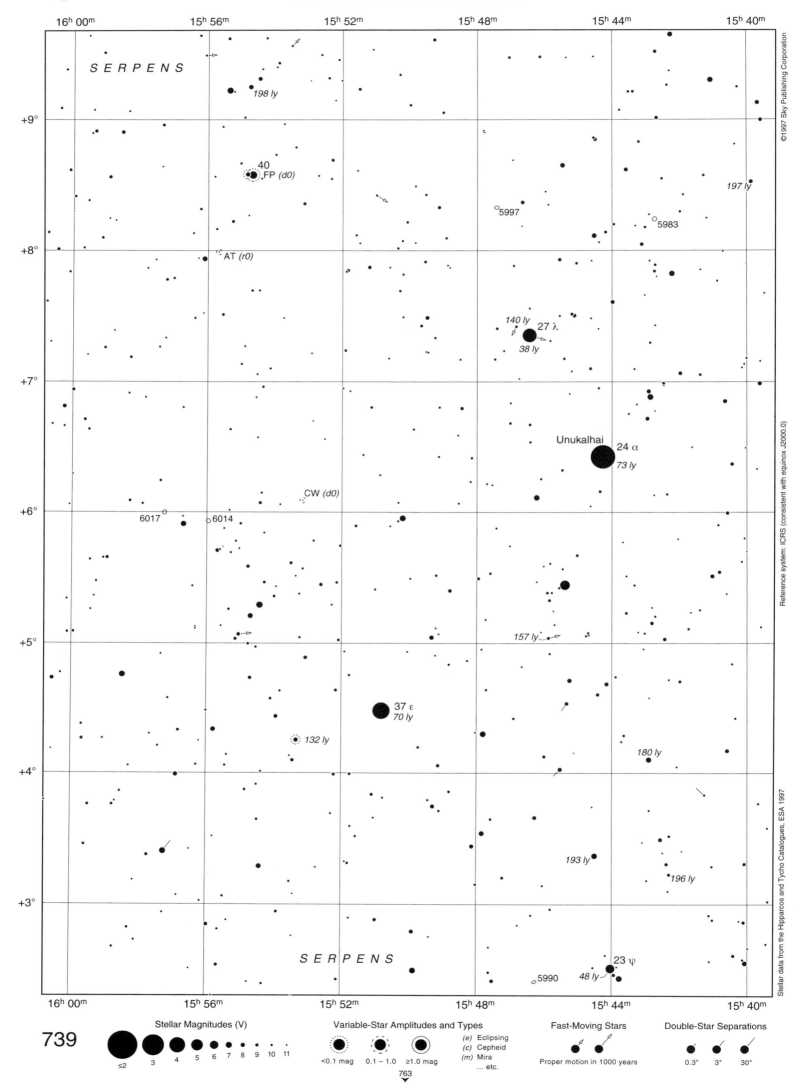

S E R P E N S

198 ly

40
FP *(d0)*

197 ly

○ 5997

○ 5983

AT *(r0)*

140 ly
27 λ
38 ly

Unukalhai   24 α
73 ly

CW *(d0)*

6017 ○   ○ 6014

157 ly

37 ε
70 ly

132 ly

180 ly

193 ly

196 ly

S E R P E N S

23 ψ

○ 5990   48 ly

©1997 Sky Publishing Corporation

Reference system: ICRS (consistent with equinox J2000.0)

Stellar data from the Hipparcos and Tycho Catalogues, ESA 1997

739

Stellar Magnitudes (V)

≤2   3   4   5   6   7   8   9   10   11

Variable-Star Amplitudes and Types

<0.1 mag   0.1 – 1.0   ≥1.0 mag

(e) Eclipsing
(c) Cepheid
(m) Mira
... etc.

Fast-Moving Stars

Proper motion in 1000 years

Double-Star Separations

0.3"   3"   30"

763

MILLENNIUM STAR ATLAS

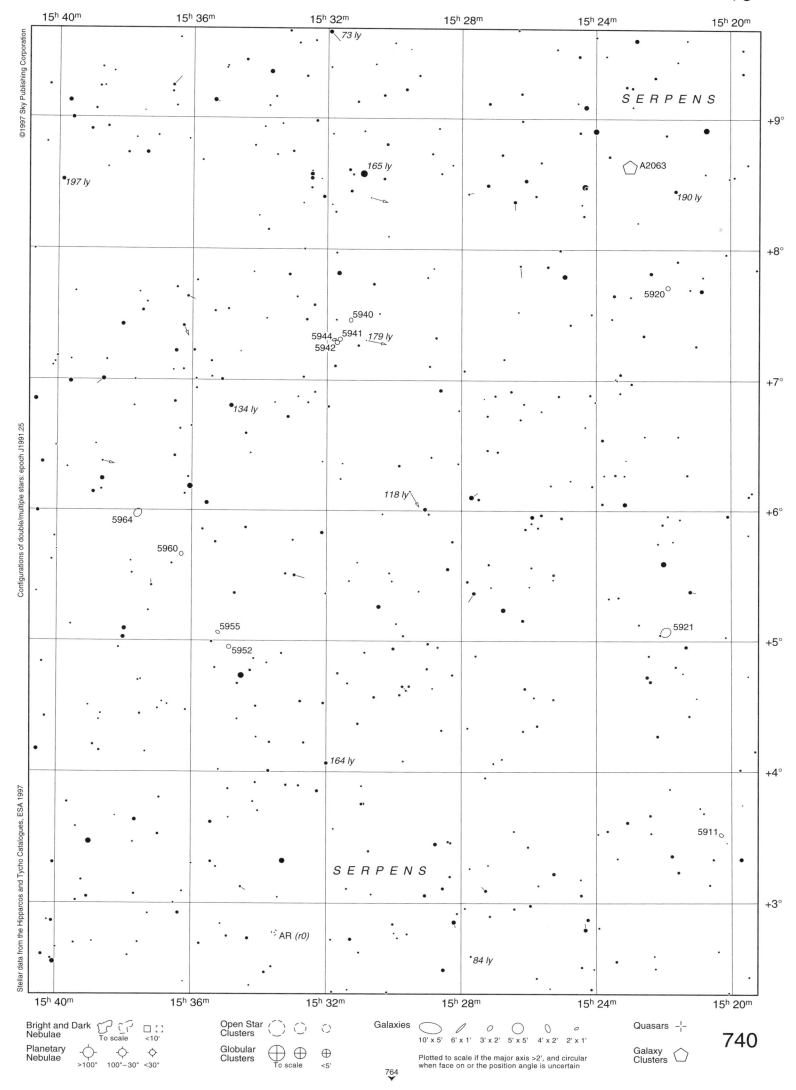

©1997 Sky Publishing Corporation

Configurations of double/multiple stars: epoch J1991.25

Stellar data from the Hipparcos and Tycho Catalogues, ESA 1997

15h 40m   15h 36m   15h 32m   15h 28m   15h 24m   15h 20m

+9°
+8°
+7°
+6°
+5°
+4°
+3°

SERPENS

A2063

73 ly
197 ly
165 ly
190 ly
5920
5940
5944 5941 179 ly
5942
134 ly
118 ly
5964
5960
5921
5955
5952
164 ly
5911
SERPENS
AR (r0)
84 ly

15h 40m   15h 36m   15h 32m   15h 28m   15h 24m   15h 20m

Bright and Dark Nebulae
To scale   <10'

Planetary Nebulae
>100"   100"–30"   <30"

Open Star Clusters

Globular Clusters
To scale   <5'

Galaxies
10' x 5'   6' x 1'   3' x 2'   5' x 5'   4' x 2'   2' x 1'

Plotted to scale if the major axis >2', and circular when face on or the position angle is uncertain

Quasars

Galaxy Clusters

740

764

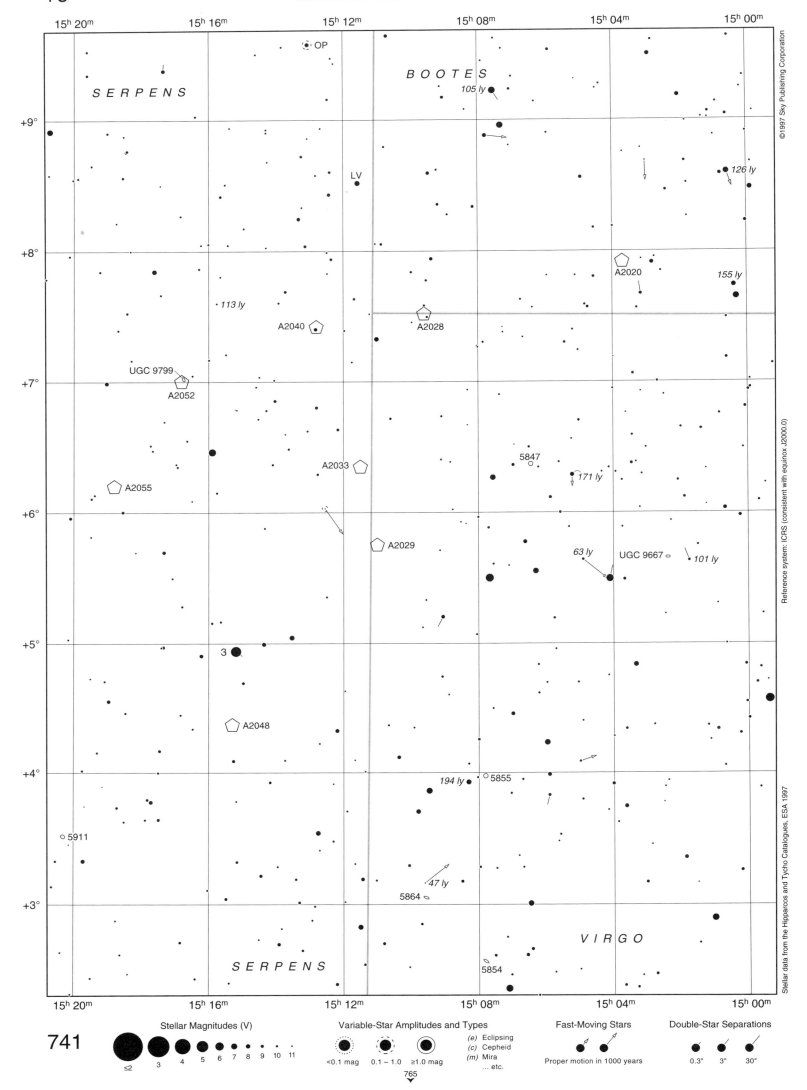

©1997 Sky Publishing Corporation

Reference system: ICRS (consistent with equinox J2000.0)

Stellar data from the Hipparcos and Tycho Catalogues, ESA 1997

15h 20m   15h 16m   15h 12m   15h 08m   15h 04m   15h 00m

B O O T E S

S E R P E N S

OP

105 ly

LV

126 ly

+9°

+8°

A2020

155 ly

113 ly

A2040

A2028

UGC 9799

+7°

A2052

5847

A2033

171 ly

A2055

+6°

A2029

63 ly   UGC 9667   101 ly

+5°

3

A2048

+4°

194 ly   5855

° 5911

47 ly

5864

+3°

V I R G O

S E R P E N S

5854

15h 20m   15h 16m   15h 12m   15h 08m   15h 04m   15h 00m

741

Stellar Magnitudes (V)

≤2   3   4   5   6   7   8   9   10   11

Variable-Star Amplitudes and Types

<0.1 mag   0.1 – 1.0   ≥1.0 mag

(e) Eclipsing
(c) Cepheid
(m) Mira
... etc.

765

Fast-Moving Stars

Proper motion in 1000 years

Double-Star Separations

0.3"   3"   30"

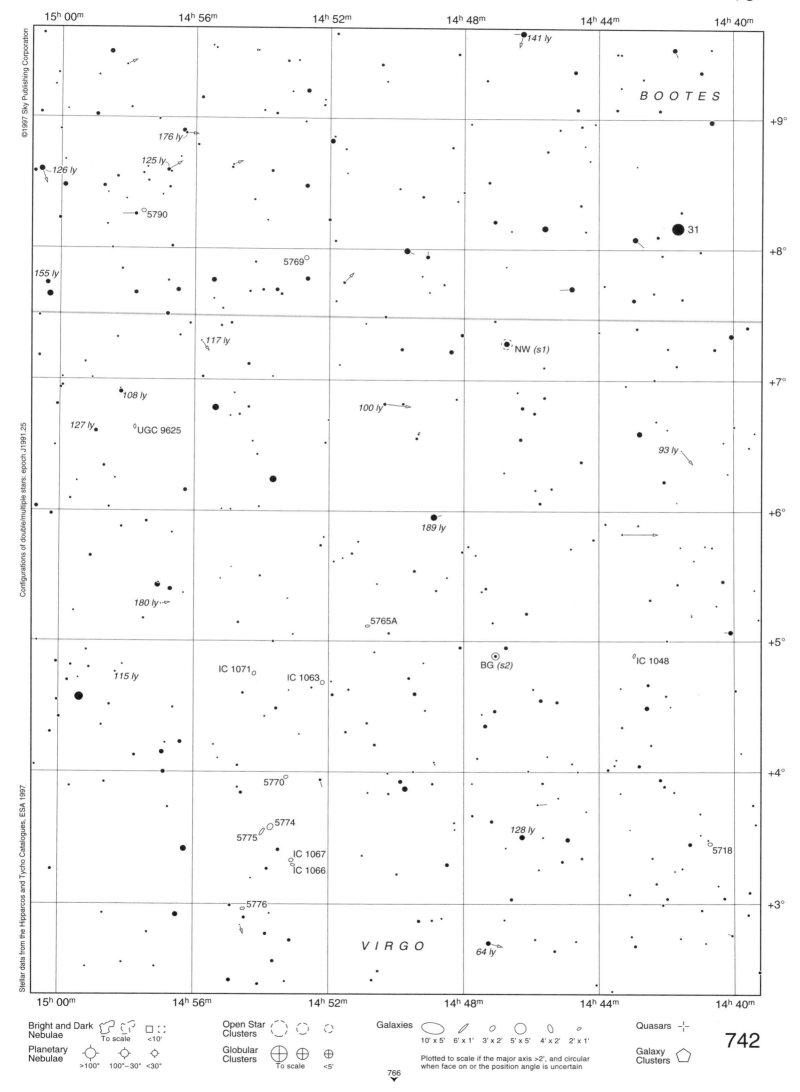

15ʰ 00ᵐ   14ʰ 56ᵐ   14ʰ 52ᵐ   14ʰ 48ᵐ   14ʰ 44ᵐ   14ʰ 40ᵐ

141 ly

BOOTES

+9°

176 ly

125 ly

126 ly

5790

31

+8°

155 ly

5769

117 ly

NW (s1)

+7°

108 ly

100 ly

127 ly

UGC 9625

93 ly

+6°

189 ly

180 ly

5765A

+5°

115 ly

IC 1071

IC 1063

BG (s2)

IC 1048

5770

5774

5775

128 ly

5718

IC 1067

IC 1066

5776

+4°

VIRGO

64 ly

+3°

15ʰ 00ᵐ   14ʰ 56ᵐ   14ʰ 52ᵐ   14ʰ 48ᵐ   14ʰ 44ᵐ   14ʰ 40ᵐ

Bright and Dark Nebulae   To scale   <10'

Open Star Clusters

Galaxies   10' x 5'   6' x 1'   3' x 2'   5' x 5'   4' x 2'   2' x 1'

Quasars

Planetary Nebulae   >100"   100"–30"   <30"

Globular Clusters   To scale   <5'

Plotted to scale if the major axis >2', and circular when face on or the position angle is uncertain

Galaxy Clusters

742

766

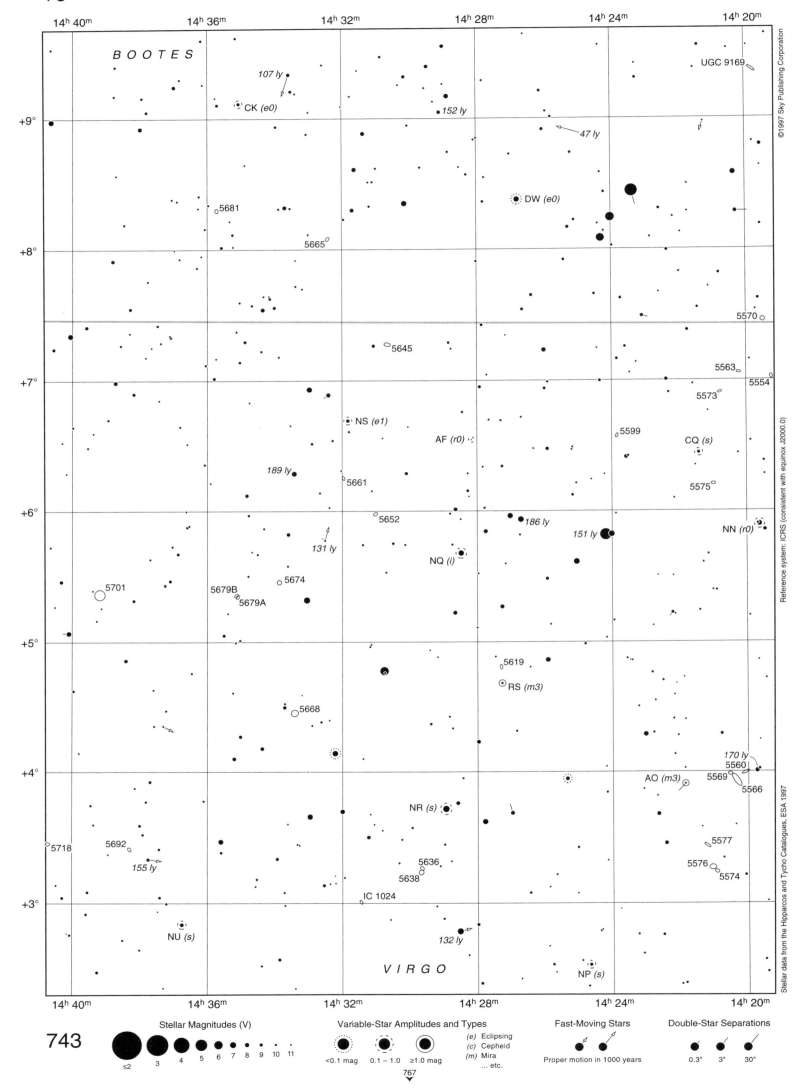

©1997 Sky Publishing Corporation

Reference system: ICRS (consistent with equinox J2000.0)

Stellar data from the Hipparcos and Tycho Catalogues, ESA 1997

BOOTES

107 ly
CK (e0)
152 ly
47 ly
UGC 9169
DW (e0)
5681
5665
5570
5645
5563
5554
5573
NS (e1)
AF (r0)
CQ (s)
5599
189 ly
5575
5661
5652
186 ly
131 ly
NN (r0)
151 ly
NQ (i)
5674
5701
5679B
5679A
5619
RS (m3)
5668
170 ly
5560
AO (m3)
5569
5566
NR (s)
5718
5692
5577
155 ly
5636
5576
5638
5574
IC 1024
NU (s)
132 ly
NP (s)
VIRGO

743

Stellar Magnitudes (V)

≤2   3   4   5   6 7 8 9 10 11

Variable-Star Amplitudes and Types

<0.1 mag   0.1 – 1.0   ≥1.0 mag

(e) Eclipsing
(c) Cepheid
(m) Mira
... etc.

Fast-Moving Stars

Proper motion in 1000 years

Double-Star Separations

0.3"   3"   30"

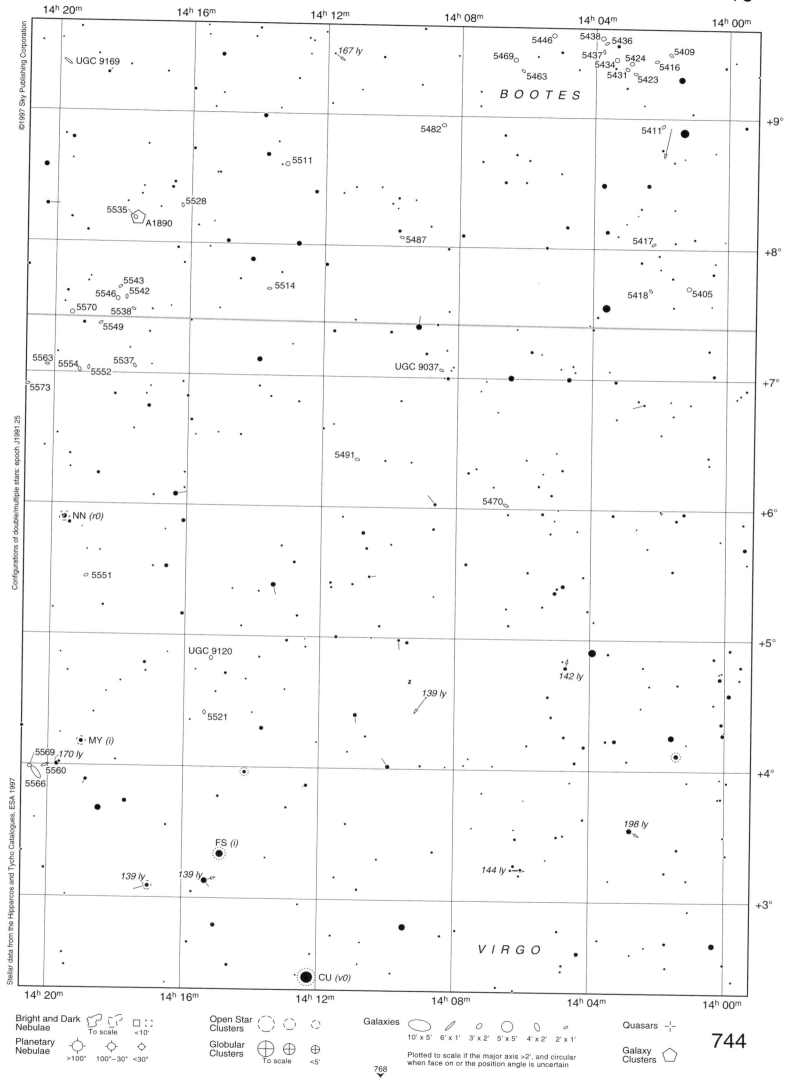

Configurations of double/multiple stars: epoch J1991.25

Stellar data from the Hipparcos and Tycho Catalogues, ESA 1997

14ʰ 20ᵐ   14ʰ 16ᵐ   14ʰ 12ᵐ   14ʰ 08ᵐ   14ʰ 04ᵐ   14ʰ 00ᵐ

UGC 9169

167 ly

5446   5438   5436
5469   5437
5463   5434   5424   5409
         5431   5423   5416

B O O T E S

5482   5411

5511

5528   5417

5535
A1890

5543   5405
5546 5542   5514   5418
5570
5538
5549

5563 5537
5554 5552   UGC 9037
5573

+9°
+8°
+7°
+6°
+5°
+4°
+3°

5491

5470

NN (r0)

5551

UGC 9120
142 ly

5521   139 ly

MY (i)
5569 170 ly
5560
5566   198 ly

FS (i)
                                        144 ly
139 ly 139 ly

V I R G O

CU (v0)

14ʰ 20ᵐ   14ʰ 16ᵐ   14ʰ 12ᵐ   14ʰ 08ᵐ   14ʰ 04ᵐ   14ʰ 00ᵐ

Bright and Dark
Nebulae   To scale   <10'

Planetary
Nebulae   >100" 100"–30" <30"

Open Star
Clusters

Globular
Clusters   To scale   <5'

Galaxies

10' x 5' 6' x 1' 3' x 2' 5' x 5' 4' x 2' 2' x 1'

Plotted to scale if the major axis >2', and circular
when face on or the position angle is uncertain

Quasars

Galaxy
Clusters

744

768

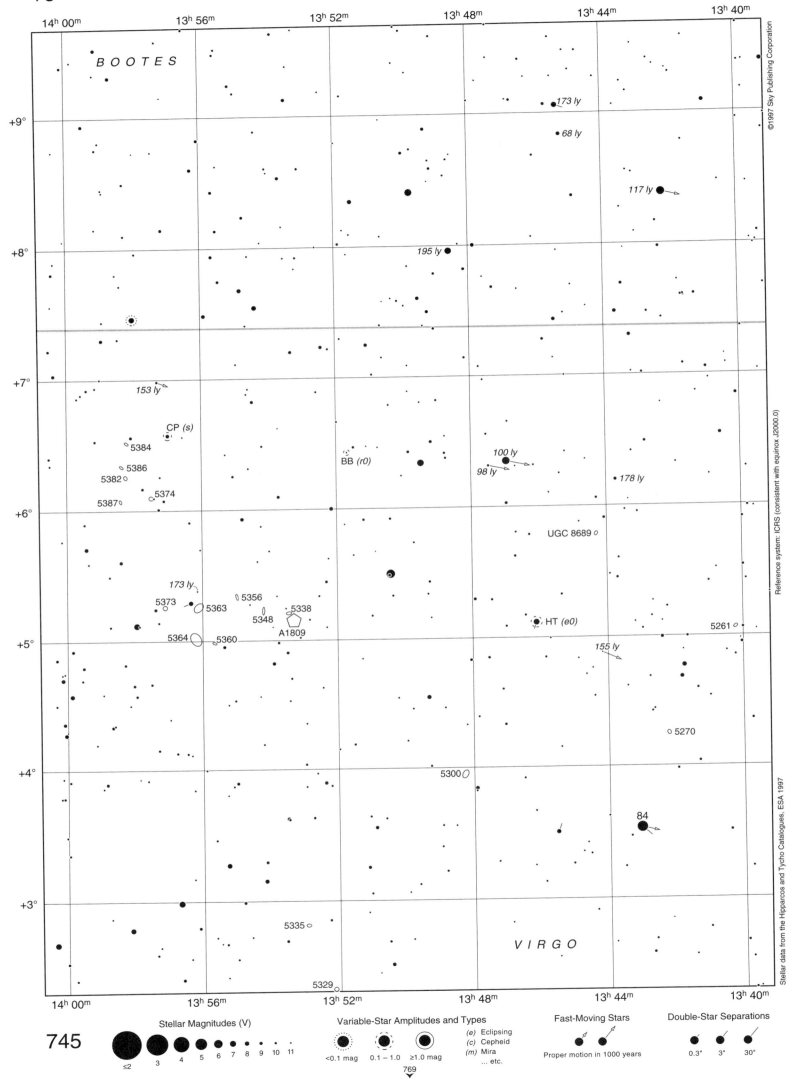

BOOTES

173 ly
68 ly
117 ly
195 ly
153 ly
CP (s)
5384
5386
5382
5374
5387
BB (r0)
100 ly
98 ly
178 ly
UGC 8689
173 ly
5373
5363
5356
5348
5338
5364
5360
A1809
HT (e0)
5261
155 ly
5270
5300
84
5335
VIRGO
5329

745

Stellar Magnitudes (V)

≤2 3 4 5 6 7 8 9 10 11

Variable-Star Amplitudes and Types

<0.1 mag   0.1 – 1.0   ≥1.0 mag

(e) Eclipsing
(c) Cepheid
(m) Mira
... etc.

Fast-Moving Stars

Proper motion in 1000 years

Double-Star Separations

0.3"   3"   30"

769

MILLENNIUM STAR ATLAS

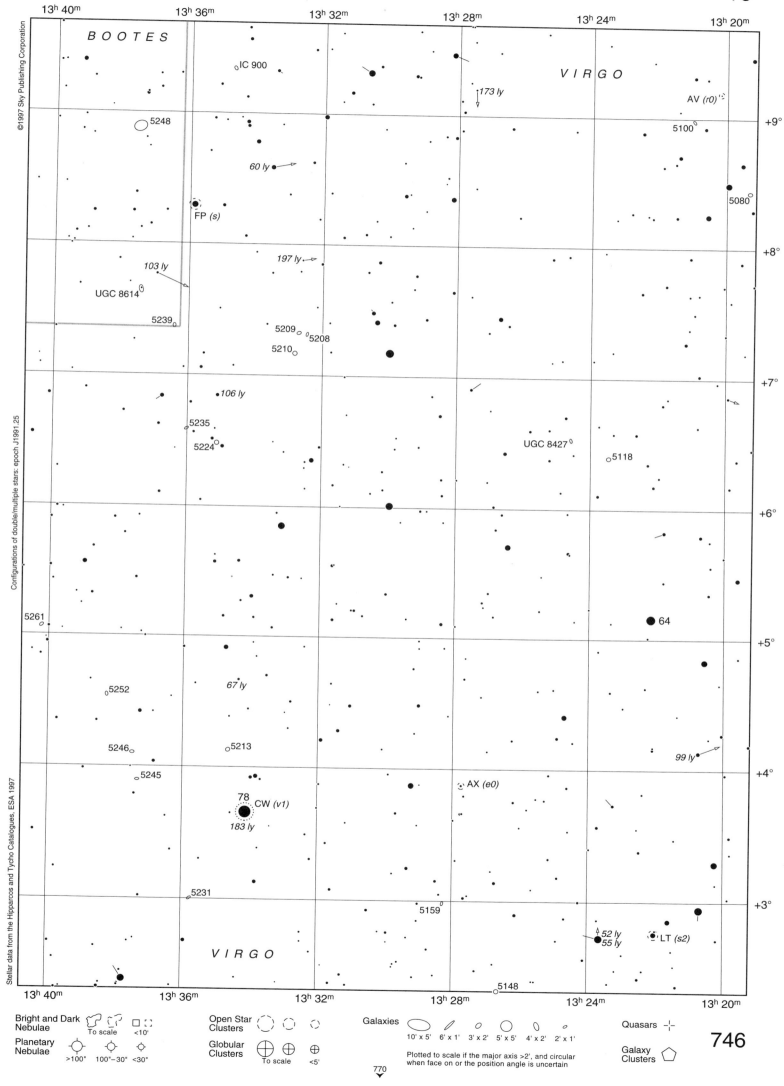

13h 40m   13h 36m   13h 32m   13h 28m   13h 24m   13h 20m

BOOTES

VIRGO

IC 900

173 ly

AV (r0)

5248

5100

60 ly

5080

FP (s)

197 ly

103 ly

UGC 8614

5239

5209   5208

5210

+9°

+8°

+7°

106 ly

5235

5224

UGC 8427

5118

+6°

5261

64

+5°

5252

67 ly

5246

5213

99 ly

5245

78

CW (v1)

AX (e0)

183 ly

5231

5159

52 ly

55 ly

LT (s2)

VIRGO

5148

+4°

+3°

13h 40m   13h 36m   13h 32m   13h 28m   13h 24m   13h 20m

Bright and Dark Nebulae   To scale   <10'

Planetary Nebulae   >100"   100"-30"   <30"

Open Star Clusters

Globular Clusters   To scale   <5'

Galaxies   10' x 5'   6' x 1'   3' x 2'   5' x 5'   4' x 2'   2' x 1'

Plotted to scale if the major axis >2', and circular when face on or the position angle is uncertain

Quasars

Galaxy Clusters

746

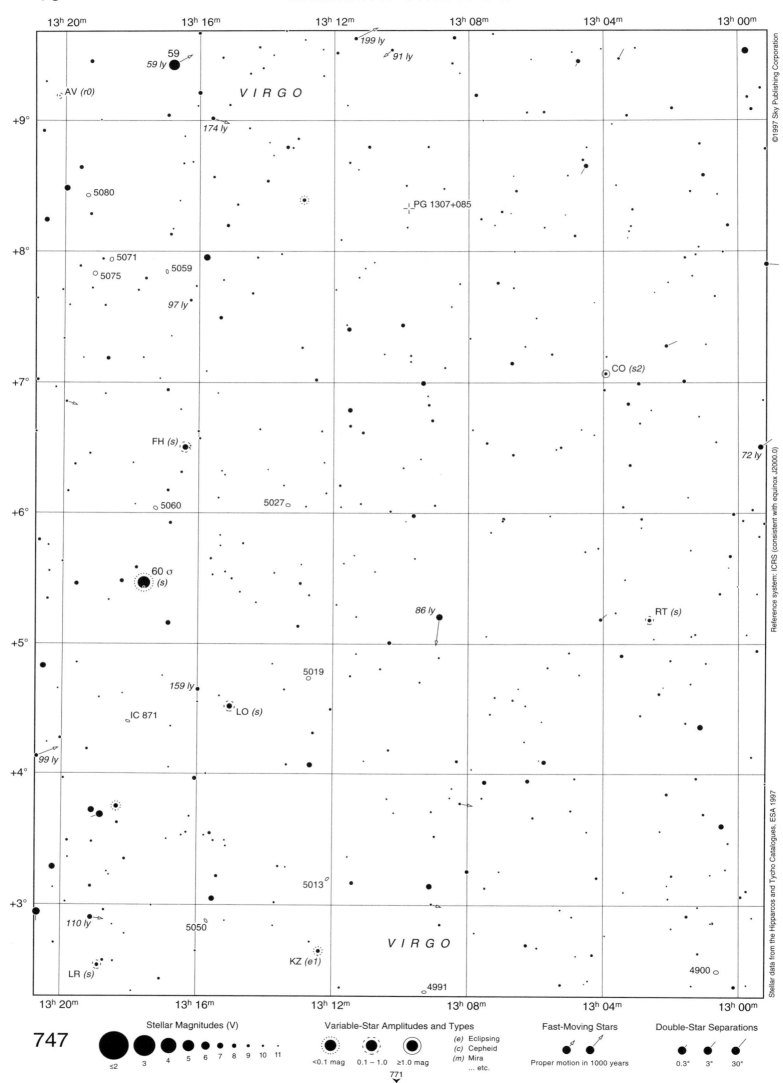

©1997 Sky Publishing Corporation

Reference system: ICRS (consistent with equinox J2000.0)

Stellar data from the Hipparcos and Tycho Catalogues, ESA 1997

VIRGO

VIRGO

59
59 ly

199 ly
91 ly

AV (r0)

174 ly

5080

PG 1307+085

5071

5075   5059

97 ly

CO (s2)

72 ly

FH (s)

5060   5027

60 σ
(s)

86 ly   RT (s)

5019

159 ly

IC 871   LO (s)

99 ly

5013

110 ly

5050

KZ (e1)

4900

LR (s)   4991

747

Stellar Magnitudes (V)
≤2 3 4 5 6 7 8 9 10 11

Variable-Star Amplitudes and Types

<0.1 mag   0.1 – 1.0   ≥1.0 mag

(e) Eclipsing
(c) Cepheid
(m) Mira
... etc.

Fast-Moving Stars

Proper motion in 1000 years

Double-Star Separations

0.3"   3"   30"

+6°

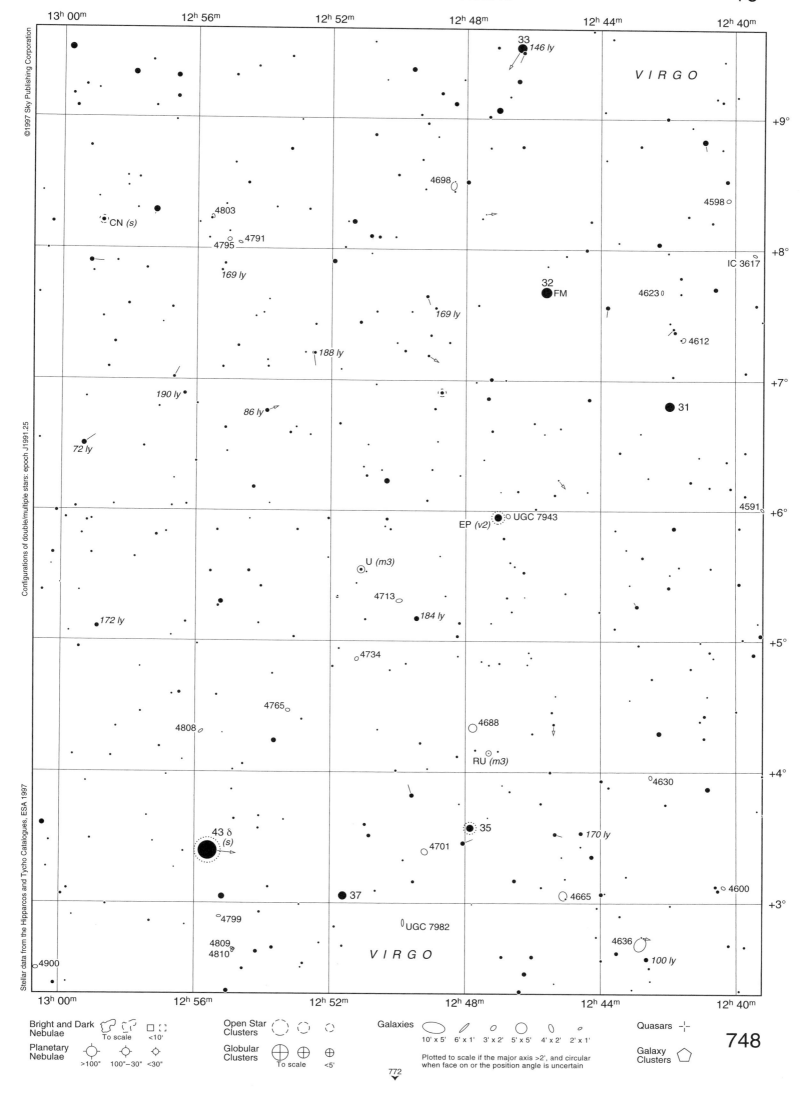

VIRGO

33   146 ly

4698

4598

4803

CN (s)

4795   4791

IC 3617

169 ly

32   FM   4623

169 ly

4612

188 ly

190 ly

86 ly

31

72 ly

4591   +6°

EP (v2)   UGC 7943

U (m3)

4713

172 ly   184 ly

4734

4765

4688

4808

RU (m3)

4630

43 δ   (s)

35   170 ly

4701

37   4665   4600

UGC 7982

4799   VIRGO

4809
4810   4636

4900   100 ly

13h 00m   12h 56m   12h 52m   12h 48m   12h 44m   12h 40m

Bright and Dark Nebulae
To scale   <10'

Planetary Nebulae
>100"   100"–30"   <30"

Open Star Clusters

Globular Clusters
To scale   <5'

Galaxies
10' x 5'   6' x 1'   3' x 2'   5' x 5'   4' x 2'   2' x 1'

Plotted to scale if the major axis >2', and circular when face on or the position angle is uncertain

Quasars

Galaxy Clusters

748

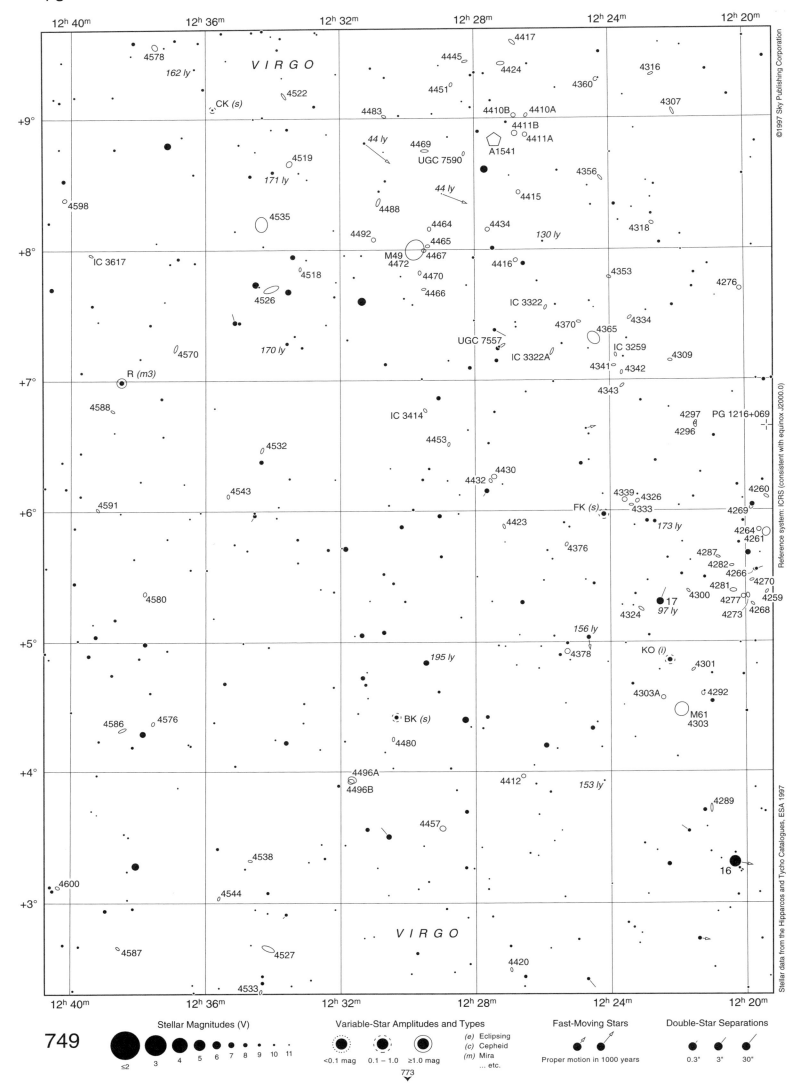

©1997 Sky Publishing Corporation

Reference system: ICRS (consistent with equinox J2000.0)

Stellar data from the Hipparcos and Tycho Catalogues, ESA 1997

749

Stellar Magnitudes (V)	Variable-Star Amplitudes and Types	Fast-Moving Stars	Double-Star Separations

Stellar Magnitudes (V)
≤2   3   4   5   6 7 8 9 10 11

Variable-Star Amplitudes and Types
<0.1 mag   0.1 – 1.0   ≥1.0 mag
(e) Eclipsing
(c) Cepheid
(m) Mira
... etc.

Fast-Moving Stars
Proper motion in 1000 years

Double-Star Separations
0.3"   3"   30"

773

MILLENNIUM STAR ATLAS

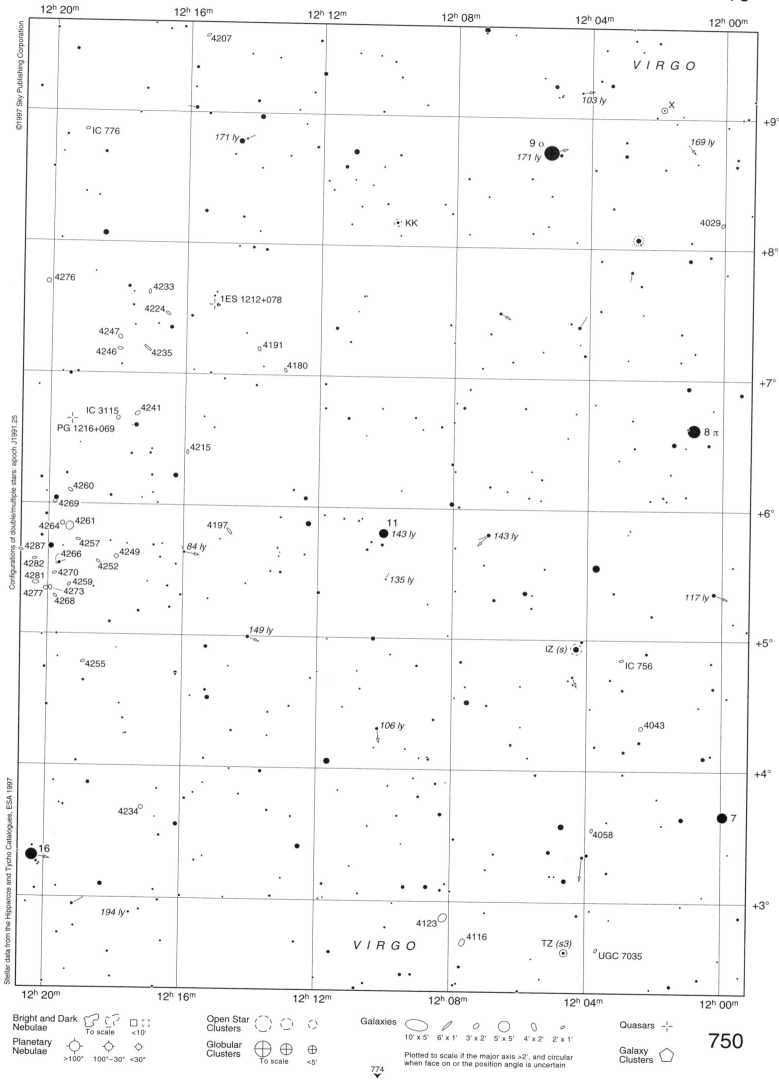

12h 20m 12h 16m 12h 12m 12h 08m 12h 04m 12h 00m

©1997 Sky Publishing Corporation

Configurations of double/multiple stars: epoch J1991.25

Stellar data from the Hipparcos and Tycho Catalogues, ESA 1997

VIRGO

4207

IC 776

171 ly

103 ly

X

9 o
171 ly

169 ly

4029

KK

+9°

+8°

4276

4233
4224

1ES 1212+078

4247
4246   4235

4191

4180

+7°

IC 3115   4241
PG 1216+069

4215

8 π

+6°

4260
4269

4264 4261
4287
4282   4257
4266
4281   4249
4277 4270   4252
4268 4273 4259

4197

84 ly

11
143 ly

143 ly

135 ly

117 ly

149 ly

IZ (s)

IC 756

+5°

4255

106 ly

4043

+4°

4234

7

16

4058

194 ly

4123

4116

TZ (s3)

UGC 7035

+3°

VIRGO

12h 20m 12h 16m 12h 12m 12h 08m 12h 04m 12h 00m

Bright and Dark Nebulae
To scale   <10'

Planetary Nebulae
>100"   100"–30"   <30"

Open Star Clusters
To scale

Globular Clusters
To scale   <5'

Galaxies
10' x 5'   6' x 1'   3' x 2'   5' x 5'   4' x 2'   2' x 1'

Plotted to scale if the major axis >2', and circular when face on or the position angle is uncertain

Quasars

Galaxy Clusters

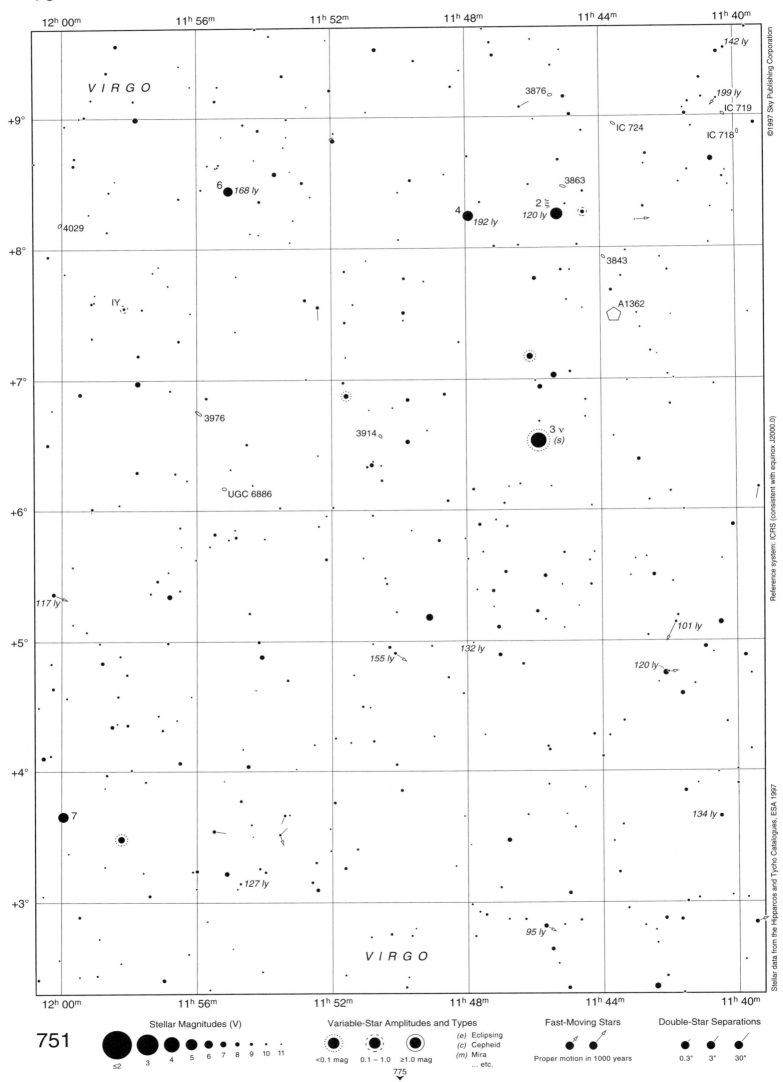

©1997 Sky Publishing Corporation

Reference system: ICRS (consistent with equinox J2000.0)

Stellar data from the Hipparcos and Tycho Catalogues, ESA 1997

751

Stellar Magnitudes (V)

≤2 3 4 5 6 7 8 9 10 11

Variable-Star Amplitudes and Types

<0.1 mag   0.1 – 1.0   ≥1.0 mag

(e) Eclipsing
(c) Cepheid
(m) Mira
... etc.

Fast-Moving Stars

Proper motion in 1000 years

Double-Star Separations

0.3"   3"   30"

775

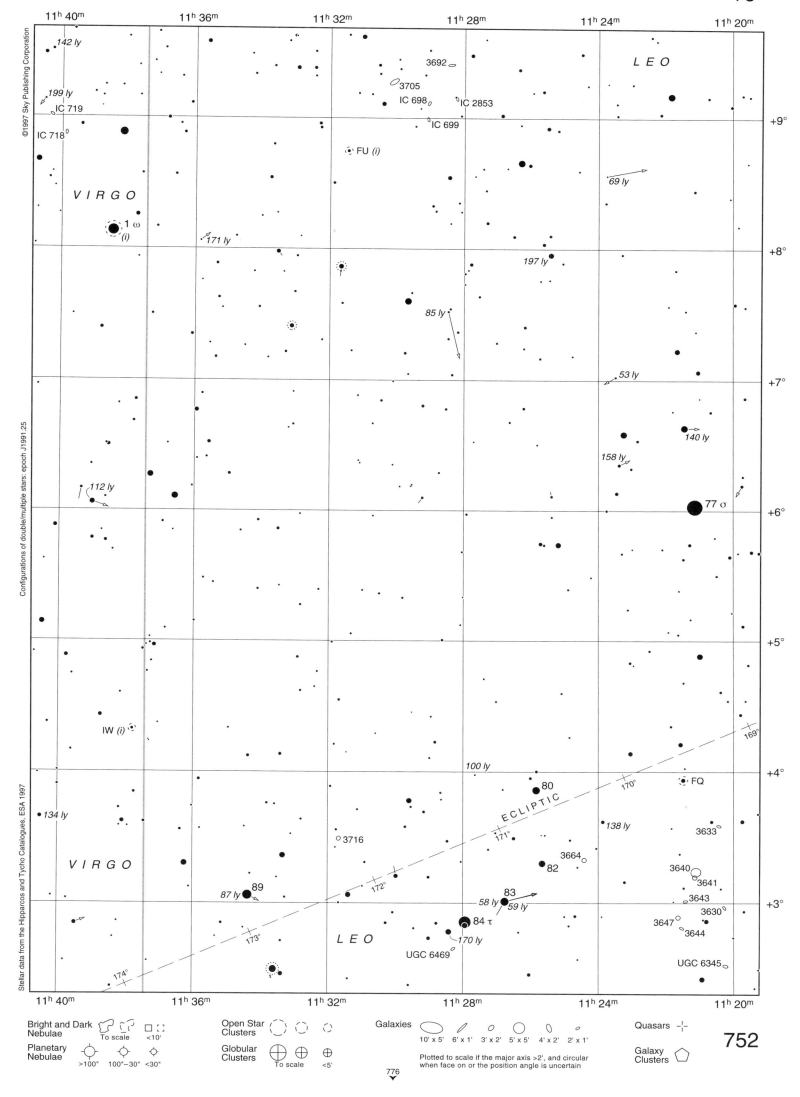

11ʰ 40ᵐ   11ʰ 36ᵐ   11ʰ 32ᵐ   11ʰ 28ᵐ   11ʰ 24ᵐ   11ʰ 20ᵐ

142 ly

LEO

199 ly

3692

IC 719

3705

IC 698   IC 2853

IC 718   IC 699   +9°

FU *(i)*

VIRGO

69 ly

1 ω   +8°
(i)

171 ly   *197 ly*

85 ly

53 ly   +7°

140 ly

158 ly

112 ly   77 σ   +6°

+5°

169°

IW *(i)*

100 ly   170°   FQ   +4°

80

134 ly   ECLIPTIC   *138 ly*   3633

171°

3716   3664   3640

VIRGO   82   3641

87 ly   89   172°   3643

83   3630

58 ly   59 ly   3647   3644

84 τ   170°   UGC 6345

173°   *LEO*

UGC 6469

174°

11ʰ 40ᵐ   11ʰ 36ᵐ   11ʰ 32ᵐ   11ʰ 28ᵐ   11ʰ 24ᵐ   11ʰ 20ᵐ   +3°

Bright and Dark Nebulae   Open Star Clusters   Galaxies   Quasars

To scale   <10'   10' x 5' 6' x 1' 3' x 2' 5' x 5' 4' x 2' 2' x 1'

Planetary Nebulae   Globular Clusters   Galaxy Clusters

>100" 100"–30" <30"   To scale <5'   Plotted to scale if the major axis >2', and circular when face on or the position angle is uncertain

752

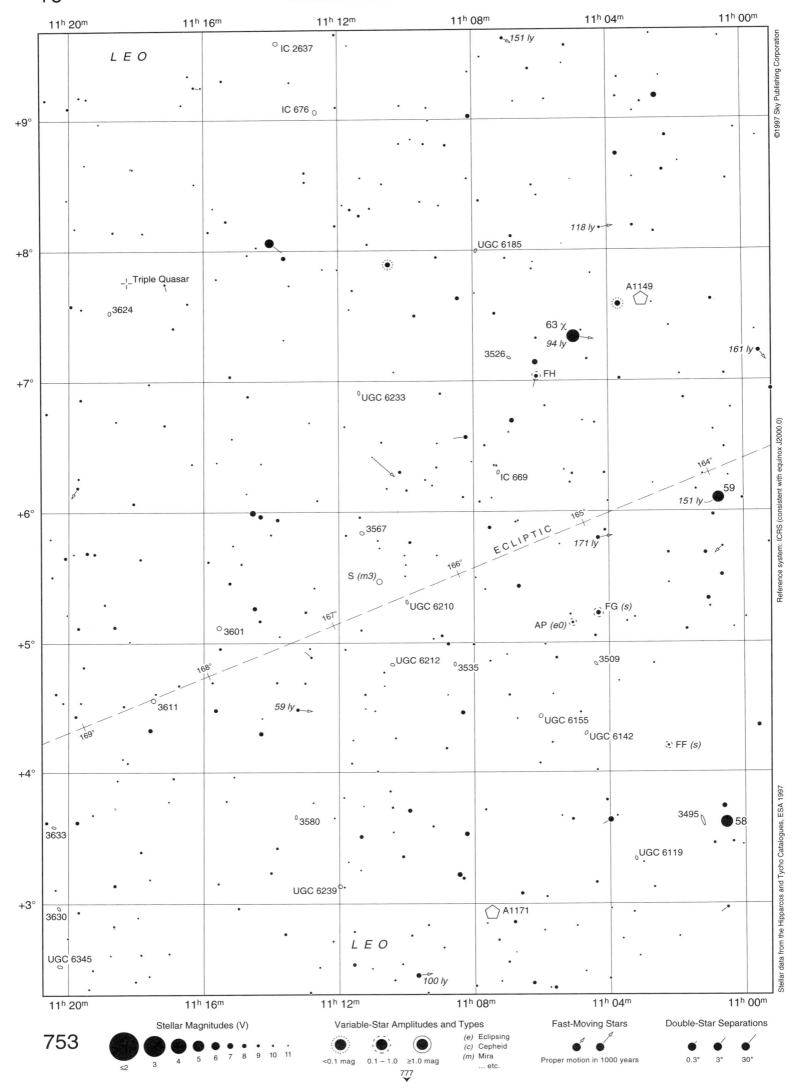

©1997 Sky Publishing Corporation

Reference system: ICRS (consistent with equinox J2000.0)

Stellar data from the Hipparcos and Tycho Catalogues, ESA 1997

LEO

IC 2637

IC 676

UGC 6185

Triple Quasar

3624

A1149

63 χ
94 ly

3526

FH

UGC 6233

151 ly

118 ly

161 ly

IC 669

164°

59
151 ly

165°

3567

ECLIPTIC

171 ly

S (m3)

166°

UGC 6210

FG (s)

AP (e0)

3601

167°

3509

UGC 6212

3535

168°

UGC 6155

3611

UGC 6142

59 ly

FF (s)

3580

3495

58

3633

UGC 6119

UGC 6239

3630

A1171

UGC 6345

LEO

100 ly

753

Stellar Magnitudes (V)

≤2   3   4   5   6 7 8 9 10 11

Variable-Star Amplitudes and Types

<0.1 mag   0.1 – 1.0   ≥1.0 mag

(e) Eclipsing
(c) Cepheid
(m) Mira
... etc.

Fast-Moving Stars

Proper motion in 1000 years

Double-Star Separations

0.3"   3"   30"

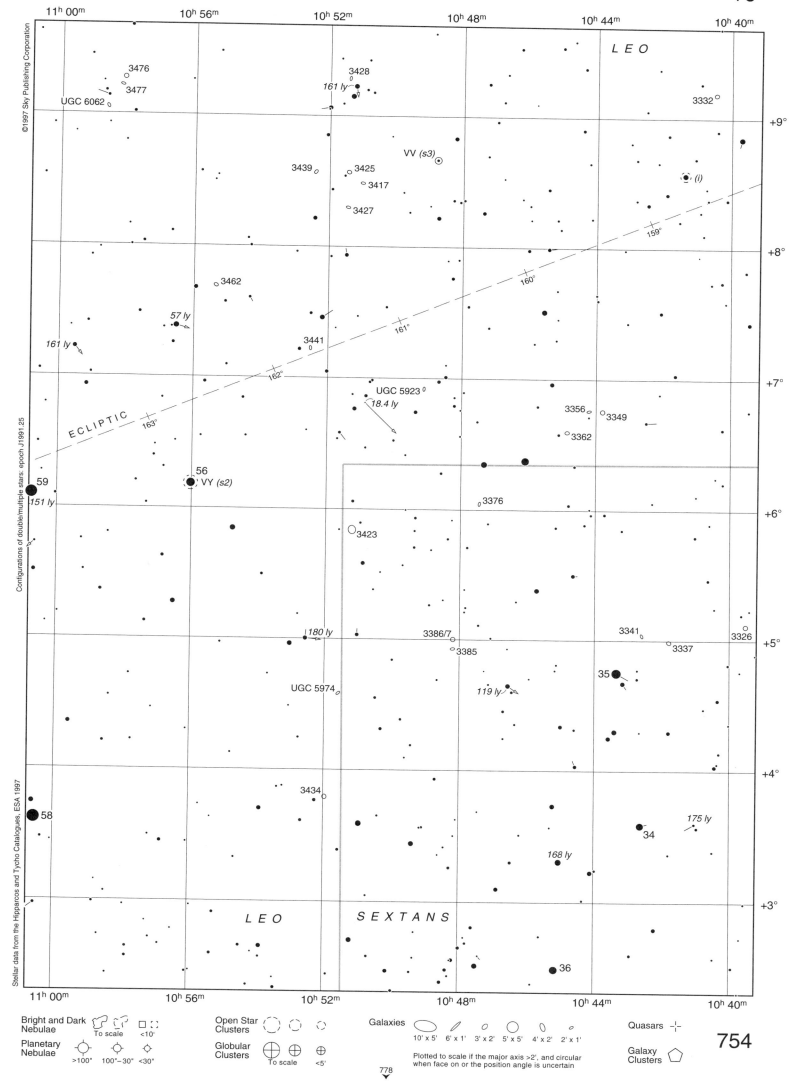

Configurations of double/multiple stars: epoch J1991.25

Stellar data from the Hipparcos and Tycho Catalogues, ESA 1997

L E O

3476
3477
UGC 6062

3428
161 ly

3439 3425
3417
3427

VV *(s3)*

3332

(i)

159°

+9°

160°

+8°

3462

57 ly

161°

161 ly

3441

162°

ECLIPTIC

163°

UGC 5923

18.4 ly

3356 3349

3362

+7°

56
VY *(s2)*

59

151 ly

3376

3423

+6°

180 ly

3386/7
3385

3341
3337

3326

+5°

UGC 5974

35

119 ly

3434

58

34

175 ly

168 ly

L E O

S E X T A N S

36

+4°

+3°

11ʰ 00ᵐ   10ʰ 56ᵐ   10ʰ 52ᵐ   10ʰ 48ᵐ   10ʰ 44ᵐ   10ʰ 40ᵐ

Bright and Dark Nebulae	Open Star Clusters	Galaxies	Quasars

Bright and Dark
Nebulae
To scale   <10'

Planetary
Nebulae
>100" 100"–30" <30"

Open Star
Clusters

Globular
Clusters
To scale   <5'

Galaxies
10' x 5' 6' x 1' 3' x 2' 5' x 5' 4' x 2' 2' x 1'

Plotted to scale if the major axis >2', and circular
when face on or the position angle is uncertain

Quasars

Galaxy
Clusters

754

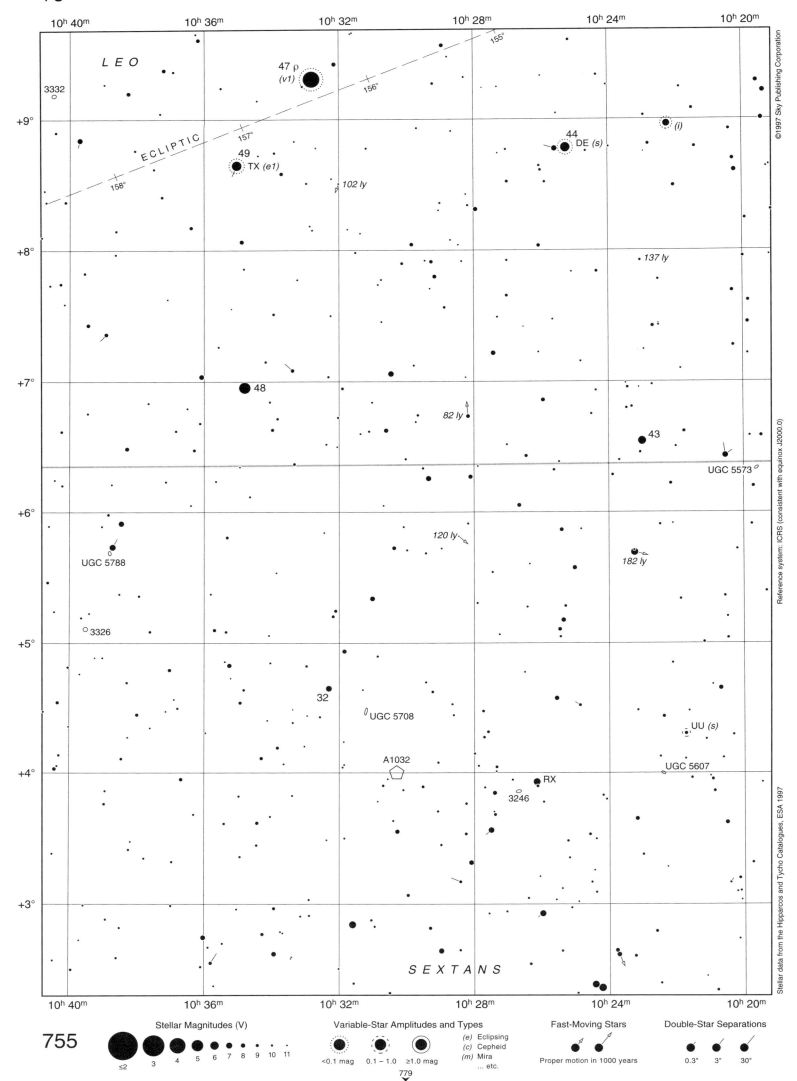

©1997 Sky Publishing Corporation

Reference system: ICRS (consistent with equinox J2000.0)

Stellar data from the Hipparcos and Tycho Catalogues, ESA 1997

LEO

3332

ECLIPTIC

47 ρ
(v1)

155°
156°
157°
158°

49
TX (e1)

102 ly

44
DE (s)

(i)

137 ly

48

82 ly

43

UGC 5573

120 ly

UGC 5788

182 ly

3326

32

UGC 5708

UU (s)

A1032

UGC 5607

RX
3246

SEXTANS

755

Stellar Magnitudes (V)

≤2 3 4 5 6 7 8 9 10 11

Variable-Star Amplitudes and Types

<0.1 mag   0.1 – 1.0   ≥1.0 mag

(e) Eclipsing
(c) Cepheid
(m) Mira
... etc.

Fast-Moving Stars

Proper motion in 1000 years

Double-Star Separations

0.3"   3"   30"

779

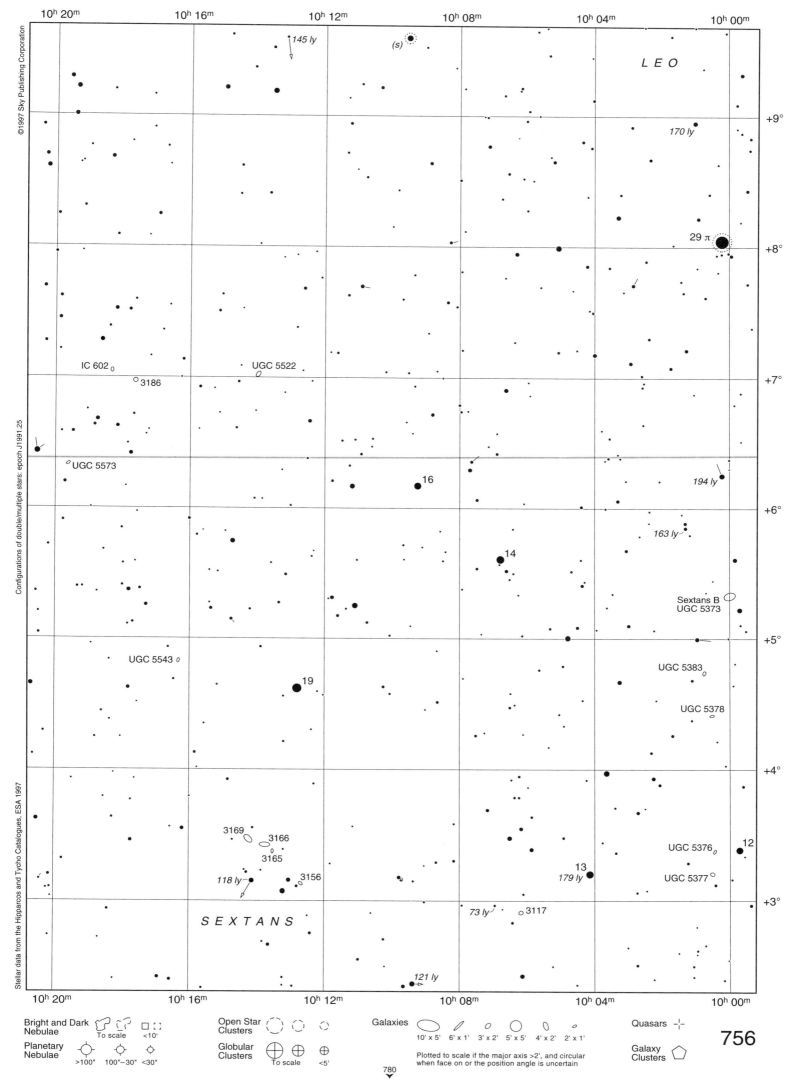

LEO

170 ly

29 π

145 ly

(s)

IC 602

UGC 5522

3186

UGC 5573

16

194 ly

163 ly

14

Sextans B
UGC 5373

UGC 5383

UGC 5543

19

UGC 5378

3169
3166
3165

3156

118 ly

13
179 ly

UGC 5376

UGC 5377

12

73 ly 3117

SEXTANS

121 ly

Bright and Dark Nebulae	Open Star Clusters	Galaxies	Quasars

To scale <10'

Planetary Nebulae
>100" 100"–30" <30"

Globular Clusters
To scale <5'

10' x 5' 6' x 1' 3' x 2' 5' x 5' 4' x 2' 2' x 1'

Galaxy Clusters

Plotted to scale if the major axis >2', and circular
when face on or the position angle is uncertain

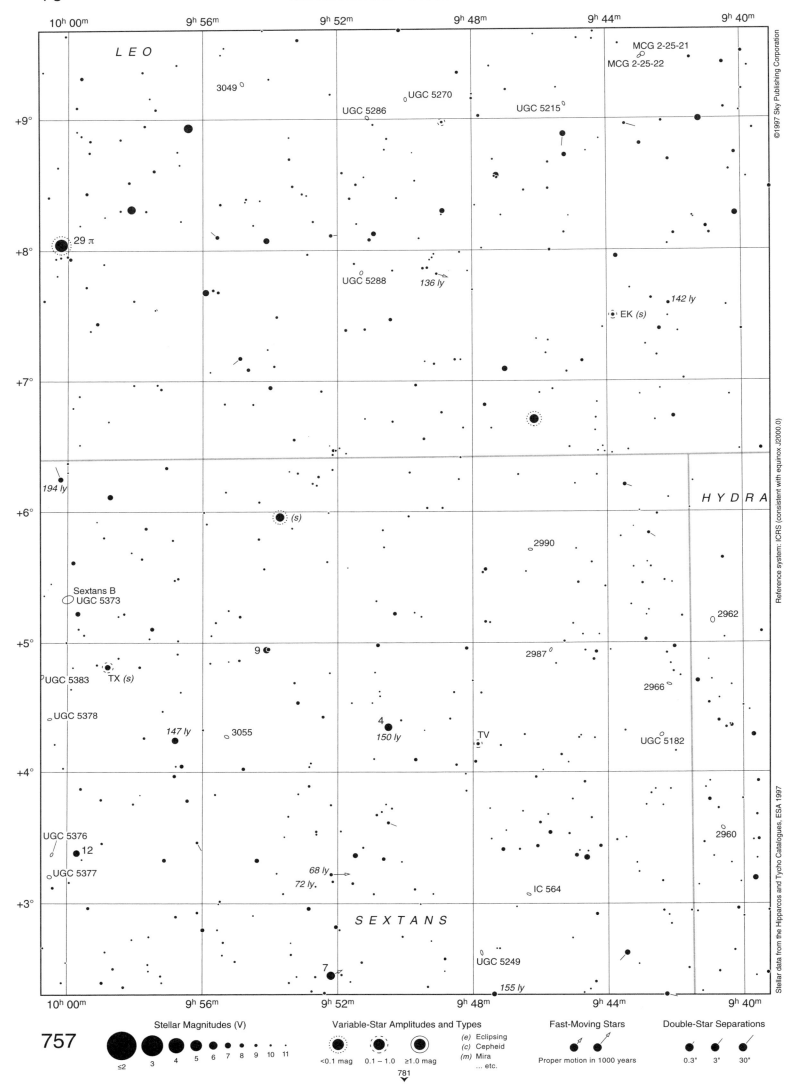

©1997 Sky Publishing Corporation

Reference system: ICRS (consistent with equinox J2000.0)

Stellar data from the Hipparcos and Tycho Catalogues, ESA 1997

LEO

MCG 2-25-21
MCG 2-25-22

3049

UGC 5270

UGC 5286

UGC 5215

UGC 5288

136 ly

142 ly

EK (s)

29 π

194 ly

HYDRA

2990

Sextans B
UGC 5373

2962

9

2987

2966

UGC 5383

TX (s)

UGC 5378

147 ly

3055

4
150 ly

TV

UGC 5182

UGC 5376

12

2960

UGC 5377

68 ly

72 ly

IC 564

SEXTANS

UGC 5249

7

155 ly

Stellar Magnitudes (V)

≤2 3 4 5 6 7 8 9 10 11

Variable-Star Amplitudes and Types

<0.1 mag   0.1 – 1.0 mag   ≥1.0 mag

781

(e) Eclipsing
(c) Cepheid
(m) Mira
... etc.

Fast-Moving Stars

Proper motion in 1000 years

Double-Star Separations

0.3"   3"   30"

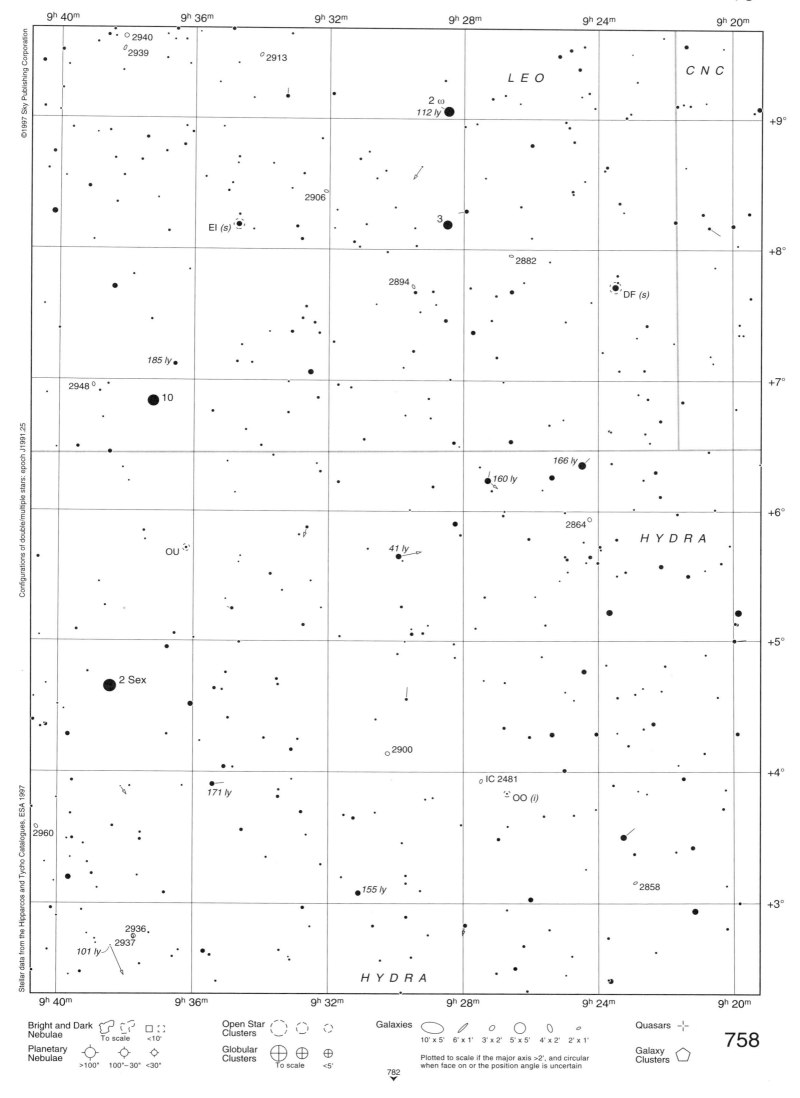

LEO

CNC

2 ω
112 ly

2913

2939
2940

2906

EI (s)

3

2882

2894

DF (s)

185 ly

2948

10

166 ly

160 ly

2864

HYDRA

OU

41 ly

2 Sex

2900

IC 2481

171 ly

OO (i)

2960

2858

155 ly

2936
2937

101 ly

HYDRA

Bright and Dark Nebulae
To scale   <10'

Planetary Nebulae
>100"   100"–30"   <30"

Open Star Clusters

Globular Clusters
To scale   <5'

Galaxies
10' x 5'   6' x 1'   3' x 2'   5' x 5'   4' x 2'   2' x 1'

Plotted to scale if the major axis >2', and circular when face on or the position angle is uncertain

Quasars

Galaxy Clusters

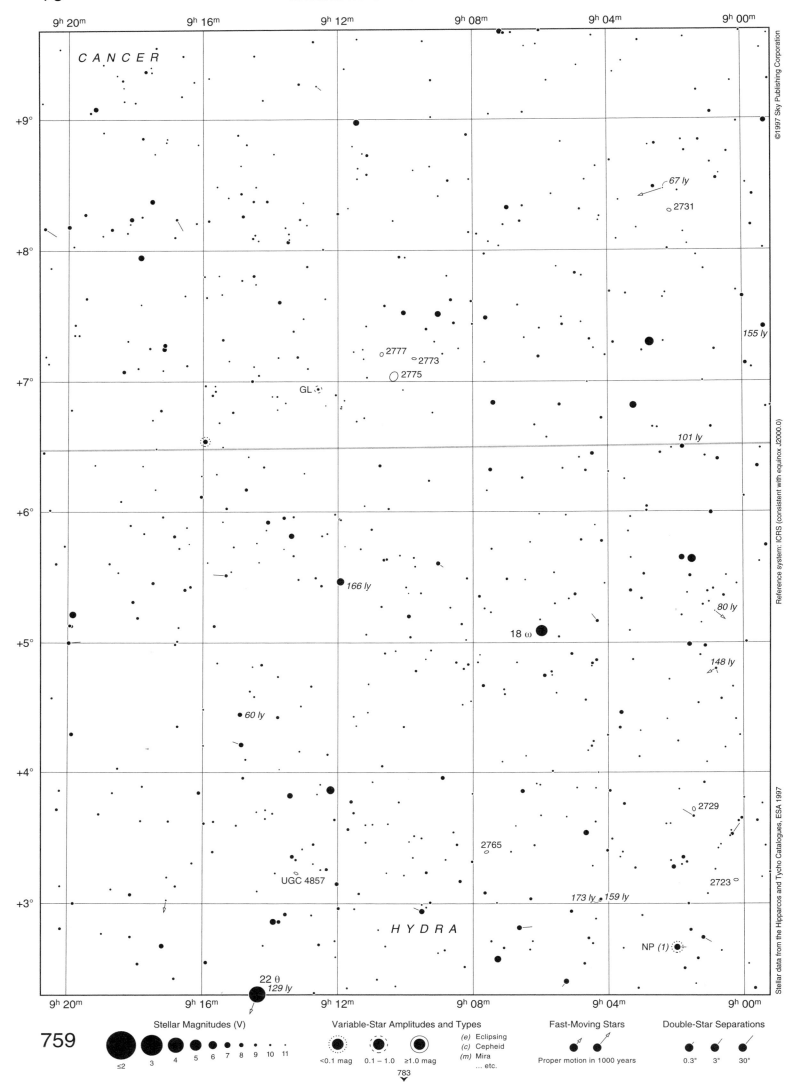

©1997 Sky Publishing Corporation

Reference system: ICRS (consistent with equinox J2000.0)

Stellar data from the Hipparcos and Tycho Catalogues, ESA 1997

CANCER

67 ly
2731

155 ly

2777   2773
2775

GL

101 ly

166 ly

60 ly

18 ω

80 ly

148 ly

2729

2765

UGC 4857

2723

173 ly 159 ly

HYDRA

NP (1)

22 θ
129 ly

Stellar Magnitudes (V)
≤2   3   4   5   6 7 8 9 10 11

Variable-Star Amplitudes and Types
<0.1 mag   0.1 – 1.0   ≥1.0 mag

(e) Eclipsing
(c) Cepheid
(m) Mira
... etc.

Fast-Moving Stars
Proper motion in 1000 years

Double-Star Separations
0.3"   3"   30"

MILLENNIUM STAR ATLAS

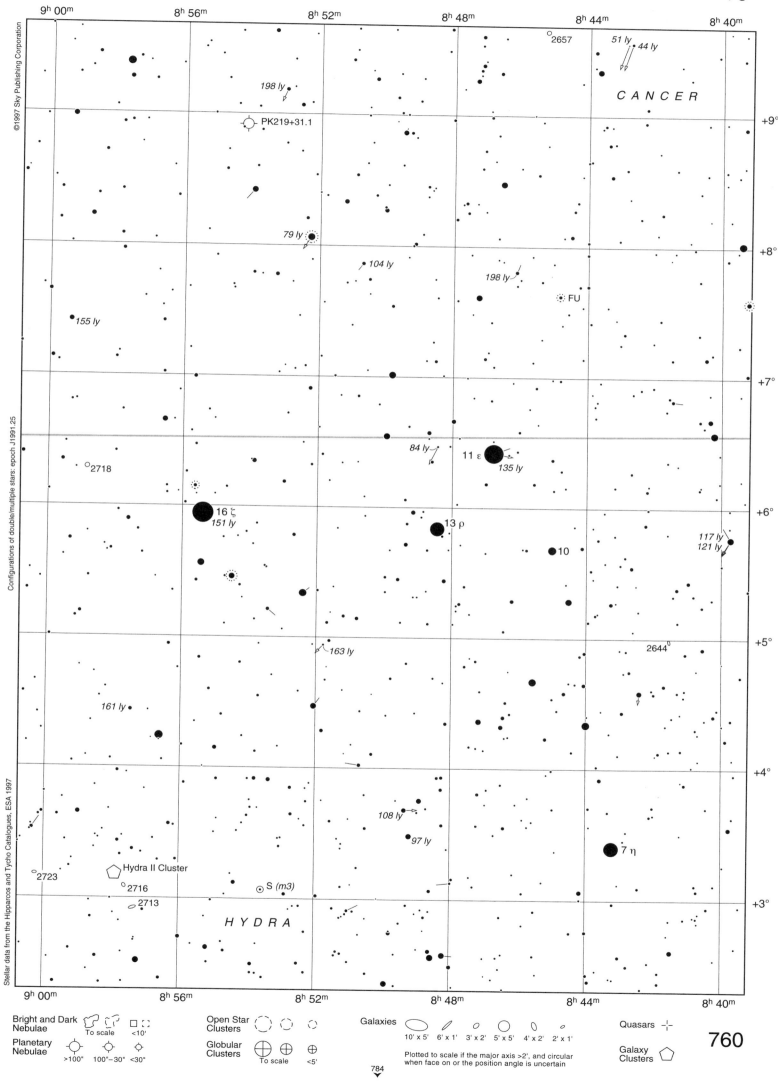

©1997 Sky Publishing Corporation

Configurations of double/multiple stars: epoch J1991.25

Stellar data from the Hipparcos and Tycho Catalogues, ESA 1997

9h 00m   8h 56m   8h 52m   8h 48m   8h 44m   8h 40m

+9°
+8°
+7°
+6°
+5°
+4°
+3°

CANCER

○ 2657
51 ly   44 ly

198 ly

⊕ PK219+31.1

79 ly ●

104 ly

198 ly

⊙ FU

155 ly

○ 2718

84 ly

11 ε ●
135 ly

16 ζ ●
151 ly

13 ρ ●

10 ●

117 ly ●
121 ly

163 ly

161 ly

2644 ○

108 ly

97 ly

7 η ●

○ 2723

⬠ Hydra II Cluster

○ 2716

⊙ S (m3)

◠ 2713

HYDRA

9h 00m   8h 56m   8h 52m   8h 48m   8h 44m   8h 40m

Bright and Dark Nebulae
To scale   <10'

Planetary Nebulae
>100"   100"–30"   <30"

Open Star Clusters

Globular Clusters
To scale   <5'

Galaxies
10' x 5'   6' x 1'   3' x 2'   5' x 5'   4' x 2'   2' x 1'

Plotted to scale if the major axis >2', and circular when face on or the position angle is uncertain

Quasars

Galaxy Clusters

760

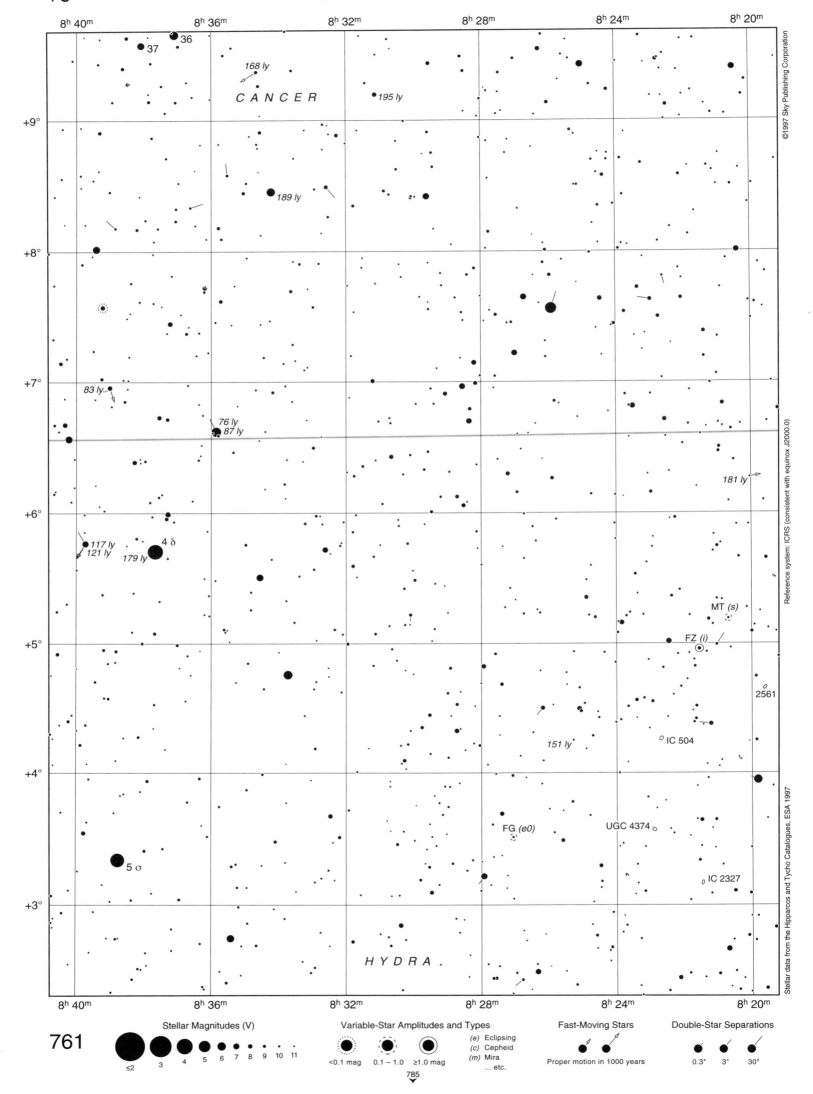

CANCER

168 ly

195 ly

189 ly

83 ly

76 ly
87 ly

181 ly

117 ly
121 ly

4 δ

179 ly

MT (s)

FZ (i)

2561

IC 504

151 ly

5 σ

FG (e0)

UGC 4374

IC 2327

HYDRA

761

Stellar Magnitudes (V)

≤2   3   4   5   6   7   8   9   10   11

Variable-Star Amplitudes and Types

<0.1 mag   0.1 – 1.0   ≥1.0 mag

(e) Eclipsing
(c) Cepheid
(m) Mira
... etc.

785

Fast-Moving Stars

Proper motion in 1000 years

Double-Star Separations

0.3"   3"   30"

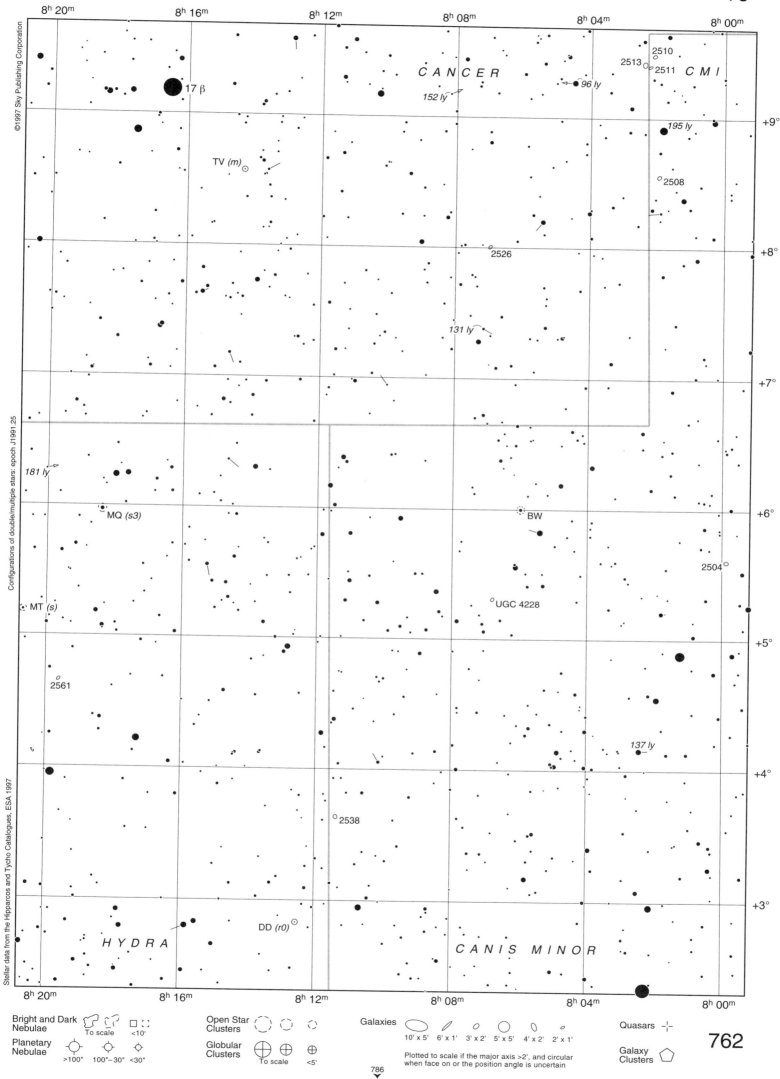

©1997 Sky Publishing Corporation

Configurations of double/multiple stars: epoch J1991.25

Stellar data from the Hipparcos and Tycho Catalogues, ESA 1997

8h 20m   8h 16m   8h 12m   8h 08m   8h 04m   8h 00m

CANCER

CMI

2510
2513   2511

96 ly

152 ly

195 ly

+9°

2508

TV (m)

+8°
2526

131 ly

+7°

181 ly

MQ (s3)

BW

+6°
2504

MT (s)

UGC 4228

+5°

2561

137 ly

+4°

2538

+3°
DD (r0)

HYDRA

CANIS MINOR

8h 20m   8h 16m   8h 12m   8h 08m   8h 04m   8h 00m

Bright and Dark Nebulae
To scale   <10'

Open Star Clusters

Galaxies

Quasars

Planetary Nebulae
>100"   100"–30"   <30"

Globular Clusters
To scale   <5'

10' x 5'   6' x 1'   3' x 2'   5' x 5'   4' x 2'   2' x 1'

Galaxy Clusters

762

Plotted to scale if the major axis >2', and circular when face on or the position angle is uncertain

786

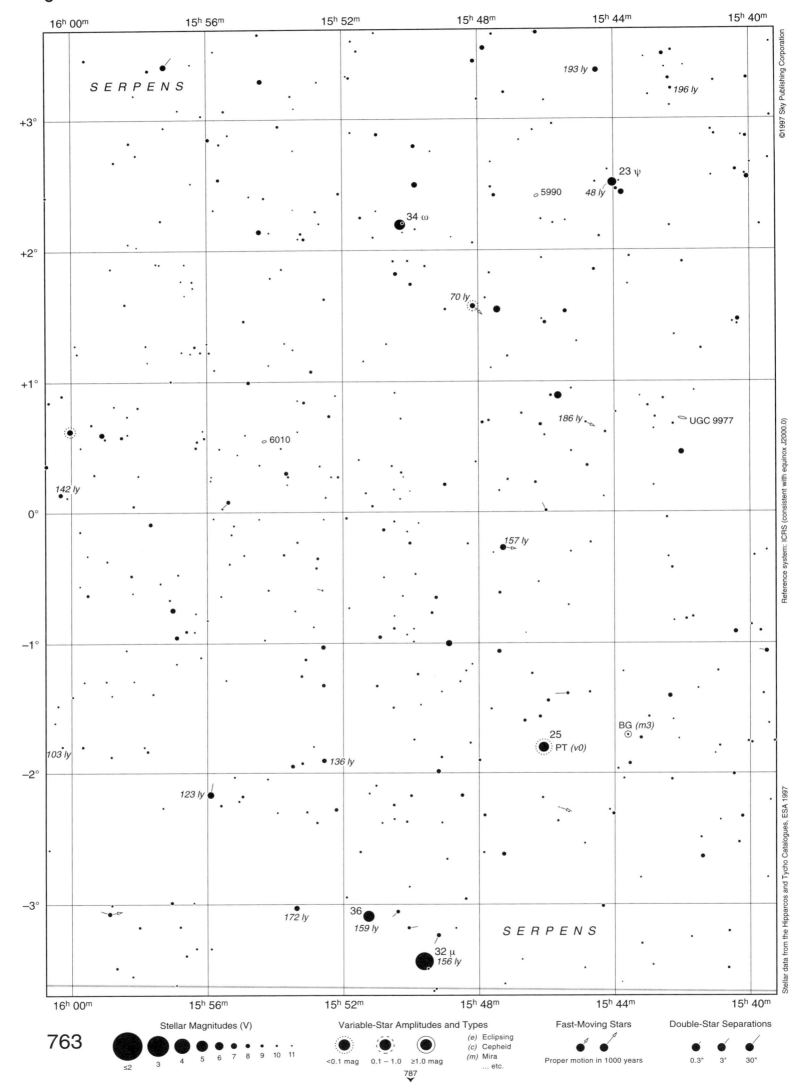

S E R P E N S

193 ly

196 ly

23 ψ

5990   48 ly

34 ω

70 ly

186 ly   UGC 9977

6010

142 ly

157 ly

103 ly

25
PT (v0)   BG (m3)

136 ly

123 ly

S E R P E N S

172 ly

36
159 ly

32 μ
156 ly

©1997 Sky Publishing Corporation

Reference system: ICRS (consistent with equinox J2000.0)

Stellar data from the Hipparcos and Tycho Catalogues, ESA 1997

763

Stellar Magnitudes (V)

≤2   3   4   5   6   7   8   9   10   11

Variable-Star Amplitudes and Types

<0.1 mag   0.1 – 1.0   ≥1.0 mag

(e) Eclipsing
(c) Cepheid
(m) Mira
... etc.

Fast-Moving Stars

Proper motion in 1000 years

Double-Star Separations

0.3"   3"   30"

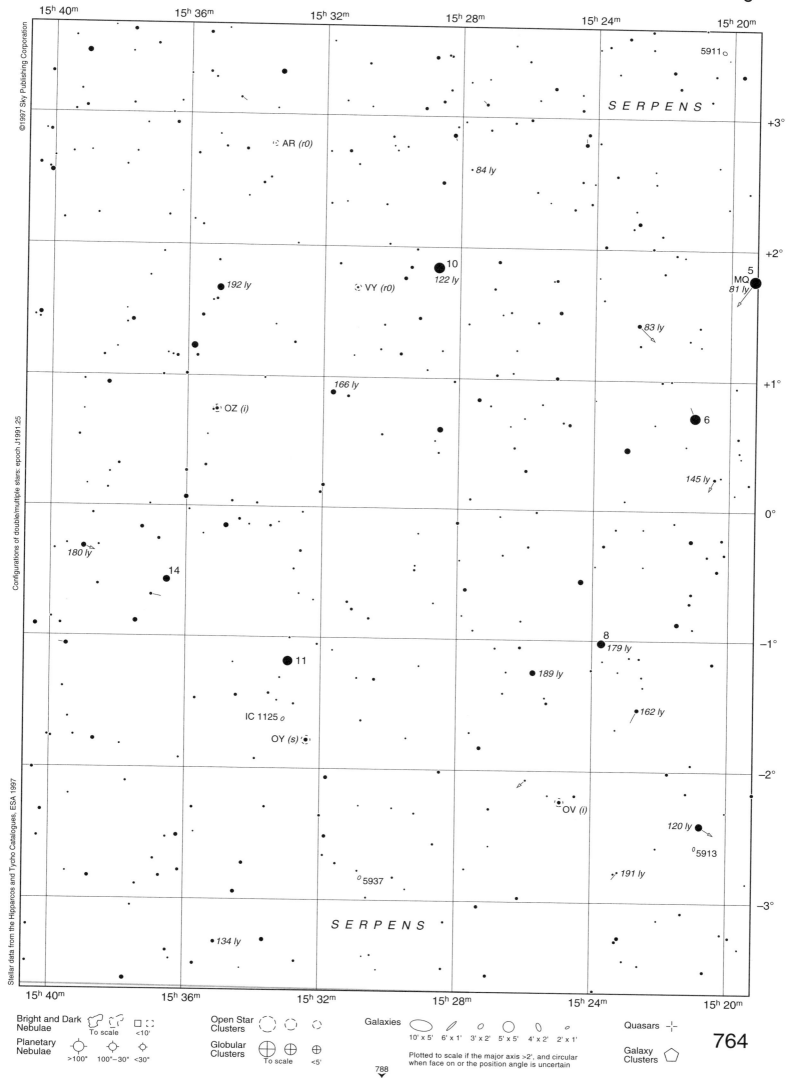

SERPENS

AR *(r0)*

84 ly

10
122 ly

192 ly

VY *(r0)*

5
MQ
81 ly

83 ly

166 ly

OZ *(i)*

6

145 ly

180 ly

14

8
179 ly

11

189 ly

IC 1125 *o*

OY *(s)*

162 ly

OV *(i)*

120 ly
5913

5937

191 ly

SERPENS

134 ly

Bright and Dark Nebulae	Open Star Clusters	Galaxies	Quasars

Bright and Dark Nebulae — To scale — <10'

Planetary Nebulae — >100" — 100"–30" — <30"

Globular Clusters — To scale — <5'

Galaxies — 10' x 5' — 6' x 1' — 3' x 2' — 5' x 5' — 4' x 2' — 2' x 1'

Plotted to scale if the major axis >2', and circular when face on or the position angle is uncertain

Quasars

Galaxy Clusters

764

788

0°

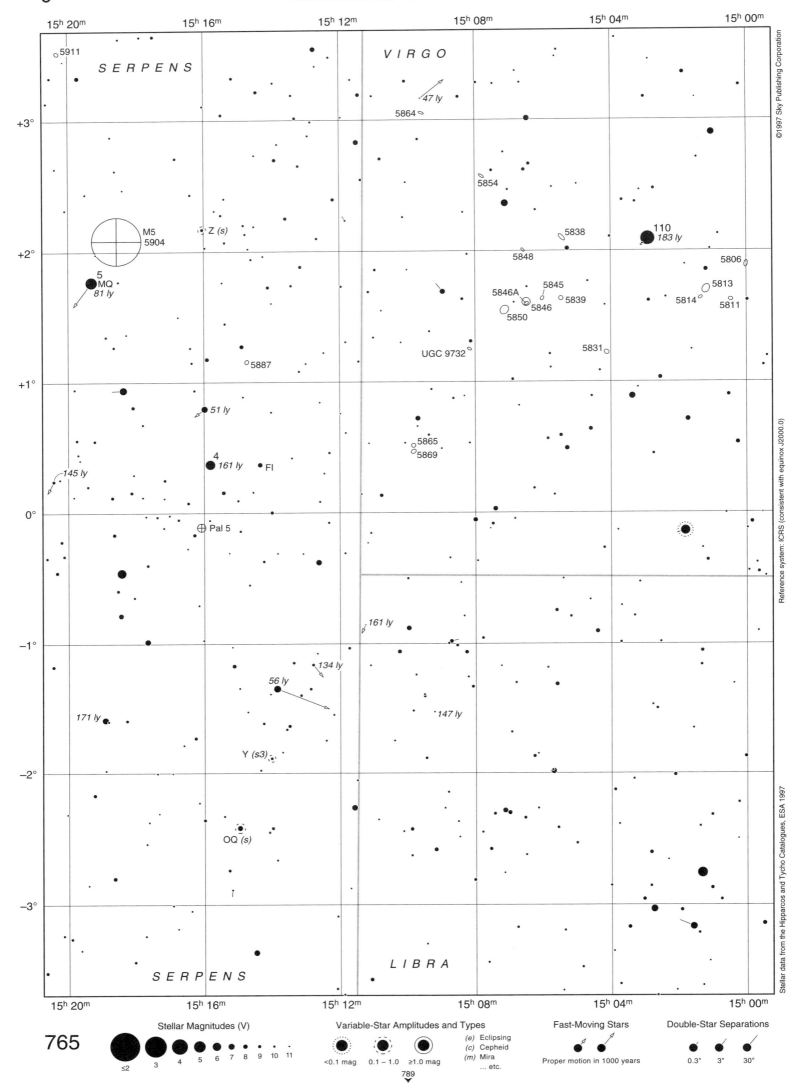

SERPENS

VIRGO

47 ly
5864

5911

5854

M5
5904

Z (s)

110
183 ly

5838

5806

5848

5
MQ
81 ly

5846A
5850

5845
5846

5839

5813

5814

5811

5887

UGC 9732

5831

51 ly

4
161 ly

FI

5865
5869

145 ly

Pal 5

161 ly

134 ly

147 ly

56 ly

171 ly

Y (s3)

OQ (s)

SERPENS

LIBRA

©1997 Sky Publishing Corporation

Reference system: ICRS (consistent with equinox J2000.0)

Stellar data from the Hipparcos and Tycho Catalogues, ESA 1997

765

Stellar Magnitudes (V)

≤2   3   4   5   6   7   8   9   10   11

Variable-Star Amplitudes and Types

<0.1 mag   0.1 – 1.0   ≥1.0 mag

(e) Eclipsing
(c) Cepheid
(m) Mira
... etc.

Fast-Moving Stars

Proper motion in 1000 years

Double-Star Separations

0.3"   3"   30"

MILLENNIUM STAR ATLAS

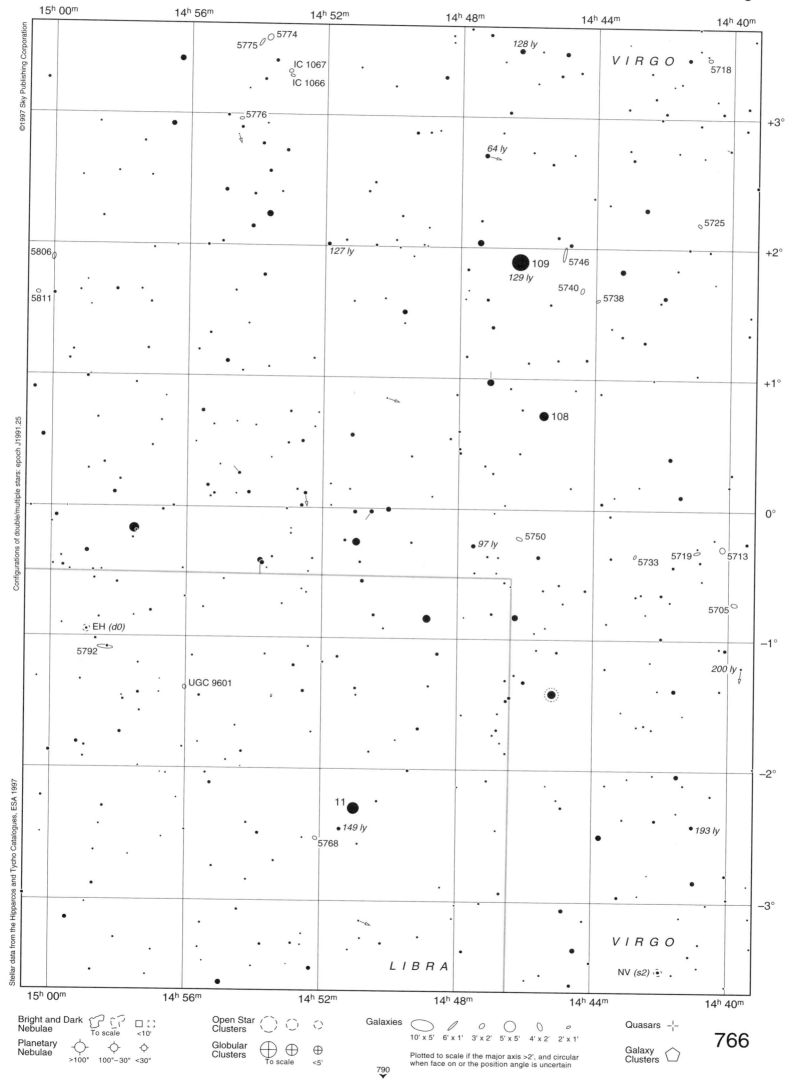

15h 00m   14h 56m   14h 52m   14h 48m   14h 44m   14h 40m

VIRGO

5775   5774

IC 1067

IC 1066

5776

5806

5811

128 ly

5718

64 ly

5725

127 ly

5746

109
129 ly

5740   5738

108

5750

97 ly

5733   5719   5713

5705

EH (d0)

5792

UGC 9601

200 ly

11

149 ly

5768

193 ly

VIRGO

LIBRA

NV (s2)

15h 00m   14h 56m   14h 52m   14h 48m   14h 44m   14h 40m

+3°
+2°
+1°
0°
-1°
-2°
-3°

| Bright and Dark Nebulae | To scale | <10' | | Open Star Clusters | | | Galaxies | 10' x 5' | 6' x 1' | 3' x 2' | 5' x 5' | 4' x 2' | 2' x 1' | Quasars |
| Planetary Nebulae | >100" | 100"-30" | <30" | Globular Clusters | To scale | <5' | | | | | | | | Galaxy Clusters |

Plotted to scale if the major axis >2', and circular
when face on or the position angle is uncertain

766

0°

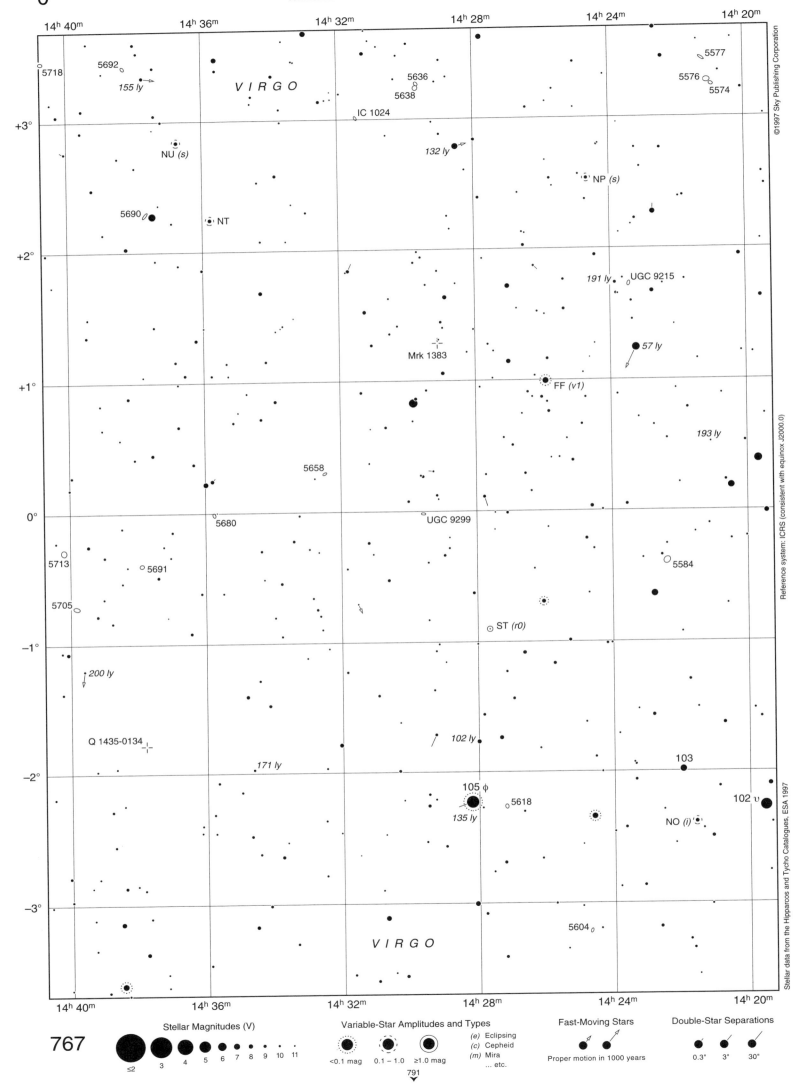

767

Stellar Magnitudes (V)									
≤2	3	4	5	6	7	8	9	10	11

Variable-Star Amplitudes and Types

<0.1 mag   0.1 – 1.0   ≥1.0 mag

(e) Eclipsing
(c) Cepheid
(m) Mira
... etc.

Fast-Moving Stars

Proper motion in 1000 years

Double-Star Separations

0.3"   3"   30"

791

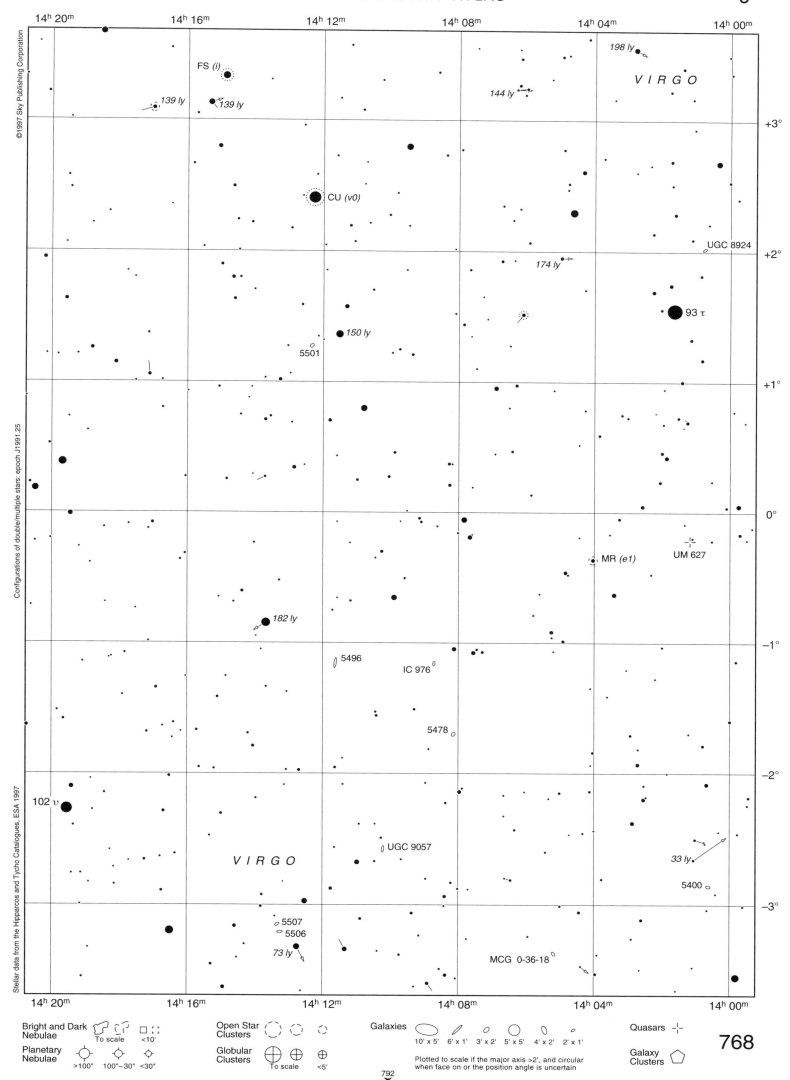

Configurations of double/multiple stars: epoch J1991.25

Stellar data from the Hipparcos and Tycho Catalogues, ESA 1997

FS *(i)*

139 ly

139 ly

VIRGO

198 ly

144 ly

CU *(v0)*

UGC 8924

174 ly

93 τ

150 ly

5501

MR *(e1)*

UM 627

182 ly

5496

IC 976

5478

102 υ

33 ly

UGC 9057

5400

VIRGO

5507

5506

73 ly

MCG 0-36-18

Bright and Dark Nebulae			Open Star Clusters			Galaxies						Quasars
To scale		<10'				10' x 5'	6' x 1'	3' x 2'	5' x 5'	4' x 2'	2' x 1'	
Planetary Nebulae			Globular Clusters									Galaxy Clusters
>100"	100"-30"	<30"	To scale		<5'							

Plotted to scale if the major axis >2', and circular when face on or the position angle is uncertain

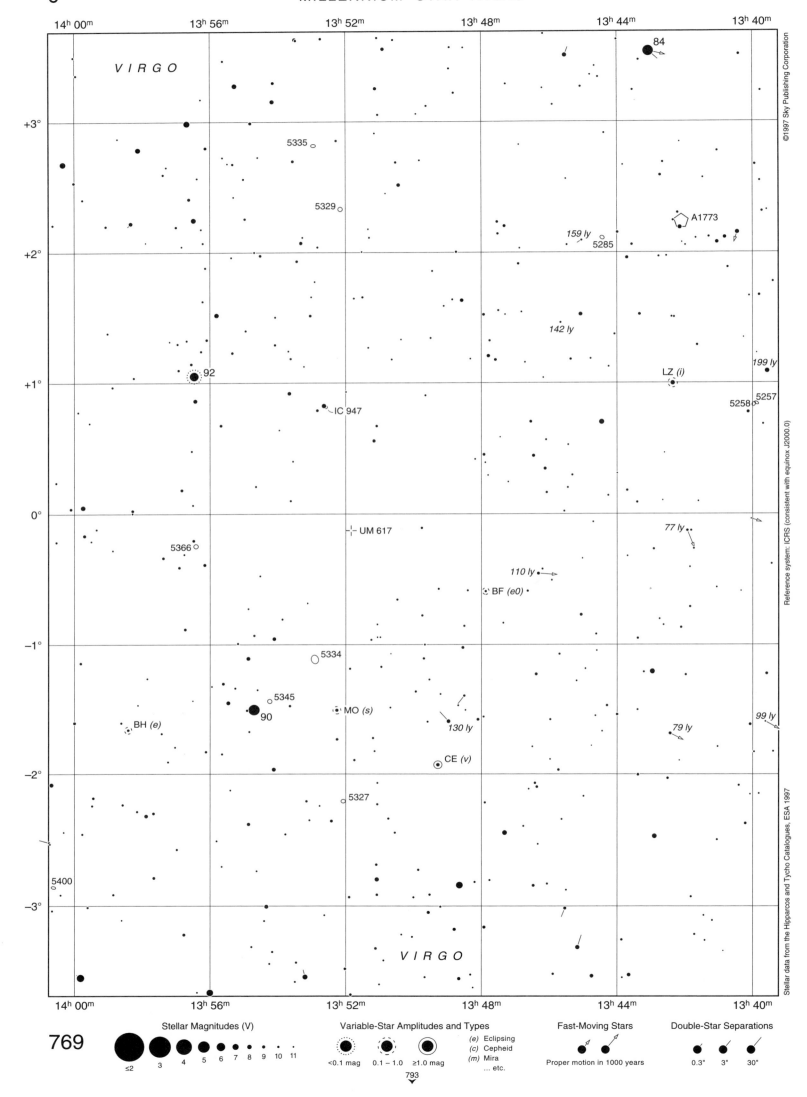

VIRGO

VIRGO

©1997 Sky Publishing Corporation

Reference system: ICRS (consistent with equinox J2000.0)

Stellar data from the Hipparcos and Tycho Catalogues, ESA 1997

769

Stellar Magnitudes (V)

≤2 3 4 5 6 7 8 9 10 11

Variable-Star Amplitudes and Types

<0.1 mag   0.1 – 1.0   ≥1.0 mag

(e) Eclipsing
(c) Cepheid
(m) Mira
... etc.

Fast-Moving Stars

Proper motion in 1000 years

Double-Star Separations

0.3" 3" 30"

793

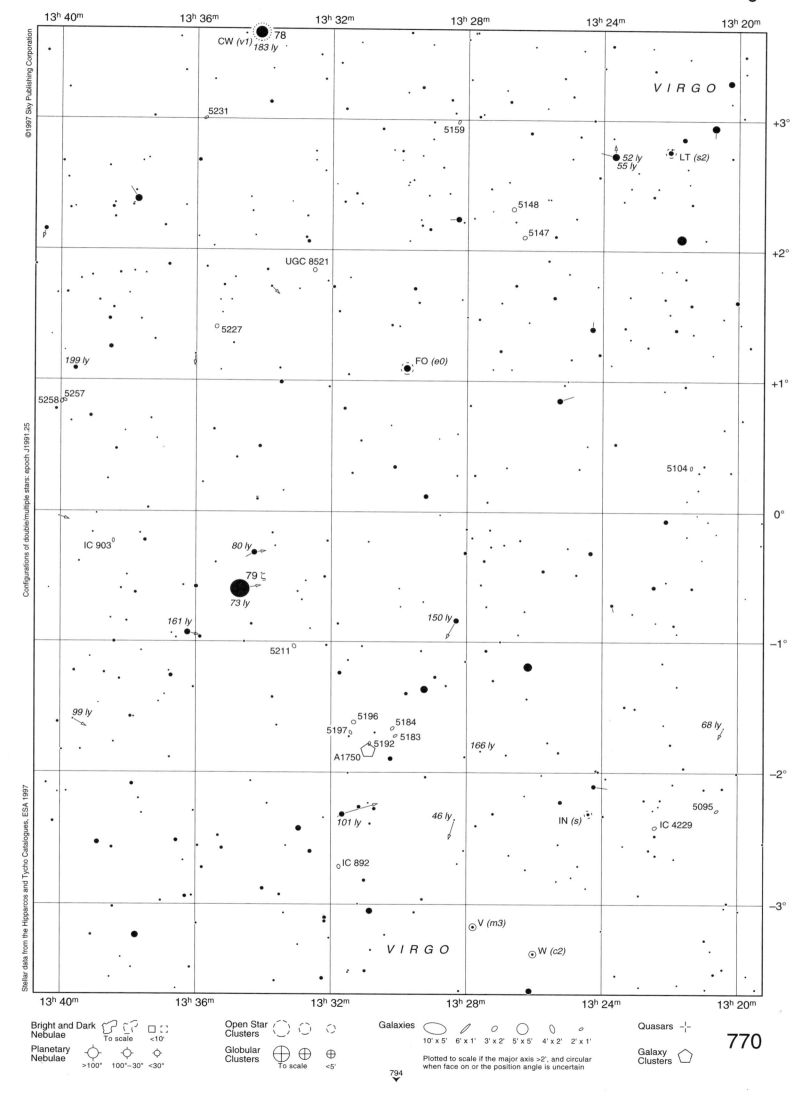

13ʰ 40ᵐ   13ʰ 36ᵐ   13ʰ 32ᵐ   13ʰ 28ᵐ   13ʰ 24ᵐ   13ʰ 20ᵐ

CW *(v1)* 78
183 ly

5231

VIRGO

5159   +3°

52 ly   LT *(s2)*
55 ly

5148

5147   +2°

UGC 8521

5227

FO *(e0)*   +1°

199 ly

5257
5258 5104   +1°

IC 903

80 ly   0°

79 ζ
73 ly

161 ly

150 ly   −1°

5211

99 ly

5196
5197   5184
       5183
       5192   68 ly
A1750

166 ly   −2°

101 ly   46 ly   IN *(s)*   5095
                               IC 4229

IC 892

−3°

V *(m3)*

VIRGO   W *(c2)*

13ʰ 40ᵐ   13ʰ 36ᵐ   13ʰ 32ᵐ   13ʰ 28ᵐ   13ʰ 24ᵐ   13ʰ 20ᵐ

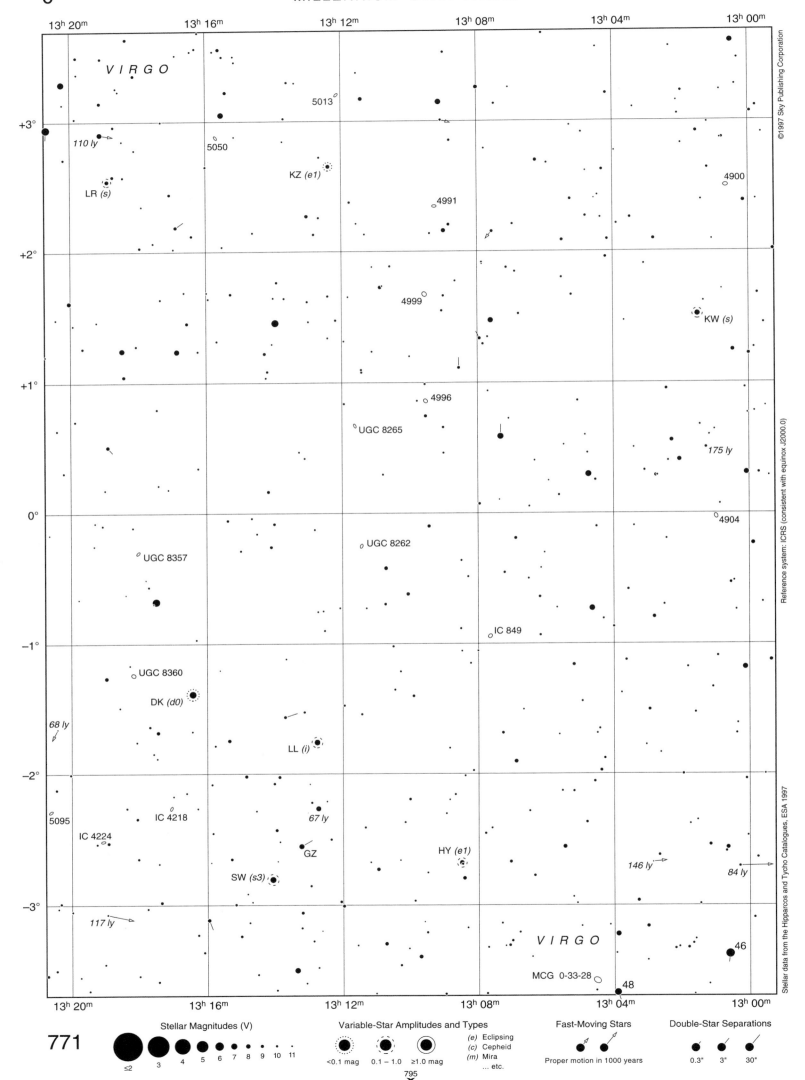

©1997 Sky Publishing Corporation

Reference system: ICRS (consistent with equinox J2000.0)

Stellar data from the Hipparcos and Tycho Catalogues, ESA 1997

V I R G O

13ʰ 20ᵐ   13ʰ 16ᵐ   13ʰ 12ᵐ   13ʰ 08ᵐ   13ʰ 04ᵐ   13ʰ 00ᵐ

5013

110 ly

5050

KZ (e1)

LR (s)

4991

4900

4999

KW (s)

4996

UGC 8265

175 ly

UGC 8357

4904

UGC 8262

IC 849

UGC 8360

DK (d0)

68 ly

LL (i)

5095

IC 4218

67 ly

IC 4224

GZ

HY (e1)

146 ly

84 ly

SW (s3)

117 ly

V I R G O

MCG 0-33-28

46

48

13ʰ 20ᵐ   13ʰ 16ᵐ   13ʰ 12ᵐ   13ʰ 08ᵐ   13ʰ 04ᵐ   13ʰ 00ᵐ

+3°
+2°
+1°
0°
−1°
−2°
−3°

771

Stellar Magnitudes (V)

≤2   3   4   5   6   7 8 9 10 11

Variable-Star Amplitudes and Types

<0.1 mag   0.1 – 1.0   ≥1.0 mag

(e) Eclipsing
(c) Cepheid
(m) Mira
... etc.

Fast-Moving Stars

Proper motion in 1000 years

Double-Star Separations

0.3"   3"   30"

795

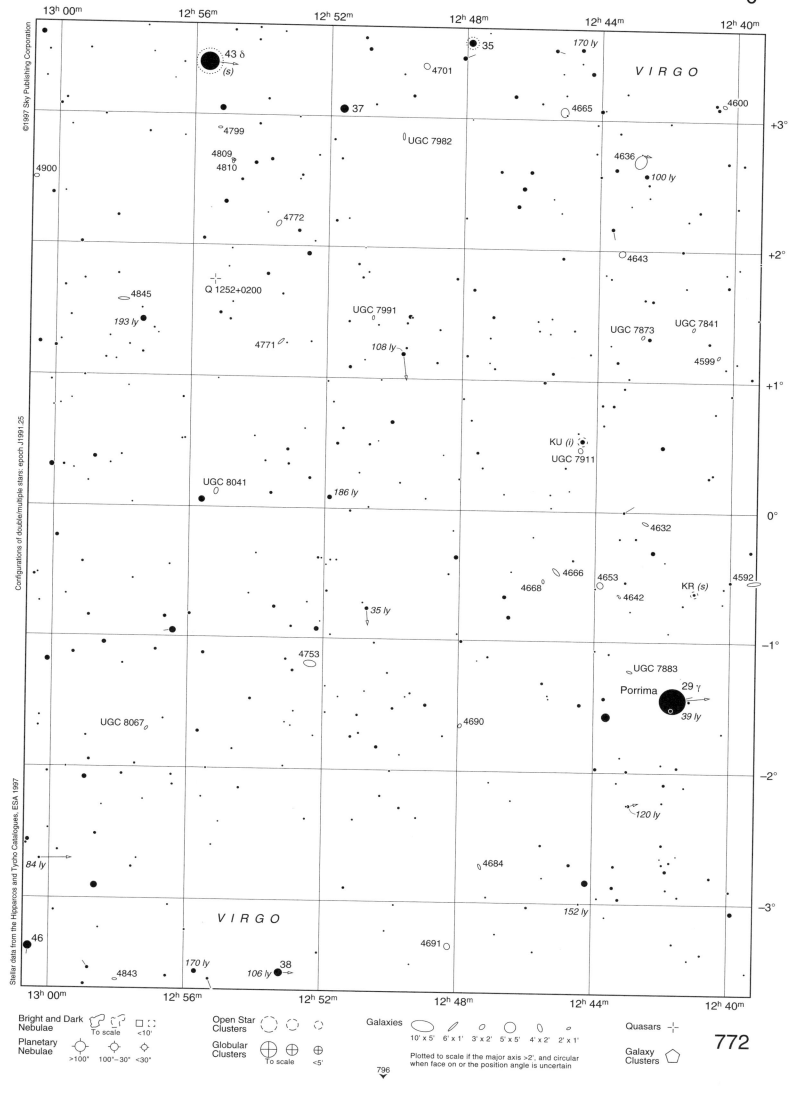

©1997 Sky Publishing Corporation

Configurations of double/multiple stars: epoch J1991.25

Stellar data from the Hipparcos and Tycho Catalogues, ESA 1997

VIRGO

VIRGO

Porrima

29 γ
39 ly

Bright and Dark Nebulae — To scale — <10'

Planetary Nebulae — >100" — 100"–30" — <30"

Open Star Clusters

Globular Clusters — To scale — <5'

Galaxies — 10' x 5' — 6' x 1' — 3' x 2' — 5' x 5' — 4' x 2' — 2' x 1'

Plotted to scale if the major axis >2', and circular when face on or the position angle is uncertain

Quasars

Galaxy Clusters

772

796

0°

749

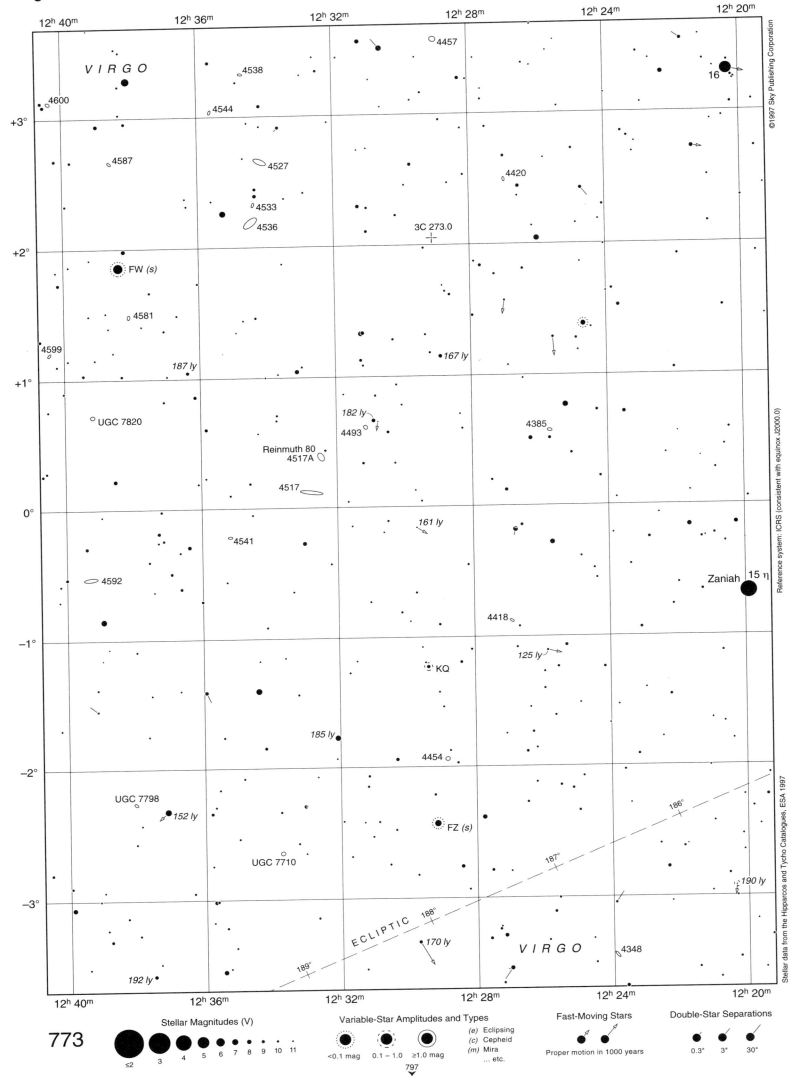

VIRGO

4600

4538

4544

4457

16

4587

4527

4533
4536

4420

3C 273.0

FW (s)

4581

4599

187 ly

167 ly

UGC 7820

182 ly
4493

4385

Reinmuth 80
4517A

4517

161 ly

4541

Zaniah   15 η

4592

4418

125 ly

KQ

185 ly

4454

UGC 7798

152 ly

FZ (s)

UGC 7710

186°

187°

190 ly

ECLIPTIC   188°

4348

189°

170 ly

VIRGO

192 ly

Reference system: ICRS (consistent with equinox J2000.0)

Stellar data from the Hipparcos and Tycho Catalogues, ESA 1997

773

Stellar Magnitudes (V)

≤2   3   4   5   6   7 8 9 10 11

Variable-Star Amplitudes and Types

<0.1 mag   0.1 – 1.0   ≥1.0 mag

(e) Eclipsing
(c) Cepheid
(m) Mira
... etc.

Fast-Moving Stars

Proper motion in 1000 years

Double-Star Separations

0.3"   3"   30"

797

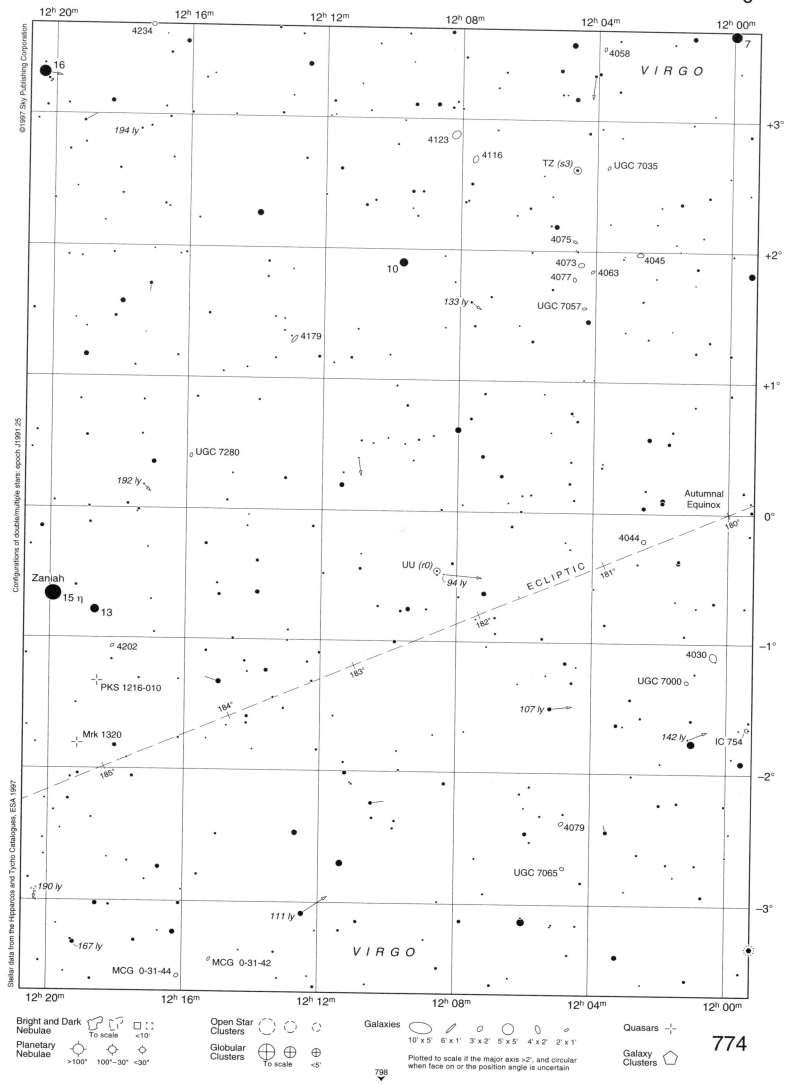

©1997 Sky Publishing Corporation

Configurations of double/multiple stars: epoch J1991.25

Stellar data from the Hipparcos and Tycho Catalogues, ESA 1997

12h 20m · 12h 16m · 12h 12m · 12h 08m · 12h 04m · 12h 00m

4234

16

VIRGO

4058

+3°

194 ly

4123

4116

TZ (s3)

UGC 7035

+2°

4075

4073 · 4045

4077 · 4063

10

UGC 7057

133 ly

4179

+1°

UGC 7280

192 ly

Autumnal Equinox

180°

0°

4044

ECLIPTIC

181°

UU (r0)

94 ly

Zaniah

15 η

13

182°

4202

−1°

4030

183°

PKS 1216-010

UGC 7000

184°

107 ly

Mrk 1320

142 ly · IC 754

185°

−2°

4079

UGC 7065

190 ly

−3°

111 ly

167 ly

VIRGO

MCG 0-31-44 · MCG 0-31-42

12h 20m · 12h 16m · 12h 12m · 12h 08m · 12h 04m · 12h 00m

Bright and Dark Nebulae — To scale — <10'

Open Star Clusters

Globular Clusters — To scale — <5'

Galaxies — 10' x 5' · 6' x 1' · 3' x 2' · 5' x 5' · 4' x 2' · 2' x 1'

Plotted to scale if the major axis >2', and circular when face on or the position angle is uncertain

Quasars

Galaxy Clusters

Planetary Nebulae — >100" · 100"–30" · <30"

774

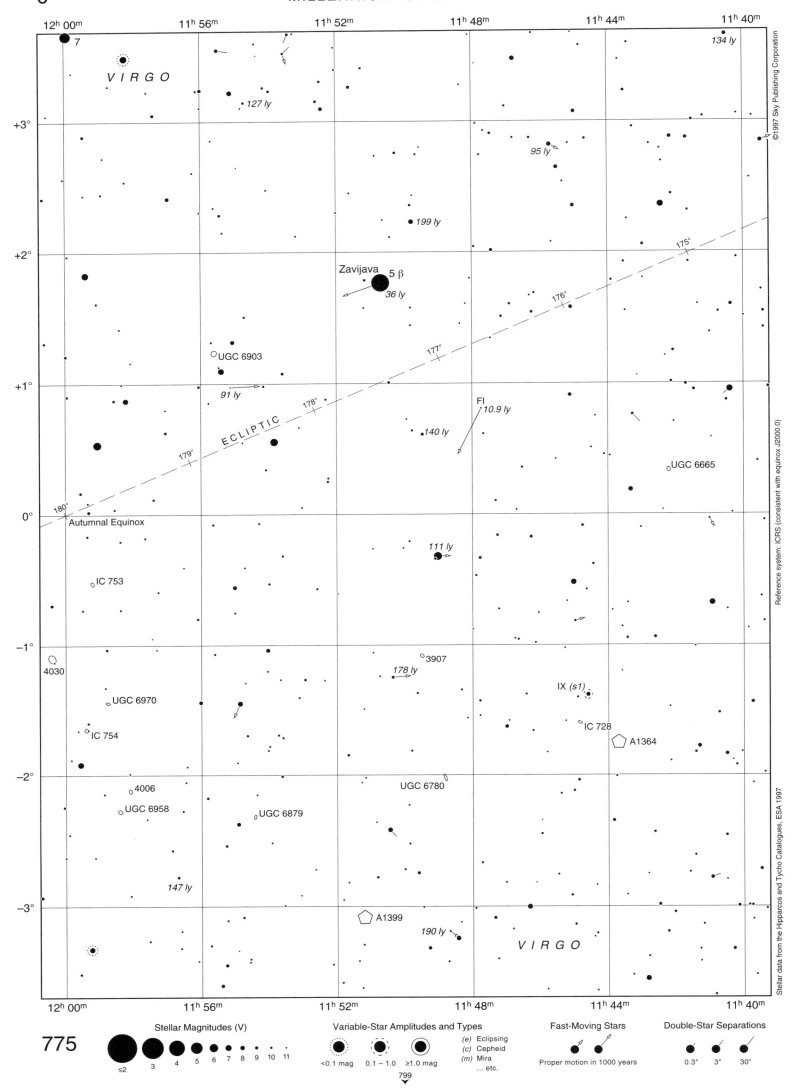

VIRGO

Zavijava 5 β
36 ly

UGC 6903

FI 10.9 ly

ECLIPTIC

Autumnal Equinox

IC 753

4030

UGC 6970

IC 754

4006

UGC 6958

UGC 6879

3907
178 ly

IX (s1)

IC 728

A1364

UGC 6780

A1399

190 ly

VIRGO

127 ly
91 ly
199 ly
140 ly
111 ly
95 ly
134 ly
147 ly

175°
176°
177°
178°
179°
180°

UGC 6665

7

©1997 Sky Publishing Corporation

Reference system: ICRS (consistent with equinox J2000.0)

Stellar data from the Hipparcos and Tycho Catalogues, ESA 1997

Stellar Magnitudes (V)
≤2 3 4 5 6 7 8 9 10 11

Variable-Star Amplitudes and Types
<0.1 mag   0.1 – 1.0   ≥1.0 mag
(e) Eclipsing
(c) Cepheid
(m) Mira
... etc.
799

Fast-Moving Stars
Proper motion in 1000 years

Double-Star Separations
0.3"   3"   30"

775

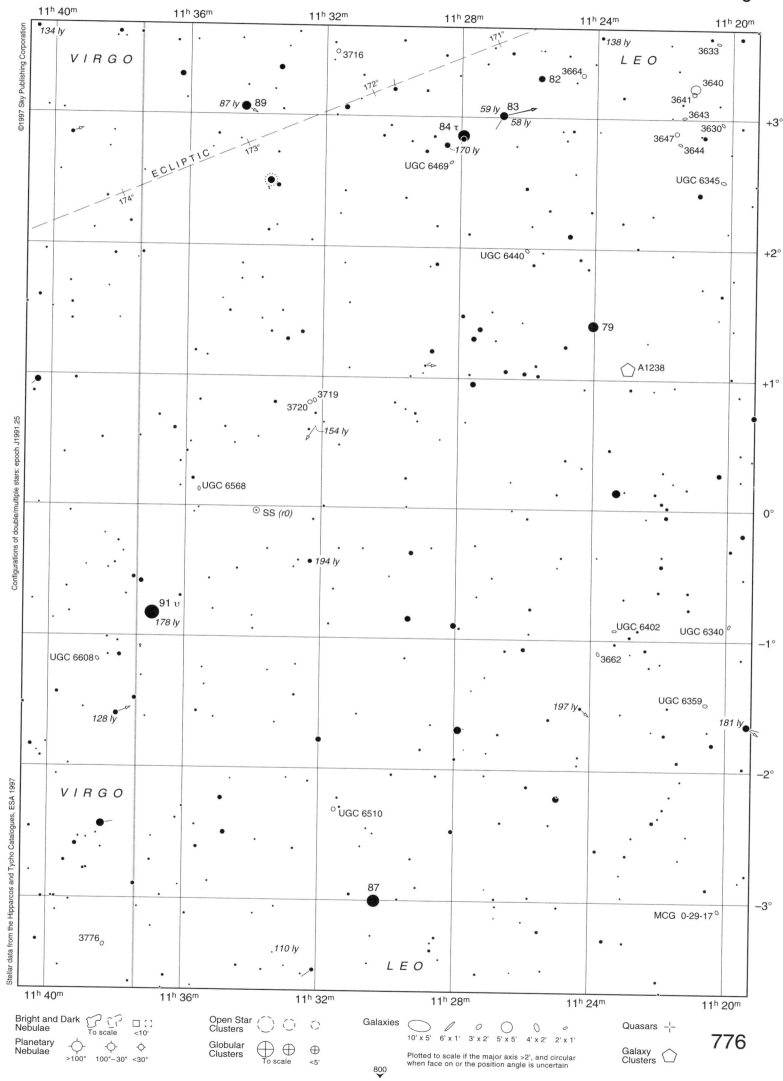

11h 40m   11h 36m   11h 32m   11h 28m   11h 24m   11h 20m

VIRGO

LEO

134 ly
3716
138 ly
3633
3664
82
3640
3641
87 ly 89
ECLIPTIC
59 ly 83
58 ly
3643
84 τ
3630
170 ly
3647
3644
UGC 6469
UGC 6345
+3°

172°
171°
173°
174°

UGC 6440
+2°

79
A1238
+1°

3720 3719
154 ly

UGC 6568
0°

SS (r0)

194 ly

91 υ
178 ly
UGC 6402   UGC 6340
-1°

UGC 6608
3662

128 ly
UGC 6359
197 ly
181 ly
-2°

VIRGO

UGC 6510

87
-3°

MCG 0-29-17

3776
110 ly

LEO

11h 40m   11h 36m   11h 32m   11h 28m   11h 24m   11h 20m

Bright and Dark Nebulae
To scale   <10'

Planetary Nebulae
>100"   100"–30"   <30"

Open Star Clusters

Globular Clusters
To scale   <5'

Galaxies
10' x 5'   6' x 1'   3' x 2'   5' x 5'   4' x 2'   2' x 1'

Plotted to scale if the major axis >2', and circular when face on or the position angle is uncertain

Quasars

Galaxy Clusters

800

MILLENNIUM STAR ATLAS

0°

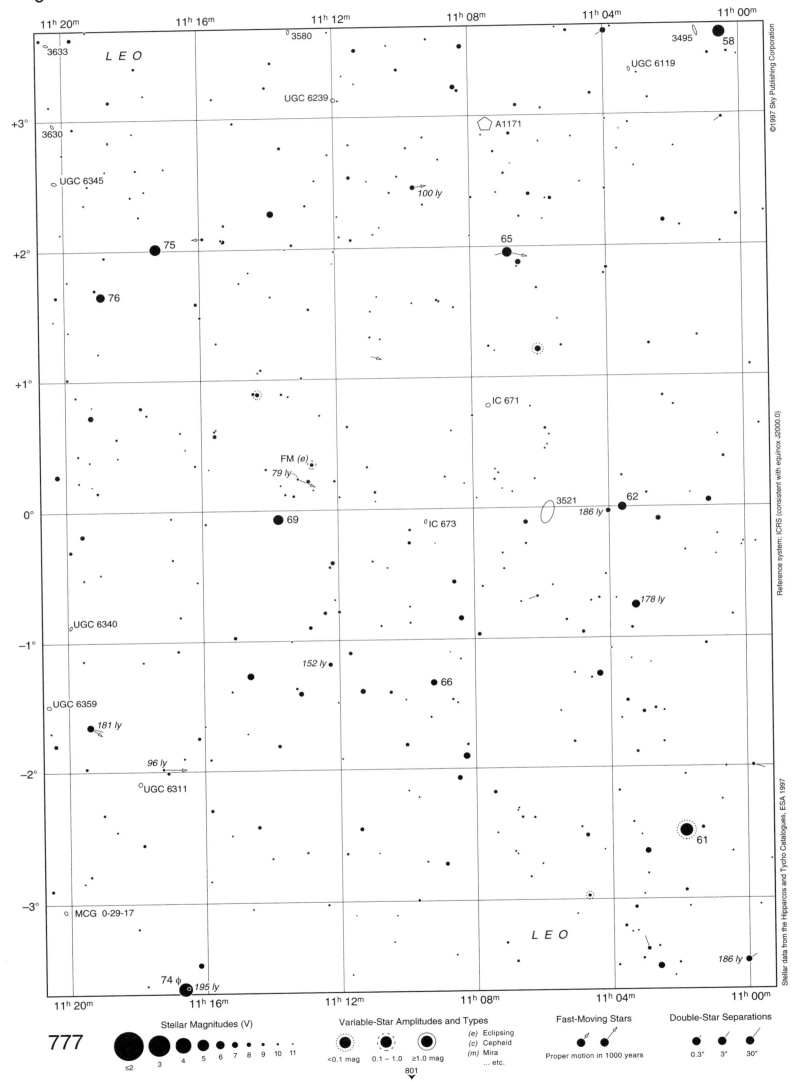

©1997 Sky Publishing Corporation

Reference system: ICRS (consistent with equinox J2000.0)

Stellar data from the Hipparcos and Tycho Catalogues, ESA 1997

LEO

3633
3630
UGC 6345
UGC 6340
UGC 6359
UGC 6311
MCG 0-29-17

3580
UGC 6239
100 ly
FM (e)
79 ly
69
152 ly
96 ly
74 φ
195 ly

A1171
IC 671
IC 673
66

3495
58
UGC 6119
65
3521
186 ly
62
178 ly
61
186 ly

LEO

11h 20m   11h 16m   11h 12m   11h 08m   11h 04m   11h 00m

+3°
+2°
+1°
0°
−1°
−2°
−3°

75
76

777

Stellar Magnitudes (V)

≤2   3   4   5   6   7   8   9   10   11

Variable-Star Amplitudes and Types

<0.1 mag   0.1 − 1.0   ≥1.0 mag

(e) Eclipsing
(c) Cepheid
(m) Mira
... etc.

Fast-Moving Stars

Proper motion in 1000 years

Double-Star Separations

0.3"   3"   30"

MILLENNIUM STAR ATLAS

0°

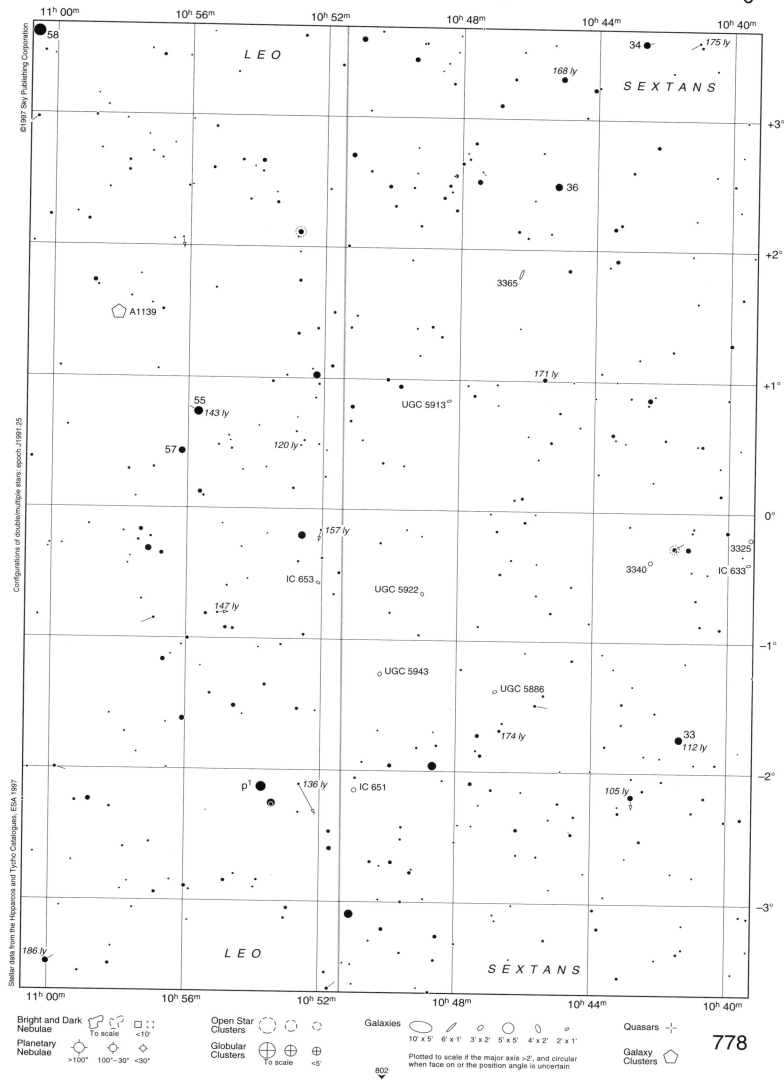

LEO

SEXTANS

Configurations of double/multiple stars: epoch J1991.25

Stellar data from the Hipparcos and Tycho Catalogues, ESA 1997

58

34

175 ly

168 ly

36

3365

A1139

55
143 ly

171 ly

57

UGC 5913

120 ly

157 ly

3340

3325

IC 633

IC 653

UGC 5922

147 ly

UGC 5943

UGC 5886

174 ly

33
112 ly

p¹

136 ly

IC 651

105 ly

186 ly

LEO

SEXTANS

+3°

+2°

+1°

0°

−1°

−2°

−3°

11ʰ 00ᵐ | 10ʰ 56ᵐ | 10ʰ 52ᵐ | 10ʰ 48ᵐ | 10ʰ 44ᵐ | 10ʰ 40ᵐ

Bright and Dark Nebulae
To scale   <10'

Planetary Nebulae
>100"   100"–30"   <30"

Open Star Clusters

Globular Clusters
To scale   <5'

Galaxies
10' x 5'   6' x 1'   3' x 2'   5' x 5'   4' x 2'   2' x 1'

Plotted to scale if the major axis >2', and circular when face on or the position angle is uncertain

Quasars

Galaxy Clusters

778

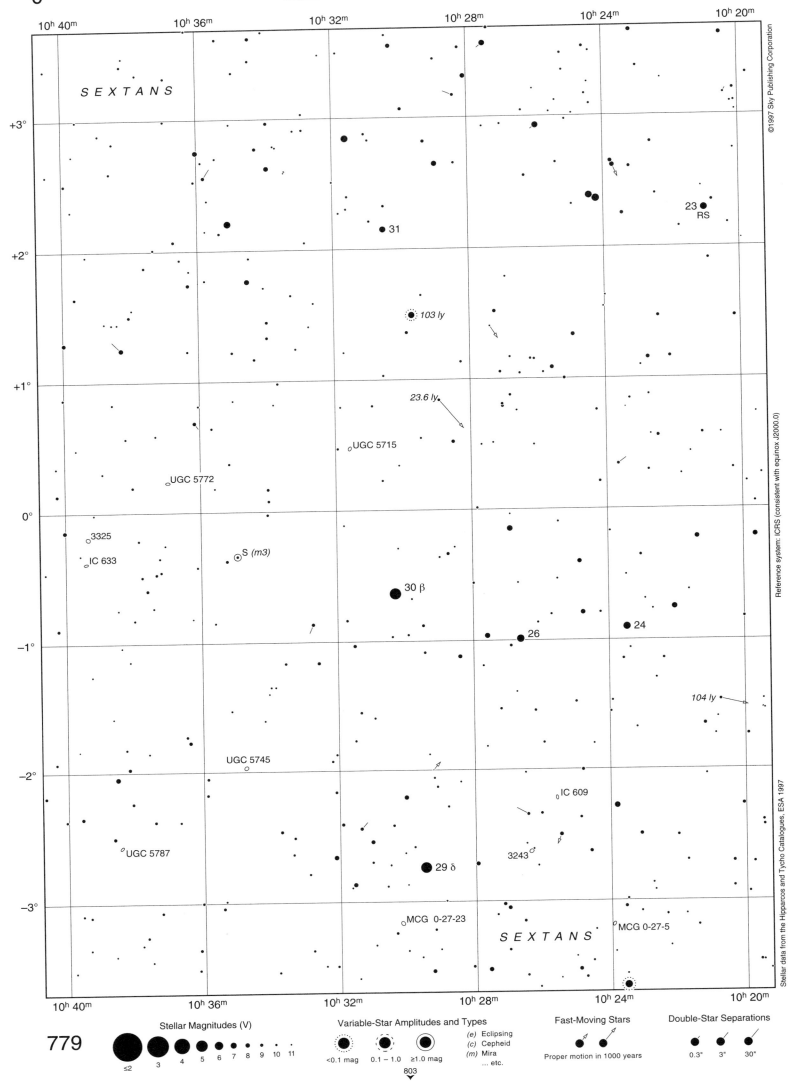

©1997 Sky Publishing Corporation

Reference system: ICRS (consistent with equinox J2000.0)

Stellar data from the Hipparcos and Tycho Catalogues, ESA 1997

S E X T A N S

31

23
RS

103 ly

23.6 ly

UGC 5715

UGC 5772

3325

IC 633

S (m3)

30 β

26

24

104 ly

UGC 5745

IC 609

UGC 5787

3243

29 δ

MCG 0-27-23

MCG 0-27-5

S E X T A N S

779

Stellar Magnitudes (V)

≤2 3 4 5 6 7 8 9 10 11

Variable-Star Amplitudes and Types

<0.1 mag   0.1 – 1.0   ≥1.0 mag

(e) Eclipsing
(c) Cepheid
(m) Mira
... etc.

Fast-Moving Stars

Proper motion in 1000 years

Double-Star Separations

0.3"   3"   30"

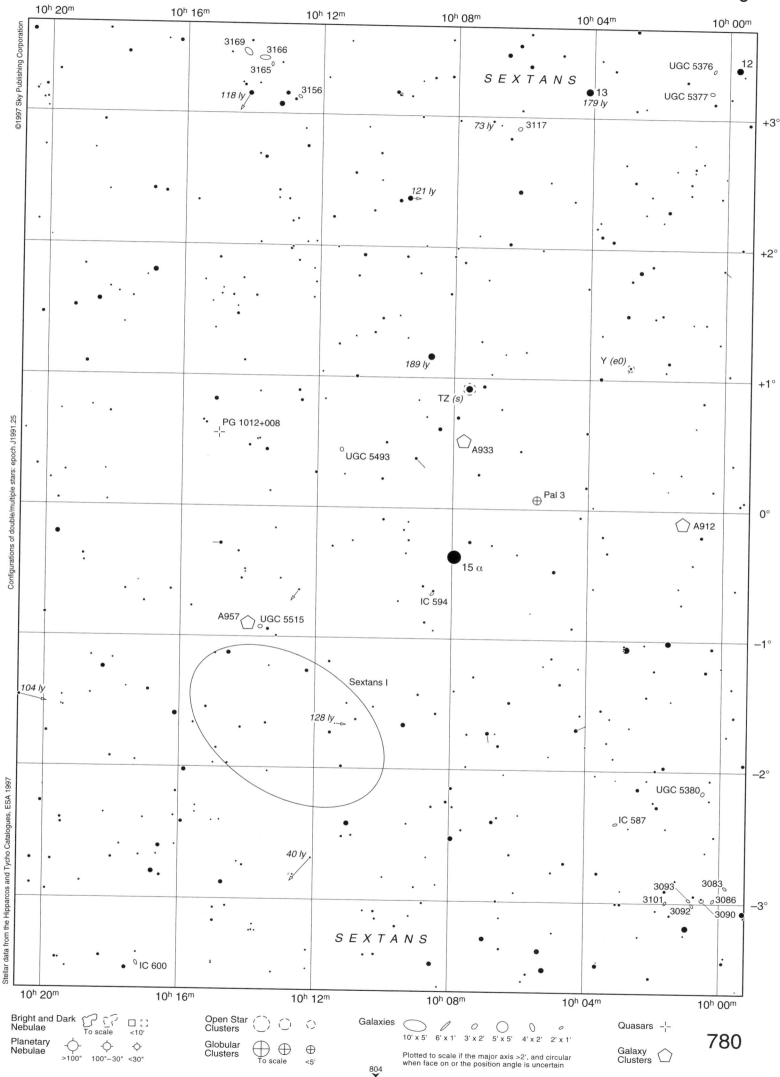

10h 20m 10h 16m 10h 12m 10h 08m 10h 04m 10h 00m

3169
3166
3165
118 ly
3156

SEXTANS

UGC 5376
12

13
179 ly

73 ly
3117
+3°

UGC 5377

121 ly
+2°

189 ly
Y (e0)
+1°

TZ (s)

PG 1012+008

A933
UGC 5493

Pal 3
0°

A912

15 α

IC 594

A957 UGC 5515
-1°

104 ly

Sextans I

128 ly

-2°

UGC 5380

IC 587

40 ly

3093 3083
3101 3086
3092 3090
-3°

SEXTANS

IC 600

10h 20m 10h 16m 10h 12m 10h 08m 10h 04m 10h 00m

Bright and Dark
Nebulae
To scale   <10'

Planetary
Nebulae
>100" 100"–30" <30"

Open Star
Clusters
To scale

Globular
Clusters
To scale   <5'

Galaxies
10' x 5' 6' x 1' 3' x 2' 5' x 5' 4' x 2' 2' x 1'

Plotted to scale if the major axis >2', and circular
when face on or the position angle is uncertain

Quasars

Galaxy
Clusters

780

804

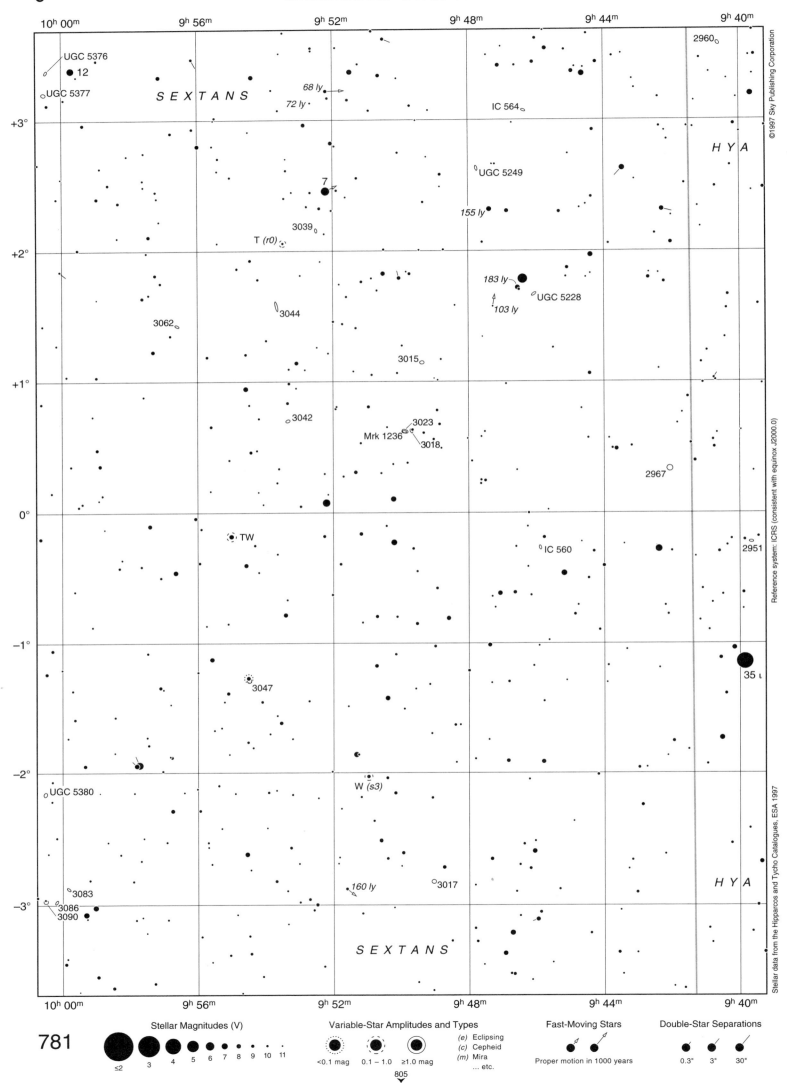

©1997 Sky Publishing Corporation

Reference system: ICRS (consistent with equinox J2000.0)

Stellar data from the Hipparcos and Tycho Catalogues, ESA 1997

Stellar Magnitudes (V)

≤2 3 4 5 6 7 8 9 10 11

781

Variable-Star Amplitudes and Types

<0.1 mag   0.1 – 1.0   ≥1.0 mag

(e) Eclipsing
(c) Cepheid
(m) Mira
... etc.

Fast-Moving Stars

Proper motion in 1000 years

Double-Star Separations

0.3"   3"   30"

805

MILLENNIUM STAR ATLAS

0°

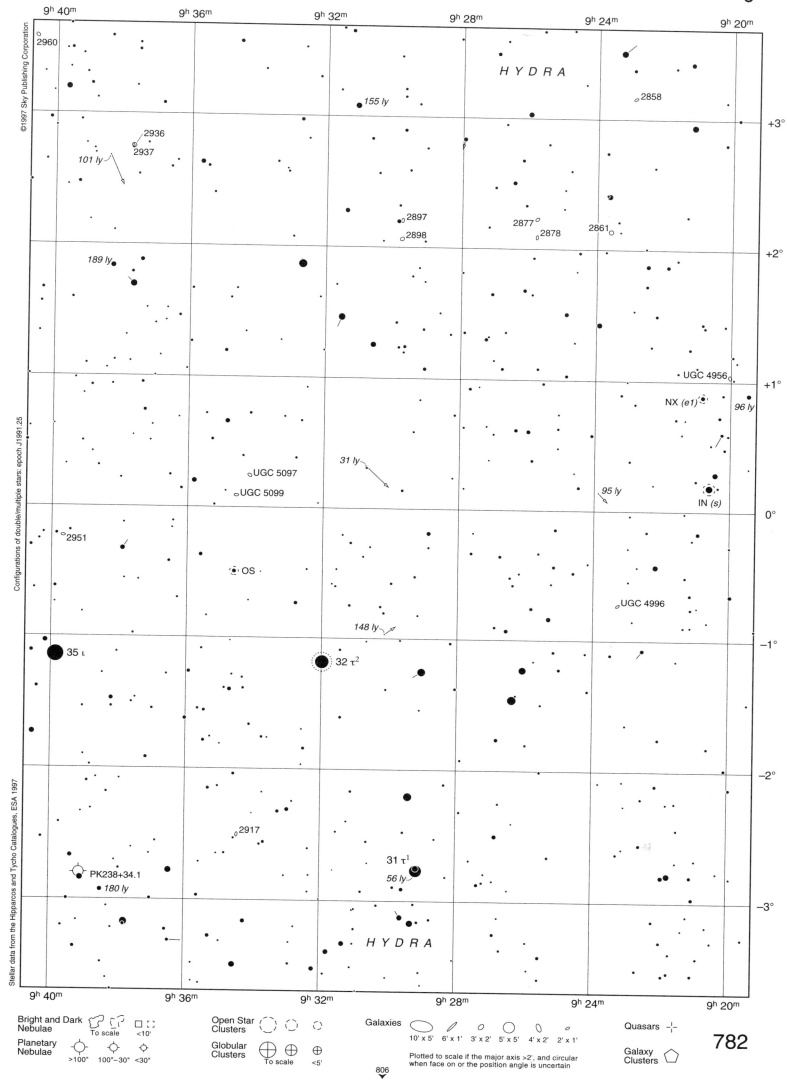

H Y D R A

2960

155 ly

2858

2936
2937

101 ly

2897
2898

2877
2878

2861

189 ly

UGC 4956

NX (e1)

96 ly

UGC 5097

UGC 5099

31 ly

95 ly

IN (s)

2951

OS

UGC 4996

148 ly

35 ι

32 τ²

PK238+34.1

2917

31 τ¹

56 ly

180 ly

H Y D R A

Configurations of double/multiple stars: epoch J1991.25

Stellar data from the Hipparcos and Tycho Catalogues, ESA 1997

Bright and Dark Nebulae				Open Star Clusters			Galaxies						Quasars	

To scale   <10'

Planetary Nebulae
>100"   100"–30"   <30"

Globular Clusters
To scale   <5'

Galaxies
10' x 5'   6' x 1'   3' x 2'   5' x 5'   4' x 2'   2' x 1'

Plotted to scale if the major axis >2', and circular when face on or the position angle is uncertain

Quasars

Galaxy Clusters

782

806

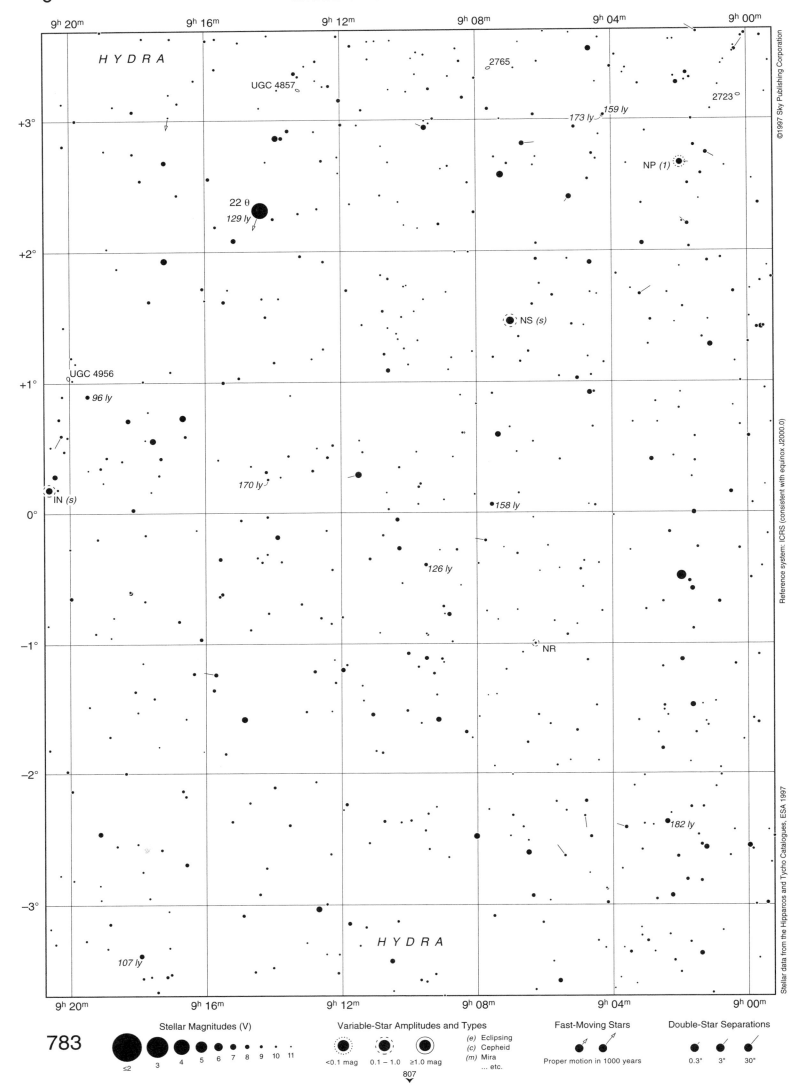

©1997 Sky Publishing Corporation

Reference system: ICRS (consistent with equinox J2000.0)

Stellar data from the Hipparcos and Tycho Catalogues, ESA 1997

HYDRA

UGC 4857

2765

2723

173 ly   159 ly

NP (1)

22 θ
129 ly

NS (s)

UGC 4956

96 ly

170 ly

158 ly

IN (s)

126 ly

NR

182 ly

HYDRA

107 ly

Stellar Magnitudes (V)

≤2   3   4   5   6   7   8   9 10 11

Variable-Star Amplitudes and Types

<0.1 mag   0.1 – 1.0   ≥1.0 mag

(e) Eclipsing
(c) Cepheid
(m) Mira
... etc.

Fast-Moving Stars

Proper motion in 1000 years

Double-Star Separations

0.3"   3"   30"

807

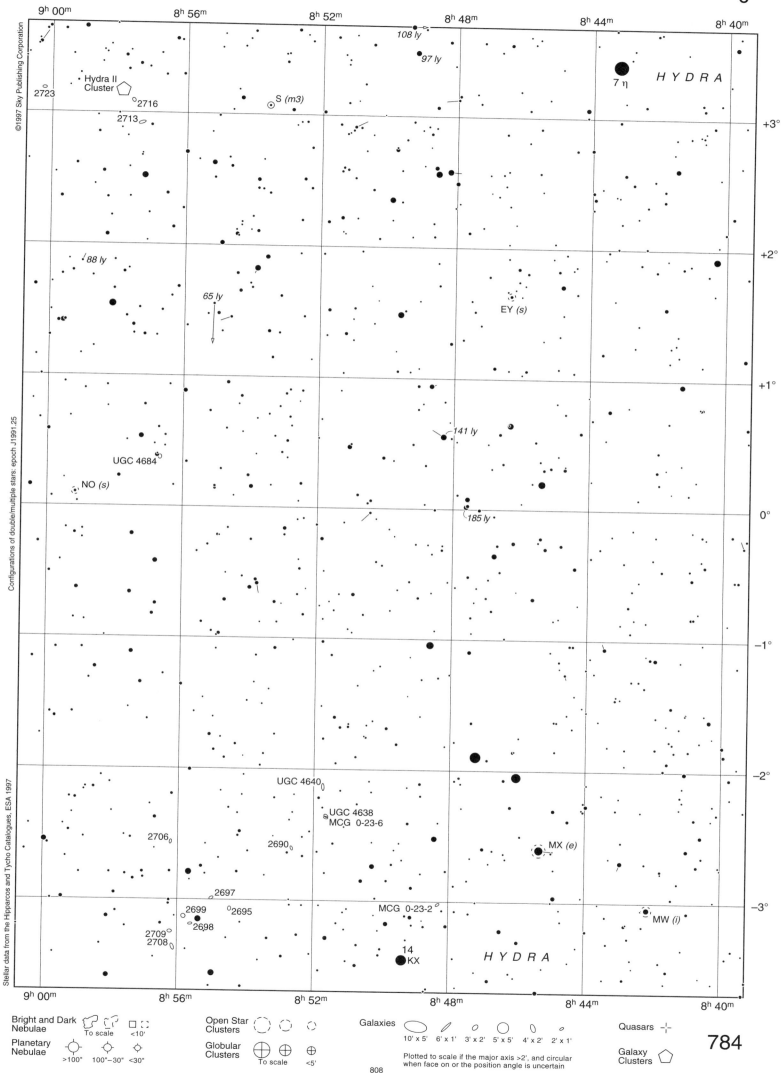

Configurations of double/multiple stars: epoch J1991.25

Stellar data from the Hipparcos and Tycho Catalogues, ESA 1997

9h 00m
8h 56m
8h 52m
8h 48m
8h 44m
8h 40m

108 ly
97 ly
7 η
HYDRA

2723
Hydra II
Cluster
2716
2713
S (m3)

+3°

88 ly
65 ly
EY (s)

+2°

141 ly

+1°

UGC 4684
NO (s)
185 ly

0°

−1°

−2°

UGC 4640
UGC 4638
MCG 0-23-6
2706
2690
MX (e)

2697
MCG 0-23-2
2699
2695
MW (i)
2698
2709
2708
14
KX
HYDRA

−3°

9h 00m
8h 56m
8h 52m
8h 48m
8h 44m
8h 40m

Bright and Dark
Nebulae
To scale
<10'
Planetary
Nebulae
>100"   100"–30"   <30"

Open Star
Clusters
Globular
Clusters
To scale   <5'

Galaxies
10' x 5'   6' x 1'   3' x 2'   5' x 5'   4' x 2'   2' x 1'

Plotted to scale if the major axis >2', and circular
when face on or the position angle is uncertain

Quasars

Galaxy
Clusters

784

808

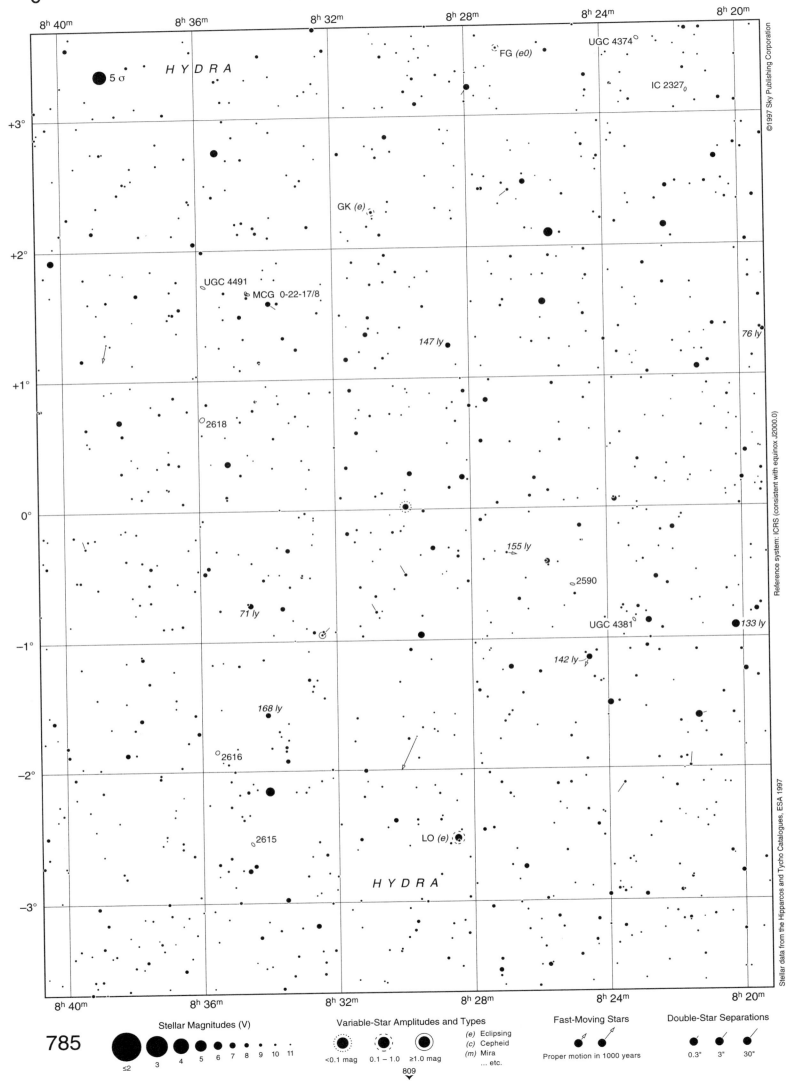

785

Stellar Magnitudes (V)
≤2 3 4 5 6 7 8 9 10 11

Variable-Star Amplitudes and Types
<0.1 mag   0.1 – 1.0   ≥1.0 mag
(e) Eclipsing
(c) Cepheid
(m) Mira
... etc.
809

Fast-Moving Stars
Proper motion in 1000 years

Double-Star Separations
0.3"   3"   30"

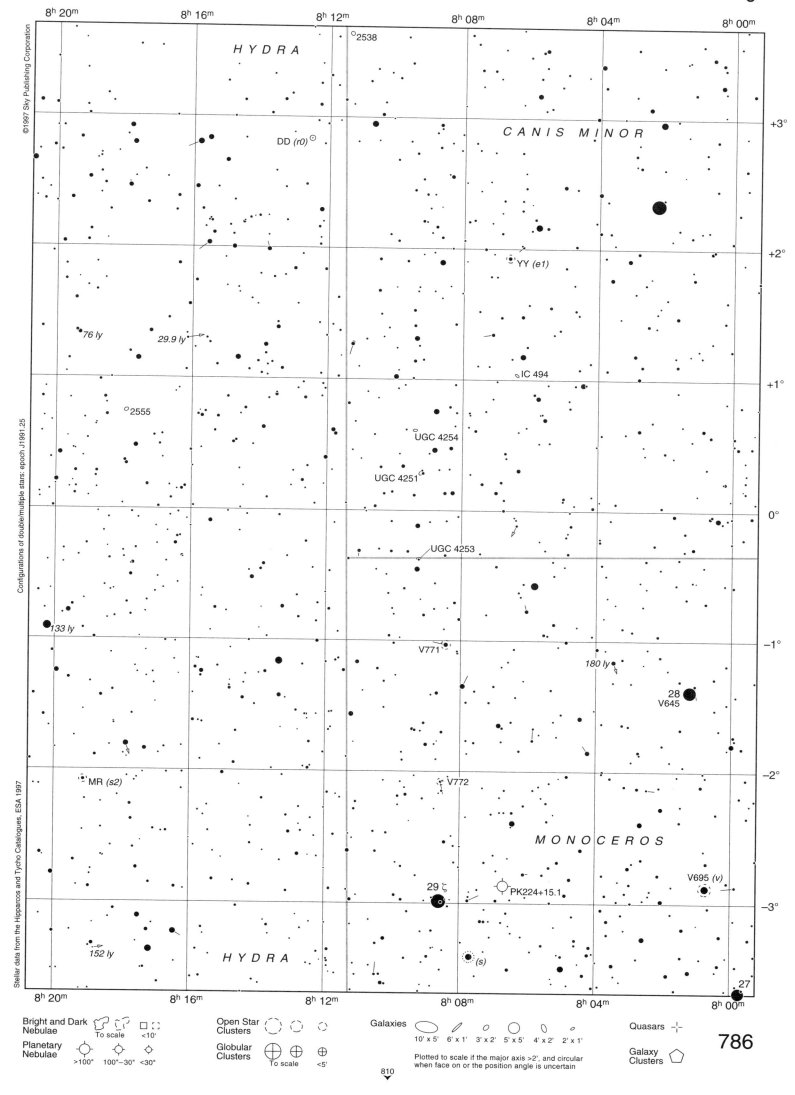

MILLENNIUM STAR ATLAS

0°

8h 20m   8h 16m   8h 12m   8h 08m   8h 04m   8h 00m

HYDRA

○ 2538

+3°

DD (r0) ⊙

CANIS MINOR

⊙ YY (e1)   +2°

76 ly   *29.9 ly*

⊙ IC 494   +1°

○ 2555

ⓤ UGC 4254

UGC 4251

0°

UGC 4253

● *133 ly*

V771   −1°

180 ly

28
V645

⊡ MR (s2)   −2°

V772

MONOCEROS

29 ζ   ○ PK224+15.1   V695 (v)

−3°

152 ly   *HYDRA*   ⊙ (s)

27

8h 20m   8h 16m   8h 12m   8h 08m   8h 04m   8h 00m

Configurations of double/multiple stars: epoch J1991.25

Stellar data from the Hipparcos and Tycho Catalogues, ESA 1997

Bright and Dark Nebulae			Open Star Clusters			Galaxies						Quasars
To scale		<10'				10' x 5'	6' x 1'	3' x 2'	5' x 5'	4' x 2'	2' x 1'	

Planetary Nebulae			Globular Clusters				Galaxy Clusters
>100"	100"–30"	<30"	To scale		<5'	Plotted to scale if the major axis >2', and circular when face on or the position angle is uncertain	

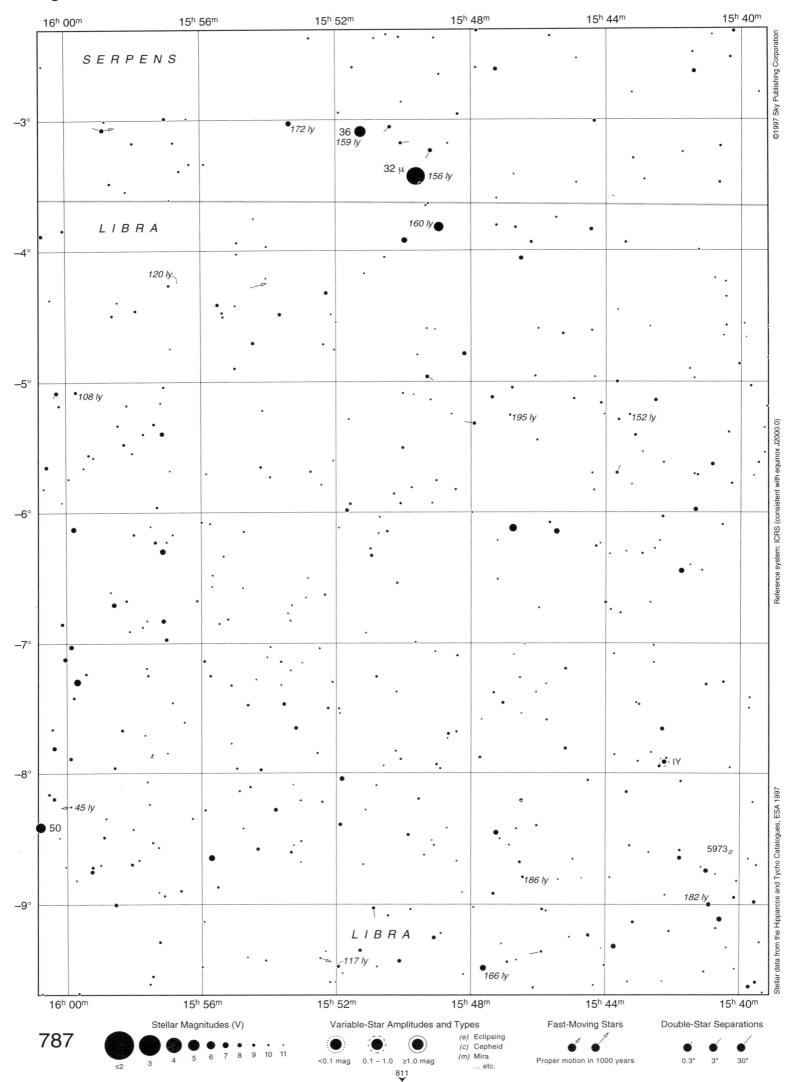

SERPENS

LIBRA

172 ly

36
159 ly

32 μ 156 ly

160 ly

120 ly

108 ly

195 ly   152 ly

IY

45 ly

50

5973₀

186 ly

182 ly

LIBRA

117 ly

166 ly

Stellar Magnitudes (V)									
≤2	3	4	5	6	7	8	9	10	11

Variable-Star Amplitudes and Types

<0.1 mag   0.1 − 1.0   ≥1.0 mag

(e) Eclipsing
(c) Cepheid
(m) Mira
... etc.

Fast-Moving Stars

Proper motion in 1000 years

Double-Star Separations

0.3"   3"   30"

MILLENNIUM STAR ATLAS

-6°

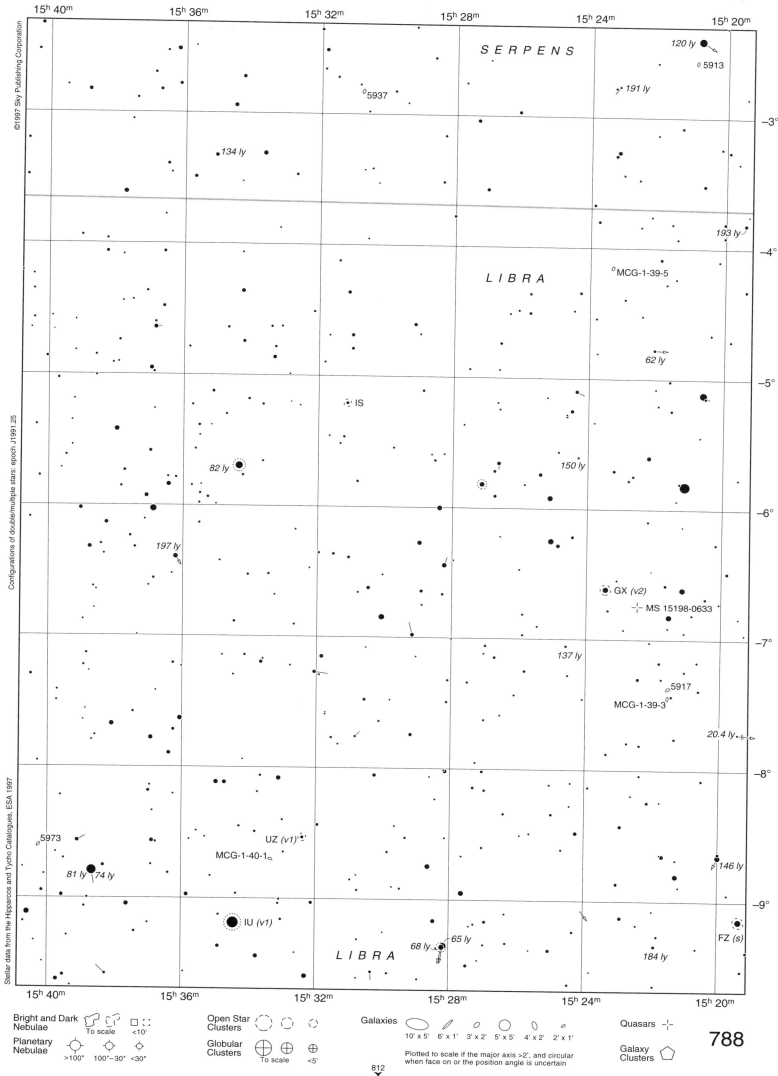

©1997 Sky Publishing Corporation

15h 40m   15h 36m   15h 32m   15h 28m   15h 24m   15h 20m

S E R P E N S

120 ly
0 5913

5937
191 ly

-3°

193 ly

134 ly

L I B R A

0 MCG-1-39-5

-4°

62 ly

-5°

IS

150 ly

82 ly

-6°

197 ly

GX *(v2)*

MS 15198-0633

137 ly

-7°

5917
MCG-1-39-3 0

20.4 ly

-8°

5973

UZ *(v1)*

MCG-1-40-1

146 ly

81 ly 74 ly

-9°

IU *(v1)*

FZ *(s)*

68 ly 65 ly

L I B R A

184 ly

Stellar data from the Hipparcos and Tycho Catalogues, ESA 1997

Configurations of double/multiple stars: epoch J1991.25

15h 40m   15h 36m   15h 32m   15h 28m   15h 24m   15h 20m

| Bright and Dark Nebulae | To scale | <10' |
| Planetary Nebulae | >100" 100"−30" <30" | |

Open Star Clusters

Globular Clusters
To scale <5'

Galaxies
10' x 5' 6' x 1' 3' x 2' 5' x 5' 4' x 2' 2' x 1'

Plotted to scale if the major axis >2', and circular when face on or the position angle is uncertain

Quasars

Galaxy Clusters

788

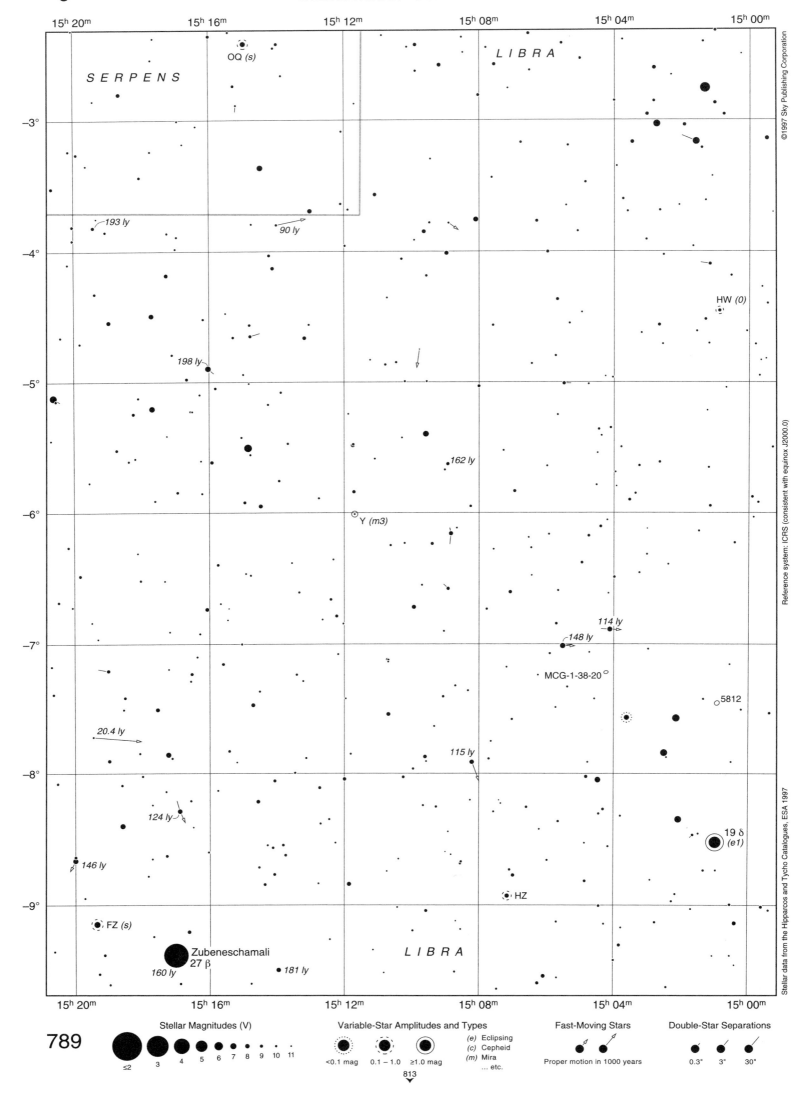

©1997 Sky Publishing Corporation

Reference system: ICRS (consistent with equinox J2000.0)

Stellar data from the Hipparcos and Tycho Catalogues, ESA 1997

SERPENS

OQ (s)

LIBRA

193 ly

90 ly

HW (0)

198 ly

162 ly

Y (m3)

114 ly

148 ly

MCG-1-38-20

5812

20.4 ly

115 ly

124 ly

19 δ
(e1)

146 ly

HZ

FZ (s)

LIBRA

Zubeneschamali
27 β

160 ly

181 ly

Stellar Magnitudes (V)

≤2   3   4   5   6   7   8   9   10   11

Variable-Star Amplitudes and Types

<0.1 mag   0.1 − 1.0   ≥1.0 mag

813

(e) Eclipsing
(c) Cepheid
(m) Mira
... etc.

Fast-Moving Stars

Proper motion in 1000 years

Double-Star Separations

0.3"   3"   30"

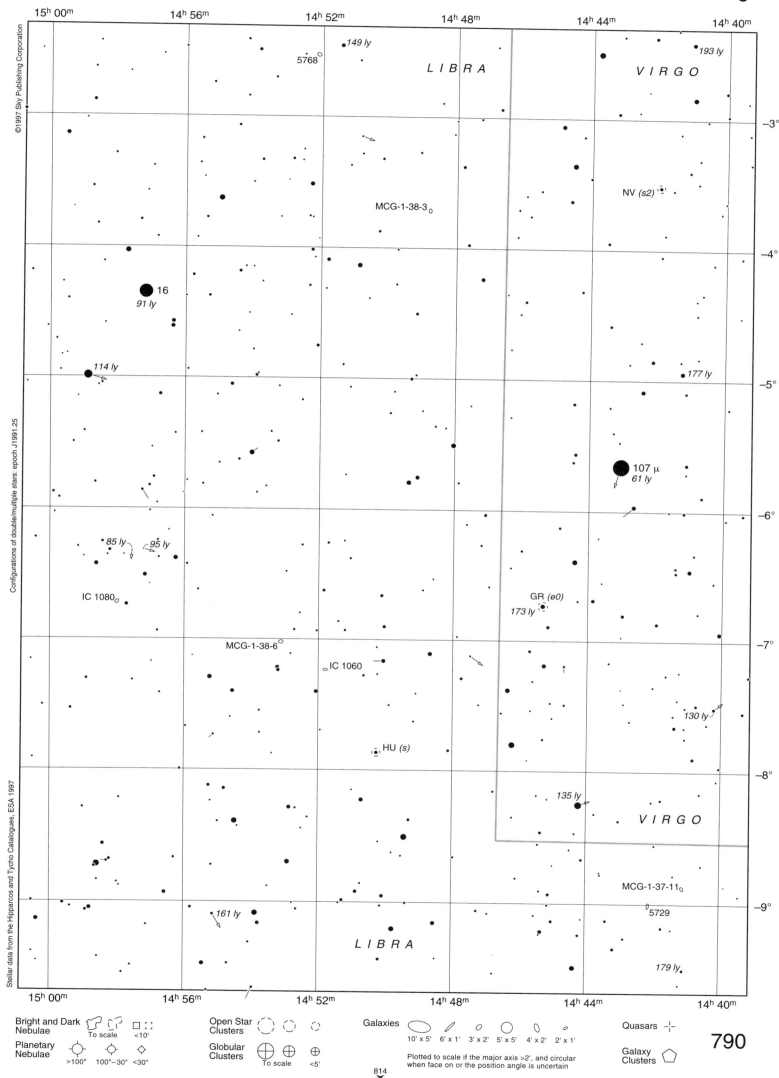

15h 00m   14h 56m   14h 52m   14h 48m   14h 44m   14h 40m

LIBRA   VIRGO

149 ly
5768

193 ly

−3°

MCG-1-38-3

NV (s2)

−4°

16
91 ly

114 ly   177 ly

−5°

107 μ
61 ly

−6°

85 ly   95 ly

IC 1080

GR (e0)
173 ly

MCG-1-38-6   −7°

IC 1060

130 ly

HU (s)

−8°

135 ly

VIRGO

MCG-1-37-11

161 ly   5729   −9°

LIBRA

179 ly

15h 00m   14h 56m   14h 52m   14h 48m   14h 44m   14h 40m

Bright and Dark
Nebulae
To scale   <10'

Open Star
Clusters

Galaxies

Quasars

Planetary
Nebulae
>100"   100"–30"   <30"

Globular
Clusters
To scale   <5'

10' x 5'   6' x 1'   3' x 2'   5' x 5'   4' x 2'   2' x 1'

Plotted to scale if the major axis >2', and circular
when face on or the position angle is uncertain

Galaxy
Clusters

790

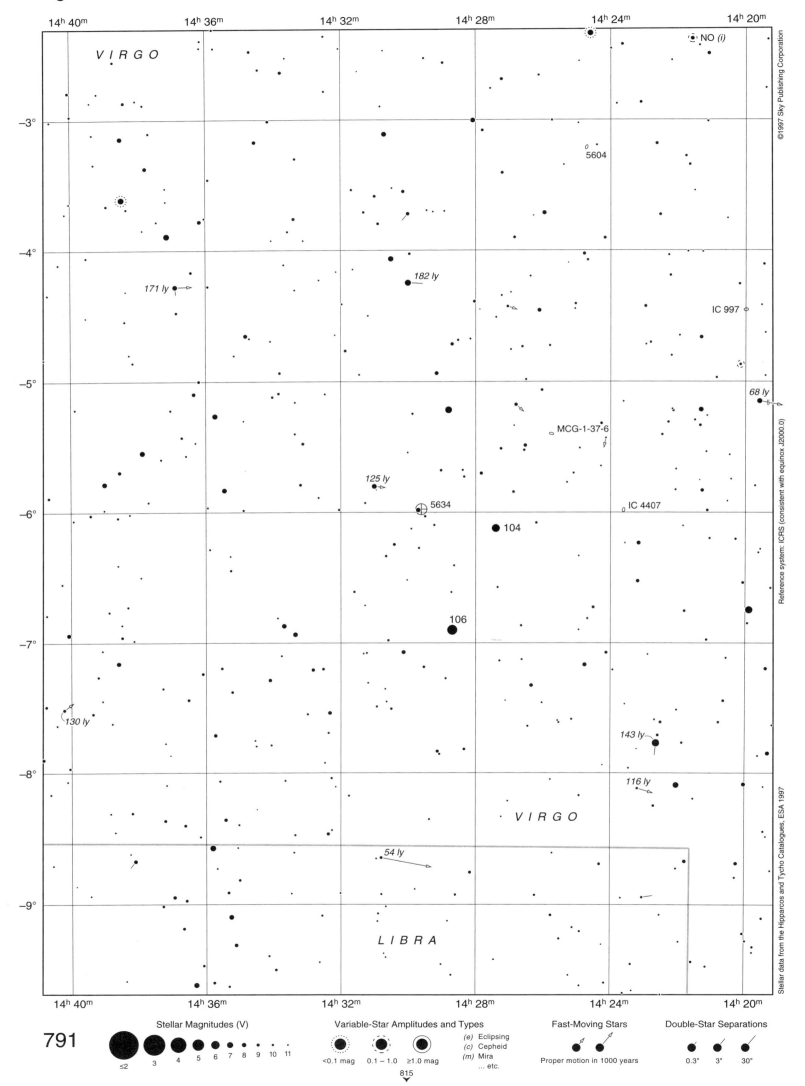

©1997 Sky Publishing Corporation

Reference system: ICRS (consistent with equinox J2000.0)

Stellar data from the Hipparcos and Tycho Catalogues, ESA 1997

VIRGO

5604

171 ly

182 ly

IC 997

68 ly

125 ly

MCG-1-37-6

5634

IC 4407

104

106

130 ly

143 ly

116 ly

VIRGO

54 ly

LIBRA

NO (i)

Stellar Magnitudes (V)

≤2   3   4   5   6 7 8 9 10 11

Variable-Star Amplitudes and Types

<0.1 mag   0.1 − 1.0   ≥1.0 mag

(e) Eclipsing
(c) Cepheid
(m) Mira
... etc.

Fast-Moving Stars

Proper motion in 1000 years

Double-Star Separations

0.3"   3"   30"

MILLENNIUM STAR ATLAS

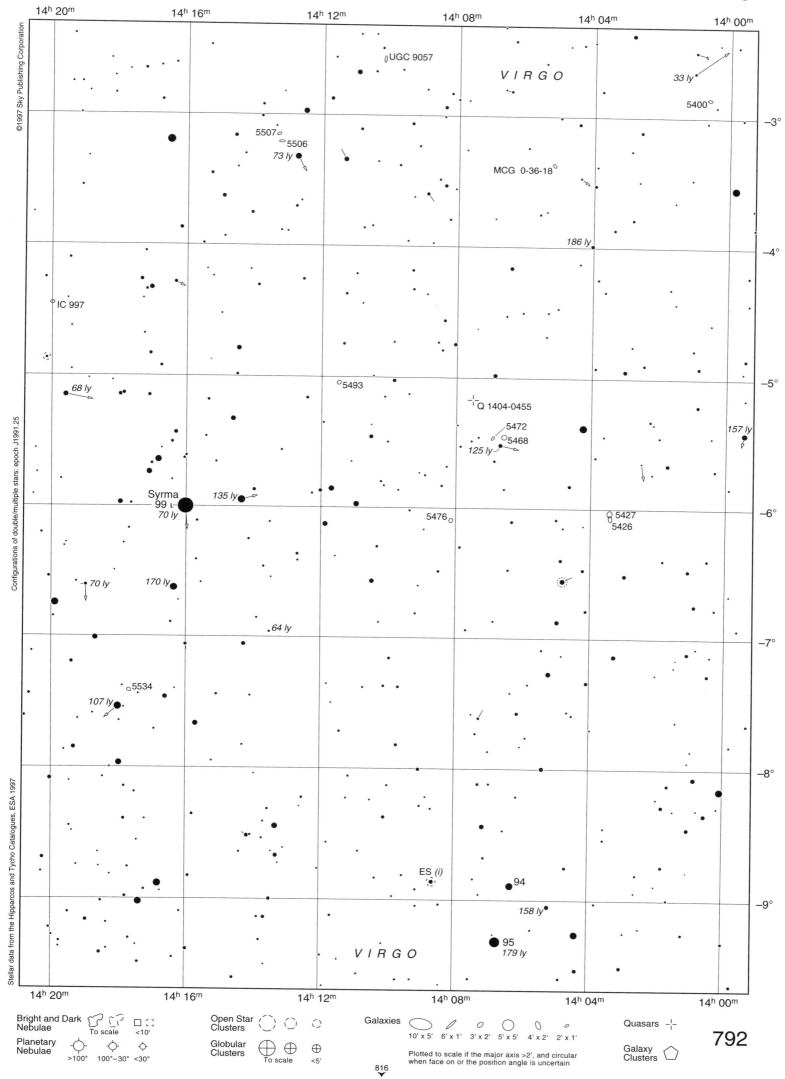

©1997 Sky Publishing Corporation

Configurations of double/multiple stars: epoch J1991.25

Stellar data from the Hipparcos and Tycho Catalogues, ESA 1997

UGC 9057

VIRGO

33 ly

5400

5507 5506

73 ly

MCG 0-36-18

186 ly

IC 997

5493

Q 1404-0455

157 ly

68 ly

5472
5468

125 ly

Syrma
99 ι
70 ly

135 ly

5476

5427
5426

70 ly   170 ly

64 ly

5534

107 ly

ES (i)

94

158 ly

95
179 ly

VIRGO

14ʰ 20ᵐ   14ʰ 16ᵐ   14ʰ 12ᵐ   14ʰ 08ᵐ   14ʰ 04ᵐ   14ʰ 00ᵐ

14ʰ 20ᵐ   14ʰ 16ᵐ   14ʰ 12ᵐ   14ʰ 08ᵐ   14ʰ 04ᵐ   14ʰ 00ᵐ

−3°
−4°
−5°
−6°
−7°
−8°
−9°

Bright and Dark Nebulae	To scale	<10'
Planetary Nebulae	>100" 100"−30" <30"	
Open Star Clusters		
Globular Clusters	To scale	<5'
Galaxies	10' x 5' 6' x 1' 3' x 2' 5' x 5' 4' x 2' 2' x 1'	
	Plotted to scale if the major axis >2', and circular when face on or the position angle is uncertain	
Quasars		
Galaxy Clusters		

792

816

−6°

MILLENNIUM STAR ATLAS

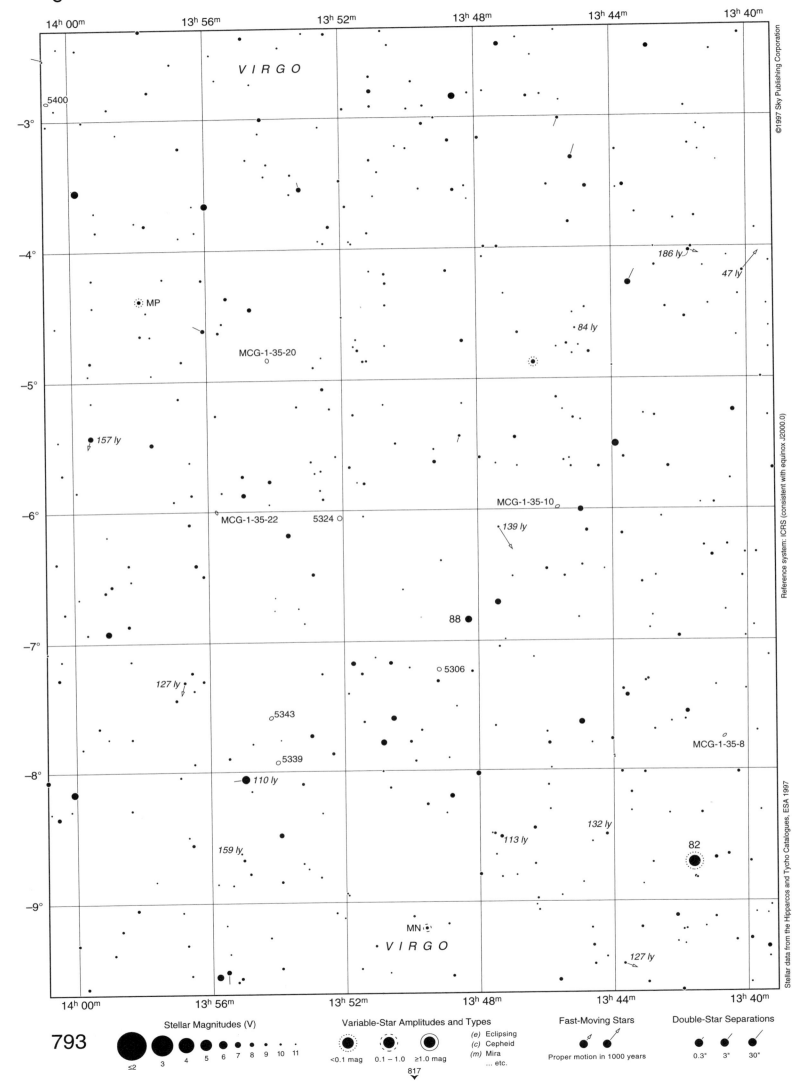

©1997 Sky Publishing Corporation

VIRGO

5400

MP

MCG-1-35-20

186 ly

47 ly

84 ly

157 ly

MCG-1-35-10

MCG-1-35-22   5324

139 ly

88

127 ly

5343

5306

5339

MCG-1-35-8

110 ly

132 ly

159 ly

113 ly

82

MN

VIRGO

127 ly

Reference system: ICRS (consistent with equinox J2000.0)

Stellar data from the Hipparcos and Tycho Catalogues, ESA 1997

793

Stellar Magnitudes (V)

≤2   3   4   5   6   7   8   9   10   11

Variable-Star Amplitudes and Types

<0.1 mag   0.1 – 1.0   ≥1.0 mag

(e) Eclipsing
(c) Cepheid
(m) Mira
… etc.

Fast-Moving Stars

Proper motion in 1000 years

Double-Star Separations

0.3"   3"   30"

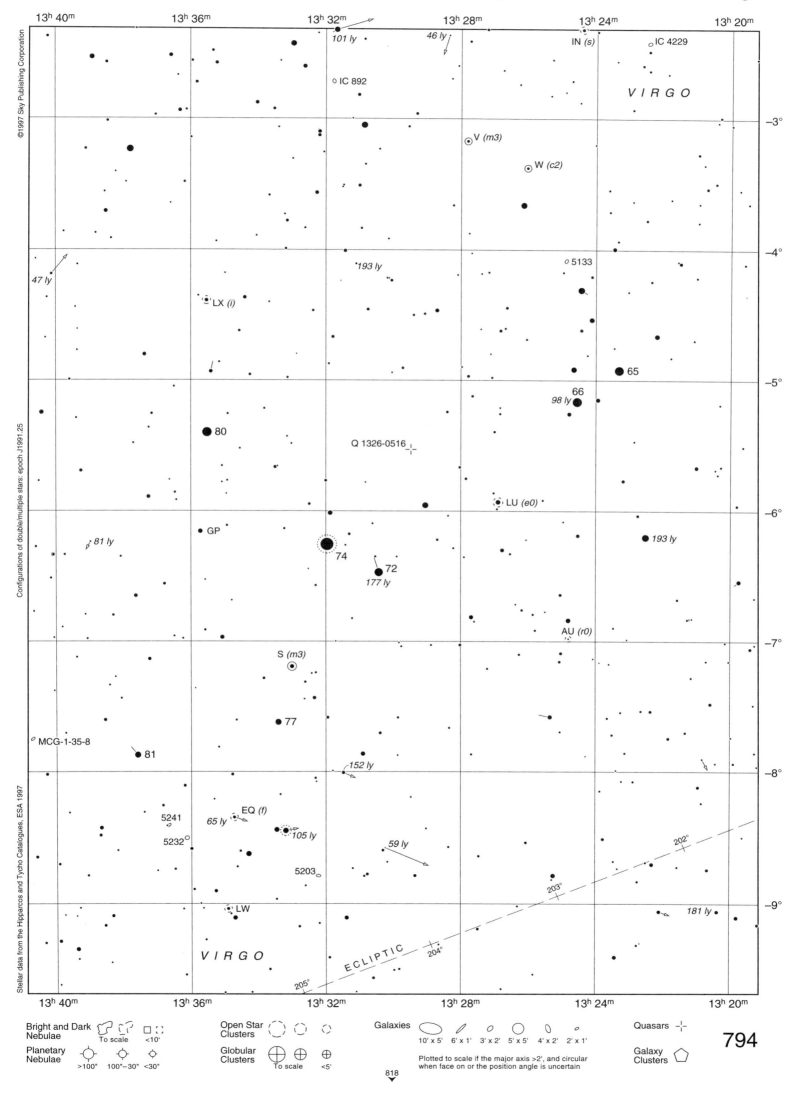

13h 40m 13h 36m 13h 32m 13h 28m 13h 24m 13h 20m

101 ly
46 ly
IN (s)
IC 4229
IC 892
VIRGO
−3°
V (m3)
W (c2)
47 ly
193 ly
5133
−4°
LX (i)
65
−5°
66
98 ly
80
Q 1326-0516
LU (e0)
81 ly
GP
193 ly
−6°
74
72
177 ly
AU (r0)
S (m3)
−7°
77
MCG-1-35-8
81
152 ly
−8°
5241
EQ (f)
5232
65 ly
105 ly
5203
59 ly
202°
203°
LW
181 ly
−9°
VIRGO
ECLIPTIC
204°
205°

13h 40m 13h 36m 13h 32m 13h 28m 13h 24m 13h 20m

Bright and Dark Nebulae
To scale   <10'
Planetary Nebulae
>100" 100"−30" <30"
Open Star Clusters
Globular Clusters
To scale   <5'
Galaxies
10' x 5' 6' x 1' 3' x 2' 5' x 5' 4' x 2' 2' x 1'
Plotted to scale if the major axis >2', and circular when face on or the position angle is uncertain
Quasars
Galaxy Clusters

794

818

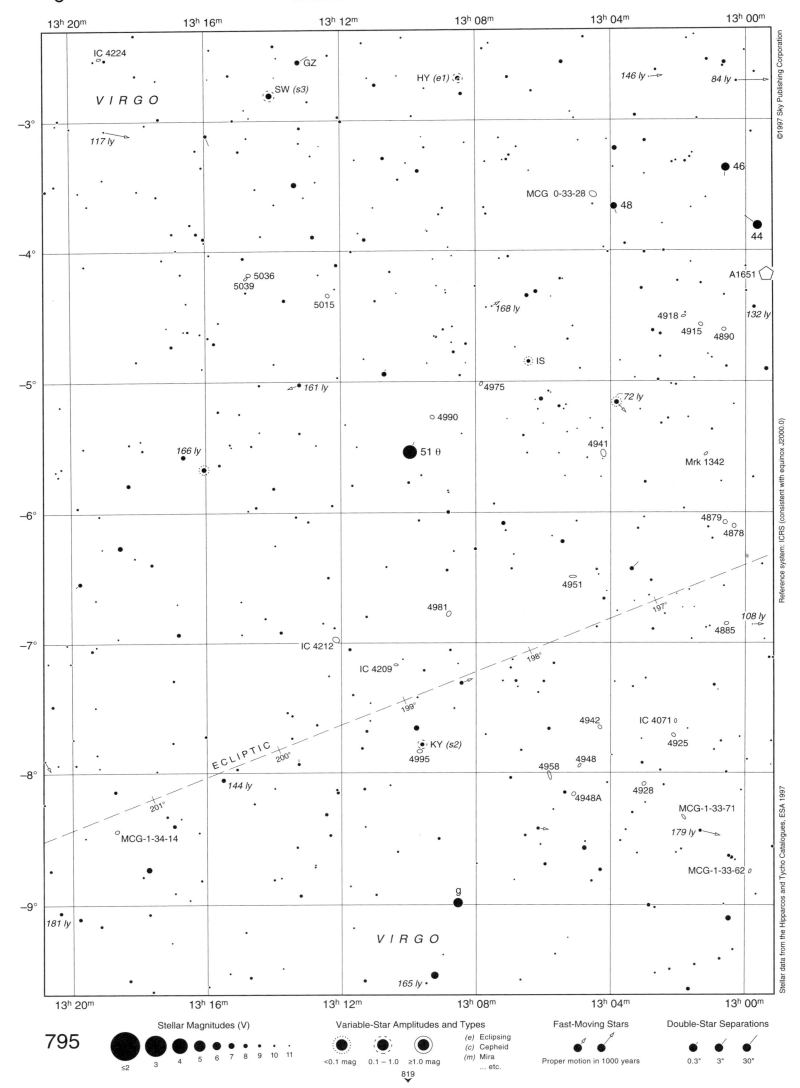

©1997 Sky Publishing Corporation

Reference system: ICRS (consistent with equinox J2000.0)

Stellar data from the Hipparcos and Tycho Catalogues, ESA 1997

IC 4224

VIRGO

GZ

SW (s3)

HY (e1)

146 ly

84 ly

46

MCG 0-33-28

48

44

A1651

-3°

117 ly

5036
5039

5015

168 ly

4918
4915   4890

132 ly

IS

-4°

161 ly

4975

72 ly

4990

4941

Mrk 1342

166 ly

51 θ

4879
4878

-5°

4951

197°

108 ly

4981

4885

IC 4212

IC 4209

198°

199°

4942   IC 4071

4925

-6°

200°

KY (s2)
4995

4958   4948

4948A

4928

MCG-1-33-71

179 ly

ECLIPTIC

144 ly

201°

MCG-1-34-14

MCG-1-33-62

-7°

g

-8°

181 ly

VIRGO

165 ly

-9°

13ʰ 20ᵐ   13ʰ 16ᵐ   13ʰ 12ᵐ   13ʰ 08ᵐ   13ʰ 04ᵐ   13ʰ 00ᵐ

795

Stellar Magnitudes (V)

≤2   3   4   5   6   7   8   9   10   11

Variable-Star Amplitudes and Types

<0.1 mag   0.1 – 1.0   ≥1.0 mag

(e) Eclipsing
(c) Cepheid
(m) Mira
... etc.

Fast-Moving Stars

Proper motion in 1000 years

Double-Star Separations

0.3"   3"   30"

MILLENNIUM STAR ATLAS

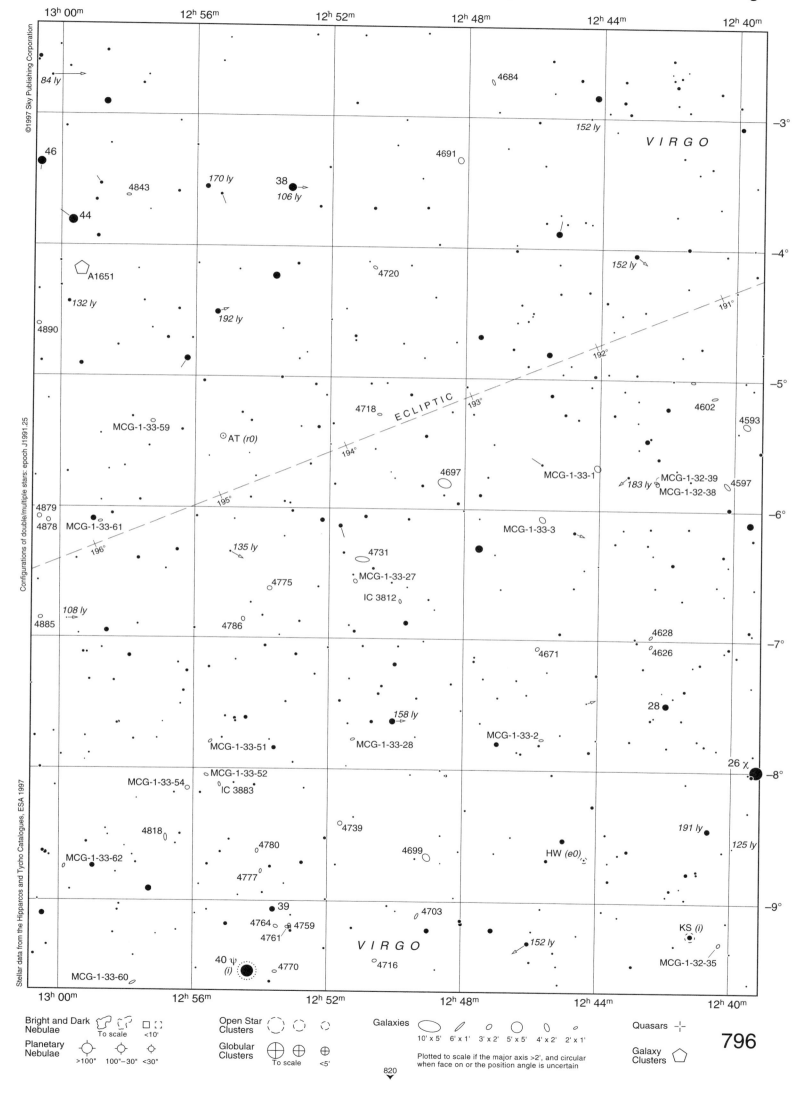

Configurations of double/multiple stars: epoch J1991.25

Stellar data from the Hipparcos and Tycho Catalogues, ESA 1997

13h 00m   12h 56m   12h 52m   12h 48m   12h 44m   12h 40m

84 ly

46

4843

170 ly

38

106 ly

4691

4684

152 ly

VIRGO

−3°

44

A1651

132 ly

4890

192 ly

4720

152 ly

191°

−4°

MCG-1-33-59

AT (r0)

4718

ECLIPTIC

193°

194°

4697

MCG-1-33-1

195°

183 ly

MCG-1-32-39

MCG-1-32-38

4602

4593

4597

−5°

4879

4878

MCG-1-33-61

196°

135 ly

4775

IC 3812

4731

MCG-1-33-27

MCG-1-33-3

−6°

108 ly

4885

4786

4628

4626

4671

−7°

158 ly

MCG-1-33-51

MCG-1-33-28

MCG-1-33-2

28

26 χ

−8°

MCG-1-33-54

MCG-1-33-52

IC 3883

4739

4699

HW (e0)

191 ly

125 ly

4818

MCG-1-33-62

4780

4777

39

4764

4761

4759

4703

VIRGO

4716

152 ly

KS (i)

MCG-1-32-35

40 ψ
(i)

4770

MCG-1-33-60

−9°

13h 00m   12h 56m   12h 52m   12h 48m   12h 44m   12h 40m

Legend

Bright and Dark Nebulae — To scale   <10'

Planetary Nebulae — >100"   100"−30"   <30"

Open Star Clusters

Globular Clusters — To scale   <5'

Galaxies — 10' x 5'   6' x 1'   3' x 2'   5' x 5'   4' x 2'   2' x 1'

Plotted to scale if the major axis >2', and circular when face on or the position angle is uncertain

Quasars

Galaxy Clusters

820

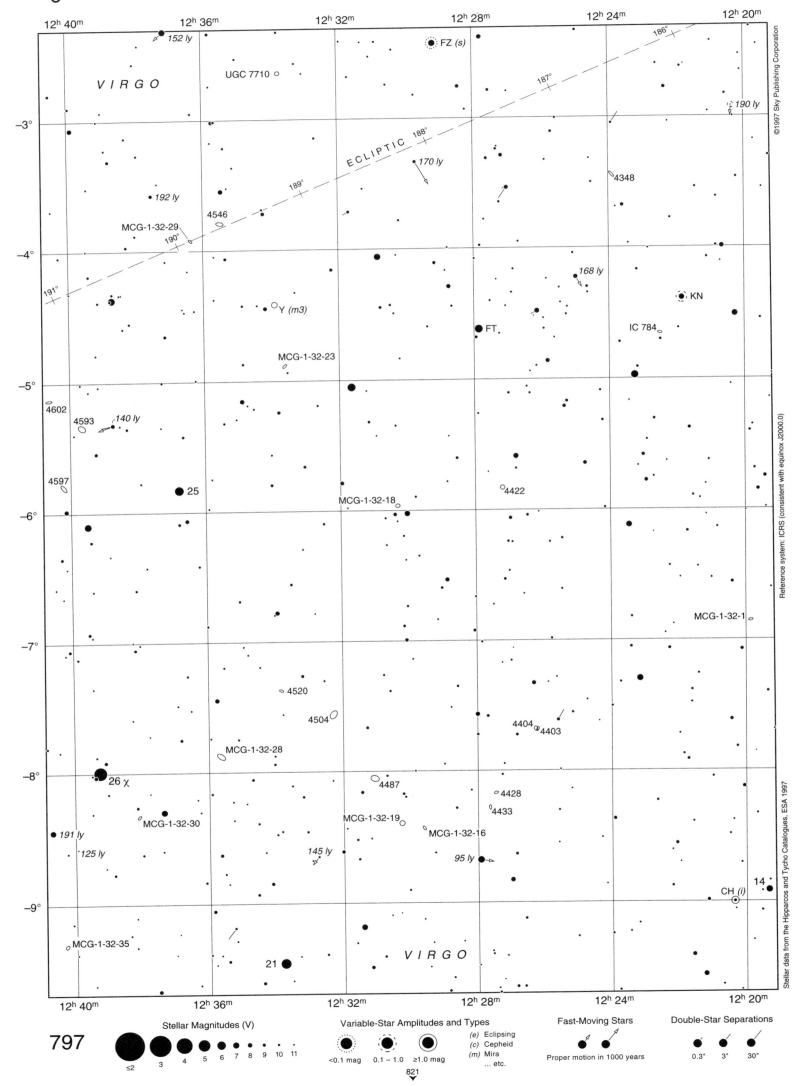

VIRGO

FZ *(s)*

UGC 7710

152 ly

190 ly

186°

187°

ECLIPTIC

188°

189°

190°

191°

192 ly

4546

MCG-1-32-29

170 ly

4348

168 ly

KN

Y *(m3)*

FT

IC 784

MCG-1-32-23

4602

4593

140 ly

4597

25

MCG-1-32-18

4422

MCG-1-32-1

4520

4504

4404 4403

MCG-1-32-28

26 χ

4487

4428

4433

MCG-1-32-30

MCG-1-32-19

MCG-1-32-16

191 ly

125 ly

145 ly

95 ly

14

CH *(i)*

MCG-1-32-35

21

VIRGO

©1997 Sky Publishing Corporation

Reference system: ICRS (consistent with equinox J2000.0)

Stellar data from the Hipparcos and Tycho Catalogues, ESA 1997

Stellar Magnitudes (V)	Variable-Star Amplitudes and Types	Fast-Moving Stars	Double-Star Separations

797

≤2   3   4   5   6   7   8   9   10   11

<0.1 mag   0.1 – 1.0   ≥1.0 mag

(e) Eclipsing
(c) Cepheid
(m) Mira
… etc.

Proper motion in 1000 years

0.3"   3"   30"

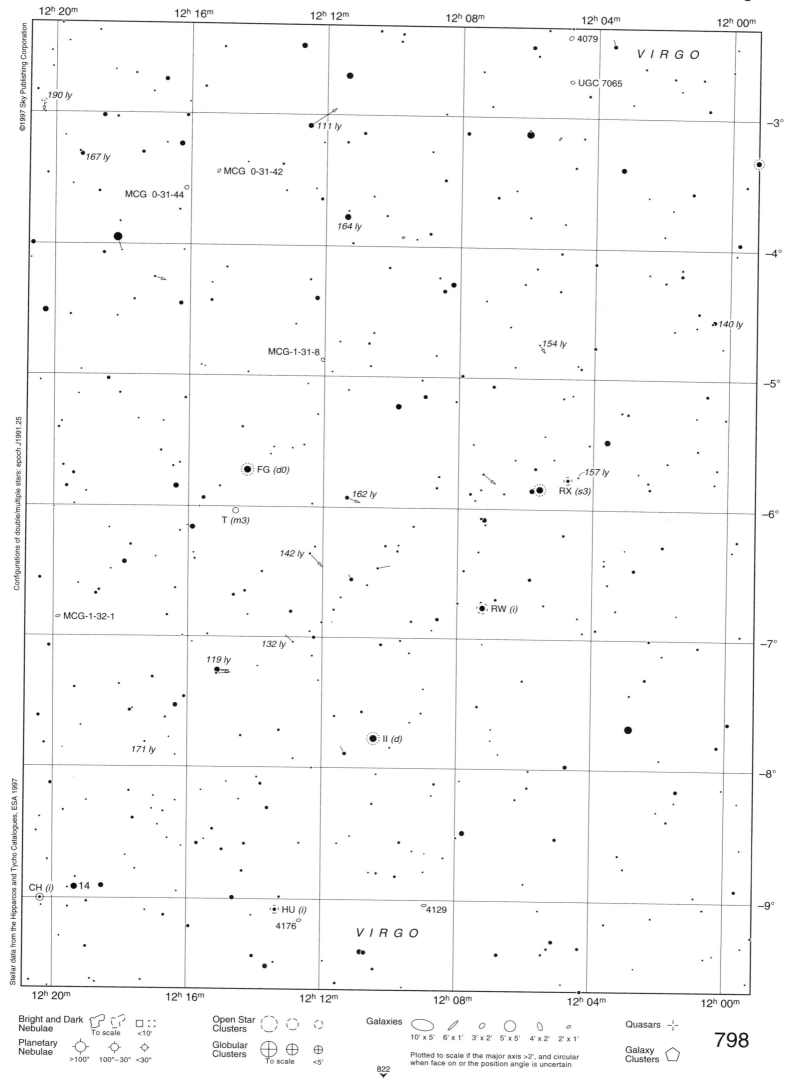

12h 20m   12h 16m   12h 12m   12h 08m   12h 04m   12h 00m

VIRGO

○ 4079

○ UGC 7065

−3°

190 ly

111 ly

167 ly

○ MCG 0-31-42

MCG 0-31-44 ○

164 ly

−4°

140 ly

MCG-1-31-8 ○

154 ly

−5°

○ FG *(d0)*

157 ly

162 ly

⊙ RX *(s3)*

○ T *(m3)*

142 ly

−6°

MCG-1-32-1 ○

⊙ RW *(i)*

132 ly

−7°

119 ly

⊙ II *(d)*

171 ly

−8°

CH *(i)*
⊙ ● 14

○ 4129

HU *(i)*
4176 ○

VIRGO

−9°

12h 20m   12h 16m   12h 12m   12h 08m   12h 04m   12h 00m

Bright and Dark Nebulae
To scale <10'

Open Star Clusters

Galaxies
10' x 5' 6' x 1' 3' x 2' 5' x 5' 4' x 2' 2' x 1'

Quasars

Planetary Nebulae
>100" 100"–30" <30"

Globular Clusters
To scale <5'

Plotted to scale if the major axis >2', and circular when face on or the position angle is uncertain

Galaxy Clusters

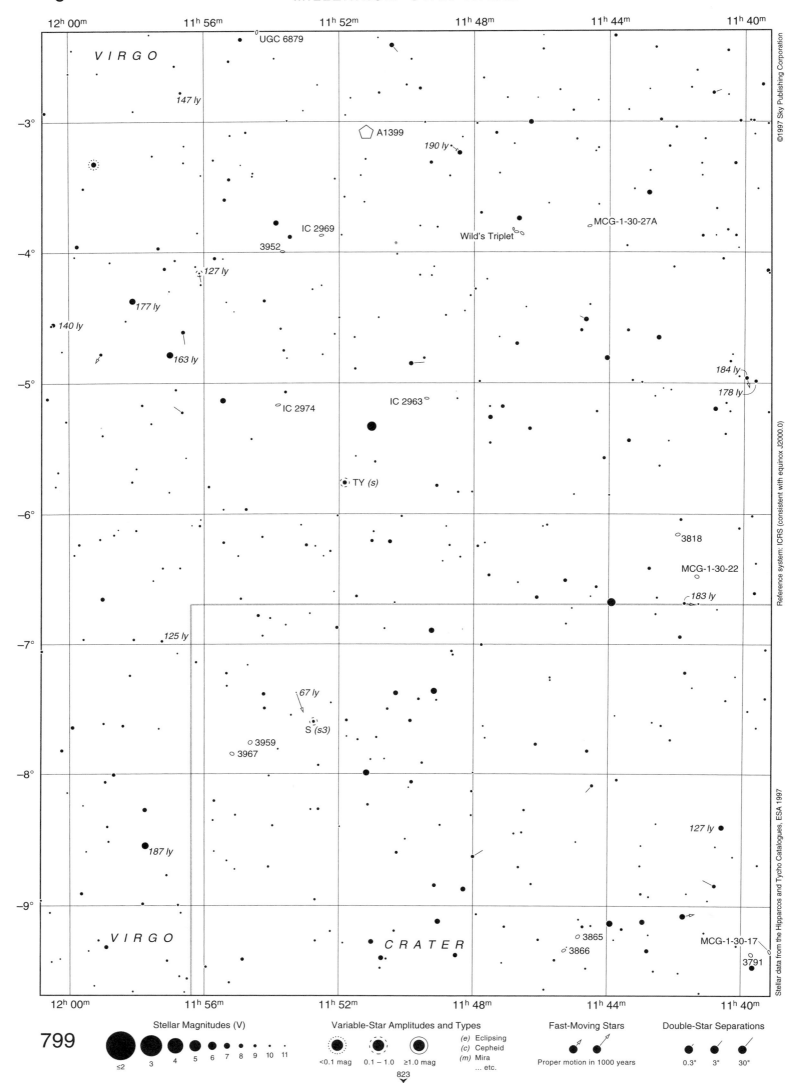

©1997 Sky Publishing Corporation

Reference system: ICRS (consistent with equinox J2000.0)

Stellar data from the Hipparcos and Tycho Catalogues, ESA 1997

VIRGO

147 ly

UGC 6879

A1399

190 ly

IC 2969

3952

MCG-1-30-27A

Wild's Triplet

127 ly

177 ly

140 ly

163 ly

184 ly

178 ly

IC 2974

IC 2963

TY (s)

3818

MCG-1-30-22

183 ly

125 ly

67 ly

S (s3)

3959

3967

187 ly

127 ly

VIRGO

CRATER

3865

3866

MCG-1-30-17

3791

799

Stellar Magnitudes (V)

≤2 3 4 5 6 7 8 9 10 11

Variable-Star Amplitudes and Types

<0.1 mag   0.1 − 1.0   ≥1.0 mag

(e) Eclipsing
(c) Cepheid
(m) Mira
... etc.

Fast-Moving Stars

Proper motion in 1000 years

Double-Star Separations

0.3"   3"   30"

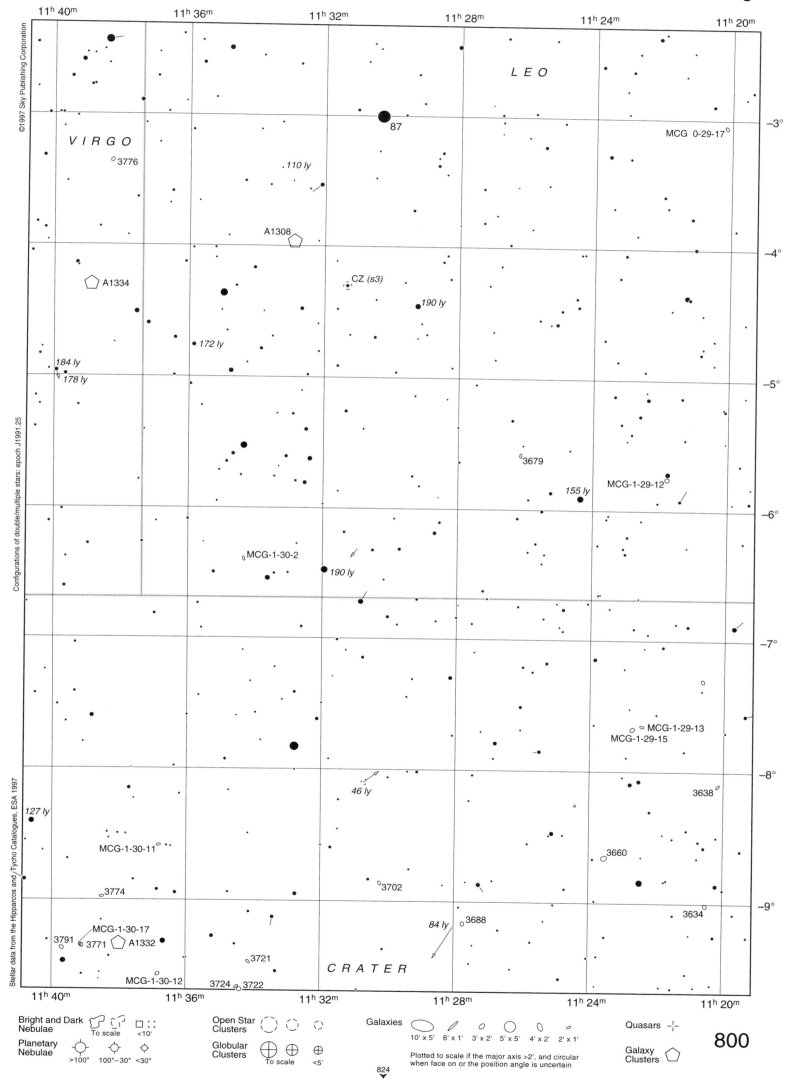

11ʰ 40ᵐ   11ʰ 36ᵐ   11ʰ 32ᵐ   11ʰ 28ᵐ   11ʰ 24ᵐ   11ʰ 20ᵐ

©1997 Sky Publishing Corporation

−3°

L E O

MCG 0-29-17

87

V I R G O

3776

.110 ly

A1308

A1334

−4°

CZ (s3)

190 ly

172 ly

184 ly

178 ly

−5°

3679

MCG-1-29-12

155 ly

−6°

MCG-1-30-2

190 ly

−7°

MCG-1-29-13
MCG-1-29-15

3638

−8°

46 ly

127 ly

MCG-1-30-11

3660

3774

3702

3634

−9°

Stellar data from the Hipparcos and Tycho Catalogues, ESA 1997

Configurations of double/multiple stars: epoch J1991.25

MCG-1-30-17

3791   3771   A1332

84 ly   3688

MCG-1-30-12   3724 3722   3721   *C R A T E R*

11ʰ 40ᵐ   11ʰ 36ᵐ   11ʰ 32ᵐ   11ʰ 28ᵐ   11ʰ 24ᵐ   11ʰ 20ᵐ

Bright and Dark
Nebulae   To scale   <10'

Planetary
Nebulae   >100" 100"−30" <30"

Open Star
Clusters

Globular
Clusters   To scale   <5'

Galaxies

10' x 5' 6' x 1' 3' x 2' 5' x 5' 4' x 2' 2' x 1'

Plotted to scale if the major axis >2', and circular
when face on or the position angle is uncertain

Quasars

Galaxy
Clusters

800

824

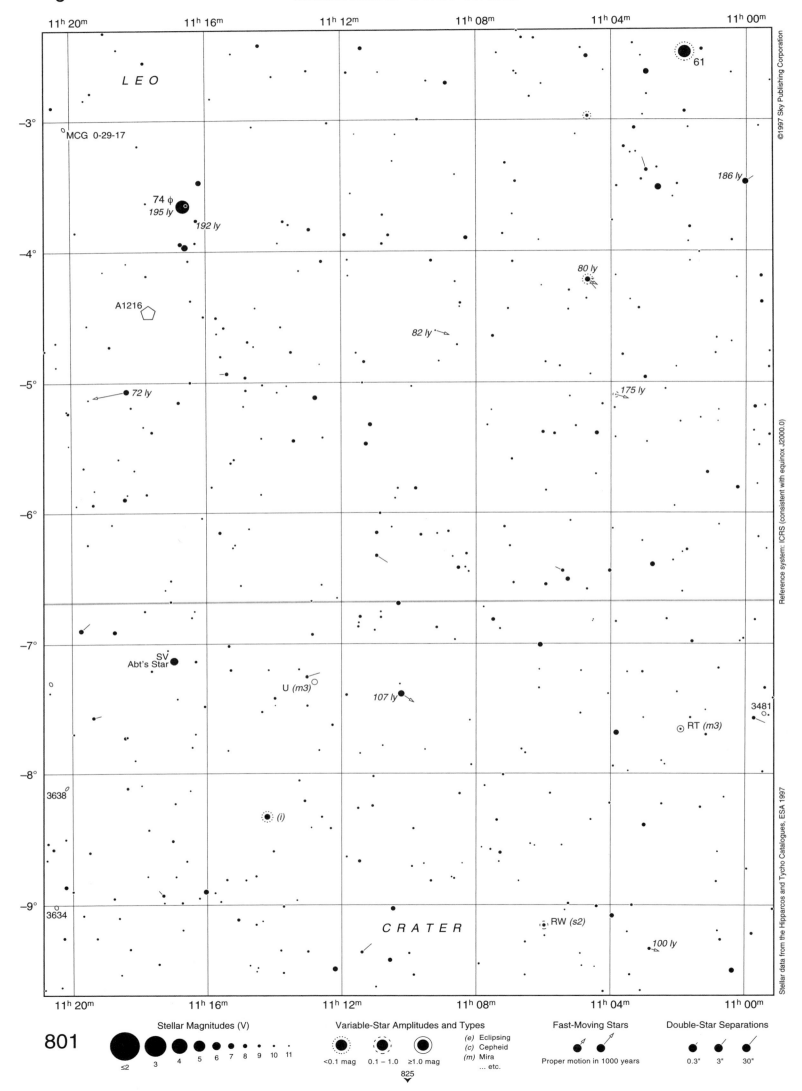

©1997 Sky Publishing Corporation

Reference system: ICRS (consistent with equinox J2000.0)

Stellar data from the Hipparcos and Tycho Catalogues, ESA 1997

801

Stellar Magnitudes (V)

≤2   3   4   5   6   7 8 9 10 11

Variable-Star Amplitudes and Types

<0.1 mag   0.1 – 1.0   ≥1.0 mag

(e) Eclipsing
(c) Cepheid
(m) Mira
... etc.

Fast-Moving Stars

Proper motion in 1000 years

Double-Star Separations

0.3"   3"   30"

825

MILLENNIUM STAR ATLAS

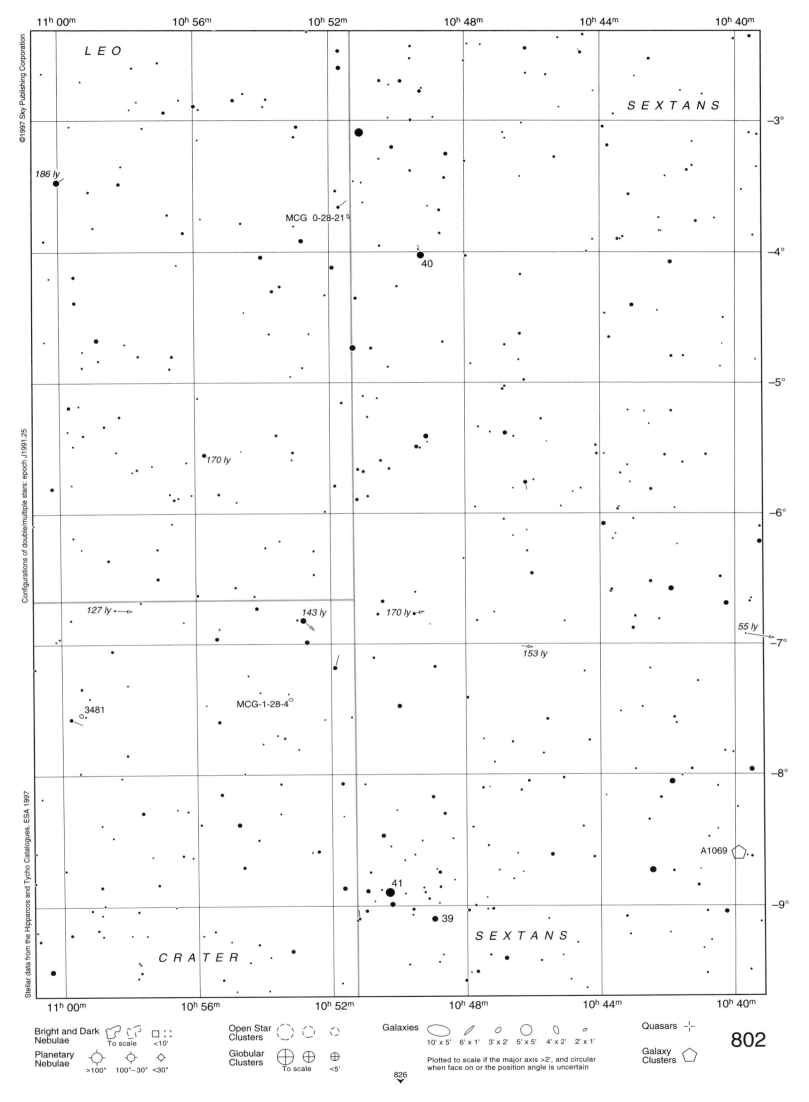

©1997 Sky Publishing Corporation

Configurations of double/multiple stars: epoch J1991.25

Stellar data from the Hipparcos and Tycho Catalogues, ESA 1997

L E O

S E X T A N S

186 ly

MCG 0-28-21

40

170 ly

127 ly   143 ly   170 ly

55 ly

153 ly

MCG-1-28-4

3481

A1069

41

39

S E X T A N S

C R A T E R

Bright and Dark Nebulae			Open Star Clusters			Galaxies							Quasars	−┼−
To scale	<10'					10' x 5'	6' x 1'	3' x 2'	5' x 5'	4' x 2'	2' x 1'			

Planetary Nebulae
>100"   100"−30"   <30"

Globular Clusters
To scale   <5'

Plotted to scale if the major axis >2', and circular when face on or the position angle is uncertain

Galaxy Clusters

802

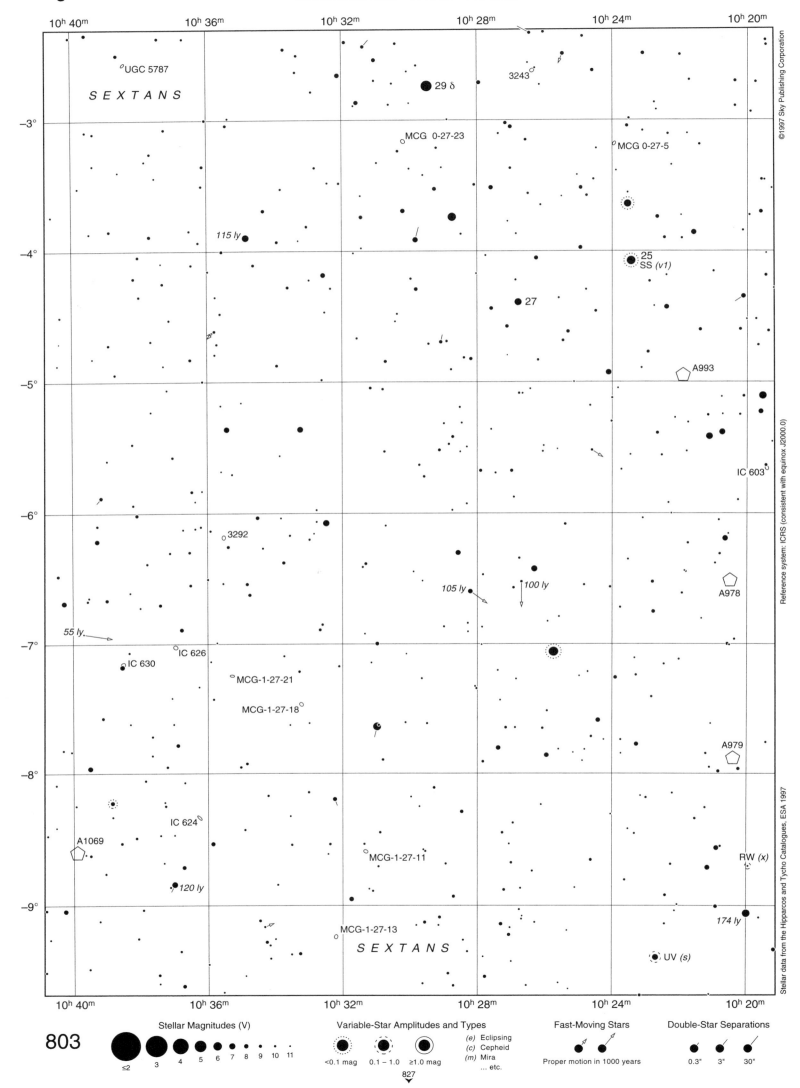

SEXTANS

UGC 5787

29 δ

MCG 0-27-23

3243

MCG 0-27-5

115 ly

25
SS (v1)

27

A993

IC 603

3292

A978

105 ly   100 ly

55 ly.

IC 626

IC 630

MCG-1-27-21

MCG-1-27-18

A979

IC 624

A1069

MCG-1-27-11

RW (x)

120 ly

174 ly

MCG-1-27-13

SEXTANS

UV (s)

©1997 Sky Publishing Corporation

Reference system: ICRS (consistent with equinox J2000.0)

Stellar data from the Hipparcos and Tycho Catalogues, ESA 1997

803

Stellar Magnitudes (V)

≤2   3   4   5   6 7 8 9 10 11

Variable-Star Amplitudes and Types

<0.1 mag   0.1 – 1.0   ≥1.0 mag

(e) Eclipsing
(c) Cepheid
(m) Mira
... etc.

Fast-Moving Stars

Proper motion in 1000 years

Double-Star Separations

0.3"   3"   30"

827

780

−6°

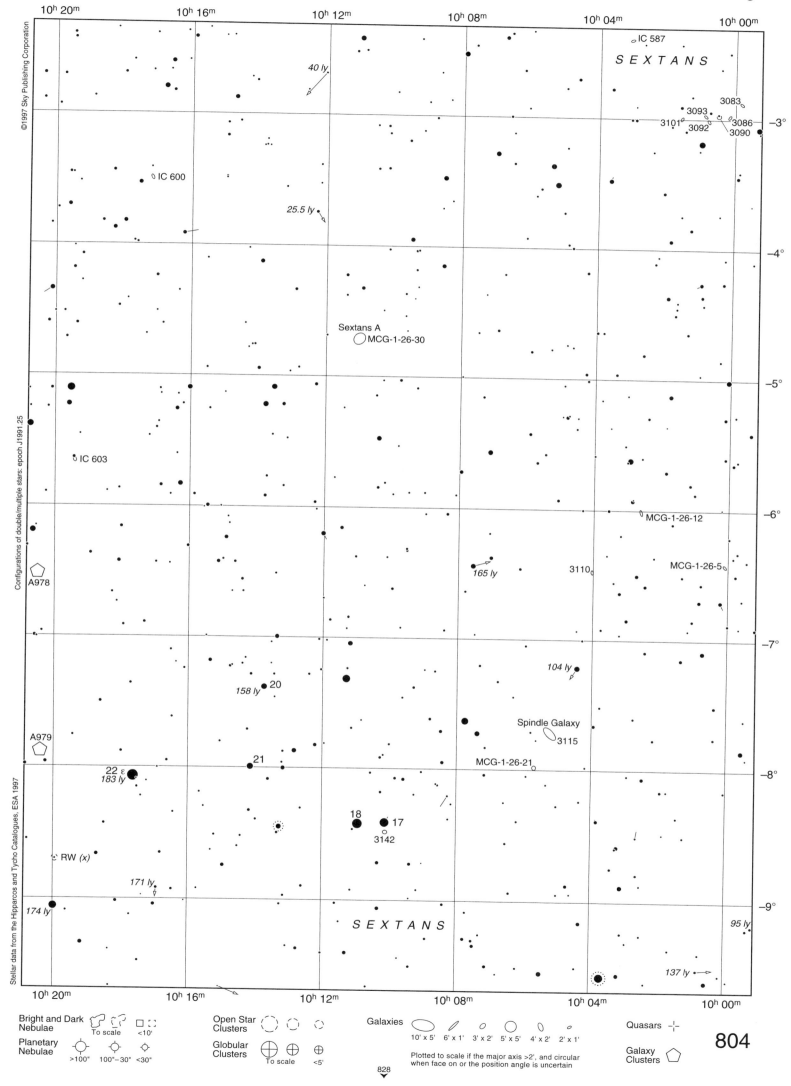

10ʰ 20ᵐ 10ʰ 16ᵐ 10ʰ 12ᵐ 10ʰ 08ᵐ 10ʰ 04ᵐ 10ʰ 00ᵐ

IC 587

S E X T A N S

3083
3093
3101 3092 3086
3090

−3°

IC 600

40 ly

25.5 ly

−4°

Sextans A
MCG-1-26-30

−5°

IC 603

MCG-1-26-12

−6°

A978

165 ly

3110

MCG-1-26-5

−7°

104 ly

158 ly 20

Spindle Galaxy
3115

A979

21

MCG-1-26-21

−8°

22 ε
183 ly

18 17
3142

RW (x)

171 ly

−9°

174 ly

S E X T A N S

95 ly

137 ly

10ʰ 20ᵐ 10ʰ 16ᵐ 10ʰ 12ᵐ 10ʰ 08ᵐ 10ʰ 04ᵐ 10ʰ 00ᵐ

Bright and Dark
Nebulae
To scale <10'

Planetary
Nebulae
>100" 100"–30" <30"

Open Star
Clusters

Globular
Clusters
To scale <5'

Galaxies
10' x 5' 6' x 1' 3' x 2' 5' x 5' 4' x 2' 2' x 1'

Plotted to scale if the major axis >2', and circular
when face on or the position angle is uncertain

Quasars –|–

Galaxy
Clusters

804

828

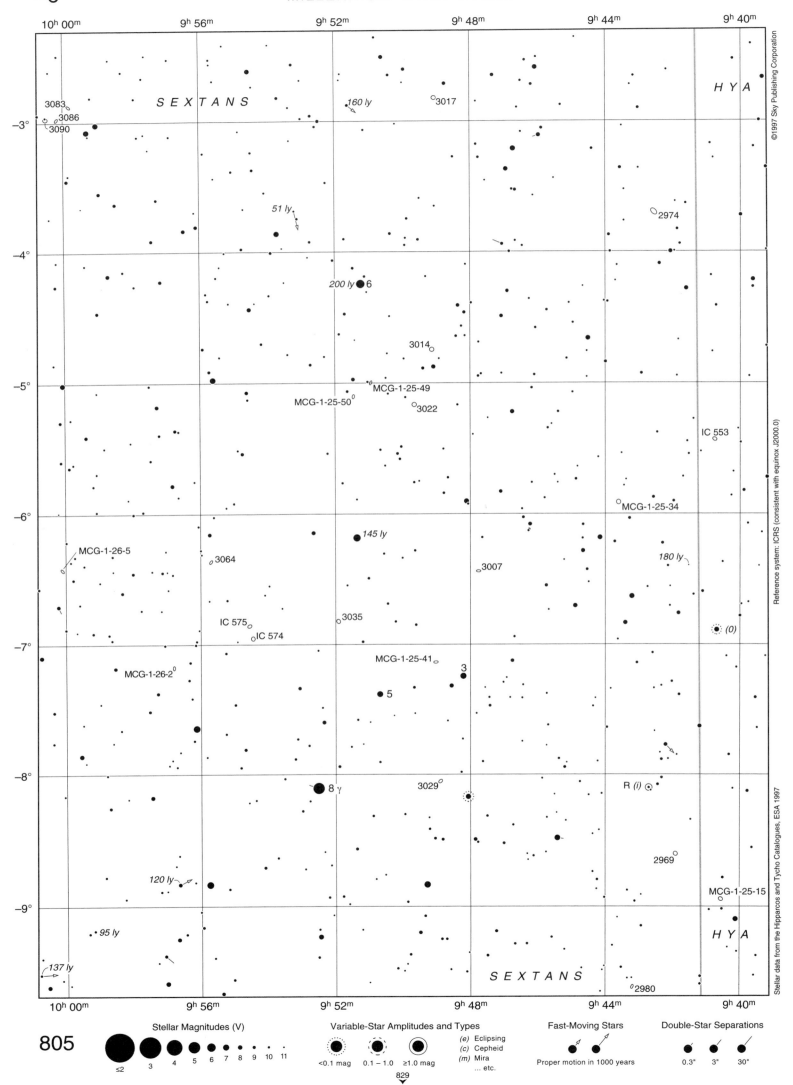

805

Stellar Magnitudes (V)

≤2   3   4   5   6   7   8   9   10   11

Variable-Star Amplitudes and Types

<0.1 mag   0.1 – 1.0   ≥1.0 mag

(e) Eclipsing
(c) Cepheid
(m) Mira
... etc.

Fast-Moving Stars

Proper motion in 1000 years

Double-Star Separations

0.3"   3"   30"

829

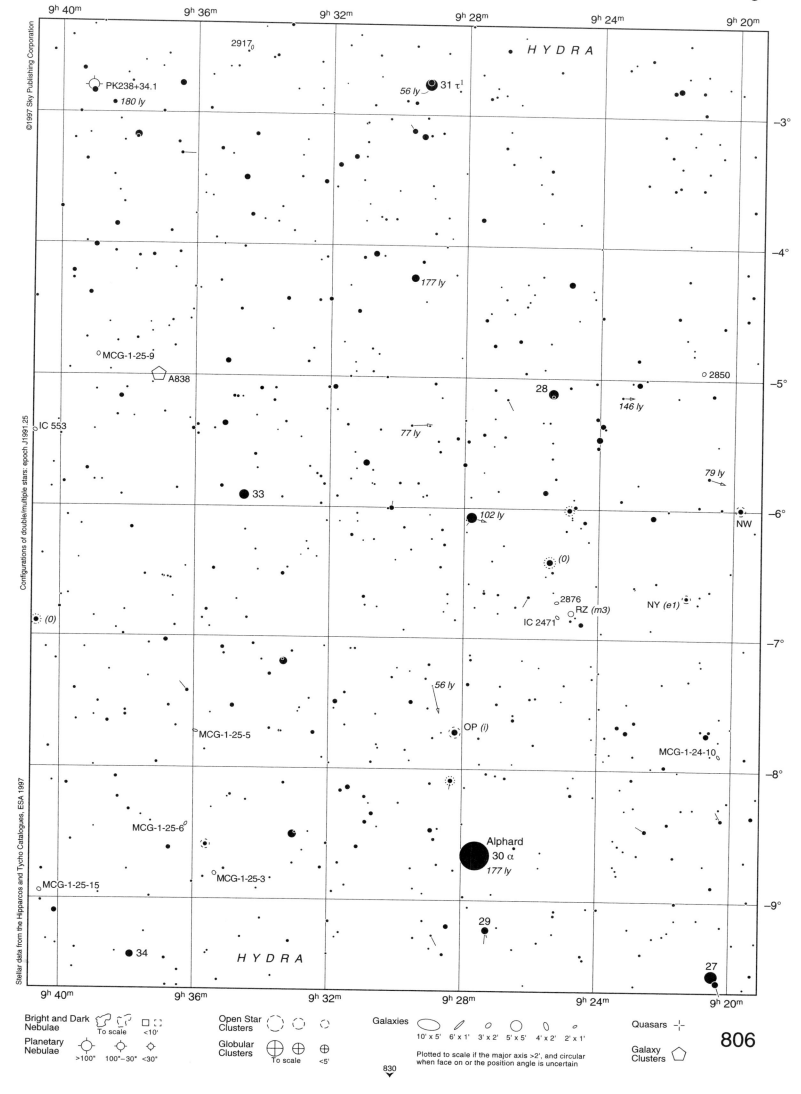

Configurations of double/multiple stars: epoch J1991.25

Stellar data from the Hipparcos and Tycho Catalogues, ESA 1997

9h 40m   9h 36m   9h 32m   9h 28m   9h 24m   9h 20m

HYDRA

2917₀

PK238+34.1
• 180 ly

56 ly 31 τ¹

177 ly

MCG-1-25-9

A838

28

2850

146 ly

IC 553

77 ly

79 ly

33

102 ly

NW

(0)

2876

NY (e1)

RZ (m3)

IC 2471

(0)

56 ly

OP (i)

MCG-1-25-5

MCG-1-24-10

MCG-1-25-6

Alphard
30 α
177 ly

MCG-1-25-15

MCG-1-25-3

29

HYDRA

34

27

−3°

−4°

−5°

−6°

−7°

−8°

−9°

Bright and Dark Nebulae	Open Star Clusters	Galaxies	Quasars

Bright and Dark Nebulae   To scale   <10'
Planetary Nebulae   >100"   100"−30"   <30"
Open Star Clusters
Globular Clusters   To scale   <5'
Galaxies   10' x 5'   6' x 1'   3' x 2'   5' x 5'   4' x 2'   2' x 1'
Plotted to scale if the major axis >2', and circular when face on or the position angle is uncertain
Quasars
Galaxy Clusters

806

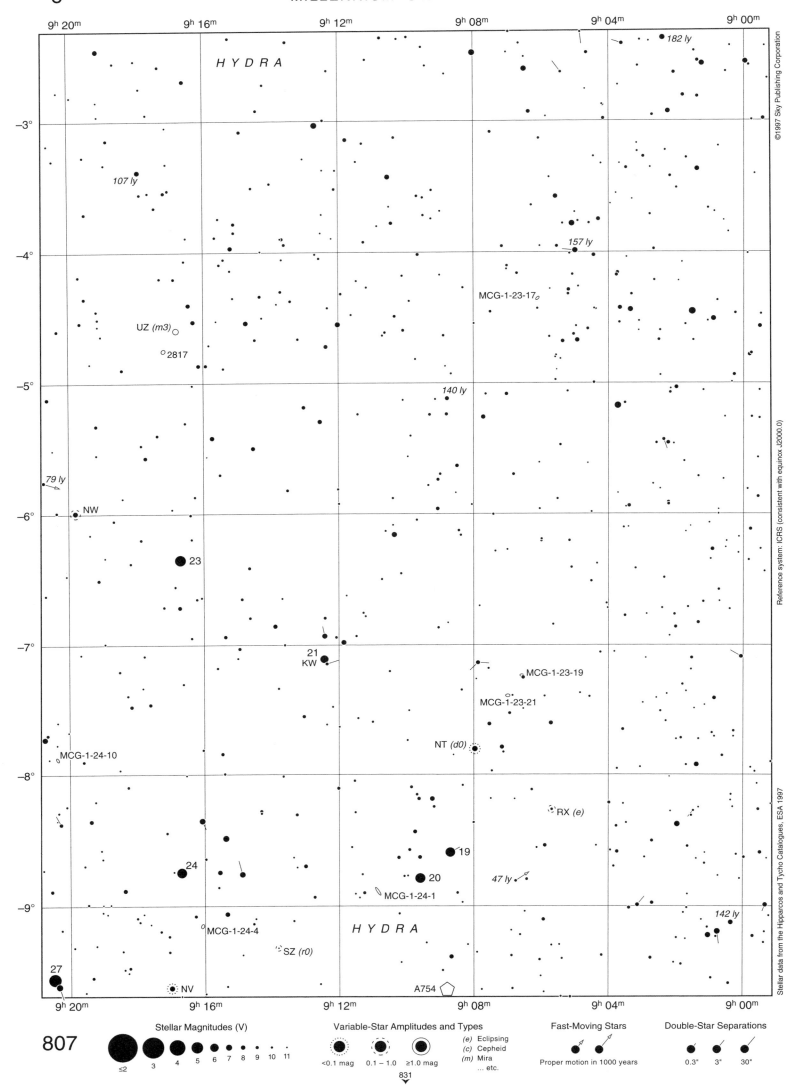

©1997 Sky Publishing Corporation

Reference system: ICRS (consistent with equinox J2000.0)

Stellar data from the Hipparcos and Tycho Catalogues, ESA 1997

HYDRA

107 ly

157 ly

182 ly

MCG-1-23-17₀

UZ (m3)

2817

140 ly

79 ly

NW

23

21
KW

MCG-1-23-19

MCG-1-23-21

NT (d0)

MCG-1-24-10

RX (e)

19

47 ly

20

24

MCG-1-24-1

MCG-1-24-4

142 ly

HYDRA

SZ (r0)

27

NV

A754

807

Stellar Magnitudes (V)	Variable-Star Amplitudes and Types	Fast-Moving Stars	Double-Star Separations

Stellar Magnitudes (V)
≤2   3   4   5   6   7   8   9   10   11

Variable-Star Amplitudes and Types
<0.1 mag   0.1 – 1.0   ≥1.0 mag
(e) Eclipsing
(c) Cepheid
(m) Mira
... etc.

Fast-Moving Stars
Proper motion in 1000 years

Double-Star Separations
0.3"   3"   30"

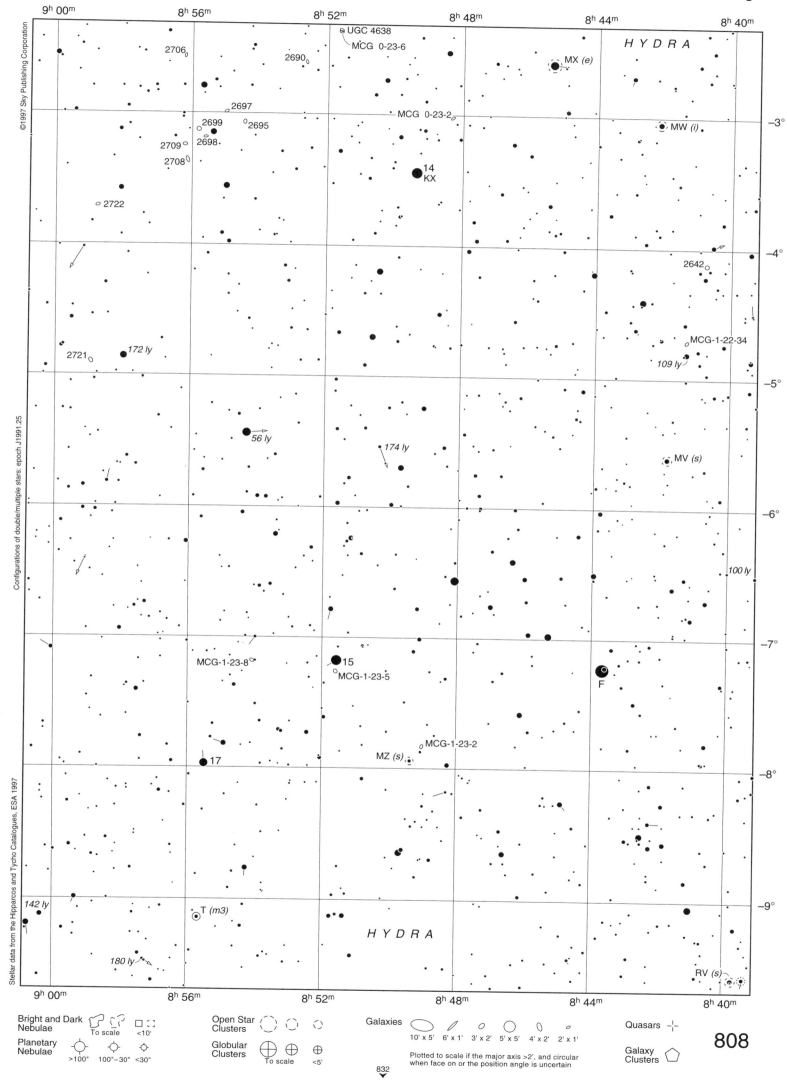

Configurations of double/multiple stars: epoch J1991.25

Stellar data from the Hipparcos and Tycho Catalogues, ESA 1997

HYDRA

UGC 4638
MCG 0-23-6
2706
2690
MX (e)
2697
MCG 0-23-2
2699
2695
MW (i)
2709
2698
2708
14
KX
2722
2642
2721   172 ly
MCG-1-22-34
109 ly
56 ly
174 ly
MV (s)
100 ly
MCG-1-23-8
15
F
MCG-1-23-5
MCG-1-23-2
17
MZ (s)
142 ly
T (m3)
HYDRA
180 ly
RV (s)

9ʰ 00ᵐ   8ʰ 56ᵐ   8ʰ 52ᵐ   8ʰ 48ᵐ   8ʰ 44ᵐ   8ʰ 40ᵐ

−3°
−4°
−5°
−6°
−7°
−8°
−9°

Bright and Dark Nebulae
To scale   <10'
Planetary Nebulae
>100"   100"−30"   <30"

Open Star Clusters
Globular Clusters
To scale   <5'

Galaxies
10' x 5'   6' x 1'   3' x 2'   5' x 5'   4' x 2'   2' x 1'
Plotted to scale if the major axis >2', and circular when face on or the position angle is uncertain

Quasars

Galaxy Clusters

808

▼
832

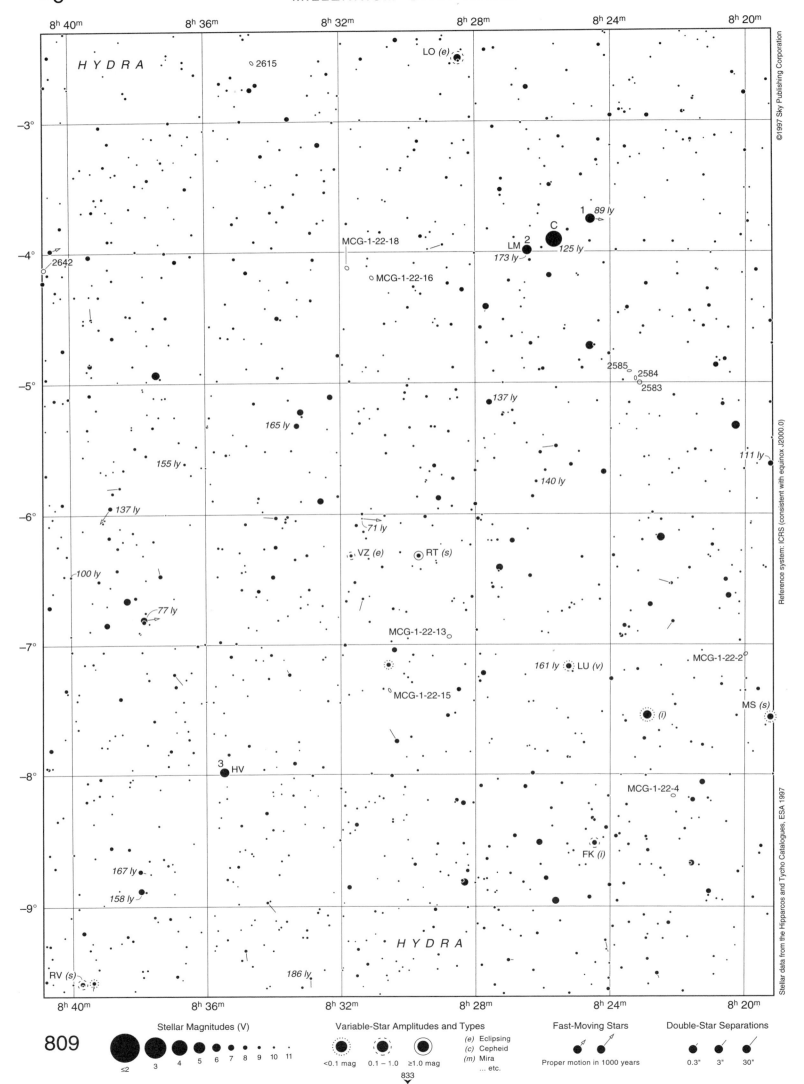

©1997 Sky Publishing Corporation

Reference system: ICRS (consistent with equinox J2000.0)

Stellar data from the Hipparcos and Tycho Catalogues, ESA 1997

HYDRA

2615

LO (e)

1 *89 ly*
C
MCG-1-22-18
LM 2
173 ly *125 ly*

MCG-1-22-16

2585
2584
2583

137 ly

165 ly

155 ly

111 ly

140 ly

137 ly

71 ly

100 ly

VZ (e)   RT (s)

77 ly

MCG-1-22-13

MCG-1-22-2

161 ly LU (v)

MCG-1-22-15

MS (s)

(i)

3 HV

MCG-1-22-4

167 ly

FK (i)

158 ly

HYDRA

RV (s)

186 ly

809

Stellar Magnitudes (V)

≤2   3   4   5   6   7   8   9 10 11

Variable-Star Amplitudes and Types

<0.1 mag   0.1 − 1.0   ≥1.0 mag

(e) Eclipsing
(c) Cepheid
(m) Mira
... etc.

Fast-Moving Stars

Proper motion in 1000 years

Double-Star Separations

0.3"   3"   30"

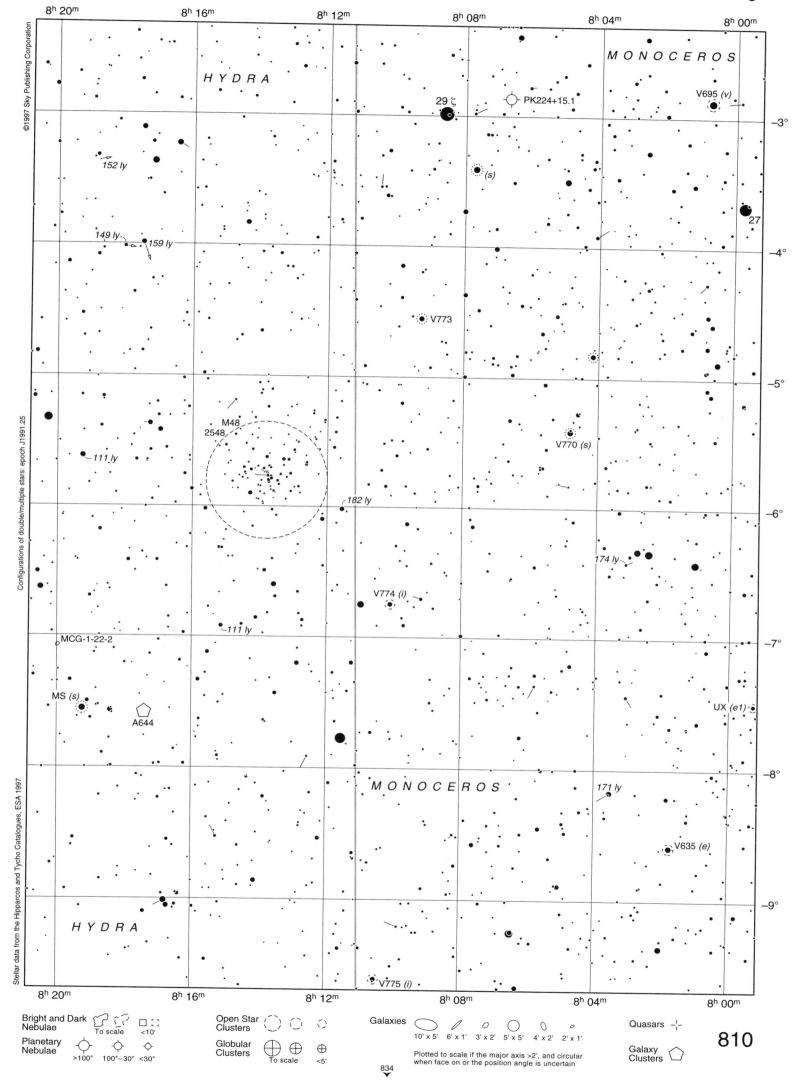

MONOCEROS

HYDRA

29 ζ

PK224+15.1

V695 (v)

(s)

27

152 ly

149 ly   159 ly

V773

111 ly

M48
2548

V770 (s)

182 ly

174 ly

V774 (i)

111 ly

MCG-1-22-2

MS (s)

UX (e1)

A644

MONOCEROS

171 ly

V635 (e)

HYDRA

V775 (i)

Stellar data from the Hipparcos and Tycho Catalogues, ESA 1997
Configurations of double/multiple stars: epoch J1991.25

Bright and Dark Nebulae	Open Star Clusters	Galaxies	Quasars

To scale   <10'

Planetary Nebulae
>100"   100"−30'   <30'

Globular Clusters
To scale   <5'

10' x 5'   6' x 1'   3' x 2'   5' x 5'   4' x 2'   2' x 1'

Plotted to scale if the major axis >2', and circular when face on or the position angle is uncertain

Galaxy Clusters

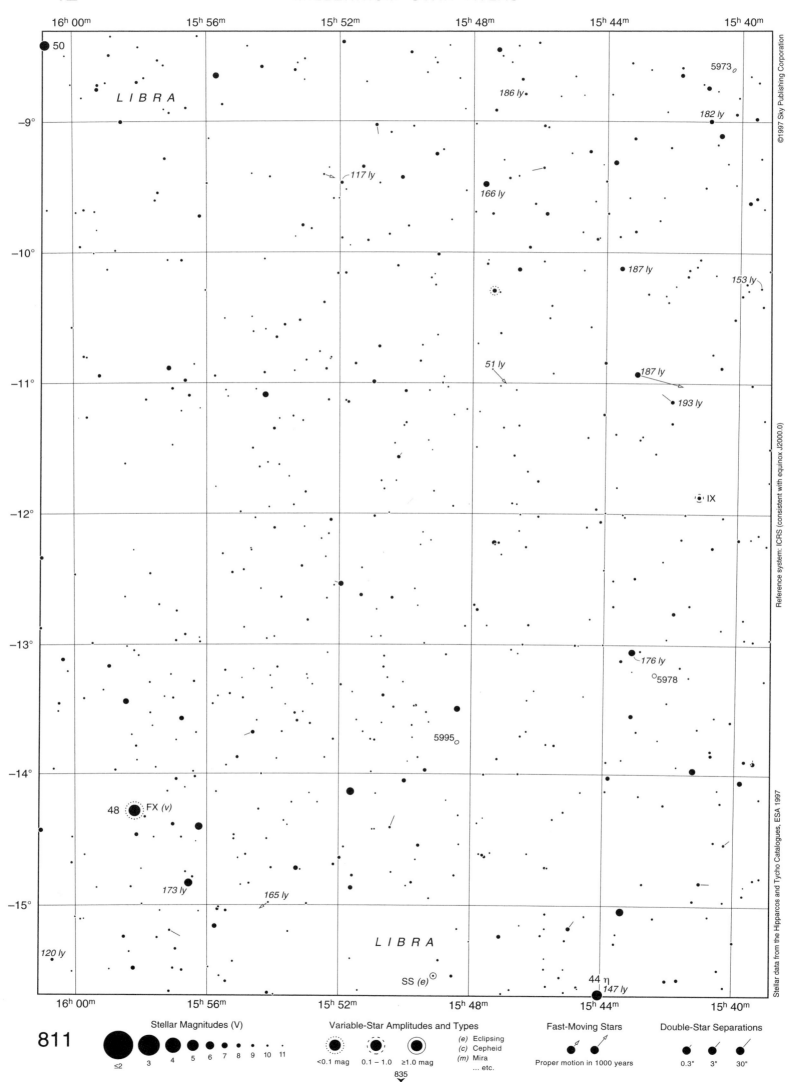

LIBRA

LIBRA

50

186 ly

182 ly

5973

117 ly

166 ly

187 ly

153 ly

51 ly

187 ly

193 ly

IX

176 ly

5978

5995

48 FX (v)

173 ly

165 ly

120 ly

SS (e)

44 η
147 ly

811

Stellar Magnitudes (V)

≤2 3 4 5 6 7 8 9 10 11

Variable-Star Amplitudes and Types

<0.1 mag   0.1 – 1.0   ≥1.0 mag

(e) Eclipsing
(c) Cepheid
(m) Mira
... etc.

Fast-Moving Stars

Proper motion in 1000 years

Double-Star Separations

0.3"   3"   30"

835

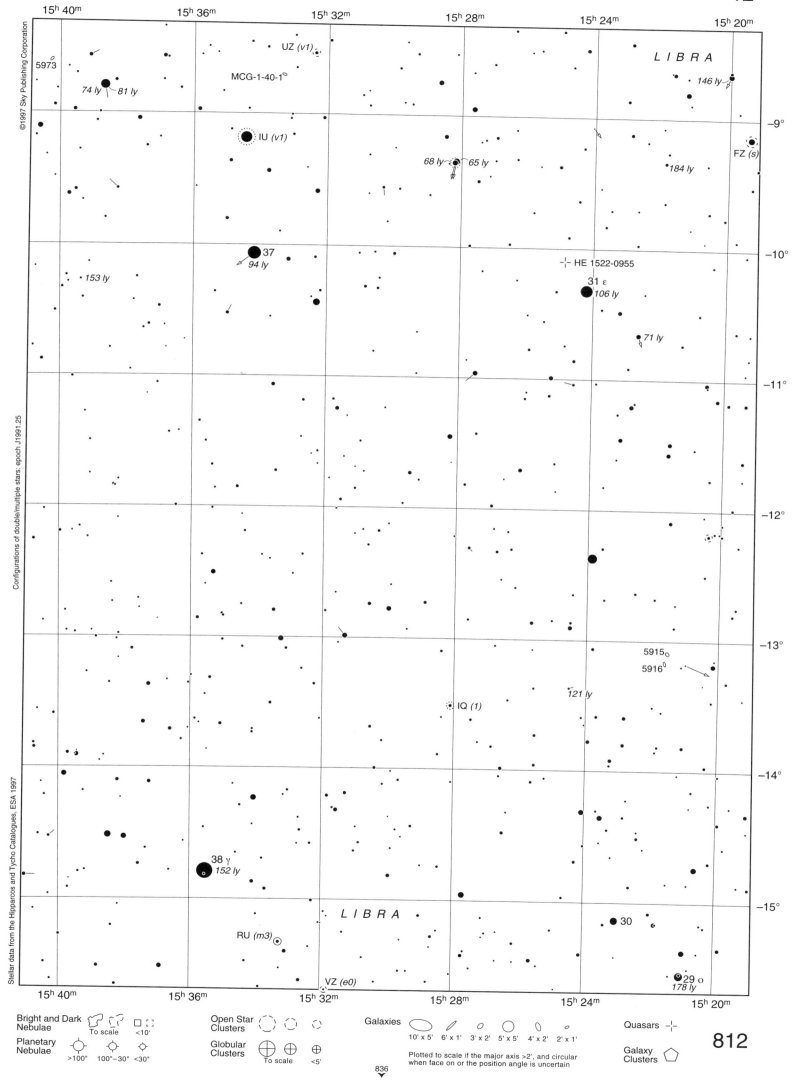

LIBRA

LIBRA

5973

74 ly — 81 ly

UZ (v1)

MCG-1-40-1

IU (v1)

68 ly — 65 ly

146 ly

FZ (s)

184 ly

37
94 ly

153 ly

HE 1522-0955

31 ε
106 ly

71 ly

5915
5916

121 ly

IQ (1)

30

38 γ
152 ly

RU (m3)

VZ (e0)

29 o
178 ly

Bright and Dark Nebulae			To scale	<10'

Planetary Nebulae
>100" 100"−30" <30"

Open Star Clusters

Globular Clusters
To scale <5'

Galaxies
10' x 5'   6' x 1'   3' x 2'   5' x 5'   4' x 2'   2' x 1'

Plotted to scale if the major axis >2', and circular when face on or the position angle is uncertain

Quasars

Galaxy Clusters

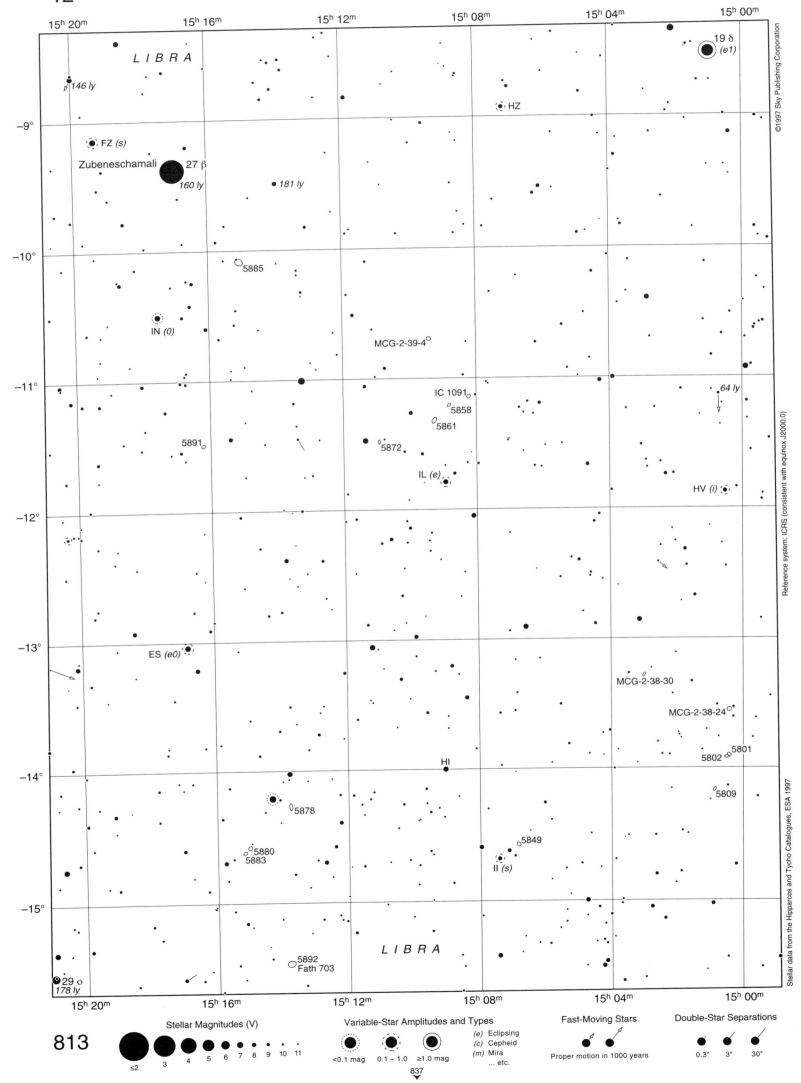

15h 20m   15h 16m   15h 12m   15h 08m   15h 04m   15h 00m

L I B R A

19 δ
(e1)

β *146 ly*

−9°   HZ

FZ *(s)*

Zubeneschamali   27 β
160 ly   • *181 ly*

−10°   5885

IN *(0)*

MCG-2-39-4

−11°   IC 1091   *64 ly*
5858
5861
5891   5872
IL *(e)*
HV *(i)*

−12°

−13°   ES *(e0)*
MCG-2-38-30
MCG-2-38-24
5802 5801

HI   −14°   5809

5878

5880   5849
5883   II *(s)*

−15°

L I B R A

5892
Fath 703
29 o
178 ly

15h 20m   15h 16m   15h 12m   15h 08m   15h 04m   15h 00m

©1997 Sky Publishing Corporation

Reference system: ICRS (consistent with equinox J2000.0)

Stellar data from the Hipparcos and Tycho Catalogues, ESA 1997

Stellar Magnitudes (V)   Variable-Star Amplitudes and Types   Fast-Moving Stars   Double-Star Separations

813   ≤2 3 4 5 6 7 8 9 10 11   <0.1 mag 0.1 – 1.0 ≥1.0 mag   *(e)* Eclipsing
(c) Cepheid
(m) Mira
… etc.   Proper motion in 1000 years   0.3" 3" 30"

837

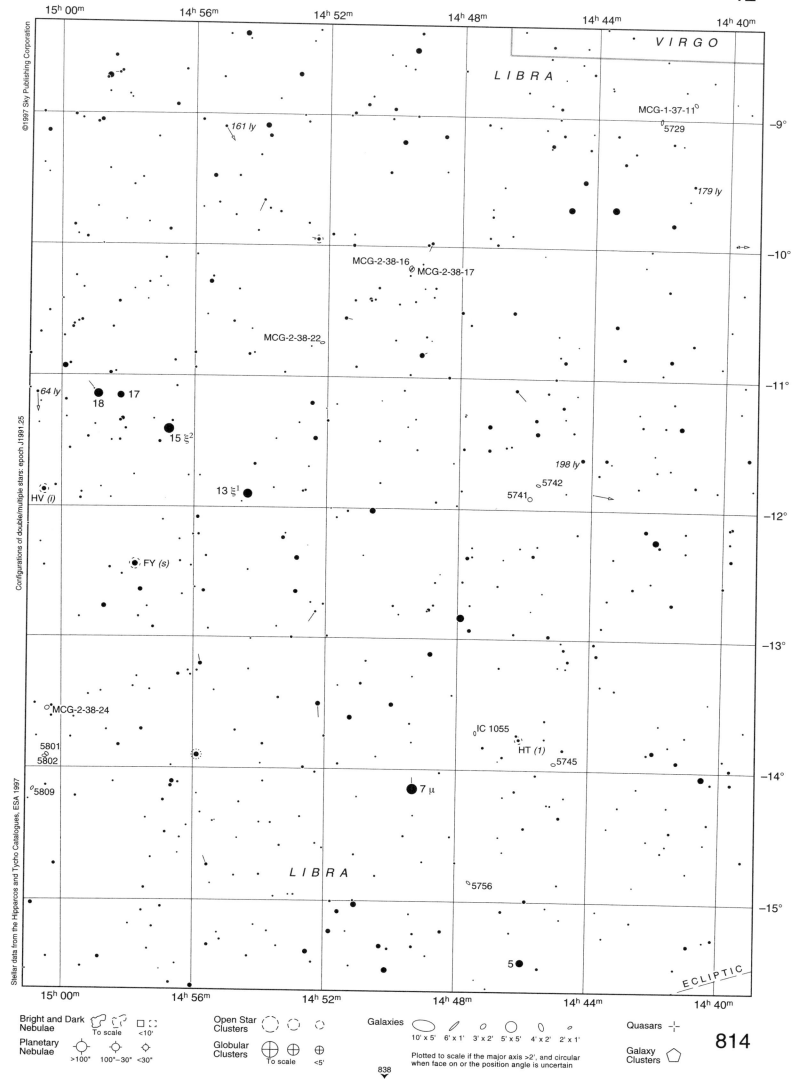

15h 00m   14h 56m   14h 52m   14h 48m   14h 44m   14h 40m

V I R G O

L I B R A

MCG-1-37-11
5729

161 ly

179 ly

−9°

MCG-2-38-16
MCG-2-38-17

MCG-2-38-22

−10°

64 ly

18   17

15 ξ²

HV *(i)*

13 ξ¹

198 ly
5742
5741

−11°

FY *(s)*

−12°

MCG-2-38-24

5801
5802

5809

IC 1055

HT *(1)*
5745

−13°

7 μ

−14°

L I B R A

5756

5

ECLIPTIC

−15°

15h 00m   14h 56m   14h 52m   14h 48m   14h 44m   14h 40m

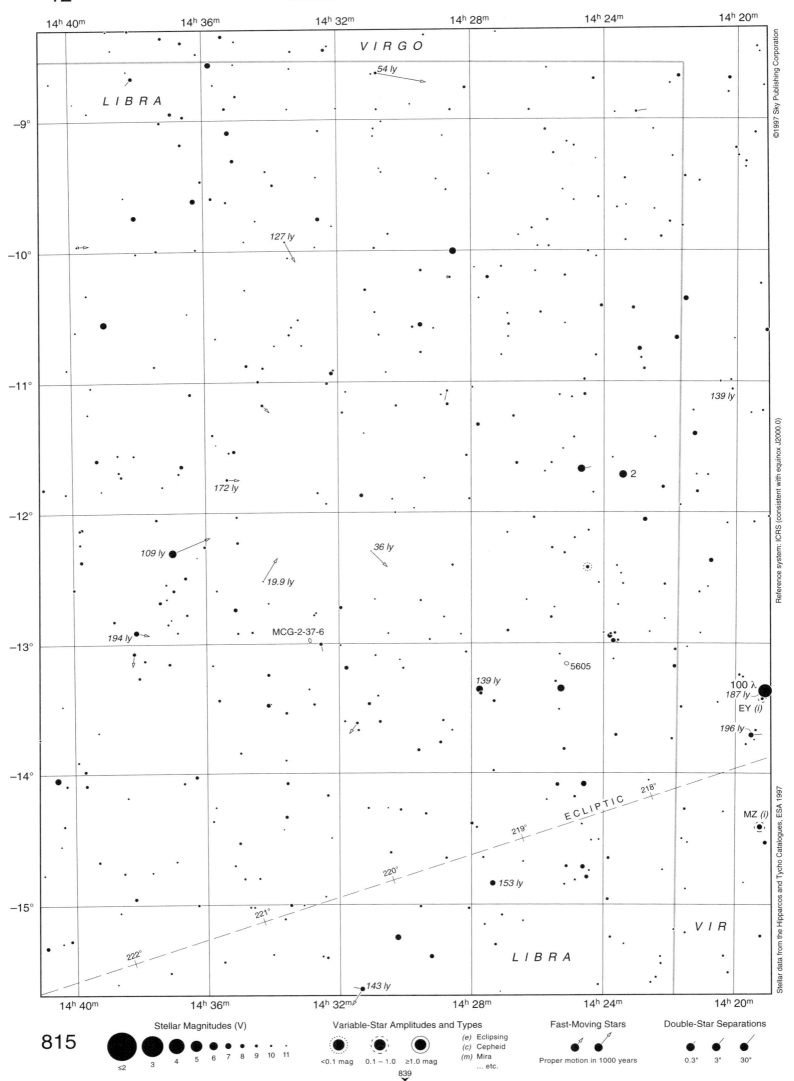

©1997 Sky Publishing Corporation

Reference system: ICRS (consistent with equinox J2000.0)

Stellar data from the Hipparcos and Tycho Catalogues, ESA 1997

VIRGO

LIBRA

54 ly

127 ly

139 ly

2

172 ly

109 ly

36 ly

19.9 ly

194 ly

MCG-2-37-6

139 ly

5605

100 λ
187 ly
EY (i)

196 ly

ECLIPTIC

218°

MZ (i)

219°

220°

153 ly

221°

VIR

222°

LIBRA

143 ly

815

Stellar Magnitudes (V)

≤2   3   4   5   6   7   8   9 10 11

Variable-Star Amplitudes and Types

<0.1 mag   0.1 – 1.0   ≥1.0 mag

(e) Eclipsing
(c) Cepheid
(m) Mira
... etc.

Fast-Moving Stars

Proper motion in 1000 years

Double-Star Separations

0.3"   3"   30"

839

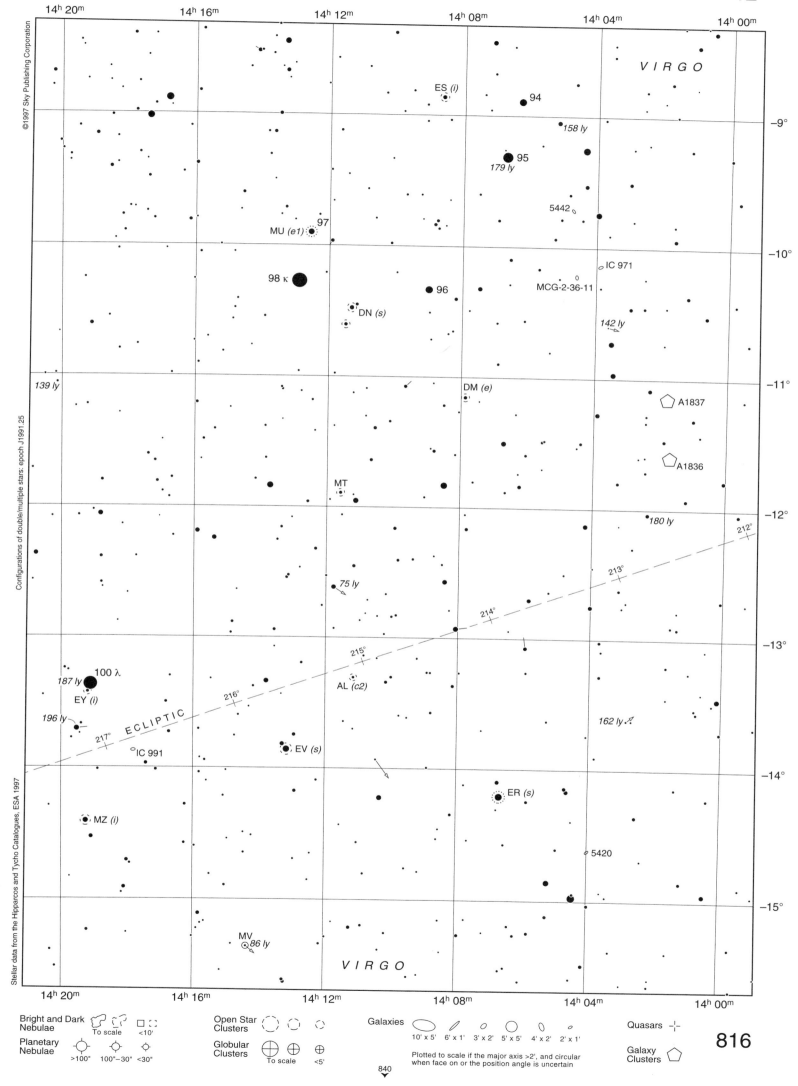

VIRGO

ES (i)
94
158 ly
95
179 ly
5442
MU (e1) 97
98 κ
96
DN (s)
IC 971
MCG-2-36-11
142 ly
139 ly
DM (e)
A1837
A1836
MT
180 ly
75 ly
212°
213°
214°
215°
100 λ
187 ly
AL (c2)
216°
EY (i)
196 ly
162 ly
217°
ECLIPTIC
IC 991
EV (s)
ER (s)
MZ (i)
5420
MV
86 ly
VIRGO

©1997 Sky Publishing Corporation

Configurations of double/multiple stars: epoch J1991.25

Stellar data from the Hipparcos and Tycho Catalogues, ESA 1997

14h 20m   14h 16m   14h 12m   14h 08m   14h 04m   14h 00m

−9°
−10°
−11°
−12°
−13°
−14°
−15°

Bright and Dark Nebulae
To scale   <10'

Planetary Nebulae
>100"   100"−30"   <30"

Open Star Clusters

Globular Clusters
To scale   <5'

Galaxies
10' x 5'   6' x 1'   3' x 2'   5' x 5'   4' x 2'   2' x 1'

Plotted to scale if the major axis >2', and circular when face on or the position angle is uncertain

Quasars

Galaxy Clusters

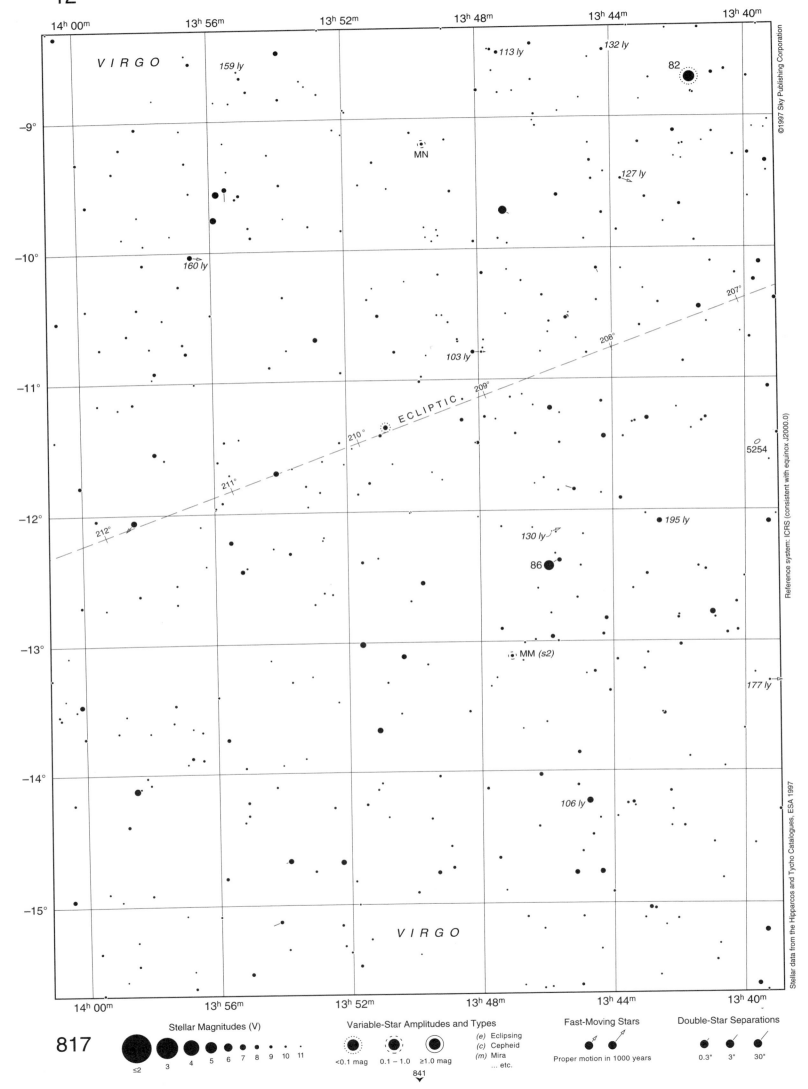

©1997 Sky Publishing Corporation

Reference system: ICRS (consistent with equinox J2000.0)

Stellar data from the Hipparcos and Tycho Catalogues, ESA 1997

VIRGO

159 ly

113 ly

132 ly

82

MN

127 ly

160 ly

103 ly

207°

208°

209°

ECLIPTIC

210°

5254

211°

195 ly

212°

130 ly

86

MM (s2)

177 ly

106 ly

VIRGO

817

Stellar Magnitudes (V)

≤2   3   4   5   6   7   8   9   10   11

Variable-Star Amplitudes and Types

<0.1 mag   0.1 – 1.0   ≥1.0 mag

(e) Eclipsing
(c) Cepheid
(m) Mira
... etc.

Fast-Moving Stars

Proper motion in 1000 years

Double-Star Separations

0.3"   3"   30"

841

MILLENNIUM STAR ATLAS

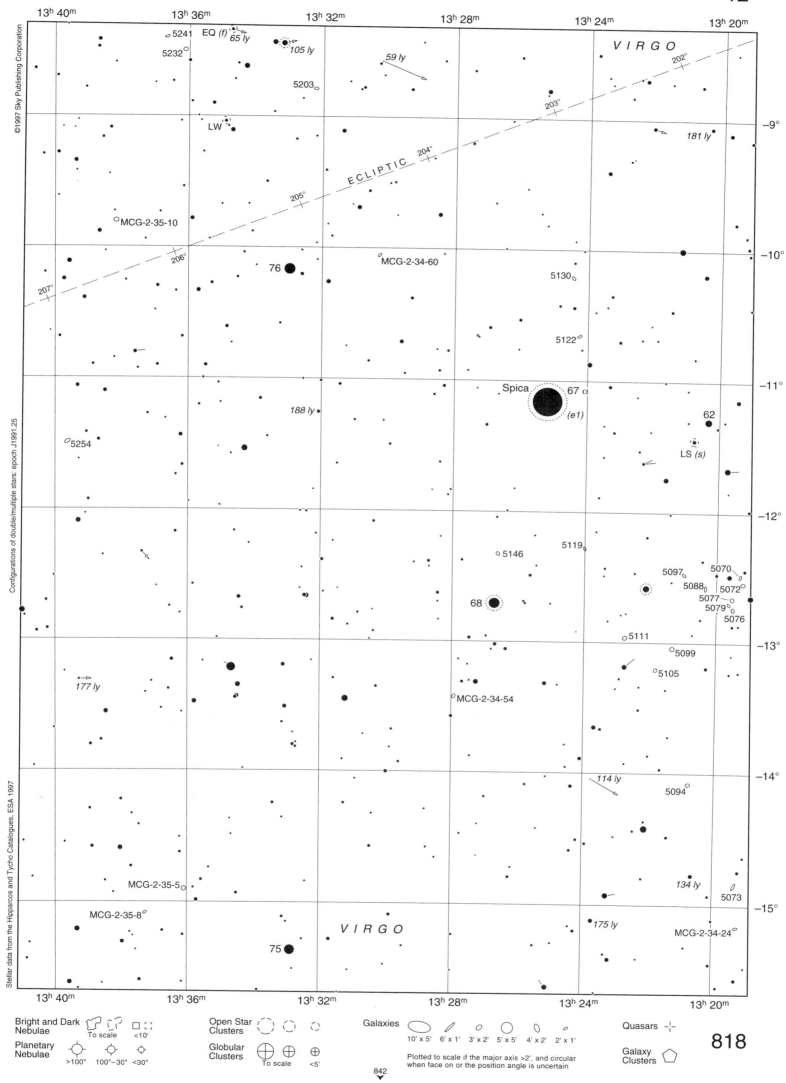

13h 40m   13h 36m   13h 32m   13h 28m   13h 24m   13h 20m

VIRGO

5241
5232
EQ (f) 65 ly
105 ly
59 ly
202°
203°
5203
−9°
181 ly
LW
MCG-2-35-10
204°
205°
206°
ECLIPTIC
207°
76
MCG-2-34-60
−10°
5130
5122
Spica   67 α
(e1)
62
188 ly
LS (s)
5254
−11°

Configurations of double/multiple stars: epoch J1991.25

−12°
5119
5146
5097   5070
5088   5072
68
5077
5079
5076
5111
5099
177 ly
5105
MCG-2-34-54
−13°
114 ly
5094
−14°
134 ly
5073
MCG-2-35-5
175 ly
MCG-2-34-24
MCG-2-35-8
−15°
VIRGO
75

Stellar data from the Hipparcos and Tycho Catalogues, ESA 1997

13h 40m   13h 36m   13h 32m   13h 28m   13h 24m   13h 20m

Bright and Dark Nebulae			Open Star Clusters			Galaxies						Quasars
	To scale	<10'				10' x 5'	6' x 1'	3' x 2'	5' x 5'	4' x 2'	2' x 1'	
Planetary Nebulae			Globular Clusters									Galaxy Clusters
>100"	100"–30"	<30"		To scale	<5'							

Plotted to scale if the major axis >2', and circular when face on or the position angle is uncertain

818

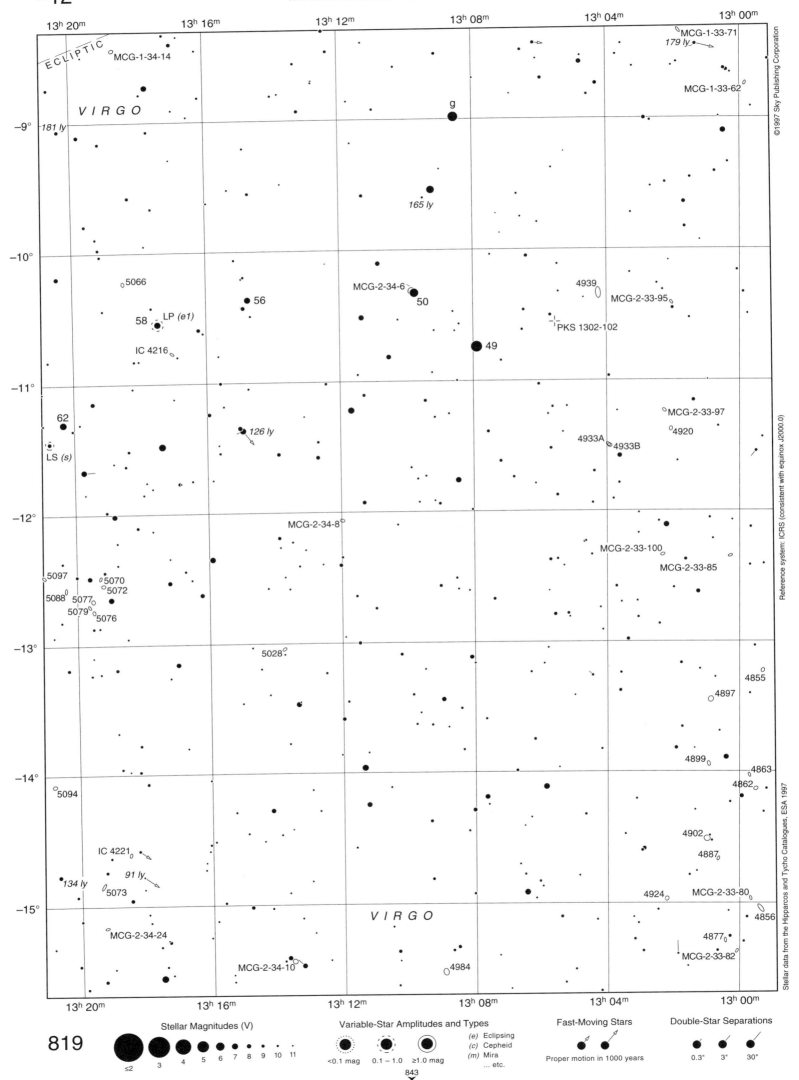

ECLIPTIC
MCG-1-34-14

VIRGO

181 ly

g

165 ly

5066

56

58   LP (e1)

IC 4216

MCG-2-34-6
50

49

MCG-1-33-71
179 ly

MCG-1-33-62

4939
MCG-2-33-95

PKS 1302-102

62

LS (s)

126 ly

MCG-2-33-97

4920

4933A   4933B

MCG-2-34-8

MCG-2-33-100

MCG-2-33-85

5097

5070
5072

5088   5077
5079   5076

5028

4855

4897

5094

4899

4863
4862

IC 4221

91 ly

134 ly

5073

4902

4887

VIRGO

4924

MCG-2-33-80

4856

MCG-2-34-24

4877

MCG-2-33-82

MCG-2-34-10

4984

819

Stellar Magnitudes (V)

≤2   3   4   5   6   7   8   9   10   11

Variable-Star Amplitudes and Types

<0.1 mag   0.1 – 1.0   ≥1.0 mag

(e) Eclipsing
(c) Cepheid
(m) Mira
... etc.

Fast-Moving Stars

Proper motion in 1000 years

Double-Star Separations

0.3"   3"   30"

843

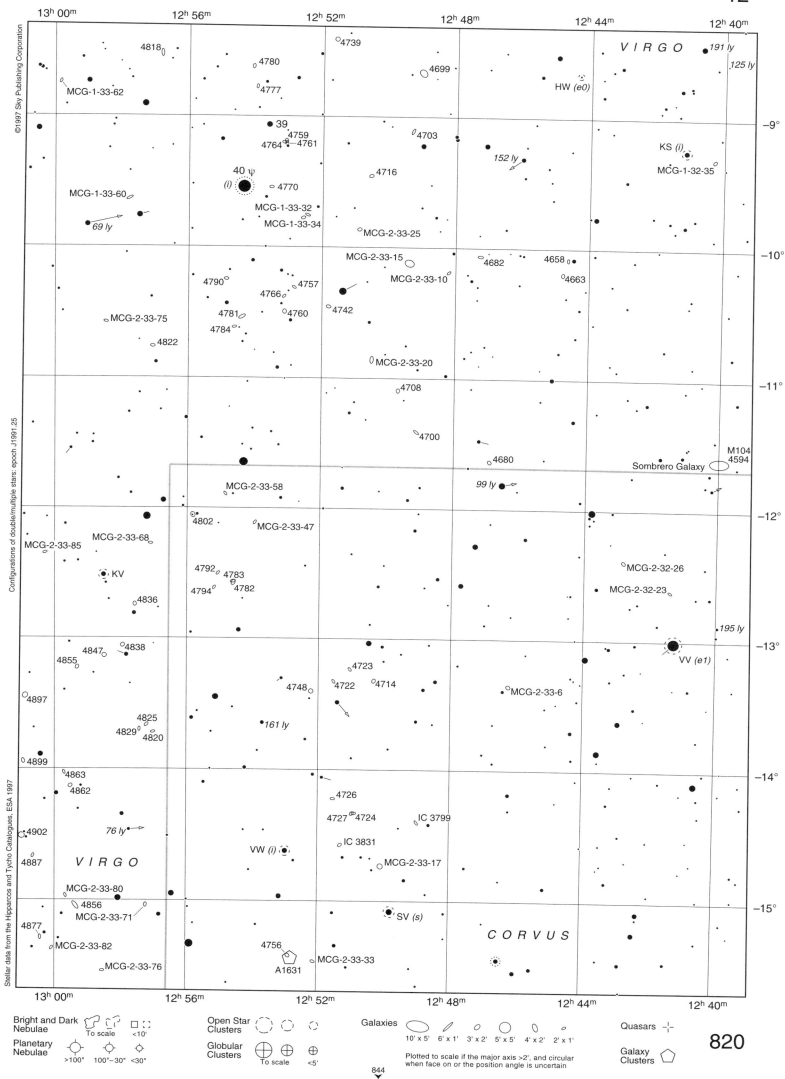

©1997 Sky Publishing Corporation

Configurations of double/multiple stars: epoch J1991.25

Stellar data from the Hipparcos and Tycho Catalogues, ESA 1997

VIRGO

191 ly
125 ly

4818
MCG-1-33-62

4739
4780
4777
4699
HW (e0)

39
4759
4764 — 4761
4703
KS (i)
152 ly
MCG-1-32-35

40 ψ
(i)
4770
4716
MCG-1-33-32
MCG-1-33-34
MCG-1-33-60
69 ly
MCG-2-33-25

MCG-2-33-15
4682
4658
4663
MCG-2-33-10
4790
4757
4766
4760
MCG-2-33-75
4781
4742
4784
4822

MCG-2-33-20

4708

4700

4680
M104
4594
Sombrero Galaxy

99 ly
MCG-2-33-58
MCG-2-33-85
4802
MCG-2-33-47
MCG-2-33-68
MCG-2-32-26
KV
MCG-2-32-23
4792
4783
4794
4782
4836
195 ly
4847
4838
4855
VV (e1)
4723
4897
4748
4722
4714
MCG-2-33-6
4825
4829
4820
161 ly
4899

4863
4862
4726
4902
4727
4724
IC 3799
4887
76 ly
IC 3831
VIRGO
VW (i)
MCG-2-33-17
MCG-2-33-80
4856
MCG-2-33-71
SV (s)
4877
CORVUS
MCG-2-33-82
4756
MCG-2-33-76
A1631
MCG-2-33-33

13h 00m
12h 56m
12h 52m
12h 48m
12h 44m
12h 40m

−9°
−10°
−11°
−12°
−13°
−14°
−15°

Bright and Dark
Nebulae
To scale   <10'
Planetary
Nebulae
>100" 100"–30" <30"

Open Star
Clusters
Globular
Clusters
To scale   <5'

Galaxies

10' x 5' 6' x 1' 3' x 2' 5' x 5' 4' x 2' 2' x 1'

Plotted to scale if the major axis >2', and circular
when face on or the position angle is uncertain

Quasars

Galaxy
Clusters

820

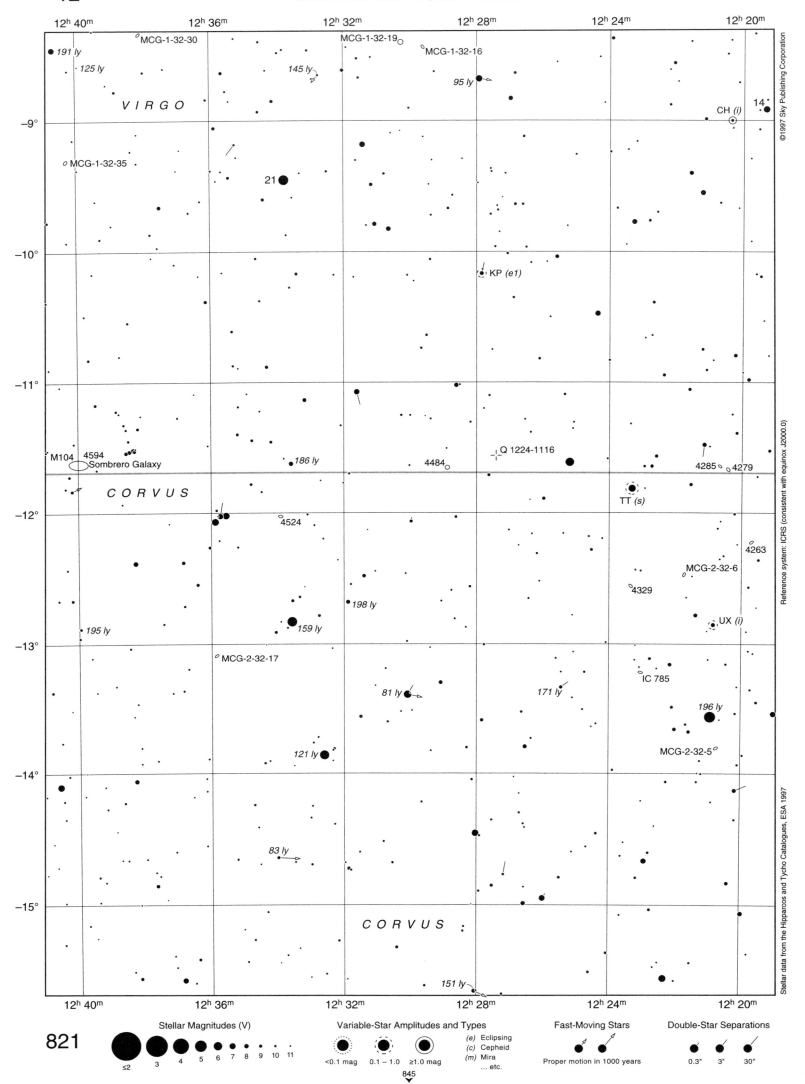

©1997 Sky Publishing Corporation

Reference system: ICRS (consistent with equinox J2000.0)

Stellar data from the Hipparcos and Tycho Catalogues, ESA 1997

VIRGO

CORVUS

CORVUS

MCG-1-32-30
191 ly
125 ly
145 ly
MCG-1-32-19
MCG-1-32-16
95 ly
CH (i)
14
MCG-1-32-35
21
KP (e1)
M104
4594
Sombrero Galaxy
186 ly
4484
Q 1224-1116
4285   4279
TT (s)
4524
4263
MCG-2-32-6
4329
198 ly
UX (i)
195 ly
159 ly
MCG-2-32-17
IC 785
81 ly
171 ly
196 ly
121 ly
MCG-2-32-5
83 ly
151 ly

Stellar Magnitudes (V)

≤2 3 4 5 6 7 8 9 10 11

Variable-Star Amplitudes and Types

<0.1 mag   0.1 − 1.0   ≥1.0 mag

(e) Eclipsing
(c) Cepheid
(m) Mira
... etc.

Fast-Moving Stars

Proper motion in 1000 years

Double-Star Separations

0.3"   3"   30"

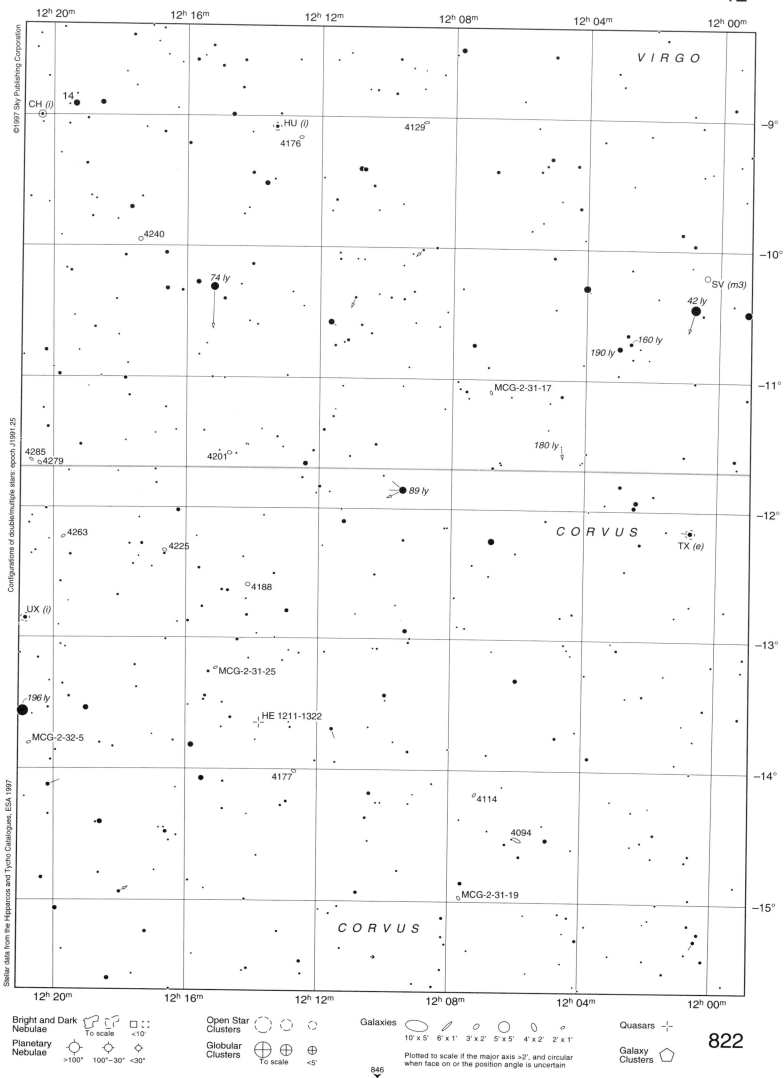

12h 20m   12h 16m   12h 12m   12h 08m   12h 04m   12h 00m

VIRGO

CH (i)   14
HU (i)
4176   4129
4240
74 ly   SV (m3)
                                        42 ly
                              160 ly
                    190 ly
                MCG-2-31-17
4285   180 ly
4279   4201
                    89 ly
                                    CORVUS
4263   TX (e)
4225
4188
UX (i)
MCG-2-31-25
196 ly
HE 1211-1322
MCG-2-32-5
4177
                        4114
                    4094
MCG-2-31-19
CORVUS

−9°
−10°
−11°
−12°
−13°
−14°
−15°

12h 20m   12h 16m   12h 12m   12h 08m   12h 04m   12h 00m

Bright and Dark Nebulae   To scale   <10'
Planetary Nebulae   >100" 100"-30" <30"
Open Star Clusters
Globular Clusters   To scale   <5'
Galaxies   10' x 5'   6' x 1'   3' x 2'   5' x 5'   4' x 2'   2' x 1'
Plotted to scale if the major axis >2', and circular when face on or the position angle is uncertain
Quasars
Galaxy Clusters

822

846

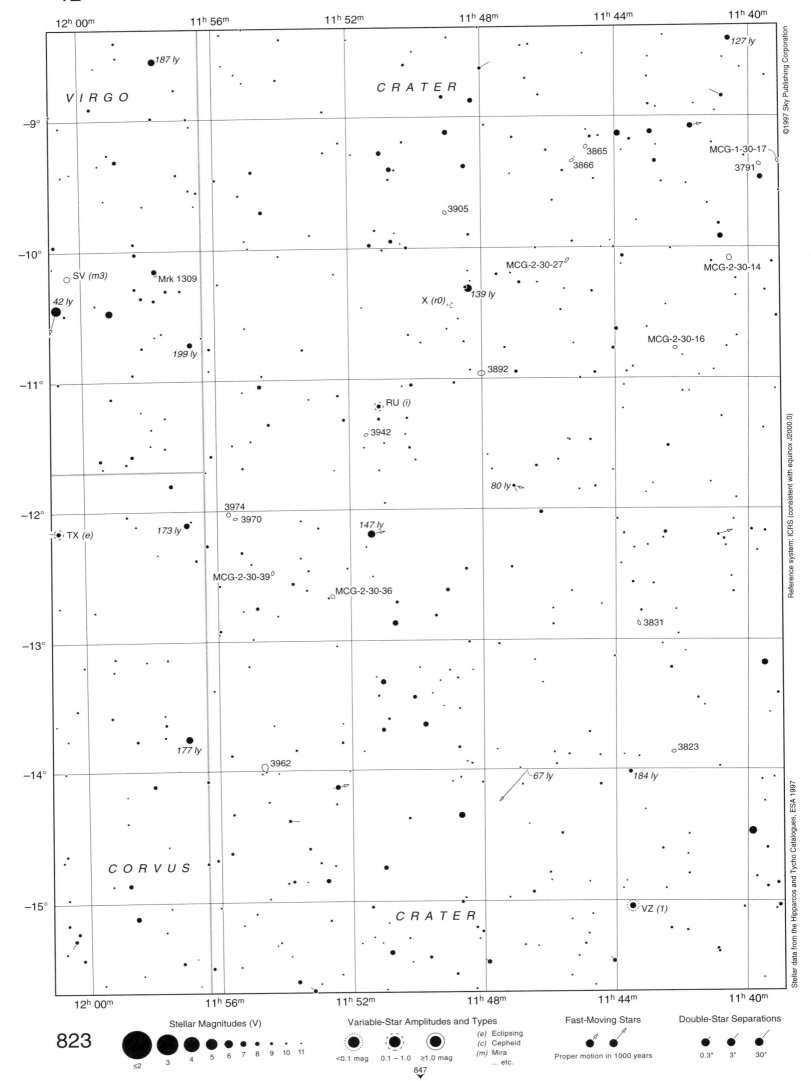

©1997 Sky Publishing Corporation

Reference system: ICRS (consistent with equinox J2000.0)

Stellar data from the Hipparcos and Tycho Catalogues, ESA 1997

823

Stellar Magnitudes (V)

≤2   3   4   5   6   7   8   9 10 11

Variable-Star Amplitudes and Types

<0.1 mag   0.1 – 1.0   ≥1.0 mag

(e) Eclipsing
(c) Cepheid
(m) Mira
... etc.

Fast-Moving Stars

Proper motion in 1000 years

Double-Star Separations

0.3"   3"   30"

847

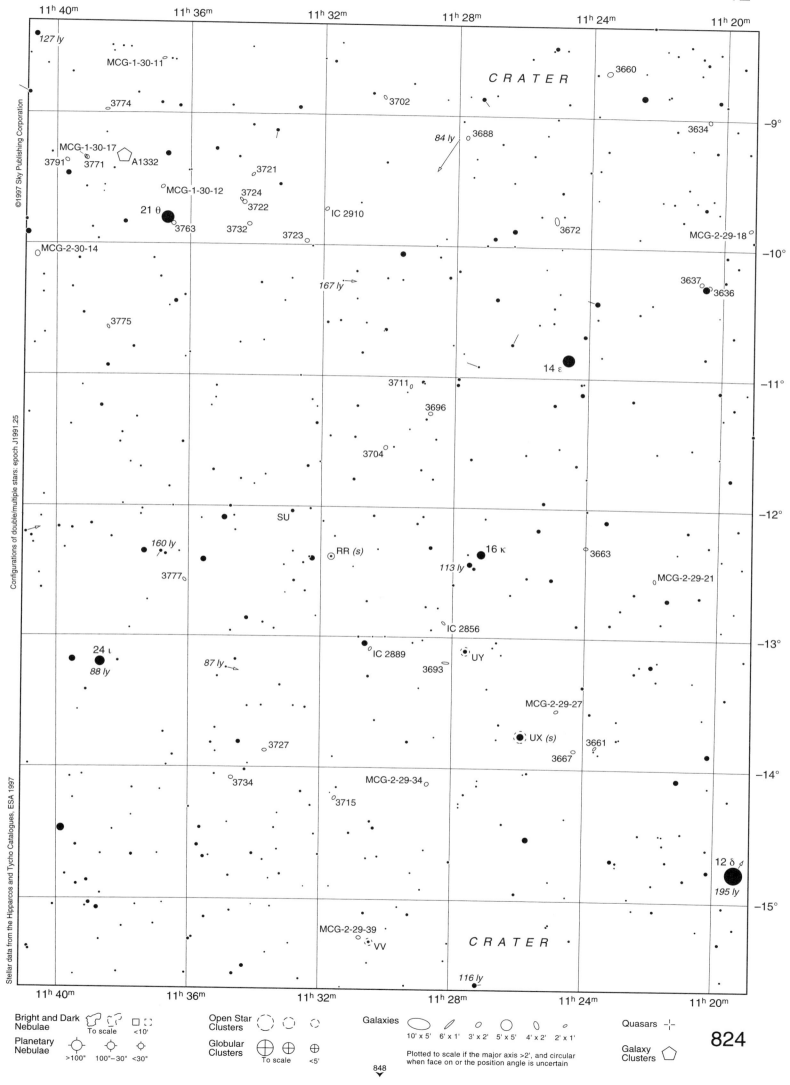

11ʰ 40ᵐ   11ʰ 36ᵐ   11ʰ 32ᵐ   11ʰ 28ᵐ   11ʰ 24ᵐ   11ʰ 20ᵐ

127 ly

MCG-1-30-11

3774

MCG-1-30-17
3791   3771   A1332

MCG-1-30-12

21 θ

3763   3732   3723

MCG-2-30-14

3775

MCG-1-30-12
3724
3721
3722

IC 2910

CRATER

3660

3702

84 ly   3688

3634

3672   MCG-2-29-18

−9°

−10°

3637   3636

167 ly

14 ε

3711   3696

3704

SU

160 ly

3777

RR (s)

16 κ   3663

113 ly   MCG-2-29-21

IC 2856

−11°

−12°

24 ι
88 ly

87 ly

IC 2889   3693

UY

MCG-2-29-27

UX (s)   3661
3667

−13°

3727

3734   MCG-2-29-34

3715

12 δ
195 ly

−14°

−15°

MCG-2-29-39
VV   CRATER

116 ly

11ʰ 40ᵐ   11ʰ 36ᵐ   11ʰ 32ᵐ   11ʰ 28ᵐ   11ʰ 24ᵐ   11ʰ 20ᵐ

Bright and Dark Nebulae   To scale   <10'
Planetary Nebulae   >100"   100"–30"   <30"

Open Star Clusters
Globular Clusters   To scale   <5'

Galaxies
10' x 5'   6' x 1'   3' x 2'   5' x 5'   4' x 2'   2' x 1'

Plotted to scale if the major axis >2', and circular when face on or the position angle is uncertain

Quasars

Galaxy Clusters

824

848

−12°

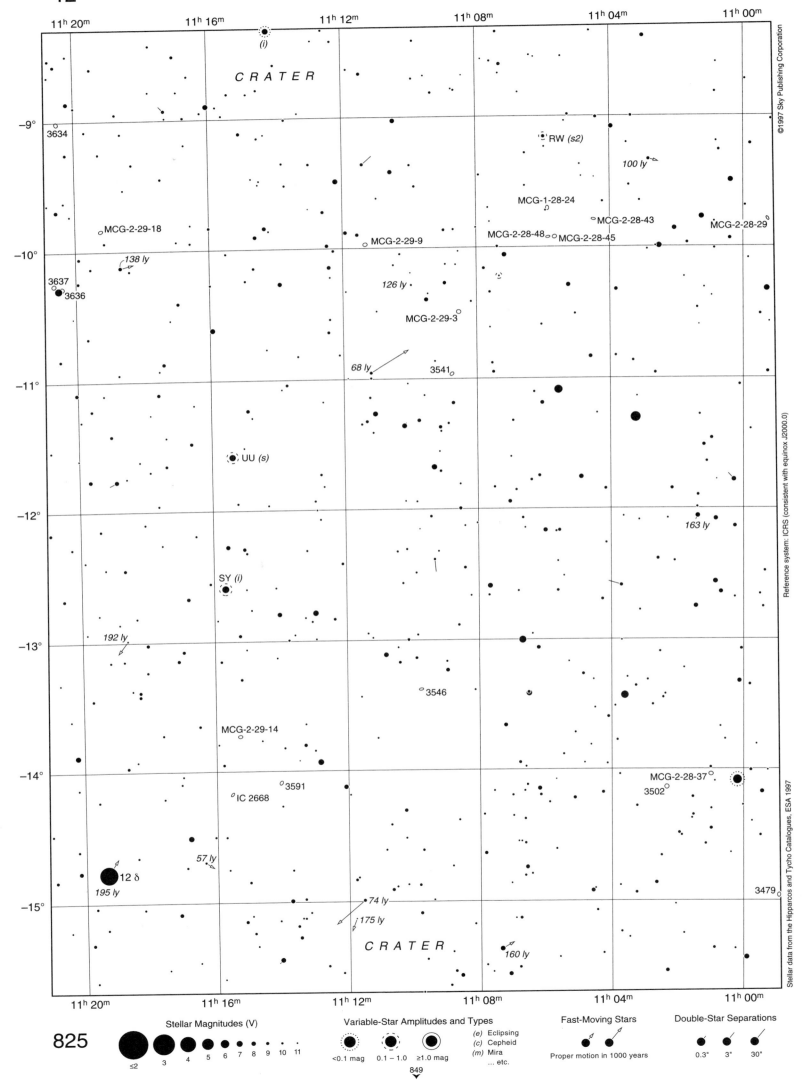

©1997 Sky Publishing Corporation

Reference system: ICRS (consistent with equinox J2000.0)

Stellar data from the Hipparcos and Tycho Catalogues, ESA 1997

CRATER

3634

MCG-2-29-18

138 ly

3637
3636

RW (s2)

100 ly

MCG-1-28-24

MCG-2-28-43

MCG-2-28-29

MCG-2-28-48 MCG-2-28-45

MCG-2-29-9

126 ly

MCG-2-29-3

68 ly

3541

UU (s)

163 ly

SY (i)

192 ly

3546

MCG-2-29-14

MCG-2-28-37
3502

3591

IC 2668

3479

57 ly

12 δ

195 ly

74 ly

175 ly

CRATER

160 ly

825

Stellar Magnitudes (V)

≤2 3 4 5 6 7 8 9 10 11

Variable-Star Amplitudes and Types

<0.1 mag   0.1 – 1.0   ≥1.0 mag

(e) Eclipsing
(c) Cepheid
(m) Mira
... etc.

Fast-Moving Stars

Proper motion in 1000 years

Double-Star Separations

0.3" 3" 30"

849

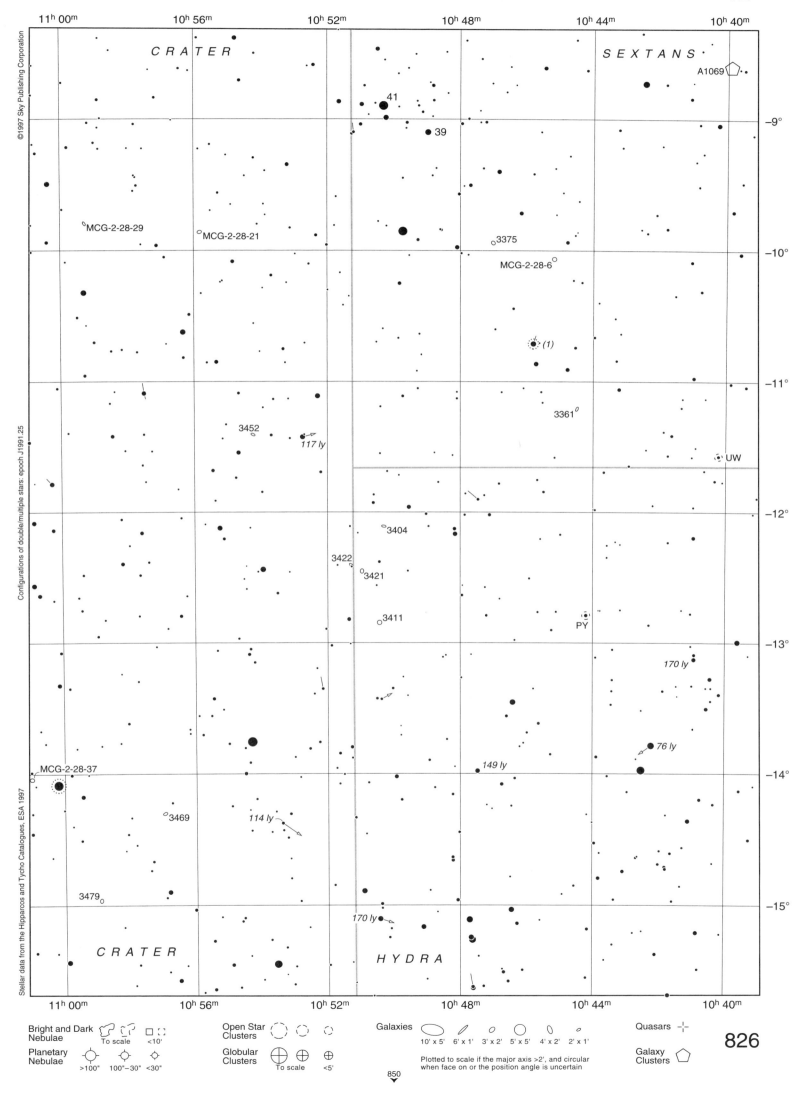

11ʰ 00ᵐ   10ʰ 56ᵐ   10ʰ 52ᵐ   10ʰ 48ᵐ   10ʰ 44ᵐ   10ʰ 40ᵐ

C R A T E R

S E X T A N S

A1069

41

39

−9°

MCG-2-28-29

MCG-2-28-21

3375

MCG-2-28-6

−10°

(1)

3361

−11°

3452

117 ly

UW

3404

−12°

3422

3421

3411

PY

−13°

170 ly

76 ly

MCG-2-28-37

149 ly

−14°

3469

114 ly

3479

−15°

170 ly

C R A T E R

H Y D R A

11ʰ 00ᵐ   10ʰ 56ᵐ   10ʰ 52ᵐ   10ʰ 48ᵐ   10ʰ 44ᵐ   10ʰ 40ᵐ

Bright and Dark Nebulae	Open Star Clusters	Galaxies	Quasars
To scale <10'		10' x 5' 6' x 1' 3' x 2' 5' x 5' 4' x 2' 2' x 1'	
Planetary Nebulae	Globular Clusters		Galaxy Clusters
>100" 100"–30" <30"	To scale <5'	Plotted to scale if the major axis >2', and circular when face on or the position angle is uncertain	

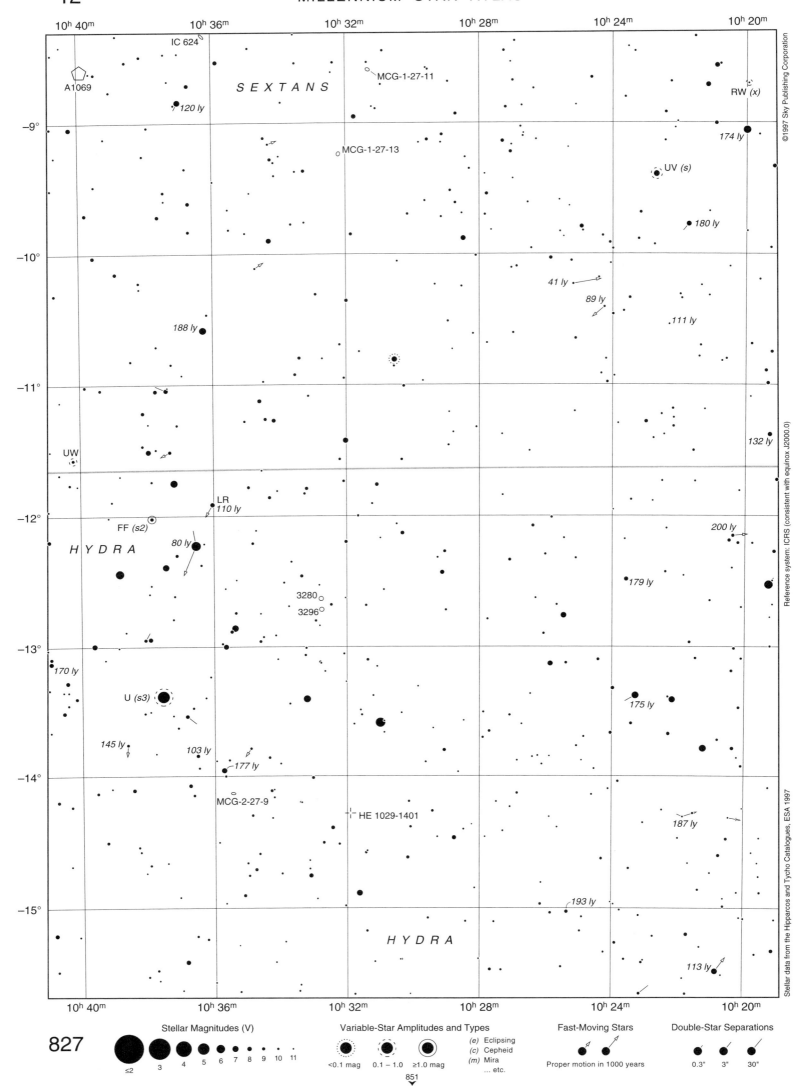

827

Stellar Magnitudes (V)

≤2   3   4   5   6 7 8 9 10 11

Variable-Star Amplitudes and Types

<0.1 mag   0.1 − 1.0 mag   ≥1.0 mag

(e) Eclipsing
(c) Cepheid
(m) Mira
… etc.

Fast-Moving Stars

Proper motion in 1000 years

Double-Star Separations

0.3"   3"   30"

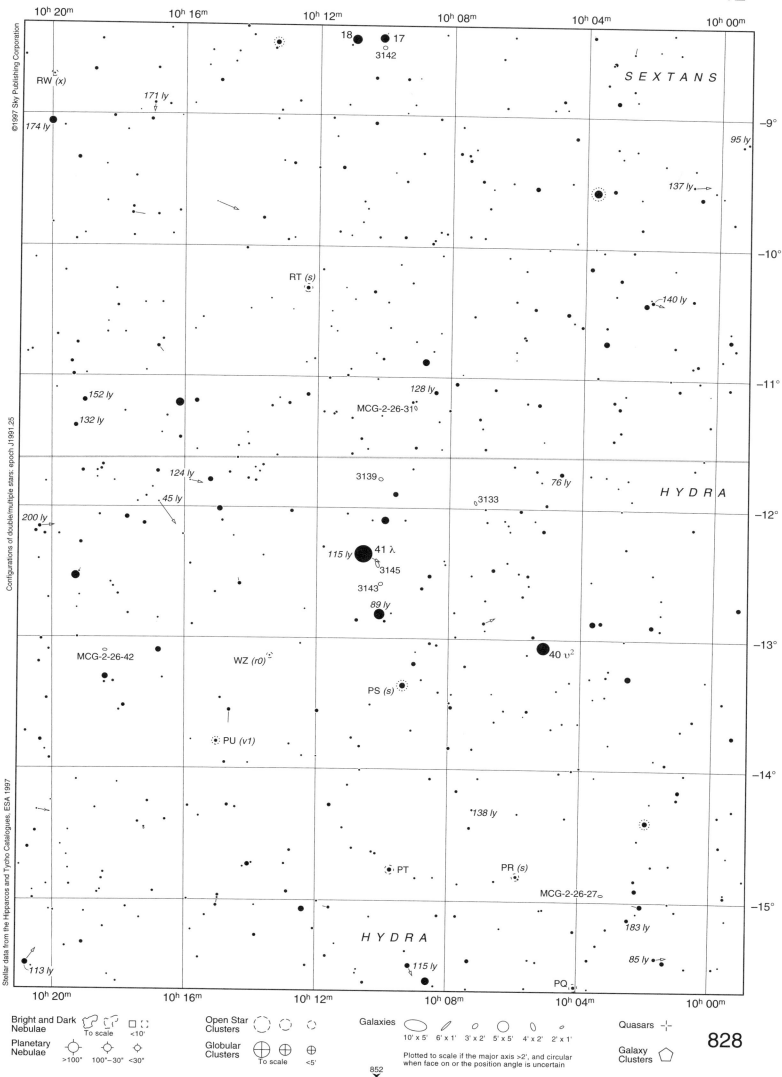

10ʰ 20ᵐ   10ʰ 16ᵐ   10ʰ 12ᵐ   10ʰ 08ᵐ   10ʰ 04ᵐ   10ʰ 00ᵐ

SEXTANS

−9°
95 ly
137 ly

RW (x)
171 ly
174 ly

−10°
RT (s)
140 ly

−11°
152 ly
132 ly
MCG-2-26-31
128 ly

124 ly
3139
76 ly
45 ly
3133
HYDRA
−12°
200 ly
115 ly   41 λ
3145
3143
89 ly

−13°
MCG-2-26-42
40 υ²
WZ (r0)
PS (s)
PU (v1)

−14°
138 ly

PT
PR (s)
MCG-2-26-27
−15°
183 ly
HYDRA
85 ly
113 ly
115 ly
PQ

©1997 Sky Publishing Corporation

Configurations of double/multiple stars: epoch J1991.25

Stellar data from the Hipparcos and Tycho Catalogues, ESA 1997

10ʰ 20ᵐ   10ʰ 16ᵐ   10ʰ 12ᵐ   10ʰ 08ᵐ   10ʰ 04ᵐ   10ʰ 00ᵐ

Bright and Dark Nebulae
To scale   <10'
Planetary Nebulae
>100"   100"–30"   <30"

Open Star Clusters
Globular Clusters
To scale   <5'

Galaxies
10' x 5'   6' x 1'   3' x 2'   5' x 5'   4' x 2'   2' x 1'
Plotted to scale if the major axis >2', and circular when face on or the position angle is uncertain

Quasars

Galaxy Clusters

828

852

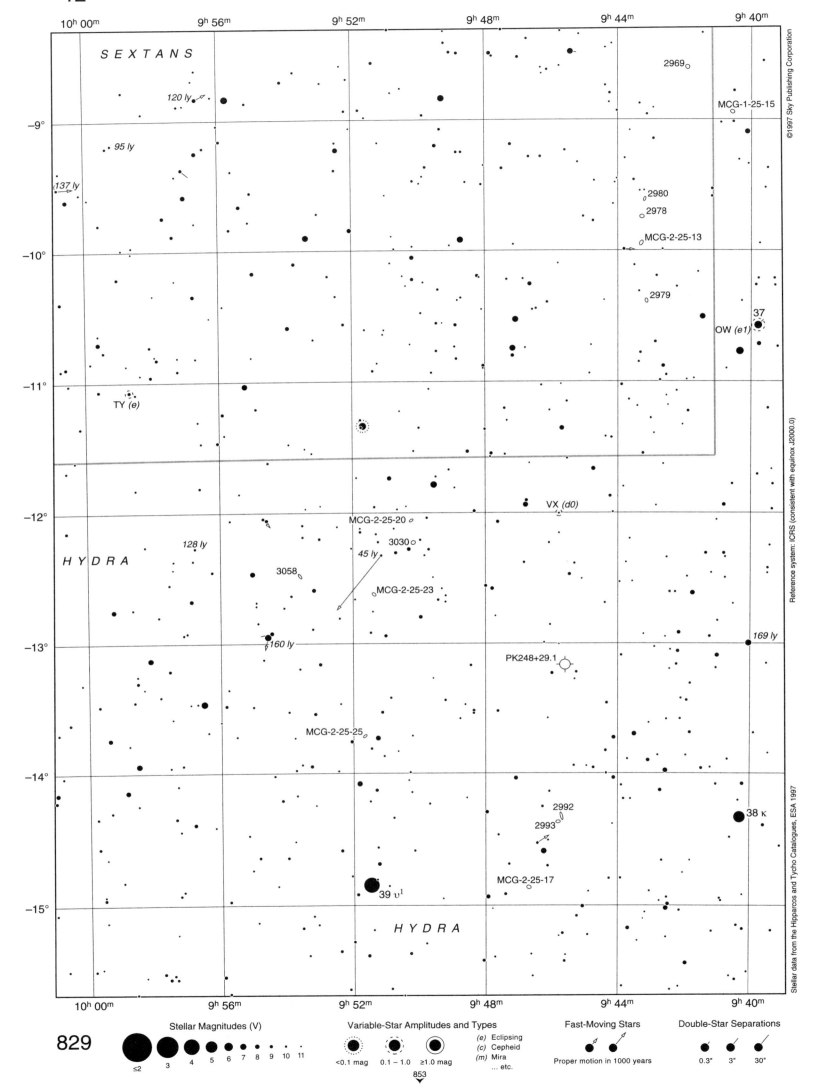

SEXTANS

120 ly

95 ly

137 ly

2969

MCG-1-25-15

2980

2978

MCG-2-25-13

2979

37

OW (e1)

TY (e)

HYDRA

128 ly

45 ly

3030

3058

MCG-2-25-20

MCG-2-25-23

VX (d0)

169 ly

160 ly

PK248+29.1

MCG-2-25-25

2992

2993

38 κ

MCG-2-25-17

39 υ¹

HYDRA

829

Stellar Magnitudes (V)

≤2 3 4 5 6 7 8 9 10 11

Variable-Star Amplitudes and Types

<0.1 mag   0.1 – 1.0   ≥1.0 mag

(e) Eclipsing
(c) Cepheid
(m) Mira
... etc.

Fast-Moving Stars

Proper motion in 1000 years

Double-Star Separations

0.3"   3"   30"

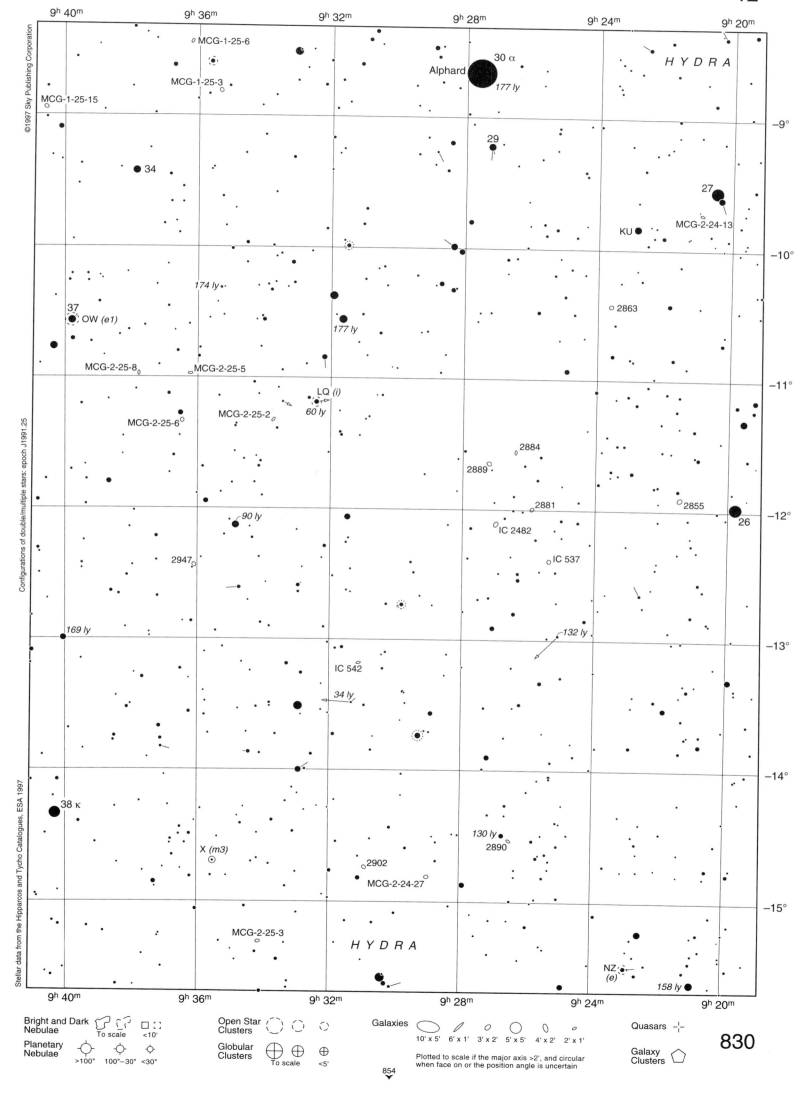

MCG-1-25-6

MCG-1-25-3

MCG-1-25-15

30 α
Alphard
177 ly

HYDRA

29

27
MCG-2-24-13
KU

34

174 ly

37
OW (e1)

2863

177 ly

MCG-2-25-8

MCG-2-25-5

LQ (i)
60 ly

MCG-2-25-6   MCG-2-25-2

2884
2889

2881   2855
IC 2482
26
2947
IC 537

90 ly

169 ly

132 ly

IC 542

34 ly

38 κ

130 ly
2890

X (m3)

2902
MCG-2-24-27

MCG-2-25-3

HYDRA

NZ
(e)
158 ly

Bright and Dark Nebulae			Open Star Clusters			Galaxies						Quasars
To scale	<10'					10' x 5'	6' x 1'	3' x 2'	5' x 5'	4' x 2'	2' x 1'	
Planetary Nebulae			Globular Clusters									Galaxy Clusters
>100"	100"–30"	<30"	To scale	<5'		Plotted to scale if the major axis >2', and circular when face on or the position angle is uncertain						

830

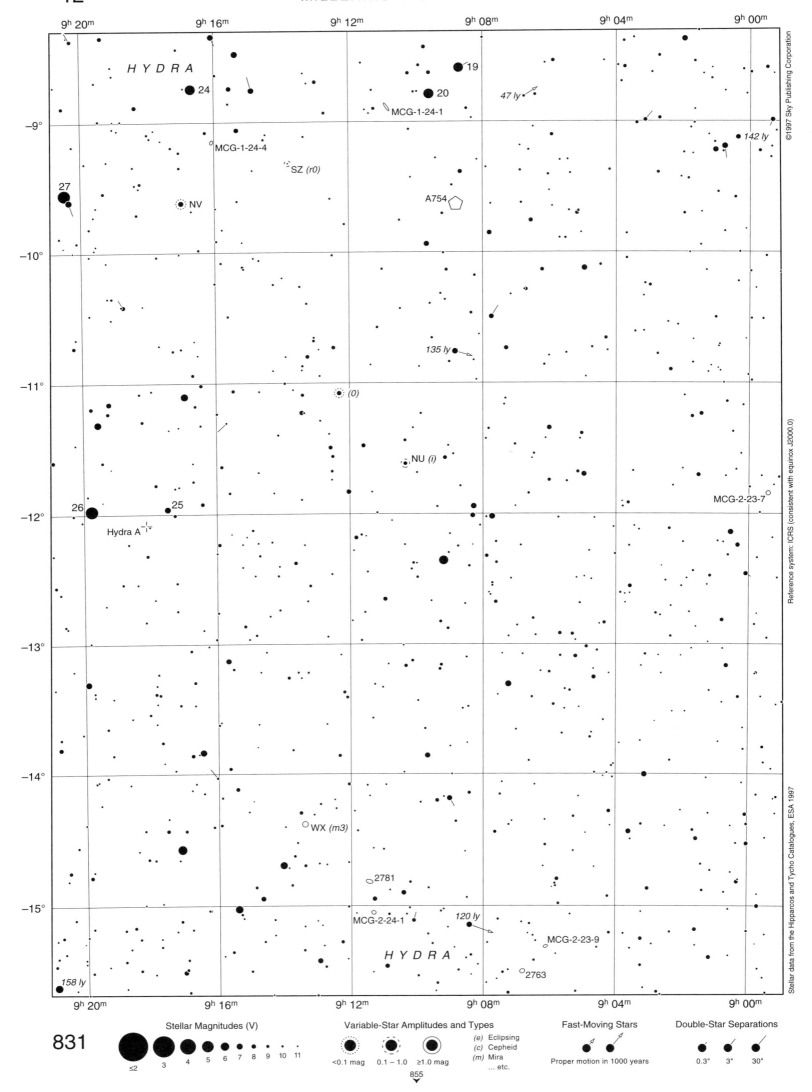

HYDRA

24

19

20

47 ly

MCG-1-24-1

MCG-1-24-4

−9°

142 ly

SZ (r0)

27

NV

A754

−10°

135 ly

(0)

NU (i)

MCG-2-23-7

26   25

−12°

Hydra A

HYDRA

−13°

−14°

WX (m3)

2781

−15°

MCG-2-24-1   120 ly

MCG-2-23-9

HYDRA

2763

158 ly

9ʰ 20ᵐ   9ʰ 16ᵐ   9ʰ 12ᵐ   9ʰ 08ᵐ   9ʰ 04ᵐ   9ʰ 00ᵐ

©1997 Sky Publishing Corporation

Reference system: ICRS (consistent with equinox J2000.0)

Stellar data from the Hipparcos and Tycho Catalogues, ESA 1997

831

Stellar Magnitudes (V)

≤2   3   4   5   6   7   8   9   10   11

Variable-Star Amplitudes and Types

<0.1 mag   0.1 – 1.0   ≥1.0 mag

(e) Eclipsing
(c) Cepheid
(m) Mira
... etc.

Fast-Moving Stars

Proper motion in 1000 years

Double-Star Separations

0.3"   3"   30"

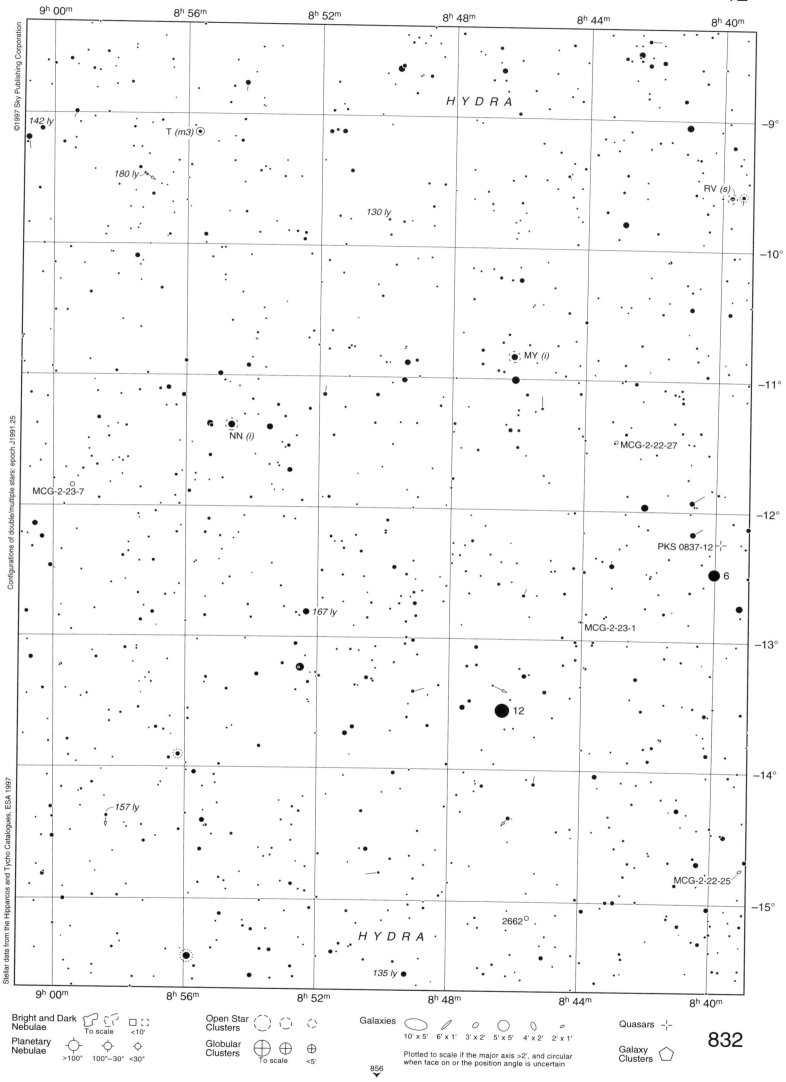

Configurations of double/multiple stars: epoch J1991.25

Stellar data from the Hipparcos and Tycho Catalogues, ESA 1997

9h 00m 8h 56m 8h 52m 8h 48m 8h 44m 8h 40m

−9°

−10°

−11°

−12°

−13°

−14°

−15°

H Y D R A

142 ly

T (m3) ⊙

180 ly

130 ly

RV (s)

MY (i)

NN (i)

MCG-2-22-27

MCG-2-23-7

MCG-2-23-1

PKS 0837-12

6

167 ly

12

157 ly

MCG-2-22-25

2662

H Y D R A

135 ly

9h 00m 8h 56m 8h 52m 8h 48m 8h 44m 8h 40m

Bright and Dark Nebulae
To scale   <10'

Planetary Nebulae
>100" 100"–30" <30"

Open Star Clusters

Globular Clusters
To scale   <5'

Galaxies
10' x 5' 6' x 1' 3' x 2' 5' x 5' 4' x 2' 2' x 1'

Plotted to scale if the major axis >2', and circular when face on or the position angle is uncertain

Quasars

Galaxy Clusters

832

856

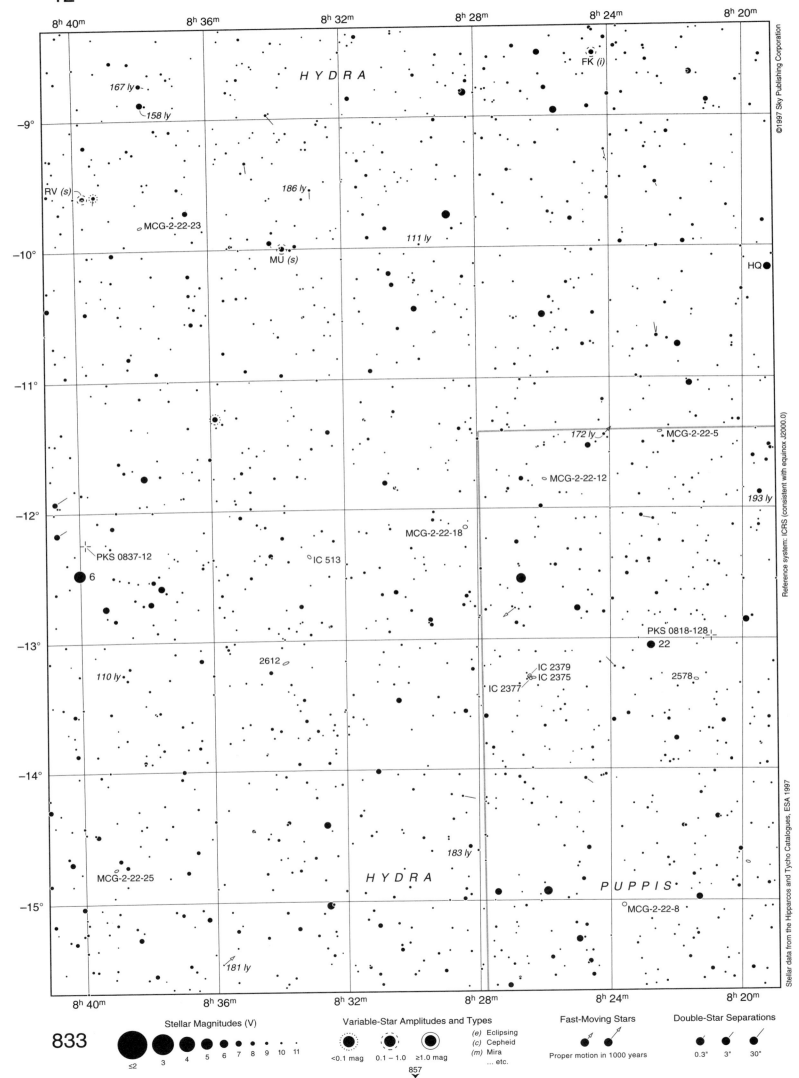

©1997 Sky Publishing Corporation

Reference system: ICRS (consistent with equinox J2000.0)

Stellar data from the Hipparcos and Tycho Catalogues, ESA 1997

HYDRA

FK (i)

167 ly
158 ly

RV (s)

186 ly

MCG-2-22-23

MU (s)

111 ly

HQ

172 ly
MCG-2-22-5

MCG-2-22-12

193 ly

MCG-2-22-18

PKS 0837-12

6

IC 513

PKS 0818-128

22

2612

IC 2379
IC 2375

2578

110 ly

IC 2377

MCG-2-22-25

183 ly

HYDRA

PUPPIS

MCG-2-22-8

181 ly

833

Stellar Magnitudes (V)

≤2   3   4   5   6   7   8   9 10 11

Variable-Star Amplitudes and Types

<0.1 mag   0.1 – 1.0   ≥1.0 mag

(e) Eclipsing
(c) Cepheid
(m) Mira
... etc.

Fast-Moving Stars

Proper motion in 1000 years

Double-Star Separations

0.3"   3"   30"

857

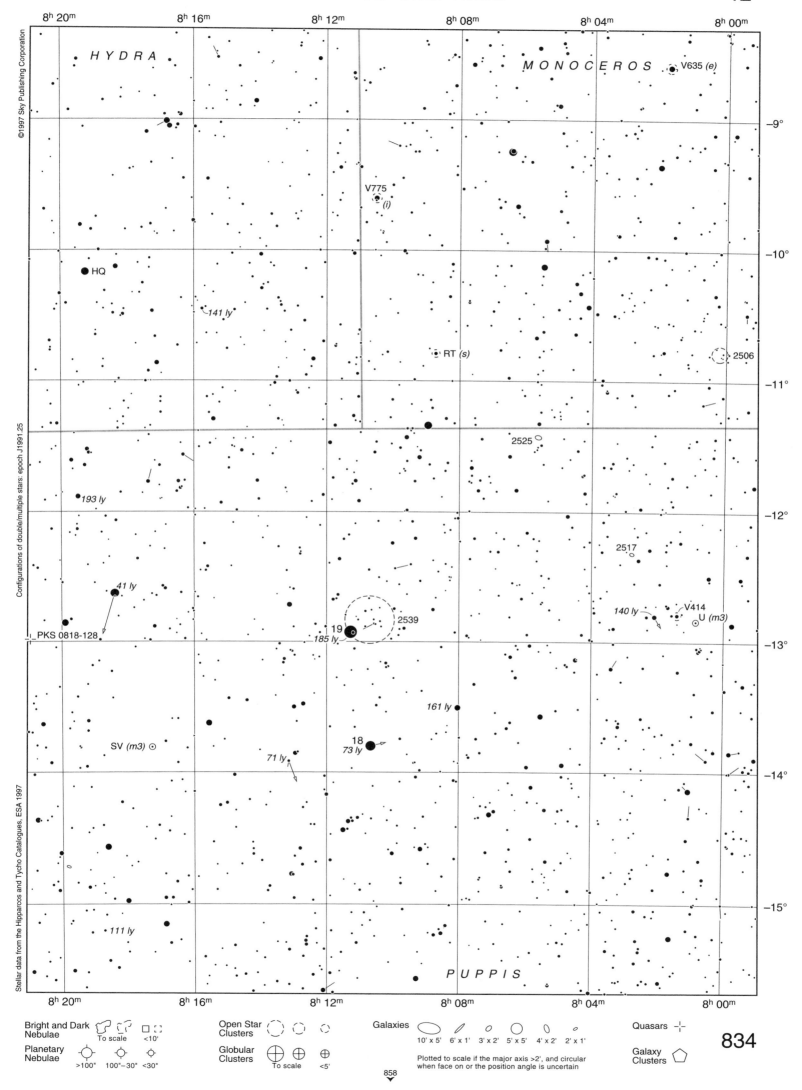

810

8h 20m   8h 16m   8h 12m   8h 08m   8h 04m   8h 00m

H Y D R A

M O N O C E R O S

V635 (e)

−9°

V775

(i)

−10°

HQ

141 ly

RT (s)

2506

−11°

193 ly

2525

−12°

2517

41 ly

140 ly   V414

U (m3)

PKS 0818-128

19

2539

185 ly

−13°

161 ly

SV (m3)

18

73 ly

71 ly

−14°

−15°

111 ly

P U P P I S

8h 20m   8h 16m   8h 12m   8h 08m   8h 04m   8h 00m

Bright and Dark
Nebulae   To scale   <10'

Planetary
Nebulae   >100" 100"-30" <30"

Open Star
Clusters

Globular
Clusters   To scale   <5'

Galaxies

10' x 5'   6' x 1'   3' x 2'   5' x 5'   4' x 2'   2' x 1'

Plotted to scale if the major axis >2', and circular
when face on or the position angle is uncertain

Quasars

Galaxy
Clusters

834

858

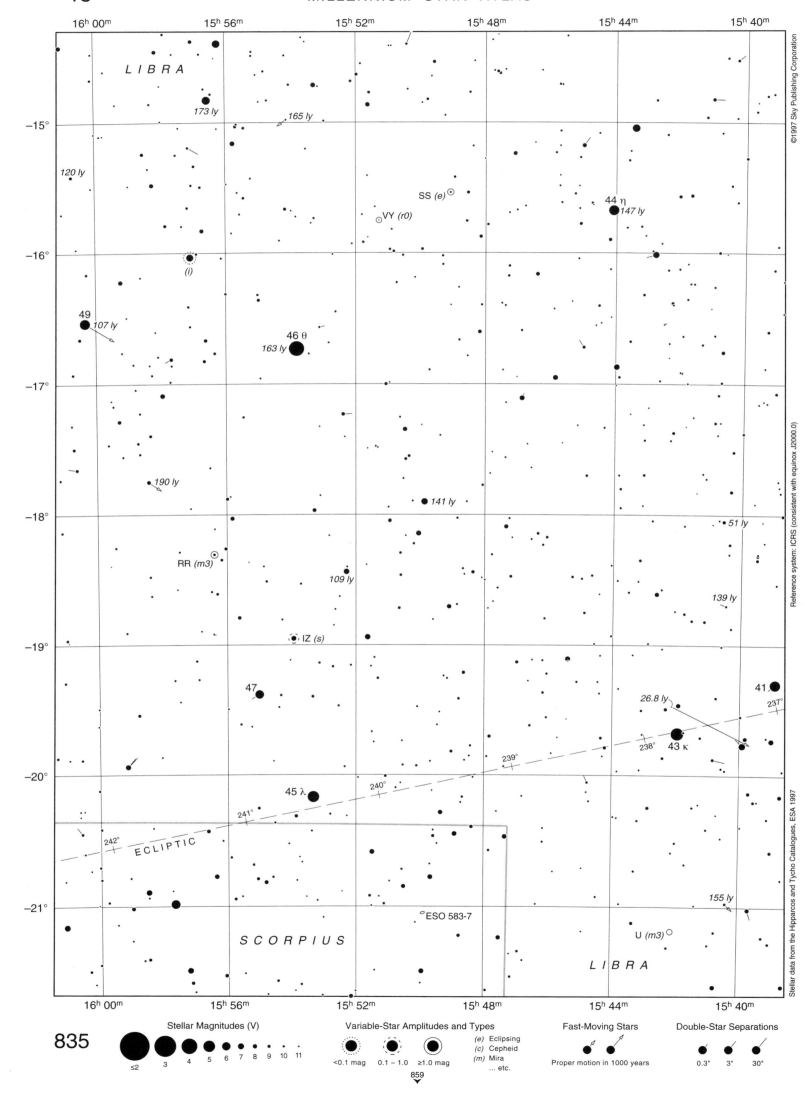

©1997 Sky Publishing Corporation

Reference system: ICRS (consistent with equinox J2000.0)

Stellar data from the Hipparcos and Tycho Catalogues, ESA 1997

L I B R A

173 ly

165 ly

120 ly

SS (e) ⊙

VY (r0) ⊙

44 η
147 ly

(i)

49
107 ly

46 θ
163 ly

190 ly

141 ly

51 ly

RR (m3) ⊙

109 ly

139 ly

IZ (s)

47

41

26.8 ly

237°

238°
43 κ

239°

45 λ

240°

241°

242°

E C L I P T I C

ESO 583-7

155 ly

U (m3) ○

S C O R P I U S

L I B R A

835

Stellar Magnitudes (V)

≤2   3   4   5   6 7 8 9 10 11

Variable-Star Amplitudes and Types

<0.1 mag   0.1 – 1.0   ≥1.0 mag

(e) Eclipsing
(c) Cepheid
(m) Mira
... etc.

Fast-Moving Stars

Proper motion in 1000 years

Double-Star Separations

0.3"   3"   30"

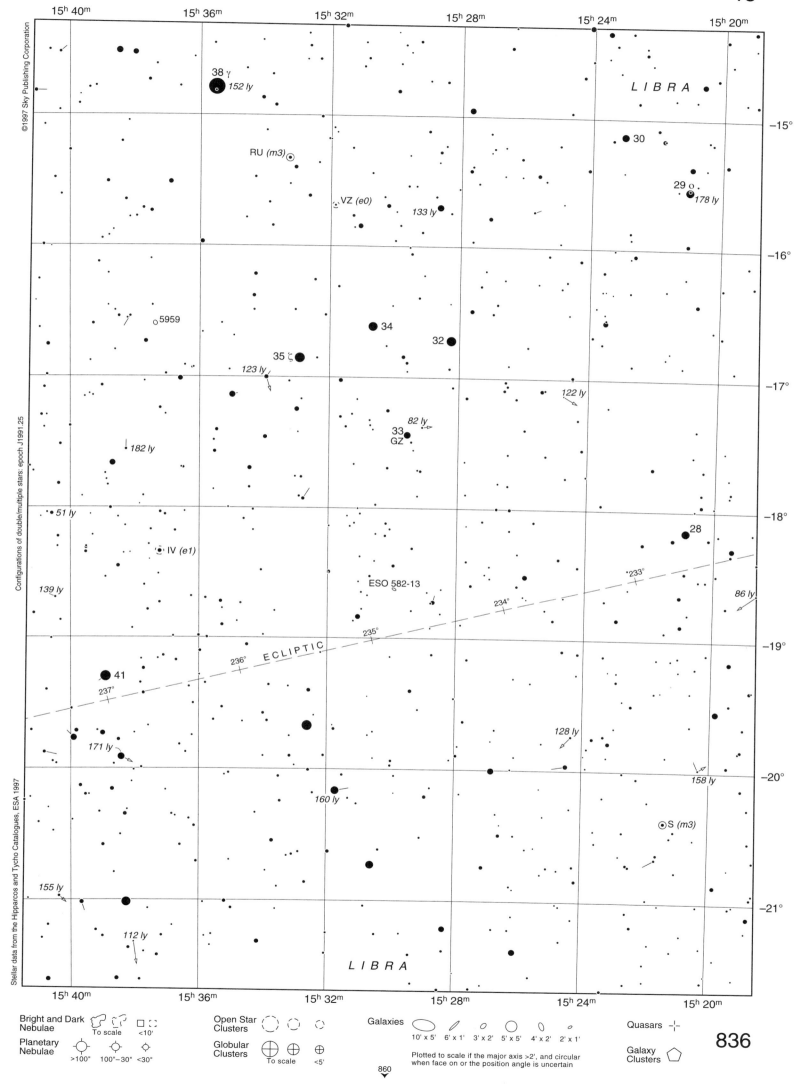

15h 40m   15h 36m   15h 32m   15h 28m   15h 24m   15h 20m

L I B R A

38 γ
152 ly

RU *(m3)*

30

VZ *(e0)*
133 ly

29 o
178 ly

−15°

○ 5959

34

32

35 ζ
123 ly

122 ly

82 ly

33
GZ

−17°

182 ly

51 ly

IV *(e1)*

28

ESO 582-13

233°

86 ly

234°

139 ly

235°

236°   E C L I P T I C

41
237°

128 ly

171 ly

158 ly

−20°

160 ly

S *(m3)*

155 ly

112 ly

L I B R A

15h 40m   15h 36m   15h 32m   15h 28m   15h 24m   15h 20m

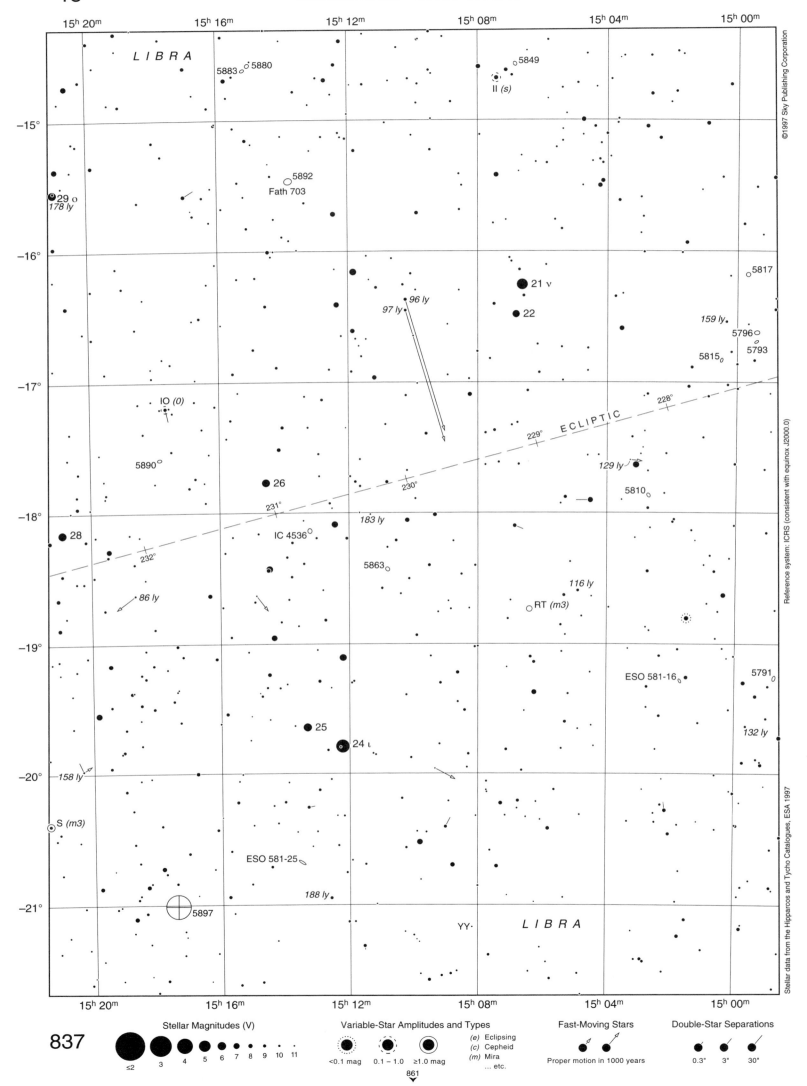

LIBRA

5883 ○ ○ 5880

5849

II (s)

5892
Fath 703

29 o
178 ly

21 ν

22

96 ly

97 ly

5817

159 ly

5796
5793

5815

IO (0)

ECLIPTIC

228°

5890

26

229°

230°

231°

129 ly

5810

28

232°

IC 4536

183 ly

5863

116 ly

RT (m3)

86 ly

ESO 581-16

5791

25

24 ι

132 ly

158 ly

S (m3)

ESO 581-25

188 ly

YY

LIBRA

5897

Stellar Magnitudes (V)

≤2   3   4   5   6   7   8   9   10   11

Variable-Star Amplitudes and Types

<0.1 mag   0.1 – 1.0   ≥1.0 mag

(e) Eclipsing
(c) Cepheid
(m) Mira
... etc.

Fast-Moving Stars

Proper motion in 1000 years

Double-Star Separations

0.3"   3"   30"

−18°

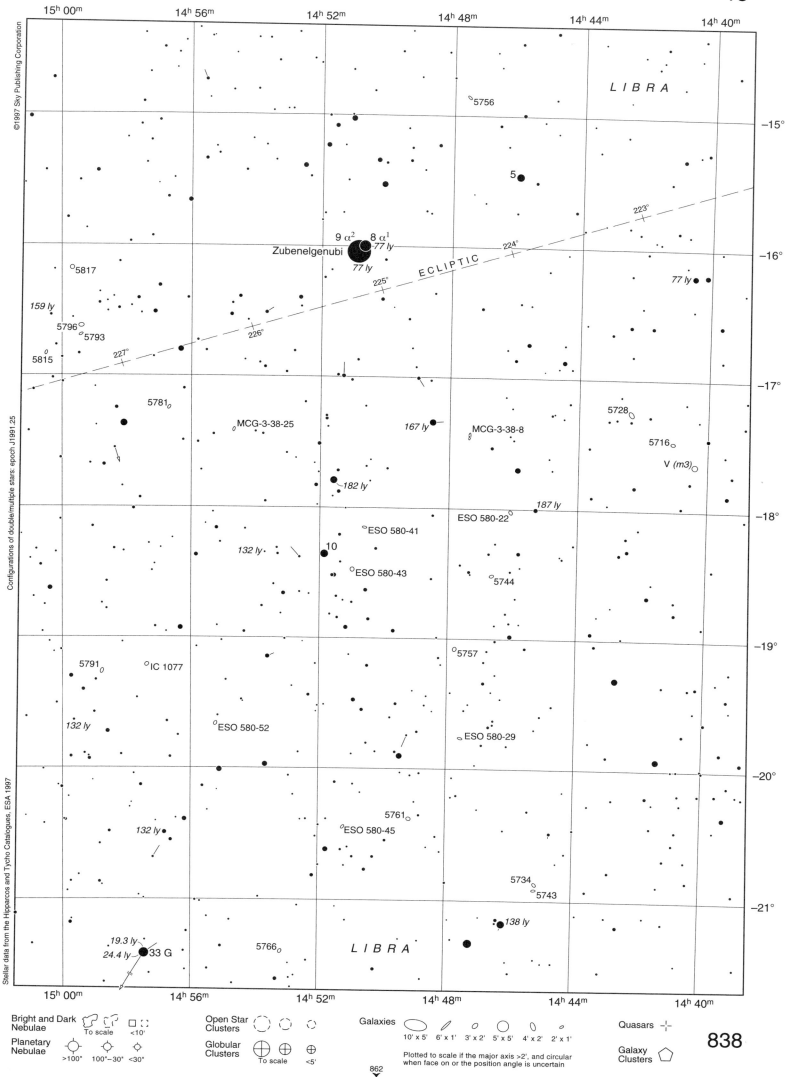

Configurations of double/multiple stars: epoch J1991.25

Stellar data from the Hipparcos and Tycho Catalogues, ESA 1997

15h 00m   14h 56m   14h 52m   14h 48m   14h 44m   14h 40m

LIBRA

5756

−15°

5

9 α² 8 α¹
Zubenelgenubi 77 ly
77 ly

ECLIPTIC

223°

224°

225°

77 ly

−16°

5817

159 ly

5796
5793

227°

5815

226°

5781

MCG-3-38-25

167 ly

MCG-3-38-8

5728

5716

V (m3)

−17°

182 ly

187 ly

ESO 580-22

−18°

132 ly

ESO 580-41

10

ESO 580-43

5744

5791

IC 1077

5757

−19°

132 ly

ESO 580-52

ESO 580-29

−20°

132 ly

5761

ESO 580-45

5734
5743

138 ly

−21°

19.3 ly
24.4 ly 33 G

5766

LIBRA

Bright and Dark Nebulae
To scale   <10'

Planetary Nebulae
>100"   100"–30"   <30"

Open Star Clusters

Globular Clusters
To scale   <5'

Galaxies
10' x 5'   6' x 1'   3' x 2'   5' x 5'   4' x 2'   2' x 1'

Plotted to scale if the major axis >2', and circular when face on or the position angle is uncertain

Quasars

Galaxy Clusters

838

862

MILLENNIUM STAR ATLAS

−18°

©1997 Sky Publishing Corporation

Reference system: ICRS (consistent with equinox J2000.0)

Stellar data from the Hipparcos and Tycho Catalogues, ESA 1997

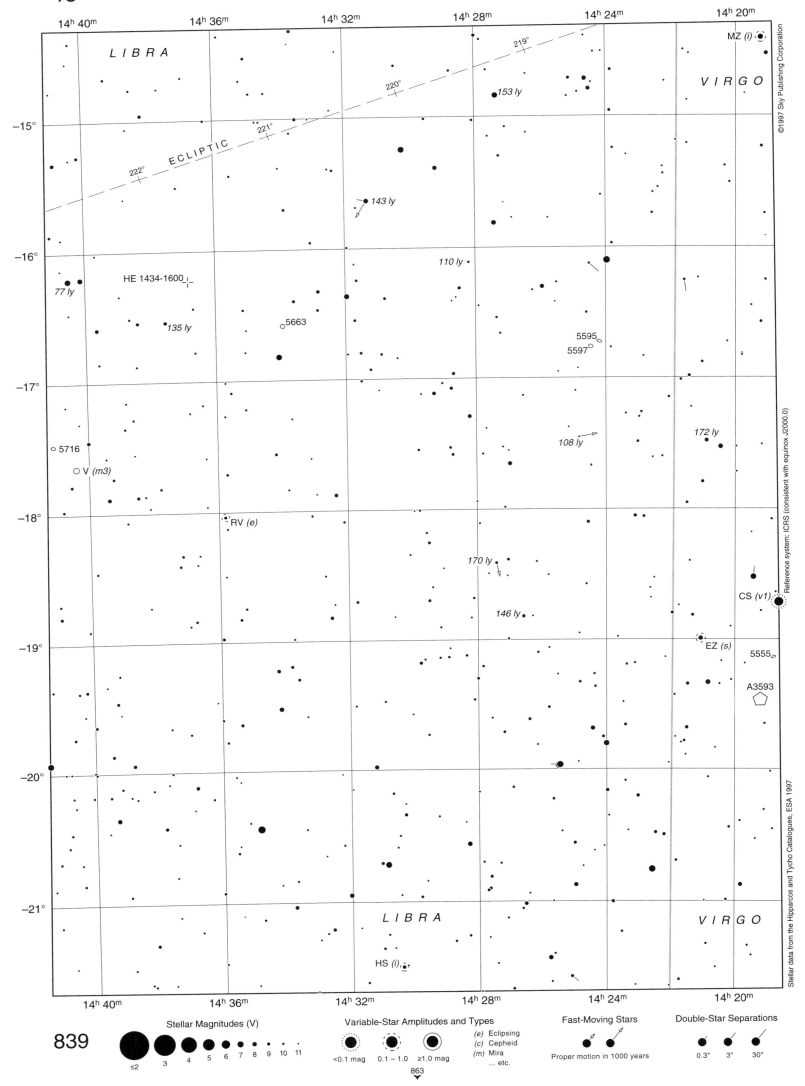

LIBRA

VIRGO

MZ (i)

153 ly

219°

220°

221°

ECLIPTIC

222°

143 ly

HE 1434-1600

77 ly

110 ly

135 ly

○5663

5595

5597

○5716

172 ly

V (m3)

108 ly

RV (e)

170 ly

CS (v1)

146 ly

EZ (s)

5555

A3593

LIBRA

VIRGO

HS (i)

839

Stellar Magnitudes (V)

≤2   3   4   5   6   7   8   9   10   11

Variable-Star Amplitudes and Types

<0.1 mag   0.1 – 1.0   ≥1.0 mag

(e) Eclipsing
(c) Cepheid
(m) Mira
... etc.

Fast-Moving Stars

Proper motion in 1000 years

Double-Star Separations

0.3"   3"   30"

MILLENNIUM STAR ATLAS

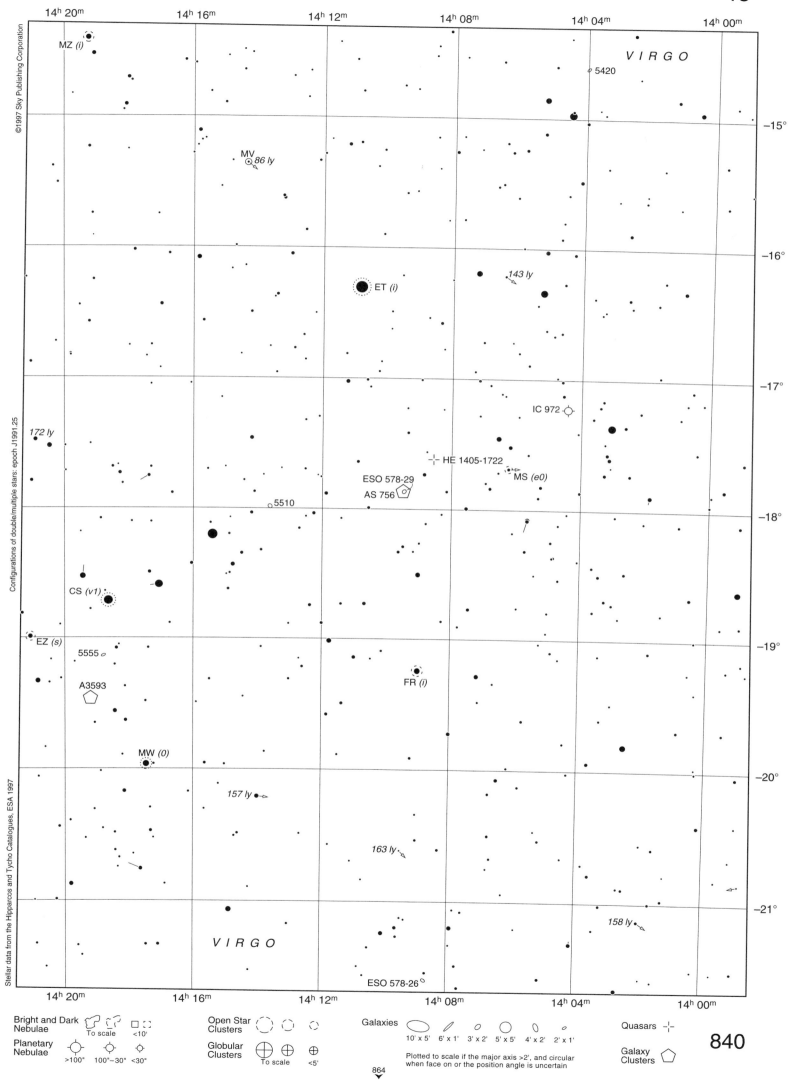

MZ *(i)*

V I R G O

5420

−15°

MV *86 ly*

ET *(i)*

143 ly

−16°

−17°

IC 972

172 ly

HE 1405-1722

ESO 578-29

MS *(e0)*

AS 756

5510

−18°

CS *(v1)*

EZ *(s)*

−19°

5555

A3593

FR *(i)*

MW *(0)*

−20°

157 ly

163 ly

−21°

158 ly

V I R G O

ESO 578-26

14ʰ 20ᵐ   14ʰ 16ᵐ   14ʰ 12ᵐ   14ʰ 08ᵐ   14ʰ 04ᵐ   14ʰ 00ᵐ

Bright and Dark Nebulae
To scale   <10'

Planetary Nebulae
>100"   100"–30"   <30"

Open Star Clusters

Globular Clusters
To scale   <5'

Galaxies
10' x 5'   6' x 1'   3' x 2'   5' x 5'   4' x 2'   2' x 1'

Plotted to scale if the major axis >2', and circular
when face on or the position angle is uncertain

Quasars

Galaxy Clusters

840

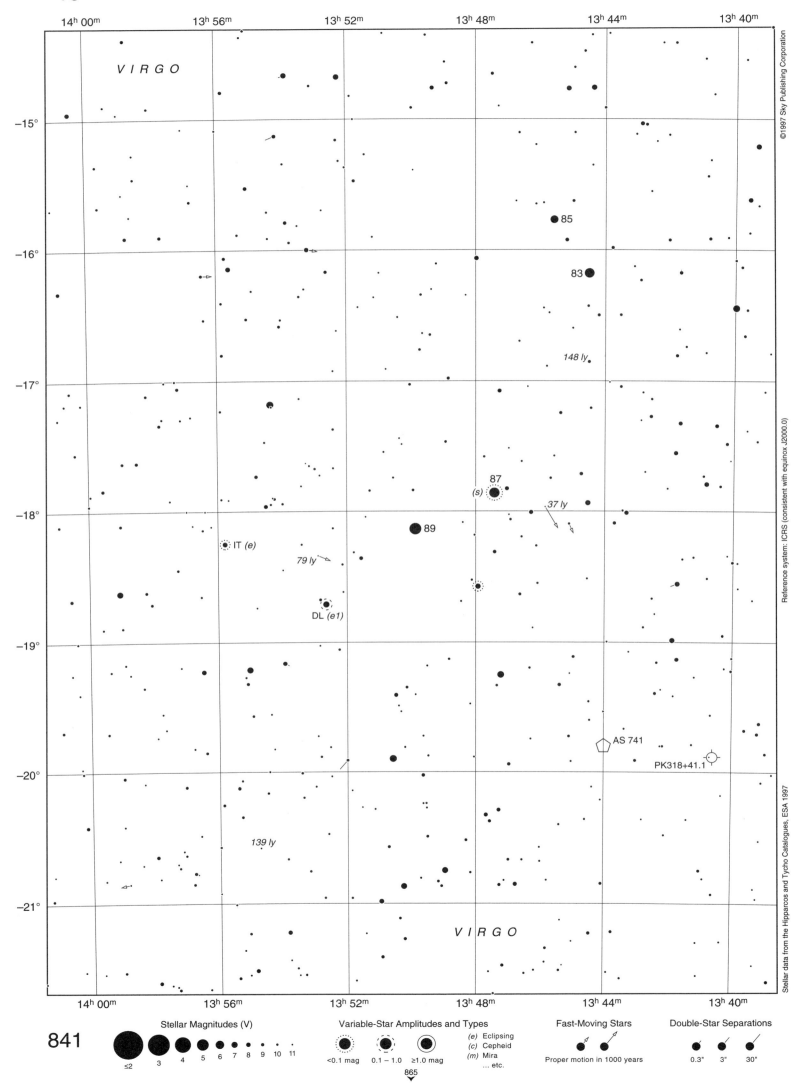

Reference system: ICRS (consistent with equinox J2000.0)

Stellar data from the Hipparcos and Tycho Catalogues, ESA 1997

VIRGO

85

83

148 ly

87
(s)

37 ly

89

IT (e)

79 ly

DL (e1)

AS 741

PK318+41.1

139 ly

VIRGO

14h 00m   13h 56m   13h 52m   13h 48m   13h 44m   13h 40m

−15°
−16°
−17°
−18°
−19°
−20°
−21°

841

Stellar Magnitudes (V)

≤2   3   4   5   6   7 8 9 10 11

Variable-Star Amplitudes and Types

<0.1 mag   0.1 − 1.0   ≥1.0 mag

(e) Eclipsing
(c) Cepheid
(m) Mira
... etc.

Fast-Moving Stars

Proper motion in 1000 years

Double-Star Separations

0.3"   3"   30"

865

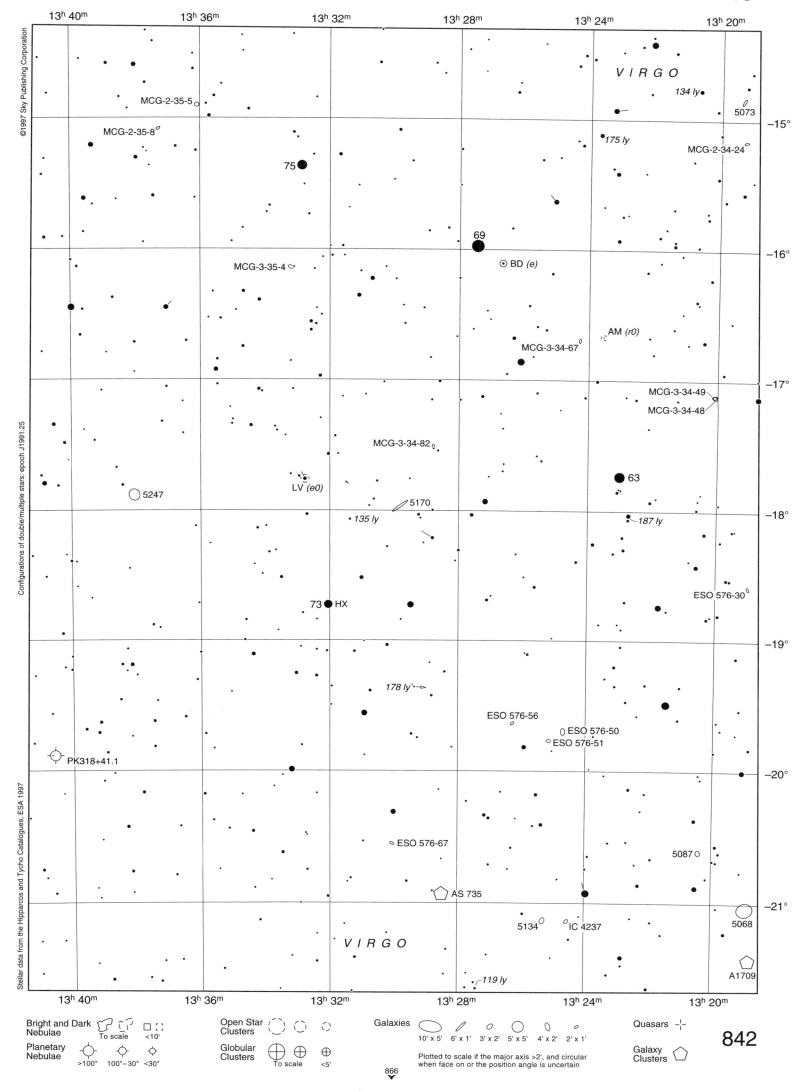

VIRGO

134 ly

5073

MCG-2-35-5

MCG-2-35-8

MCG-2-34-24

−15°

175 ly

75

69

⊙ BD (e)

−16°

MCG-3-35-4

AM (r0)

MCG-3-34-67

MCG-3-34-49

MCG-3-34-48

−17°

MCG-3-34-82

63

5247

LV (e0)

5170

187 ly

135 ly

ESO 576-30

73 ● HX

−19°

178 ly

ESO 576-56

ESO 576-50

ESO 576-51

PK318+41.1

−20°

ESO 576-67

5087

AS 735

−21°

5134

IC 4237

5068

VIRGO

A1709

119 ly

Bright and Dark Nebulae
To scale   <10'

Open Star Clusters

Galaxies
10' x 5'   6' x 1'   3' x 2'   5' x 5'   4' x 2'   2' x 1'

Quasars

Planetary Nebulae
>100"   100"−30"   <30'

Globular Clusters
To scale   <5'

Plotted to scale if the major axis >2', and circular when face on or the position angle is uncertain

Galaxy Clusters

MILLENNIUM STAR ATLAS

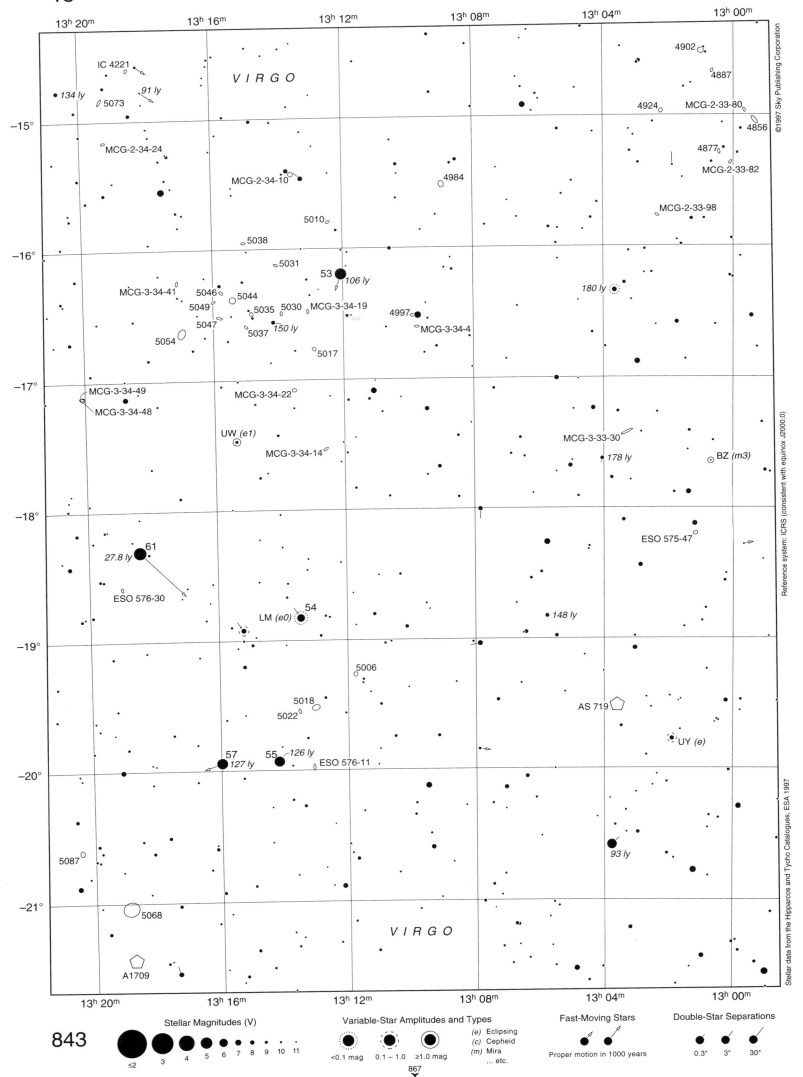

−18°

−15°

−16°

−17°

−18°

−19°

−20°

−21°

13h 20m　13h 16m　13h 12m　13h 08m　13h 04m　13h 00m

VIRGO

IC 4221

134 ly

91 ly

5073

MCG-2-34-24

MCG-2-34-10

4984

4902
4887
4924　MCG-2-33-80
4856
4877　MCG-2-33-82
MCG-2-33-98

5010

5038

5031

MCG-3-34-41

5046

5049

5044

53　*106 ly*

180 ly

5035　5030　MCG-3-34-19

5047

5054

5037　*150 ly*

5017

4997　MCG-3-34-4

MCG-3-34-49

MCG-3-34-48

MCG-3-34-22

UW *(e1)*

MCG-3-34-14

MCG-3-33-30

178 ly

BZ *(m3)*

ESO 575-47

61

27.8 ly

ESO 576-30

LM *(e0)*　54

148 ly

5006

AS 719

5018

5022

UY *(e)*

57　*127 ly*

55　*126 ly*

ESO 576-11

93 ly

5087

5068

VIRGO

A1709

13h 20m　13h 16m　13h 12m　13h 08m　13h 04m　13h 00m

843

Stellar Magnitudes (V)

≤2　3　4　5　6　7　8　9　10　11

Variable-Star Amplitudes and Types

<0.1 mag　0.1 − 1.0　≥1.0 mag

(e) Eclipsing
(c) Cepheid
(m) Mira
... etc.

Fast-Moving Stars

Proper motion in 1000 years

Double-Star Separations

0.3"　3"　30"

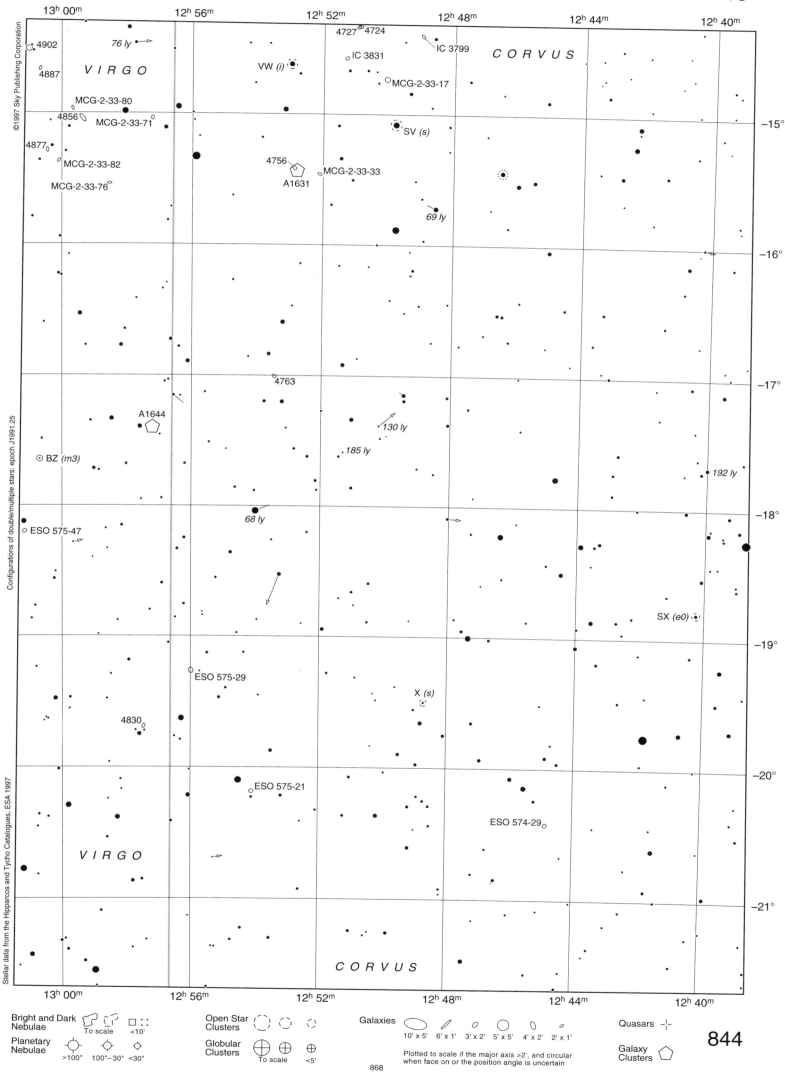

Configurations of double/multiple stars: epoch J1991.25

Stellar data from the Hipparcos and Tycho Catalogues, ESA 1997

13h 00m   12h 56m   12h 52m   12h 48m   12h 44m   12h 40m

4902
4887
VIRGO
76 ly
4727 4724
IC 3831
IC 3799
CORVUS
VW (i)
MCG-2-33-17
MCG-2-33-80
4856
MCG-2-33-71
SV (s)
−15°
4877
MCG-2-33-82
4756
MCG-2-33-33
MCG-2-33-76
A1631
69 ly
−16°
4763
−17°
A1644
130 ly
BZ (m3)
185 ly
192 ly
−18°
68 ly
ESO 575-47
SX (e0)
ESO 575-29
−19°
X (s)
4830
−20°
ESO 575-21
VIRGO
ESO 574-29
−21°
CORVUS

13h 00m   12h 56m   12h 52m   12h 48m   12h 44m   12h 40m

Bright and Dark Nebulae   To scale   <10'
Open Star Clusters
Galaxies   10' x 5'   6' x 1'   3' x 2'   5' x 5'   4' x 2'   2' x 1'
Quasars
Planetary Nebulae   >100"   100"–30"   <30"
Globular Clusters   To scale   <5'
Plotted to scale if the major axis >2', and circular when face on or the position angle is uncertain
Galaxy Clusters

844

868

MILLENNIUM STAR ATLAS

−18°

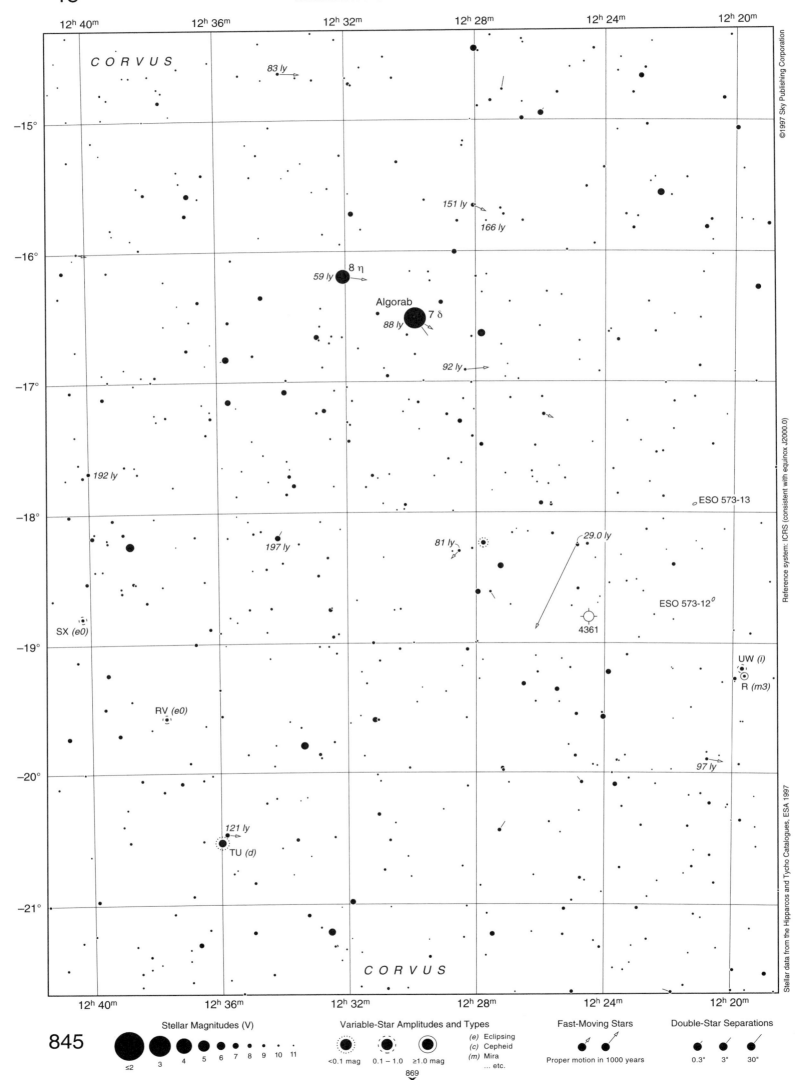

©1997 Sky Publishing Corporation

Reference system: ICRS (consistent with equinox J2000.0)

Stellar data from the Hipparcos and Tycho Catalogues, ESA 1997

12ʰ 40ᵐ 12ʰ 36ᵐ 12ʰ 32ᵐ 12ʰ 28ᵐ 12ʰ 24ᵐ 12ʰ 20ᵐ

−15°
−16°
−17°
−18°
−19°
−20°
−21°

CORVUS

83 ly

151 ly
166 ly

8 η
59 ly

Algorab
88 ly   7 δ

92 ly

192 ly

197 ly

81 ly

29.0 ly

ESO 573-13

ESO 573-12⁰
4361

SX (e0)

RV (e0)

UW (i)
R (m3)

97 ly

121 ly
TU (d)

CORVUS

845

Stellar Magnitudes (V)
≤2 3 4 5 6 7 8 9 10 11

Variable-Star Amplitudes and Types
<0.1 mag   0.1 – 1.0   ≥1.0 mag

(e) Eclipsing
(c) Cepheid
(m) Mira
... etc.

Fast-Moving Stars
Proper motion in 1000 years

Double-Star Separations
0.3"   3"   30"

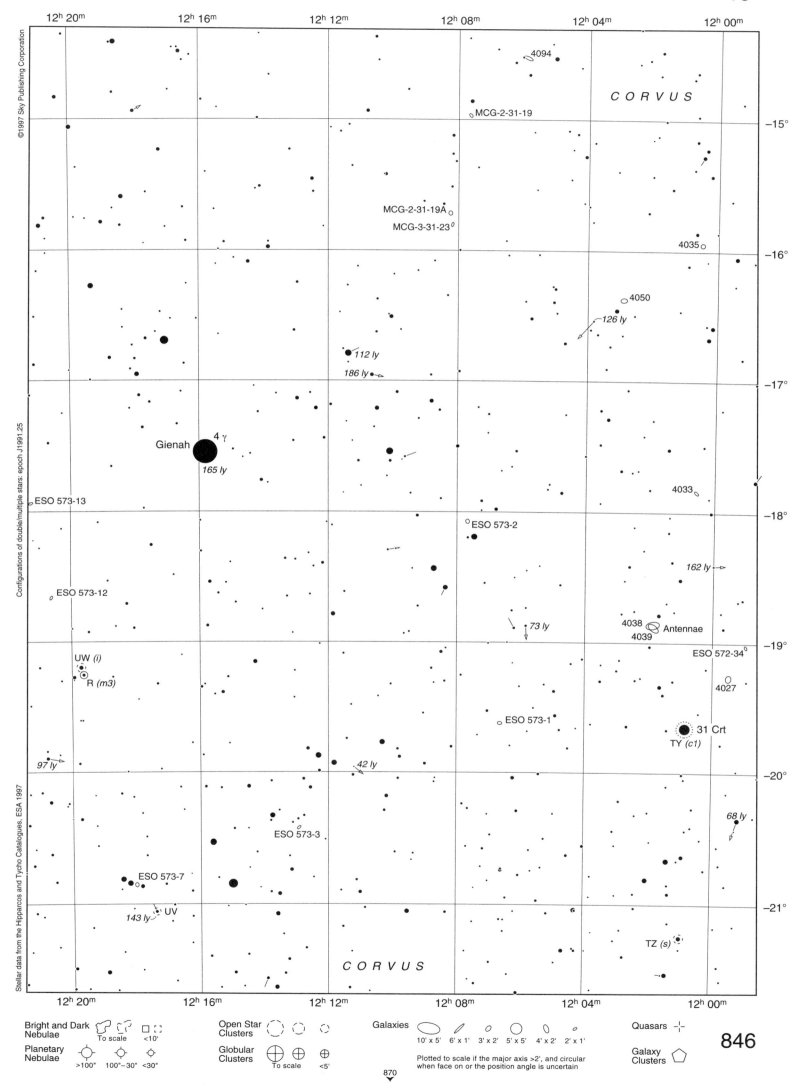

©1997 Sky Publishing Corporation

Configurations of double/multiple stars: epoch J1991.25

Stellar data from the Hipparcos and Tycho Catalogues, ESA 1997

CORVUS

4094
MCG-2-31-19

−15°

MCG-2-31-19A
MCG-3-31-23

4035

−16°

4050
126 ly

112 ly
186 ly

−17°

Gienah 4 γ
165 ly

4033

ESO 573-13

−18°

ESO 573-2

162 ly

ESO 573-12

73 ly

4038 Antennae
4039

ESO 572-34

−19°

UW (i)
R (m3)

4027

ESO 573-1

31 Crt
TY (c1)

97 ly

42 ly

68 ly

−20°

ESO 573-3

ESO 573-7

TZ (s)

143 ly UV

CORVUS

−21°

12^h 20^m   12^h 16^m   12^h 12^m   12^h 08^m   12^h 04^m   12^h 00^m

| Bright and Dark Nebulae | To scale   <10' | Open Star Clusters | Galaxies | 10' x 5'   6' x 1'   3' x 2'   5' x 5'   4' x 2'   2' x 1' | Quasars |
| Planetary Nebulae | >100"   100"–30"   <30" | Globular Clusters   To scale   <5' | | Plotted to scale if the major axis >2', and circular when face on or the position angle is uncertain | Galaxy Clusters |

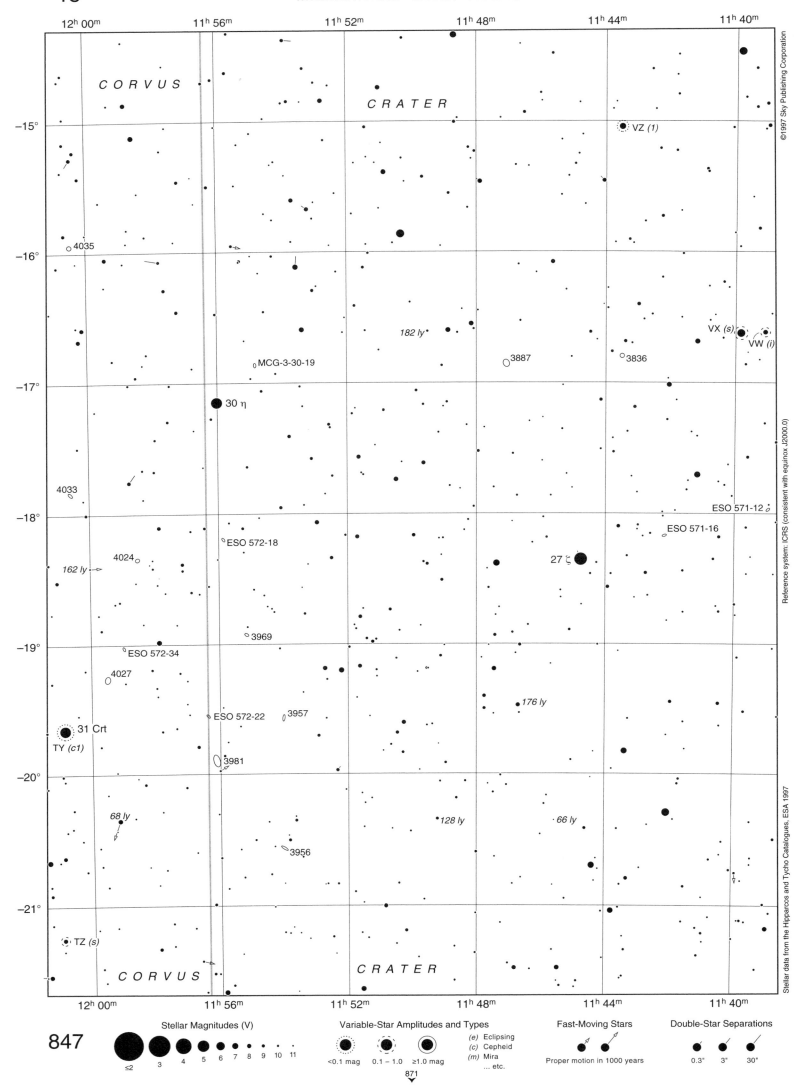

©1997 Sky Publishing Corporation

Reference system: ICRS (consistent with equinox J2000.0)

Stellar data from the Hipparcos and Tycho Catalogues, ESA 1997

C O R V U S

C R A T E R

○ 4035

VZ *(l)*

182 *ly*

VX *(s)*
VW *(i)*

○ MCG-3-30-19

○ 3887   ○ 3836

30 η

4033

ESO 571-12 ○

ESO 571-16 ○

○ ESO 572-18

4024 ○

162 *ly*

27 ζ

○ 3969

○ ESO 572-34

4027

176 *ly*

○ ESO 572-22   ○ 3957

31 Crt

TY *(c1)*

○ 3981

68 *ly*

128 *ly*   66 *ly*

○ 3956

TZ *(s)*

C O R V U S   C R A T E R

847

Stellar Magnitudes (V)

≤2   3   4   5   6   7   8   9 10 11

Variable-Star Amplitudes and Types

<0.1 mag   0.1 – 1.0   ≥1.0 mag

(e) Eclipsing
(c) Cepheid
(m) Mira
... etc.

Fast-Moving Stars

Proper motion in 1000 years

Double-Star Separations

0.3"   3"   30"

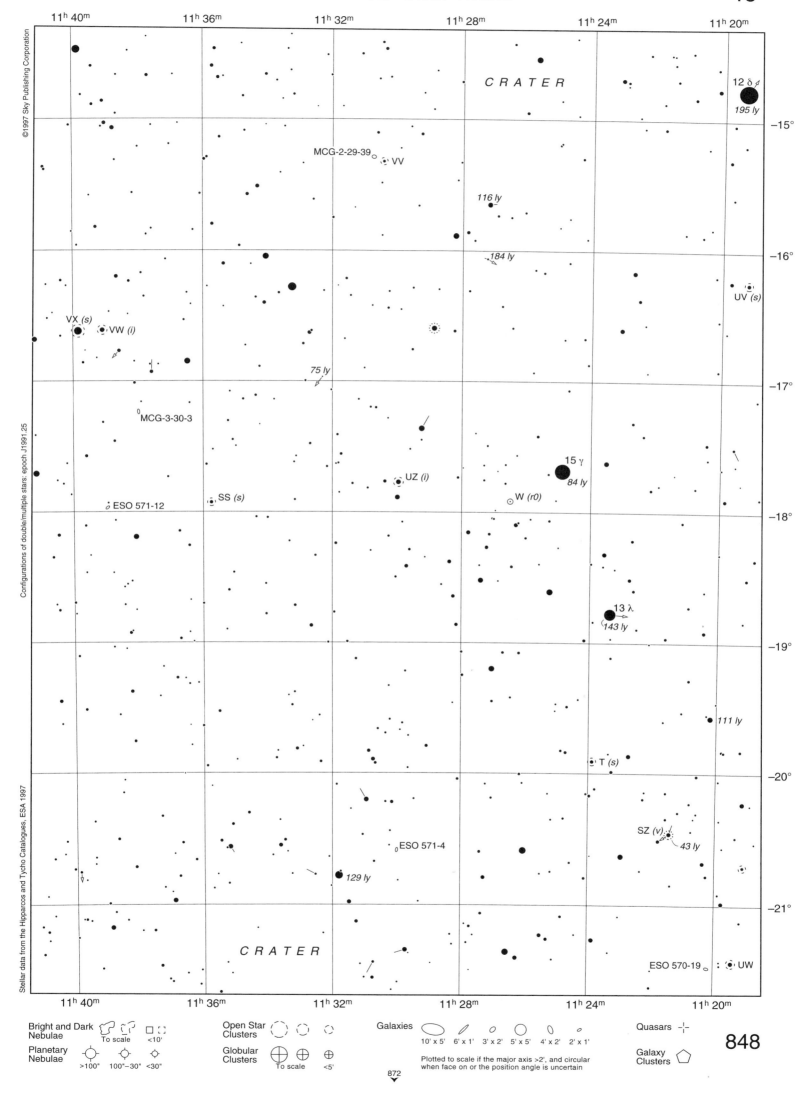

©1997 Sky Publishing Corporation

Configurations of double/multiple stars: epoch J1991.25

Stellar data from the Hipparcos and Tycho Catalogues, ESA 1997

11ʰ 40ᵐ   11ʰ 36ᵐ   11ʰ 32ᵐ   11ʰ 28ᵐ   11ʰ 24ᵐ   11ʰ 20ᵐ

−15°

C R A T E R

12 δ   195 ly

MCG-2-29-39   VV

116 ly

−16°

184 ly

UV (s)

VX (s)   VW (i)

75 ly

MCG-3-30-3

15 γ   84 ly

UZ (i)   W (r0)

SS (s)

ESO 571-12

−18°

13 λ   143 ly

−19°

111 ly

T (s)

−20°

SZ (v)   43 ly

ESO 571-4

129 ly

−21°

C R A T E R

ESO 570-19   UW

11ʰ 40ᵐ   11ʰ 36ᵐ   11ʰ 32ᵐ   11ʰ 28ᵐ   11ʰ 24ᵐ   11ʰ 20ᵐ

Bright and Dark Nebulae   To scale   <10'

Planetary Nebulae   >100"   100"−30"   <30"

Open Star Clusters

Globular Clusters   To scale   <5'

Galaxies   10' x 5'   6' x 1'   3' x 2'   5' x 5'   4' x 2'   2' x 1'

Plotted to scale if the major axis >2', and circular when face on or the position angle is uncertain

Quasars

Galaxy Clusters

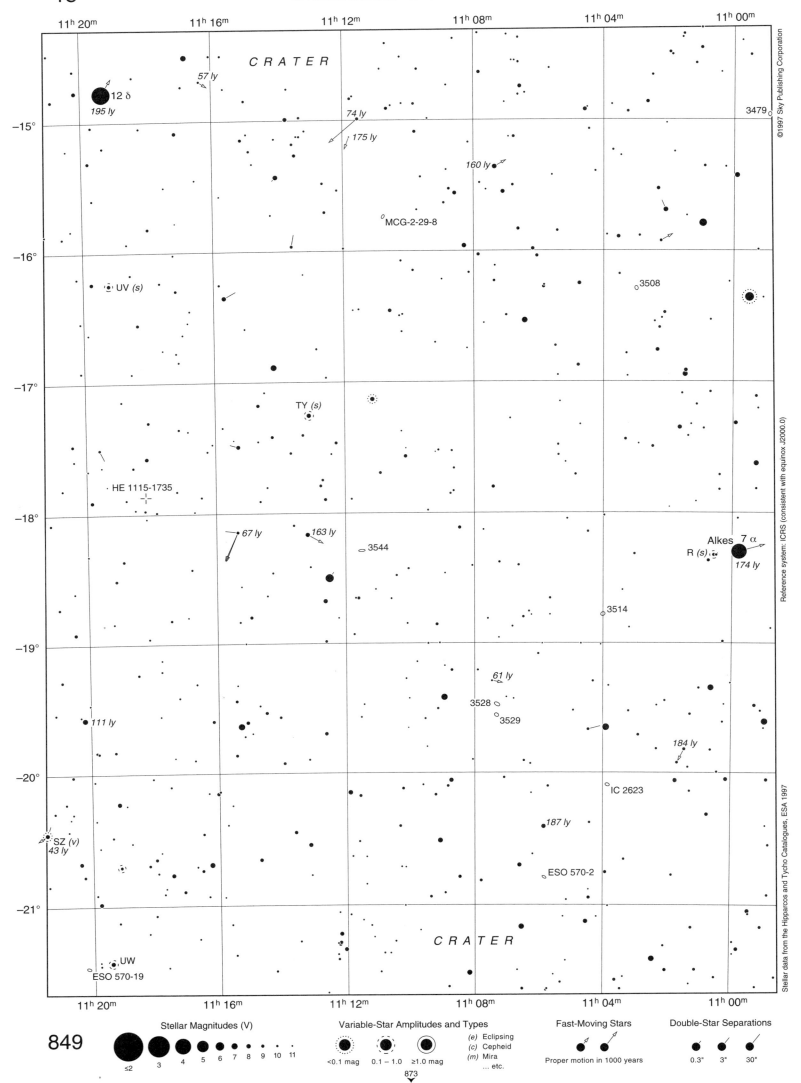

©1997 Sky Publishing Corporation

Reference system: ICRS (consistent with equinox J2000.0)

Stellar data from the Hipparcos and Tycho Catalogues, ESA 1997

849

| Stellar Magnitudes (V) | Variable-Star Amplitudes and Types | Fast-Moving Stars | Double-Star Separations |

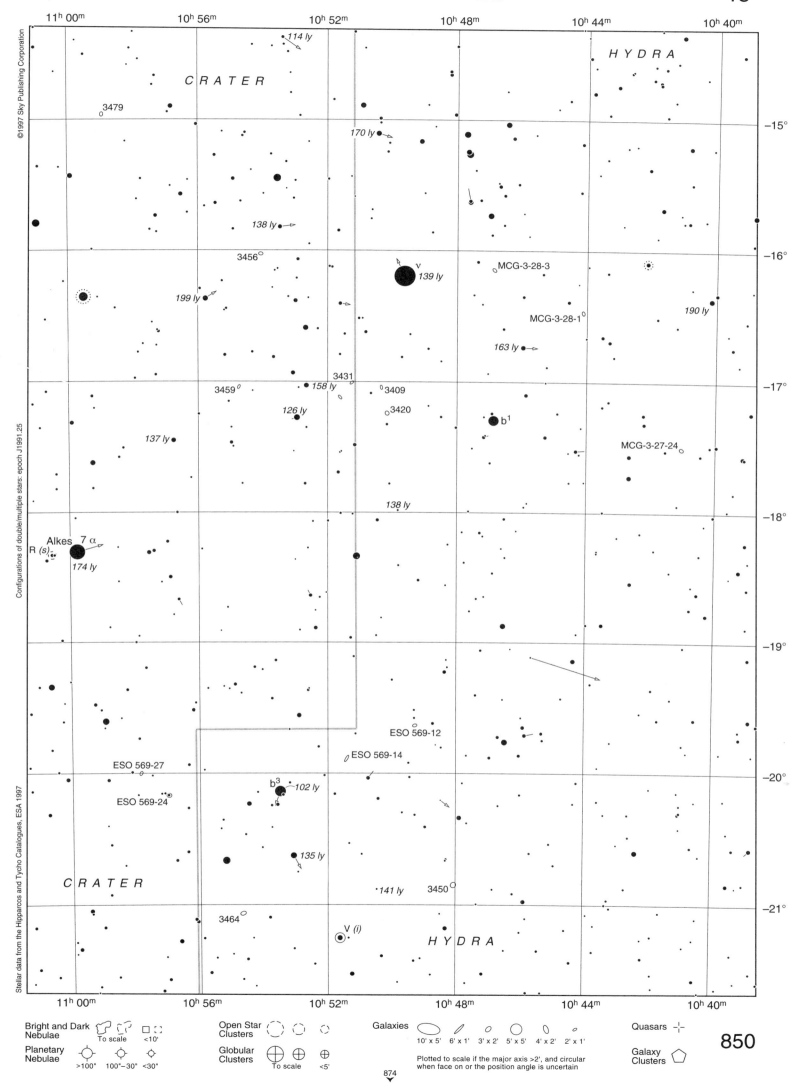

Bright and Dark Nebulae			Open Star Clusters			Galaxies							Quasars

To scale   <10'

Planetary Nebulae
>100"   100"−30"   <30'

Globular Clusters
To scale   <5'

Galaxies
10' x 5'   6' x 1'   3' x 2'   5' x 5'   4' x 2'   2' x 1'

Plotted to scale if the major axis >2', and circular
when face on or the position angle is uncertain

Quasars

Galaxy Clusters

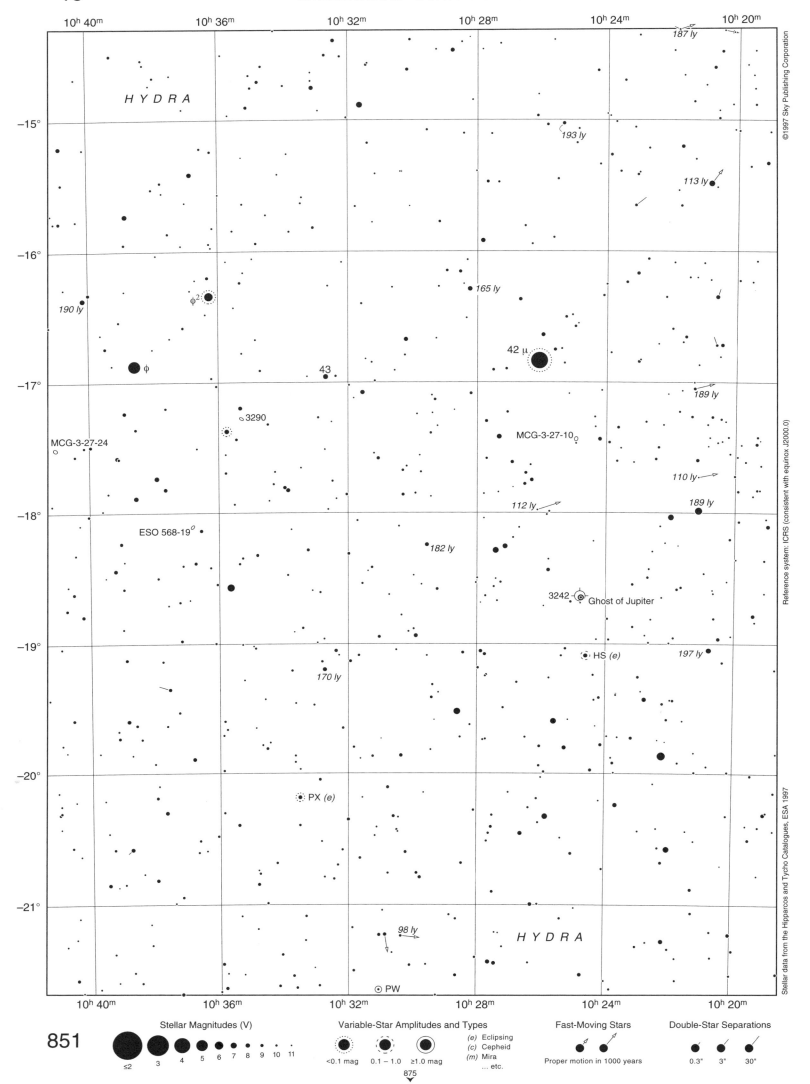

HYDRA

187 ly

193 ly

113 ly

190 ly

φ²

165 ly

42 μ

φ

43

189 ly

3290

MCG-3-27-24

MCG-3-27-10

110 ly

189 ly

112 ly

ESO 568-19

182 ly

3242 Ghost of Jupiter

HS (e)

197 ly

170 ly

PX (e)

98 ly

HYDRA

PW

851

Stellar Magnitudes (V)

≤2   3   4   5   6 7 8 9 10 11

Variable-Star Amplitudes and Types

<0.1 mag   0.1 – 1.0   ≥1.0 mag

(e) Eclipsing
(c) Cepheid
(m) Mira
... etc.

Fast-Moving Stars

Proper motion in 1000 years

Double-Star Separations

0.3"   3"   30"

875

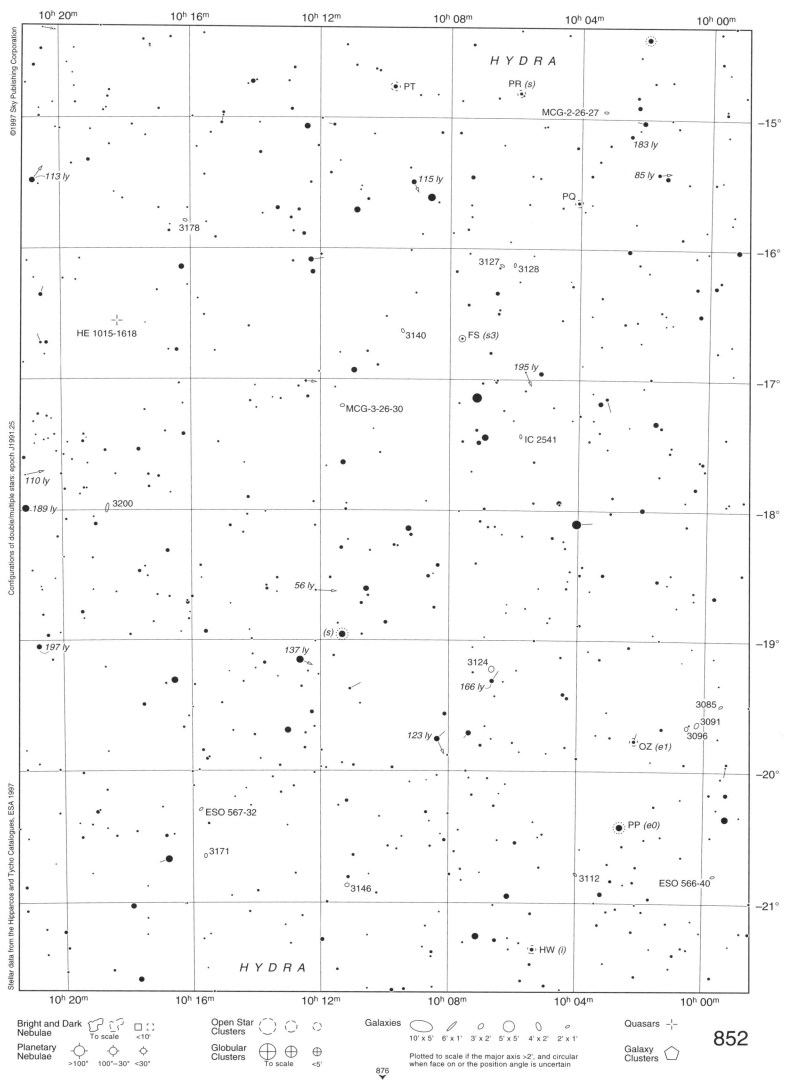

HYDRA

PT
PR *(s)*
MCG-2-26-27
183 ly
113 ly
115 ly
85 ly
PQ
3178
3127
3128
HE 1015-1618
3140
FS *(s3)*
195 ly
110 ly
MCG-3-26-30
189 ly
3200
IC 2541
56 ly
(s)
197 ly
137 ly
3124
166 ly
3085
3091
3096
123 ly
OZ *(e1)*
ESO 567-32
PP *(e0)*
3171
3112
ESO 566-40
3146
HW *(i)*

HYDRA

−15°
−16°
−17°
−18°
−19°
−20°
−21°

10ʰ 20ᵐ 10ʰ 16ᵐ 10ʰ 12ᵐ 10ʰ 08ᵐ 10ʰ 04ᵐ 10ʰ 00ᵐ

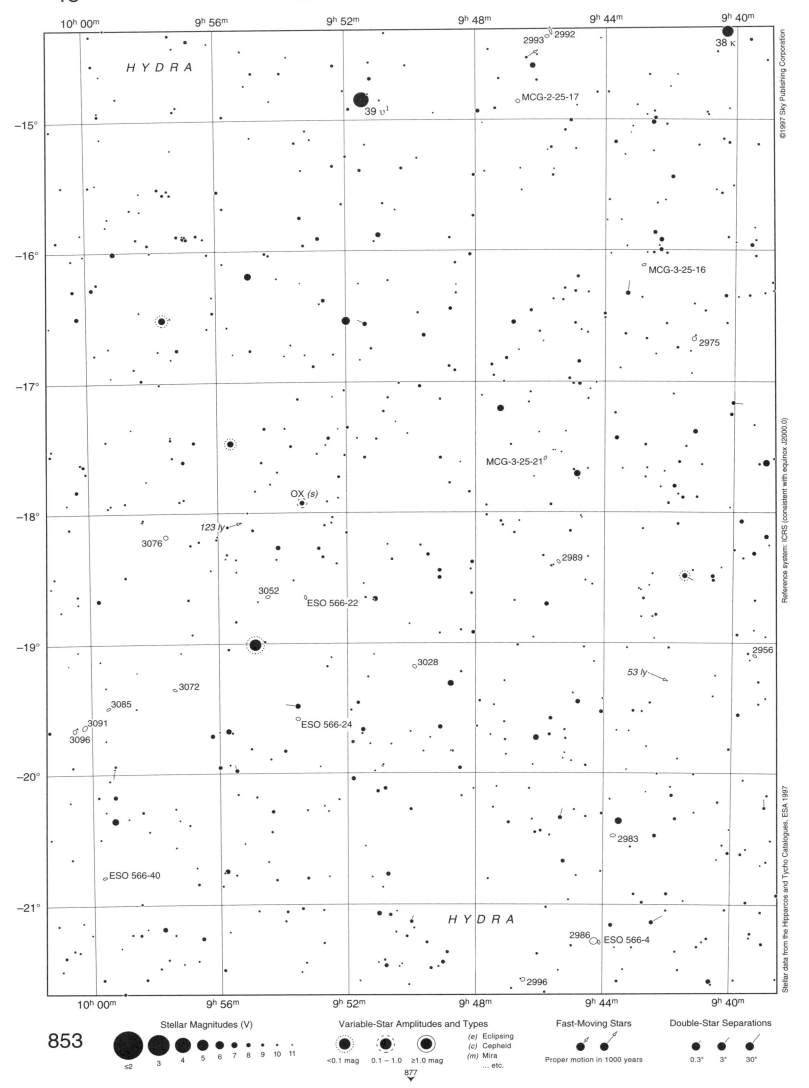

©1997 Sky Publishing Corporation

Reference system: ICRS (consistent with equinox J2000.0)

Stellar data from the Hipparcos and Tycho Catalogues, ESA 1997

853

Stellar Magnitudes (V)

≤2   3   4   5   6   7 8 9 10 11

Variable-Star Amplitudes and Types

<0.1 mag   0.1 – 1.0   ≥1.0 mag

(e) Eclipsing
(c) Cepheid
(m) Mira
... etc.

Fast-Moving Stars

Proper motion in 1000 years

Double-Star Separations

0.3"   3"   30"

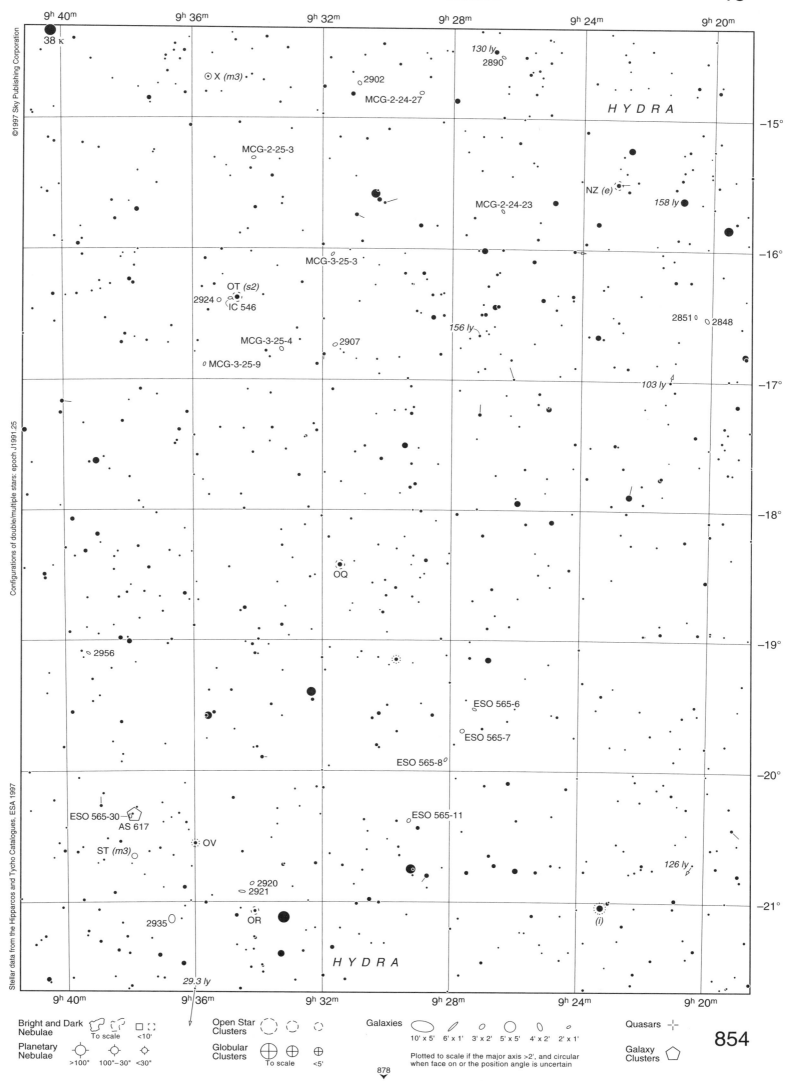

38 κ

⊙ X *(m3)*

2902

MCG-2-24-27

2890
130 ly

H Y D R A

−15°

MCG-2-25-3

NZ *(e)*

MCG-2-24-23

158 ly

MCG-3-25-3

−16°

OT *(s2)*

2924 IC 546

2851 2848

MCG-3-25-4   2907

156 ly

MCG-3-25-9

103 ly

−17°

−18°

OQ

2956

−19°

ESO 565-6

ESO 565-7

ESO 565-8

−20°

ESO 565-30
AS 617

ESO 565-11

ST *(m3)*

OV

126 ly

(i)

2920
2921

−21°

2935

OR

H Y D R A

29.3 ly

Bright and Dark
Nebulae
To scale   <10'

Planetary
Nebulae
>100" 100"−30" <30"

Open Star
Clusters

Globular
Clusters
To scale   <5'

Galaxies
10' x 5' 6' x 1' 3' x 2' 5' x 5' 4' x 2' 2' x 1'

Plotted to scale if the major axis >2', and circular
when face on or the position angle is uncertain

Quasars

Galaxy
Clusters

878

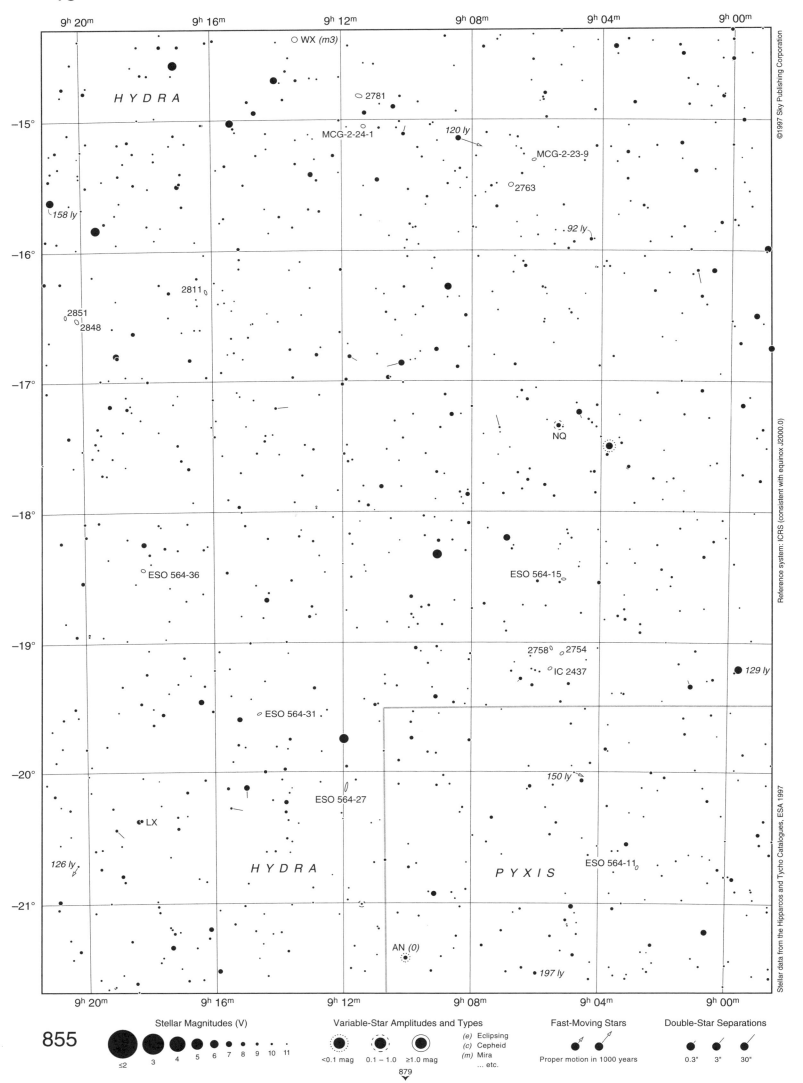

©1997 Sky Publishing Corporation

Reference system: ICRS (consistent with equinox J2000.0)

Stellar data from the Hipparcos and Tycho Catalogues, ESA 1997

9h 20m   9h 16m   9h 12m   9h 08m   9h 04m   9h 00m

HYDRA

○ WX (m3)

○ 2781

MCG-2-24-1   ○

120 ly

MCG-2-23-9

○ 2763

−15°

158 ly

92 ly

2811 ○

−16°

2851 ○
○ 2848

NQ ⊙

−17°

ESO 564-36 ○

ESO 564-15 ○

−18°

2758 ○ ○ 2754

○ IC 2437

129 ly

ESO 564-31 ○

−19°

ESO 564-27

150 ly

LX

ESO 564-11 ○

126 ly

HYDRA

PYXIS

−20°

AN (0)

197 ly

−21°

9h 20m   9h 16m   9h 12m   9h 08m   9h 04m   9h 00m

855

Stellar Magnitudes (V)

≤2   3   4   5   6   7   8   9   10   11

Variable-Star Amplitudes and Types

<0.1 mag   0.1 – 1.0   ≥1.0 mag

(e) Eclipsing
(c) Cepheid
(m) Mira
... etc.

Fast-Moving Stars

Proper motion in 1000 years

Double-Star Separations

0.3"   3"   30"

879

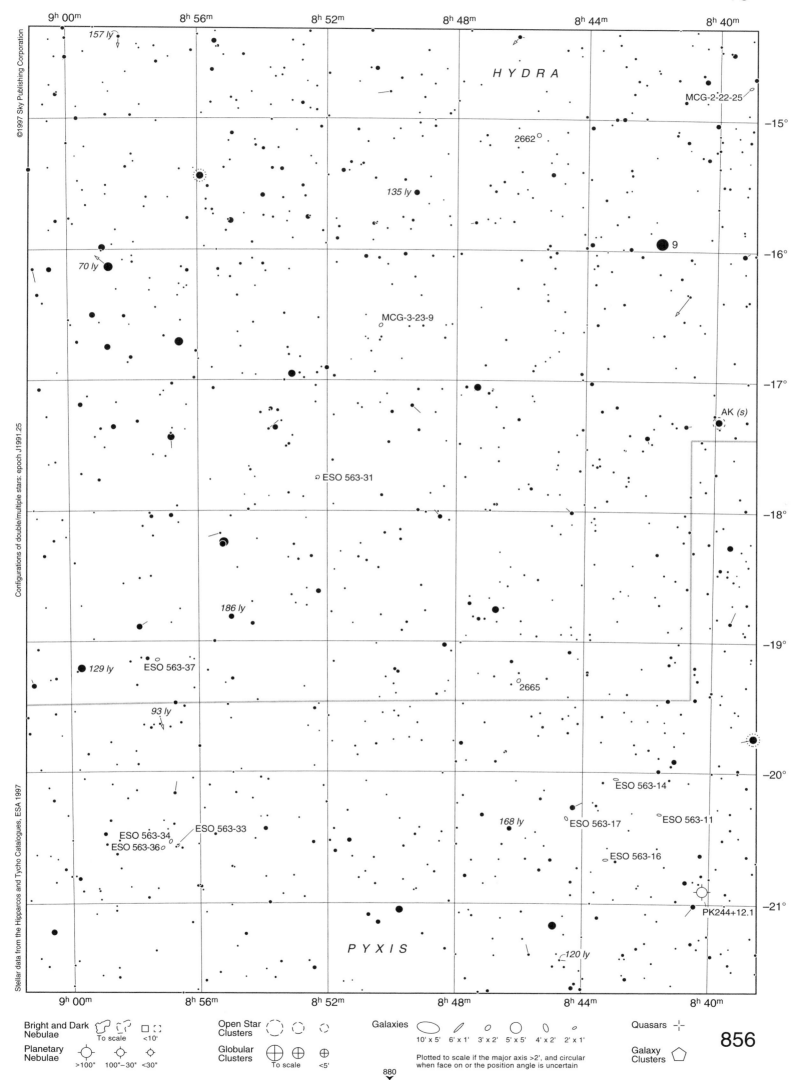

©1997 Sky Publishing Corporation

Configurations of double/multiple stars: epoch J1991.25

Stellar data from the Hipparcos and Tycho Catalogues, ESA 1997

9h 00m   8h 56m   8h 52m   8h 48m   8h 44m   8h 40m

H Y D R A

MCG-2-22-25

−15°

2662

135 ly

9   −16°

70 ly

MCG-3-23-9

−17°

AK *(s)*

ESO 563-31

−18°

186 ly

−19°

129 ly   ESO 563-37

2665

93 ly

−20°

ESO 563-14

168 ly   ESO 563-17   ESO 563-11

ESO 563-34   ESO 563-33

ESO 563-36   ESO 563-16

PK244+12.1   −21°

P Y X I S

120 ly

9h 00m   8h 56m   8h 52m   8h 48m   8h 44m   8h 40m

Bright and Dark Nebulae			Open Star Clusters			Galaxies						Quasars
	To scale	<10'				10' x 5'	6' x 1'	3' x 2'	5' x 5'	4' x 2'	2' x 1'	
Planetary Nebulae			Globular Clusters									Galaxy Clusters
>100"	100"–30"	<30"		To scale	<5'							

Plotted to scale if the major axis >2', and circular when face on or the position angle is uncertain

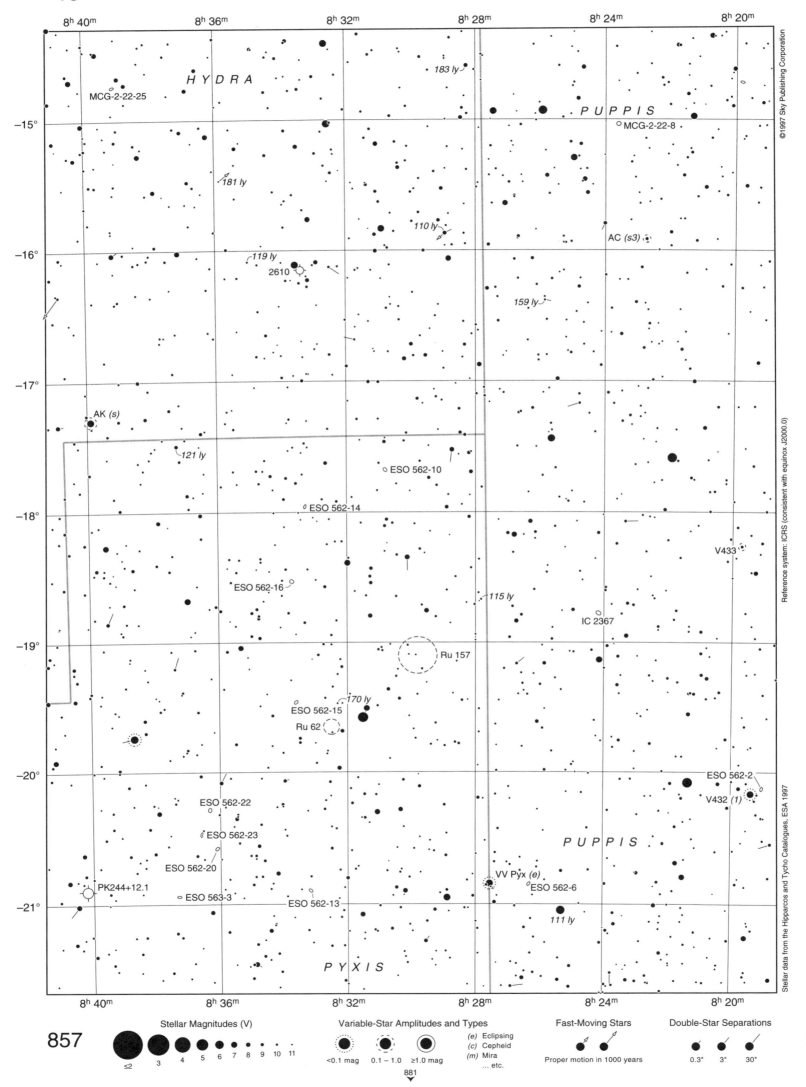

©1997 Sky Publishing Corporation

Reference system: ICRS (consistent with equinox J2000.0)

Stellar data from the Hipparcos and Tycho Catalogues, ESA 1997

857

Stellar Magnitudes (V)

≤2   3   4   5   6   7   8   9   10   11

Variable-Star Amplitudes and Types

<0.1 mag   0.1 – 1.0   ≥1.0 mag

(e) Eclipsing
(c) Cepheid
(m) Mira
... etc.

Fast-Moving Stars

Proper motion in 1000 years

Double-Star Separations

0.3"   3"   30"

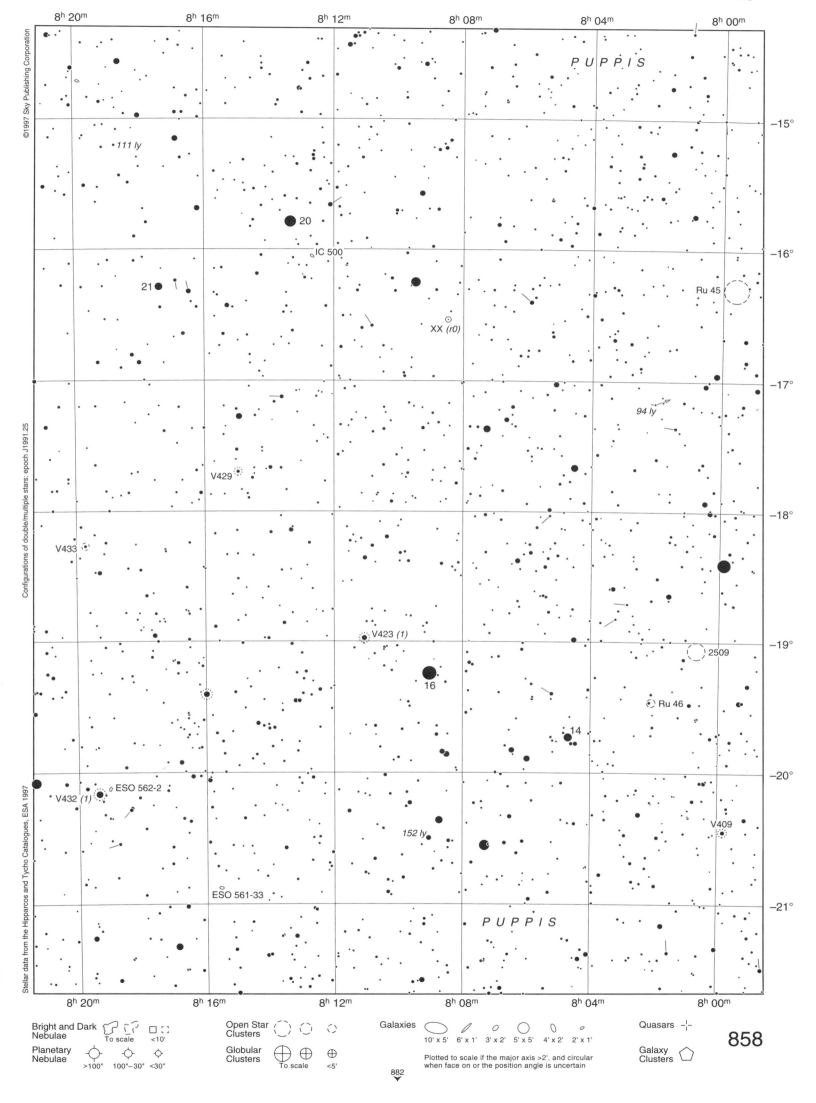

8h 20m   8h 16m   8h 12m   8h 08m   8h 04m   8h 00m

PUPPIS

−15°

111 ly

20

IC 500

−16°

21

Ru 45

XX (r0)

−17°

94 ly

V429

−18°

V433

V423 (1)

−19°

2509

16

Ru 46

14

−20°

o ESO 562-2

V432 (1)

V409

152 ly

ESO 561-33

−21°

PUPPIS

8h 20m   8h 16m   8h 12m   8h 08m   8h 04m   8h 00m

Bright and Dark Nebulae	To scale	<10'		Open Star Clusters			Galaxies							Quasars

Galaxies
10' x 5'   6' x 1'   3' x 2'   5' x 5'   4' x 2'   2' x 1'

Planetary Nebulae
>100"   100"-30"   <30"

Globular Clusters
To scale   <5'

Plotted to scale if the major axis >2', and circular when face on or the position angle is uncertain

Quasars

Galaxy Clusters

882

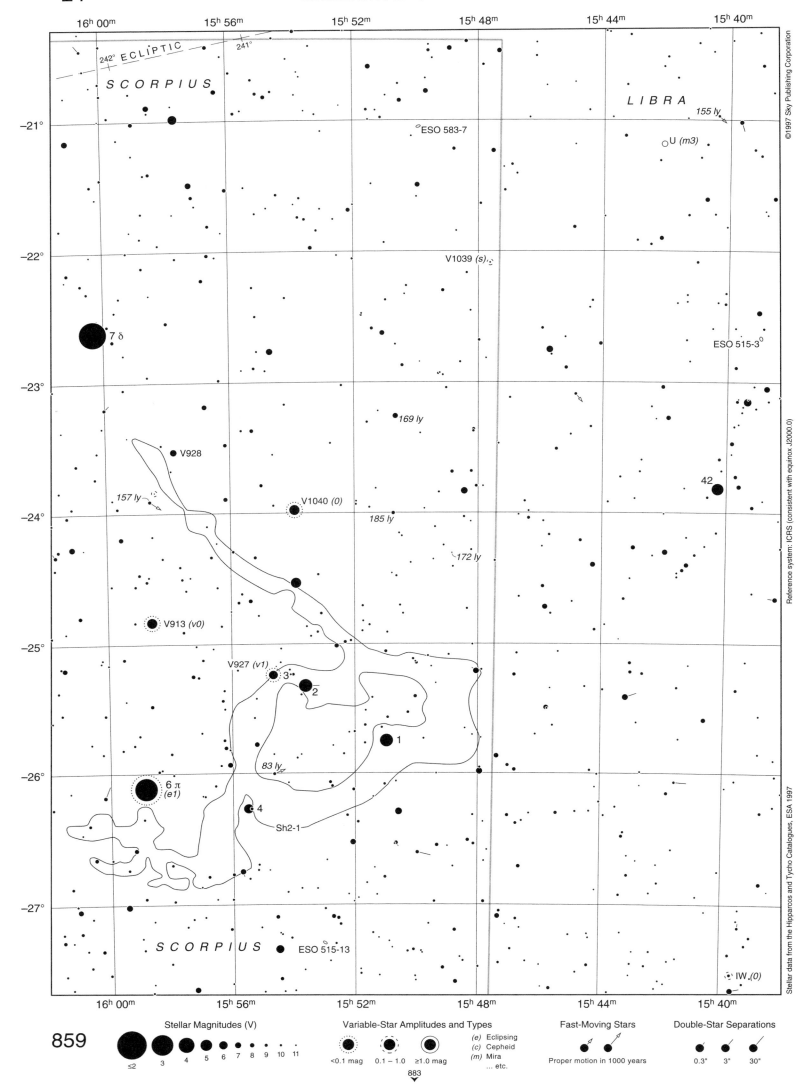

Stellar Magnitudes (V)
≤2 3 4 5 6 7 8 9 10 11

Variable-Star Amplitudes and Types
<0.1 mag   0.1 – 1.0   ≥1.0 mag
(e) Eclipsing
(c) Cepheid
(m) Mira
... etc.

Fast-Moving Stars
Proper motion in 1000 years

Double-Star Separations
0.3"   3"   30"

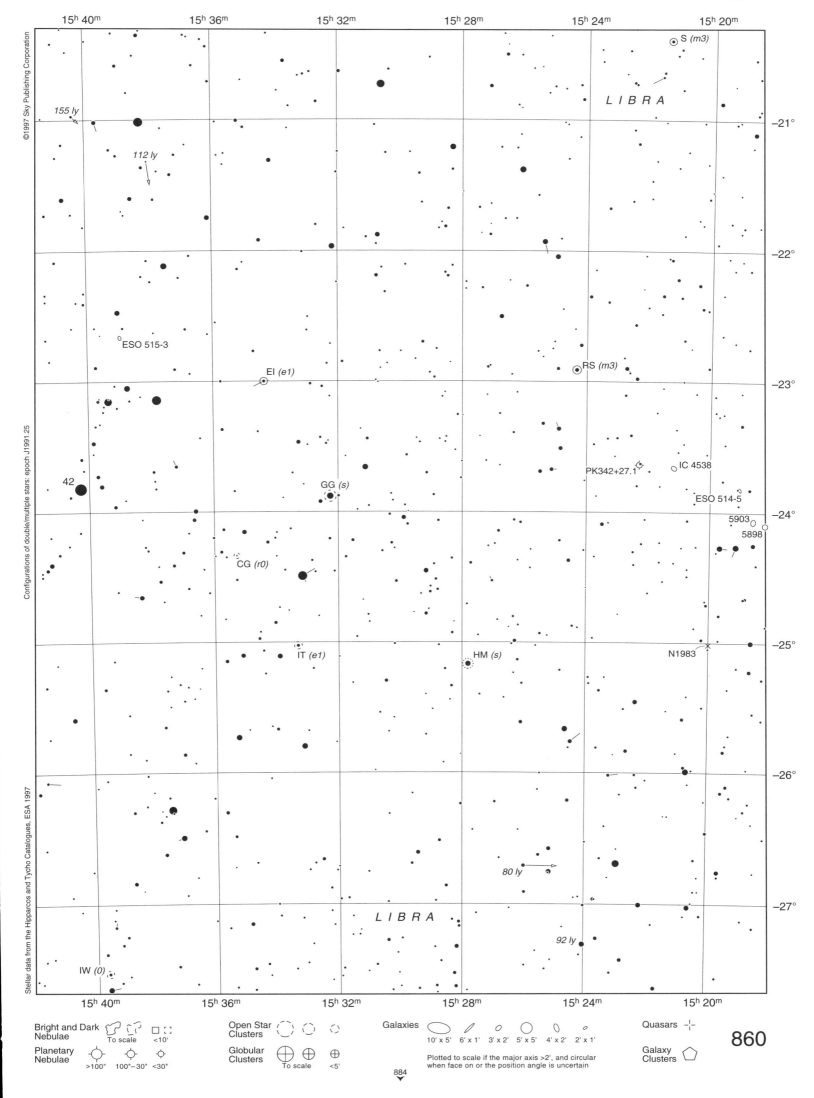

©1997 Sky Publishing Corporation

Configurations of double/multiple stars: epoch J1991.25

Stellar data from the Hipparcos and Tycho Catalogues, ESA 1997

15ʰ 40ᵐ   15ʰ 36ᵐ   15ʰ 32ᵐ   15ʰ 28ᵐ   15ʰ 24ᵐ   15ʰ 20ᵐ

S (m3)

LIBRA

−21°

155 ly

112 ly

−22°

ESO 515-3

EI (e1)

RS (m3)

−23°

PK342+27.1   IC 4538

42   GG (s)   ESO 514-5

5903
5898

−24°

CG (r0)

IT (e1)   HM (s)   N1983

−25°

−26°

80 ly

LIBRA

92 ly

−27°

IW (0)

15ʰ 40ᵐ   15ʰ 36ᵐ   15ʰ 32ᵐ   15ʰ 28ᵐ   15ʰ 24ᵐ   15ʰ 20ᵐ

Bright and Dark Nebulae	Open Star Clusters	Galaxies	Quasars

Bright and Dark Nebulae   To scale   <10'

Planetary Nebulae   >100" 100"−30" <30"

Open Star Clusters

Globular Clusters   To scale   <5'

Galaxies   10' x 5' 6' x 1' 3' x 2' 5' x 5' 4' x 2' 2' x 1'

Plotted to scale if the major axis >2', and circular when face on or the position angle is uncertain

Quasars

Galaxy Clusters

884

860

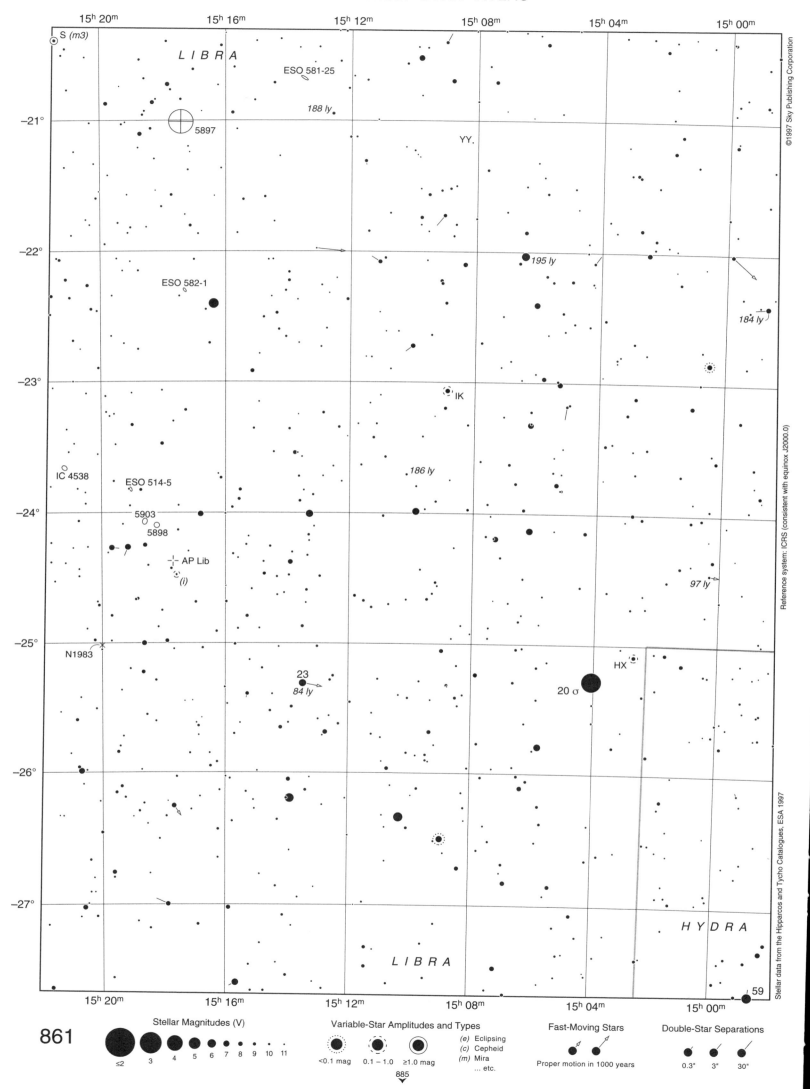

©1997 Sky Publishing Corporation

Reference system: ICRS (consistent with equinox J2000.0)

Stellar data from the Hipparcos and Tycho Catalogues, ESA 1997

S (m3)

LIBRA

ESO 581-25

188 ly

YY.

5897

195 ly

ESO 582-1

184 ly

IK

186 ly

IC 4538

ESO 514-5

5903

5898

AP Lib

(i)

97 ly

N1983

HX

23

20 σ

84 ly

HYDRA

LIBRA

59

Stellar Magnitudes (V)

≤2   3   4   5   6   7   8   9 10 11

Variable-Star Amplitudes and Types

<0.1 mag   0.1 – 1.0   ≥1.0 mag

(e) Eclipsing
(c) Cepheid
(m) Mira
... etc.

Fast-Moving Stars

Proper motion in 1000 years

Double-Star Separations

0.3"   3"   30"

885

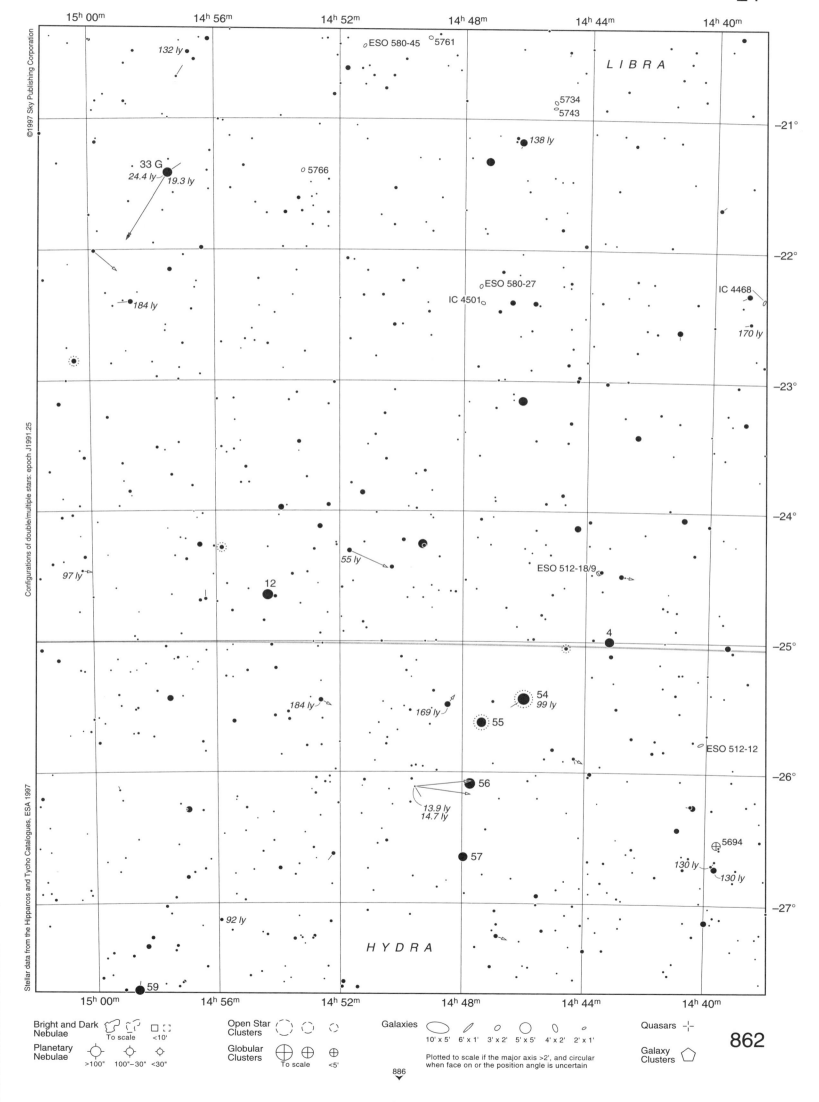

LIBRA

HYDRA

ESO 580-45   5761
5734
5743
138 ly
132 ly
33 G
24.4 ly   19.3 ly
5766
184 ly
ESO 580-27
IC 4501   IC 4468
170 ly
97 ly
55 ly
12
ESO 512-18/9
4
54
99 ly
184 ly   169 ly
55
ESO 512-12
56
13.9 ly
14.7 ly
5694
57
130 ly
130 ly
92 ly
59

Bright and Dark Nebulae				Open Star Clusters			Galaxies						Quasars
To scale		<10'					10' x 5'	6' x 1'	3' x 2'	5' x 5'	4' x 2'	2' x 1'	
Planetary Nebulae				Globular Clusters									Galaxy Clusters
>100"	100"–30"	<30"		To scale		<5'							

Plotted to scale if the major axis >2', and circular when face on or the position angle is uncertain

MILLENNIUM STAR ATLAS

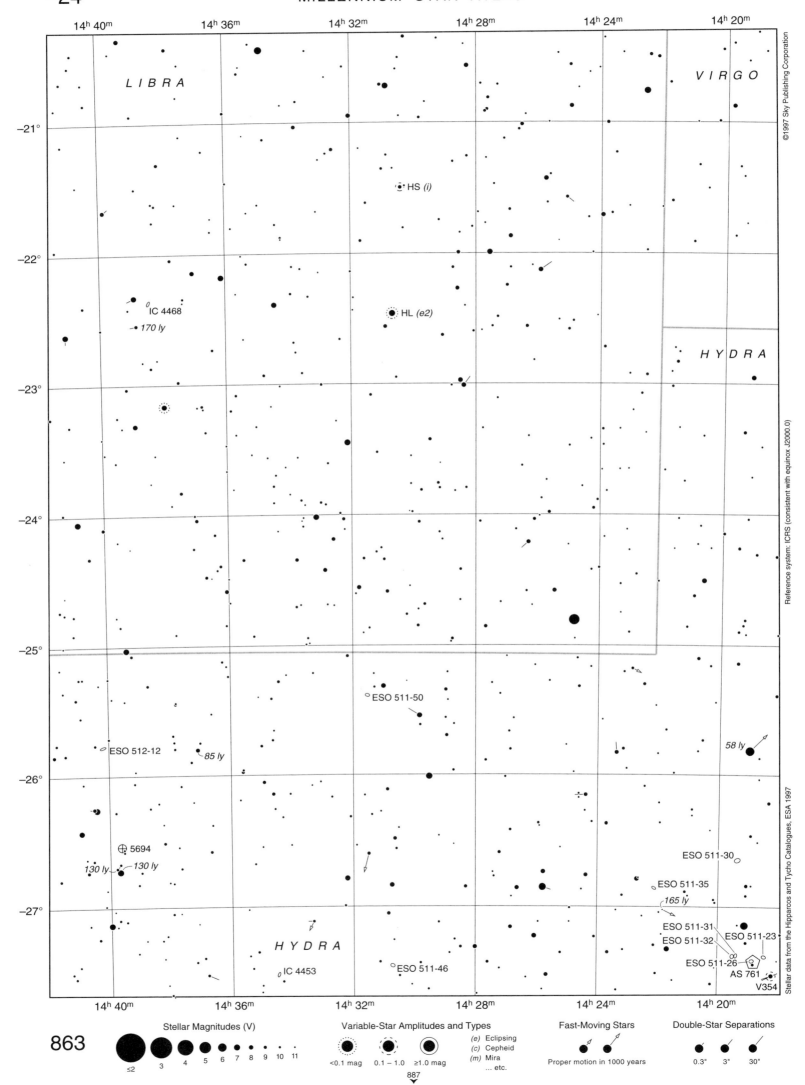

LIBRA

VIRGO

−21°

HS *(i)*

−22°

IC 4468

170 ly

HL *(e2)*

HYDRA

−23°

−24°

−25°

ESO 511-50

ESO 512-12

85 ly

58 ly

−26°

5694

ESO 511-30

130 ly   130 ly

ESO 511-35

165 ly

ESO 511-31

ESO 511-23

−27°

HYDRA

ESO 511-32

IC 4453

ESO 511-46

ESO 511-26

AS 761

V354

©1997 Sky Publishing Corporation

Reference system: ICRS (consistent with equinox J2000.0)

Stellar data from the Hipparcos and Tycho Catalogues, ESA 1997

863

Stellar Magnitudes (V)

≤2   3   4   5   6   7   8   9   10   11

Variable-Star Amplitudes and Types

<0.1 mag   0.1 – 1.0   ≥1.0 mag

(e) Eclipsing
(c) Cepheid
(m) Mira
... etc.

Fast-Moving Stars

Proper motion in 1000 years

Double-Star Separations

0.3"   3"   30"

MILLENNIUM STAR ATLAS

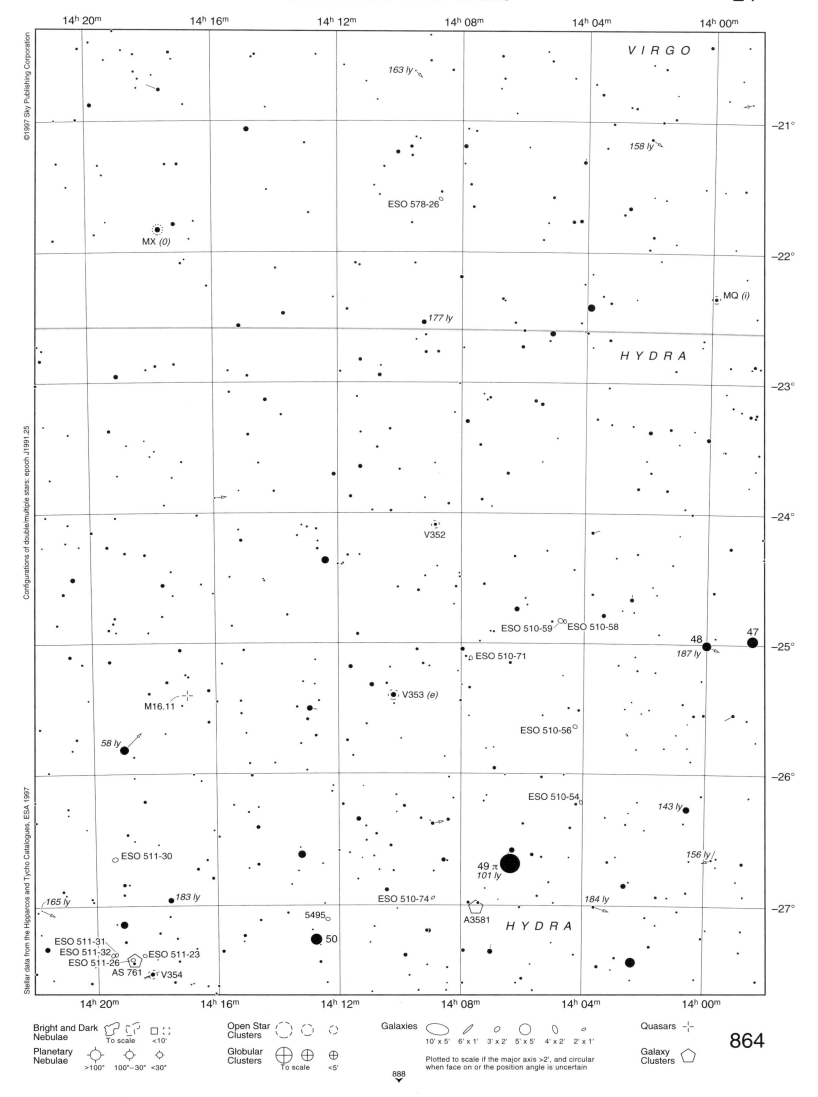

VIRGO

163 ly

158 ly

ESO 578-26

MX (0)

177 ly

HYDRA

MQ (i)

V352

ESO 510-59 ESO 510-58

ESO 510-71

48   47
187 ly

M16.11

V353 (e)

ESO 510-56

58 ly

ESO 510-54

143 ly

ESO 511-30

156 ly

49 π
101 ly

165 ly

183 ly

ESO 510-74

184 ly

5495

A3581

HYDRA

50

ESO 511-31
ESO 511-32
ESO 511-26   ESO 511-23
AS 761   V354

Bright and Dark Nebulae				Open Star Clusters			Galaxies							Quasars	
	To scale	<10'					10' x 5'	6' x 1'	3' x 2'	5' x 5'	4' x 2'	2' x 1'			
Planetary Nebulae				Globular Clusters										Galaxy Clusters	
	>100"	100"–30"	<30"		To scale	<5'									

Plotted to scale if the major axis >2', and circular when face on or the position angle is uncertain

864

888

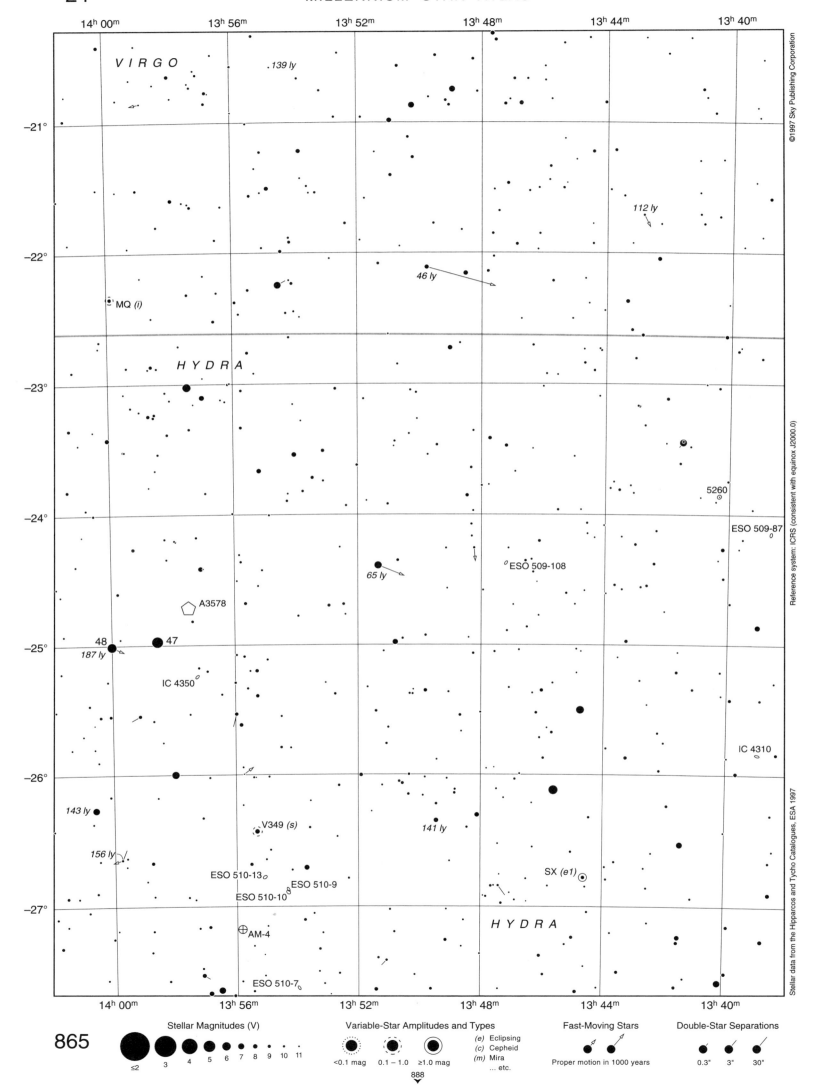

©1997 Sky Publishing Corporation

Reference system: ICRS (consistent with equinox J2000.0)

Stellar data from the Hipparcos and Tycho Catalogues, ESA 1997

V I R G O

.139 ly

MQ (i)

112 ly

46 ly

H Y D R A

5260

ESO 509-87

ESO 509-108

65 ly

A3578

48   47

187 ly

IC 4350

141 ly

143 ly

V349 (s)

IC 4310

156 ly

ESO 510-13

ESO 510-9

SX (e1)

ESO 510-10

AM-4

H Y D R A

ESO 510-7

865

Stellar Magnitudes (V)

≤2   3   4   5   6   7   8   9   10   11

Variable-Star Amplitudes and Types

<0.1 mag   0.1 – 1.0   ≥1.0 mag

(e) Eclipsing
(c) Cepheid
(m) Mira
... etc.

Fast-Moving Stars

Proper motion in 1000 years

Double-Star Separations

0.3"   3"   30"

888

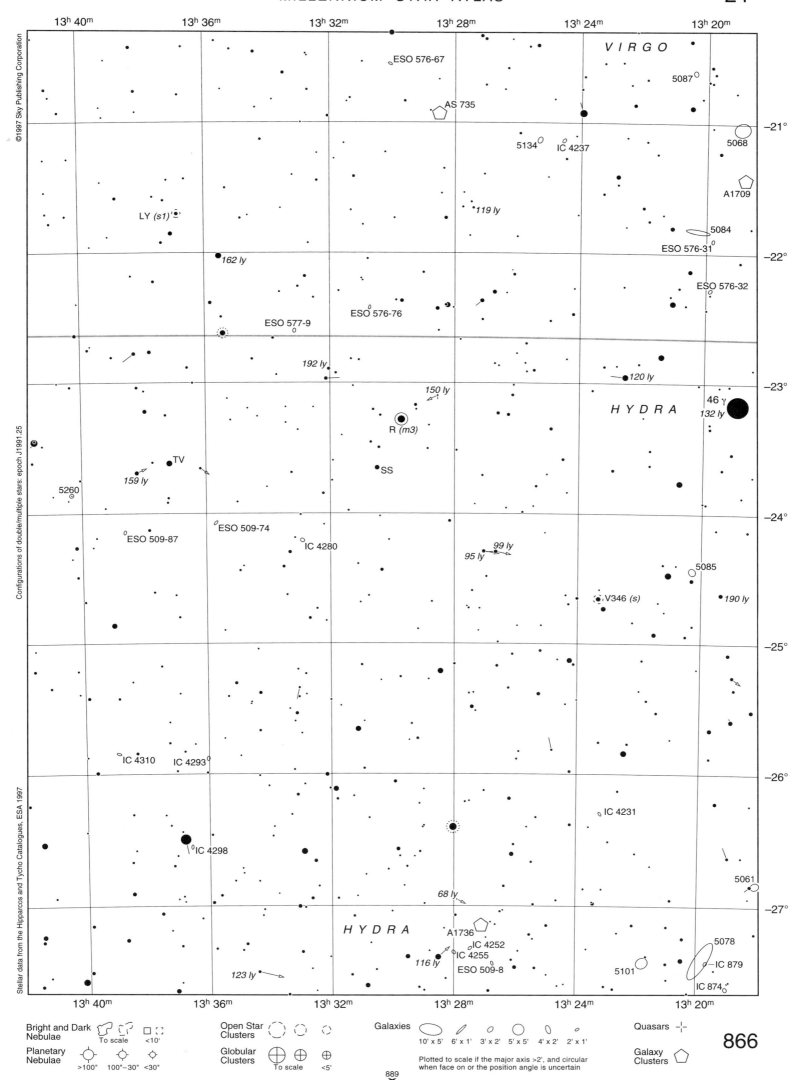

MILLENNIUM STAR ATLAS

13ʰ 40ᵐ   13ʰ 36ᵐ   13ʰ 32ᵐ   13ʰ 28ᵐ   13ʰ 24ᵐ   13ʰ 20ᵐ

VIRGO

ESO 576-67

AS 735

5087

−21°

5134   IC 4237

5068

119 ly

A1709

5084

LY (s1)

ESO 576-31

162 ly

−22°

ESO 576-76

ESO 576-32

ESO 577-9

192 ly

150 ly

120 ly

−23°

HYDRA

46 γ

132 ly

R (m3)

TV

SS

5260

159 ly

−24°

ESO 509-74

ESO 509-87

IC 4280

99 ly

95 ly

5085

V346 (s)

190 ly

−25°

IC 4310   IC 4293

IC 4231

−26°

IC 4298

5061

68 ly

−27°

HYDRA

A1736

IC 4252

5078

IC 4255

116 ly

IC 879

123 ly

ESO 509-8

5101

IC 874

13ʰ 40ᵐ   13ʰ 36ᵐ   13ʰ 32ᵐ   13ʰ 28ᵐ   13ʰ 24ᵐ   13ʰ 20ᵐ

Bright and Dark Nebulae	Open Star Clusters	Galaxies	Quasars

Bright and Dark Nebulae — To scale <10'

Planetary Nebulae — >100" 100"–30" <30"

Open Star Clusters

Globular Clusters — To scale <5'

Galaxies — 10' x 5' 6' x 1' 3' x 2' 5' x 5' 4' x 2' 2' x 1'

Plotted to scale if the major axis >2', and circular when face on or the position angle is uncertain

Quasars

Galaxy Clusters

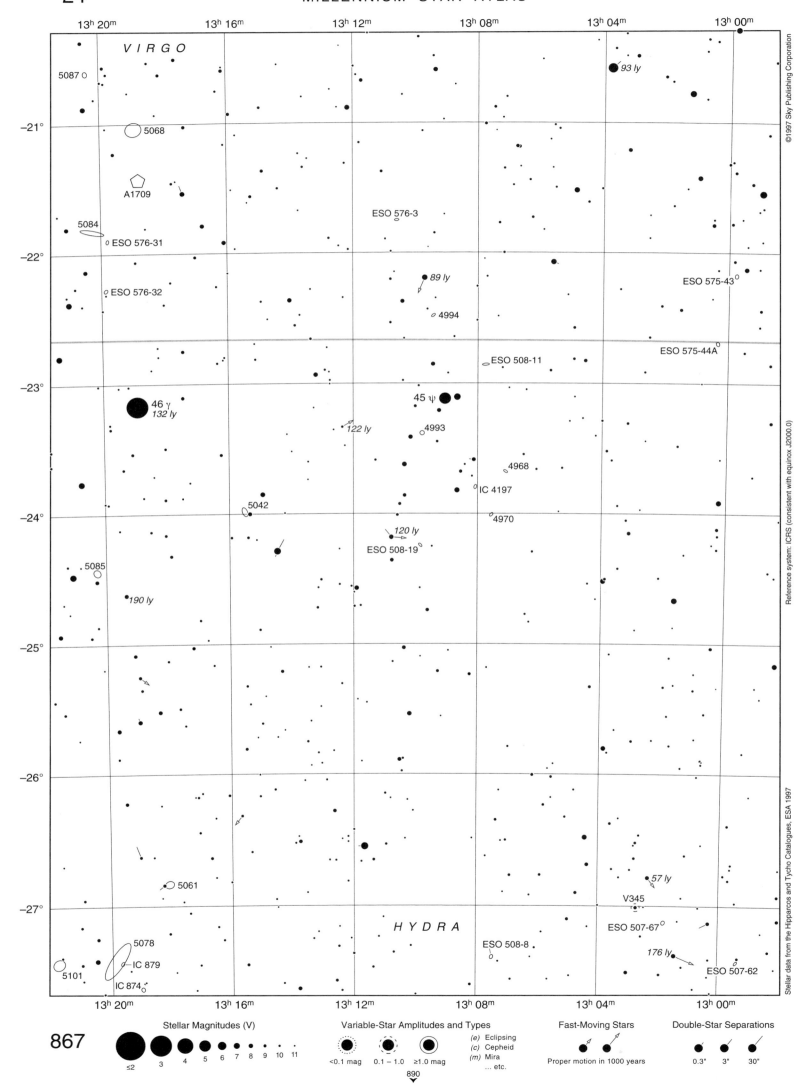

©1997 Sky Publishing Corporation

Reference system: ICRS (consistent with equinox J2000.0)

Stellar data from the Hipparcos and Tycho Catalogues, ESA 1997

VIRGO

5087

5068

A1709

5084

ESO 576-31

ESO 576-3

ESO 576-32

93 ly

89 ly

4994

ESO 575-43

ESO 575-44A

ESO 508-11

46 γ
132 ly

45 ψ

122 ly

4993

4968

IC 4197

4970

5042

120 ly

ESO 508-19

5085

190 ly

5061

HYDRA

57 ly

V345

ESO 507-67

ESO 508-8

5078

IC 879

5101

176 ly

ESO 507-62

IC 874

Stellar Magnitudes (V)

≤2   3   4   5   6   7   8   9 10 11

Variable-Star Amplitudes and Types

<0.1 mag   0.1 – 1.0   ≥1.0 mag

(e) Eclipsing
(c) Cepheid
(m) Mira
... etc.

Fast-Moving Stars

Proper motion in 1000 years

Double-Star Separations

0.3"   3"   30"

890

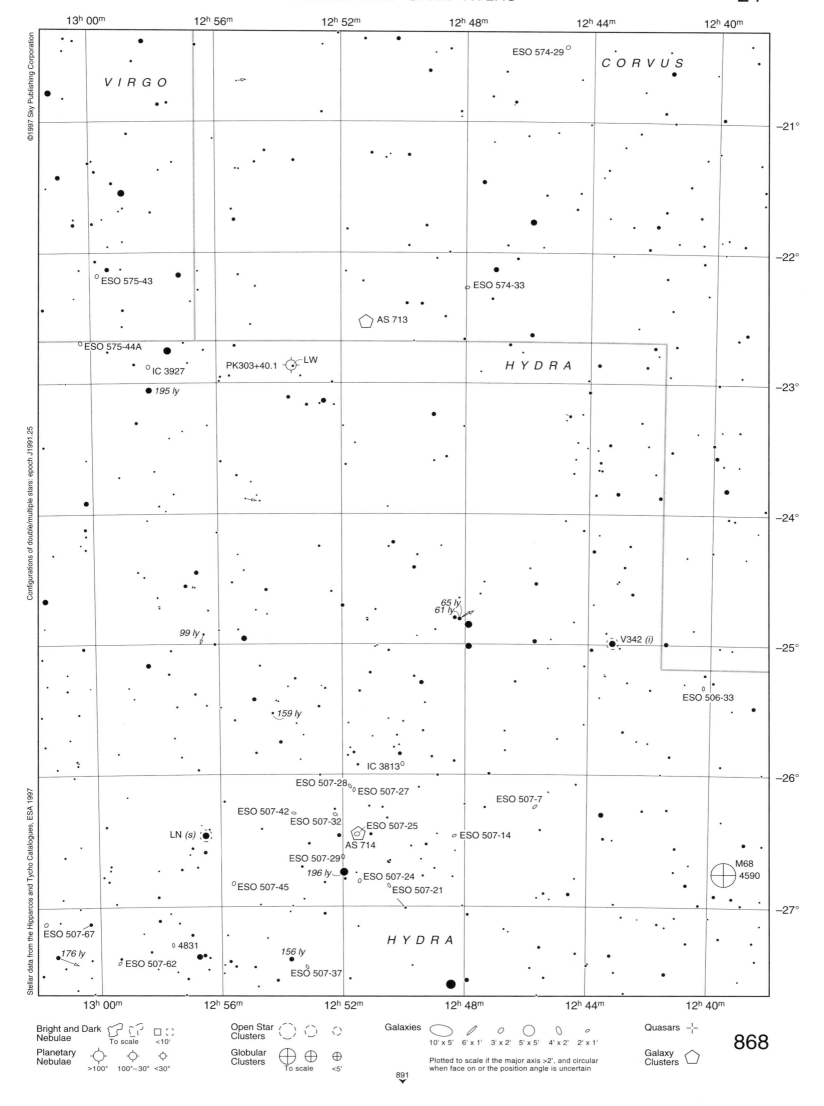

©1997 Sky Publishing Corporation

Configurations of double/multiple stars: epoch J1991.25

Stellar data from the Hipparcos and Tycho Catalogues, ESA 1997

VIRGO

CORVUS

ESO 574-29

−21°

−22°

ESO 575-43

ESO 574-33

AS 713

ESO 575-44A

HYDRA

IC 3927

PK303+40.1 LW

195 ly

−23°

65 ly
61 ly

V342 (i)

99 ly

−25°

ESO 506-33

159 ly

IC 3813

−26°

ESO 507-28
ESO 507-27

ESO 507-7

ESO 507-42
ESO 507-32

ESO 507-25

ESO 507-14

LN (s)

AS 714

ESO 507-29

196 ly
ESO 507-24

M68
4590

ESO 507-45

ESO 507-21

−27°

ESO 507-67

HYDRA

176 ly

4831

156 ly

ESO 507-62

ESO 507-37

Bright and Dark Nebulae
To scale   <10'

Planetary Nebulae
>100"   100"−30"   <30"

Open Star Clusters

Globular Clusters
To scale   <5'

Galaxies
10' x 5'   6' x 1'   3' x 2'   5' x 5'   4' x 2'   2' x 1'

Plotted to scale if the major axis >2', and circular when face on or the position angle is uncertain

Quasars

Galaxy Clusters

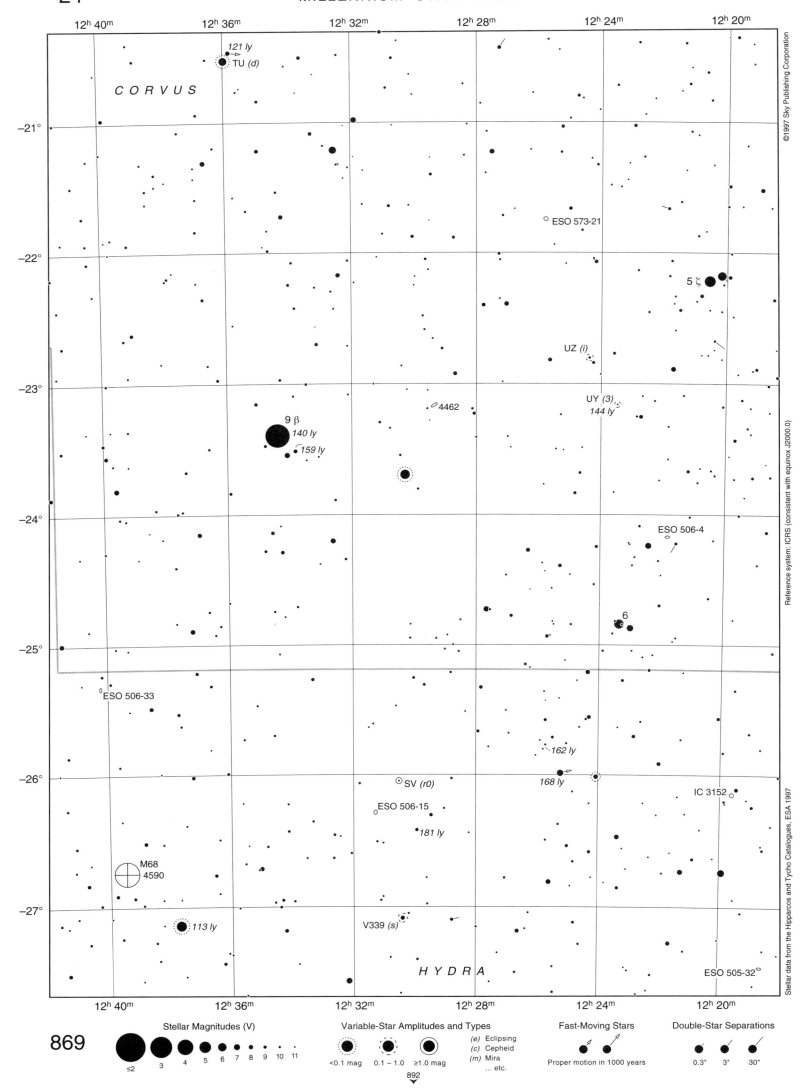

©1997 Sky Publishing Corporation

Reference system: ICRS (consistent with equinox J2000.0)

Stellar data from the Hipparcos and Tycho Catalogues, ESA 1997

121 ly
TU *(d)*

C O R V U S

○ ESO 573-21

5 ζ

UZ *(i)*

○ 4462

UY *(3)*
144 ly

9 β
140 ly
159 ly

ESO 506-4

6

ESO 506-33

162 ly

⊙ SV *(r0)*

168 ly

IC 3152 ○

ESO 506-15

181 ly

M68
4590

113 ly

V339 *(s)*

H Y D R A

ESO 505-32 ○

869

Stellar Magnitudes (V)	Variable-Star Amplitudes and Types	Fast-Moving Stars	Double-Star Separations

Stellar Magnitudes (V)

≤2   3   4   5 6 7 8 9 10 11

Variable-Star Amplitudes and Types

<0.1 mag   0.1 – 1.0   ≥1.0 mag

(e) Eclipsing
(c) Cepheid
(m) Mira
… etc.

Fast-Moving Stars

Proper motion in 1000 years

Double-Star Separations

0.3"   3"   30"

MILLENNIUM STAR ATLAS

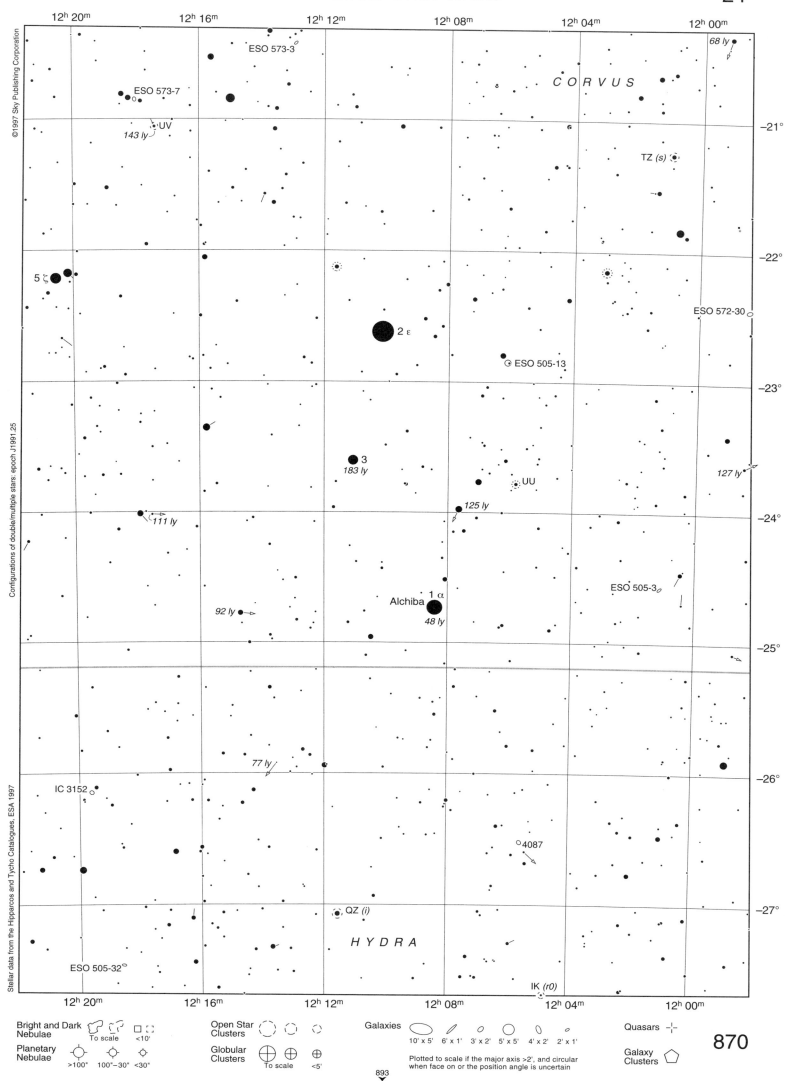

ESO 573-3

ESO 573-7

UV
143 ly

CORVUS

68 ly

TZ (s)

−21°

5 ζ

2 ε

ESO 505-13

ESO 572-30

−22°

−23°

3
183 ly

UU

127 ly

125 ly

111 ly

ESO 505-3

−24°

Alchiba   1 α
48 ly

92 ly

−25°

77 ly

IC 3152

4087

−26°

ESO 505-32

QZ (i)

HYDRA

IK (r0)

−27°

12h 20m   12h 16m   12h 12m   12h 08m   12h 04m   12h 00m

Legend

Bright and Dark Nebulae			Open Star Clusters			Galaxies						Quasars
To scale	<10'					10' x 5'	6' x 1'	3' x 2'	5' x 5'	4' x 2'	2' x 1'	

Planetary Nebulae			Globular Clusters				Galaxy Clusters
>100"	100"–30"	<30"	To scale	<5'			

Plotted to scale if the major axis >2', and circular when face on or the position angle is uncertain

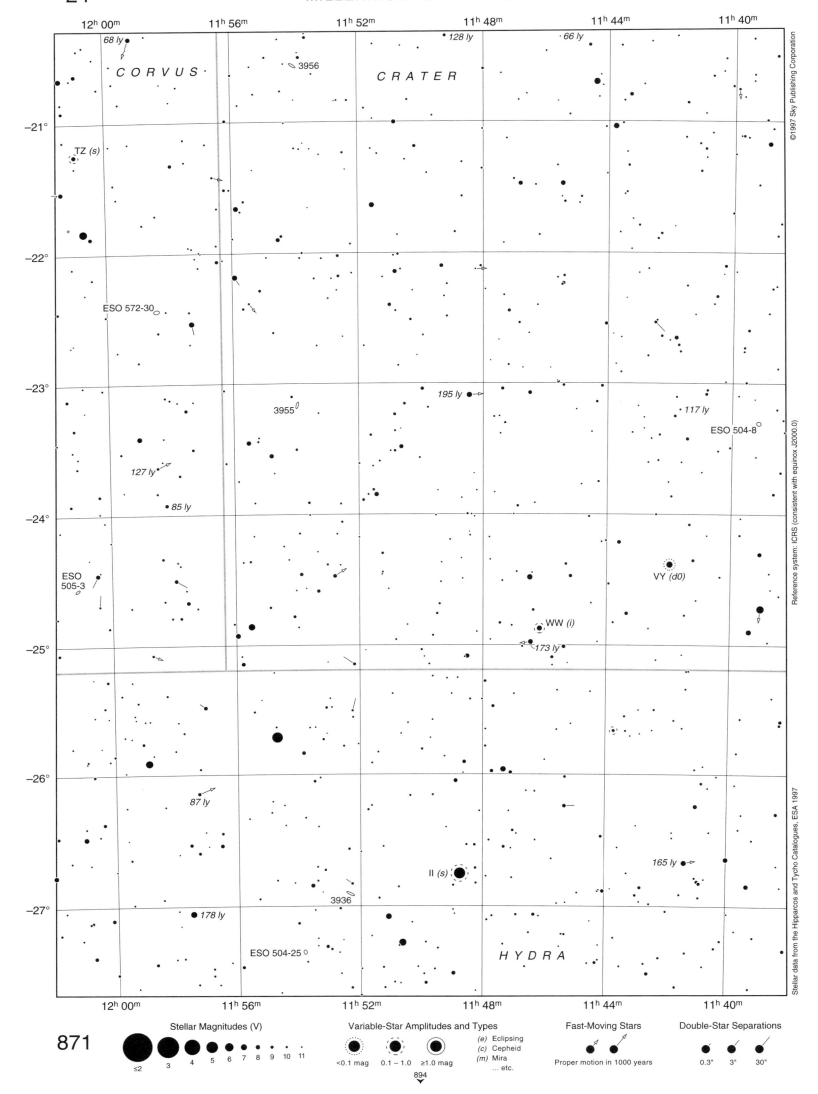

CORVUS

CRATER

HYDRA

68 ly

3956

128 ly · 66 ly

TZ (s)

ESO 572-30

195 ly

3955

117 ly

ESO 504-8

127 ly

85 ly

VY (d0)

ESO 505-3

WW (i)

173 ly

87 ly

II (s)

165 ly

3936

178 ly

ESO 504-25

Stellar Magnitudes (V)

≤2   3   4   5 6 7 8 9 10 11

Variable-Star Amplitudes and Types

<0.1 mag   0.1 – 1.0   ≥1.0 mag

(e) Eclipsing
(c) Cepheid
(m) Mira
... etc.

Fast-Moving Stars

Proper motion in 1000 years

Double-Star Separations

0.3"   3"   30"

894

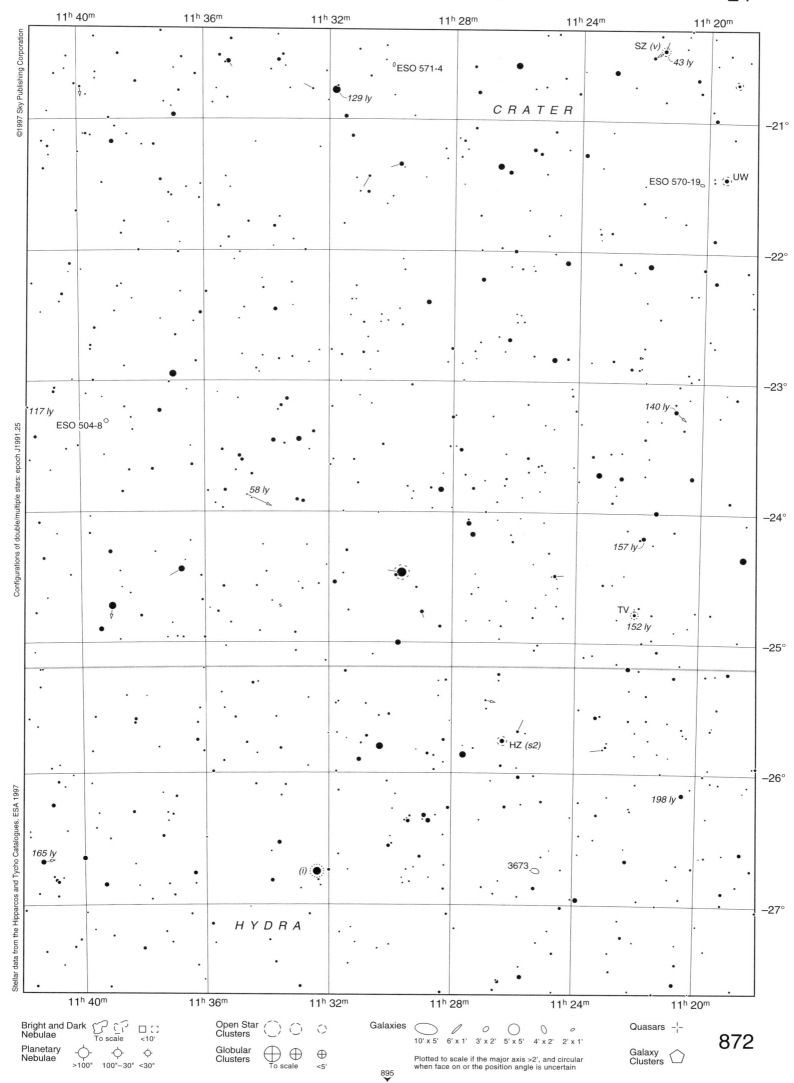

Configurations of double/multiple stars: epoch J1991.25

Stellar data from the Hipparcos and Tycho Catalogues, ESA 1997

11ʰ 40ᵐ   11ʰ 36ᵐ   11ʰ 32ᵐ   11ʰ 28ᵐ   11ʰ 24ᵐ   11ʰ 20ᵐ

SZ *(v)*
43 ly
ESO 571-4
129 ly

C R A T E R

−21°

ESO 570-19 ∘ ⊙ UW

−22°

117 ly
ESO 504-8 ∘
140 ly

−23°

58 ly
157 ly

−24°

TV
152 ly

−25°

HZ *(s2)*

−26°

198 ly

165 ly
(i)
3673

−27°

H Y D R A

11ʰ 40ᵐ   11ʰ 36ᵐ   11ʰ 32ᵐ   11ʰ 28ᵐ   11ʰ 24ᵐ   11ʰ 20ᵐ

Bright and Dark Nebulae · To scale · <10'
Planetary Nebulae · >100" · 100"–30" · <30"
Open Star Clusters
Globular Clusters · To scale · <5'
Galaxies · 10' x 5' · 6' x 1' · 3' x 2' · 5' x 5' · 4' x 2' · 2' x 1'
Plotted to scale if the major axis >2', and circular when face on or the position angle is uncertain
Quasars
Galaxy Clusters

872

895

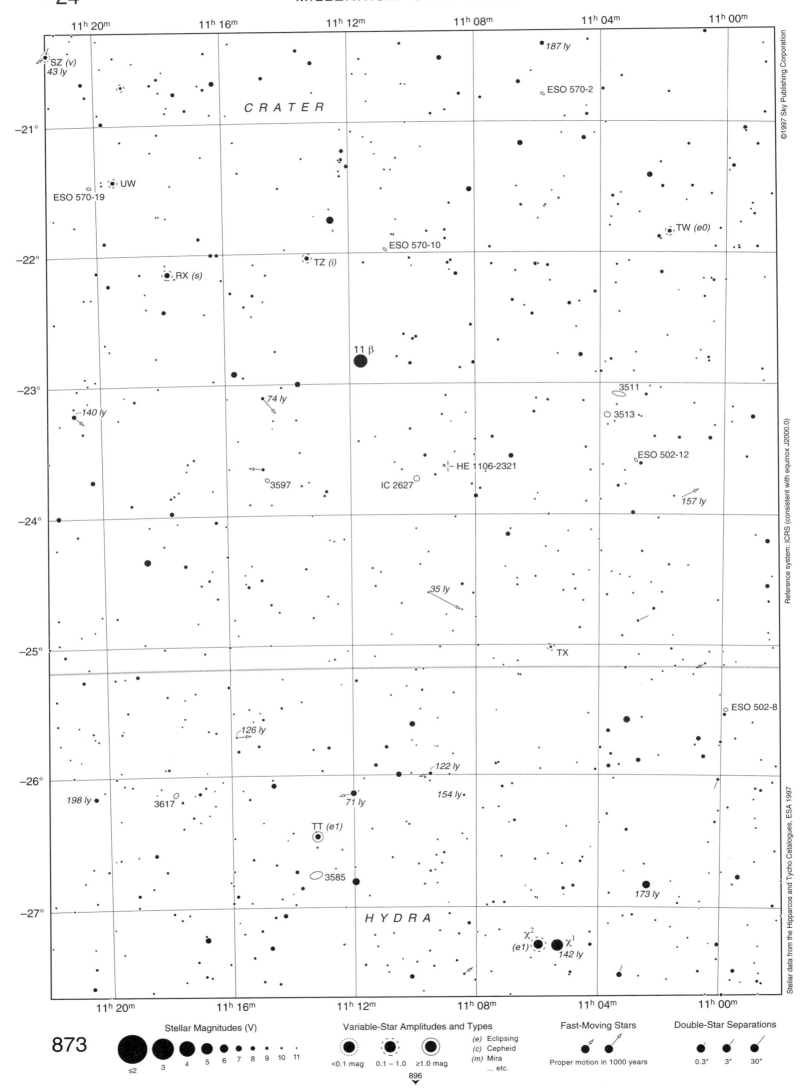

11h 20m 11h 16m 11h 12m 11h 08m 11h 04m 11h 00m

SZ (v)
43 ly

CRATER

187 ly

ESO 570-2

−21°

UW
ESO 570-19

TW (e0)

ESO 570-10

−22°

TZ (i)

RX (s)

11 β

−23°

3511

140 ly

74 ly

3513

ESO 502-12

HE 1106-2321

3597

IC 2627

157 ly

−24°

35 ly

−25°

TX

ESO 502-8

126 ly

122 ly

−26°

198 ly

3617

71 ly

154 ly

TT (e1)

3585

173 ly

−27°

HYDRA

χ²
(e1)   χ¹
142 ly

11h 20m 11h 16m 11h 12m 11h 08m 11h 04m 11h 00m

©1997 Sky Publishing Corporation

Reference system: ICRS (consistent with equinox J2000.0)

Stellar data from the Hipparcos and Tycho Catalogues, ESA 1997

873

Stellar Magnitudes (V)

≤2 3 4 5 6 7 8 9 10 11

Variable-Star Amplitudes and Types

<0.1 mag   0.1 – 1.0   ≥1.0 mag

(e) Eclipsing
(c) Cepheid
(m) Mira
… etc.

Fast-Moving Stars

Proper motion in 1000 years

Double-Star Separations

0.3"   3"   30"

896

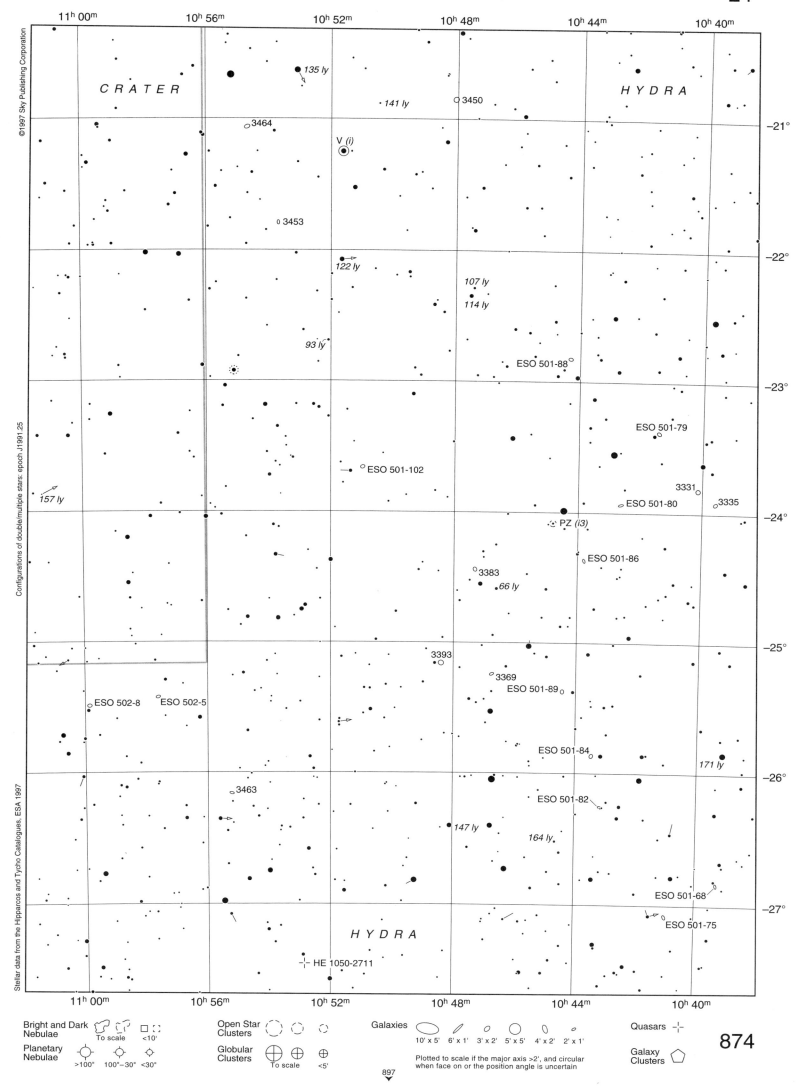

CRATER

HYDRA

135 ly

141 ly

○ 3450

○ 3464

V (i)

○ 3453

−21°

122 ly

107 ly

114 ly

93 ly

ESO 501-88 ○

−22°

ESO 501-79

ESO 501-102 ○

3331 ○

ESO 501-80 ○

3335 ○

PZ (i3)

−23°

ESO 501-86 ○

3383 ○

66 ly

−24°

3393 ○

3369 ○

ESO 501-89 ○

ESO 502-8 ○

ESO 502-5 ○

ESO 501-84 ○

171 ly

−25°

3463 ○

ESO 501-82 ○

147 ly

164 ly

ESO 501-68

−26°

ESO 501-75 ○

HYDRA

HE 1050-2711

−27°

11h 00m   10h 56m   10h 52m   10h 48m   10h 44m   10h 40m

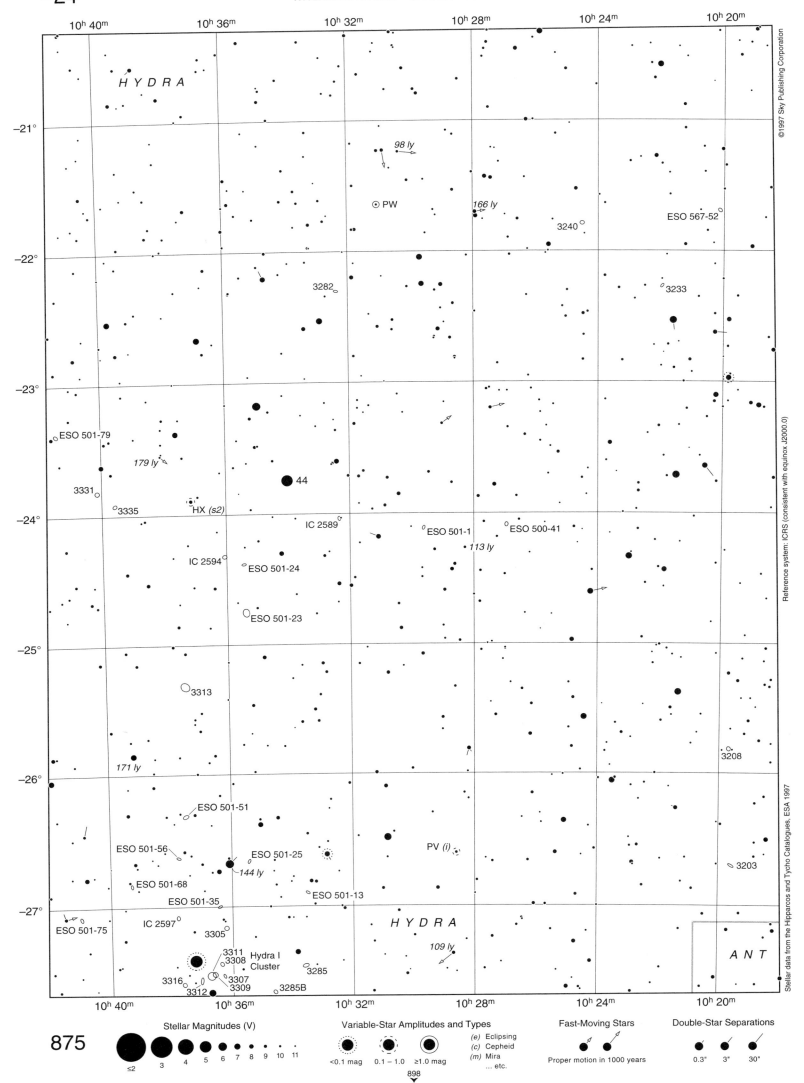

851

©1997 Sky Publishing Corporation

Reference system: ICRS (consistent with equinox J2000.0)

Stellar data from the Hipparcos and Tycho Catalogues, ESA 1997

HYDRA

98 ly

⊙ PW

166 ly

ESO 567-52

3240 ○

3282

3233

ESO 501-79

179 ly

3331

3335

44

HX (s2)

IC 2589

ESO 501-1

ESO 500-41

IC 2594

113 ly

ESO 501-24

ESO 501-23

3313

3208

171 ly

ESO 501-51

ESO 501-56

ESO 501-25

PV (i)

ESO 501-68

144 ly

3203

ESO 501-35

ESO 501-13

HYDRA

ESO 501-75

IC 2597

3305

109 ly

ANT

3311

Hydra I Cluster

3308

3316

3307

3285

3312

3309

3285B

875

898

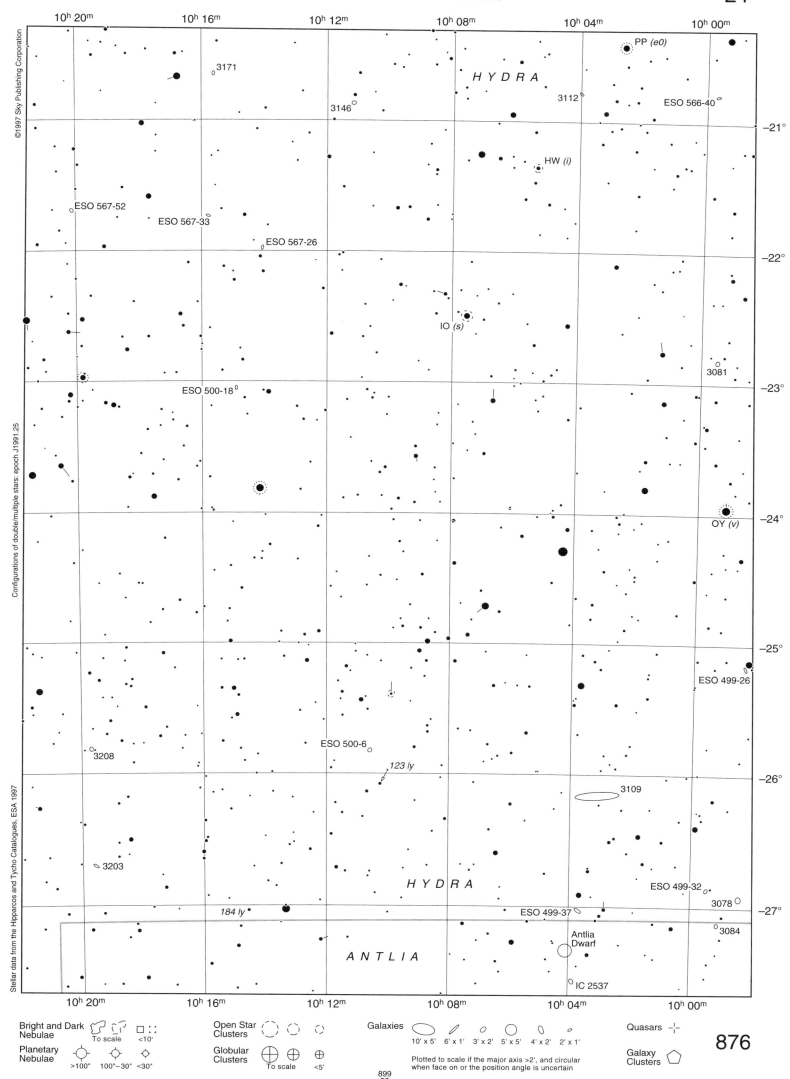

HYDRA

PP *(e0)*

3112

ESO 566-40

−21°

HW *(i)*

ESO 567-52

ESO 567-33

ESO 567-26

−22°

IO *(s)*

3081

3171

3146

ESO 500-18

−23°

OY *(v)*

−24°

ESO 499-26

−25°

ESO 500-6

123 ly

3109

3208

−26°

3203

HYDRA

ESO 499-32

3078

184 ly

ESO 499-37

3084

−27°

Antlia
Dwarf

ANTLIA

IC 2537

Bright and Dark Nebulae
To scale   <10'

Planetary Nebulae
>100"   100"–30"   <30"

Open Star Clusters

Globular Clusters
To scale   <5'

Galaxies
10' x 5'   6' x 1'   3' x 2'   5' x 5'   4' x 2'   2' x 1'

Plotted to scale if the major axis >2', and circular when face on or the position angle is uncertain

Quasars

Galaxy Clusters

876

899 ▼

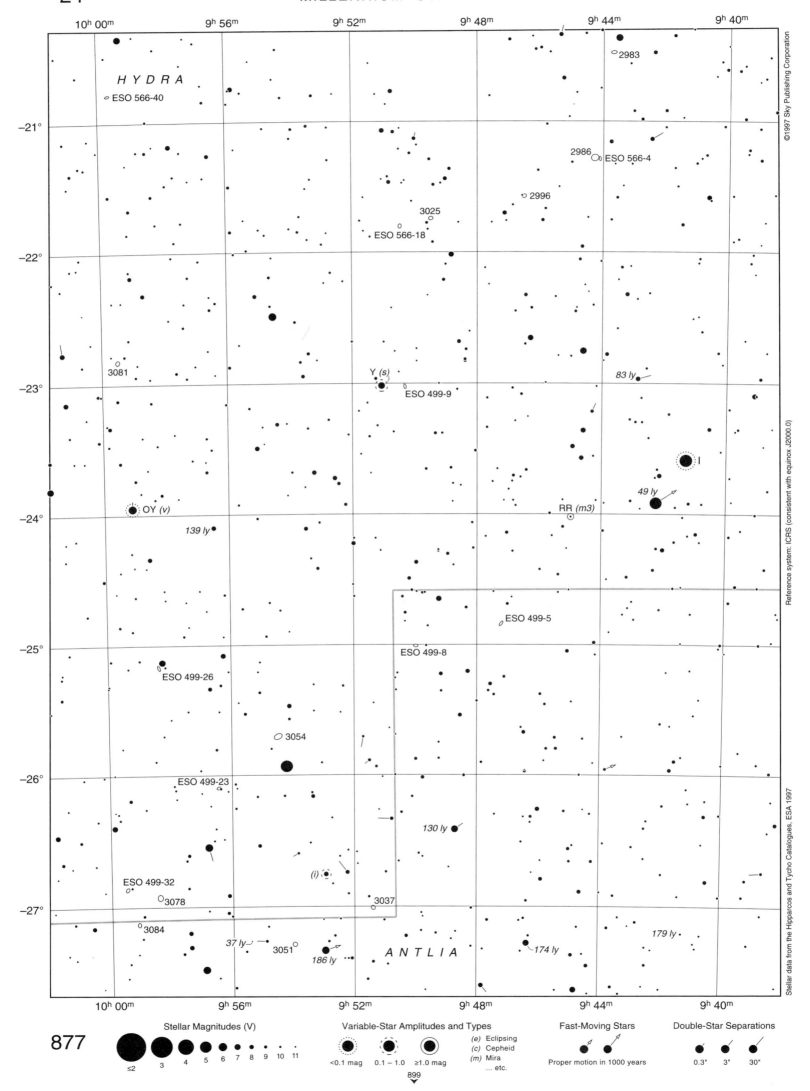

©1997 Sky Publishing Corporation

Reference system: ICRS (consistent with equinox J2000.0)

Stellar data from the Hipparcos and Tycho Catalogues, ESA 1997

HYDRA

ESO 566-40

−21°

2983

2986 ESO 566-4

2996

3025
ESO 566-18

−22°

3081

Y (s)
ESO 499-9

83 ly

I

49 ly

OY (v)

RR (m3)

−24°

139 ly

ESO 499-5

ESO 499-8

−25°

ESO 499-26

3054

130 ly

ESO 499-23

−26°

ESO 499-32

(i)

3078

3037

179 ly

−27°

3084

37 ly

3051

174 ly

186 ly

ANTLIA

877

Stellar Magnitudes (V)

≤2   3   4   5   6   7 8 9 10 11

Variable-Star Amplitudes and Types

<0.1 mag   0.1 – 1.0   ≥1.0 mag

(e) Eclipsing
(c) Cepheid
(m) Mira
... etc.

Fast-Moving Stars

Proper motion in 1000 years

Double-Star Separations

0.3"   3"   30"

899

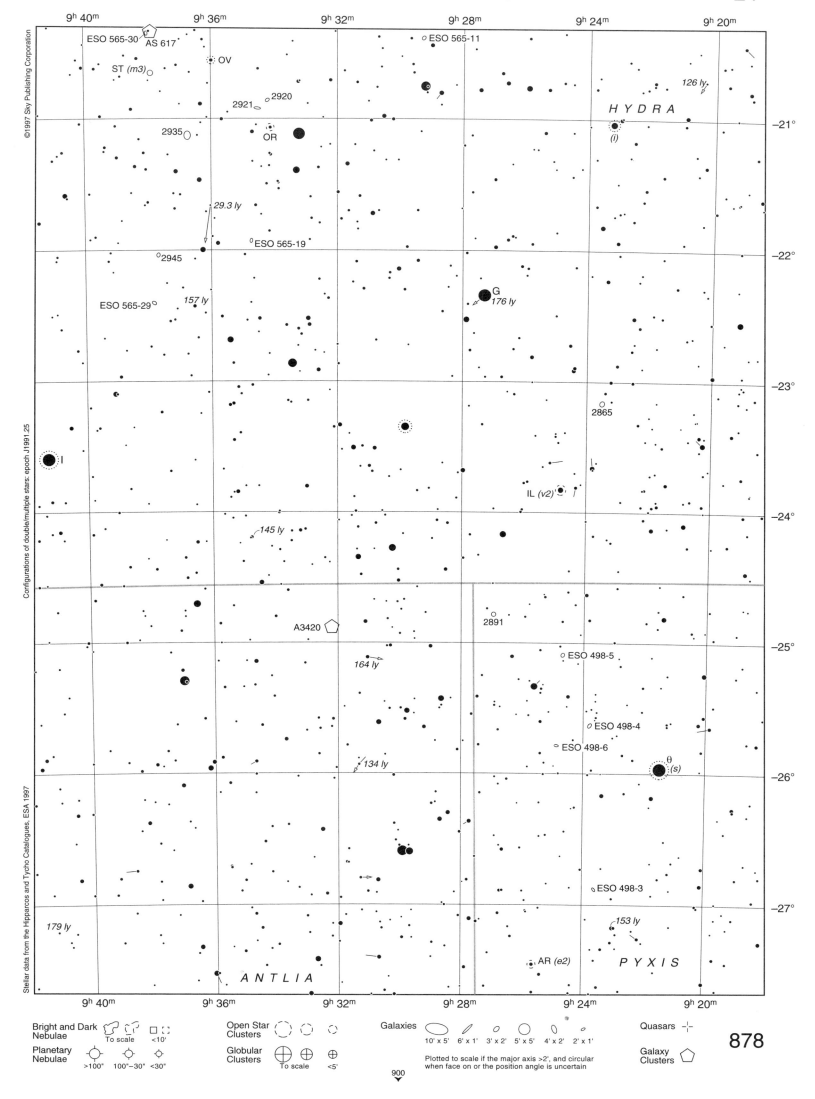

ESO 565-30
AS 617
OV
ST *(m3)*
2921 2920
2935
OR
29.3 ly
ESO 565-19
2945
ESO 565-29
157 ly

ESO 565-11

HYDRA

126 ly

(i)

G
176 ly

2865

IL *(v2)*

I

145 ly

A3420

164 ly

2891

ESO 498-5

ESO 498-4

ESO 498-6

θ
(s)

134 ly

ESO 498-3

179 ly

153 ly

AR *(e2)*

PYXIS

ANTLIA

Bright and Dark Nebulae				Open Star Clusters			Galaxies							Quasars
To scale	<10'						10' x 5'	6' x 1'	3' x 2'	5' x 5'	4' x 2'	2' x 1'		
Planetary Nebulae				Globular Clusters										Galaxy Clusters
>100"	100"−30"	<30"		To scale	<5'		Plotted to scale if the major axis >2', and circular when face on or the position angle is uncertain							

878

900

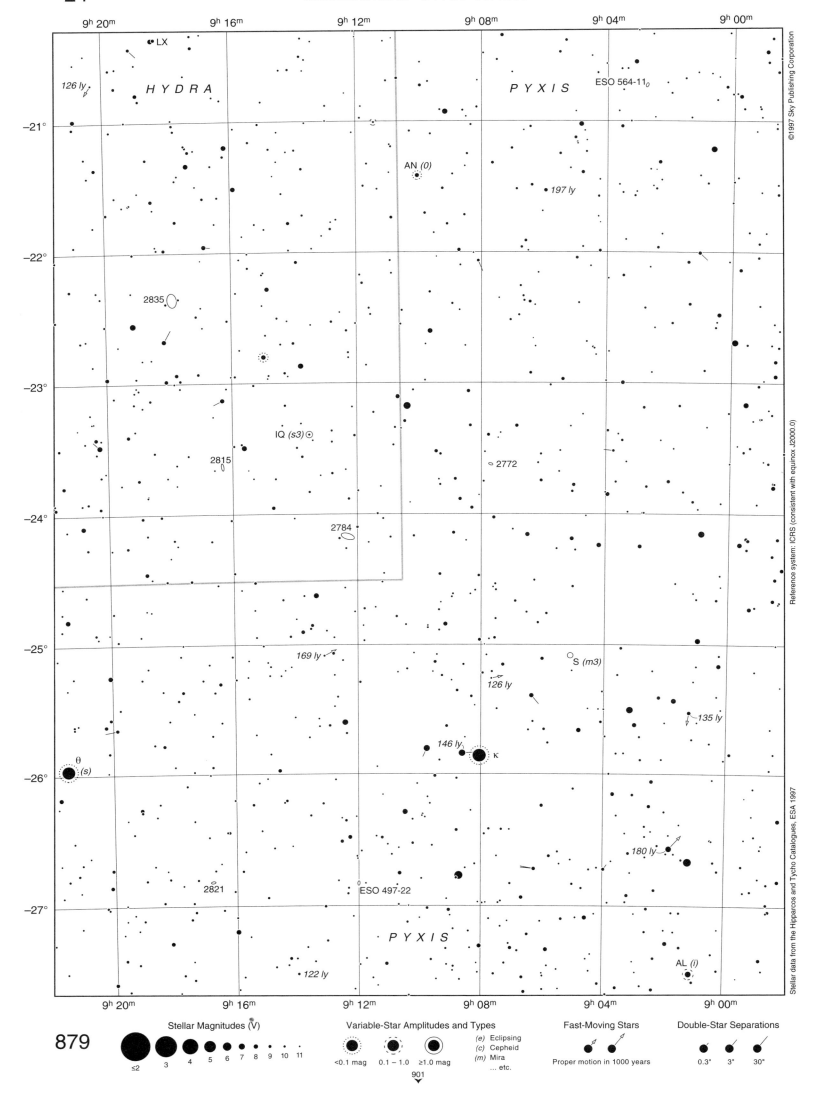

Reference system: ICRS (consistent with equinox J2000.0)

Stellar data from the Hipparcos and Tycho Catalogues, ESA 1997

879

901

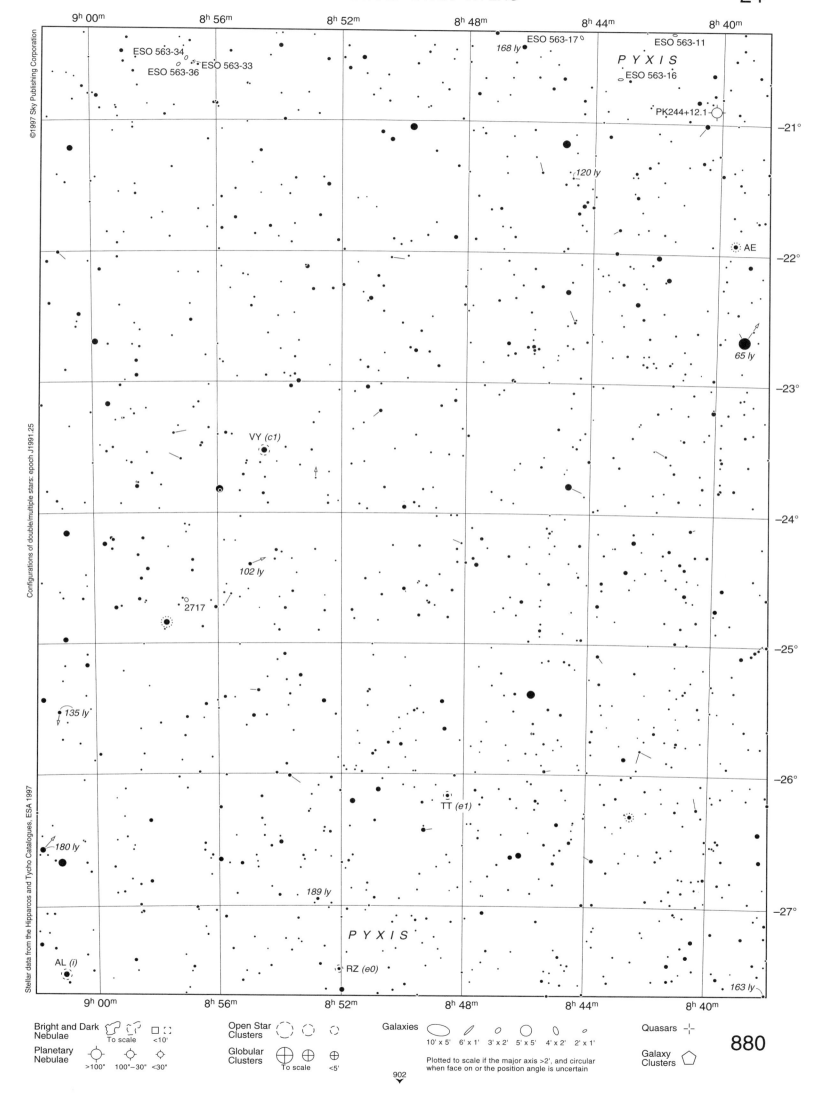

9h 00m   8h 56m   8h 52m   8h 48m   8h 44m   8h 40m

ESO 563-34
ESO 563-36   ESO 563-33

ESO 563-17
168 ly   ESO 563-11

PYXIS

ESO 563-16

PK244+12.1

−21°

120 ly

AE

−22°

65 ly

−23°

VY (c1)

−24°

102 ly

2717

−25°

135 ly

−26°

TT (e1)

180 ly

189 ly

−27°

PYXIS

AL (i)

RZ (e0)

163 ly

9h 00m   8h 56m   8h 52m   8h 48m   8h 44m   8h 40m

Bright and Dark
Nebulae
To scale   <10'

Open Star
Clusters

Galaxies

10' x 5' 6' x 1' 3' x 2' 5' x 5' 4' x 2' 2' x 1'

Quasars

Planetary
Nebulae
>100" 100"–30" <30"

Globular
Clusters
To scale   <5'

Plotted to scale if the major axis >2', and circular
when face on or the position angle is uncertain

Galaxy
Clusters

880

902

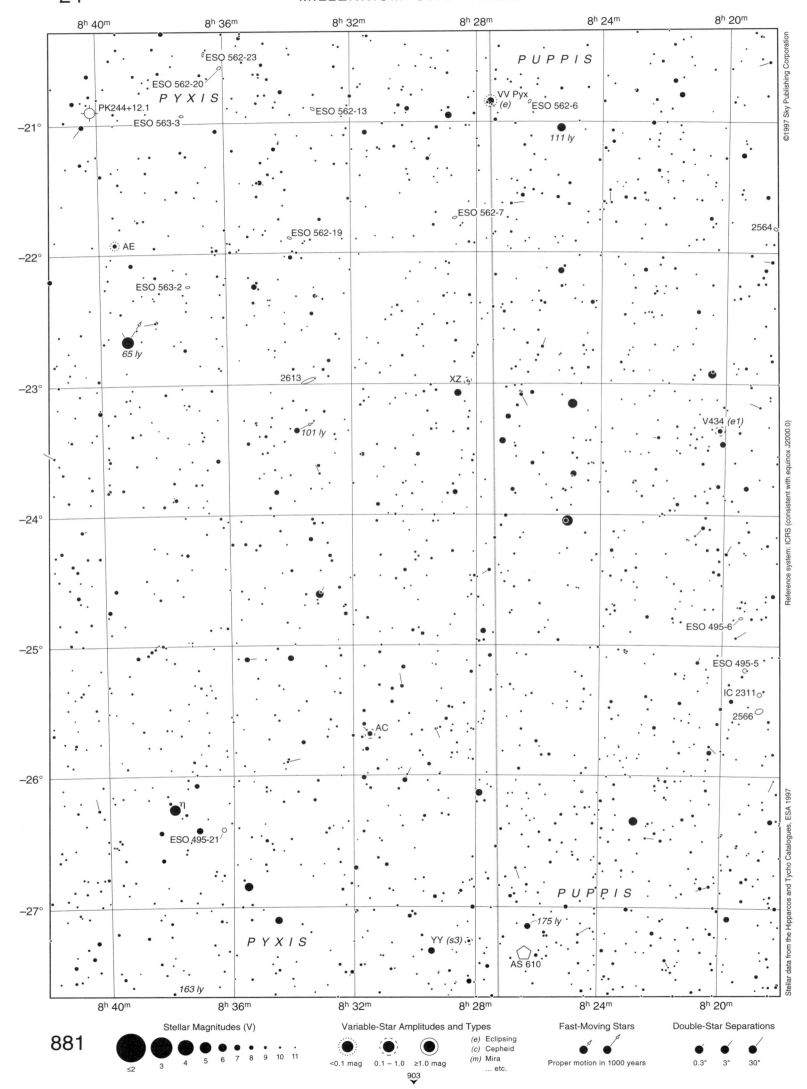

©1997 Sky Publishing Corporation

Reference system: ICRS (consistent with equinox J2000.0)

Stellar data from the Hipparcos and Tycho Catalogues, ESA 1997

857

PUPPIS

8ʰ 40ᵐ   8ʰ 36ᵐ   8ʰ 32ᵐ   8ʰ 28ᵐ   8ʰ 24ᵐ   8ʰ 20ᵐ

ESO 562-23
ESO 562-20
PYXIS
PK244+12.1
ESO 563-3
VV Pyx (e)
ESO 562-13
ESO 562-6
111 ly
−21°

ESO 562-7
ESO 562-19
2564

AE
−22°
ESO 563-2
65 ly

2613
XZ
−23°
101 ly
V434 (e1)

−24°

ESO 495-6
−25°
ESO 495-5
IC 2311
AC
2566

η
−26°
ESO 495-21
PUPPIS

−27°
PYXIS
175 ly
YY (s3)
AS 610
163 ly

8ʰ 40ᵐ   8ʰ 36ᵐ   8ʰ 32ᵐ   8ʰ 28ᵐ   8ʰ 24ᵐ   8ʰ 20ᵐ

881

Stellar Magnitudes (V)
≤2   3   4   5   6   7   8   9   10   11

Variable-Star Amplitudes and Types
<0.1 mag   0.1 – 1.0   ≥1.0 mag

(e) Eclipsing
(c) Cepheid
(m) Mira
... etc.

Fast-Moving Stars
Proper motion in 1000 years

Double-Star Separations
0.3"   3"   30"

MILLENNIUM STAR ATLAS

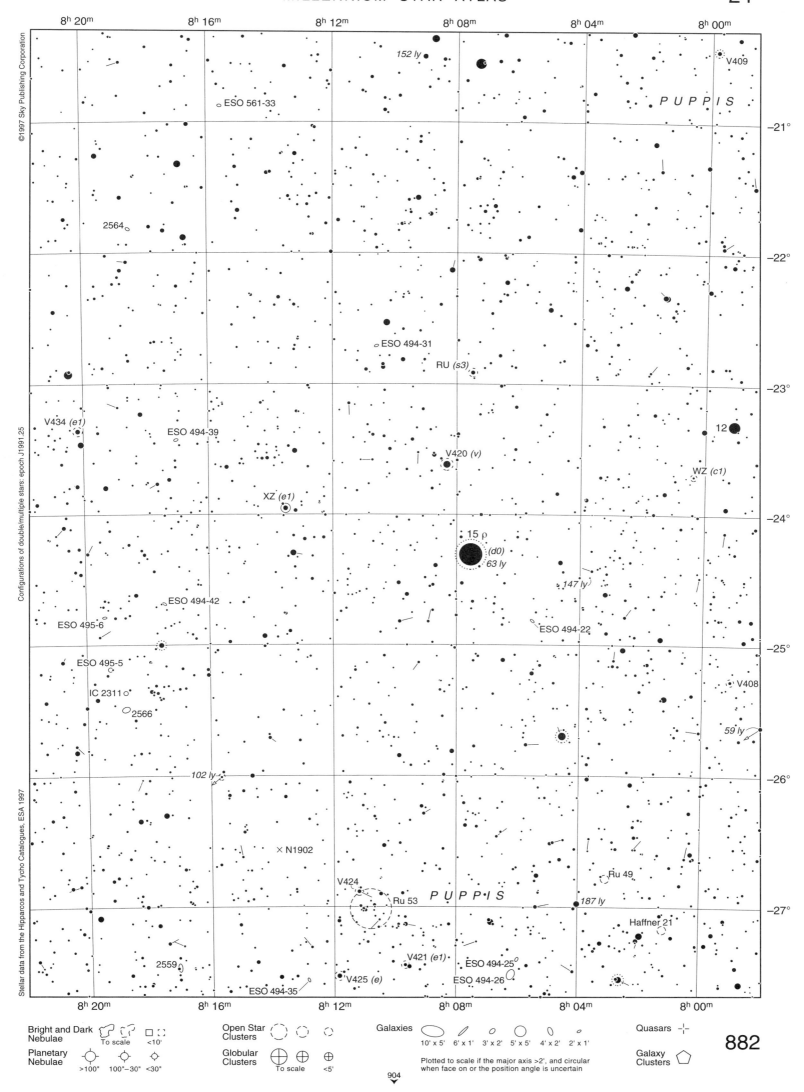

©1997 Sky Publishing Corporation

Configurations of double/multiple stars: epoch J1991.25

Stellar data from the Hipparcos and Tycho Catalogues, ESA 1997

PUPPIS

V409

ESO 561-33

152 ly

2564

ESO 494-31

RU (s3)

V434 (e1)

ESO 494-39

12

WZ (c1)

V420 (v)

XZ (e1)

15 ρ

(d0)
63 ly

147 ly

ESO 494-42

ESO 494-22

ESO 495-6

ESO 495-5

V408

IC 2311

2566

59 ly

102 ly

× N1902

Ru 49

V424

Ru 53   PUPPIS   187 ly

Haffner 21

2559

V421 (e1)

ESO 494-25

V425 (e)   ESO 494-26

ESO 494-35

Bright and Dark Nebulae
To scale   <10'

Planetary Nebulae
>100" 100"−30" <30'

Open Star Clusters

Globular Clusters
To scale   <5'

Galaxies
10' x 5' 6' x 1' 3' x 2' 5' x 5' 4' x 2' 2' x 1'

Plotted to scale if the major axis >2', and circular
when face on or the position angle is uncertain

Quasars

Galaxy Clusters

882

904

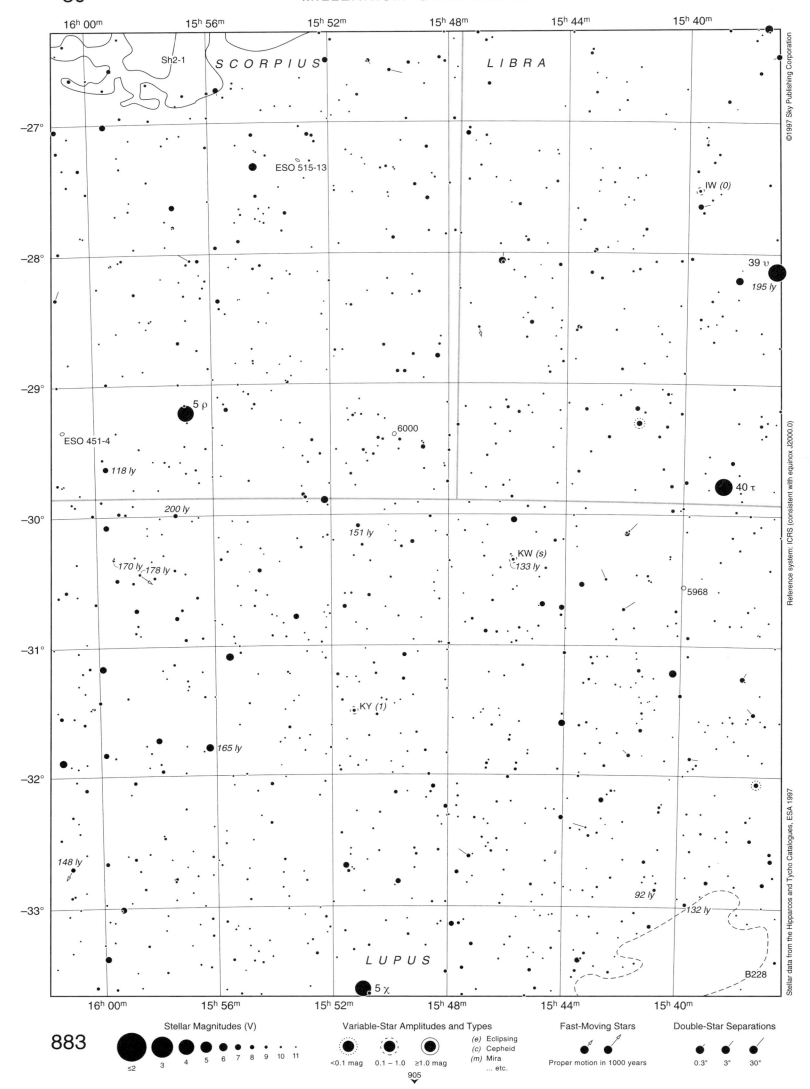

Sh2-1

S C O R P I U S

L I B R A

−27°

ESO 515-13

IW *(0)*

39 υ

−28°

195 ly

5 ρ

ESO 451-4

6000

40 τ

118 ly

−29°

200 ly

151 ly

−30°

KW *(s)*

133 ly

170 ly 178 ly

5968

−31°

KY *(1)*

165 ly

−32°

148 ly

92 ly

−33°

132 ly

B228

L U P U S

5 χ

©1997 Sky Publishing Corporation

Reference system: ICRS (consistent with equinox J2000.0)

Stellar data from the Hipparcos and Tycho Catalogues, ESA 1997

883

Stellar Magnitudes (V)

≤2   3   4   5   6 7 8 9 10 11

Variable-Star Amplitudes and Types

<0.1 mag   0.1 – 1.0   ≥1.0 mag

(e) Eclipsing
(c) Cepheid
(m) Mira
... etc.

Fast-Moving Stars

Proper motion in 1000 years

Double-Star Separations

0.3"   3"   30"

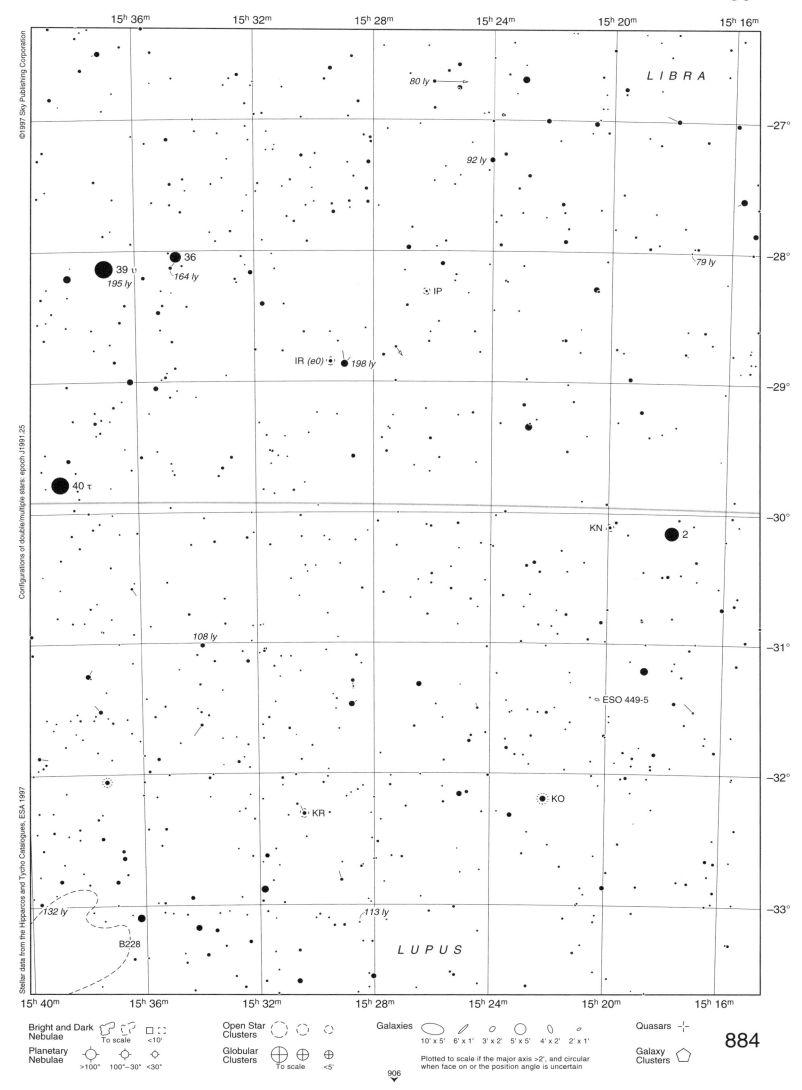

Configurations of double/multiple stars: epoch J1991.25

Stellar data from the Hipparcos and Tycho Catalogues, ESA 1997

L I B R A

80 ly

92 ly

79 ly

36

39 υ
195 ly
164 ly

IP

IR (e0)
198 ly

40 τ

KN
2

108 ly

ESO 449-5

KR

KO

132 ly
113 ly

B228

L U P U S

15ʰ 36ᵐ 15ʰ 32ᵐ 15ʰ 28ᵐ 15ʰ 24ᵐ 15ʰ 20ᵐ 15ʰ 16ᵐ

−27°
−28°
−29°
−30°
−31°
−32°
−33°

15ʰ 40ᵐ 15ʰ 36ᵐ 15ʰ 32ᵐ 15ʰ 28ᵐ 15ʰ 24ᵐ 15ʰ 20ᵐ 15ʰ 16ᵐ

Bright and Dark
Nebulae
To scale   <10'

Planetary
Nebulae
>100" 100"–30" <30"

Open Star
Clusters

Globular
Clusters
To scale   <5'

Galaxies
10' x 5' 6' x 1' 3' x 2' 5' x 5' 4' x 2' 2' x 1'

Plotted to scale if the major axis >2', and circular
when face on or the position angle is uncertain

Quasars

Galaxy
Clusters

884

906

MILLENNIUM STAR ATLAS

−30°

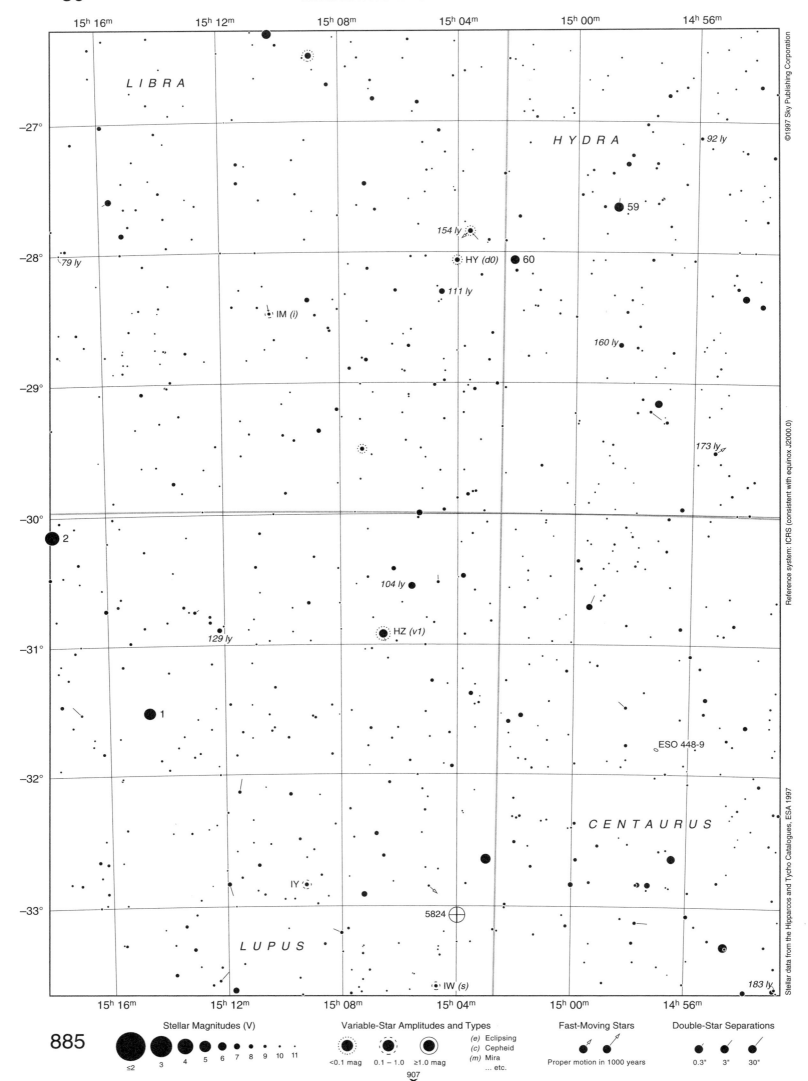

Reference system: ICRS (consistent with equinox J2000.0)

Stellar data from the Hipparcos and Tycho Catalogues, ESA 1997

LIBRA

HYDRA

92 ly

59

154 ly

79 ly

HY *(d0)* 60

111 ly

IM *(i)*

160 ly

173 ly

2

104 ly

HZ *(v1)*

129 ly

1

ESO 448-9

CENTAURUS

IY

5824

LUPUS

IW *(s)*

183 ly

885

Stellar Magnitudes (V)	Variable-Star Amplitudes and Types	Fast-Moving Stars	Double-Star Separations
≤2 3 4 5 6 7 8 9 10 11	<0.1 mag 0.1 − 1.0 ≥1.0 mag	Proper motion in 1000 years	0.3" 3" 30"

(e) Eclipsing
(c) Cepheid
(m) Mira
... etc.

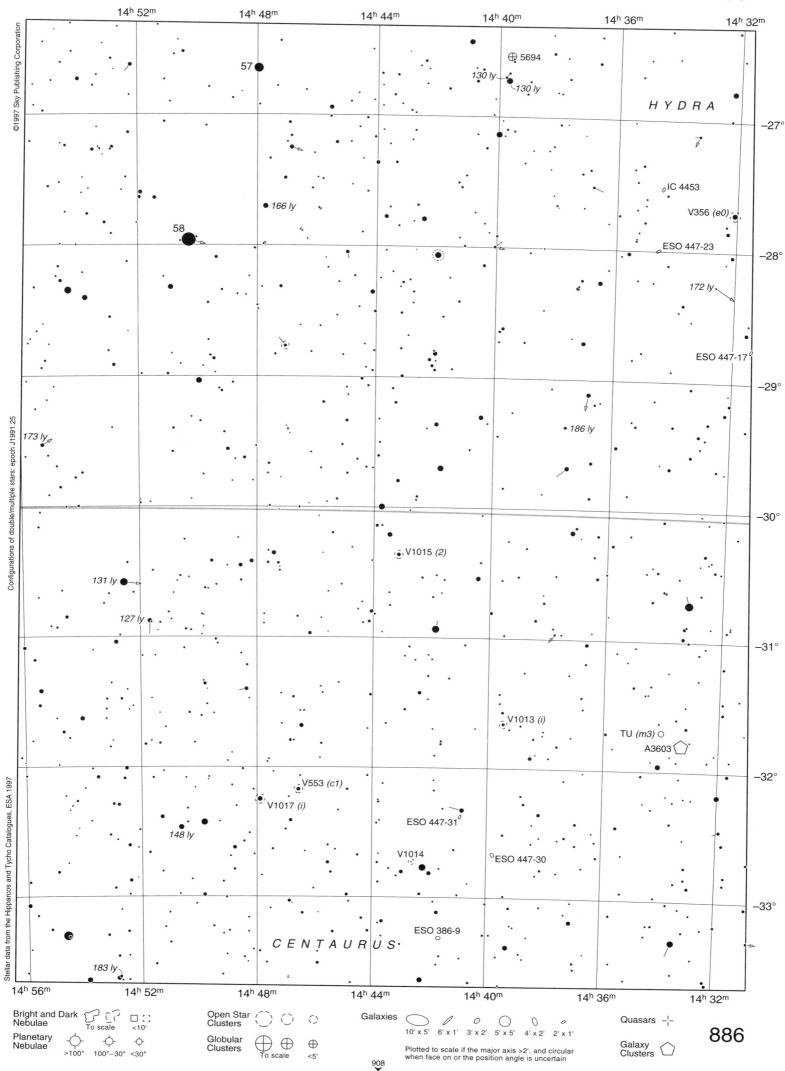

©1997 Sky Publishing Corporation

Configurations of double/multiple stars: epoch J1991.25

Stellar data from the Hipparcos and Tycho Catalogues, ESA 1997

14h 52m 14h 48m 14h 44m 14h 40m 14h 36m 14h 32m

HYDRA

57

⊕ 5694

130 ly
130 ly

166 ly

IC 4453

V356 *(e0)*

58

ESO 447-23

−28°

172 ly

ESO 447-17

−29°

173 ly

186 ly

−30°

V1015 *(2)*

131 ly

127 ly

−31°

V1013 *(i)*

TU *(m3)*
A3603

−32°

V553 *(c1)*

V1017 *(i)*

ESO 447-31

148 ly

V1014

ESO 447-30

−33°

ESO 386-9

CENTAURUS

183 ly

14h 56m 14h 52m 14h 48m 14h 44m 14h 40m 14h 36m 14h 32m

Bright and Dark Nebulae	To scale	<10'	Open Star Clusters	Galaxies	10' x 5'	6' x 1'	3' x 2'	5' x 5'	4' x 2'	2' x 1'	Quasars

Planetary Nebulae >100" 100"−30" <30"

Globular Clusters To scale <5'

Galaxies Plotted to scale if the major axis >2', and circular when face on or the position angle is uncertain

Galaxy Clusters

886

MILLENNIUM STAR ATLAS

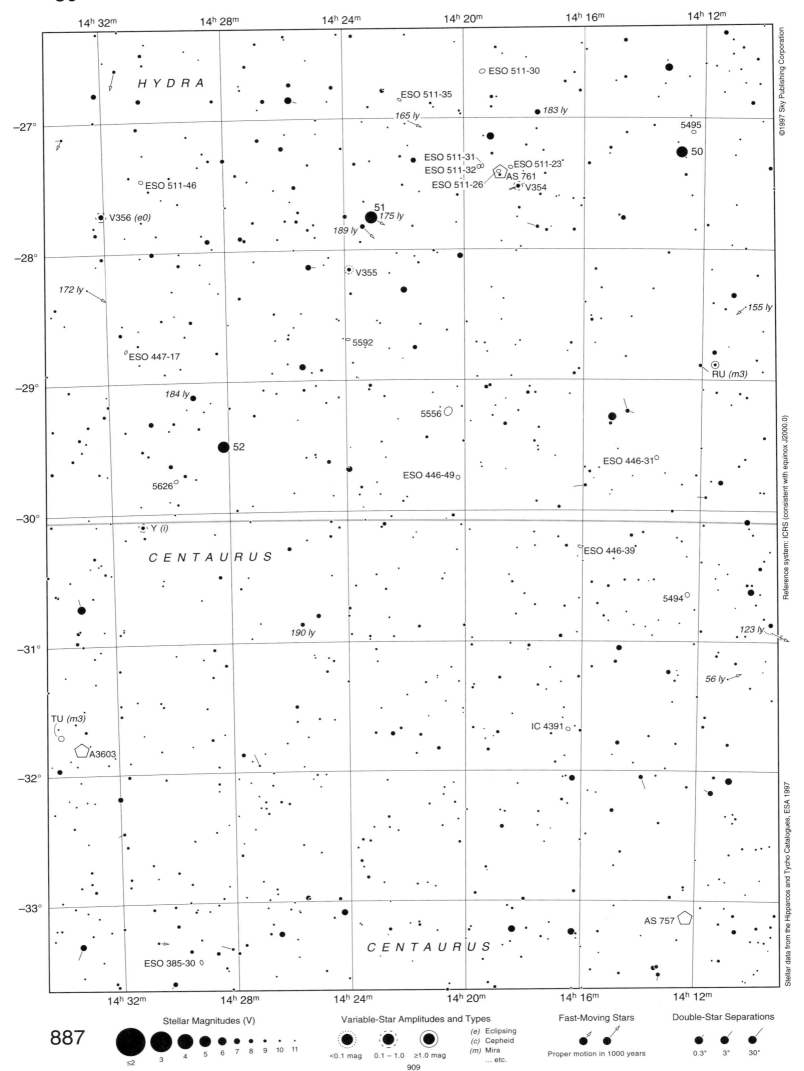

©1997 Sky Publishing Corporation

Reference system: ICRS (consistent with equinox J2000.0)

Stellar data from the Hipparcos and Tycho Catalogues, ESA 1997

887

Stellar Magnitudes (V)
≤2 3 4 5 6 7 8 9 10 11

Variable-Star Amplitudes and Types
<0.1 mag   0.1 – 1.0   ≥1.0 mag

(e) Eclipsing
(c) Cepheid
(m) Mira
... etc.

Fast-Moving Stars
Proper motion in 1000 years

Double-Star Separations
0.3" 3" 30"

909

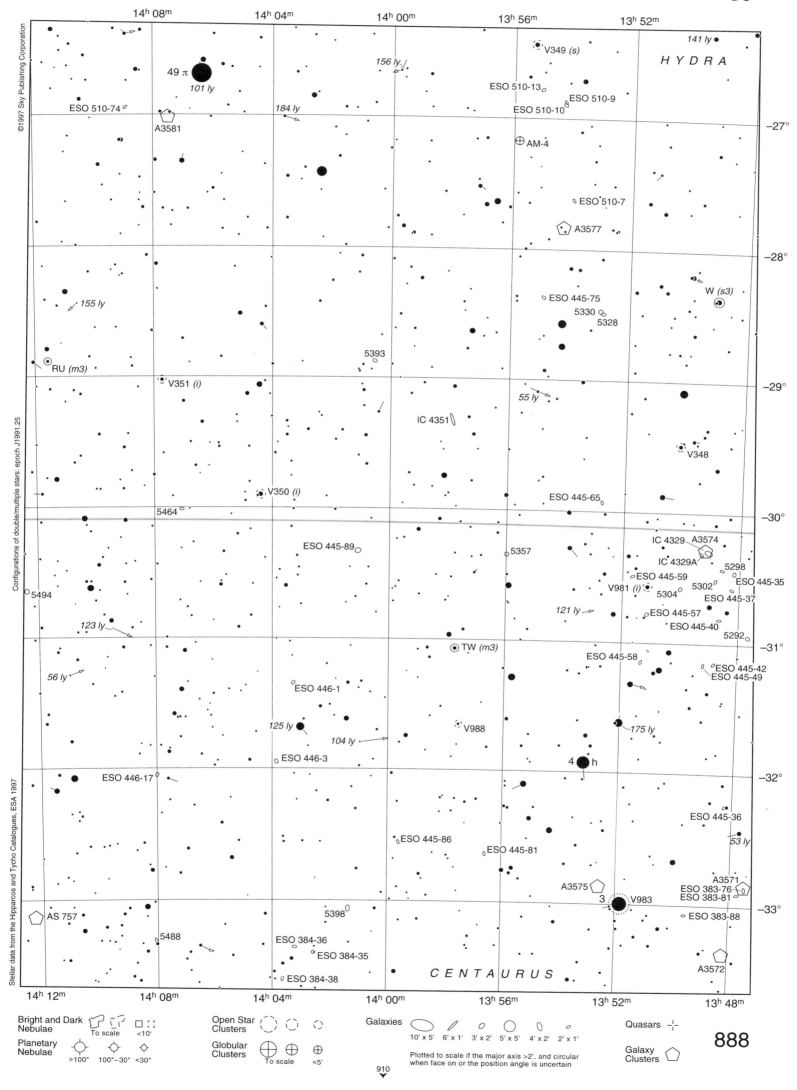

14h 08m   14h 04m   14h 00m   13h 56m   13h 52m

141 ly

V349 (s)

H Y D R A

ESO 510-13

ESO 510-9

ESO 510-74   ESO 510-10

A3581

49 π

101 ly

184 ly

AM-4

−27°

ESO 510-7

A3577

155 ly

ESO 445-75

W (s3)

5330

5328

RU (m3)

5393

V351 (i)

−28°

IC 4351

55 ly

V348

V350 (i)

ESO 445-65

−29°

5464

IC 4329 A3574

ESO 445-89

5357   IC 4329A

5298   ESO 445-35

5494   ESO 445-59

5302   ESO 445-37

V981 (i)   5304

121 ly   ESO 445-57   5292

ESO 445-40

−30°

123 ly

56 ly

TW (m3)

ESO 445-58

ESO 445-42
ESO 445-49

ESO 446-1

175 ly

125 ly   104 ly   V988

4 h

−31°

ESO 446-3

ESO 446-17

ESO 445-36

53 ly

ESO 445-86

ESO 445-81

−32°

A3575   A3571

3 V983   ESO 383-76
ESO 383-81

AS 757   5398   ESO 383-88

−33°

5488

ESO 384-36

ESO 384-35

A3572

ESO 384-38   *C E N T A U R U S*

14h 12m   14h 08m   14h 04m   14h 00m   13h 56m   13h 52m   13h 48m

Bright and Dark Nebulae	Open Star Clusters	Galaxies						Quasars
To scale <10'		10' x 5' 6' x 1' 3' x 2' 5' x 5' 4' x 2' 2' x 1'						
Planetary Nebulae	Globular Clusters							Galaxy Clusters
>100" 100"−30" <30"	To scale <5'	Plotted to scale if the major axis >2', and circular when face on or the position angle is uncertain						

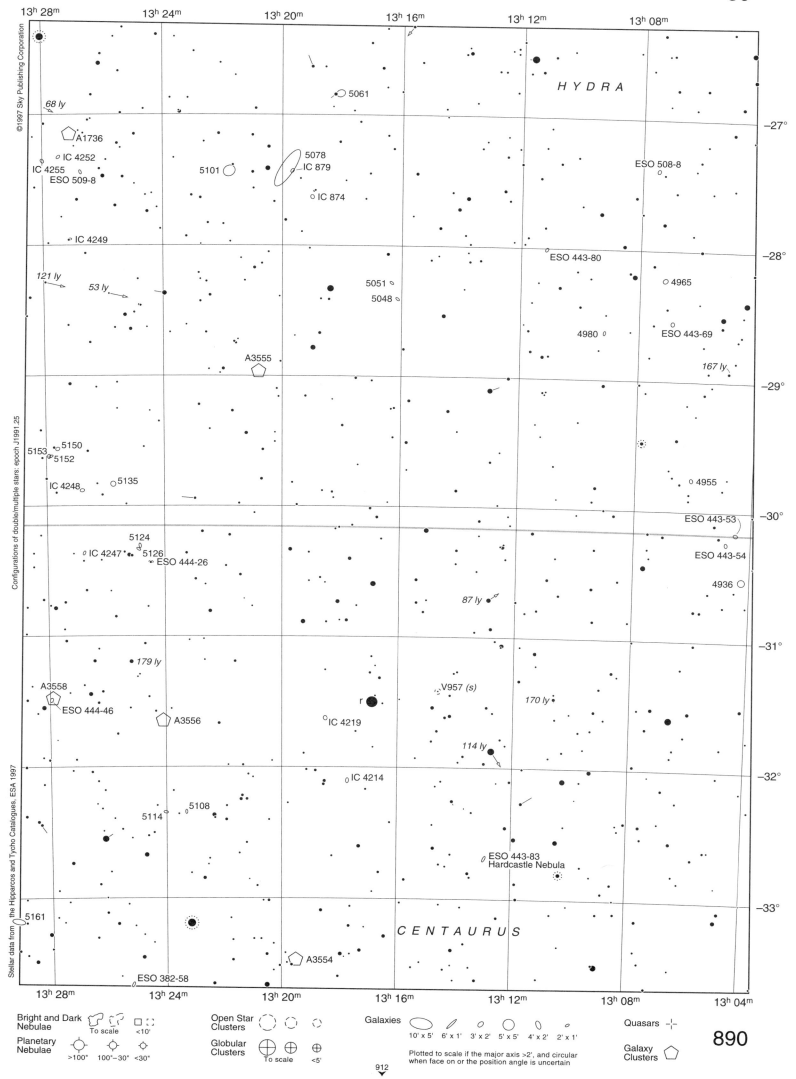

13h 28m   13h 24m   13h 20m   13h 16m   13h 12m   13h 08m

©1997 Sky Publishing Corporation

68 ly

A1736

IC 4252
IC 4255
ESO 509-8

IC 4249

5061

5101

5078
IC 879

IC 874

HYDRA

ESO 508-8

ESO 443-80

−27°

−28°

121 ly   *53 ly*

5051
5048

A3555

4965

4980

ESO 443-69

167 ly

−29°

Configurations of double/multiple stars: epoch J1991.25

5153 5150
5152

IC 4248   5135

4955

ESO 443-53

−30°

5124
IC 4247   5126
ESO 444-26

87 ly

ESO 443-54

4936

−31°

Stellar data from the Hipparcos and Tycho Catalogues, ESA 1997

179 ly

A3558
ESO 444-46

A3556

r

IC 4219

V957 (s)

170 ly

114 ly

−32°

IC 4214

5114   5108

ESO 443-83
Hardcastle Nebula

−33°

5161

CENTAURUS

A3554

ESO 382-58

13h 28m   13h 24m   13h 20m   13h 16m   13h 12m   13h 08m   13h 04m

Bright and Dark
Nebulae
    To scale   <10'

Planetary
Nebulae
    >100" 100"−30" <30"

Open Star
Clusters

Globular
Clusters
    To scale   <5'

Galaxies

10' x 5' 6' x 1' 3' x 2' 5' x 5' 4' x 2' 2' x 1'

Plotted to scale if the major axis >2', and circular
when face on or the position angle is uncertain

Quasars

Galaxy
Clusters

890

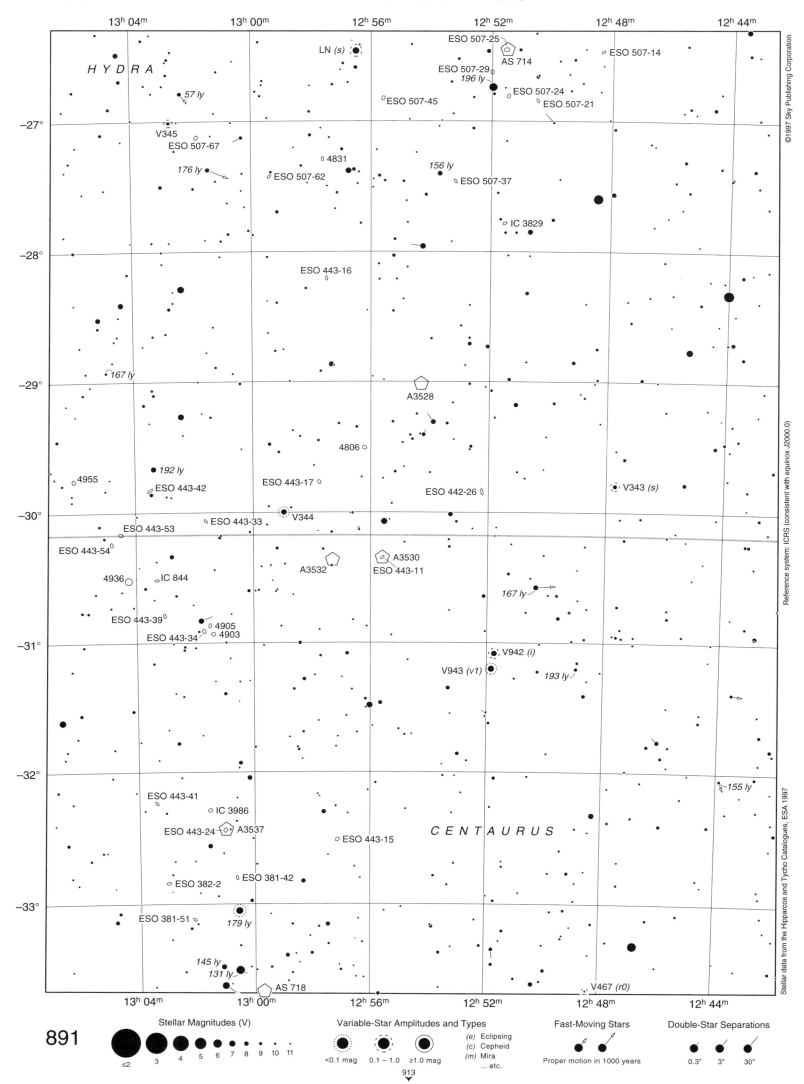

HYDRA

CENTAURUS

©1997 Sky Publishing Corporation

Reference system: ICRS (consistent with equinox J2000.0)

Stellar data from the Hipparcos and Tycho Catalogues, ESA 1997

LN (s)
ESO 507-25
AS 714
ESO 507-29
196 ly
ESO 507-45
ESO 507-24
ESO 507-21
57 ly
V345
ESO 507-67
ESO 507-14
176 ly
4831
156 ly
ESO 507-62
ESO 507-37
IC 3829
ESO 443-16
167 ly
A3528
4806
V343 (s)
4955
192 ly
ESO 443-42
ESO 443-17
ESO 442-26
ESO 443-33
V344
ESO 443-53
A3532
A3530
ESO 443-54
ESO 443-11
167 ly
4936
IC 844
ESO 443-39
4905
V942 (i)
ESO 443-34
4903
V943 (v1)
193 ly
155 ly
ESO 443-41
IC 3986
ESO 443-24
A3537
ESO 443-15
ESO 382-2
ESO 381-42
ESO 381-51
179 ly
145 ly
131 ly
AS 718
V467 (r0)

Stellar Magnitudes (V)
≤2 3 4 5 6 7 8 9 10 11

Variable-Star Amplitudes and Types
<0.1 mag   0.1 – 1.0   ≥1.0 mag
(e) Eclipsing
(c) Cepheid
(m) Mira
... etc.

Fast-Moving Stars
Proper motion in 1000 years

Double-Star Separations
0.3"   3"   30"

913
▽

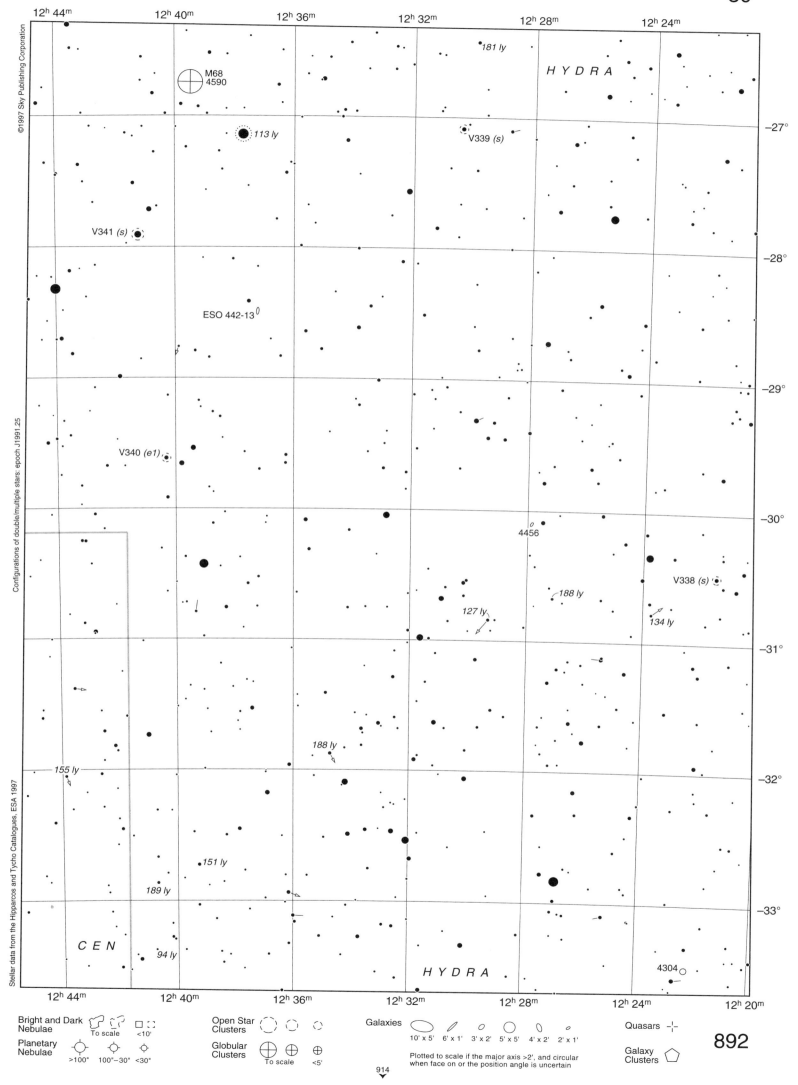

12h 44m   12h 40m   12h 36m   12h 32m   12h 28m   12h 24m

181 ly

H Y D R A

M68
4590

−27°

113 ly

V339 (s)

V341 (s)

−28°

ESO 442-13

−29°

V340 (e1)

4456

−30°

V338 (s)

188 ly

127 ly

134 ly

−31°

188 ly

155 ly

−32°

151 ly

189 ly

−33°

C E N

94 ly

H Y D R A

4304

12h 44m   12h 40m   12h 36m   12h 32m   12h 28m   12h 24m   12h 20m

Bright and Dark
Nebulae
To scale   <10'

Planetary
Nebulae
>100" 100"–30" <30"

Open Star
Clusters

Globular
Clusters
To scale   <5'

Galaxies

10' x 5' 6' x 1' 3' x 2' 5' x 5' 4' x 2' 2' x 1'

Plotted to scale if the major axis >2', and circular
when face on or the position angle is uncertain

Quasars

Galaxy
Clusters

892

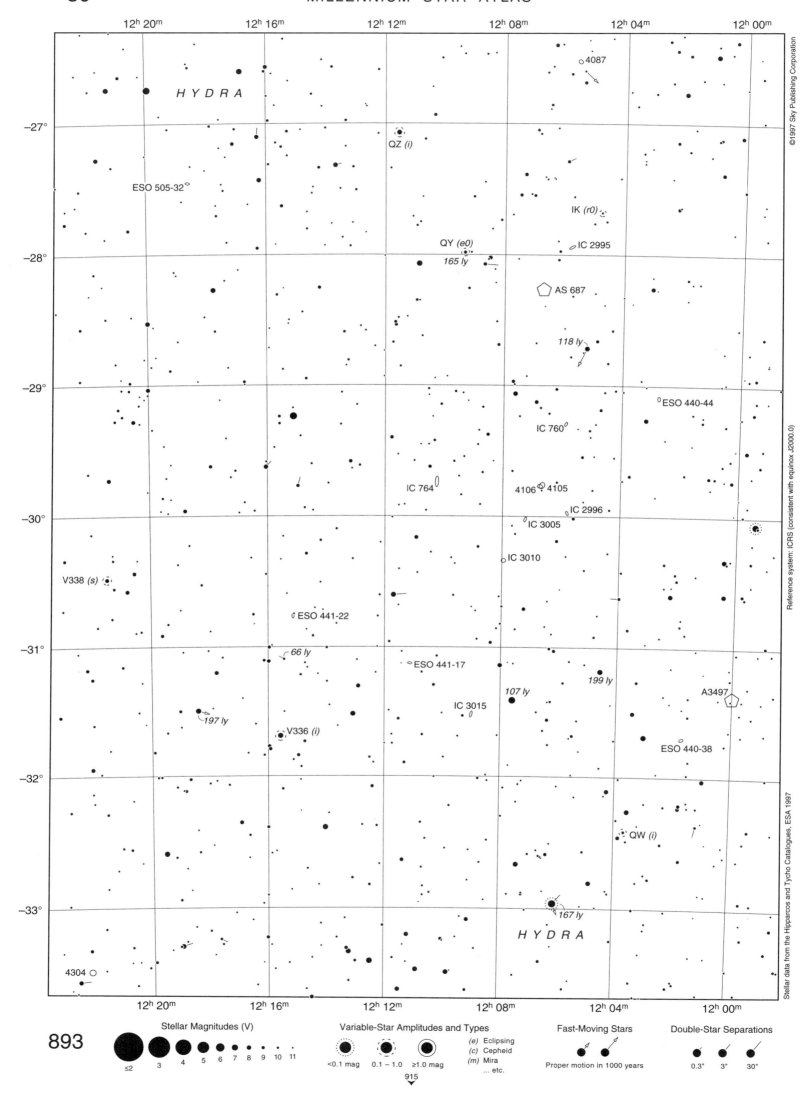

©1997 Sky Publishing Corporation

Reference system: ICRS (consistent with equinox J2000.0)

Stellar data from the Hipparcos and Tycho Catalogues, ESA 1997

HYDRA

12h 20m 12h 16m 12h 12m 12h 08m 12h 04m 12h 00m

4087

QZ (i)

ESO 505-32

IK (r0)

QY (e0)   IC 2995

165 ly

AS 687

118 ly

ESO 440-44

IC 760

IC 764   4106 4105

IC 2996

IC 3005

IC 3010

V338 (s)

ESO 441-22

66 ly

ESO 441-17

199 ly

107 ly   A3497

197 ly

IC 3015

V336 (i)

ESO 440-38

QW (i)

167 ly

HYDRA

4304

Stellar Magnitudes (V)

≤2 3 4 5 6 7 8 9 10 11

Variable-Star Amplitudes and Types

<0.1 mag   0.1 – 1.0   ≥1.0 mag

(e) Eclipsing
(c) Cepheid
(m) Mira
... etc.

Fast-Moving Stars

Proper motion in 1000 years

Double-Star Separations

0.3"   3"   30"

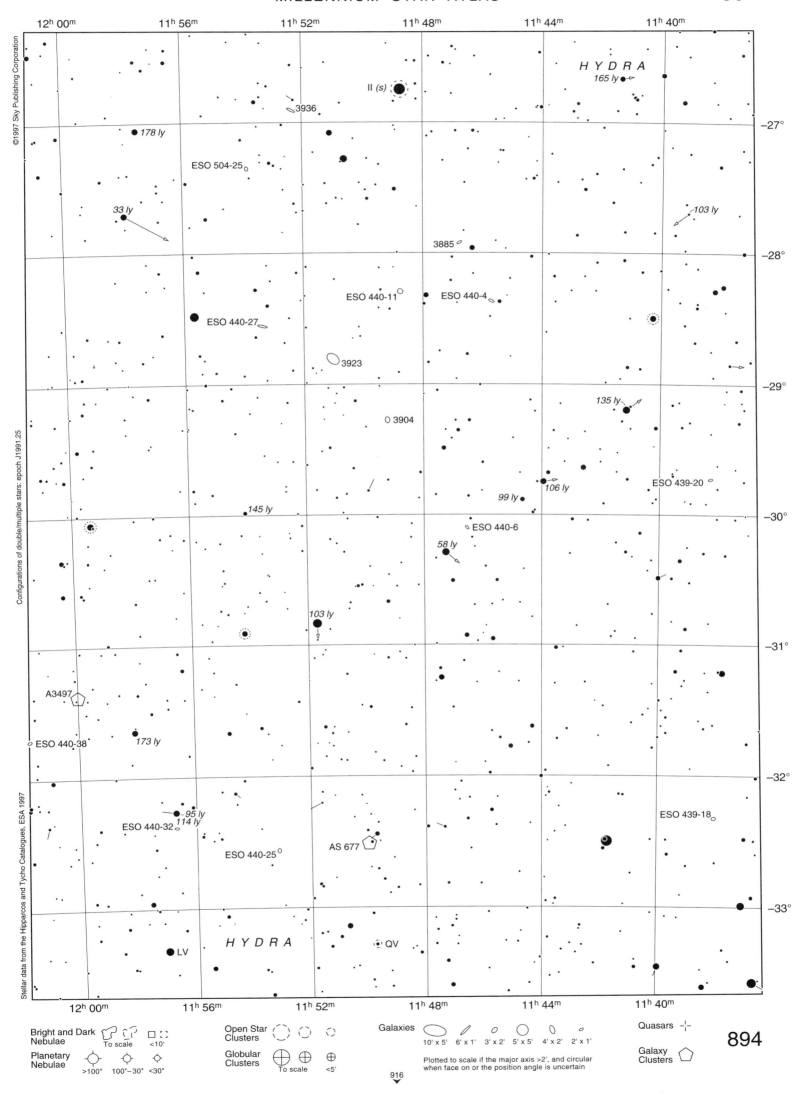

HYDRA

165 ly

II (s)

3936

© 1997 Sky Publishing Corporation

178 ly

ESO 504-25

103 ly

33 ly

3885

ESO 440-11   ESO 440-4

ESO 440-27

3923

135 ly

O 3904

ESO 439-20

106 ly

99 ly

145 ly

ESO 440-6

58 ly

103 ly

A3497

ESO 440-38   173 ly

ESO 439-18

95 ly
ESO 440-32   114 ly

AS 677

ESO 440-25

HYDRA

LV   QV

Configurations of double/multiple stars: epoch J1991.25

Stellar data from the Hipparcos and Tycho Catalogues, ESA 1997

Bright and Dark Nebulae	To scale <10'	
Planetary Nebulae	>100" 100"−30" <30"	
Open Star Clusters		
Globular Clusters	To scale <5'	
Galaxies	10' x 5' 6' x 1' 3' x 2' 5' x 5' 4' x 2' 2' x 1'	
	Plotted to scale if the major axis >2', and circular when face on or the position angle is uncertain	
Quasars		
Galaxy Clusters		

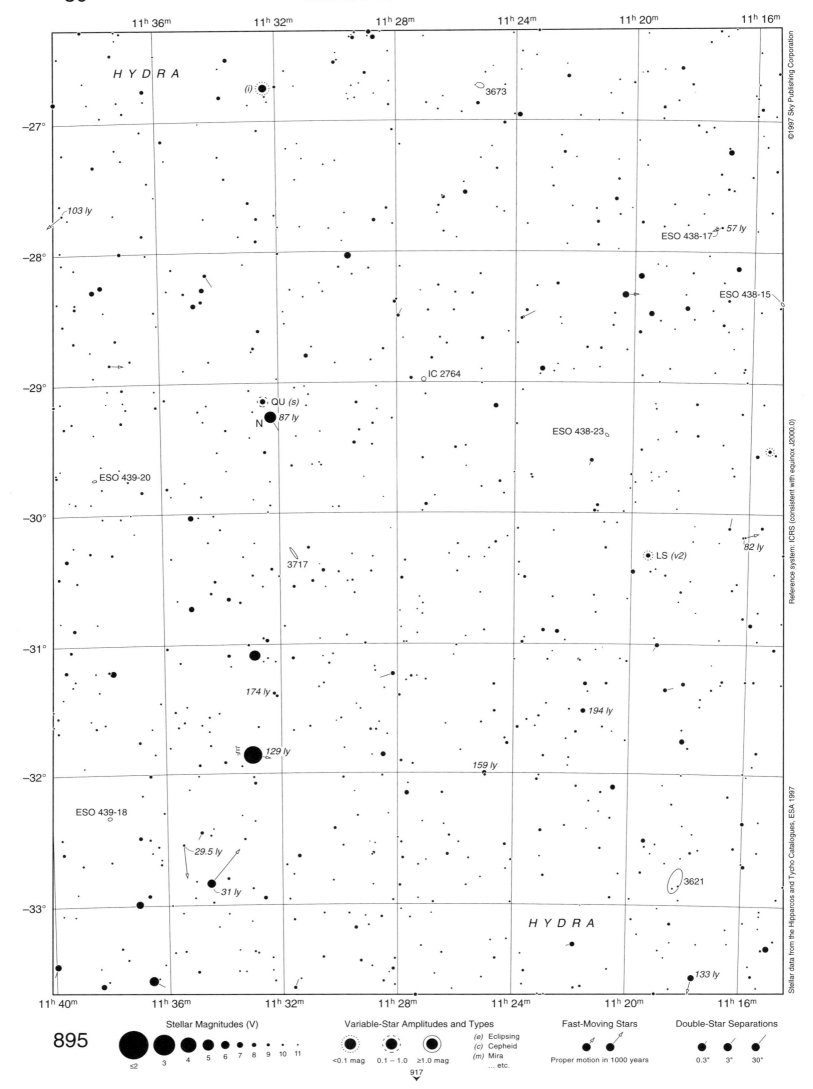

HYDRA

11ʰ 36ᵐ   11ʰ 32ᵐ   11ʰ 28ᵐ   11ʰ 24ᵐ   11ʰ 20ᵐ   11ʰ 16ᵐ

(i)

3673

−27°

103 ly

ESO 438-17   57 ly

−28°

ESO 438-15

IC 2764

−29°

QU (s)
N   87 ly

ESO 438-23

ESO 439-20

−30°

3717

LS (v2)

82 ly

−31°

174 ly

194 ly

129 ly

159 ly

ESO 439-18

29.5 ly

3621

31 ly

−32°

−33°

HYDRA

133 ly

11ʰ 40ᵐ   11ʰ 36ᵐ   11ʰ 32ᵐ   11ʰ 28ᵐ   11ʰ 24ᵐ   11ʰ 20ᵐ   11ʰ 16ᵐ

©1997 Sky Publishing Corporation

Reference system: ICRS (consistent with equinox J2000.0)

Stellar data from the Hipparcos and Tycho Catalogues, ESA 1997

Stellar Magnitudes (V)

895

≤2   3   4   5   6   7   8   9   10   11

Variable-Star Amplitudes and Types

<0.1 mag   0.1 – 1.0   ≥1.0 mag

(e) Eclipsing
(c) Cepheid
(m) Mira
... etc.

917

Fast-Moving Stars

Proper motion in 1000 years

Double-Star Separations

0.3"   3"   30"

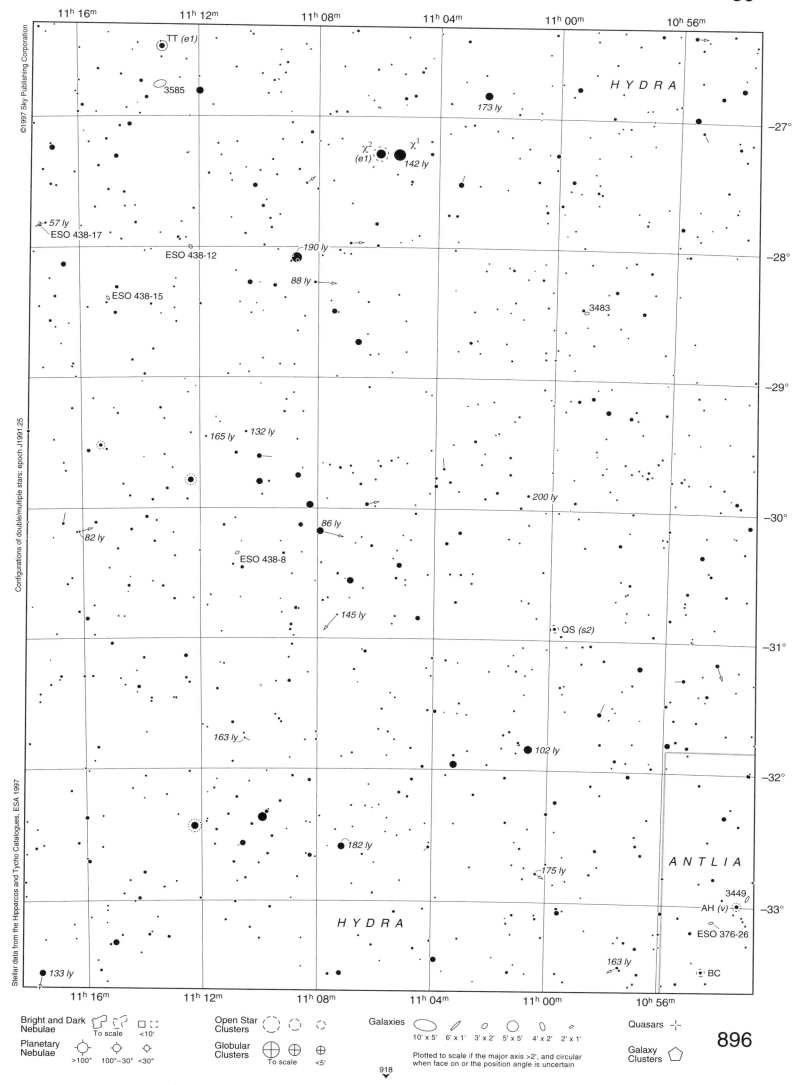

11ʰ 16ᵐ   11ʰ 12ᵐ   11ʰ 08ᵐ   11ʰ 04ᵐ   11ʰ 00ᵐ   10ʰ 56ᵐ

−27°
−28°
−29°
−30°
−31°
−32°
−33°

TT (e1)
3585
173 ly
HYDRA
χ² (e1)   χ¹
142 ly
57 ly
ESO 438-17
ESO 438-12
190 ly
88 ly
ESO 438-15
3483
165 ly   132 ly
200 ly
82 ly
86 ly
ESO 438-8
145 ly
QS (s2)
163 ly
102 ly
182 ly
175 ly
HYDRA
ANTLIA
3449
AH (v)
ESO 376-26
163 ly
BC
133 ly

11ʰ 16ᵐ   11ʰ 12ᵐ   11ʰ 08ᵐ   11ʰ 04ᵐ   11ʰ 00ᵐ   10ʰ 56ᵐ

Bright and Dark
Nebulae
To scale   <10'

Open Star
Clusters

Globular
Clusters
To scale   <5'

Galaxies
10' x 5'   6' x 1'   3' x 2'   5' x 5'   4' x 2'   2' x 1'

Plotted to scale if the major axis >2', and circular
when face on or the position angle is uncertain

Planetary
Nebulae
>100"   100"−30"   <30"

Quasars

Galaxy
Clusters

896

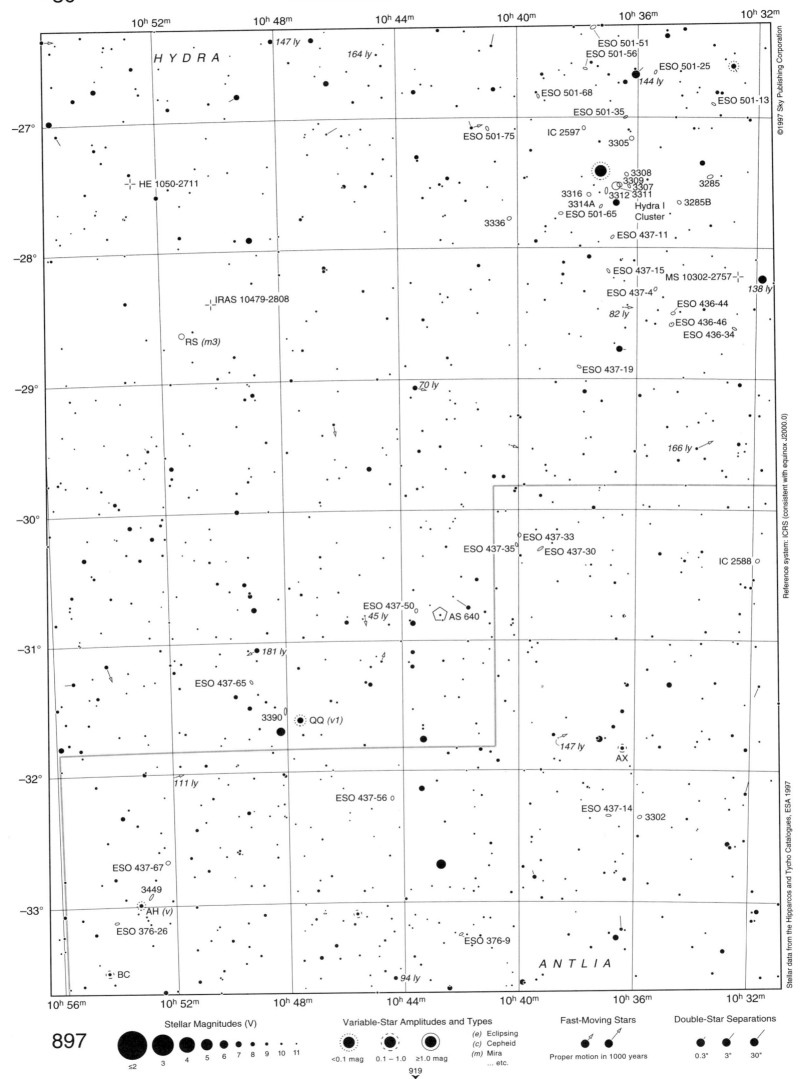

H Y D R A

147 ly
164 ly

ESO 501-51
ESO 501-56
ESO 501-25
ESO 501-68
144 ly
ESO 501-13
ESO 501-35
ESO 501-75
IC 2597
3305
3308
3309
3307
3285
3316
3312 3311
3314A
3285B
ESO 501-65
Hydra I
Cluster
ESO 437-11

HE 1050-2711

ESO 437-15
MS 10302-2757
ESO 437-4
138 ly
ESO 436-44
82 ly
ESO 436-46
ESO 436-34

IRAS 10479-2808

RS (m3)

ESO 437-19

70 ly

166 ly

ESO 437-33
ESO 437-35
ESO 437-30
IC 2588

ESO 437-50
AS 640

ESO 437-65

181 ly

3390
QQ (v1)

147 ly
AX

111 ly

ESO 437-56
ESO 437-14
3302

ESO 437-67

3449
AH (v)
ESO 376-26

ESO 376-9

A N T L I A

BC
94 ly

10h 52m 10h 48m 10h 44m 10h 40m 10h 36m 10h 32m
−27°
−28°
−29°
−30°
−31°
−32°
−33°
10h 56m 10h 52m 10h 48m 10h 44m 10h 40m 10h 36m 10h 32m

Stellar Magnitudes (V)

● ● ● ● ● • · ·
≤2   3   4   5   6   7 8 9 10 11

Variable-Star Amplitudes and Types

<0.1 mag   0.1 – 1.0   ≥1.0 mag

(e) Eclipsing
(c) Cepheid
(m) Mira
... etc.

Fast-Moving Stars

Proper motion in 1000 years

Double-Star Separations

0.3"   3"   30"

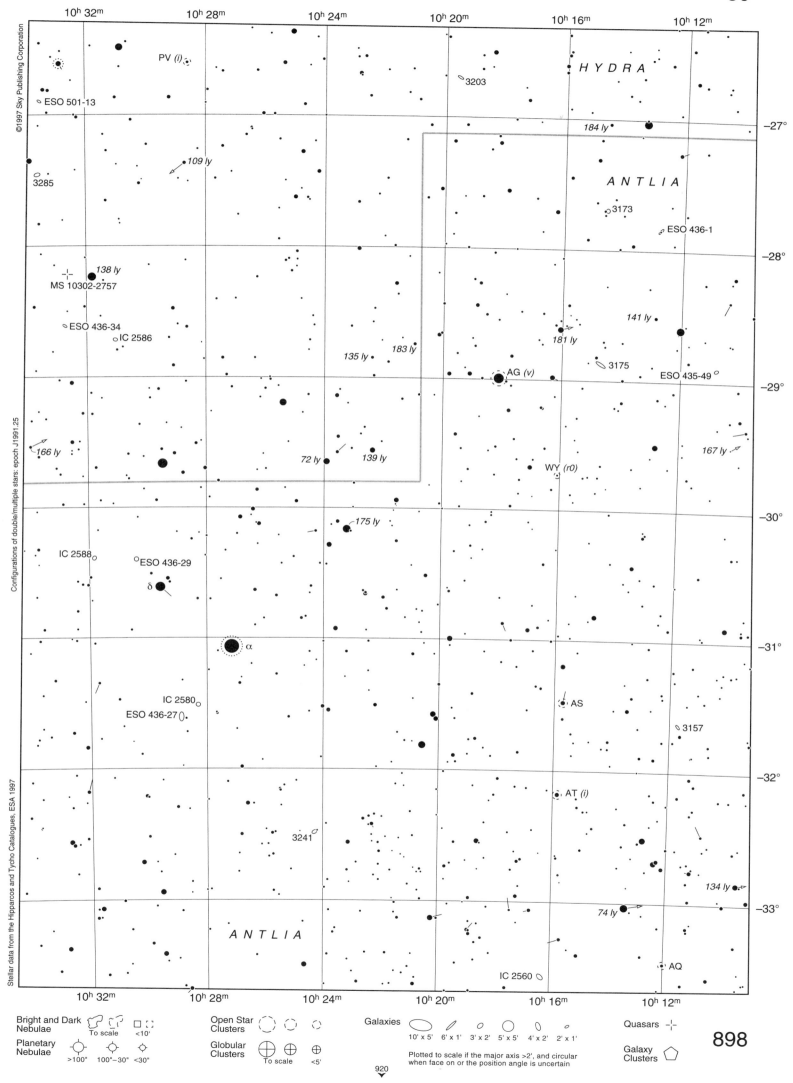

Configurations of double/multiple stars: epoch J1991.25

Stellar data from the Hipparcos and Tycho Catalogues, ESA 1997

HYDRA

ANTLIA

ANTLIA

PV (i)

ESO 501-13

3285

109 ly

3203

184 ly

3173

ESO 436-1

138 ly
MS 10302-2757

ESO 436-34

IC 2586

141 ly

181 ly

183 ly

135 ly

3175

ESO 435-49

AG (v)

166 ly

72 ly

139 ly

167 ly

WY (r0)

175 ly

IC 2588

ESO 436-29

δ

α

AS

IC 2580

3157

ESO 436-27

AT (i)

3241

134 ly

74 ly

ANTLIA

IC 2560

AQ

| 10ʰ 32ᵐ | 10ʰ 28ᵐ | 10ʰ 24ᵐ | 10ʰ 20ᵐ | 10ʰ 16ᵐ | 10ʰ 12ᵐ |

−27°
−28°
−29°
−30°
−31°
−32°
−33°

| 10ʰ 32ᵐ | 10ʰ 28ᵐ | 10ʰ 24ᵐ | 10ʰ 20ᵐ | 10ʰ 16ᵐ | 10ʰ 12ᵐ |

Bright and Dark Nebulae
To scale   <10'

Planetary Nebulae
>100"   100"–30"   <30"

Open Star Clusters

Globular Clusters
To scale   <5'

Galaxies
10' x 5'   6' x 1'   3' x 2'   5' x 5'   4' x 2'   2' x 1'

Plotted to scale if the major axis >2', and circular when face on or the position angle is uncertain

Quasars

Galaxy Clusters

898

920

MILLENNIUM STAR ATLAS

−30°

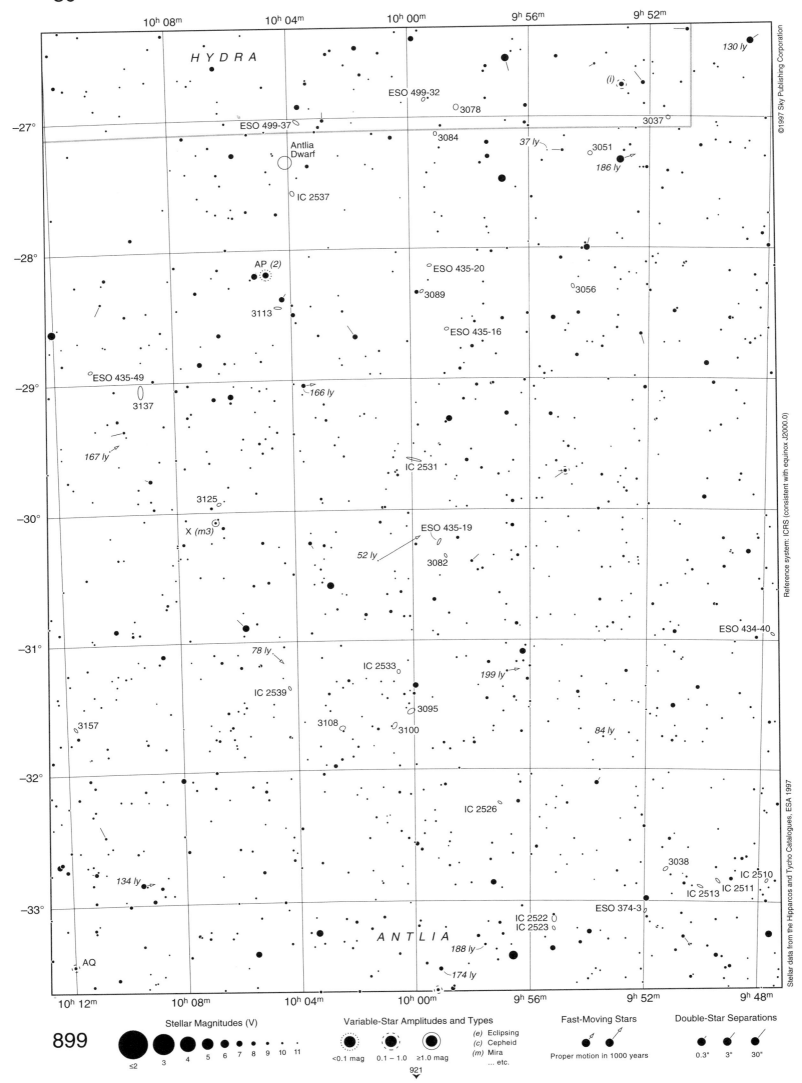

HYDRA

ESO 499-32

ESO 499-37

Antlia
Dwarf

IC 2537

AP (2)

3113

ESO 435-20

3089

ESO 435-16

ESO 435-49

3137

166 ly

167 ly

3125

X (m3)

ESO 435-19

52 ly

3082

78 ly

IC 2533

IC 2539

3108

3100

3095

3157

199 ly

84 ly

IC 2531

IC 2526

3038

IC 2510

IC 2513

IC 2511

ESO 374-3

IC 2522

IC 2523

ANTLIA

188 ly

174 ly

AQ

134 ly

3078

3084

3051

37 ly

186 ly

3056

3037

130 ly

(i)

ESO 434-40

10h 08m 10h 04m 10h 00m 9h 56m 9h 52m

−27°

−28°

−29°

−30°

−31°

−32°

−33°

10h 12m 10h 08m 10h 04m 10h 00m 9h 56m 9h 52m 9h 48m

©1997 Sky Publishing Corporation

Reference system: ICRS (consistent with equinox J2000.0)

Stellar data from the Hipparcos and Tycho Catalogues, ESA 1997

899

Stellar Magnitudes (V)

≤2   3   4   5   6   7   8   9   10   11

Variable-Star Amplitudes and Types

<0.1 mag   0.1 – 1.0   ≥1.0 mag

(e) Eclipsing
(c) Cepheid
(m) Mira
... etc.

Fast-Moving Stars

Proper motion in 1000 years

Double-Star Separations

0.3"   3"   30"

921

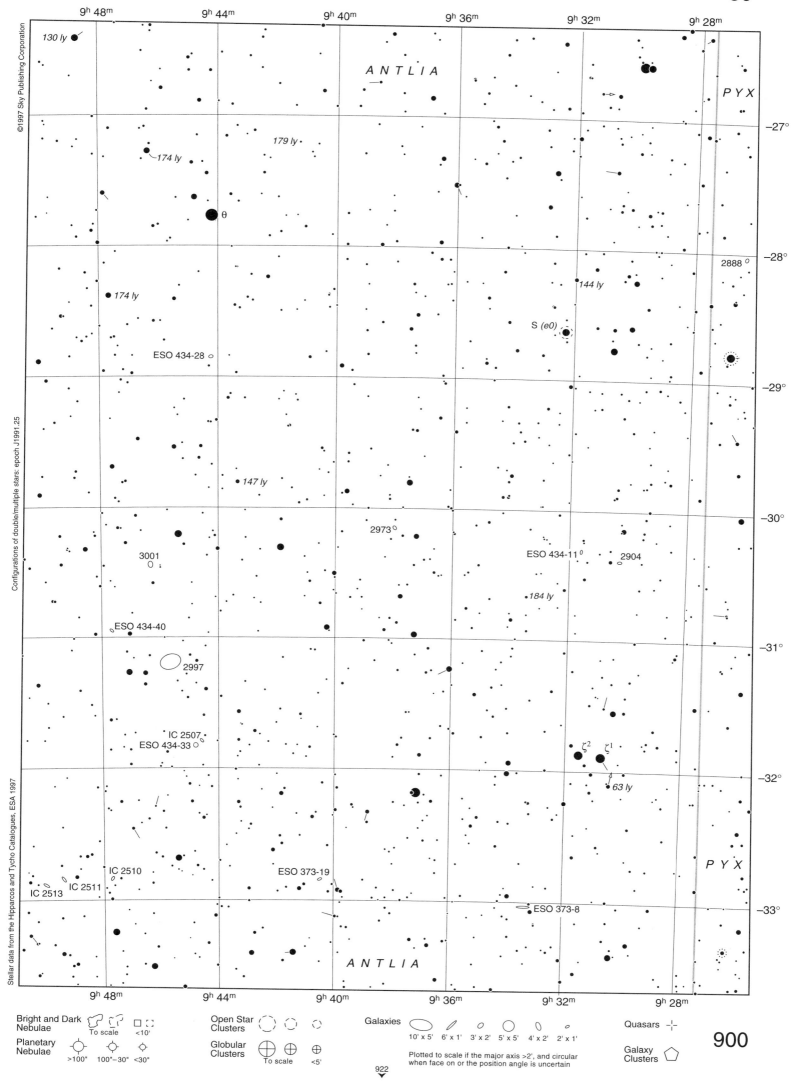

ANTLIA

PYX

PYX

ANTLIA

130 ly

179 ly

174 ly

174 ly

θ

ESO 434-28

2888

144 ly

S (e0)

147 ly

2973

3001

ESO 434-11

2904

184 ly

ESO 434-40

2997

IC 2507
ESO 434-33

ζ² ζ¹

63 ly

IC 2510

ESO 373-19

IC 2511
IC 2513

ESO 373-8

9h 48m   9h 44m   9h 40m   9h 36m   9h 32m   9h 28m

−27°
−28°
−29°
−30°
−31°
−32°
−33°

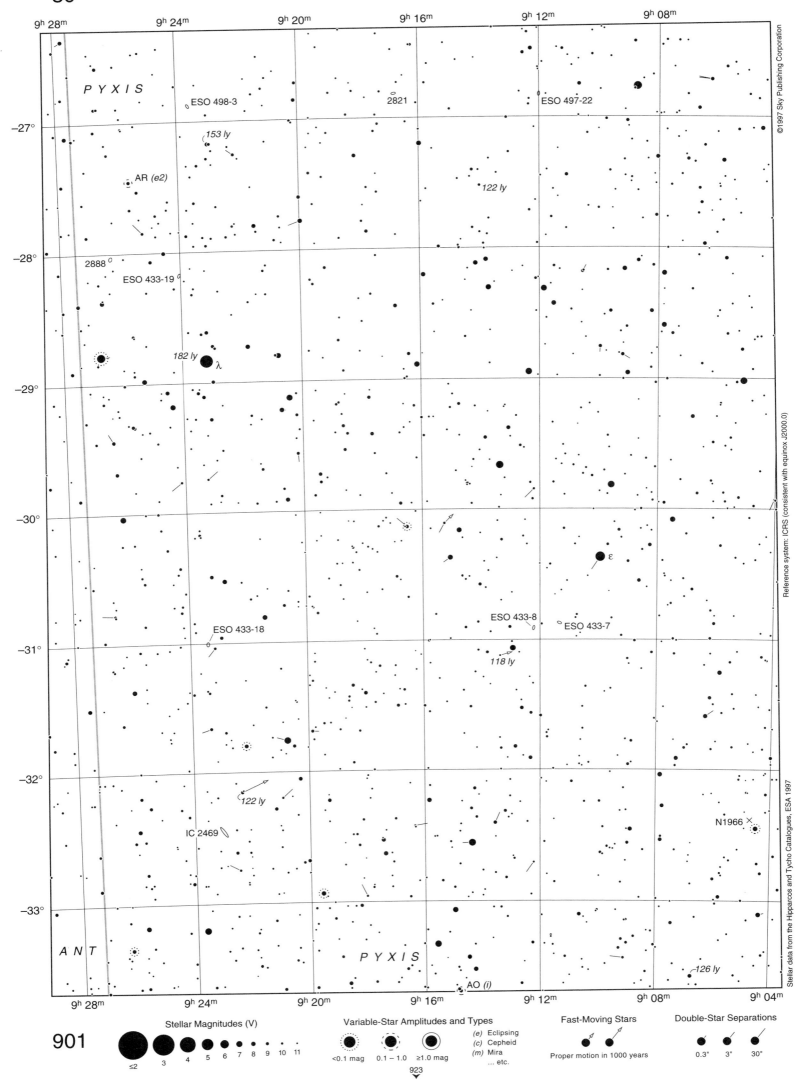

PYXIS

ESO 498-3

2821

ESO 497-22

153 ly

AR (e2)

122 ly

2888

ESO 433-19

182 ly   λ

ε

ESO 433-8

ESO 433-18   ESO 433-7

118 ly

122 ly

IC 2469

N1966

ANT

PYXIS

AO (i)

126 ly

©1997 Sky Publishing Corporation

Reference system: ICRS (consistent with equinox J2000.0)

Stellar data from the Hipparcos and Tycho Catalogues, ESA 1997

901

Stellar Magnitudes (V)	Variable-Star Amplitudes and Types	Fast-Moving Stars	Double-Star Separations

≤2   3   4   5   6   7   8   9   10   11

<0.1 mag   0.1 − 1.0   ≥1.0 mag

923

(e) Eclipsing
(c) Cepheid
(m) Mira
... etc.

Proper motion in 1000 years

0.3"   3"   30"

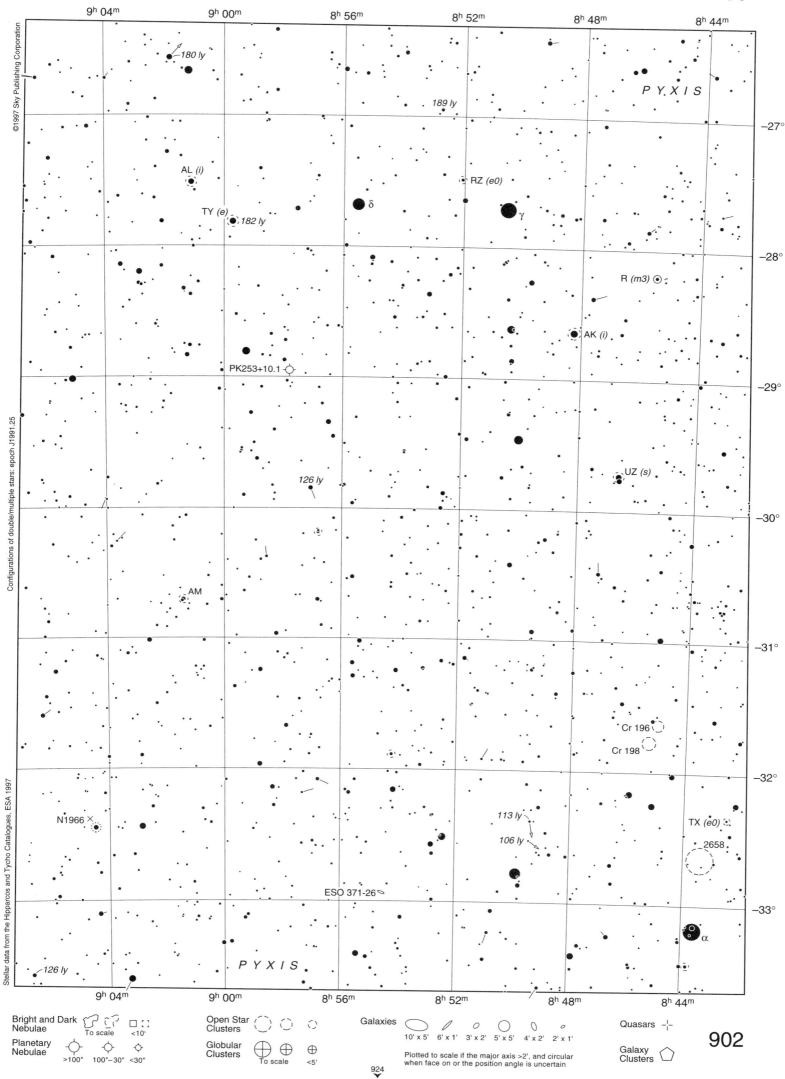

P Y X I S

9h 04m   9h 00m   8h 56m   8h 52m   8h 48m   8h 44m

−27°
−28°
−29°
−30°
−31°
−32°
−33°

180 ly
189 ly
AL (i)
RZ (e0)
TY (e)   182 ly
δ
γ
R (m3)
AK (i)
PK253+10.1
126 ly
UZ (s)
AM
Cr 196
Cr 198
N1966
113 ly
106 ly
TX (e0)
2658
ESO 371-26
126 ly
α

P Y X I S

9h 04m   9h 00m   8h 56m   8h 52m   8h 48m   8h 44m

Bright and Dark
Nebulae
To scale   <10'

Planetary
Nebulae
>100"   100"–30"   <30"

Open Star
Clusters

Globular
Clusters
To scale   <5'

Galaxies
10' x 5'   6' x 1'   3' x 2'   5' x 5'   4' x 2'   2' x 1'

Plotted to scale if the major axis >2', and circular
when face on or the position angle is uncertain

Quasars

Galaxy
Clusters

902

924

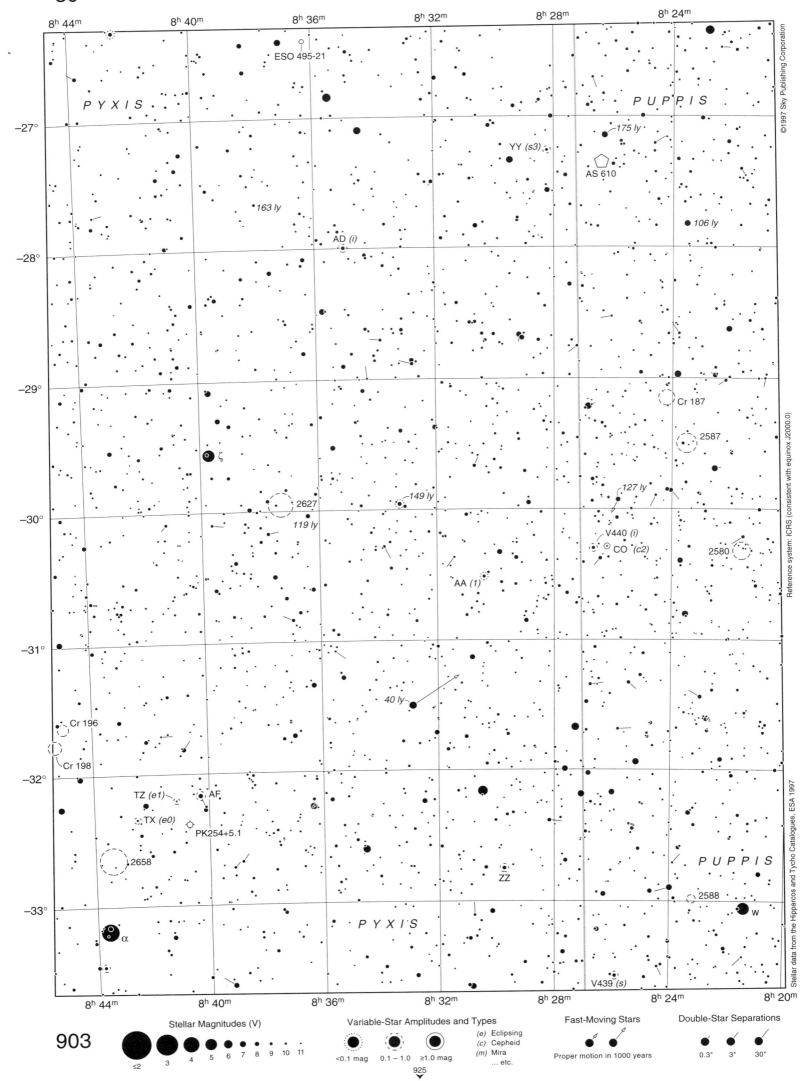

© 1997 Sky Publishing Corporation

Reference system: ICRS (consistent with equinox J2000.0)

Stellar data from the Hipparcos and Tycho Catalogues, ESA 1997

903

Stellar Magnitudes (V)

≤2   3   4   5   6   7   8   9   10   11

Variable-Star Amplitudes and Types

<0.1 mag   0.1 – 1.0   ≥1.0 mag

(e) Eclipsing
(c) Cepheid
(m) Mira
... etc.

925

Fast-Moving Stars

Proper motion in 1000 years

Double-Star Separations

0.3"   3"   30"

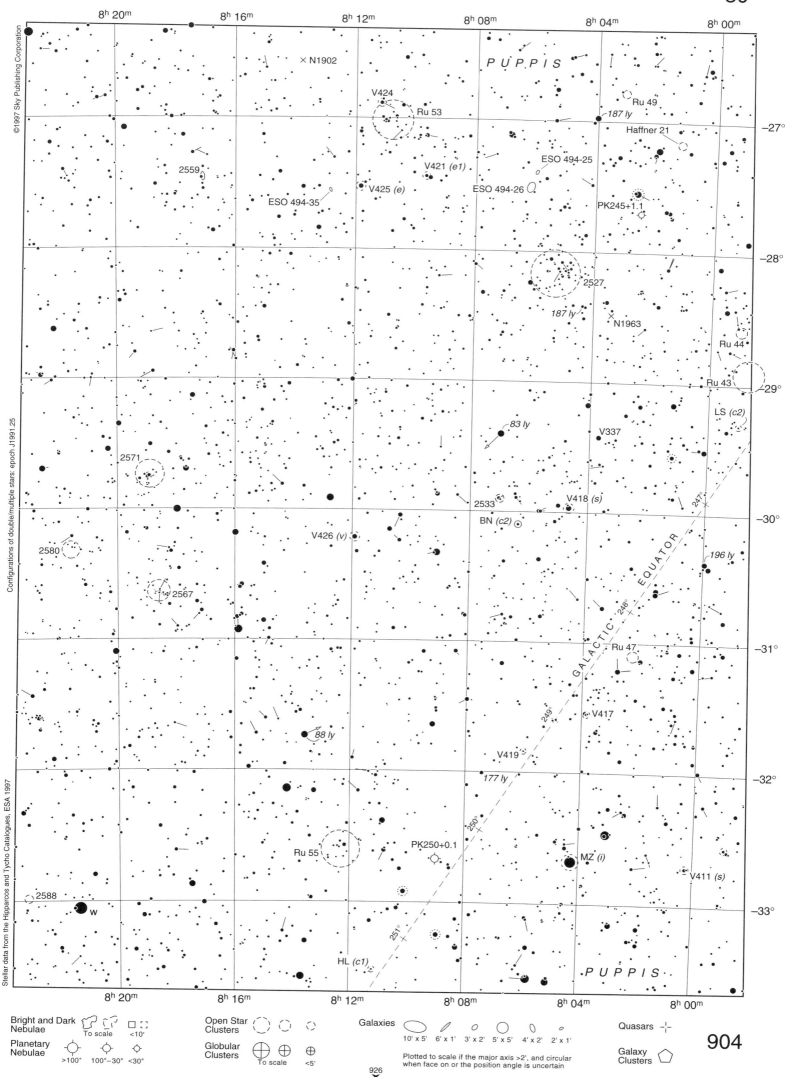

PUPPIS

× N1902

V424
Ru 53

Ru 49
187 ly

Haffner 21

2559

V421 (e1)

ESO 494-25

V425 (e)

ESO 494-26

ESO 494-35

PK245+1.1

−27°

2527

187 ly

× N1963

Ru 44

−28°

Ru 43

LS (c2)

83 ly

V337

2571

−29°

2533

V418 (s)

BN (c2)

247°

V426 (v)

2580

196 ly

2567

−30°

GALACTIC EQUATOR

248°

Ru 47

249°

V417

88 ly

V419

177 ly

−31°

250°

Ru 55

PK250+0.1

MZ (i)

V411 (s)

251°

2588

w

HL (c1)

PUPPIS

−32°

−33°

8ʰ 20ᵐ   8ʰ 16ᵐ   8ʰ 12ᵐ   8ʰ 08ᵐ   8ʰ 04ᵐ   8ʰ 00ᵐ

Bright and Dark Nebulae
To scale   <10'

Planetary Nebulae
>100"   100"–30"   <30"

Open Star Clusters

Globular Clusters
To scale   <5'

Galaxies
10' x 5'   6' x 1'   3' x 2'   5' x 5'   4' x 2'   2' x 1'

Plotted to scale if the major axis >2', and circular when face on or the position angle is uncertain

Quasars

Galaxy Clusters

904

926

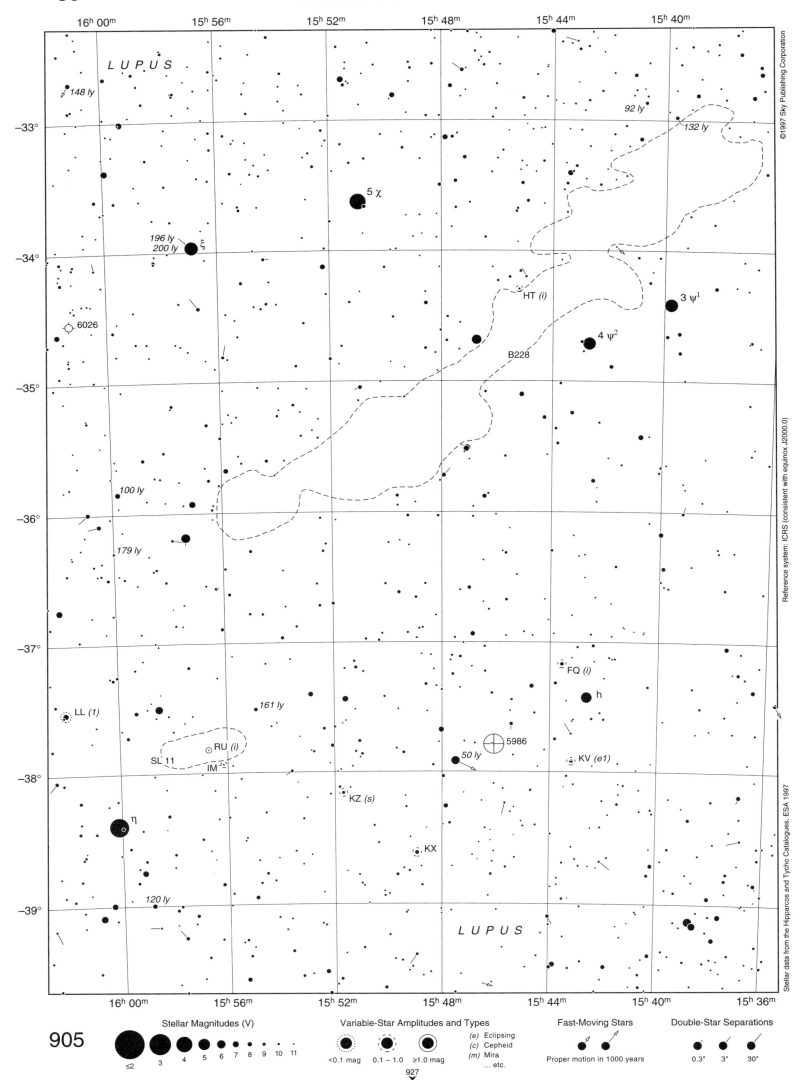

©1997 Sky Publishing Corporation

Reference system: ICRS (consistent with equinox J2000.0)

Stellar data from the Hipparcos and Tycho Catalogues, ESA 1997

LUPUS

148 ly

92 ly

132 ly

5 χ

196 ly
200 ly   ξ

6026

HT (i)

3 ψ¹

4 ψ²

B228

100 ly

179 ly

FQ (i)

h

LL (1)

161 ly

5986

RU (i)

SL 11

50 ly

KV (e1)

IM

KZ (s)

η

KX

120 ly

LUPUS

905

Stellar Magnitudes (V)

≤2   3   4   5   6   7   8   9   10   11

Variable-Star Amplitudes and Types

<0.1 mag   0.1 – 1.0   ≥1.0 mag

(e) Eclipsing
(c) Cepheid
(m) Mira
... etc.

Fast-Moving Stars

Proper motion in 1000 years

Double-Star Separations

0.3"   3"   30"

927

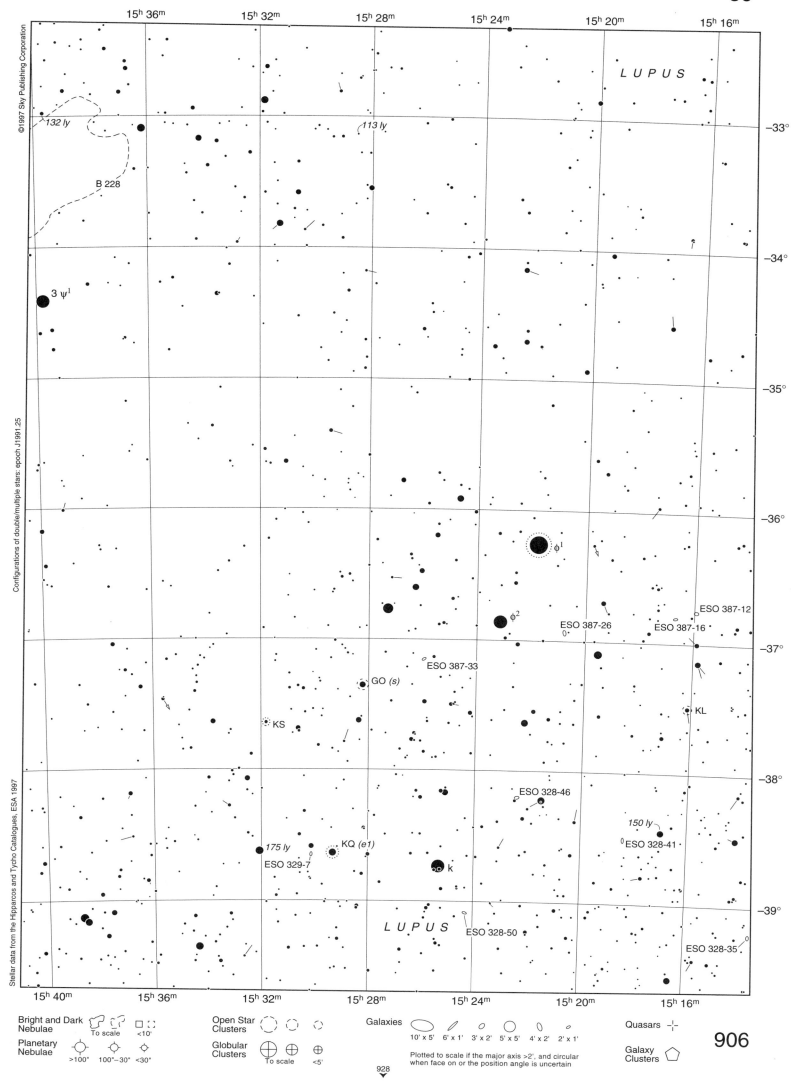

©1997 Sky Publishing Corporation

Configurations of double/multiple stars: epoch J1991.25

Stellar data from the Hipparcos and Tycho Catalogues, ESA 1997

15h 36m   15h 32m   15h 28m   15h 24m   15h 20m   15h 16m

LUPUS

−33°

132 ly

B 228

113 ly

−34°

3 ψ¹

−35°

−36°

φ¹

ESO 387-12

φ²

ESO 387-26   ESO 387-16

ESO 387-33

−37°

GO *(s)*

KS

KL

−38°

ESO 328-46

150 ly

175 ly

KQ *(e1)*   ESO 328-41

ESO 329-7

k

LUPUS   ESO 328-50

−39°

ESO 328-35

15h 40m   15h 36m   15h 32m   15h 28m   15h 24m   15h 20m   15h 16m

Bright and Dark Nebulae
To scale   <10'

Planetary Nebulae
>100"   100"−30"   <30"

Open Star Clusters

Globular Clusters
To scale   <5'

Galaxies
10' x 5'   6' x 1'   3' x 2'   5' x 5'   4' x 2'   2' x 1'

Plotted to scale if the major axis >2', and circular when face on or the position angle is uncertain

Quasars

Galaxy Clusters

906

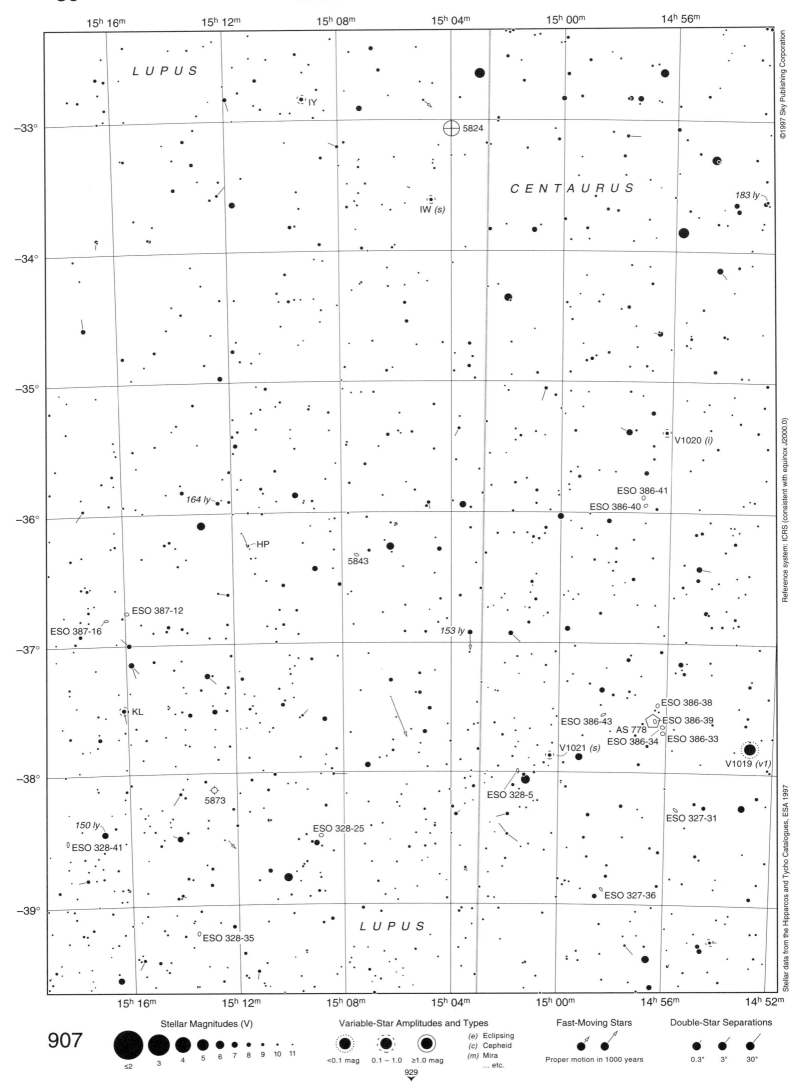

©1997 Sky Publishing Corporation

Reference system: ICRS (consistent with equinox J2000.0)

Stellar data from the Hipparcos and Tycho Catalogues, ESA 1997

LUPUS

CENTAURUS

IY

5824

IW (s)

183 ly

V1020 (i)

164 ly

ESO 386-41
ESO 386-40

HP

5843

153 ly

ESO 387-12

ESO 387-16

ESO 386-38
ESO 386-43   ESO 386-39
AS 778   ESO 386-33
ESO 386-34

KL

V1021 (s)

V1019 (v1)

ESO 328-5

5873

ESO 327-31

150 ly

ESO 328-41

ESO 328-25

ESO 327-36

LUPUS

ESO 328-35

907

Stellar Magnitudes (V)

≤2   3   4   5   6   7   8   9   10   11

Variable-Star Amplitudes and Types

<0.1 mag   0.1 − 1.0   ≥1.0 mag

(e) Eclipsing
(c) Cepheid
(m) Mira
... etc.

Fast-Moving Stars

Proper motion in 1000 years

Double-Star Separations

0.3"   3"   30"

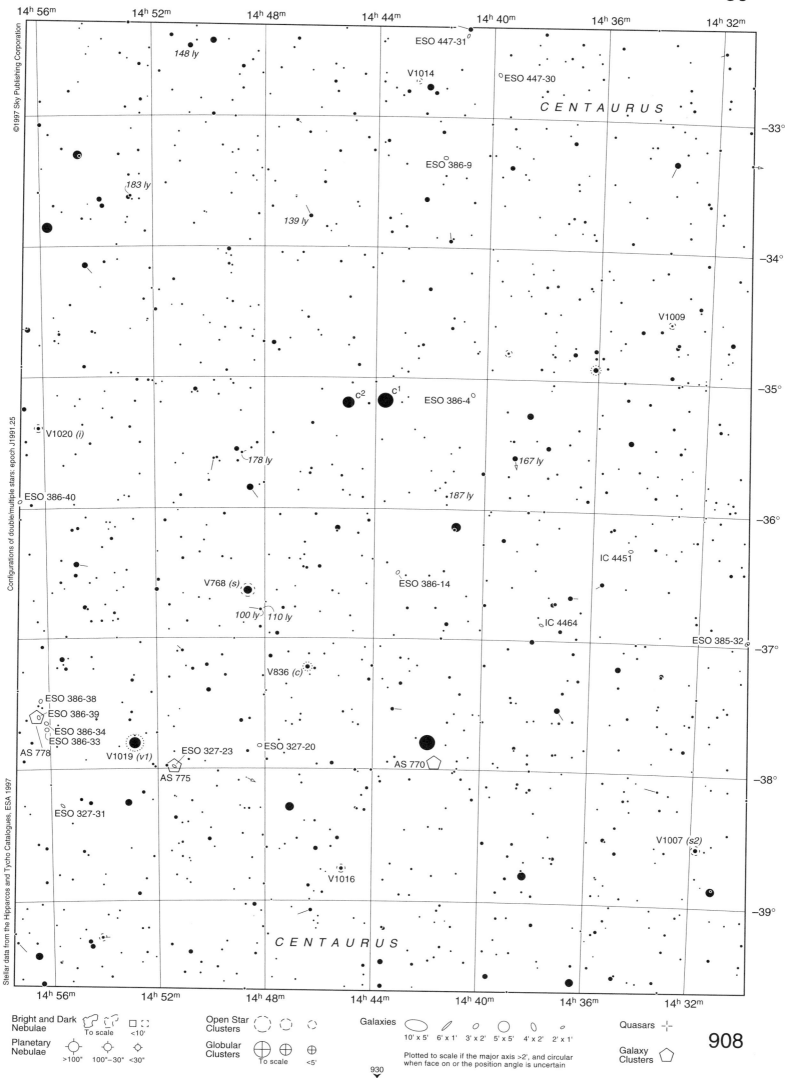

14h 56m 14h 52m 14h 48m 14h 44m 14h 40m 14h 36m 14h 32m

ESO 447-31

148 ly

V1014 ESO 447-30

C E N T A U R U S

−33°

ESO 386-9

183 ly

139 ly

−34°

V1009

c² c¹ ESO 386-4

−35°

V1020 (i)

178 ly

167 ly

187 ly

ESO 386-40

−36°

IC 4451

V768 (s)

ESO 386-14

100 ly 110 ly

IC 4464

ESO 385-32

−37°

V836 (c)

ESO 386-38
ESO 386-39
ESO 386-34
ESO 386-33
AS 778

ESO 327-23 ESO 327-20

V1019 (v1) AS 770

AS 775

−38°

ESO 327-31

V1007 (s2)

V1016

−39°

C E N T A U R U S

14h 56m 14h 52m 14h 48m 14h 44m 14h 40m 14h 36m 14h 32m

Bright and Dark Nebulae
To scale   <10'

Planetary Nebulae
>100" 100"–30" <30"

Open Star Clusters

Globular Clusters
To scale   <5'

Galaxies
10' x 5' 6' x 1' 3' x 2' 5' x 5' 4' x 2' 2' x 1'
Plotted to scale if the major axis >2', and circular when face on or the position angle is uncertain

Quasars

Galaxy Clusters

908

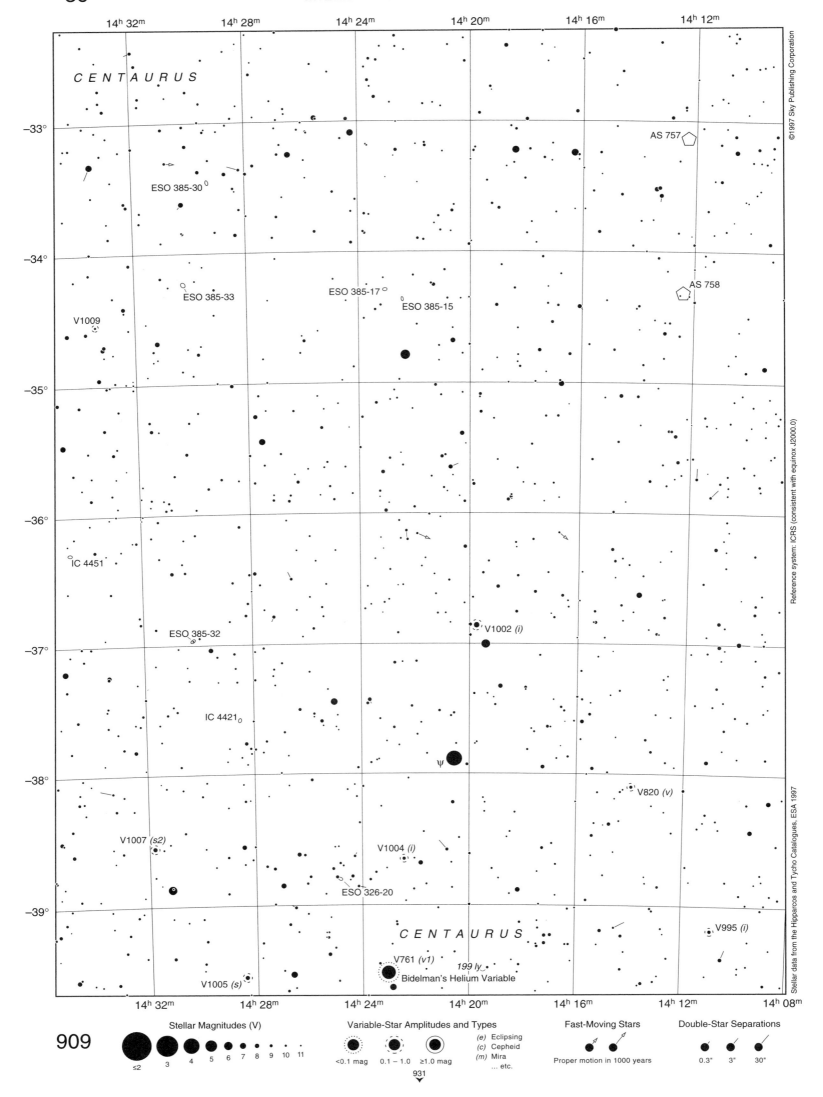

©1997 Sky Publishing Corporation

Reference system: ICRS (consistent with equinox J2000.0)

Stellar data from the Hipparcos and Tycho Catalogues, ESA 1997

CENTAURUS

ESO 385-30

AS 757

ESO 385-33

ESO 385-17

ESO 385-15

AS 758

V1009

IC 4451

ESO 385-32

V1002 (i)

IC 4421

ψ

V820 (v)

V1007 (s2)

V1004 (i)

ESO 326-20

V995 (i)

CENTAURUS

V761 (v1)
199 ly
Bidelman's Helium Variable

V1005 (s)

909

Stellar Magnitudes (V)

≤2 3 4 5 6 7 8 9 10 11

Variable-Star Amplitudes and Types

<0.1 mag   0.1 – 1.0   ≥1.0 mag

(e) Eclipsing
(c) Cepheid
(m) Mira
... etc.

Fast-Moving Stars

Proper motion in 1000 years

Double-Star Separations

0.3"   3"   30"

931

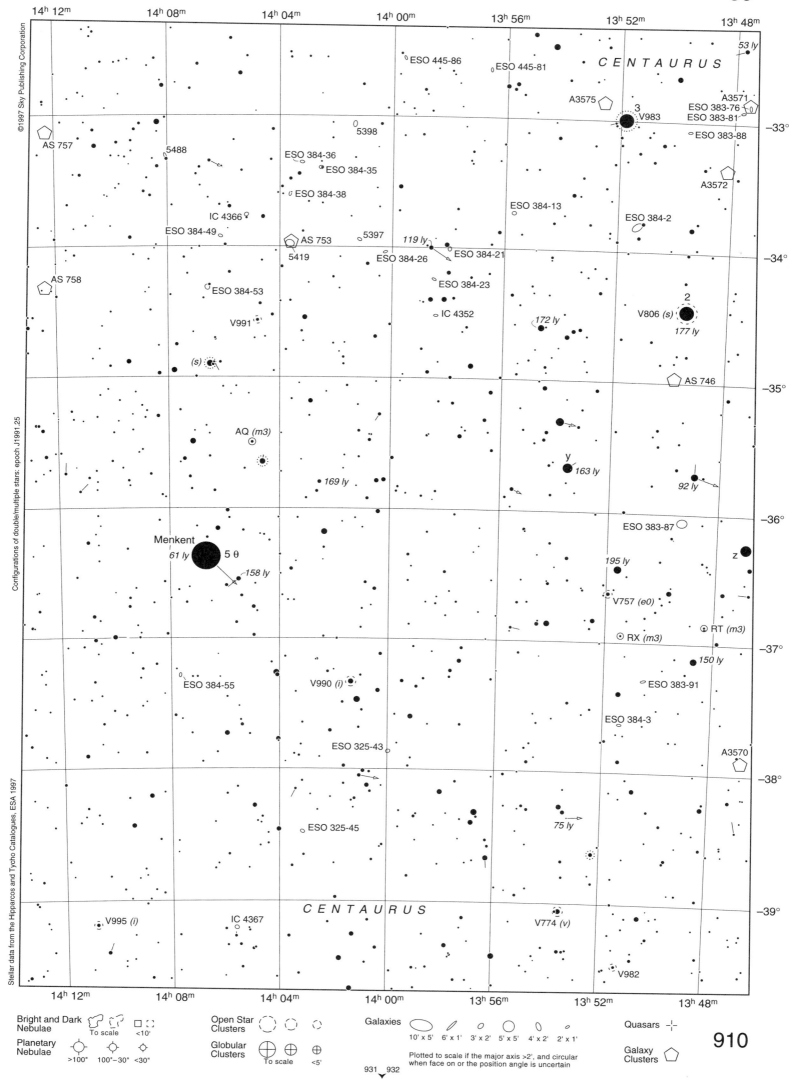

CENTAURUS

ESO 445-86
ESO 445-81
53 ly
A3575
3
V983
A3571
ESO 383-76
ESO 383-81
A3572
ESO 383-88
AS 757
5488
5398
ESO 384-36
ESO 384-35
ESO 384-38
ESO 384-13
ESO 384-2
IC 4366
ESO 384-49
AS 753
5397
119 ly
ESO 384-21
5419
ESO 384-26
AS 758
ESO 384-53
ESO 384-23
V806 (s)
2
V991
IC 4352
172 ly
177 ly
(s)
AS 746
AQ (m3)
y
163 ly
169 ly
92 ly
ESO 383-87
Menkent
z
61 ly
5 θ
195 ly
158 ly
V757 (e0)
RT (m3)
RX (m3)
150 ly
ESO 384-55
ESO 383-91
V990 (i)
ESO 384-3
ESO 325-43
A3570
ESO 325-45
75 ly
CENTAURUS
V995 (i)
IC 4367
V774 (v)
V982

Bright and Dark Nebulae		Open Star Clusters	Galaxies							Quasars
To scale	<10'		10' x 5'	6' x 1'	3' x 2'	5' x 5'	4' x 2'	2' x 1'		

Planetary Nebulae
>100" 100"–30" <30"

Globular Clusters
To scale <5'

Plotted to scale if the major axis >2', and circular when face on or the position angle is uncertain

Galaxy Clusters

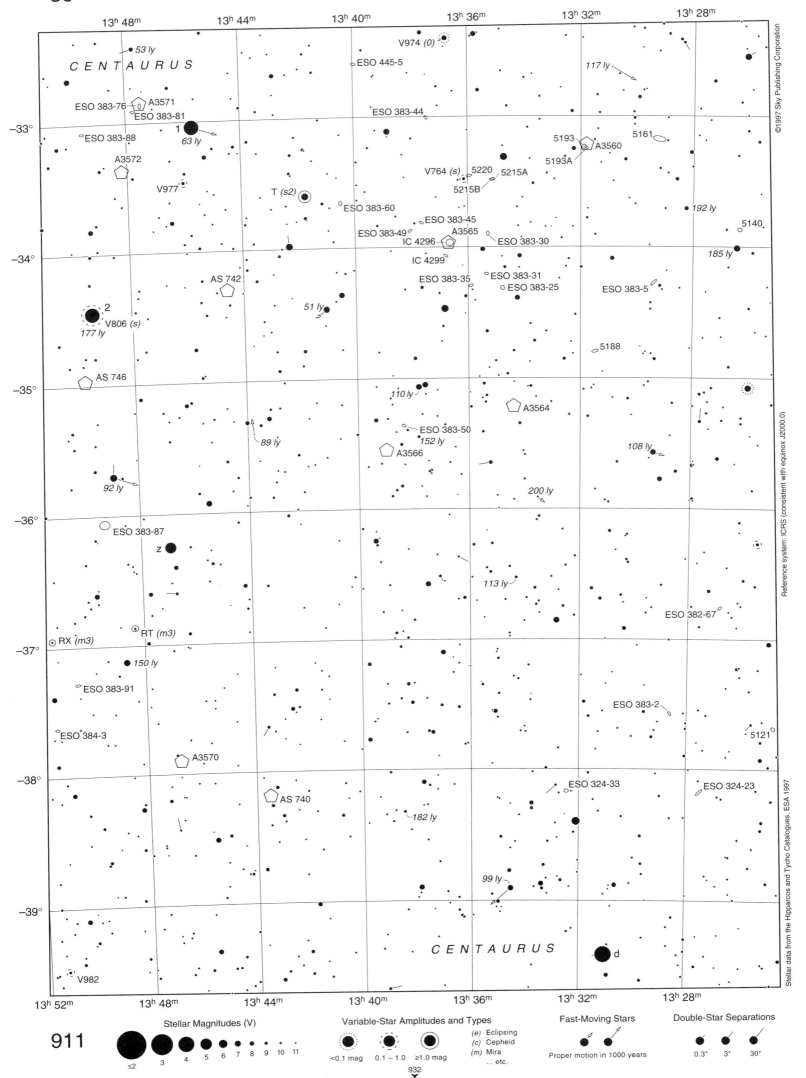

911

Stellar Magnitudes (V)

≤2   3   4   5   6   7   8   9   10   11

Variable-Star Amplitudes and Types

<0.1 mag   0.1 – 1.0   ≥1.0 mag

(e) Eclipsing
(c) Cepheid
(m) Mira
... etc.

Fast-Moving Stars

Proper motion in 1000 years

Double-Star Separations

0.3"   3"   30"

932

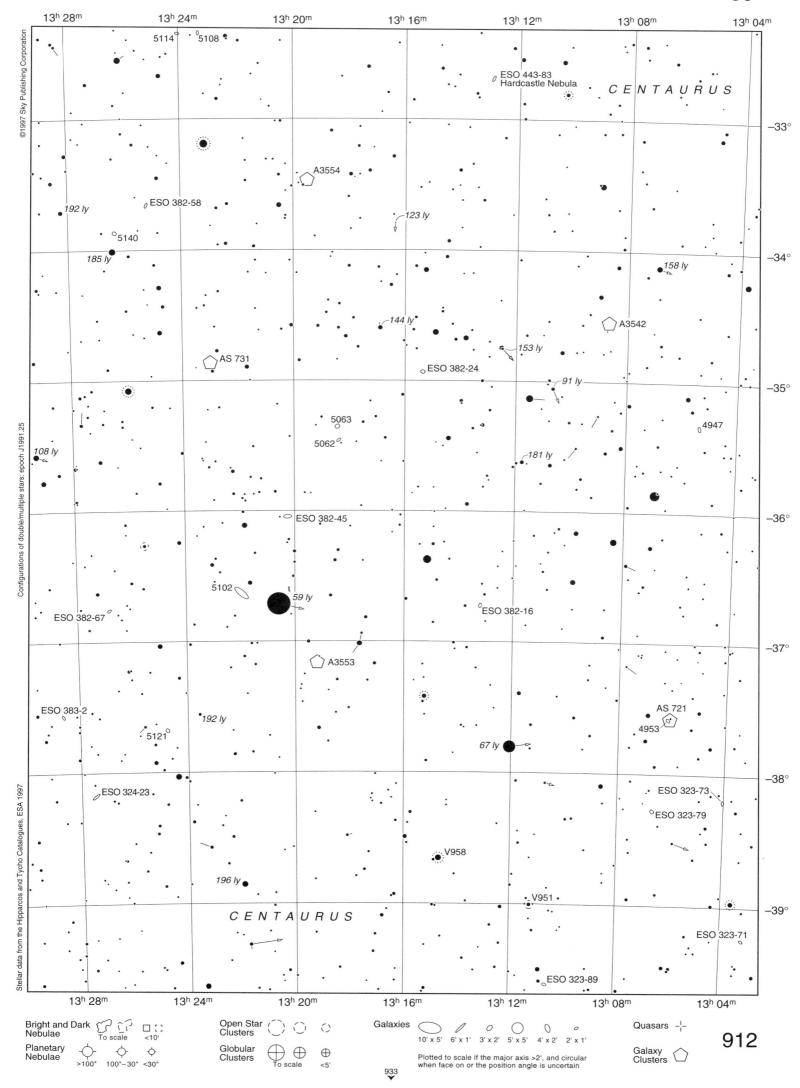

912

Bright and Dark Nebulae
To scale   <10'

Open Star Clusters

Galaxies
10' x 5'   6' x 1'   3' x 2'   5' x 5'   4' x 2'   2' x 1'

Quasars

Planetary Nebulae
>100"   100"−30"   <30"

Globular Clusters
To scale   <5'

Plotted to scale if the major axis >2', and circular when face on or the position angle is uncertain

Galaxy Clusters

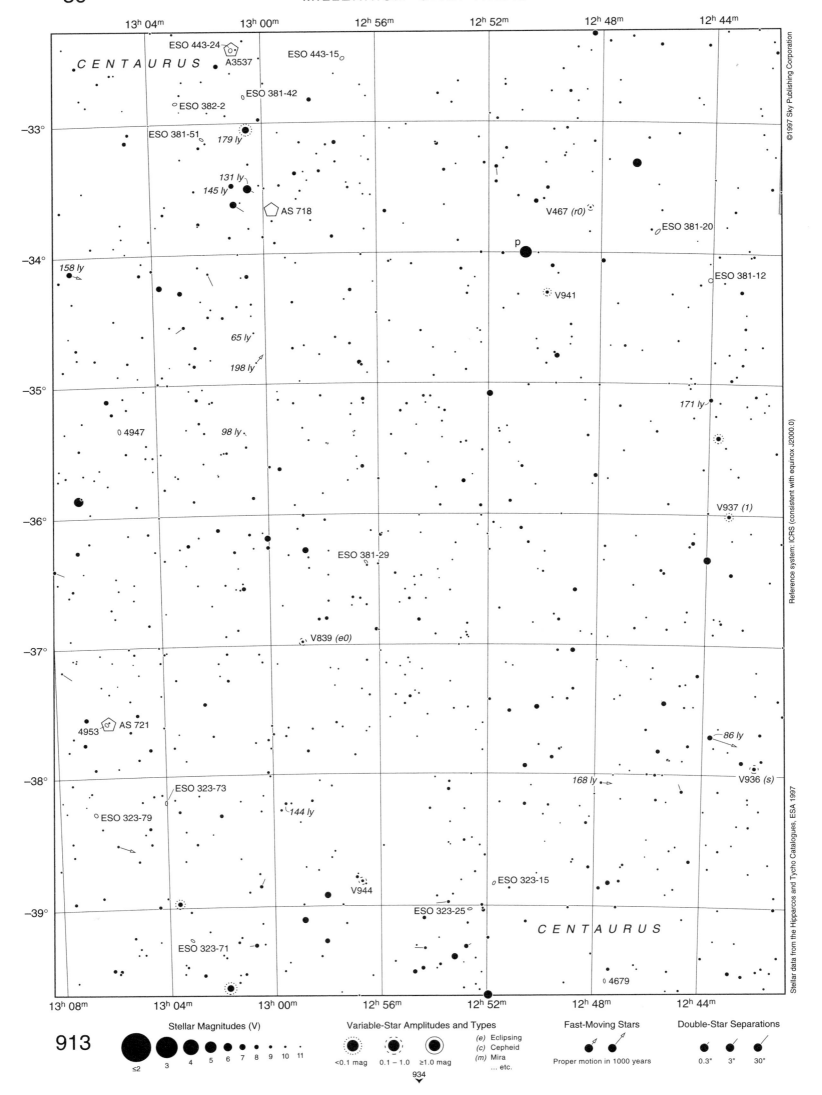

©1997 Sky Publishing Corporation

Reference system: ICRS (consistent with equinox J2000.0)

Stellar data from the Hipparcos and Tycho Catalogues, ESA 1997

CENTAURUS

ESO 443-24
A3537
ESO 443-15
ESO 381-42
ESO 382-2
ESO 381-51   179 ly
131 ly
145 ly
AS 718
V467 (r0)
ESO 381-20
p
ESO 381-12
158 ly
V941
65 ly
198 ly
171 ly
0 4947   98 ly
V937 (1)
ESO 381-29
V839 (e0)
4953   AS 721
86 ly
168 ly
V936 (s)
ESO 323-73
ESO 323-79
144 ly
ESO 323-15
V944
ESO 323-25
CENTAURUS
ESO 323-71
4679

913

934

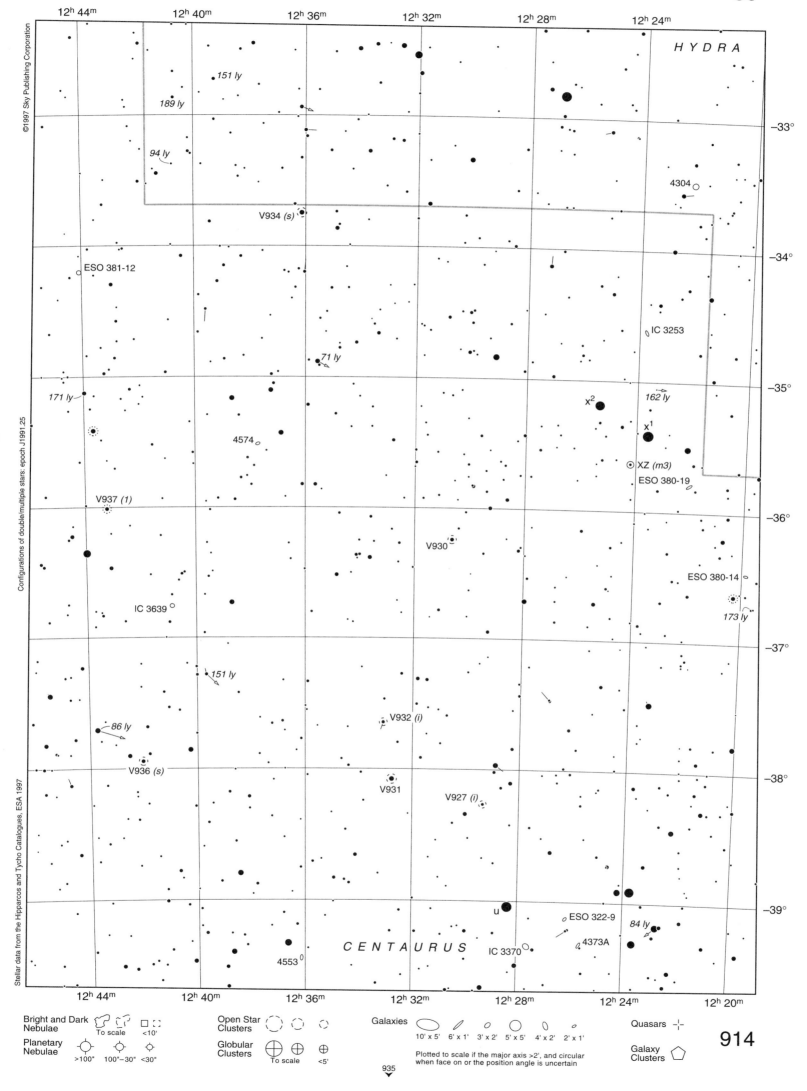

H Y D R A

151 ly

189 ly

94 ly

4304

V934 (s)

ESO 381-12

IC 3253

71 ly

171 ly

4574

x²

162 ly

x¹

XZ (m3)

ESO 380-19

V937 (1)

V930

ESO 380-14

IC 3639

173 ly

151 ly

86 ly

V932 (i)

V936 (s)

V931

V927 (i)

u

ESO 322-9

84 ly

C E N T A U R U S

IC 3370

4373A

4553

Bright and Dark Nebulae
To scale   <10'

Planetary Nebulae
>100"   100"−30"   <30"

Open Star Clusters

Globular Clusters
To scale   <5'

Galaxies
10' x 5'   6' x 1'   3' x 2'   5' x 5'   4' x 2'   2' x 1'

Plotted to scale if the major axis >2', and circular when face on or the position angle is uncertain

Quasars

Galaxy Clusters

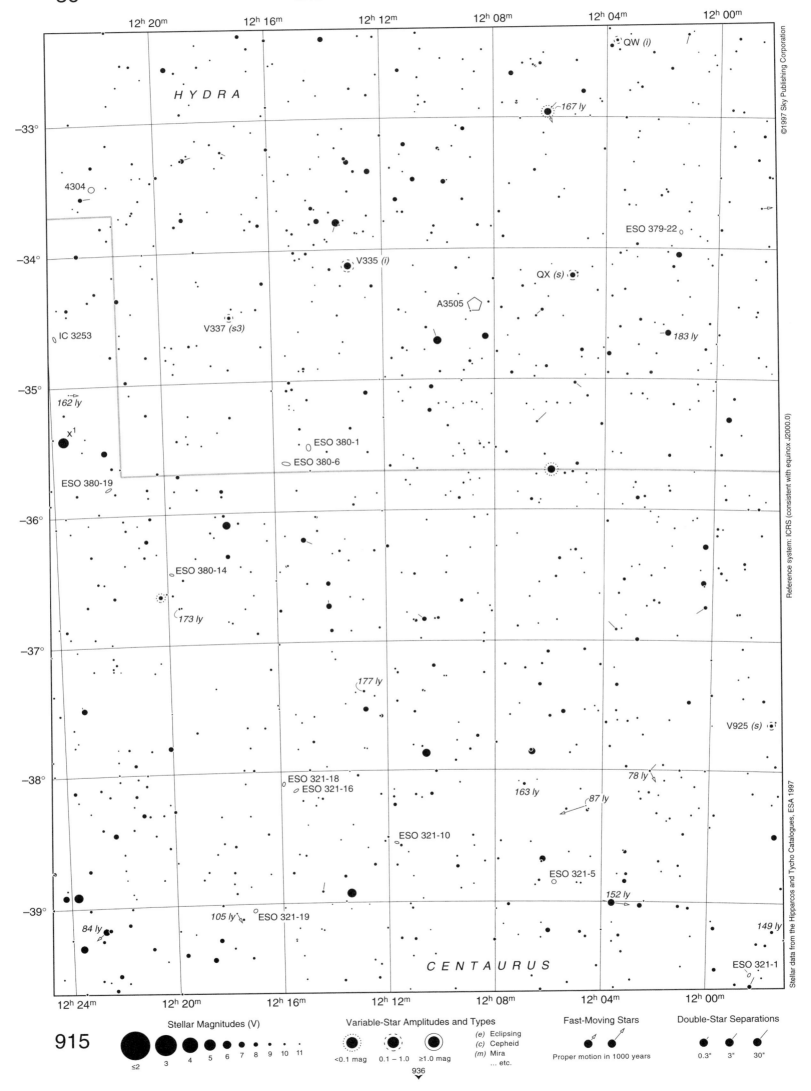

©1997 Sky Publishing Corporation

Reference system: ICRS (consistent with equinox J2000.0)

Stellar data from the Hipparcos and Tycho Catalogues, ESA 1997

Stellar Magnitudes (V)

Variable-Star Amplitudes and Types

Fast-Moving Stars

Double-Star Separations

915

≤2   3   4   5   6   7   8   9 10 11

<0.1 mag   0.1 – 1.0   ≥1.0 mag

(e) Eclipsing
(c) Cepheid
(m) Mira
... etc.

Proper motion in 1000 years

0.3"   3"   30"

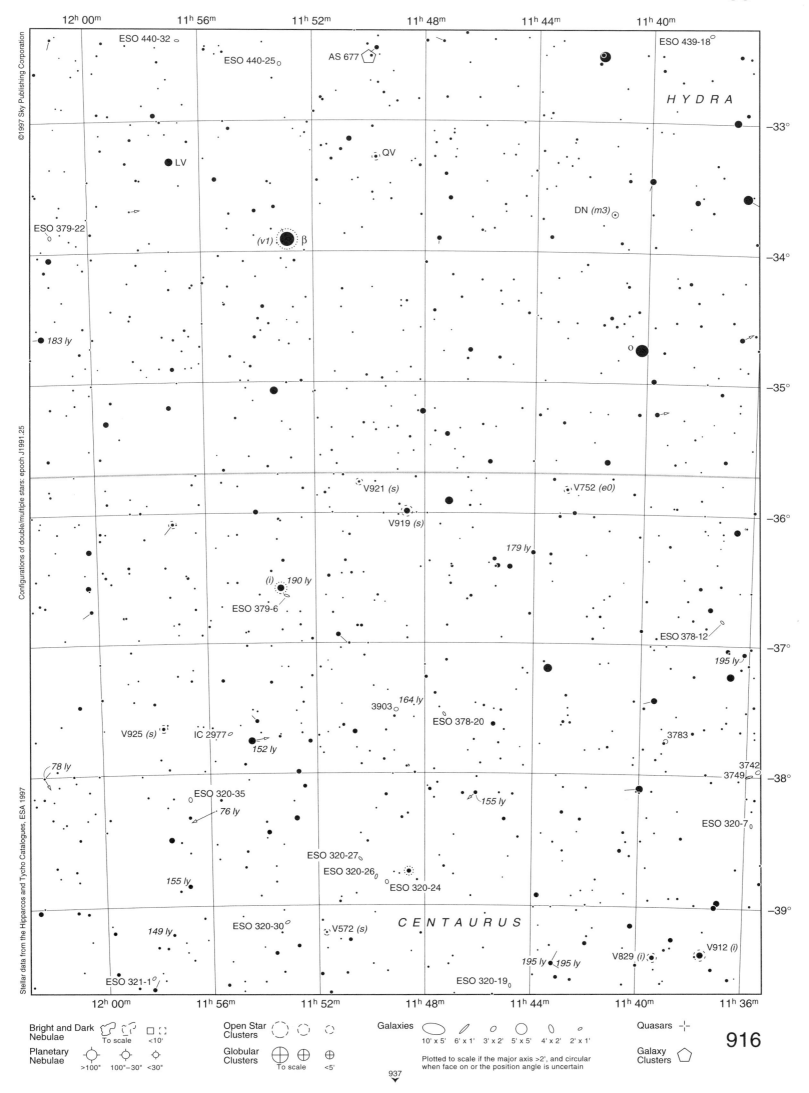

HYDRA

CENTAURUS

ESO 440-32

ESO 440-25

AS 677

ESO 439-18

LV

QV

DN *(m3)*

ESO 379-22

(v1) β

183 ly

o

V921 *(s)*

V752 *(e0)*

V919 *(s)*

179 ly

(i) *190 ly*

ESO 379-6

ESO 378-12

195 ly

164 ly

3903

ESO 378-20

3783

V925 *(s)*

IC 2977

152 ly

78 ly

3742
3749

ESO 320-35

155 ly

76 ly

ESO 320-7

ESO 320-27

ESO 320-26

155 ly

ESO 320-24

ESO 320-30

149 ly

V572 *(s)*

195 ly *195 ly*

V829 *(i)*

V912 *(i)*

ESO 321-1

ESO 320-19

12h 00m   11h 56m   11h 52m   11h 48m   11h 44m   11h 40m   11h 36m

−33°
−34°
−35°
−36°
−37°
−38°
−39°

Bright and Dark
Nebulae
To scale   <10'

Planetary
Nebulae
>100"   100"−30"   <30"

Open Star
Clusters

Globular
Clusters
To scale   <5'

Galaxies
10' x 5'   6' x 1'   3' x 2'   5' x 5'   4' x 2'   2' x 1'

Plotted to scale if the major axis >2', and circular
when face on or the position angle is uncertain

Quasars

Galaxy
Clusters

916

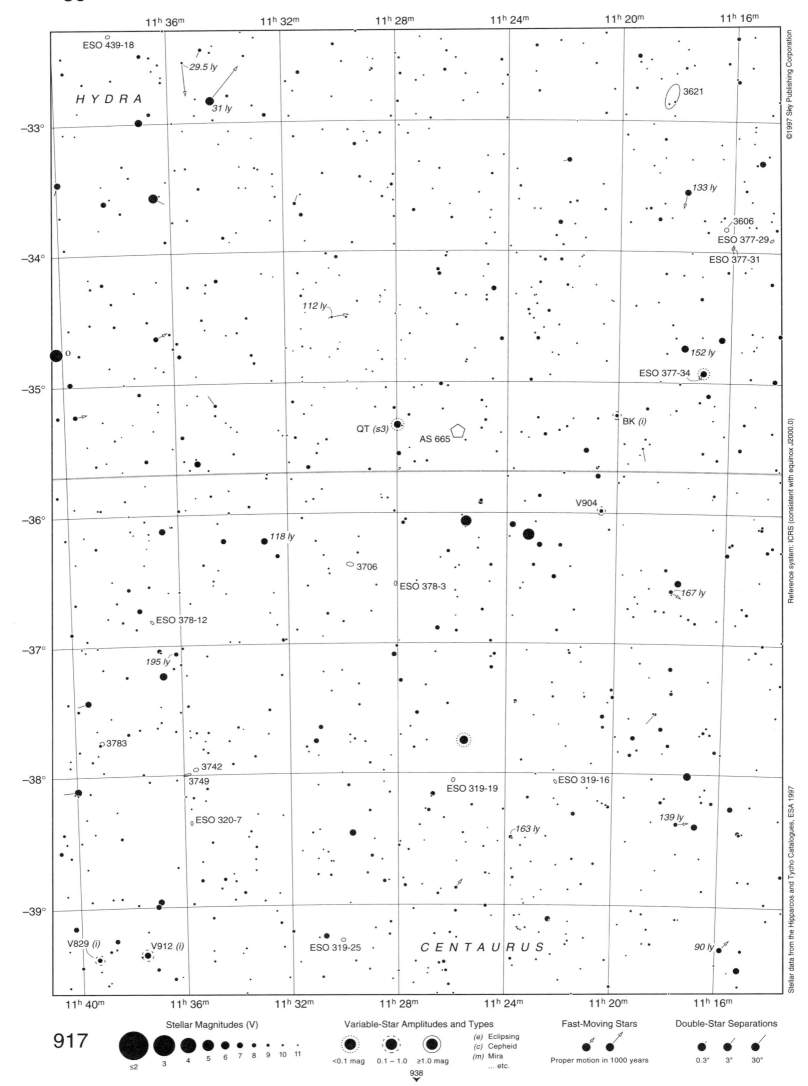

917

Stellar Magnitudes (V)

≤2 3 4 5 6 7 8 9 10 11

Variable-Star Amplitudes and Types

<0.1 mag   0.1 – 1.0   ≥1.0 mag

(e) Eclipsing
(c) Cepheid
(m) Mira
... etc.

Fast-Moving Stars

Proper motion in 1000 years

Double-Star Separations

0.3"   3"   30"

938

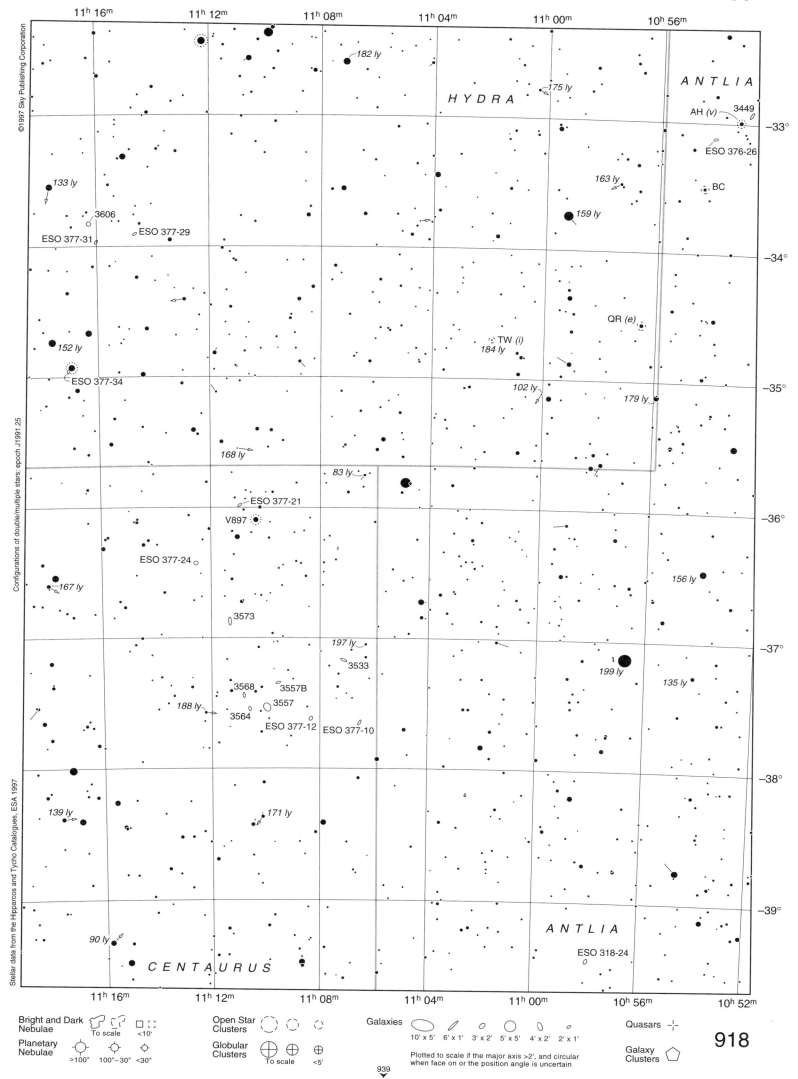

Bright and Dark Nebulae
To scale   <10'

Planetary Nebulae
>100"   100"–30"   <30"

Open Star Clusters

Globular Clusters
To scale   <5'

Galaxies
10' x 5'   6' x 1'   3' x 2'   5' x 5'   4' x 2'   2' x 1'

Plotted to scale if the major axis >2', and circular when face on or the position angle is uncertain

Quasars

Galaxy Clusters

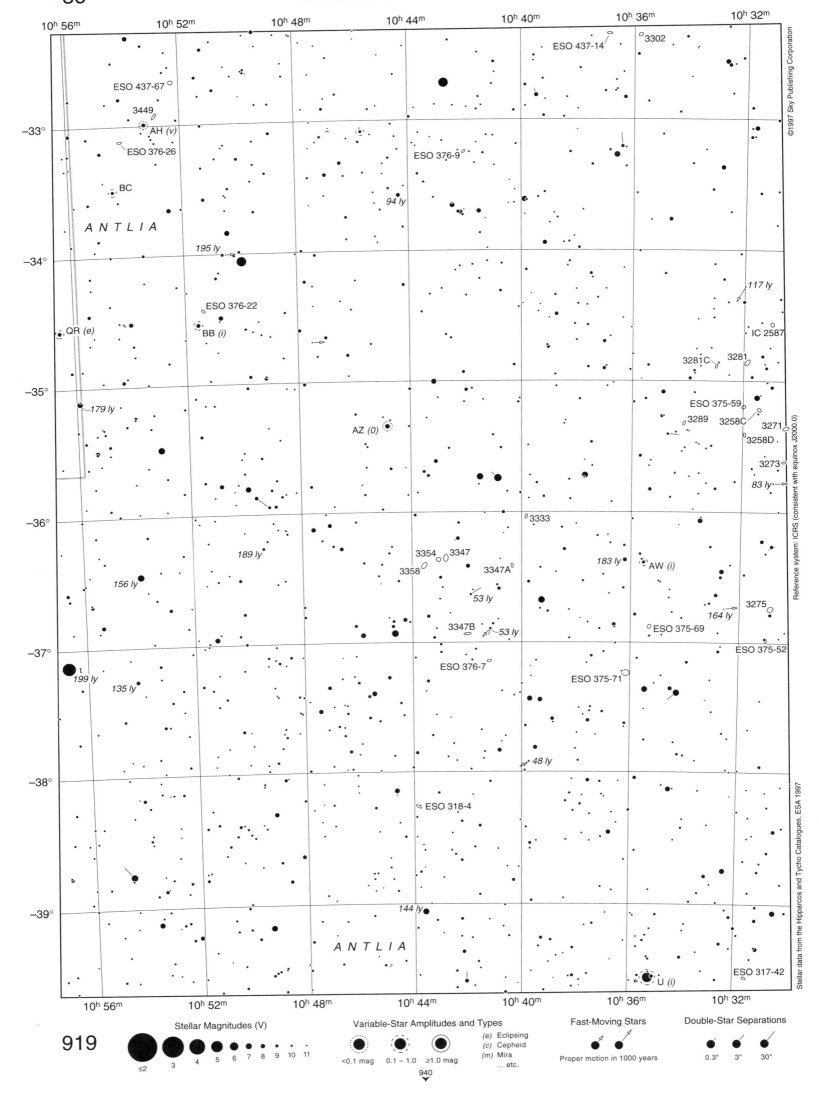

ESO 437-14
3302
ESO 437-67
3449
AH (v)
ESO 376-26
BC
ANTLIA
ESO 376-9
94 ly
195 ly
117 ly
ESO 376-22
IC 2587
BB (i)
QR (e)
3281C   3281
179 ly
ESO 375-59
AZ (0)
3289   3258C   3271
3258D
3273
83 ly
3333
189 ly
3354   3347
3358   3347A
183 ly   AW (i)
156 ly
53 ly
164 ly   3275
3347B   53 ly
ESO 375-69
ESO 375-52
ι
199 ly   ESO 376-7
135 ly
ESO 375-71
48 ly
ESO 318-4
144 ly
ANTLIA
U (i)
ESO 317-42

-33°
-34°
-35°
-36°
-37°
-38°
-39°

10ʰ 56ᵐ   10ʰ 52ᵐ   10ʰ 48ᵐ   10ʰ 44ᵐ   10ʰ 40ᵐ   10ʰ 36ᵐ   10ʰ 32ᵐ

919

Stellar Magnitudes (V)
≤2   3   4   5   6   7   8   9   10   11

Variable-Star Amplitudes and Types
<0.1 mag   0.1 – 1.0   ≥1.0 mag
(e) Eclipsing
(c) Cepheid
(m) Mira
... etc.
940

Fast-Moving Stars
Proper motion in 1000 years

Double-Star Separations
0.3"   3"   30"

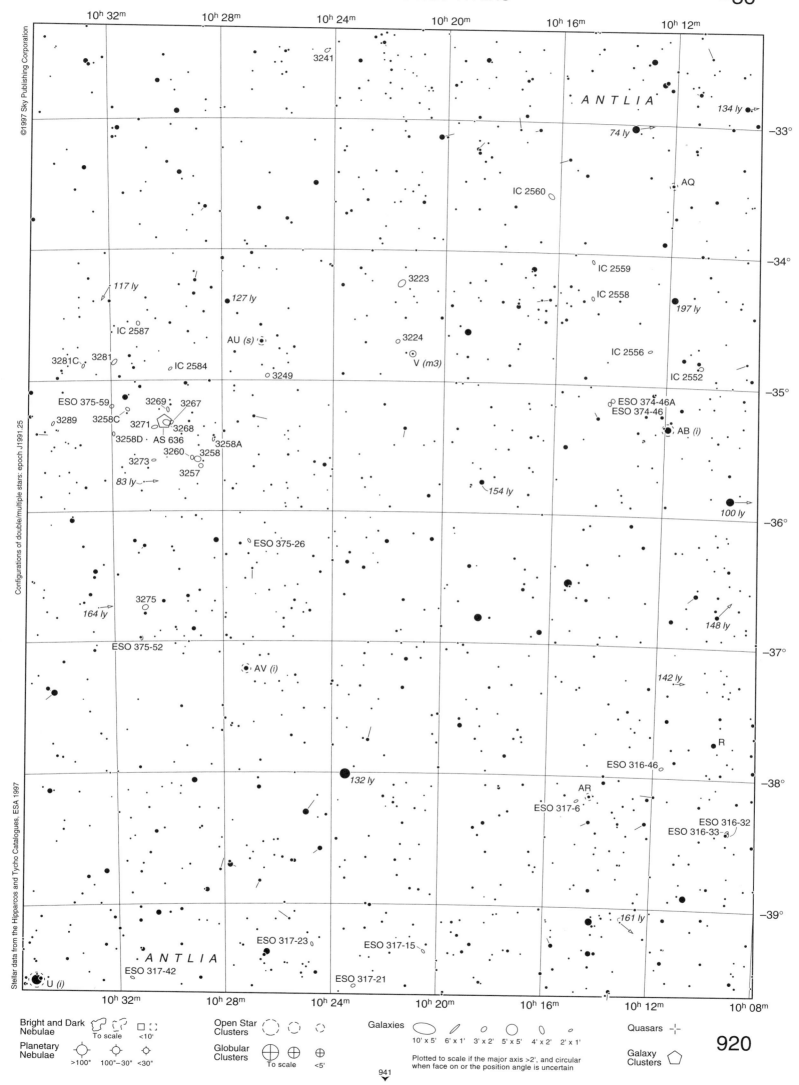

Bright and Dark Nebulae			Open Star Clusters		Galaxies	Quasars
Planetary Nebulae			Globular Clusters			Galaxy Clusters

920

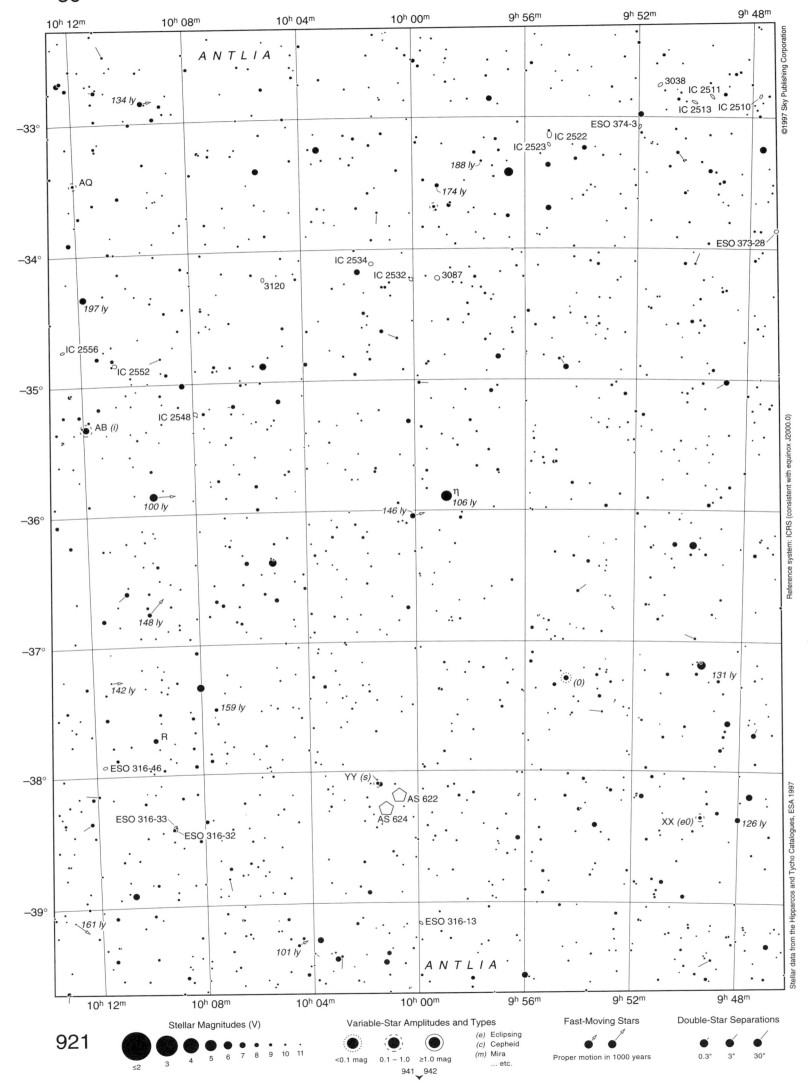

©1997 Sky Publishing Corporation

Reference system: ICRS (consistent with equinox J2000.0)

Stellar data from the Hipparcos and Tycho Catalogues, ESA 1997

921

Stellar Magnitudes (V)

≤2 3 4 5 6 7 8 9 10 11

Variable-Star Amplitudes and Types

<0.1 mag   0.1 – 1.0   ≥1.0 mag

(e) Eclipsing
(c) Cepheid
(m) Mira
... etc.

941 942

Fast-Moving Stars

Proper motion in 1000 years

Double-Star Separations

0.3" 3" 30"

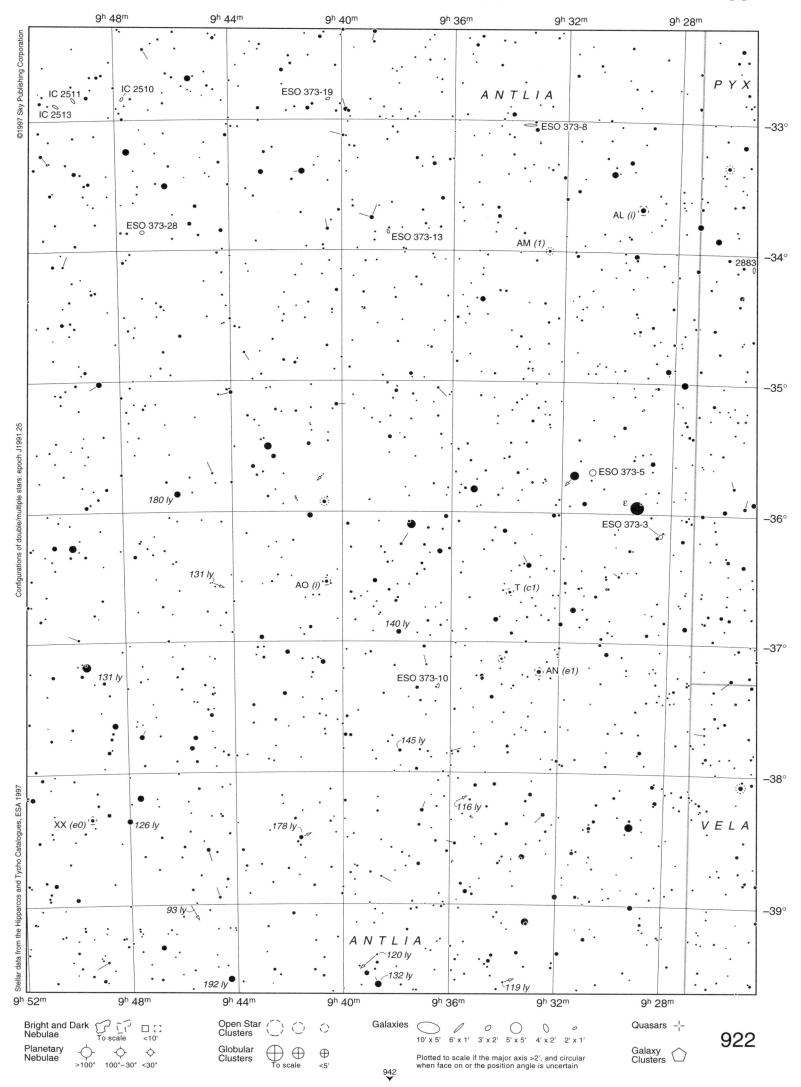

PYX

ANTLIA

IC 2511
IC 2510
IC 2513
ESO 373-19
ESO 373-8
ESO 373-28
ESO 373-13
AL (i)
AM (1)
2883
ESO 373-5
ε
ESO 373-3
180 ly
131 ly
AO (i)
T (c1)
140 ly
ESO 373-10
AN (e1)
131 ly
145 ly
XX (e0)
126 ly
178 ly
116 ly
VELA
93 ly
ANTLIA
120 ly
192 ly
132 ly
119 ly

Bright and Dark Nebulae			Open Star Clusters			Galaxies						Quasars
To scale		<10'				10' x 5'	6' x 1'	3' x 2'	5' x 5'	4' x 2'	2' x 1'	
Planetary Nebulae			Globular Clusters									Galaxy Clusters
>100"	100"–30"	<30"	To scale		<5'	Plotted to scale if the major axis >2', and circular when face on or the position angle is uncertain						

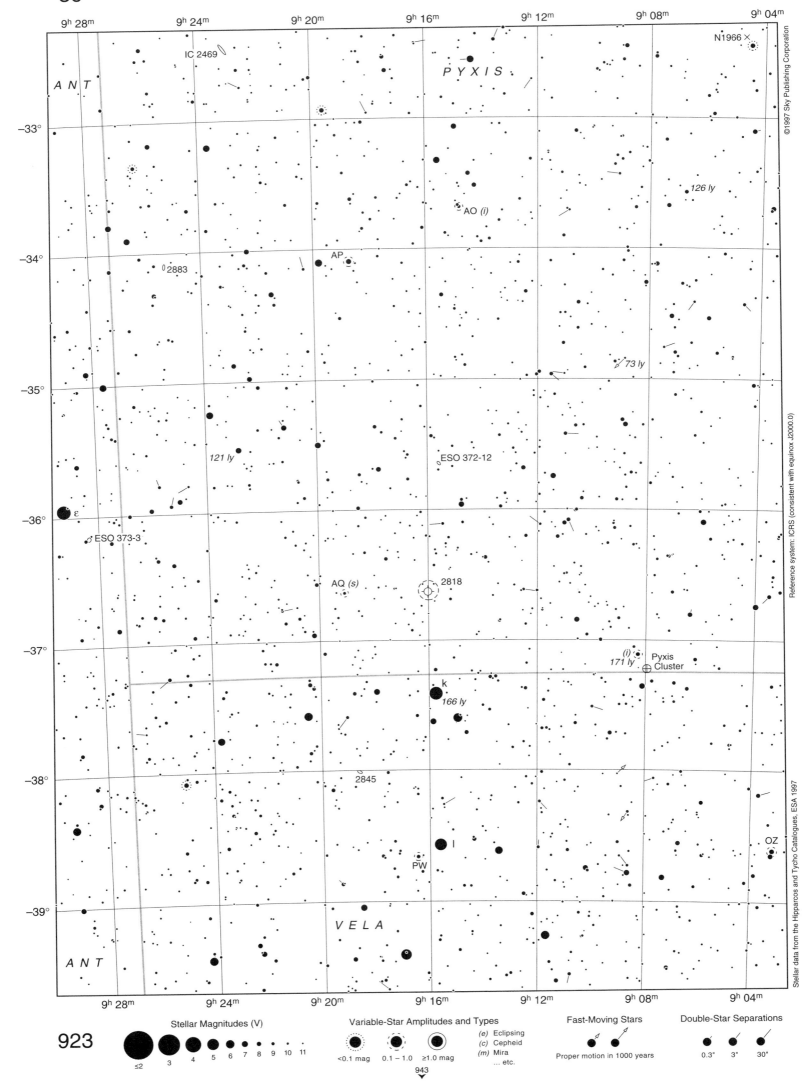

©1997 Sky Publishing Corporation

Reference system: ICRS (consistent with equinox J2000.0)

Stellar data from the Hipparcos and Tycho Catalogues, ESA 1997

IC 2469

A N T

P Y X I S

N1966 ×

126 ly

AO (i)

2883

AP

73 ly

121 ly

ESO 372-12

ε

ESO 373-3

AQ (s)

2818

Pyxis
Cluster

(i)
171 ly

k

166 ly

2845

l

PW

OZ

V E L A

A N T

923

Stellar Magnitudes (V)

≤2   3   4   5   6   7   8   9   10   11

Variable-Star Amplitudes and Types

<0.1 mag   0.1 – 1.0   ≥1.0 mag

(e) Eclipsing
(c) Cepheid
(m) Mira
... etc.

Fast-Moving Stars

Proper motion in 1000 years

Double-Star Separations

0.3"   3"   30"

943

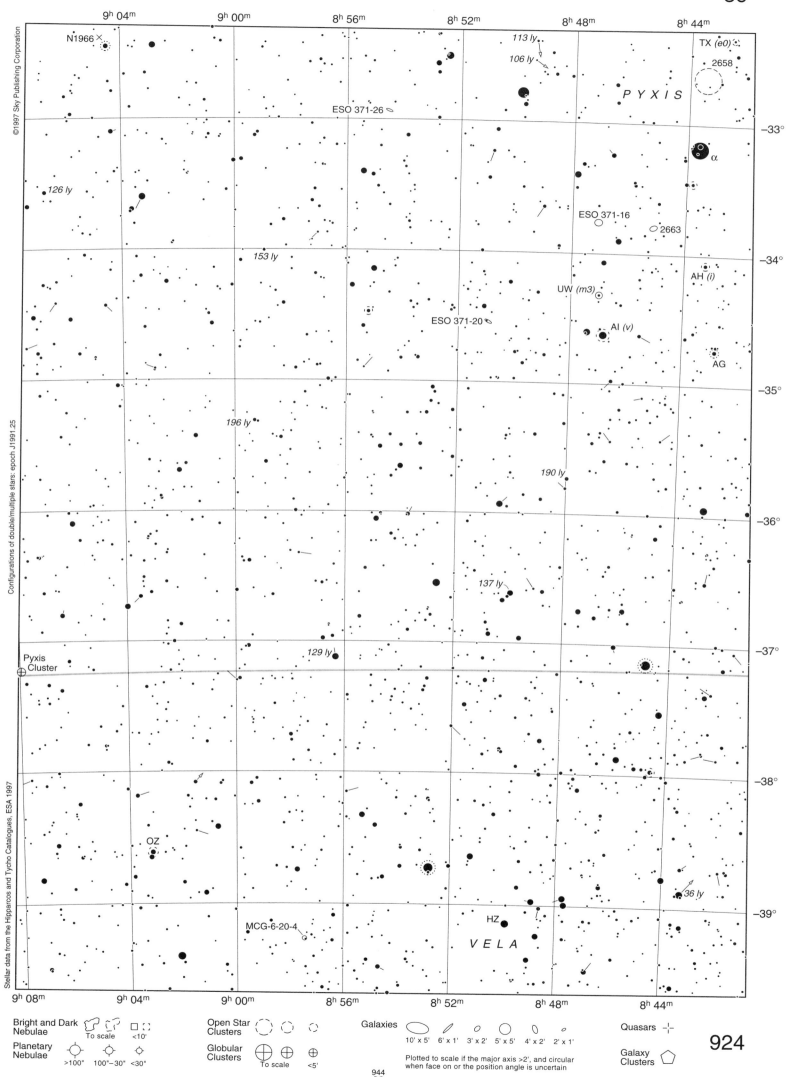

9h 04m
9h 00m
8h 56m
8h 52m
8h 48m
8h 44m

N1966 ×

113 ly

106 ly

TX (e0)

2658

P Y X I S

−33°

ESO 371-26

126 ly

α

ESO 371-16

2663

153 ly

AH (i)

UW (m3)

−34°

ESO 371-20

AI (v)

AG

−35°

196 ly

190 ly

−36°

137 ly

129 ly

Pyxis Cluster

−37°

OZ

36 ly

−38°

MCG-6-20-4

HZ

−39°

V E L A

9h 08m
9h 04m
9h 00m
8h 56m
8h 52m
8h 48m
8h 44m

Bright and Dark Nebulae
To scale
<10'

Planetary Nebulae
>100"   100"–30"   <30"

Open Star Clusters

Globular Clusters
To scale
<5'

Galaxies
10' x 5'   6' x 1'   3' x 2'   5' x 5'   4' x 2'   2' x 1'

Plotted to scale if the major axis >2', and circular when face on or the position angle is uncertain

Quasars

Galaxy Clusters

924

944

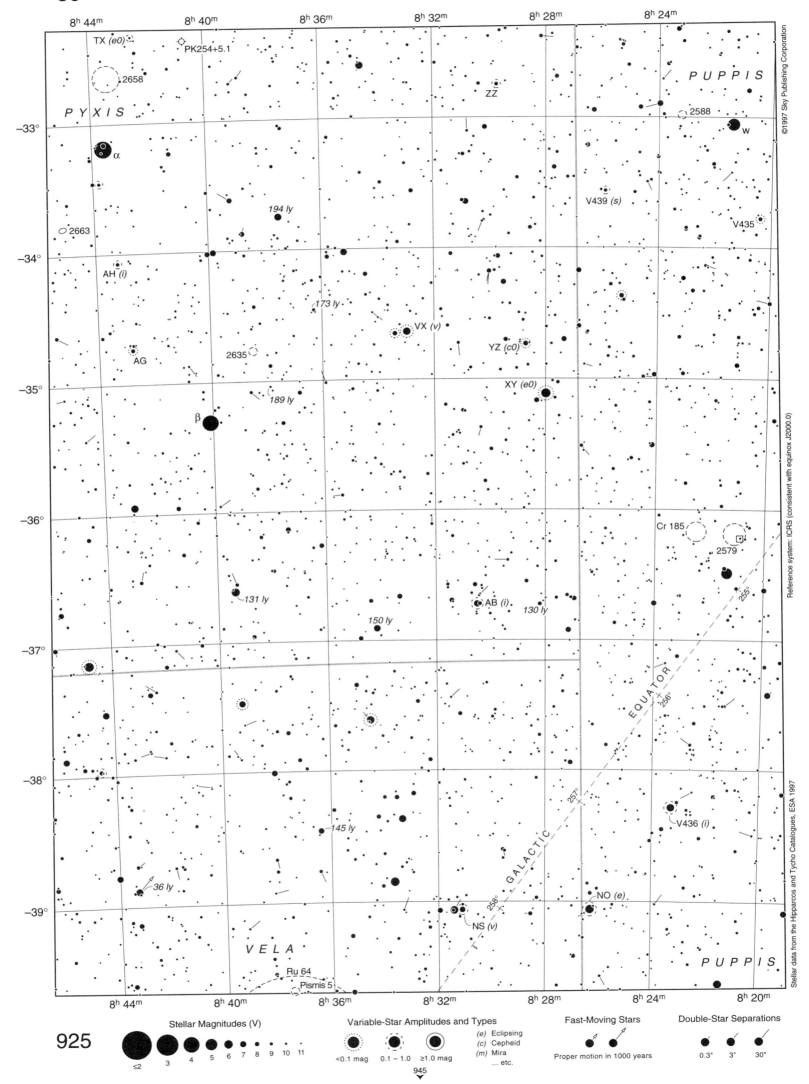

©1997 Sky Publishing Corporation

Reference system: ICRS (consistent with equinox J2000.0)

Stellar data from the Hipparcos and Tycho Catalogues, ESA 1997

TX *(e0)*
PK254+5.1
2658
P Y X I S
P U P P I S
ZZ
2588
w
α
V439 *(s)*
194 ly
V435
2663
AH *(i)*
173 ly
AG
2635
VX *(v)*
YZ *(c0)*
189 ly
XY *(e0)*
β
Cr 185
2579
131 ly
AB *(i)*
130 ly
150 ly
EQUATOR
145 ly
V436 *(i)*
36 ly
GALACTIC
NO *(e)*
NS *(v)*
V E L A
P U P P I S
Ru 64
Pismis 5

925

Stellar Magnitudes (V)
≤2   3   4   5   6   7   8   9 10 11

Variable-Star Amplitudes and Types
<0.1 mag   0.1 – 1.0   ≥1.0 mag

(e) Eclipsing
(c) Cepheid
(m) Mira
... etc.

Fast-Moving Stars
Proper motion in 1000 years

Double-Star Separations
0.3″   3″   30″

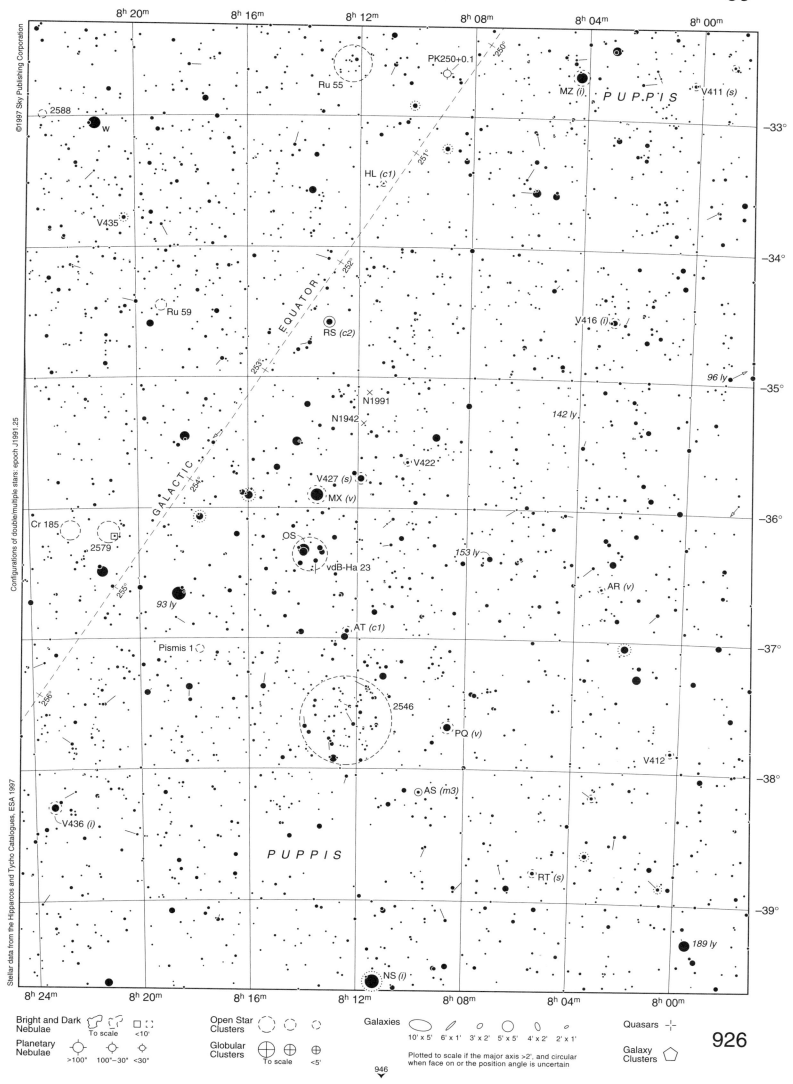

PK250+0.1

Ru 55

2588

w

MZ *(i)*

P U P P I S

V411 *(s)*

−33°

HL *(c1)*

V435

251°

252°

EQUATOR

Ru 59

RS *(c2)*

V416 *(i)*

−34°

253°

96 ly

N1991

−35°

N1942

142 ly

GALACTIC

254°

V422

V427 *(s)*

MX *(v)*

Cr 185

OS

153 ly

−36°

2579

vdB-Ha 23

255°

AR *(v)*

93 ly

AT *(c1)*

Pismis 1

−37°

256°

2546

PQ *(v)*

V412

AS *(m3)*

−38°

V436 *(i)*

P U P P I S

RT *(s)*

−39°

189 ly

NS *(i)*

8ʰ 24ᵐ   8ʰ 20ᵐ   8ʰ 16ᵐ   8ʰ 12ᵐ   8ʰ 08ᵐ   8ʰ 04ᵐ   8ʰ 00ᵐ

Bright and Dark Nebulae
To scale   <10'

Planetary Nebulae
>100"   100"–30"   <30"

Open Star Clusters

Globular Clusters
To scale   <5'

Galaxies
10' x 5'   6' x 1'   3' x 2'   5' x 5'   4' x 2'   2' x 1'

Plotted to scale if the major axis >2', and circular when face on or the position angle is uncertain

Quasars

Galaxy Clusters

926

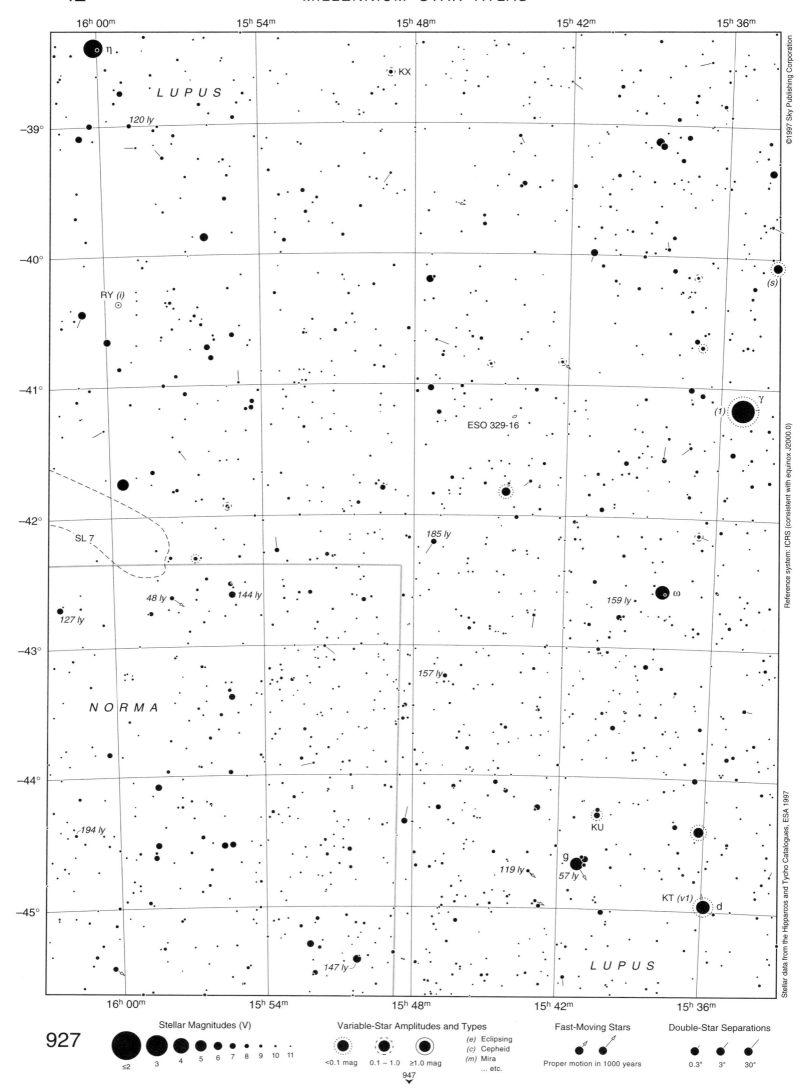

©1997 Sky Publishing Corporation

Reference system: ICRS (consistent with equinox J2000.0)

Stellar data from the Hipparcos and Tycho Catalogues, ESA 1997

927

Stellar Magnitudes (V)

≤2 3 4 5 6 7 8 9 10 11

Variable-Star Amplitudes and Types

<0.1 mag   0.1 – 1.0   ≥1.0 mag

(e) Eclipsing
(c) Cepheid
(m) Mira
... etc.

Fast-Moving Stars

Proper motion in 1000 years

Double-Star Separations

0.3"   3"   30"

947

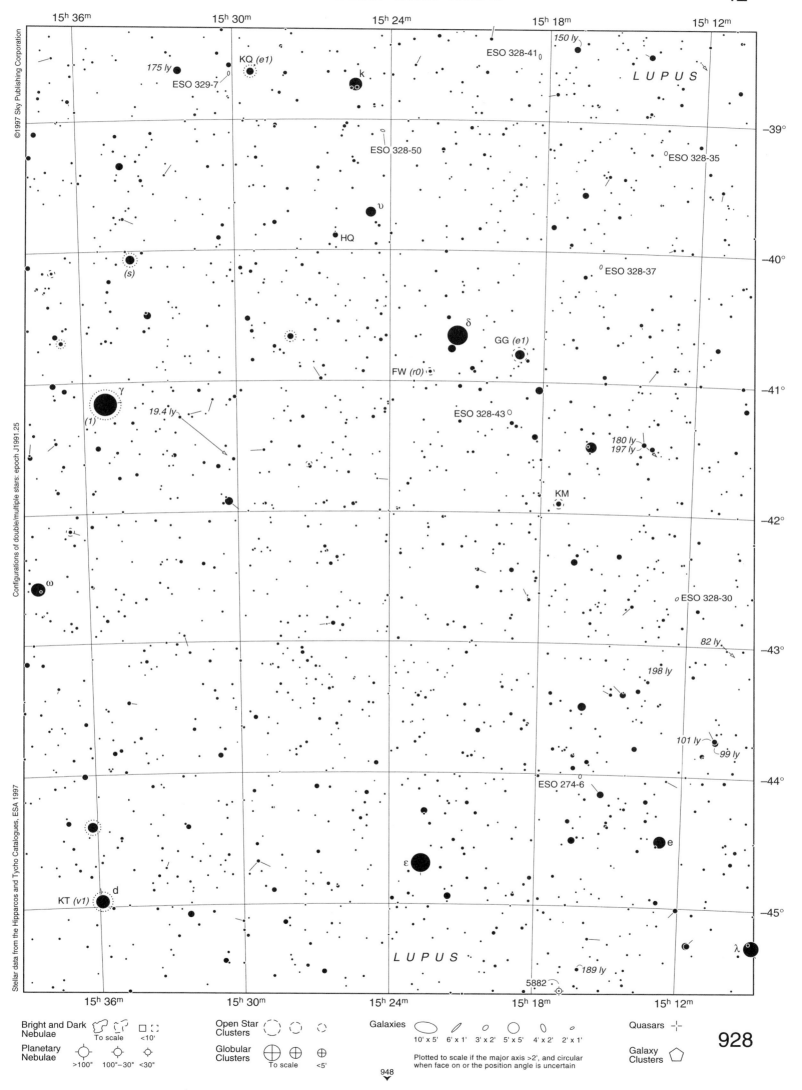

906

15h 36m   15h 30m   15h 24m   15h 18m   15h 12m

−39°

−40°

−41°

−42°

−43°

−44°

−45°

LUPUS

LUPUS

150 ly
ESO 328-41
KQ *(e1)*
175 ly
ESO 329-7
k
ESO 328-35
ESO 328-50
υ
HQ
(s)
ESO 328-37
δ
GG *(e1)*
FW *(r0)*
γ
(1)
19.4 ly
ESO 328-43
180 ly
197 ly
KM
ESO 328-30
82 ly
198 ly
101 ly
99 ly
ESO 274-6
e
ω
ε
KT *(v1)*   d
λ
189 ly
5882

15h 36m   15h 30m   15h 24m   15h 18m   15h 12m

Bright and Dark Nebulae		To scale	<10'	Open Star Clusters			Galaxies						Quasars	

Bright and Dark Nebulae   To scale   <10'

Open Star Clusters

Galaxies
10' x 5'   6' x 1'   3' x 2'   5' x 5'   4' x 2'   2' x 1'

Quasars

Planetary Nebulae
>100"   100"–30"   <30"

Globular Clusters
To scale   <5'

Plotted to scale if the major axis >2', and circular when face on or the position angle is uncertain

Galaxy Clusters

928

948

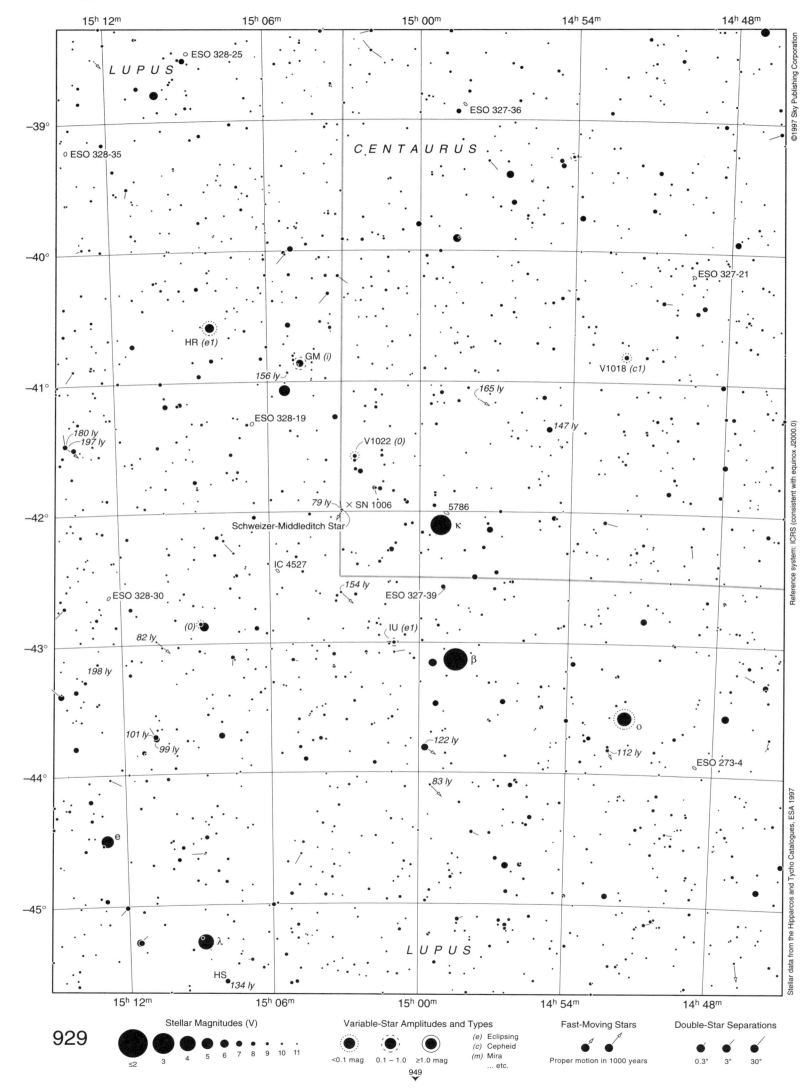

©1997 Sky Publishing Corporation

Reference system: ICRS (consistent with equinox J2000.0)

Stellar data from the Hipparcos and Tycho Catalogues, ESA 1997

LUPUS

ESO 328-25

CENTAURUS

ESO 327-36

ESO 328-35

ESO 327-21

HR (e1)

GM (i)

V1018 (c1)

156 ly

165 ly

ESO 328-19

147 ly

180 ly
197 ly

V1022 (0)

79 ly × SN 1006

5786

κ

Schweizer-Middleditch Star

IC 4527

154 ly

ESO 327-39

ESO 328-30

(0)

IU (e1)

82 ly

198 ly

β

o

101 ly

122 ly

99 ly

112 ly

ESO 273-4

83 ly

e

LUPUS

λ

HS
134 ly

Stellar Magnitudes (V)

929

≤2   3   4   5   6   7   8   9   10   11

Variable-Star Amplitudes and Types

<0.1 mag   0.1 – 1.0   ≥1.0 mag

(e) Eclipsing
(c) Cepheid
(m) Mira
… etc.

Fast-Moving Stars

Proper motion in 1000 years

Double-Star Separations

0.3″   3″   30″

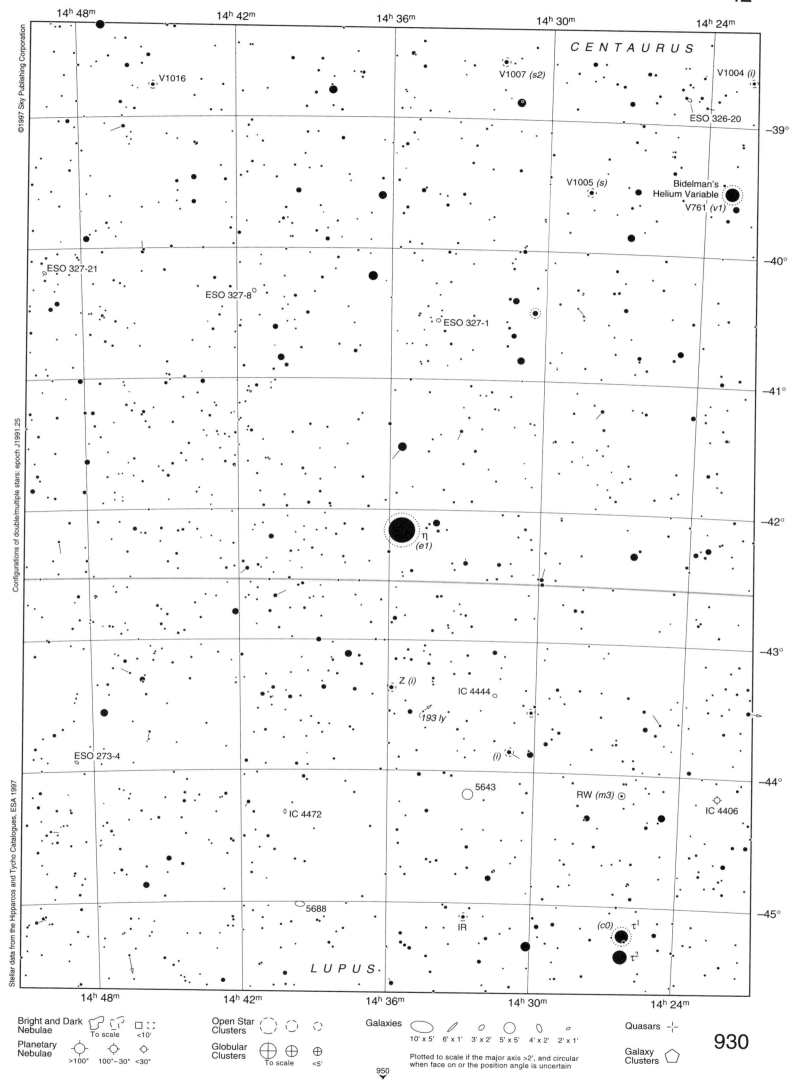

©1997 Sky Publishing Corporation

Configurations of double/multiple stars: epoch J1991.25

Stellar data from the Hipparcos and Tycho Catalogues, ESA 1997

14h 48m   14h 42m   14h 36m   14h 30m   14h 24m

C E N T A U R U S

V1016

V1007 (s2)   V1004 (i)

ESO 326-20

−39°

V1005 (s)   Bidelman's
                                 Helium Variable

                                 V761 (v1)

ESO 327-21   −40°

ESO 327-8

ESO 327-1

−41°

η
(e1)   −42°

Z (i)   IC 4444   −43°

193 ly

(i)

ESO 273-4

                        5643   RW (m3)   IC 4406   −44°

IC 4472

5688   −45°

IR

(c0) τ¹

τ²

L U P U S

14h 48m   14h 42m   14h 36m   14h 30m   14h 24m

Bright and Dark
Nebulae   To scale   <10'

Planetary
Nebulae   >100" 100"−30" <30"

Open Star
Clusters

Globular
Clusters   To scale   <5'

Galaxies
            10' x 5' 6' x 1' 3' x 2' 5' x 5' 4' x 2' 2' x 1'

Plotted to scale if the major axis >2', and circular
when face on or the position angle is uncertain

Quasars

Galaxy
Clusters

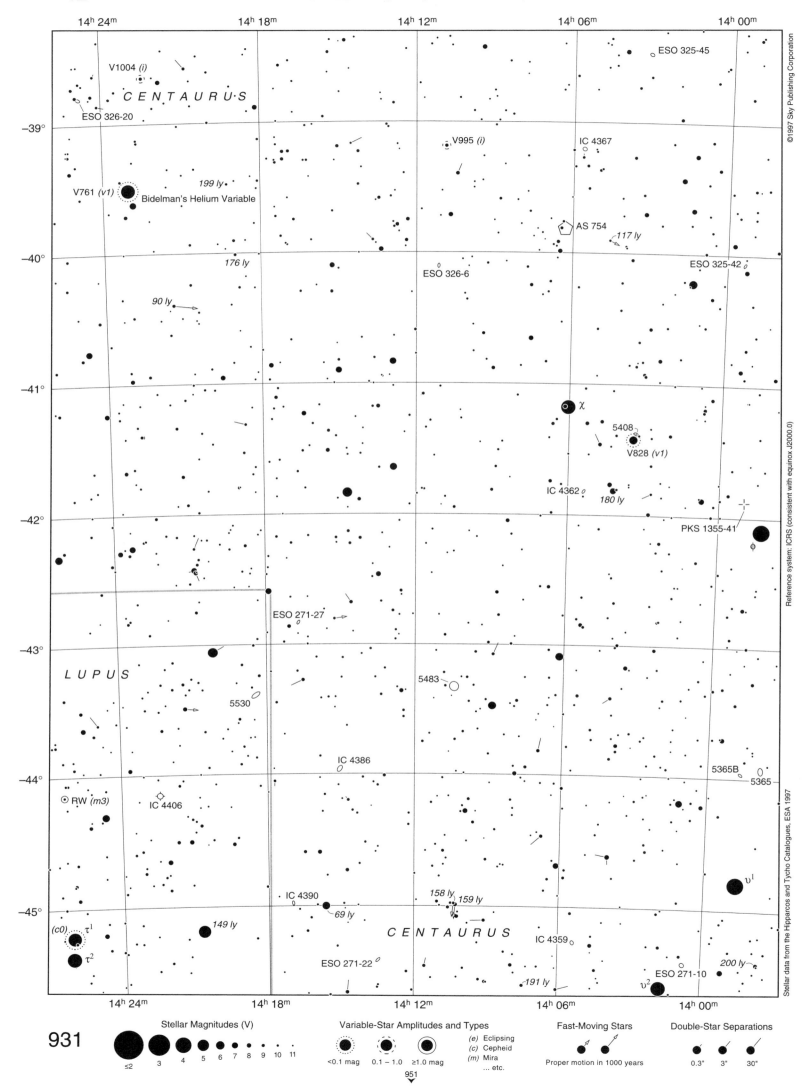

©1997 Sky Publishing Corporation

Reference system: ICRS (consistent with equinox J2000.0)

Stellar data from the Hipparcos and Tycho Catalogues, ESA 1997

931

Stellar Magnitudes (V)

≤2   3   4   5   6 7 8 9 10 11

Variable-Star Amplitudes and Types

<0.1 mag   0.1 − 1.0   ≥1.0 mag

(e) Eclipsing
(c) Cepheid
(m) Mira
... etc.

Fast-Moving Stars

Proper motion in 1000 years

Double-Star Separations

0.3"   3"   30"

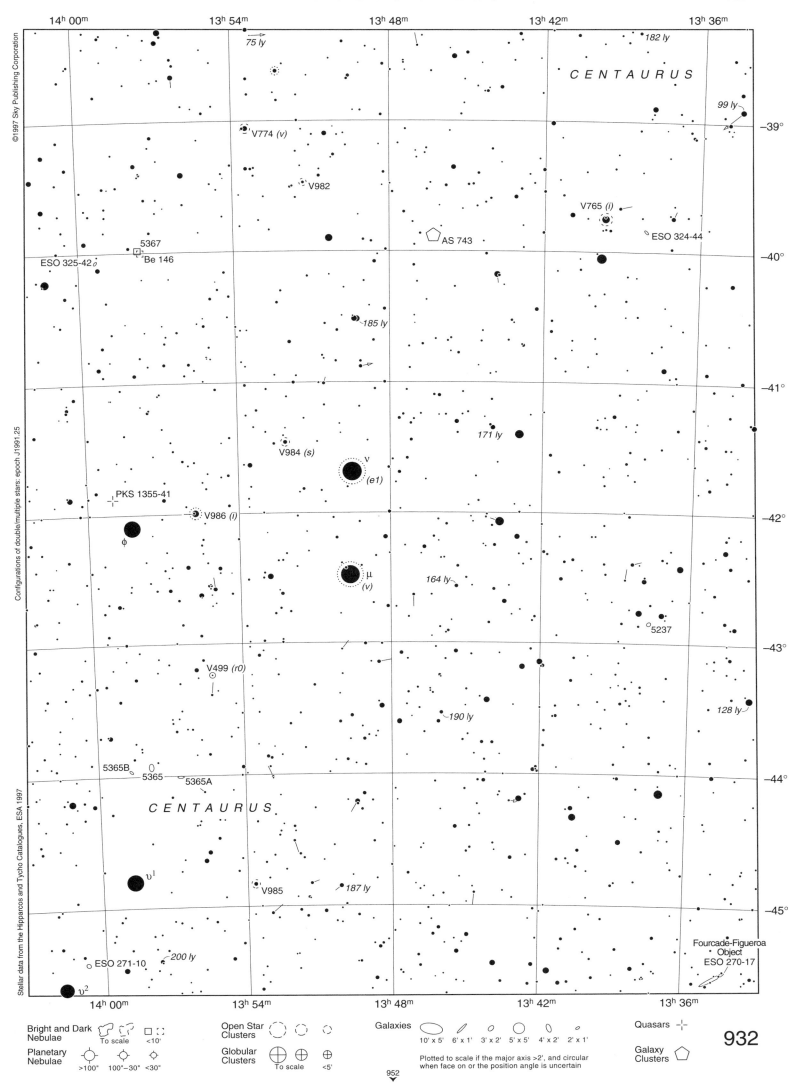

14h 00m   13h 54m   13h 48m   13h 42m   13h 36m

CENTAURUS

182 ly

99 ly

75 ly

V774 (v)

V982

V765 (i)

AS 743

ESO 324-44

5367

Be 146

ESO 325-42

−39°

−40°

185 ly

171 ly

V984 (s)

ν (e1)

PKS 1355-41

V986 (i)

φ

−41°

−42°

μ (v)

164 ly

5237

V499 (r0)

190 ly

128 ly

−43°

5365B

5365   5365A

CENTAURUS

−44°

υ¹

V985   187 ly

−45°

200 ly

ESO 271-10

Fourcade-Figueroa
Object
ESO 270-17

υ²

14h 00m   13h 54m   13h 48m   13h 42m   13h 36m

Bright and Dark Nebulae
To scale   <10'

Planetary Nebulae
>100"   100"−30"   <30"

Open Star Clusters

Globular Clusters
To scale   <5'

Galaxies
10' x 5'   6' x 1'   3' x 2'   5' x 5'   4' x 2'   2' x 1'

Plotted to scale if the major axis >2', and circular when face on or the position angle is uncertain

Quasars

Galaxy Clusters

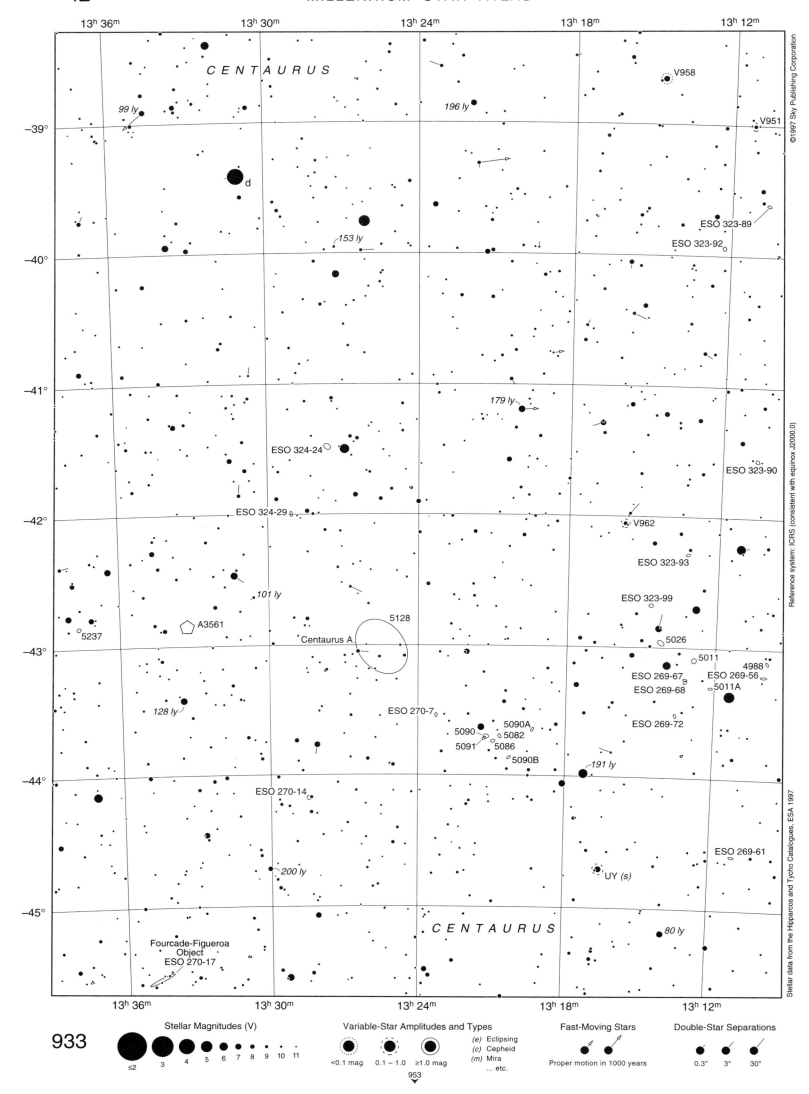

CENTAURUS

V958

99 ly

196 ly

V951

d

ESO 323-89

ESO 323-92

153 ly

179 ly

ESO 324-24

ESO 323-90

ESO 324-29

V962

ESO 323-93

ESO 323-99

101 ly

5026

5237

A3561

5128

5011

4988

Centaurus A

ESO 269-67

ESO 269-56

5011A

ESO 269-68

128 ly

ESO 270-7

ESO 269-72

5090A

5090   5082

5091   5086

5090B

191 ly

ESO 270-14

ESO 269-61

200 ly

UY (s)

CENTAURUS

80 ly

Fourcade-Figueroa
Object
ESO 270-17

©1997 Sky Publishing Corporation

Reference system: ICRS (consistent with equinox J2000.0)

Stellar data from the Hipparcos and Tycho Catalogues, ESA 1997

Stellar Magnitudes (V)

≤2   3   4   5   6   7 8 9 10 11

Variable-Star Amplitudes and Types

<0.1 mag   0.1 – 1.0   ≥1.0 mag

(e) Eclipsing
(c) Cepheid
(m) Mira
... etc.

Fast-Moving Stars

Proper motion in 1000 years

Double-Star Separations

0.3"   3"   30"

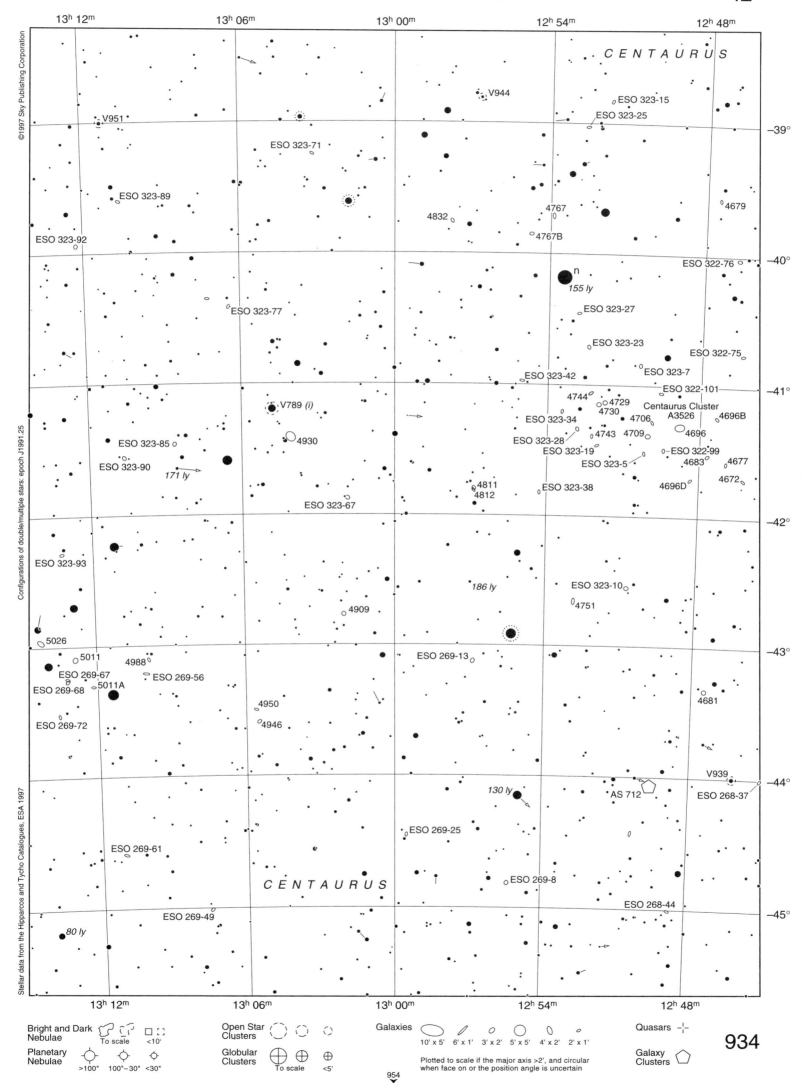

©1997 Sky Publishing Corporation

Configurations of double/multiple stars: epoch J1991.25

Stellar data from the Hipparcos and Tycho Catalogues, ESA 1997

13h 12m   13h 06m   13h 00m   12h 54m   12h 48m

CENTAURUS

V944
ESO 323-15
ESO 323-25

−39°

V951
ESO 323-71
4767
4679

ESO 323-89
4832
4767B

ESO 323-92
n
−40°
155 ly
ESO 322-76

ESO 323-77
ESO 323-27

ESO 323-23
ESO 322-75

ESO 323-42
ESO 323-7

V789 (i)
4744   4729   ESO 322-101
−41°
4730   Centaurus Cluster   4696B
ESO 323-34   4706   A3526

4930
ESO 323-28   4743   4709   4696
ESO 323-85
ESO 323-19   4683   4677
ESO 323-90
ESO 323-5   ESO 322-99
171 ly
4811   4696D   4672
4812   ESO 323-38
ESO 323-67

−42°
ESO 323-93

186 ly   ESO 323-10
4751

5026
4909

5011   ESO 269-13   −43°
ESO 269-67   4988
5011A   ESO 269-56   4681
ESO 269-68
4950
ESO 269-72   4946

V939
130 ly   AS 712   ESO 268-37
−44°
ESO 269-61
ESO 269-25

CENTAURUS   ESO 269-8
ESO 268-44
−45°
ESO 269-49

80 ly

Bright and Dark
Nebulae   Open Star
                 Clusters   Galaxies   Quasars
To scale   <10'   Galaxy
Planetary   Clusters
Nebulae   Globular   10' x 5' 6' x 1' 3' x 2' 5' x 5' 4' x 2' 2' x 1'
           Clusters
>100" 100"–30" <30"   To scale   <5'   Plotted to scale if the major axis >2', and circular
                                             when face on or the position angle is uncertain

934

954

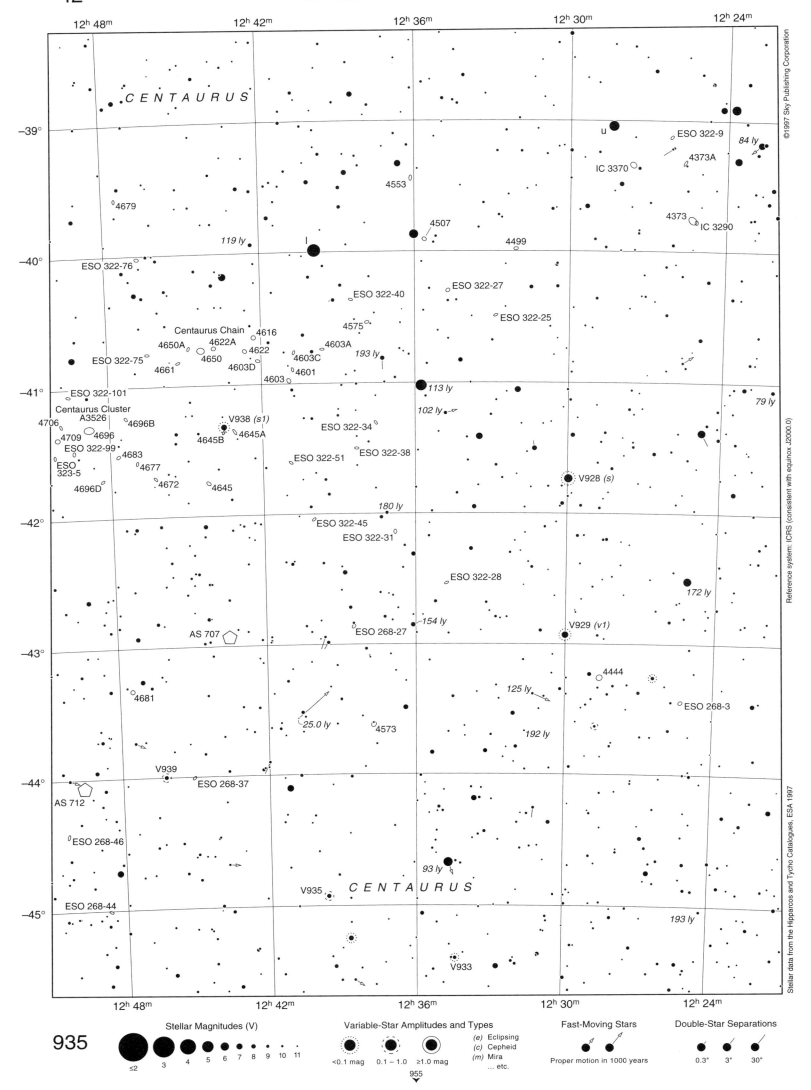

©1997 Sky Publishing Corporation

Reference system: ICRS (consistent with equinox J2000.0)

Stellar data from the Hipparcos and Tycho Catalogues, ESA 1997

CENTAURUS

12ʰ 48ᵐ   12ʰ 42ᵐ   12ʰ 36ᵐ   12ʰ 30ᵐ   12ʰ 24ᵐ

−39°

u

ESO 322-9

84 ly

IC 3370

4373A

4553

4373   IC 3290

4679

4507

119 ly   l   4499

−40°

ESO 322-76

ESO 322-40   ESO 322-27

4575   ESO 322-25

Centaurus Chain   4616

4650A   4622A   4603A

ESO 322-75   4622   193 ly

4650   4603C

4661   4603D   4601

4603

−41°   ESO 322-101   4603   113 ly

Centaurus Cluster   102 ly   79 ly

A3526   4696B

4706   V938 (s1)

4696   ESO 322-34

4709   4645A

ESO 322-99   4645B

ESO   4683   ESO 322-51   ESO 322-38

323-5   4677   V928 (s)

4696D   4672   4645

180 ly

−42°   ESO 322-45

ESO 322-31

ESO 322-28   172 ly

AS 707   V929 (v1)

154 ly

−43°   4444

ESO 268-27

4681   125 ly   ESO 268-3

25.0 ly   4573   192 ly

V939

−44°   ESO 268-37

AS 712

ESO 268-46   93 ly

V935   CENTAURUS

−45°   ESO 268-44   193 ly

V933

12ʰ 48ᵐ   12ʰ 42ᵐ   12ʰ 36ᵐ   12ʰ 30ᵐ   12ʰ 24ᵐ

935

Stellar Magnitudes (V)

≤2   3   4   5   6   7   8   9   10   11

Variable-Star Amplitudes and Types

<0.1 mag   0.1 − 1.0   ≥1.0 mag

(e) Eclipsing
(c) Cepheid
(m) Mira
... etc.

Fast-Moving Stars

Proper motion in 1000 years

Double-Star Separations

0.3"   3"   30"

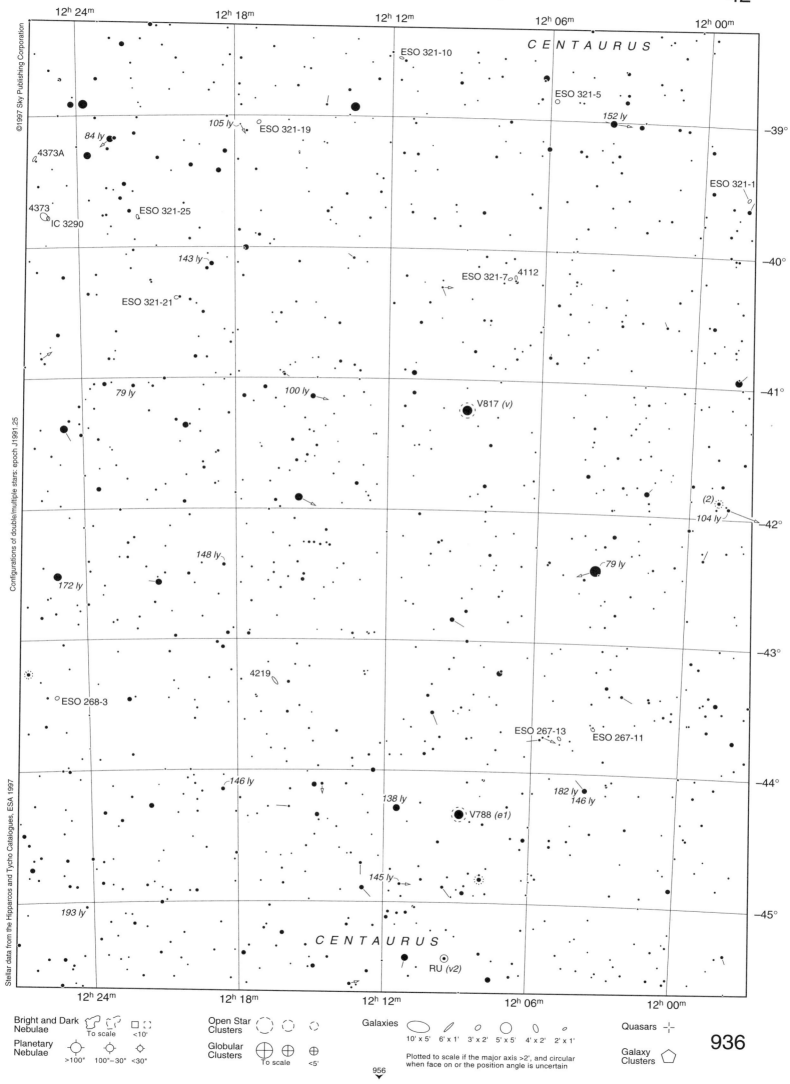

Configurations of double/multiple stars: epoch J1991.25

Stellar data from the Hipparcos and Tycho Catalogues, ESA 1997

CENTAURUS

ESO 321-10

ESO 321-5

152 ly

ESO 321-19

105 ly

84 ly

4373A

4373
IC 3290

ESO 321-25

ESO 321-1

−39°

143 ly

ESO 321-7 4112

ESO 321-21

−40°

79 ly

100 ly

V817 (v)

(2)
104 ly

−41°

148 ly

79 ly

172 ly

−42°

4219

ESO 268-3

−43°

ESO 267-13   ESO 267-11

146 ly

182 ly
146 ly

138 ly

V788 (e1)

−44°

145 ly

193 ly

−45°

CENTAURUS

RU (v2)

12h 24m   12h 18m   12h 12m   12h 06m   12h 00m

Bright and Dark Nebulae

To scale   <10'

Planetary Nebulae

>100"   100"−30"   <30"

Open Star Clusters

Globular Clusters

To scale   <5'

Galaxies

10' x 5'   6' x 1'   3' x 2'   5' x 5'   4' x 2'   2' x 1'

Plotted to scale if the major axis >2', and circular
when face on or the position angle is uncertain

Quasars

Galaxy Clusters

936

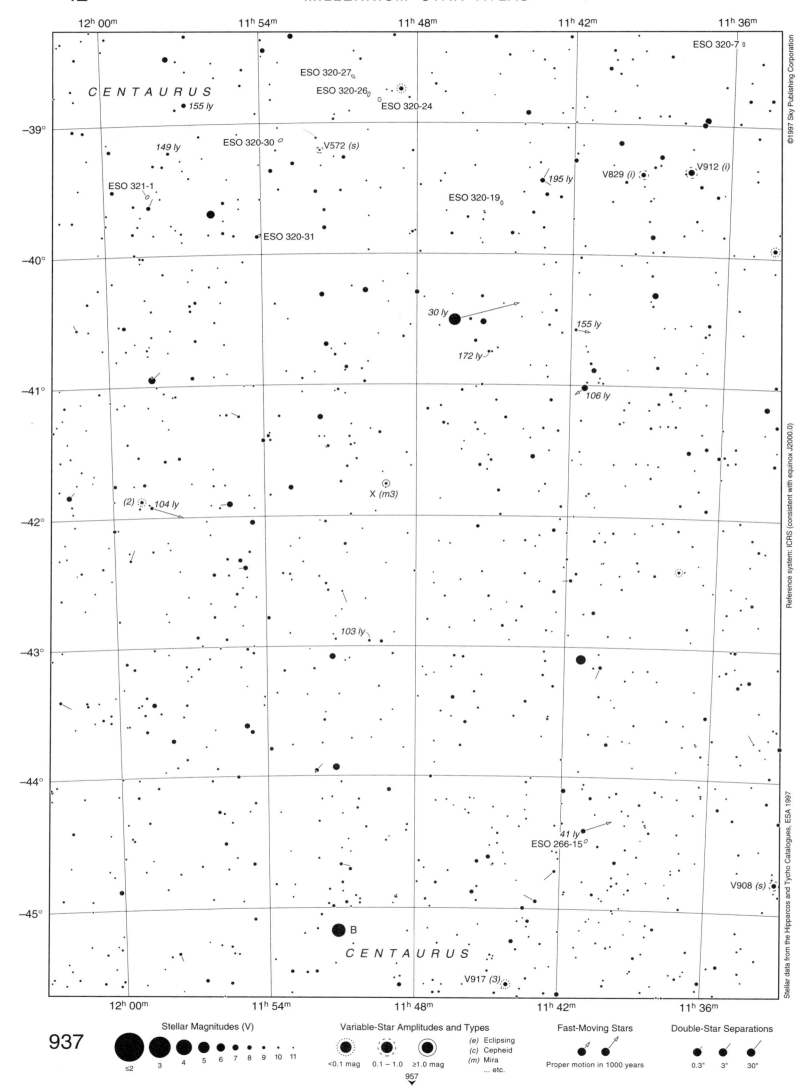

©1997 Sky Publishing Corporation

Reference system: ICRS (consistent with equinox J2000.0)

Stellar data from the Hipparcos and Tycho Catalogues, ESA 1997

C E N T A U R U S

155 ly

149 ly

ESO 320-30

ESO 321-1

ESO 320-31

ESO 320-27

ESO 320-26

ESO 320-24

V572 (s)

ESO 320-19

ESO 320-7

V829 (i)

V912 (i)

195 ly

30 ly

155 ly

172 ly

106 ly

(2)   104 ly

X (m3)

103 ly

41 ly

ESO 266-15

V908 (s)

B

C E N T A U R U S

V917 (3)

Stellar Magnitudes (V)

≤2   3   4   5   6   7   8   9   10   11

Variable-Star Amplitudes and Types

<0.1 mag   0.1 − 1.0   ≥1.0 mag

(e) Eclipsing
(c) Cepheid
(m) Mira
... etc.

957

Fast-Moving Stars

Proper motion in 1000 years

Double-Star Separations

0.3"   3"   30"

MILLENNIUM STAR ATLAS

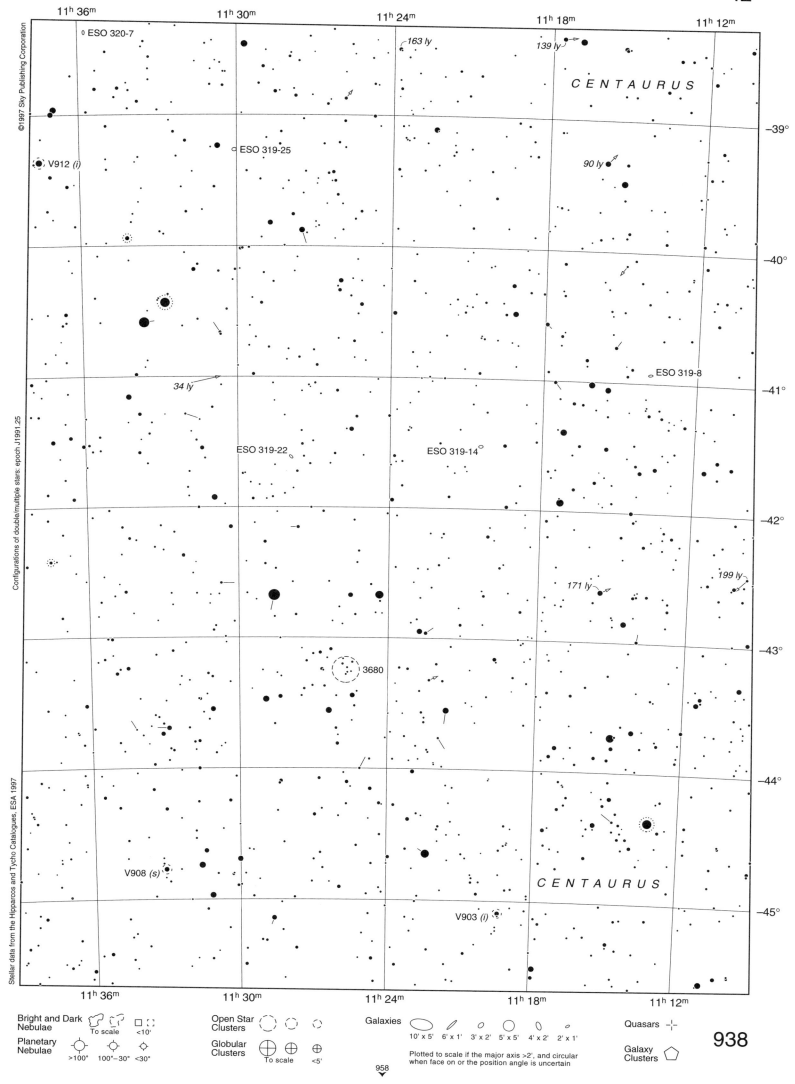

11h 36m   11h 30m   11h 24m   11h 18m   11h 12m

0 ESO 320-7

163 ly

139 ly

C E N T A U R U S

−39°

ESO 319-25

90 ly

V912 (i)

−40°

ESO 319-8

34 ly

−41°

ESO 319-22   ESO 319-14

199 ly

171 ly

−42°

3680

−43°

−44°

V908 (s)

C E N T A U R U S

−45°

V903 (i)

11h 36m   11h 30m   11h 24m   11h 18m   11h 12m

Configurations of double/multiple stars: epoch J1991.25

Stellar data from the Hipparcos and Tycho Catalogues, ESA 1997

Bright and Dark Nebulae		Open Star Clusters	Galaxies

Bright and Dark Nebulae   To scale   <10'

Planetary Nebulae   >100"   100"−30"   <30"

Open Star Clusters

Globular Clusters   To scale   <5'

Galaxies   10' x 5'   6' x 1'   3' x 2'   5' x 5'   4' x 2'   2' x 1'

Plotted to scale if the major axis >2', and circular when face on or the position angle is uncertain

Quasars   −|−

Galaxy Clusters

938

958

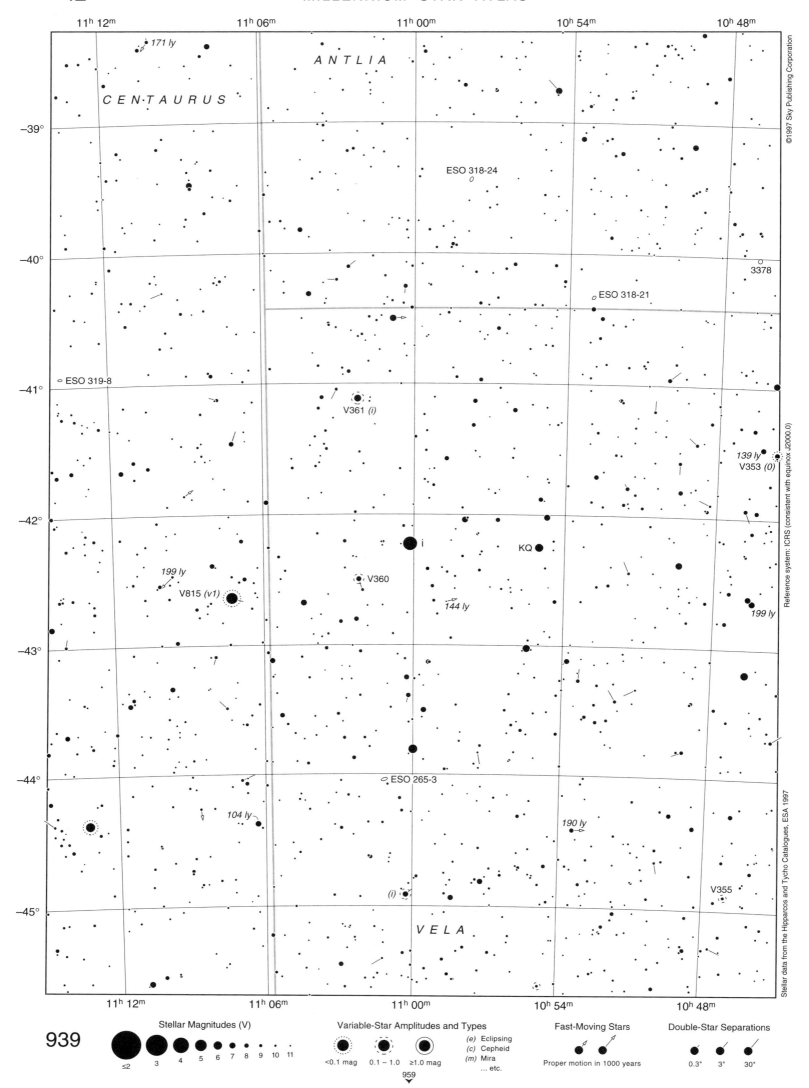

CENTAURUS

171 ly

ANTLIA

ESO 318-24

o

○ 3378

○ ESO 318-21

○ ESO 319-8

V361 *(i)*

139 ly
V353 *(0)*

i

KQ

199 ly
V815 *(v1)*

V360

144 ly

199 ly

ESO 265-3

104 ly

190 ly

V355

(i)

VELA

©1997 Sky Publishing Corporation

Reference system: ICRS (consistent with equinox J2000.0)

Stellar data from the Hipparcos and Tycho Catalogues, ESA 1997

939

Stellar Magnitudes (V)	Variable-Star Amplitudes and Types	Fast-Moving Stars	Double-Star Separations

Stellar Magnitudes (V)
≤2 3 4 5 6 7 8 9 10 11

Variable-Star Amplitudes and Types
<0.1 mag   0.1 – 1.0   ≥1.0 mag

(e) Eclipsing
(c) Cepheid
(m) Mira
... etc.

Fast-Moving Stars
Proper motion in 1000 years

Double-Star Separations
0.3"   3"   30"

959

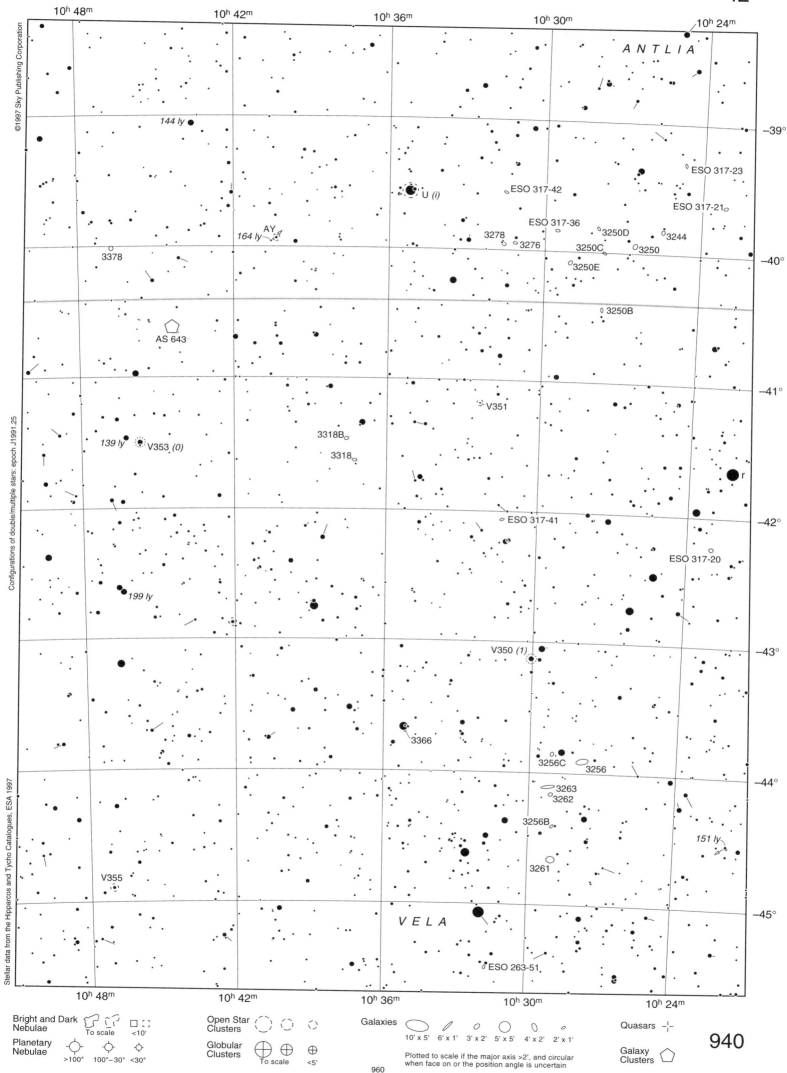

ANTLIA

10ʰ 48ᵐ   10ʰ 42ᵐ   10ʰ 36ᵐ   10ʰ 30ᵐ   10ʰ 24ᵐ

144 ly

−39°

⁰ ESO 317-23

U (i)   ⁰ ESO 317-42   ESO 317-21 ₒ
ESO 317-36   ₒ3250D   ₒ3244
164 ly   AY   3278   3250C   ₒ3250
3378   ₒ3276   ₒ3250E
−40°

⁰ 3250B

AS 643   −41°

V351
3318B ₒ   r
139 ly   V353 (0)   3318 ₒ
ₒ ESO 317-41   −42°
199 ly   ESO 317-20 ₒ

V350 (1)   −43°

3366
3256C   3256   −44°
3263
3262
3256B   151 ly
3261
V355   −45°

VELA   ₒ ESO 263-51

Stellar data from the Hipparcos and Tycho Catalogues, ESA 1997
Configurations of double/multiple stars: epoch J1991.25

10ʰ 48ᵐ   10ʰ 42ᵐ   10ʰ 36ᵐ   10ʰ 30ᵐ   10ʰ 24ᵐ

Bright and Dark Nebulae   To scale   <10'
Planetary Nebulae   >100"   100"–30"   <30"
Open Star Clusters
Globular Clusters   To scale   <5'
Galaxies   10' x 5'   6' x 1'   3' x 2'   5' x 5'   4' x 2'   2' x 1'
Plotted to scale if the major axis >2', and circular when face on or the position angle is uncertain
Quasars
Galaxy Clusters

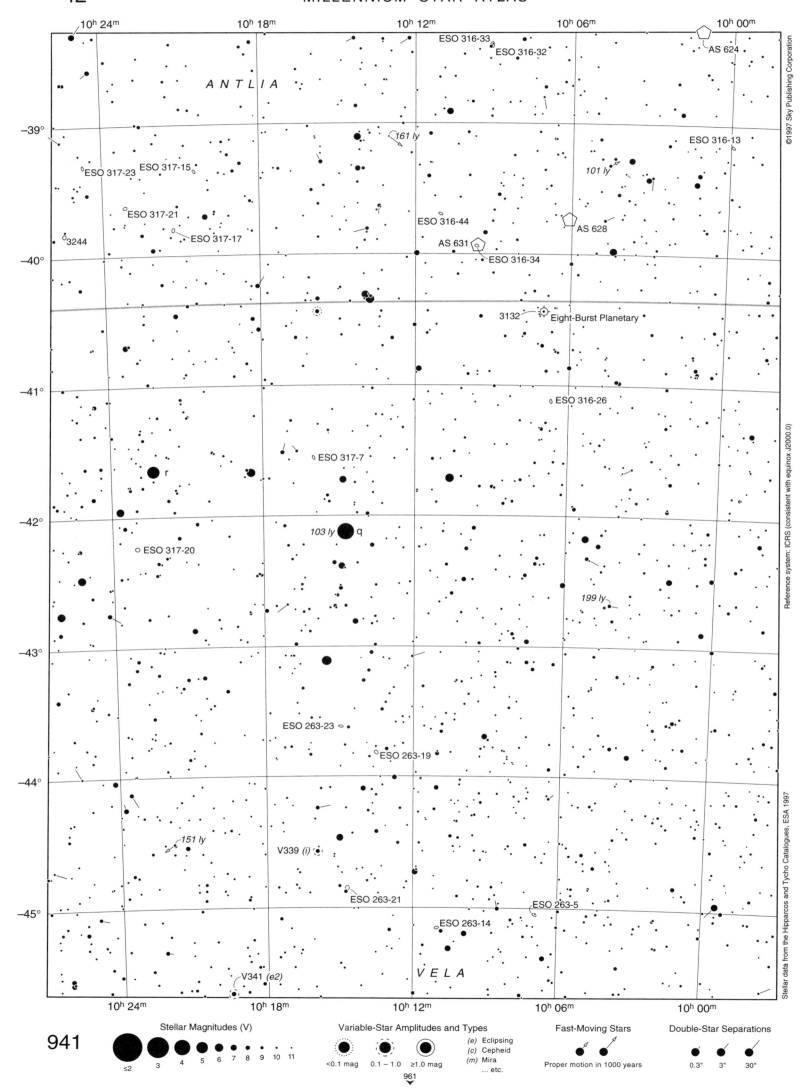

©1997 Sky Publishing Corporation

Reference system: ICRS (consistent with equinox J2000.0)

Stellar data from the Hipparcos and Tycho Catalogues, ESA 1997

941

Stellar Magnitudes (V)

≤2   3   4   5   6   7   8   9   10   11

Variable-Star Amplitudes and Types

<0.1 mag   0.1 – 1.0   ≥1.0 mag

(e) Eclipsing
(c) Cepheid
(m) Mira
... etc.

Fast-Moving Stars

Proper motion in 1000 years

Double-Star Separations

0.3"   3"   30"

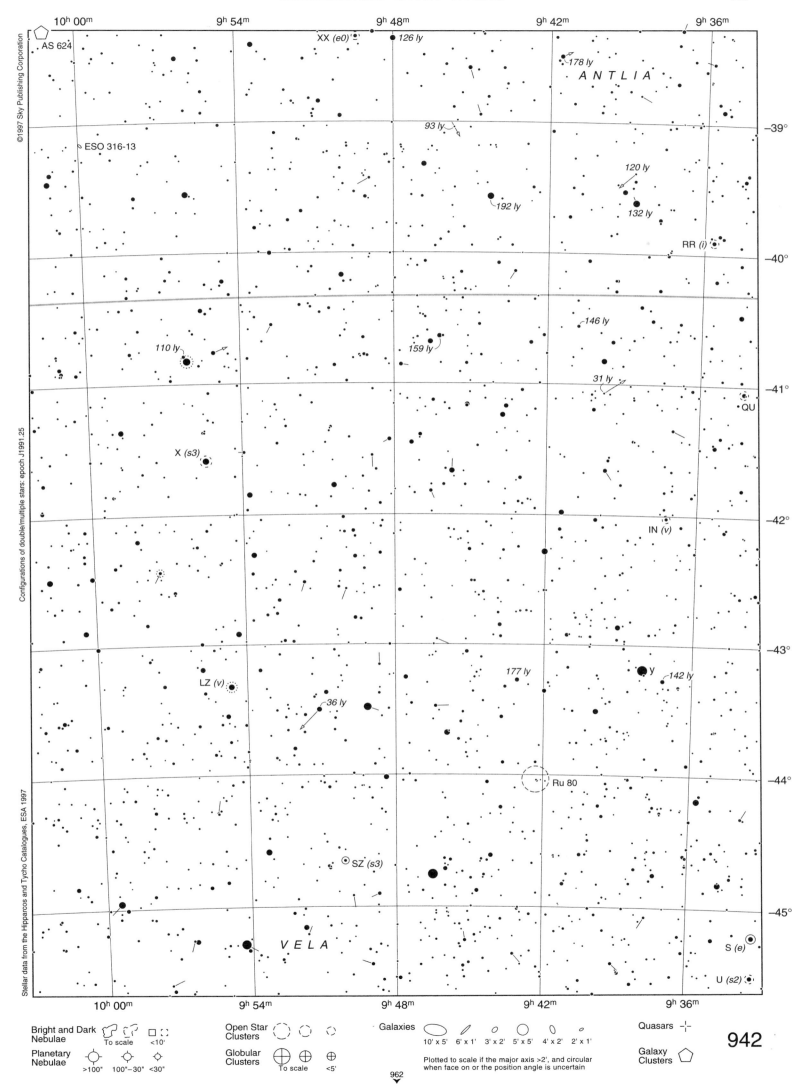

AS 624

ESO 316-13

XX (e0)   126 ly

178 ly

ANTLIA

93 ly

120 ly

192 ly

132 ly

RR (i)

146 ly

110 ly   159 ly

31 ly

QU

X (s3)

IN (v)

LZ (v)

177 ly   y   142 ly

36 ly

Ru 80

SZ (s3)

VELA   S (e)

U (s2)

Bright and Dark
Nebulae   To scale   <10'

Open Star
Clusters

Galaxies   Quasars

10' x 5' 6' x 1' 3' x 2' 5' x 5' 4' x 2' 2' x 1'

Planetary
Nebulae
>100" 100"−30" <30"

Globular
Clusters   To scale   <5'

Plotted to scale if the major axis >2', and circular
when face on or the position angle is uncertain

Galaxy
Clusters

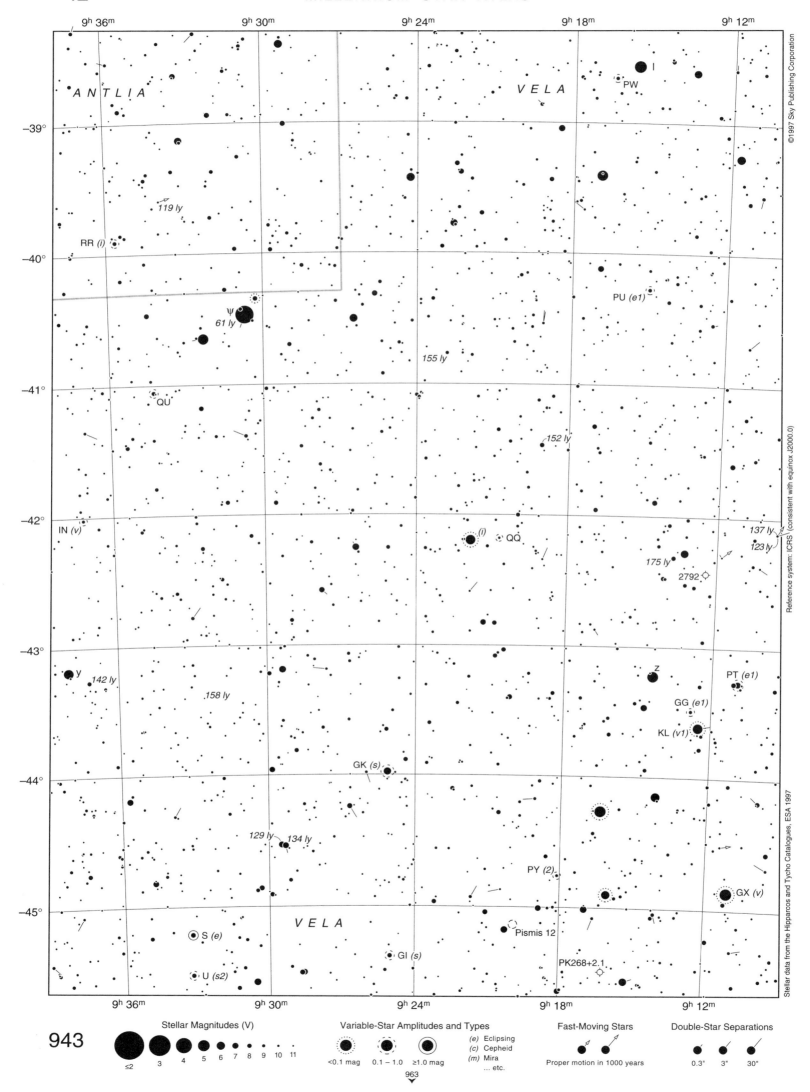

943

Stellar Magnitudes (V)									
≤2	3	4	5	6	7	8	9	10	11

Variable-Star Amplitudes and Types

<0.1 mag   0.1 – 1.0   ≥1.0 mag

(e) Eclipsing
(c) Cepheid
(m) Mira
… etc.

Fast-Moving Stars

Proper motion in 1000 years

Double-Star Separations

0.3"   3"   30"

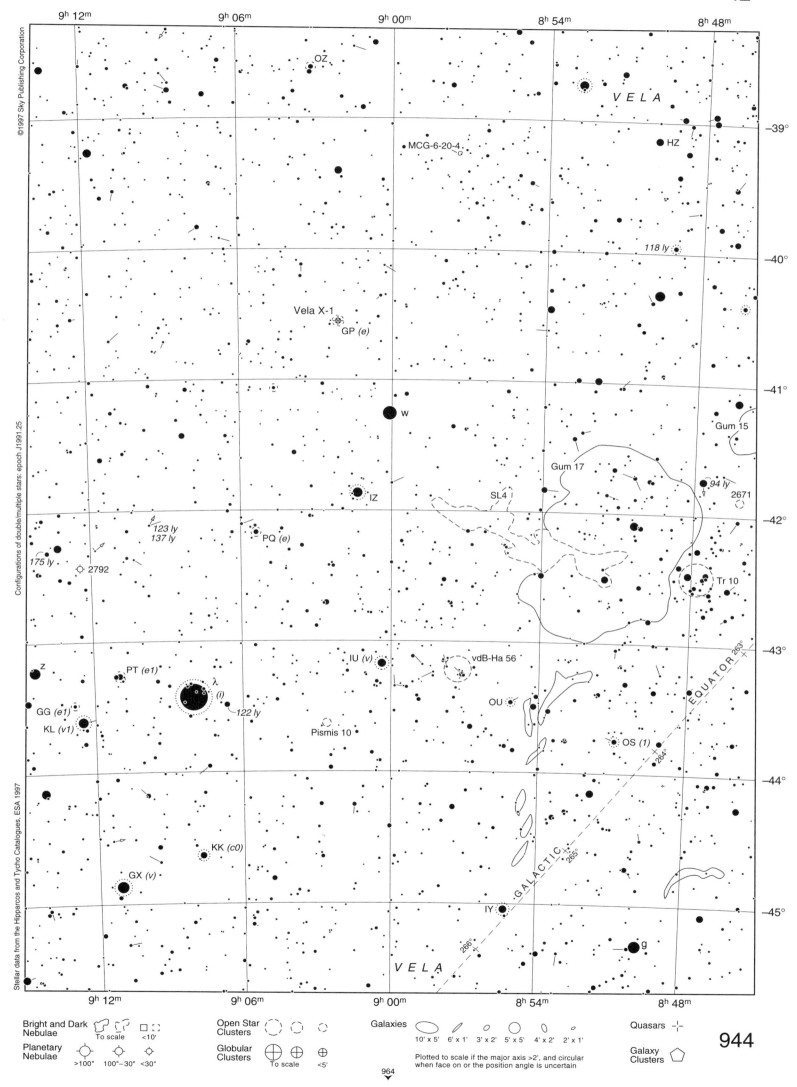

OZ

VELA

MCG-6-20-4

HZ

−39°

118 ly

−40°

Vela X-1
GP *(e)*

w

−41°

Gum 15

Gum 17

IZ

SL4

94 ly
2671

−42°

123 ly
137 ly

PQ *(e)*

175 ly   2792

Tr 10

−43°

EQUATOR 263°

Z

PT *(e1)*

IU *(v)*

vdB-Ha 56

λ
(i)

OU

GG *(e1)*

122 ly

KL *(v1)*

Pismis 10

OS *(1)*

264°

GALACTIC 265°

−44°

KK *(c0)*

GX *(v)*

IY

g

266°

VELA

−45°

| Bright and Dark Nebulae | Open Star Clusters | Galaxies | Quasars −┼─ |
| To scale   <10' | | 10' x 5'   6' x 1'   3' x 2'   5' x 5'   4' x 2'   2' x 1' | |

| Planetary Nebulae | Globular Clusters | Plotted to scale if the major axis >2', and circular when face on or the position angle is uncertain | Galaxy Clusters |
| >100" 100"–30" <30" | To scale   <5' | | |

9h 12m   9h 06m   9h 00m   8h 54m   8h 48m

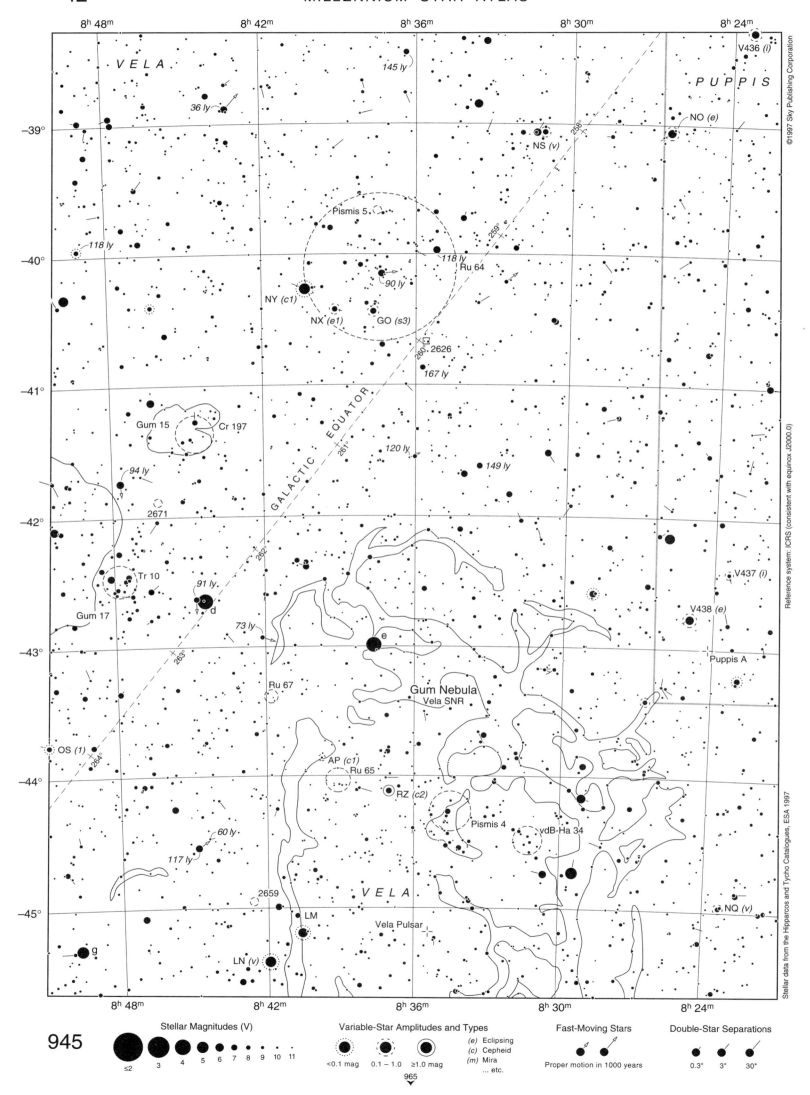

945

Stellar Magnitudes (V)
≤2 3 4 5 6 7 8 9 10 11

Variable-Star Amplitudes and Types
<0.1 mag   0.1 – 1.0   ≥1.0 mag

(e) Eclipsing
(c) Cepheid
(m) Mira
... etc.

Fast-Moving Stars
Proper motion in 1000 years

Double-Star Separations
0.3"   3"   30"

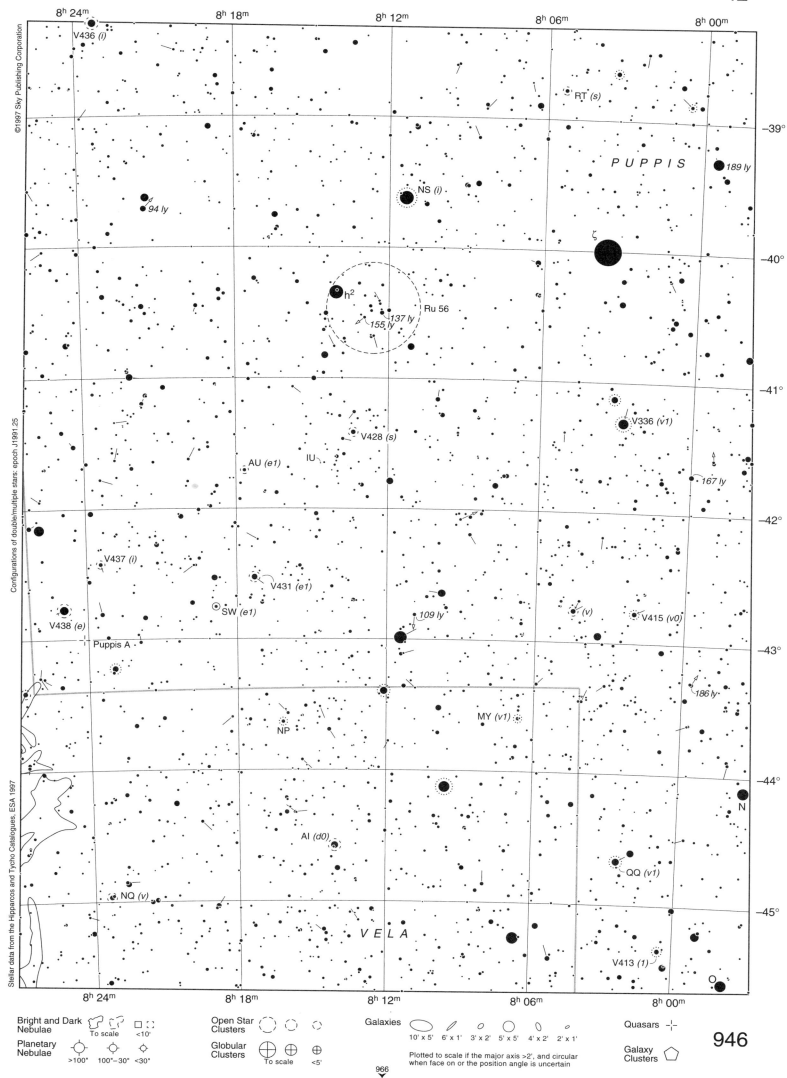

8h 24m   8h 18m   8h 12m   8h 06m   8h 00m

V436 *(i)*

PUPPIS

RT *(s)*

189 ly   −39°

94 ly

NS *(i)*

ζ   −40°

h²

Ru 56
137 ly
155 ly

−41°

V428 *(s)*

V336 *(v1)*

AU *(e1)*   IU

167 ly

−42°

V437 *(i)*

V431 *(e1)*

SW *(e1)*   *(v)*   V415 *(v0)*

V438 *(e)*

Puppis A

109 ly   186 ly   −43°

NP   MY *(v1)*

−44°

AI *(d0)*   N

QQ *(v1)*

NQ *(v)*

−45°

VELA

V413 *(1)*

8h 24m   8h 18m   8h 12m   8h 06m   8h 00m

Bright and Dark
Nebulae
To scale   <10'

Open Star
Clusters

Globular
Clusters
To scale   <5'

Galaxies

10' x 5'   6' x 1'   3' x 2'   5' x 5'   4' x 2'   2' x 1'

Quasars

946

Planetary
Nebulae
>100" 100"–30" <30"

Plotted to scale if the major axis >2', and circular
when face on or the position angle is uncertain

Galaxy
Clusters

966

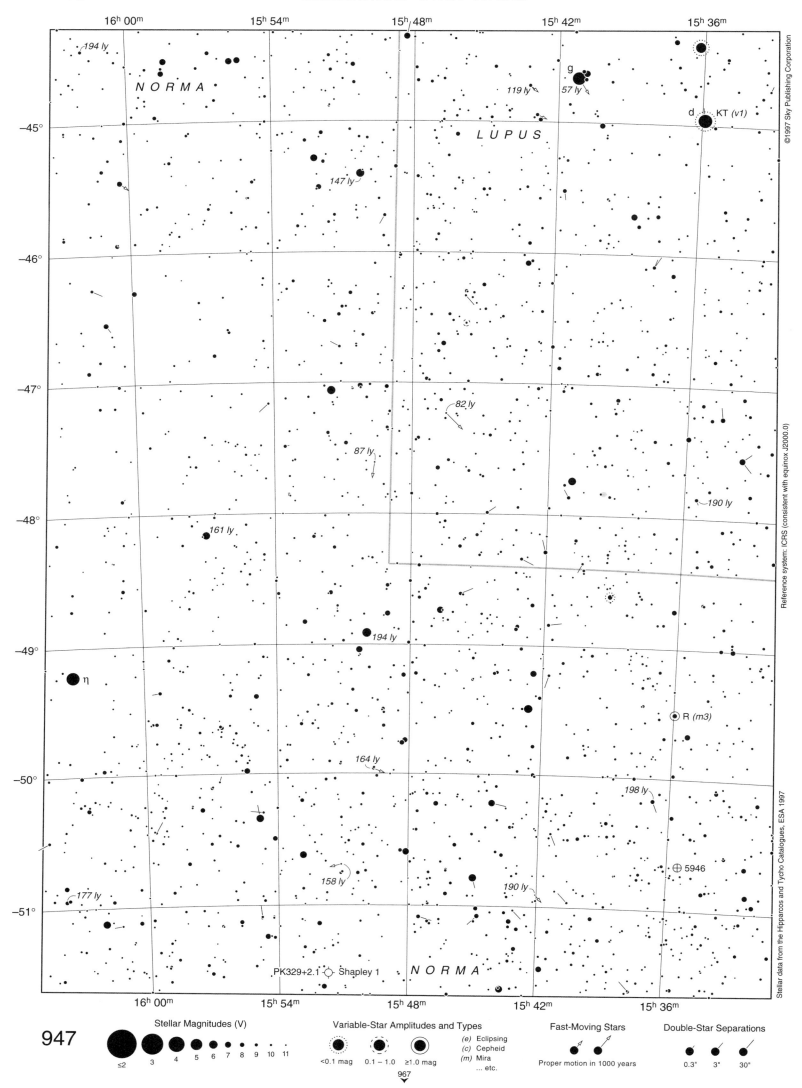

Reference system: ICRS (consistent with equinox J2000.0)

Stellar data from the Hipparcos and Tycho Catalogues, ESA 1997

947

Stellar Magnitudes (V)										
≤2	3	4	5	6	7	8	9	10	11	

Variable-Star Amplitudes and Types

<0.1 mag   0.1 – 1.0   ≥1.0 mag

(e) Eclipsing
(c) Cepheid
(m) Mira
... etc.

Fast-Moving Stars

Proper motion in 1000 years

Double-Star Separations

0.3"   3"   30"

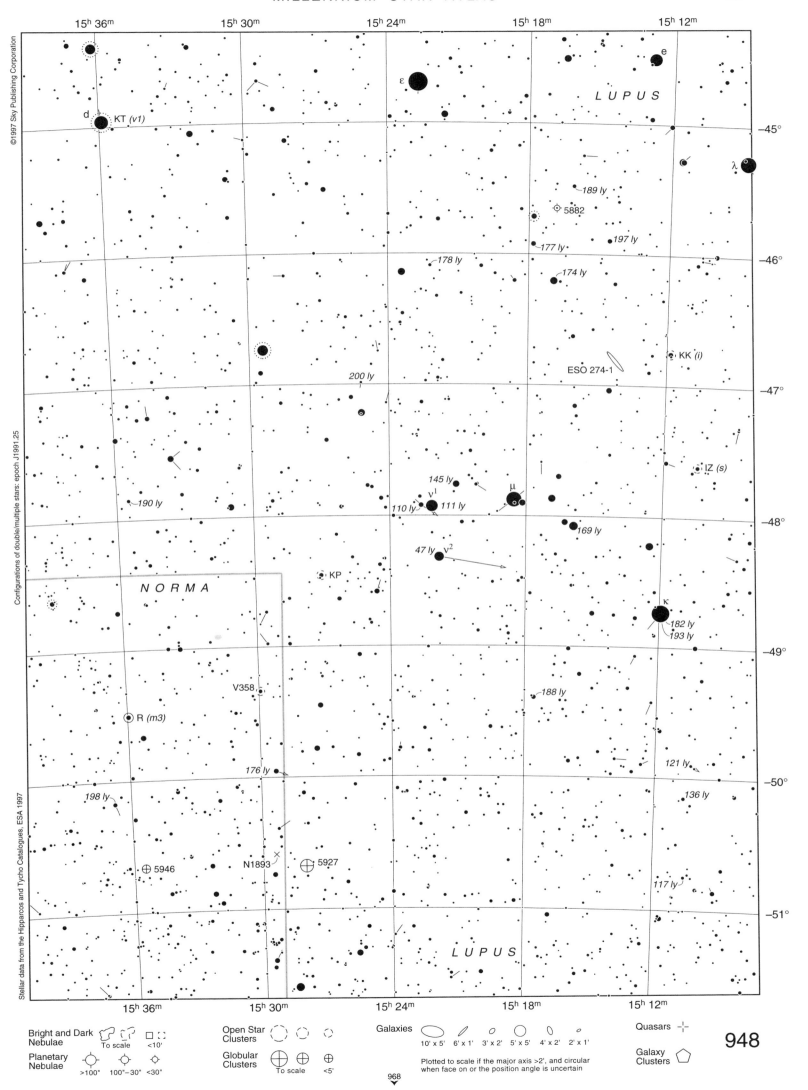

15h 36m 15h 30m 15h 24m 15h 18m 15h 12m

−45°
−46°
−47°
−48°
−49°
−50°
−51°

L U P U S

N O R M A

L U P U S

e

d KT *(v1)*

ε

λ

189 ly

5882

177 ly

197 ly

178 ly

174 ly

KK *(i)*

ESO 274-1

200 ly

IZ *(s)*

145 ly

ν¹ μ

110 ly 111 ly

190 ly

169 ly

47 ly ν²

KP

κ

182 ly

193 ly

V358

188 ly

R *(m3)*

121 ly

176 ly

198 ly

136 ly

5946 N1893 5927

117 ly

Bright and Dark Nebulae			
To scale	<10'		

Planetary Nebulae
>100" 100"–30" <30"

Open Star Clusters

Globular Clusters
To scale <5'

Galaxies
10' x 5' 6' x 1' 3' x 2' 5' x 5' 4' x 2' 2' x 1'

Plotted to scale if the major axis >2', and circular when face on or the position angle is uncertain

Quasars

Galaxy Clusters

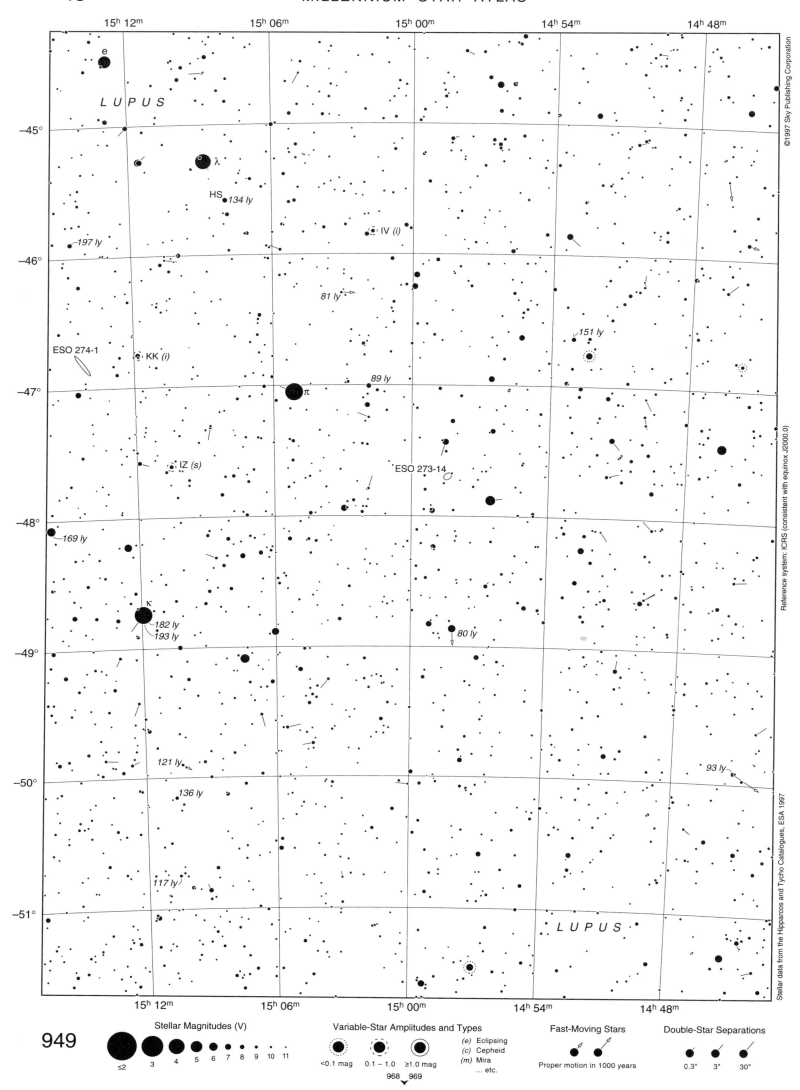

LUPUS

e

λ

HS ●134 ly

IV (i)

●197 ly

81 ly

151 ly

ESO 274-1

KK (i)

89 ly

π

IZ (s)

ESO 273-14

●169 ly

κ

182 ly
193 ly

80 ly

121 ly

136 ly

93 ly

117 ly

LUPUS

15ʰ 12ᵐ   15ʰ 06ᵐ   15ʰ 00ᵐ   14ʰ 54ᵐ   14ʰ 48ᵐ

−45°
−46°
−47°
−48°
−49°
−50°
−51°

949

Stellar Magnitudes (V)

≤2   3   4   5   6   7   8   9   10   11

Variable-Star Amplitudes and Types

<0.1 mag   0.1 – 1.0   ≥1.0 mag

(e) Eclipsing
(c) Cepheid
(m) Mira
... etc.

968   969

Fast-Moving Stars

Proper motion in 1000 years

Double-Star Separations

0.3"   3"   30"

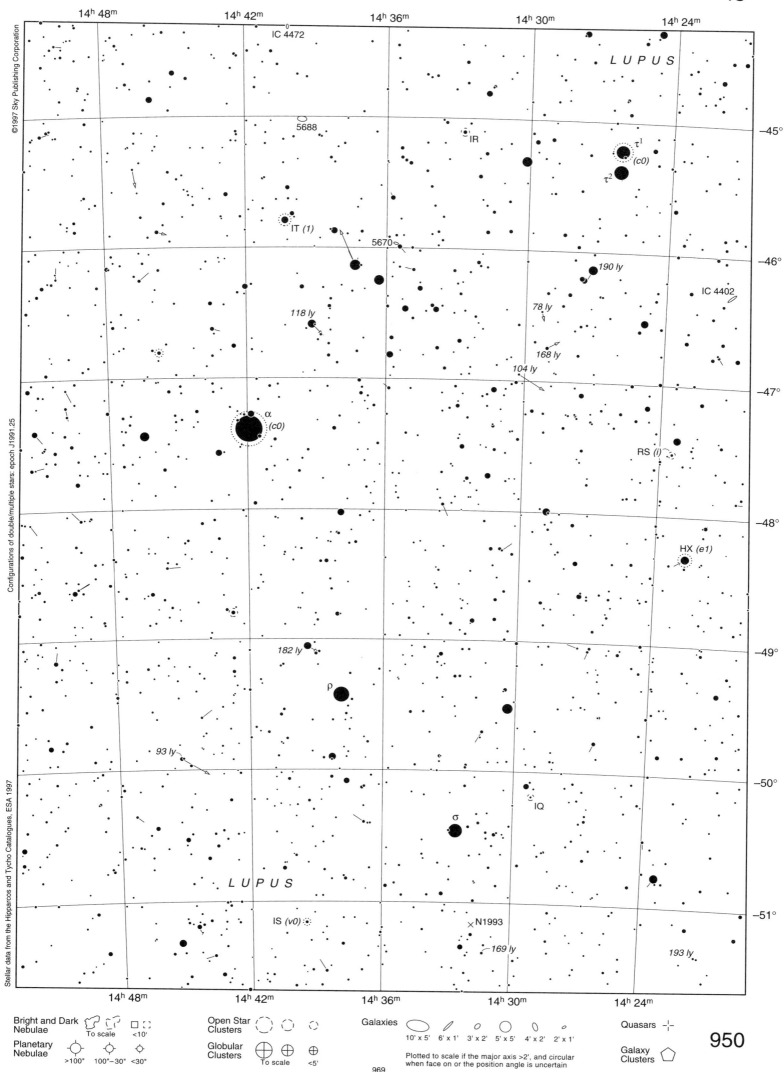

14h 48m 14h 42m 14h 36m 14h 30m 14h 24m

IC 4472

L U P U S

5688

−45°

IR

τ^1
(c0)

τ^2

IT *(1)*

5670

−46°

190 ly

IC 4402

118 ly

78 ly

168 ly

104 ly

−47°

α
(c0)

RS *(i)*

−48°

HX *(e1)*

182 ly

−49°

ρ

93 ly

−50°

IQ

σ

L U P U S

−51°

IS *(v0)*

N1993

169 ly

193 ly

14h 48m 14h 42m 14h 36m 14h 30m 14h 24m

Bright and Dark Nebulae	Open Star Clusters	Galaxies	Quasars −⊢−
To scale <10'	To scale <5'	10' x 5' 6' x 1' 3' x 2' 5' x 5' 4' x 2' 2' x 1'	
Planetary Nebulae	Globular Clusters		Galaxy Clusters
>100" 100"−30" <30"	To scale <5'	Plotted to scale if the major axis >2', and circular when face on or the position angle is uncertain	

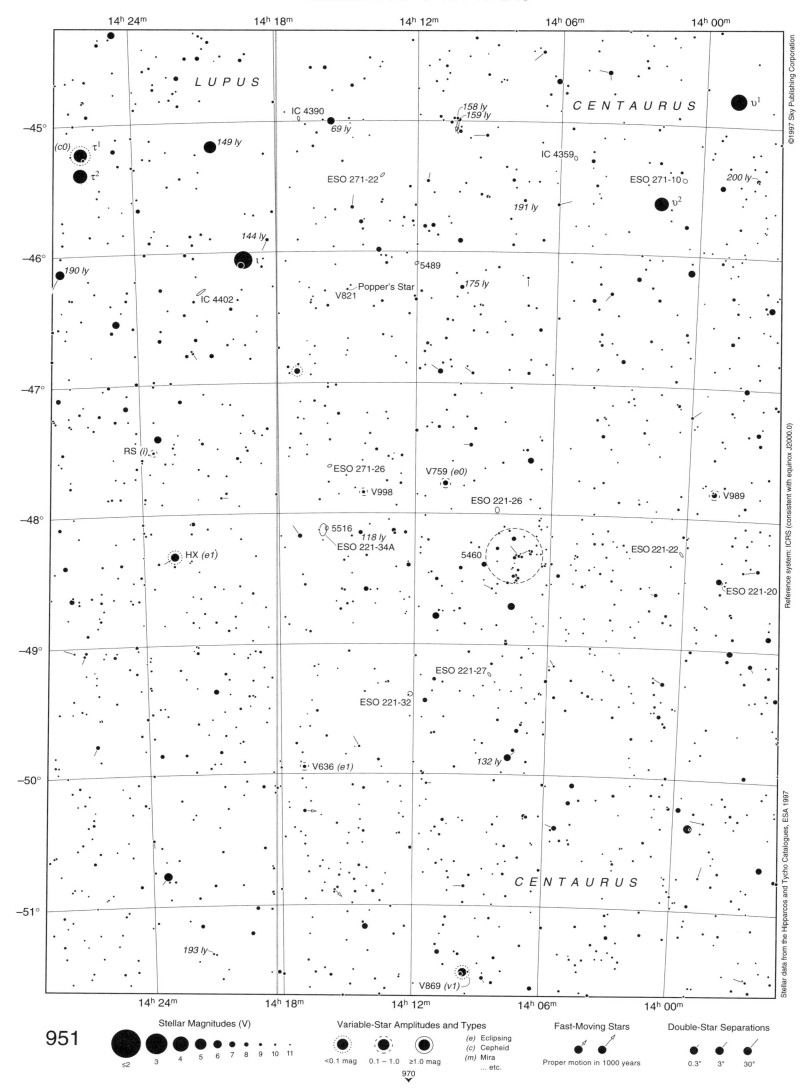

©1997 Sky Publishing Corporation

Reference system: ICRS (consistent with equinox J2000.0)

Stellar data from the Hipparcos and Tycho Catalogues, ESA 1997

LUPUS

CENTAURUS

CENTAURUS

IC 4390
69 ly

158 ly
159 ly

IC 4359

(c0) τ¹
τ²

149 ly

ESO 271-22

ESO 271-10

υ¹

200 ly

191 ly

υ²

144 ly
ι

190 ly

5489

175 ly

IC 4402

Popper's Star
V821

RS (i)

ESO 271-26

V759 (e0)

V989

V998

ESO 221-26

HX (e1)

5516
118 ly
ESO 221-34A

5460

ESO 221-22

ESO 221-20

ESO 221-27

ESO 221-32

132 ly

V636 (e1)

193 ly

V869 (v1)

951

Stellar Magnitudes (V)

≤2   3   4   5 6 7 8 9 10 11

Variable-Star Amplitudes and Types

<0.1 mag   0.1 – 1.0   ≥1.0 mag

(e) Eclipsing
(c) Cepheid
(m) Mira
... etc.

Fast-Moving Stars

Proper motion in 1000 years

Double-Star Separations

0.3"   3"   30"

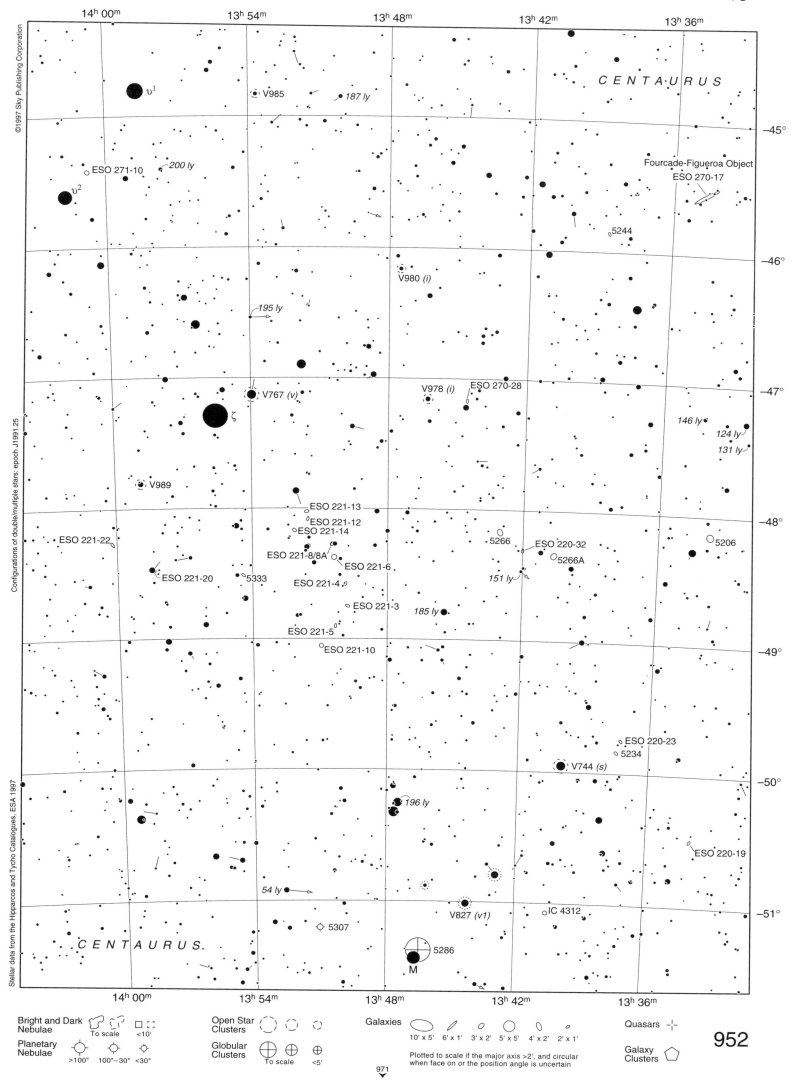

CENTAURUS

−45°

Fourcade-Figueroa Object
ESO 270-17

5244

−46°

υ¹
V985
187 ly

ESO 271-10
200 ly
υ²

195 ly

V980 (i)

V978 (i)   ESO 270-28

−47°

V767 (v)

146 ly
124 ly
131 ly

V989

ESO 221-13
ESO 221-12
ESO 221-14

−48°

ESO 221-22

ESO 221-8/8A
ESO 221-6

5266   ESO 220-32
5266A
151 ly

5206

ESO 221-20
5333
ESO 221-4

ESO 221-3
185 ly

ESO 221-5

ESO 221-10

−49°

ESO 220-23
5234

V744 (s)

−50°

196 ly

ESO 220-19

54 ly

V827 (v1)   IC 4312

−51°

5307

CENTAURUS.

5286
M

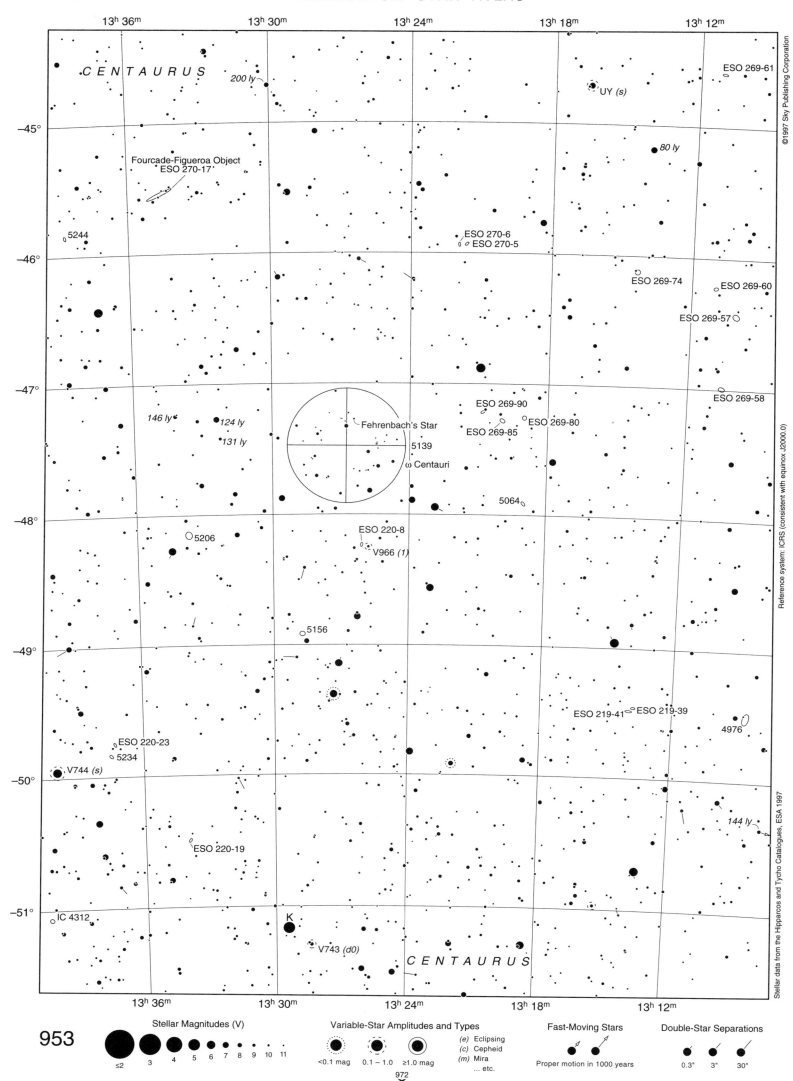

©1997 Sky Publishing Corporation

Reference system: ICRS (consistent with equinox J2000.0)

Stellar data from the Hipparcos and Tycho Catalogues, ESA 1997

13h 36m   13h 30m   13h 24m   13h 18m   13h 12m

CENTAURUS

200 ly

ESO 269-61

UY *(s)*

−45°

80 ly

Fourcade-Figueroa Object
ESO 270-17

ESO 270-6
ESO 270-5

5244

−46°

ESO 269-74

ESO 269-60

ESO 269-57

−47°

ESO 269-90

ESO 269-80
ESO 269-85

ESO 269-58

146 ly   124 ly

131 ly

Fehrenbach's Star

5139
ω Centauri

5064

−48°

5206

ESO 220-8
V966 *(1)*

5156

−49°

ESO 219-41   ESO 219-39

4976

ESO 220-23
5234

−50°

V744 *(s)*

144 ly

ESO 220-19

−51°

IC 4312

K

CENTAURUS

V743 *(d0)*

13h 36m   13h 30m   13h 24m   13h 18m   13h 12m

Stellar Magnitudes (V)	Variable-Star Amplitudes and Types	Fast-Moving Stars	Double-Star Separations

≤2   3   4   5   6   7   8   9   10   11

<0.1 mag   0.1 – 1.0   ≥1.0 mag

(e) Eclipsing
(c) Cepheid
(m) Mira
... etc.

Proper motion in 1000 years

0.3"   3"   30"

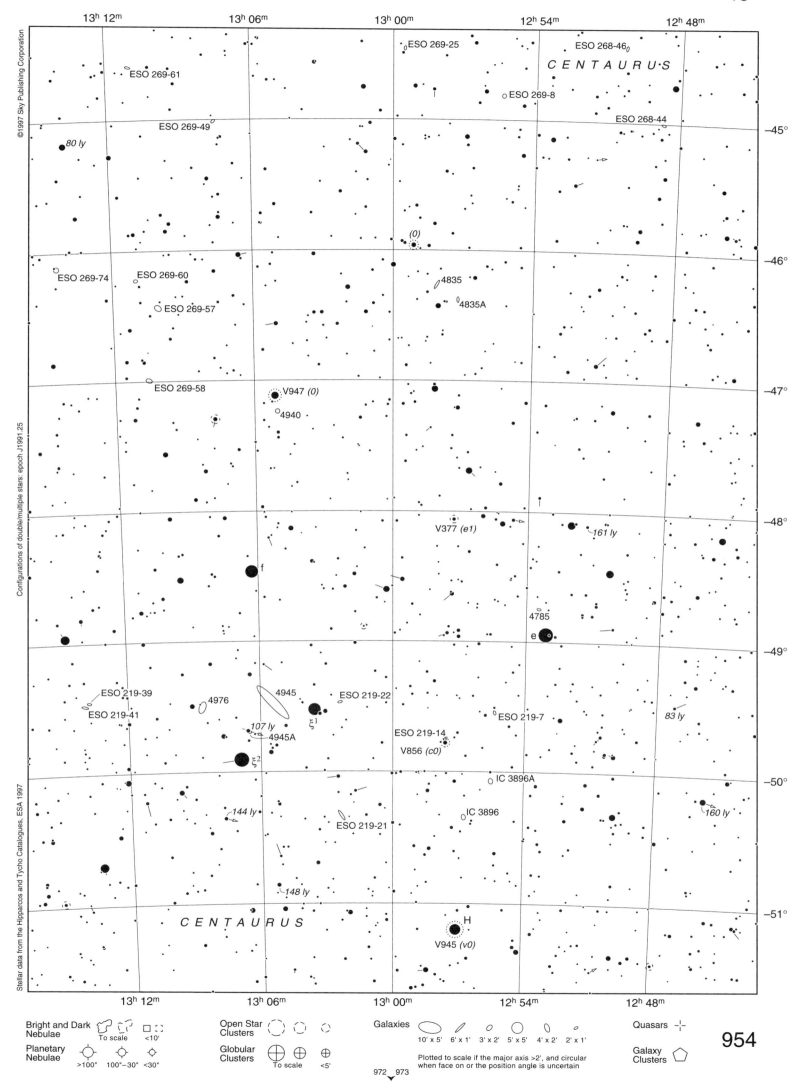

CENTAURUS

ESO 269-25
ESO 268-46
ESO 269-8
ESO 268-44
ESO 269-61
ESO 269-49
80 ly
ESO 269-74
ESO 269-60
ESO 269-57
4835
4835A
ESO 269-58
V947 (0)
4940
(0)
V377 (e1)
161 ly
f
4785
e
ESO 219-39
4976
4945
ESO 219-22
ESO 219-41
107 ly
4945A
ξ¹
ESO 219-7
83 ly
ESO 219-14
V856 (c0)
ξ²
IC 3896A
144 ly
160 ly
IC 3896
ESO 219-21
148 ly
CENTAURUS
H
V945 (v0)

−45°
−46°
−47°
−48°
−49°
−50°
−51°

13ʰ 12ᵐ
13ʰ 06ᵐ
13ʰ 00ᵐ
12ʰ 54ᵐ
12ʰ 48ᵐ

972 973

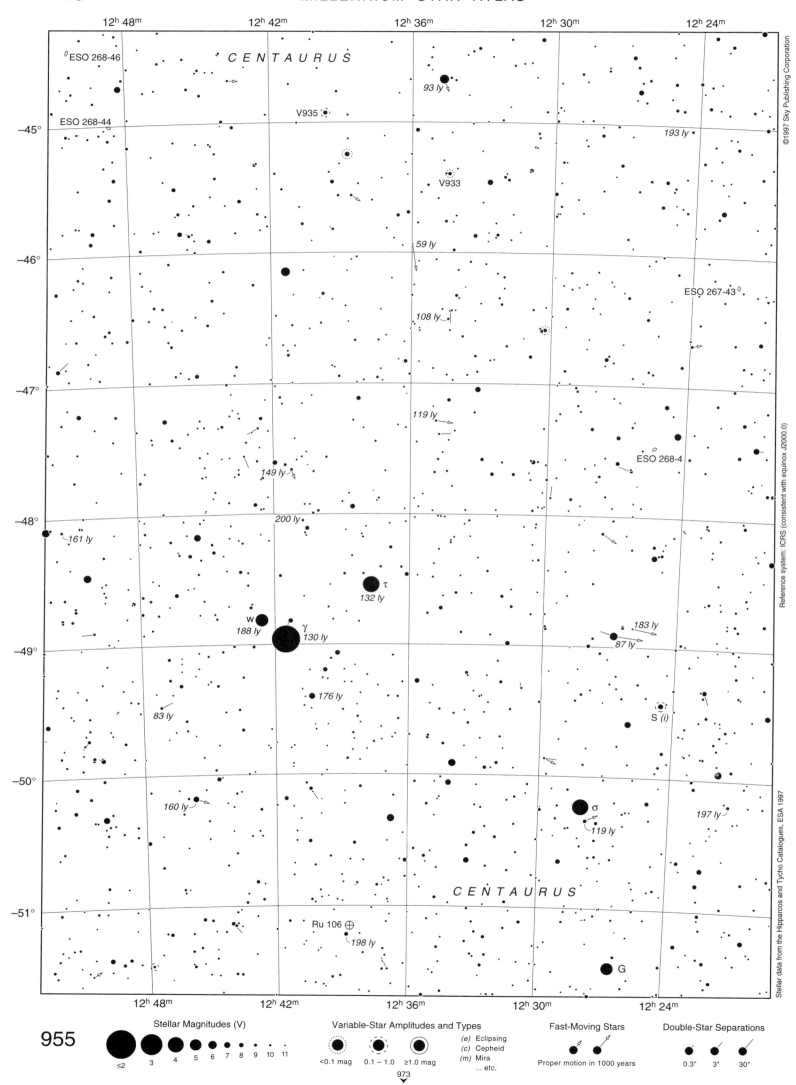

©1997 Sky Publishing Corporation

Reference system: ICRS (consistent with equinox J2000.0)

Stellar data from the Hipparcos and Tycho Catalogues, ESA 1997

955

Stellar Magnitudes (V)

≤2   3   4   5   6   7   8   9 10 11

Variable-Star Amplitudes and Types

<0.1 mag   0.1 − 1.0   ≥1.0 mag

(e) Eclipsing
(c) Cepheid
(m) Mira
... etc.

Fast-Moving Stars

Proper motion in 1000 years

Double-Star Separations

0.3"   3"   30"

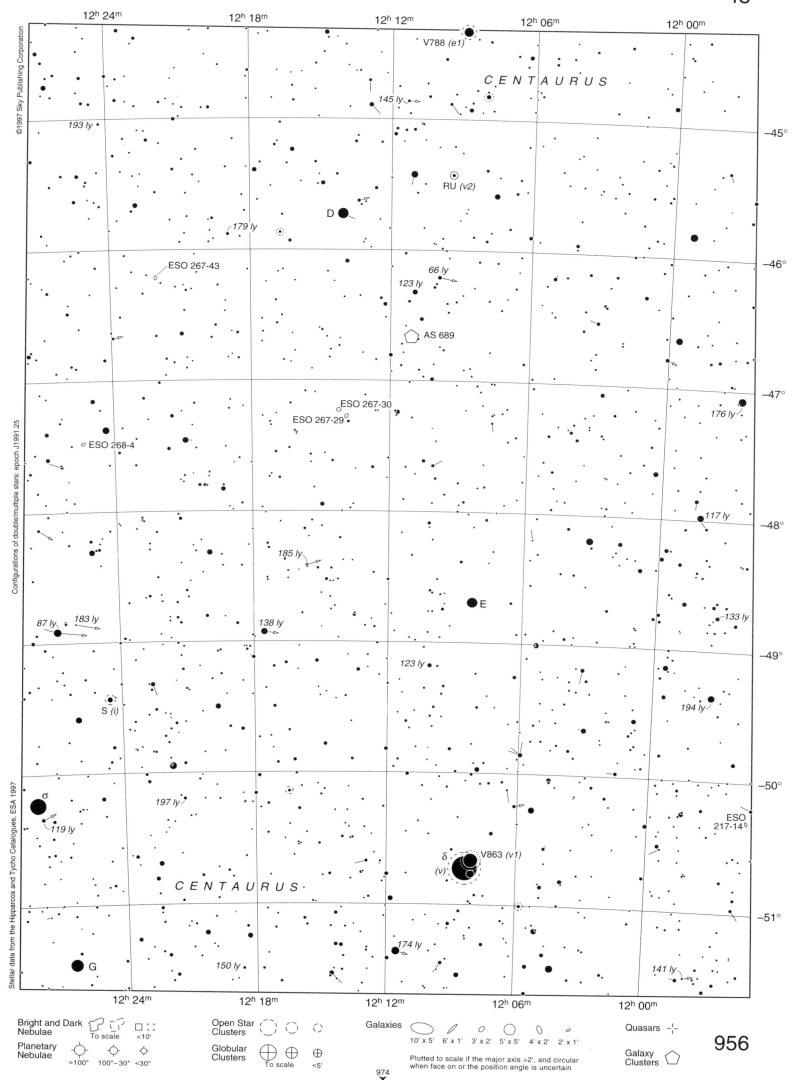

12h 24m 12h 18m 12h 12m 12h 06m 12h 00m

V788 (e1)

CENTAURUS

−45°

©1997 Sky Publishing Corporation

193 ly

RU (v2)

D

179 ly

−46°

ESO 267-43

66 ly

123 ly

AS 689

−47°

ESO 267-30
ESO 267-29

176 ly

ESO 268-4

Configurations of double/multiple stars: epoch J1991.25

117 ly

−48°

185 ly

E

133 ly

87 ly   183 ly

138 ly

−49°

123 ly

194 ly

S (i)

Stellar data from the Hipparcos and Tycho Catalogues, ESA 1997

197 ly

−50°

σ

ESO
217-14

119 ly

δ   V863 (v1)
(v)

CENTAURUS

−51°

174 ly

G

150 ly

141 ly

12h 24m 12h 18m 12h 12m 12h 06m 12h 00m

Bright and Dark
Nebulae   To scale   <10'

Open Star
Clusters

Galaxies

Quasars

Planetary
Nebulae
>100" 100"−30" <30'

Globular
Clusters
To scale   <5'

10' x 5' 6' x 1' 3' x 2' 5' x 5' 4' x 2' 2' x 1'

Plotted to scale if the major axis >2', and circular
when face on or the position angle is uncertain

Galaxy
Clusters

956

974

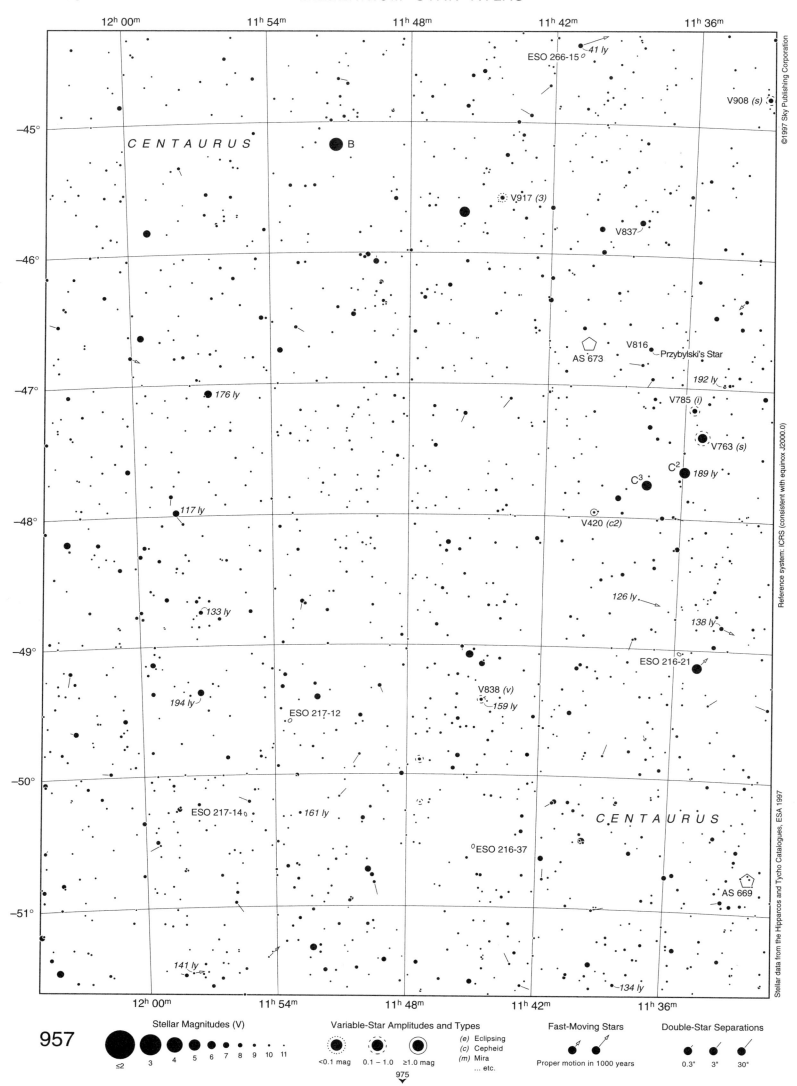

CENTAURUS

ESO 266-15

41 ly

V908 (s)

V917 (3)

V837

V816   Przybylski's Star

AS 673

192 ly

176 ly

V785 (i)

V763 (s)

C² 189 ly

C³

117 ly

V420 (c2)

126 ly

138 ly

133 ly

ESO 216-21

194 ly

V838 (v)

ESO 217-12

159 ly

ESO 217-14

161 ly

CENTAURUS

ESO 216-37

AS 669

141 ly

134 ly

©1997 Sky Publishing Corporation

Reference system: ICRS (consistent with equinox J2000.0)

Stellar data from the Hipparcos and Tycho Catalogues, ESA 1997

957

Stellar Magnitudes (V)	Variable-Star Amplitudes and Types	Fast-Moving Stars	Double-Star Separations
≤2 3 4 5 6 7 8 9 10 11	<0.1 mag 0.1 − 1.0 ≥1.0 mag (e) Eclipsing (c) Cepheid (m) Mira ... etc.	Proper motion in 1000 years	0.3" 3" 30"

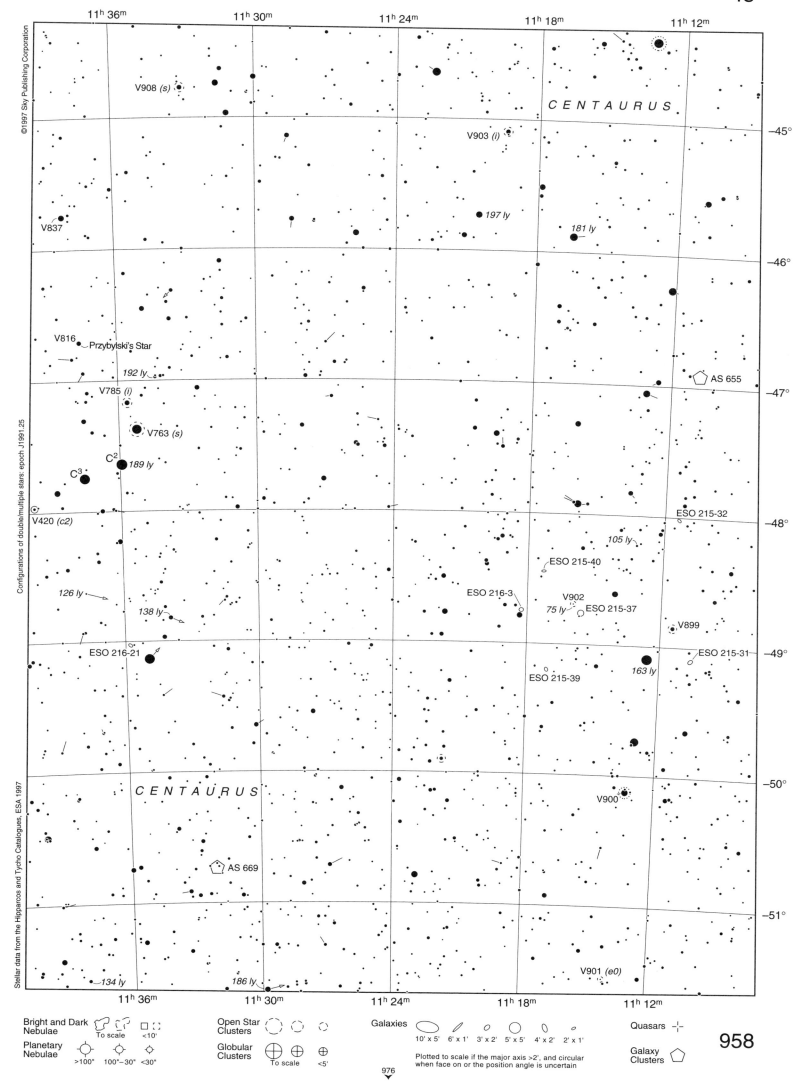

CENTAURUS

V908 (s)

V903 (i)

197 ly

181 ly

V837

V816
Przybylski's Star

192 ly

V785 (i)

V763 (s)

C²   189 ly

C³

V420 (c2)

AS 655

ESO 215-32

105 ly

ESO 215-40

126 ly

138 ly

ESO 216-3

ESO 216-21

V902
75 ly   ESO 215-37

V899

ESO 215-31

163 ly

ESO 215-39

CENTAURUS

V900

AS 669

V901 (e0)

134 ly

186 ly

Bright and Dark
Nebulae
To scale   <10'

Planetary
Nebulae
>100" 100"−30" <30"

Open Star
Clusters

Globular
Clusters
To scale   <5'

Galaxies
10' x 5' 6' x 1' 3' x 2' 5' x 5' 4' x 2' 2' x 1'

Plotted to scale if the major axis >2', and circular
when face on or the position angle is uncertain

Quasars

Galaxy
Clusters

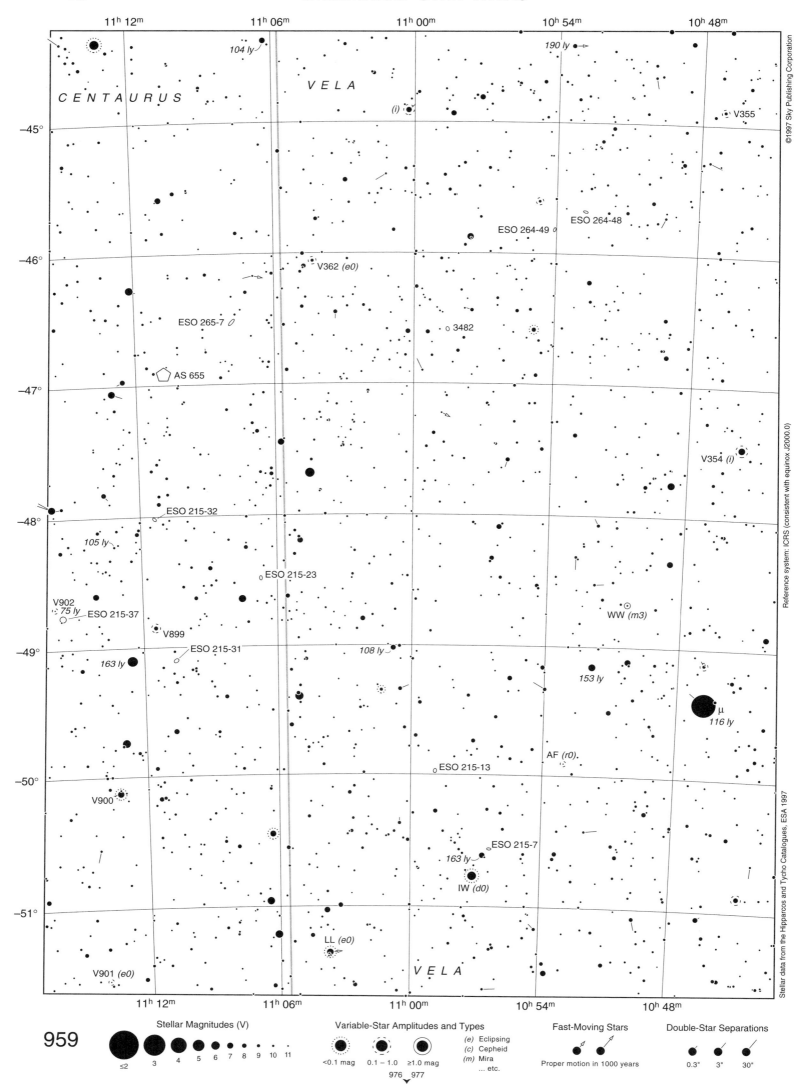

MILLENNIUM STAR ATLAS

©1997 Sky Publishing Corporation

Reference system: ICRS (consistent with equinox J2000.0)

Stellar data from the Hipparcos and Tycho Catalogues, ESA 1997

11ʰ 12ᵐ   11ʰ 06ᵐ   11ʰ 00ᵐ   10ʰ 54ᵐ   10ʰ 48ᵐ

104 ly
190 ly

C E N T A U R U S   V E L A

V355

(i)

–45°

ESO 264-49   ESO 264-48

–46°   V362 (e0)

ESO 265-7   ○ 3482

AS 655

–47°

V354 (i)

ESO 215-32

–48°   105 ly

○ ESO 215-23

V902   WW (m3)
75 ly   ESO 215-37
V899

–49°   ESO 215-31   108 ly
163 ly   153 ly

μ
116 ly

AF (r0)

○ ESO 215-13

–50°   V900

ESO 215-7
163 ly

IW (d0)

LL (e0)

–51°

V901 (e0)   V E L A

11ʰ 12ᵐ   11ʰ 06ᵐ   11ʰ 00ᵐ   10ʰ 54ᵐ   10ʰ 48ᵐ

959

Stellar Magnitudes (V)

≤2   3   4   5   6   7   8   9   10   11

Variable-Star Amplitudes and Types

<0.1 mag   0.1 – 1.0   ≥1.0 mag

(e) Eclipsing
(c) Cepheid
(m) Mira
... etc.

976   977

Fast-Moving Stars

Proper motion in 1000 years

Double-Star Separations

0.3"   3"   30"

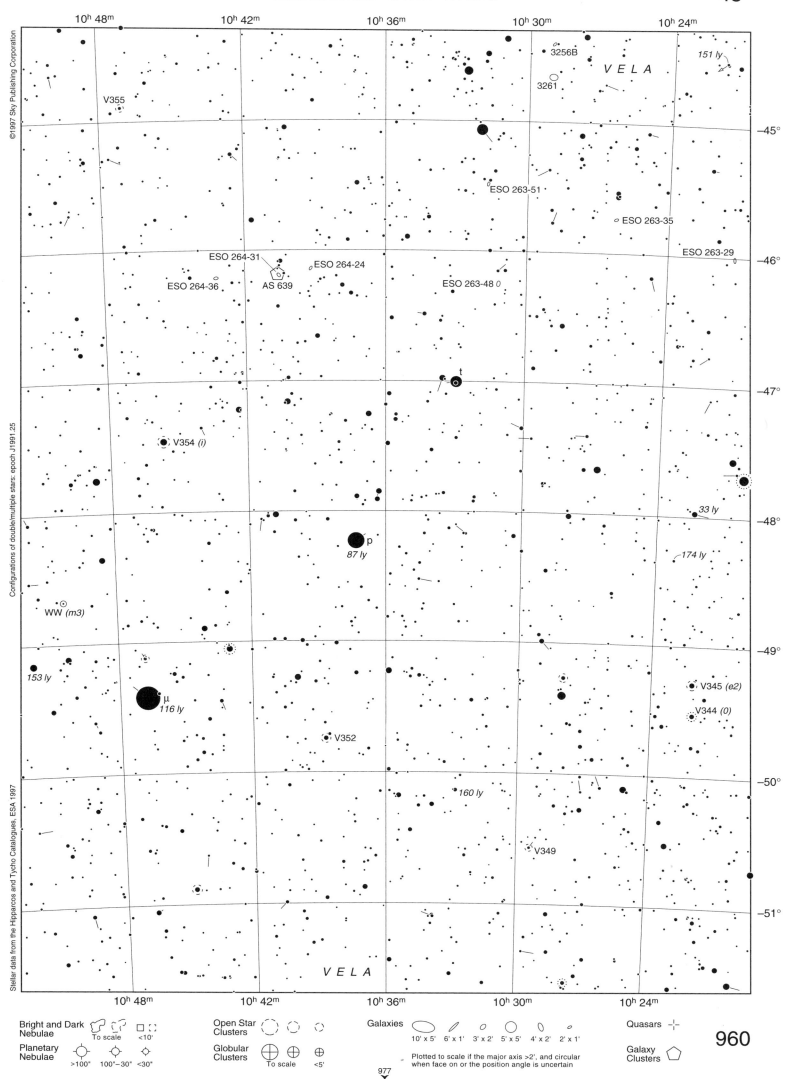

10h 48m   10h 42m   10h 36m   10h 30m   10h 24m

−45°

−46°

−47°

−48°

−49°

−50°

−51°

V E L A

3256B
3261
151 ly

ESO 263-51

ESO 263-35

ESO 263-29

ESO 264-31
ESO 264-36   ESO 264-24
AS 639   ESO 263-48 0

t

V354 (i)

33 ly

p
87 ly

174 ly

WW (m3)

153 ly

V345 (e2)

μ
116 ly

V344 (0)

V352

160 ly

V349

V E L A

10h 48m   10h 42m   10h 36m   10h 30m   10h 24m

Bright and Dark
Nebulae
To scale   <10'

Open Star
Clusters

Galaxies

10' x 5' 6' x 1' 3' x 2' 5' x 5' 4' x 2' 2' x 1'

Quasars

Planetary
Nebulae
>100" 100"−30" <30"

Globular
Clusters
To scale   <5'

Plotted to scale if the major axis >2', and circular
when face on or the position angle is uncertain

Galaxy
Clusters

MILLENNIUM STAR ATLAS

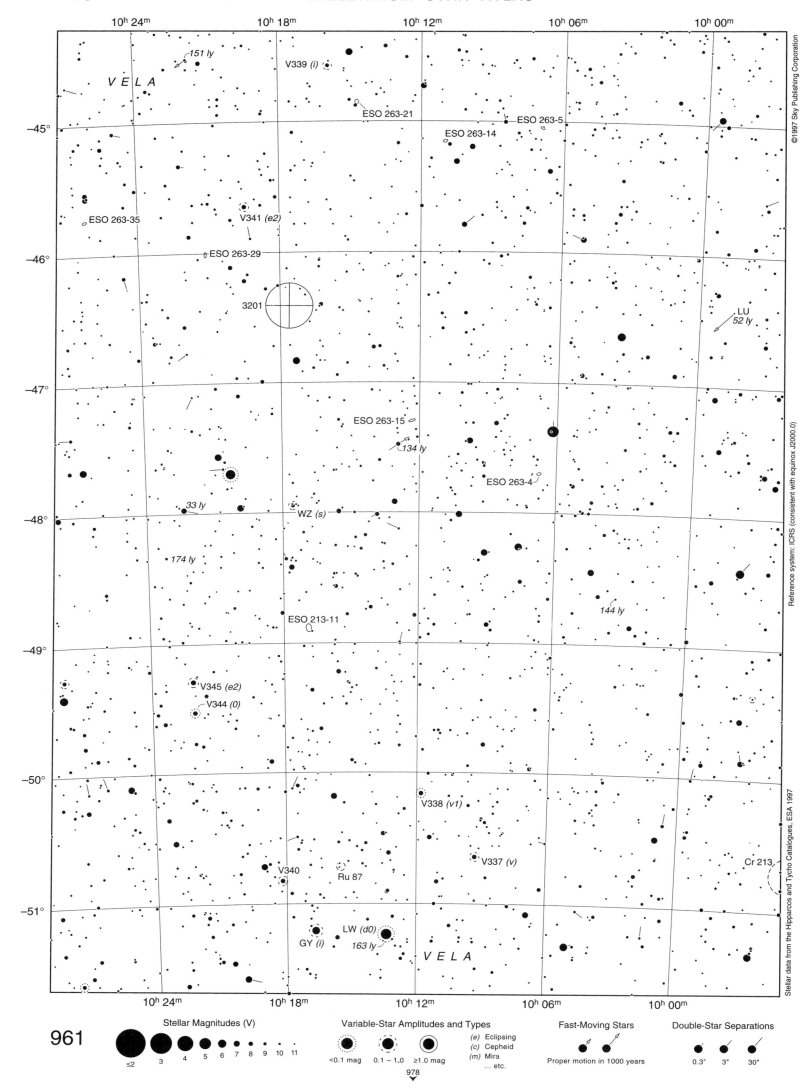

©1997 Sky Publishing Corporation

Reference system: ICRS (consistent with equinox J2000.0)

Stellar data from the Hipparcos and Tycho Catalogues, ESA 1997

10ʰ 24ᵐ   10ʰ 18ᵐ   10ʰ 12ᵐ   10ʰ 06ᵐ   10ʰ 00ᵐ

VELA

151 ly

V339 *(i)*

ESO 263-21

ESO 263-5

ESO 263-14

−45°

ESO 263-35

V341 *(e2)*

ESO 263-29

3201

LU
52 ly

−46°

ESO 263-15

134 ly

ESO 263-4

33 ly

WZ *(s)*

−48°

174 ly

144 ly

ESO 213-11

−49°

V345 *(e2)*

V344 *(0)*

−50°

V338 *(v1)*

V337 *(v)*

Cr 213

V340

Ru 87

LW *(d0)*

GY *(i)*

163 ly

VELA

−51°

10ʰ 24ᵐ   10ʰ 18ᵐ   10ʰ 12ᵐ   10ʰ 06ᵐ   10ʰ 00ᵐ

961

Stellar Magnitudes (V)

≤2   3   4   5   6   7   8   9   10   11

Variable-Star Amplitudes and Types

<0.1 mag   0.1 – 1.0   ≥1.0 mag

(e) Eclipsing
(c) Cepheid
(m) Mira
... etc.

Fast-Moving Stars

Proper motion in 1000 years

Double-Star Separations

0.3"   3"   30"

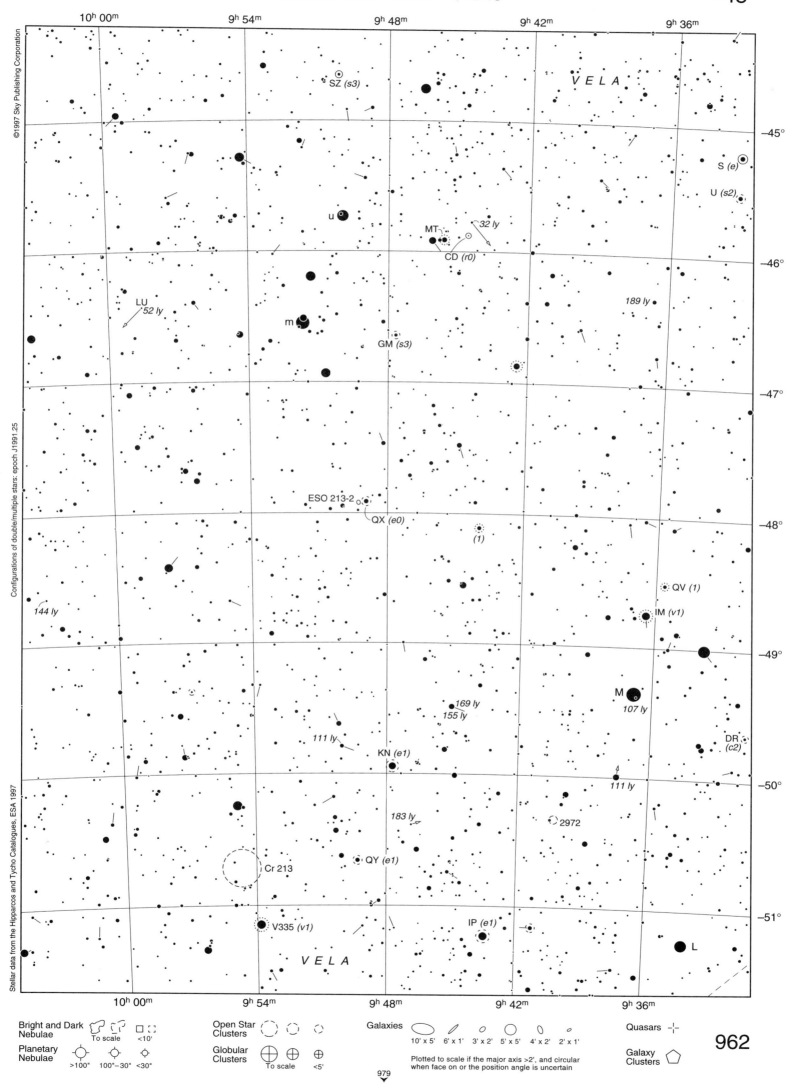

VELA

−45°

SZ (s3)

S (e)

U (s2)

u

MT
32 ly
CD (r0)

189 ly

−46°

LU
52 ly

m

GM (s3)

−47°

ESO 213-2

QX (e0)

(1)

−48°

QV (1)

IM (v1)

144 ly

−49°

M
107 ly

169 ly
155 ly

DR
(c2)

111 ly

KN (e1)

111 ly

−50°

183 ly

2972

QY (e1)

Cr 213

−51°

V335 (v1)

IP (e1)

L

VELA

10h 00m   9h 54m   9h 48m   9h 42m   9h 36m

Bright and Dark
Nebulae
To scale   <10'

Planetary
Nebulae
>100"   100"–30"   <30"

Open Star
Clusters

Globular
Clusters
To scale   <5'

Galaxies
10' x 5'   6' x 1'   3' x 2'   5' x 5'   4' x 2'   2' x 1'

Plotted to scale if the major axis >2', and circular
when face on or the position angle is uncertain

Quasars

Galaxy
Clusters

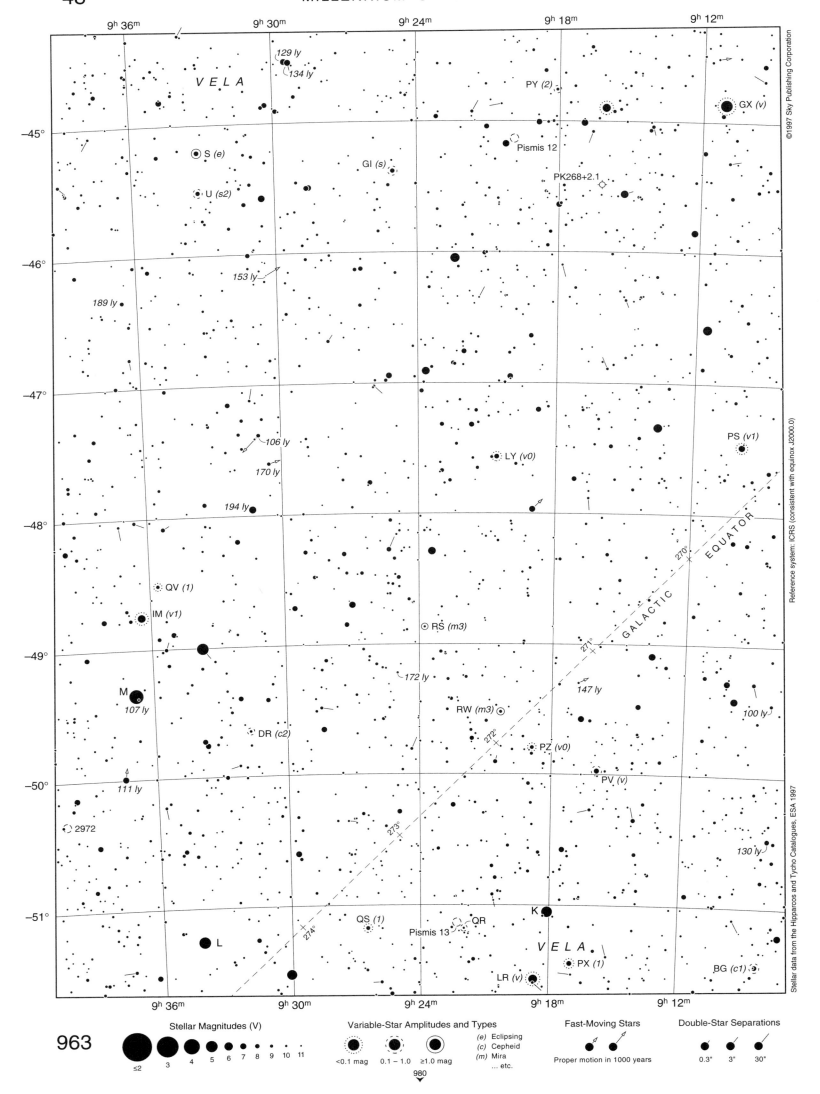

©1997 Sky Publishing Corporation

Reference system: ICRS (consistent with equinox J2000.0)

Stellar data from the Hipparcos and Tycho Catalogues, ESA 1997

Stellar Magnitudes (V)

≤2 3 4 5 6 7 8 9 10 11

Variable-Star Amplitudes and Types

<0.1 mag   0.1 − 1.0   ≥1.0 mag

(e) Eclipsing
(c) Cepheid
(m) Mira
... etc.

Fast-Moving Stars

Proper motion in 1000 years

Double-Star Separations

0.3"   3"   30"

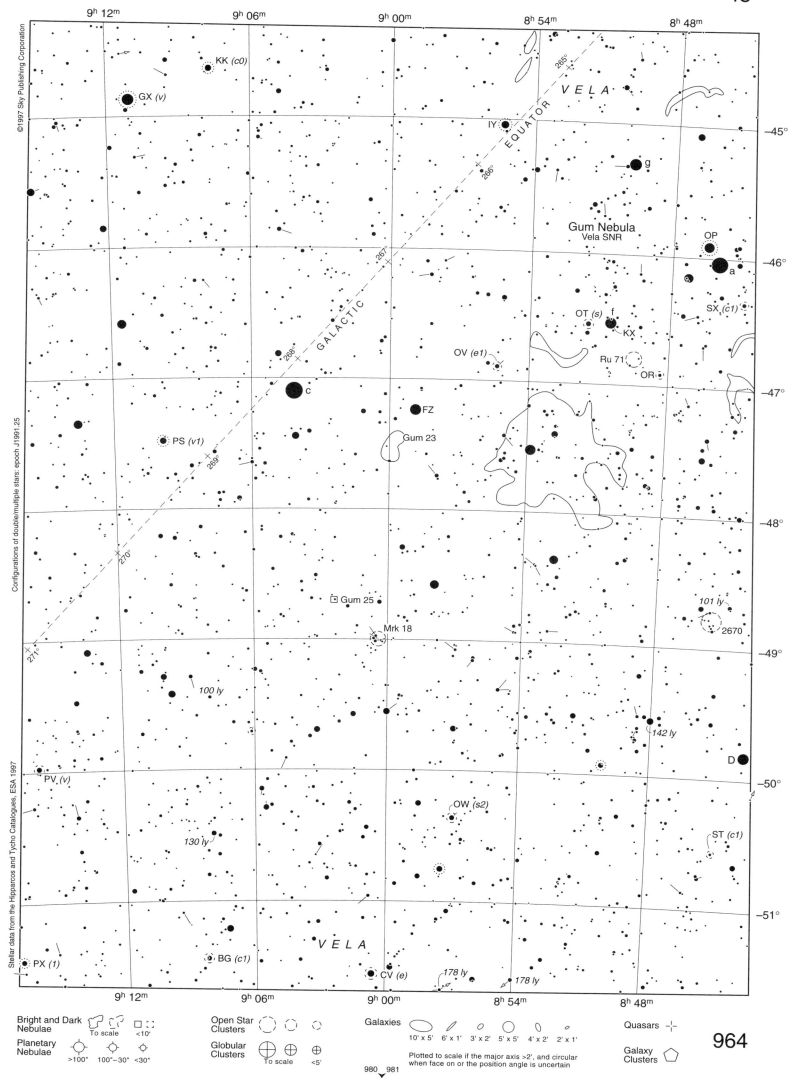

VELA

EQUATOR

KK (c0)

GX (v)

IY

g

Gum Nebula
Vela SNR

OP

a

SX (c1)

OT (s)   f
KX

OV (e1)

Ru 71

OR

c

FZ

Gum 23

PS (v1)

Gum 25

101 ly
2670

Mrk 18

100 ly

142 ly

D

PV (v)

OW (s2)

ST (c1)

130 ly

VELA

PX (1)

BG (c1)

CV (e)

178 ly   178 ly

Bright and Dark
Nebulae
To scale   <10'

Planetary
Nebulae
>100"   100"−30"   <30"

Open Star
Clusters

Globular
Clusters
To scale   <5'

Galaxies
10' x 5'   6' x 1'   3' x 2'   5' x 5'   4' x 2'   2' x 1'

Plotted to scale if the major axis >2', and circular
when face on or the position angle is uncertain

Quasars

Galaxy
Clusters

964

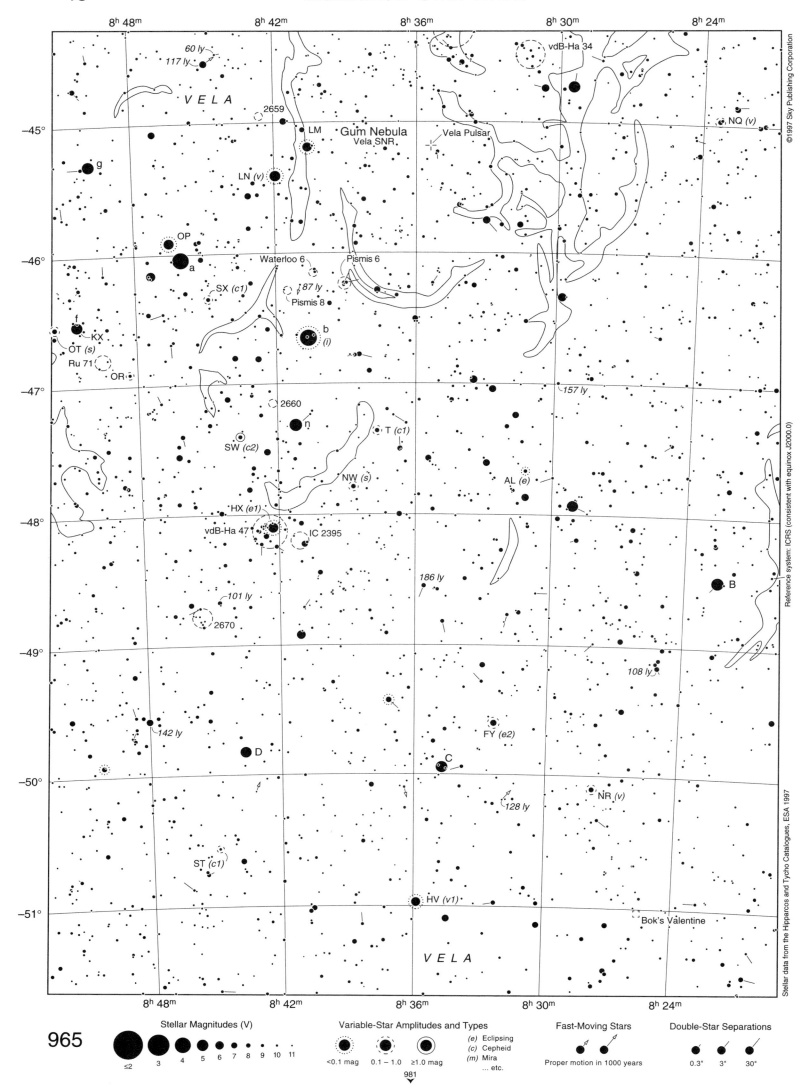

©1997 Sky Publishing Corporation

Reference system: ICRS (consistent with equinox J2000.0)

Stellar data from the Hipparcos and Tycho Catalogues, ESA 1997

Stellar Magnitudes (V)

≤2   3   4   5   6   7   8   9   10   11

Variable-Star Amplitudes and Types

<0.1 mag   0.1 − 1.0   ≥1.0 mag

(e) Eclipsing
(c) Cepheid
(m) Mira
... etc.

Fast-Moving Stars

Proper motion in 1000 years

Double-Star Separations

0.3"   3"   30"

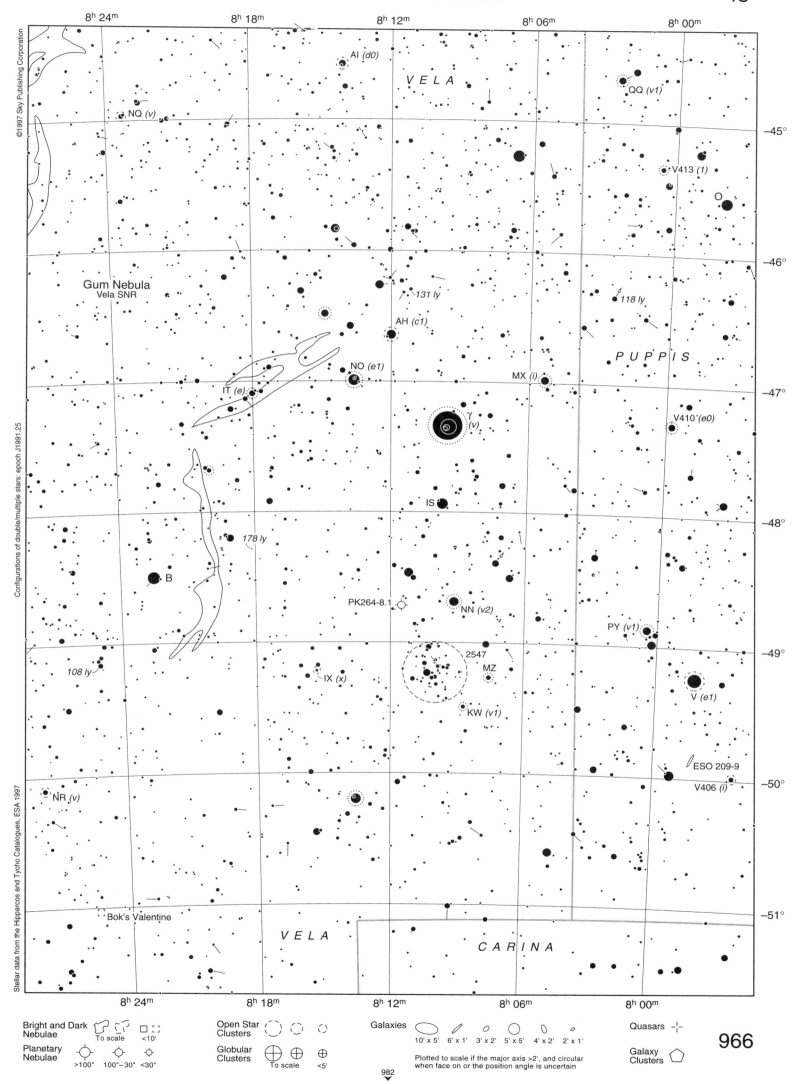

8h 24m 8h 18m 8h 12m 8h 06m 8h 00m

AI *(d0)*

VELA

QQ *(v1)*

NQ *(v)*

−45°

V413 *(1)*

Gum Nebula
Vela SNR

118 ly

−46°

131 ly

AH *(c1)*

PUPPIS

NO *(e1)*

MX *(i)*

IT *(e)*

−47°

γ
(v)

V410 *(e0)*

IS

−48°

178 ly

B

PK264-8.1

NN *(v2)*

PY *(v1)*

−49°

2547

MZ

IX *(x)*

V *(e1)*

KW *(v1)*

108 ly

ESO 209-9

−50°

NR *(v)*

V406 *(i)*

−51°

Bok's Valentine

VELA *CARINA*

8h 24m 8h 18m 8h 12m 8h 06m 8h 00m

Bright and Dark Nebulae		Open Star Clusters			Galaxies						Quasars
	To scale <10'				10' x 5'	6' x 1'	3' x 2'	5' x 5'	4' x 2'	2' x 1'	

Planetary Nebulae
>100" 100"–30" <30"

Globular Clusters
To scale <5'

Plotted to scale if the major axis >2', and circular
when face on or the position angle is uncertain

Galaxy Clusters

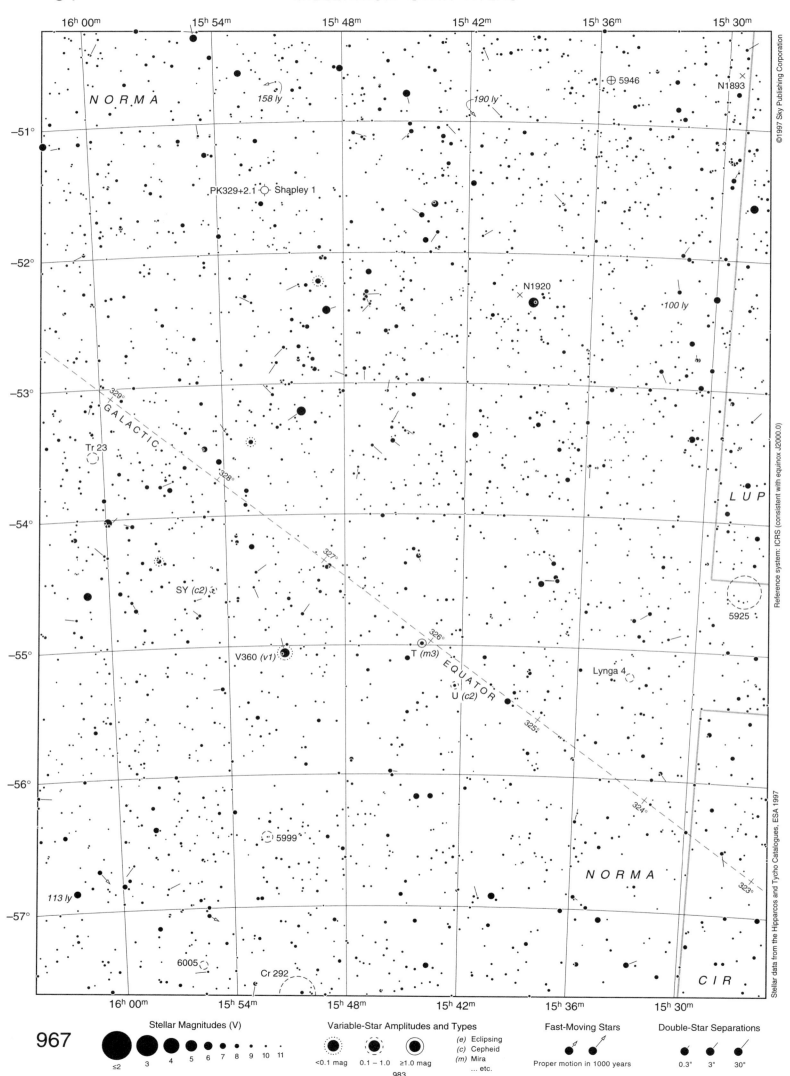

©1997 Sky Publishing Corporation

Reference system: ICRS (consistent with equinox J2000.0)

Stellar data from the Hipparcos and Tycho Catalogues, ESA 1997

967

Stellar Magnitudes (V)

≤2   3   4   5   6   7   8   9   10   11

Variable-Star Amplitudes and Types

<0.1 mag   0.1 − 1.0   ≥1.0 mag

(e) Eclipsing
(c) Cepheid
(m) Mira
... etc.

Fast-Moving Stars

Proper motion in 1000 years

Double-Star Separations

0.3"   3"   30"

983

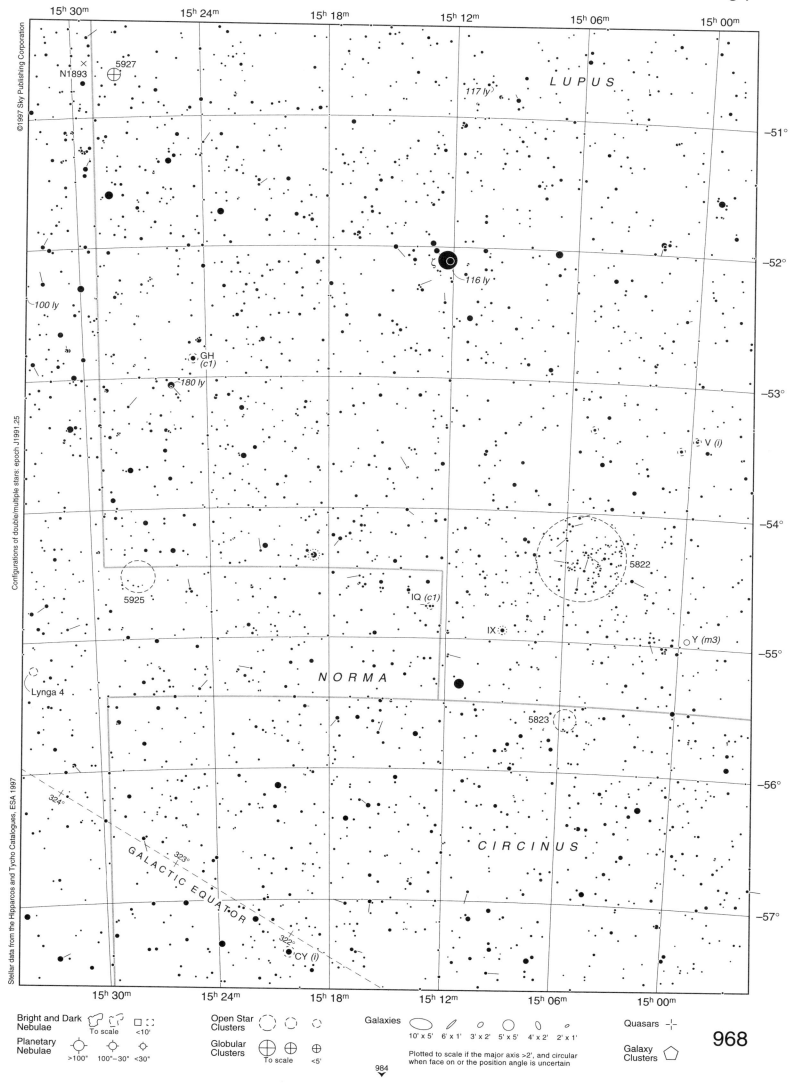

15h 30m   15h 24m   15h 18m   15h 12m   15h 06m   15h 00m

−51°
−52°
−53°
−54°
−55°
−56°
−57°

LUPUS

N1893   5927

117 ly

ζ   116 ly

100 ly

GH (c1)

180 ly

V (i)

5925

IQ (c1)

5822

IX

Y (m3)

NORMA

5823

Lynga 4

324°

GALACTIC EQUATOR

323°

CIRCINUS

322°

CY (i)

15h 30m   15h 24m   15h 18m   15h 12m   15h 06m   15h 00m

Bright and Dark
Nebulae
To scale   <10'

Planetary
Nebulae
>100" 100"−30" <30"

Open Star
Clusters

Globular
Clusters
To scale   <5'

Galaxies
10' x 5'   6' x 1'   3' x 2'   5' x 5'   4' x 2'   2' x 1'

Plotted to scale if the major axis >2', and circular
when face on or the position angle is uncertain

Quasars

Galaxy
Clusters

968

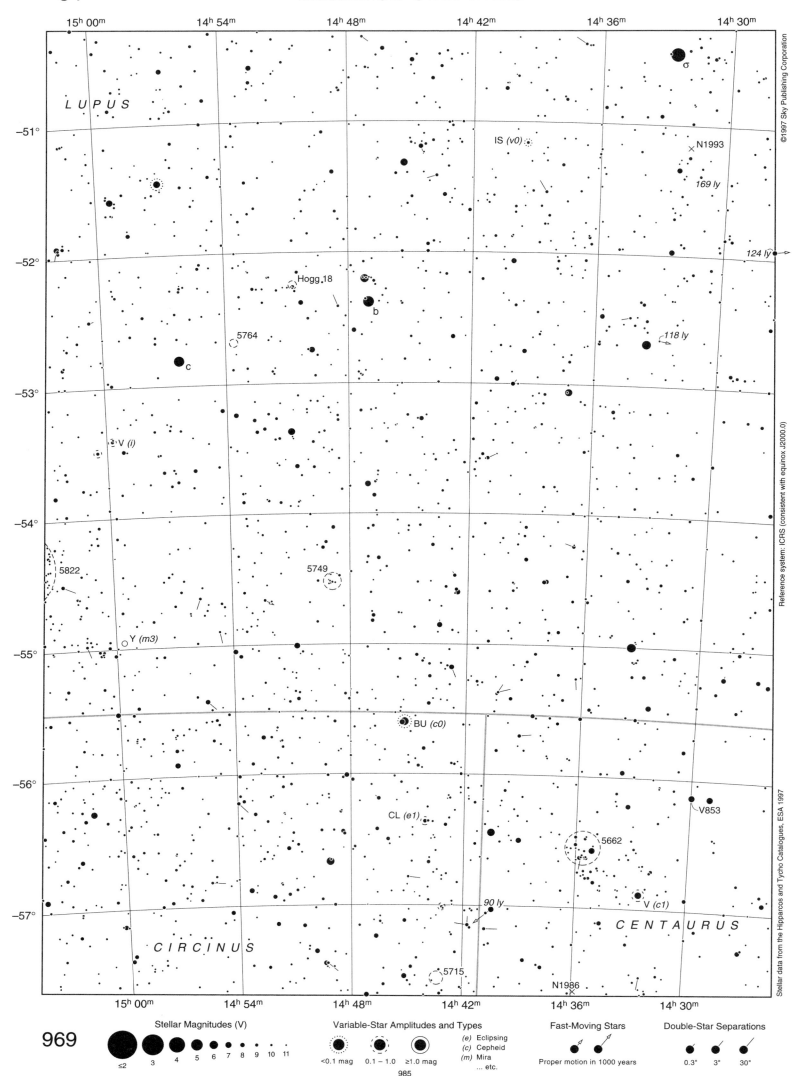

Reference system: ICRS (consistent with equinox J2000.0)

Stellar data from the Hipparcos and Tycho Catalogues, ESA 1997

LUPUS

CIRCINUS

CENTAURUS

σ

IS (v0)

N1993

169 ly

124 ly

Hogg 18

b

118 ly

5764

c

V (i)

5822

Y (m3)

5749

BU (c0)

CL (e1)

V853

5662

90 ly

V (c1)

5715

N1986

969

| Stellar Magnitudes (V) | | Variable-Star Amplitudes and Types | | Fast-Moving Stars | Double-Star Separations |

Stellar Magnitudes (V)

≤2   3   4   5   6   7   8   9   10   11

Variable-Star Amplitudes and Types

<0.1 mag   0.1 – 1.0   ≥1.0 mag

(e) Eclipsing
(c) Cepheid
(m) Mira
... etc.

Fast-Moving Stars

Proper motion in 1000 years

Double-Star Separations

0.3"   3"   30"

950

985

MILLENNIUM STAR ATLAS

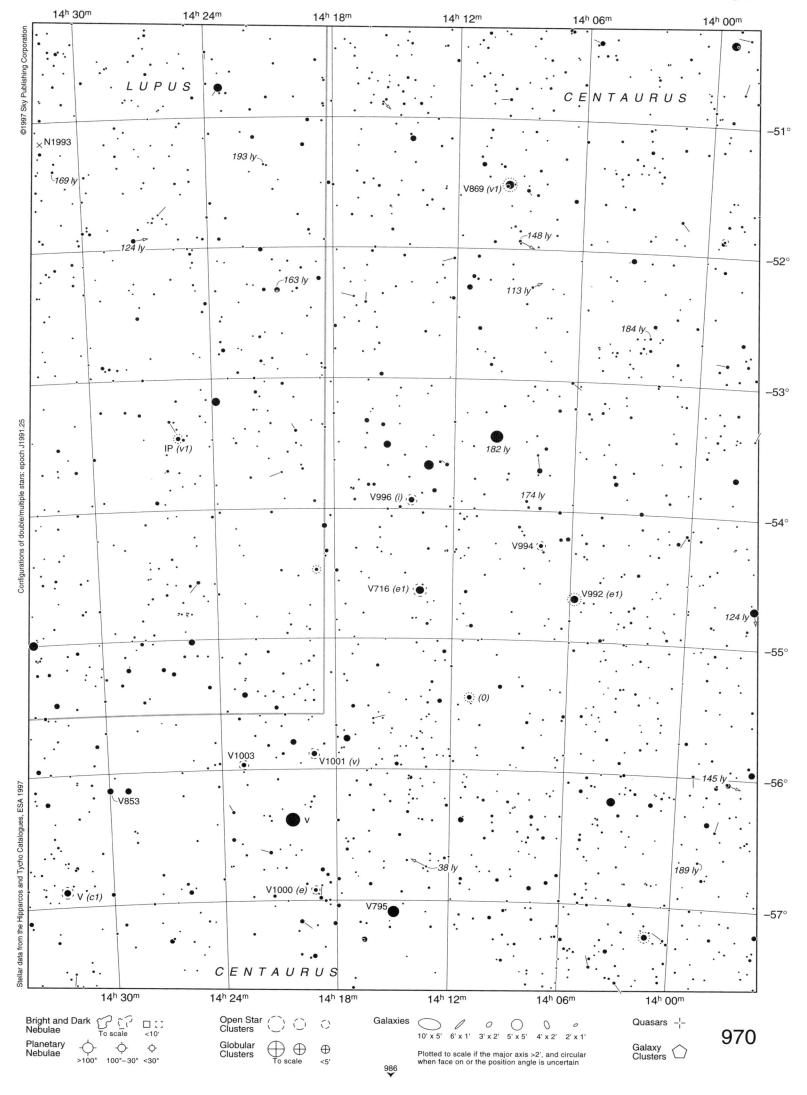

14h 30m   14h 24m   14h 18m   14h 12m   14h 06m   14h 00m

L U P U S

C E N T A U R U S

×N1993

169 ly

193 ly

124 ly

163 ly

V869 (v1)

148 ly

113 ly

184 ly

IP (v1)

182 ly

174 ly

V996 (i)

V994

V716 (e1)

V992 (e1)

124 ly

(0)

V1003   V1001 (v)

145 ly

V853

V

38 ly

189 ly

V1000 (e)

V (c1)

V795

C E N T A U R U S

14h 30m   14h 24m   14h 18m   14h 12m   14h 06m   14h 00m

−51°

−52°

−53°

−54°

−55°

−56°

−57°

©1997 Sky Publishing Corporation

Configurations of double/multiple stars: epoch J1991.25

Stellar data from the Hipparcos and Tycho Catalogues, ESA 1997

Bright and Dark Nebulae
To scale   <10'

Planetary Nebulae
>100"   100"–30"   <30"

Open Star Clusters

Globular Clusters
To scale   <5'

Galaxies
10' x 5'   6' x 1'   3' x 2'   5' x 5'   4' x 2'   2' x 1'

Plotted to scale if the major axis >2', and circular when face on or the position angle is uncertain

Quasars

Galaxy Clusters

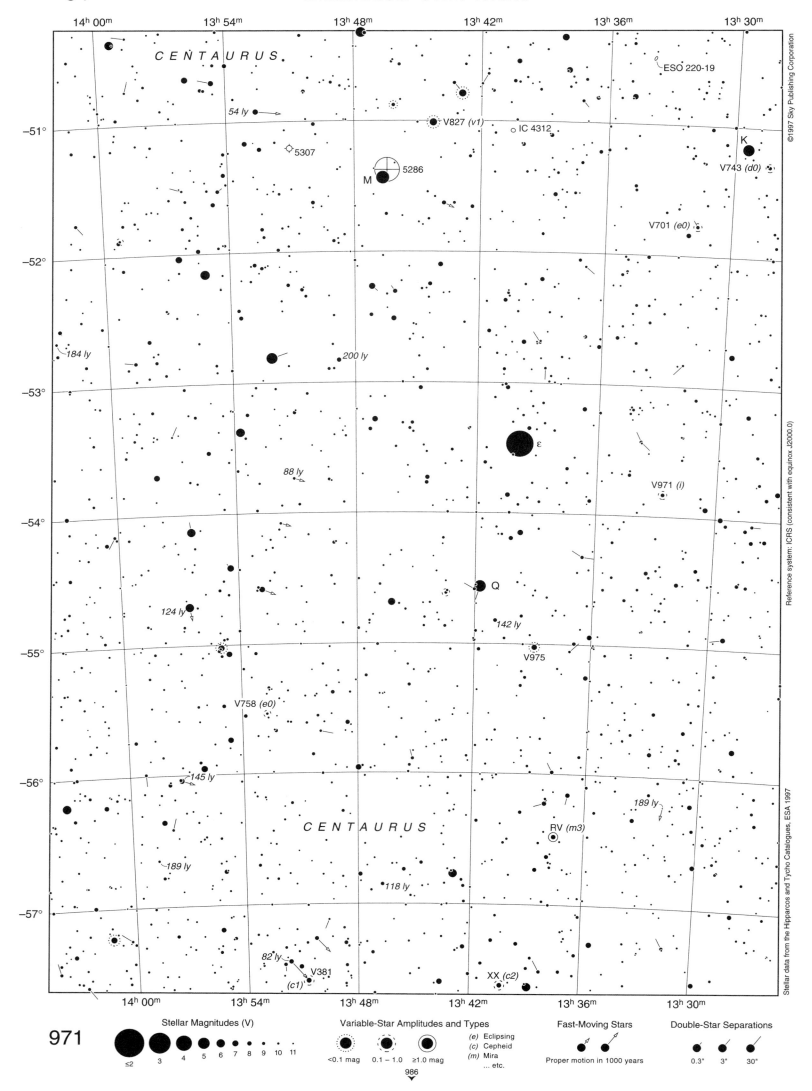

−54°

MILLENNIUM STAR ATLAS

©1997 Sky Publishing Corporation

Reference system: ICRS (consistent with equinox J2000.0)

Stellar data from the Hipparcos and Tycho Catalogues, ESA 1997

CENTAURUS

54 ly

V827 *(v1)*

ESO 220-19

IC 4312

K

V743 *(d0)*

5307

M 5286

V701 *(e0)*

184 ly

200 ly

ε

88 ly

V971 *(i)*

Q

124 ly

142 ly

V975

V758 *(e0)*

145 ly

CENTAURUS

RV *(m3)*

189 ly

189 ly

118 ly

82 ly

V381

(c1)

XX *(c2)*

971

Stellar Magnitudes (V)

≤2   3   4   5   6   7   8   9   10   11

Variable-Star Amplitudes and Types

<0.1 mag   0.1 – 1.0   ≥1.0 mag

(e) Eclipsing
(c) Cepheid
(m) Mira
... etc.

Fast-Moving Stars

Proper motion in 1000 years

Double-Star Separations

0.3"   3"   30"

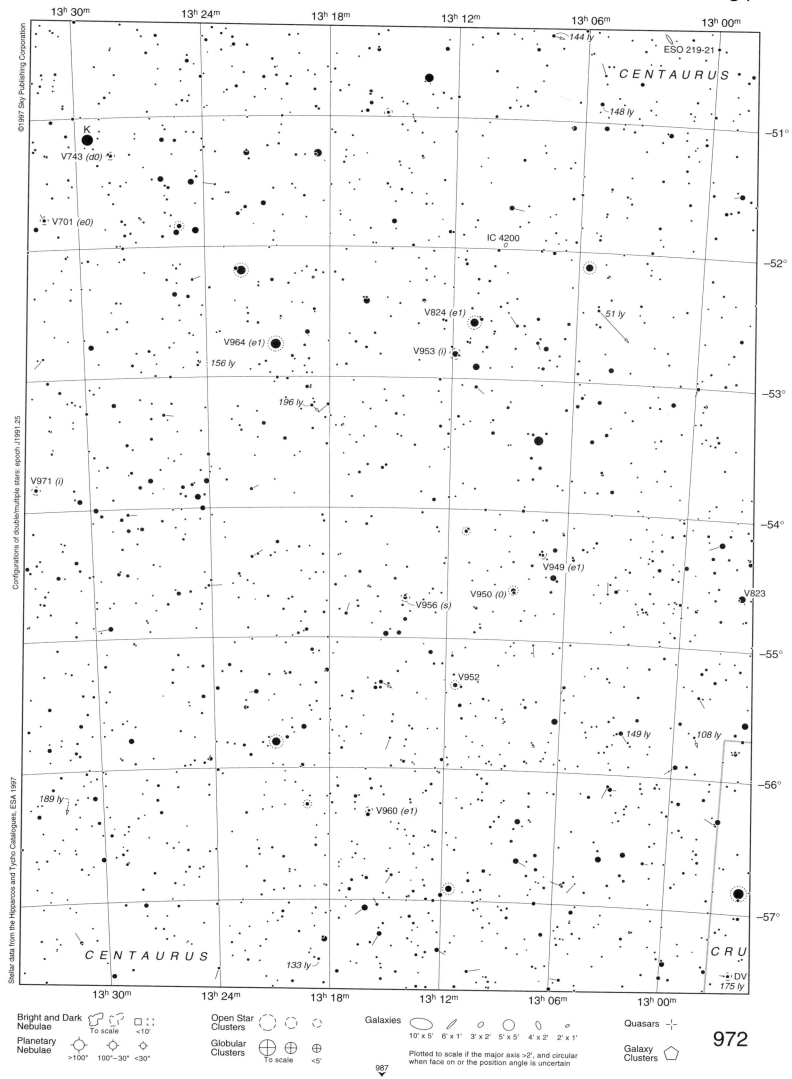

13h 30m · 13h 24m · 13h 18m · 13h 12m · 13h 06m · 13h 00m

144 ly

ESO 219-21

C E N T A U R U S

148 ly

−51°

K

V743 (d0)

V701 (e0)

IC 4200

−52°

V824 (e1)

51 ly

V964 (e1)

V953 (i)

156 ly

196 ly

−53°

V971 (i)

−54°

V949 (e1)

V950 (0)

V823

V956 (s)

−55°

V952

149 ly

108 ly

−56°

189 ly

V960 (e1)

C E N T A U R U S

133 ly

C R U

−57°

DV
175 ly

13h 30m · 13h 24m · 13h 18m · 13h 12m · 13h 06m · 13h 00m

Configurations of double/multiple stars: epoch J1991.25

Stellar data from the Hipparcos and Tycho Catalogues, ESA 1997

Bright and Dark Nebulae
To scale   <10'

Planetary Nebulae
>100"   100"–30"   <30"

Open Star Clusters

Globular Clusters
To scale   <5'

Galaxies
10' x 5'   6' x 1'   3' x 2'   5' x 5'   4' x 2'   2' x 1'

Plotted to scale if the major axis >2', and circular when face on or the position angle is uncertain

Quasars

Galaxy Clusters

972

987

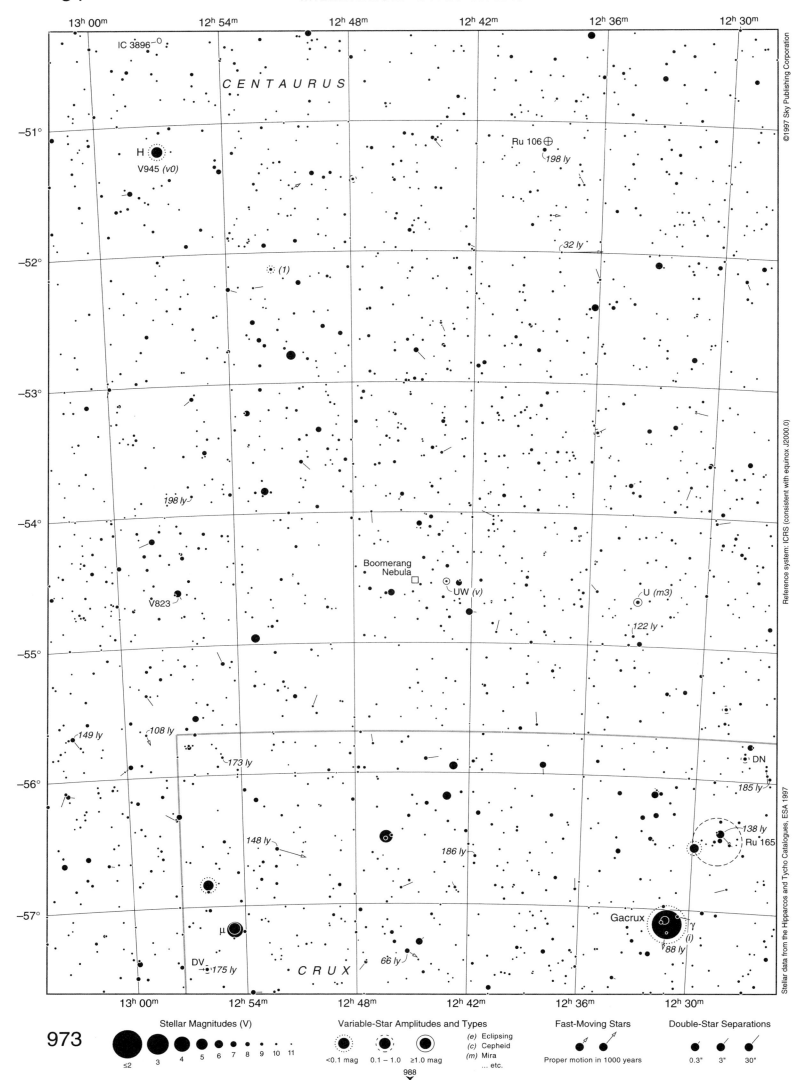

13h 00m   12h 54m   12h 48m   12h 42m   12h 36m   12h 30m

–51°

IC 3896

CENTAURUS

H
V945 (v0)

Ru 106
198 ly

32 ly

–52°

(1)

–53°

198 ly

–54°

Boomerang
Nebula

UW (v)

U (m3)

V823

122 ly

–55°

149 ly   108 ly

DN

173 ly

185 ly

–56°

138 ly
Ru 165

148 ly

186 ly

–57°

μ

Gacrux   γ
(i)

88 ly

DV   175 ly

CRUX

66 ly

13h 00m   12h 54m   12h 48m   12h 42m   12h 36m   12h 30m

©1997 Sky Publishing Corporation

Reference system: ICRS (consistent with equinox J2000.0)

Stellar data from the Hipparcos and Tycho Catalogues, ESA 1997

973

Stellar Magnitudes (V)

≤2   3   4   5   6   7 8 9 10 11

Variable-Star Amplitudes and Types

<0.1 mag   0.1 – 1.0   ≥1.0 mag

(e) Eclipsing
(c) Cepheid
(m) Mira
... etc.

Fast-Moving Stars

Proper motion in 1000 years

Double-Star Separations

0.3"   3"   30"

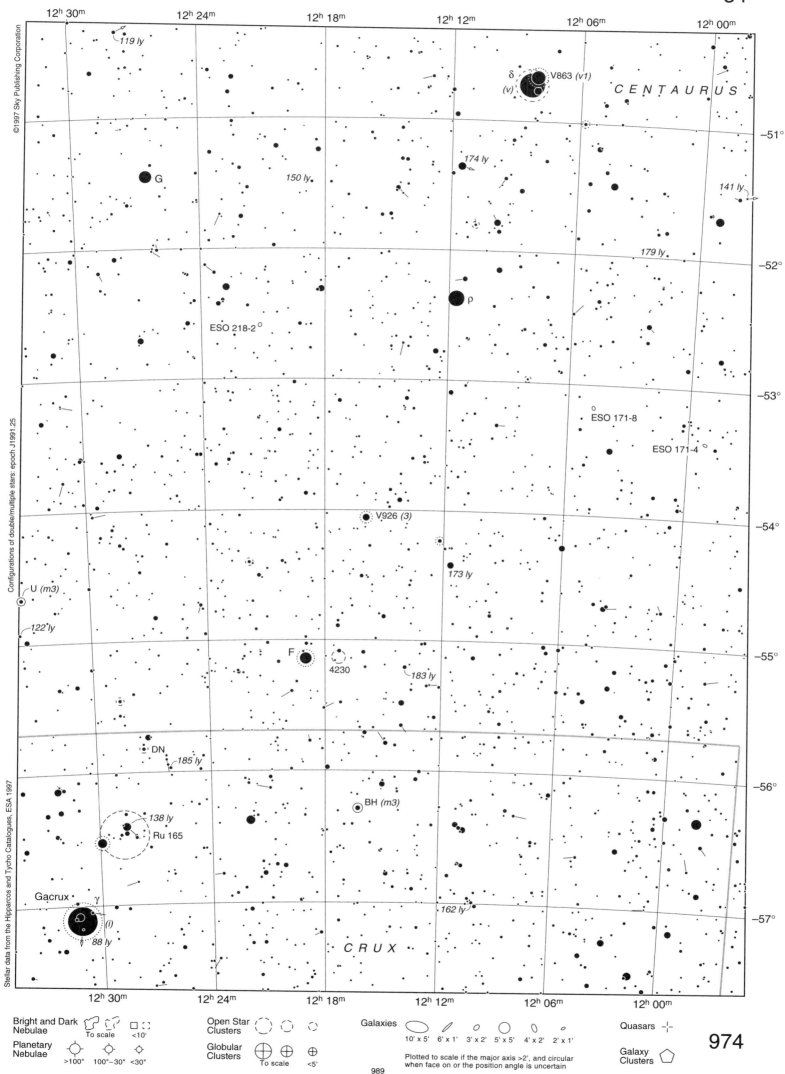

CENTAURUS

CRUX

119 ly

δ
(v)
V863 (v1)

G

150 ly

174 ly

141 ly

179 ly

ρ

ESO 218-2

ESO 171-8

ESO 171-4

V926 (3)

173 ly

U (m3)

122 ly

F

4230

183 ly

DN

185 ly

BH (m3)

138 ly
Ru 165

Gacrux
γ
(i)
88 ly

162 ly

12ʰ 30ᵐ   12ʰ 24ᵐ   12ʰ 18ᵐ   12ʰ 12ᵐ   12ʰ 06ᵐ   12ʰ 00ᵐ

−51°
−52°
−53°
−54°
−55°
−56°
−57°

12ʰ 30ᵐ   12ʰ 24ᵐ   12ʰ 18ᵐ   12ʰ 12ᵐ   12ʰ 06ᵐ   12ʰ 00ᵐ

Bright and Dark Nebulae			Open Star Clusters			Galaxies						Quasars
To scale		<10'				10' x 5'	6' x 1'	3' x 2'	5' x 5'	4' x 2'	2' x 1'	

Planetary Nebulae
>100"   100"−30"   <30"

Globular Clusters
To scale   <5'

Plotted to scale if the major axis >2', and circular when face on or the position angle is uncertain

Galaxy Clusters

974

989

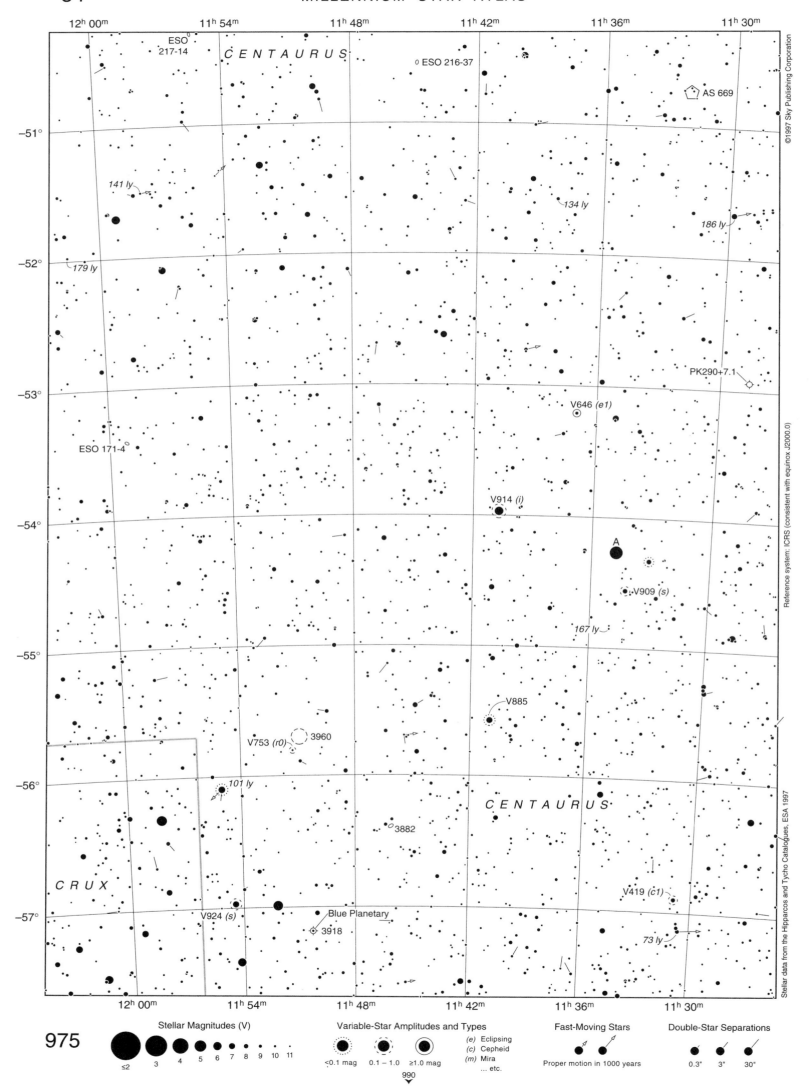

©1997 Sky Publishing Corporation

Reference system: ICRS (consistent with equinox J2000.0)

Stellar data from the Hipparcos and Tycho Catalogues, ESA 1997

CENTAURUS

ESO 217-14

ESO 216-37

AS 669

141 ly

134 ly

186 ly

179 ly

PK290+7.1

ESO 171-4

V646 (e1)

V914 (i)

A

V909 (s)

167 ly

V885

V753 (r0)   3960

101 ly

CENTAURUS

3882

CRUX

V419 (c1)

V924 (s)   Blue Planetary

73 ly

3918

975

Stellar Magnitudes (V)

≤2   3   4   5   6   7   8   9   10   11

Variable-Star Amplitudes and Types

<0.1 mag   0.1 – 1.0   ≥1.0 mag

(e) Eclipsing
(c) Cepheid
(m) Mira
... etc.

Fast-Moving Stars

Proper motion in 1000 years

Double-Star Separations

0.3"   3"   30"

990

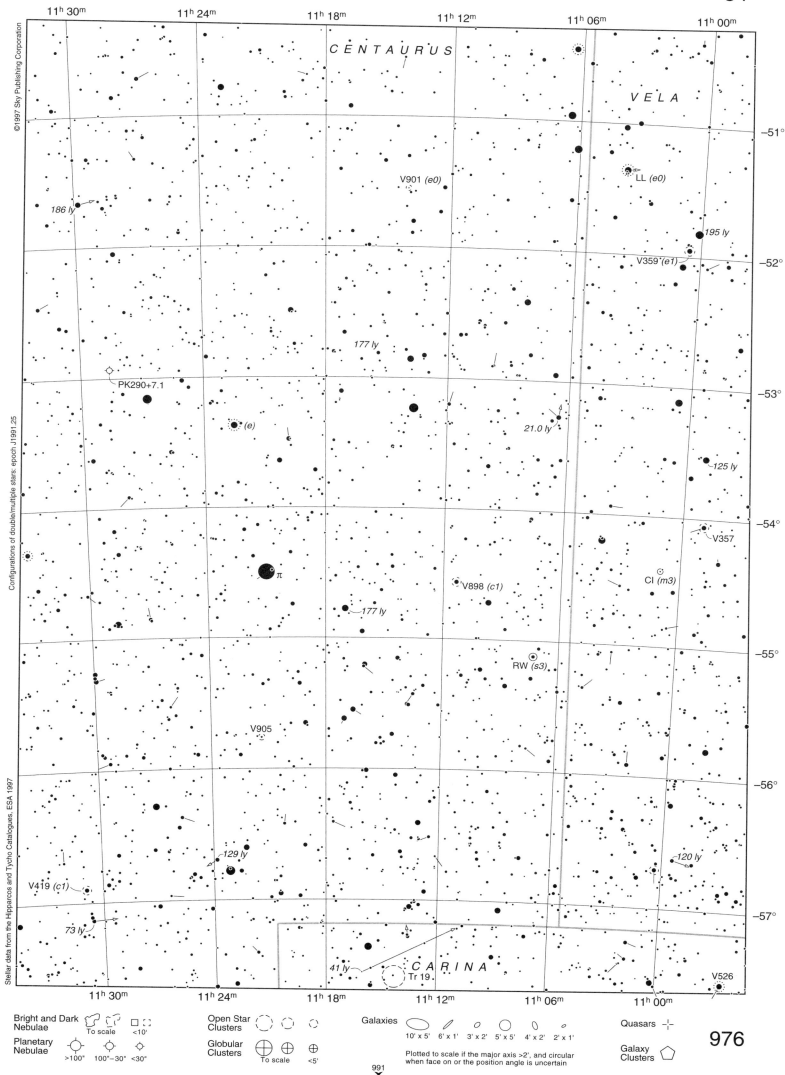

11ʰ 30ᵐ   11ʰ 24ᵐ   11ʰ 18ᵐ   11ʰ 12ᵐ   11ʰ 06ᵐ   11ʰ 00ᵐ

C E N T A U R U S

V E L A

−51°

V901 (e0)

LL (e0)

186 ly

195 ly

V359 (e1)

−52°

177 ly

PK290+7.1

21.0 ly

−53°

(e)

125 ly

−54°

V357

π

V898 (c1)

CI (m3)

177 ly

−55°

RW (s3)

V905

−56°

129 ly

120 ly

V419 (c1)

−57°

73 ly

41 ly

C A R I N A

Tr 19

V526

11ʰ 30ᵐ   11ʰ 24ᵐ   11ʰ 18ᵐ   11ʰ 12ᵐ   11ʰ 06ᵐ   11ʰ 00ᵐ

Bright and Dark Nebulae
To scale   <10'

Planetary Nebulae
>100"   100"–30"   <30"

Open Star Clusters

Globular Clusters
To scale   <5'

Galaxies
10' x 5'   6' x 1'   3' x 2'   5' x 5'   4' x 2'   2' x 1'

Plotted to scale if the major axis >2', and circular when face on or the position angle is uncertain

Quasars

Galaxy Clusters

976

MILLENNIUM STAR ATLAS

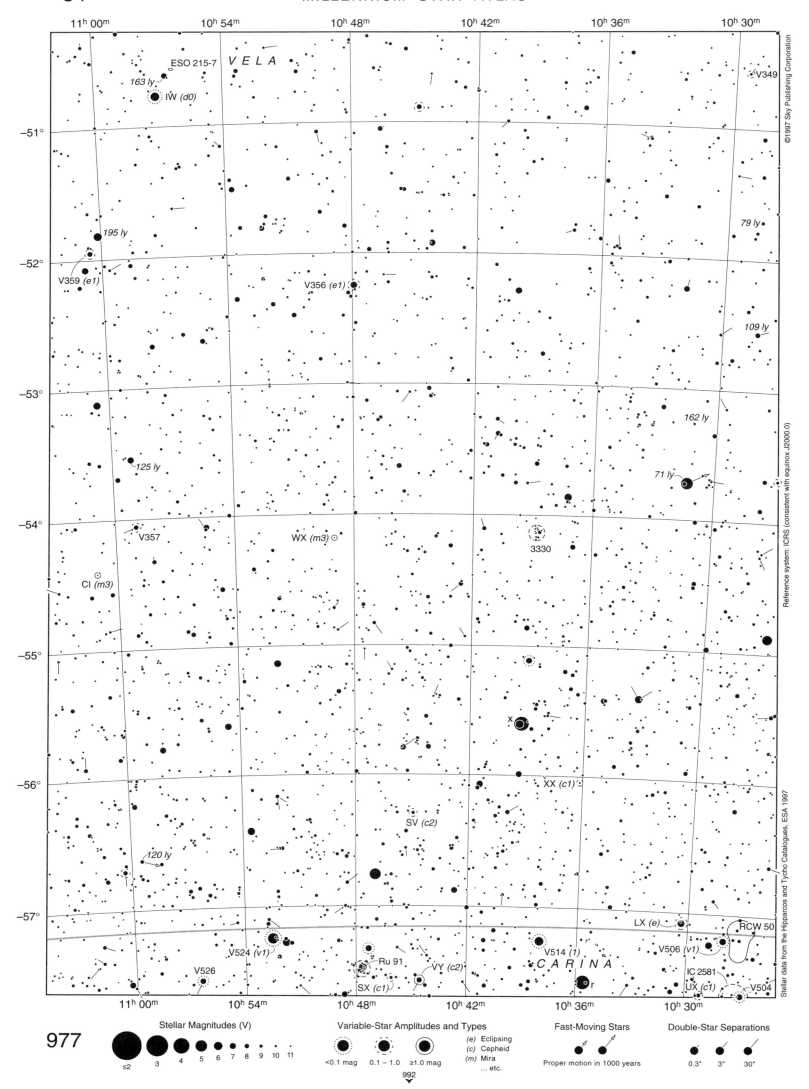

©1997 Sky Publishing Corporation

Reference system: ICRS (consistent with equinox J2000.0)

Stellar data from the Hipparcos and Tycho Catalogues, ESA 1997

977

Stellar Magnitudes (V)

≤2 3 4 5 6 7 8 9 10 11

Variable-Star Amplitudes and Types

<0.1 mag   0.1 – 1.0   ≥1.0 mag

(e) Eclipsing
(c) Cepheid
(m) Mira
... etc.

Fast-Moving Stars

Proper motion in 1000 years

Double-Star Separations

0.3"   3"   30"

MILLENNIUM STAR ATLAS

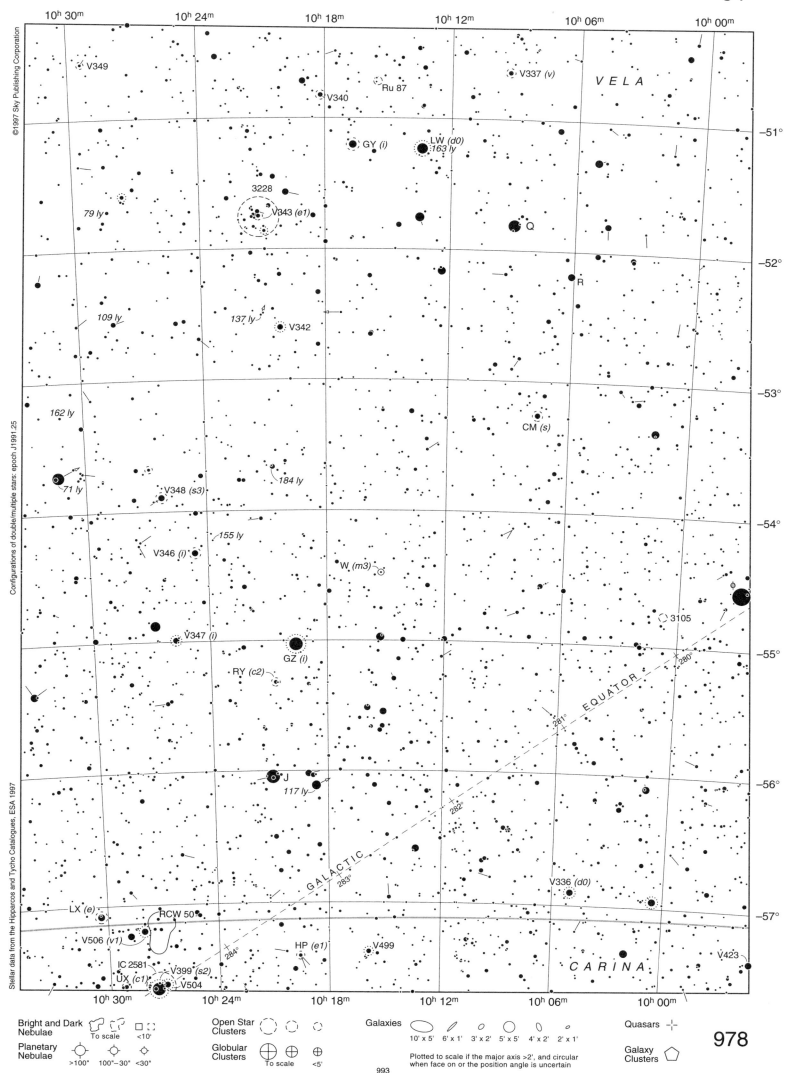

©1997 Sky Publishing Corporation

Configurations of double/multiple stars: epoch J1991.25

Stellar data from the Hipparcos and Tycho Catalogues, ESA 1997

V349

V340

Ru 87

V337 (v)

VELA

GY (i)

LW (d0)
163 ly

3228

V343 (e1)

79 ly

Q

R

109 ly

137 ly

V342

162 ly

CM (s)

184 ly

71 ly

V348 (s3)

155 ly

V346 (i)

W (m3)

φ

3105

V347 (i)

GZ (i)

280°

RY (c2)

281° EQUATOR

J

117 ly

282°

GALACTIC

283°

V336 (d0)

LX (e)

RCW 50

284°

HP (e1)

V499

V506 (v1)

CARINA

IC 2581

V423

UX (c1)

V399 (s2)

V504

10h 30m   10h 24m   10h 18m   10h 12m   10h 06m   10h 00m

−51°

−52°

−53°

−54°

−55°

−56°

−57°

Bright and Dark Nebulae	Open Star Clusters	Galaxies						Quasars
To scale <10'		10' x 5' 6' x 1' 3' x 2' 5' x 5' 4' x 2' 2' x 1'						
Planetary Nebulae	Globular Clusters							Galaxy Clusters
>100" 100"–30" <30"	To scale <5'	Plotted to scale if the major axis >2', and circular when face on or the position angle is uncertain						

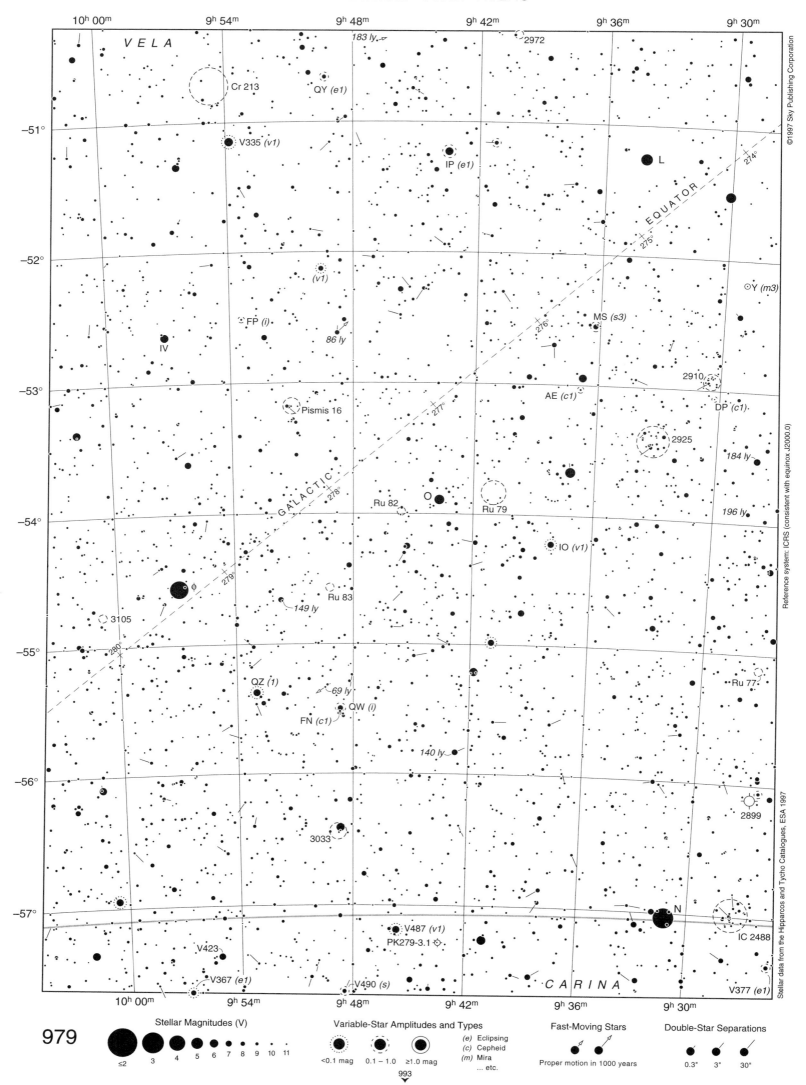

Stellar Magnitudes (V)

≤2   3   4   5   6   7   8   9   10   11

Variable-Star Amplitudes and Types

<0.1 mag   0.1 – 1.0   ≥1.0 mag

(e) Eclipsing
(c) Cepheid
(m) Mira
... etc.

993

Fast-Moving Stars

Proper motion in 1000 years

Double-Star Separations

0.3"   3"   30"

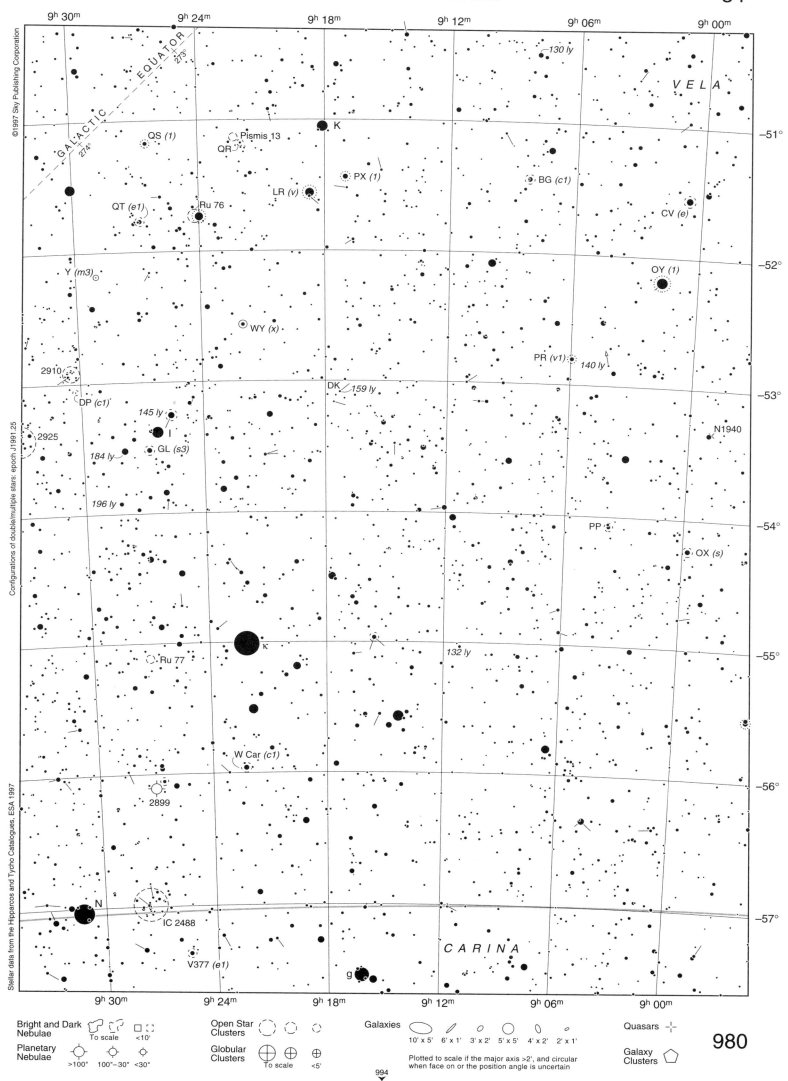

9h 30m   9h 24m   9h 18m   9h 12m   9h 06m   9h 00m

GALACTIC
EQUATOR
273°
274°

VELA

−51°

QS (1)   Pismis 13   K
QR

PX (1)

BG (c1)

LR (v)

CV (e)

QT (e1)   Ru 76

Y (m3)

OY (1)

WY (x)

2910

PR (v1)   140 ly

DP (c1)

DK   159 ly

145 ly   I

2925   GL (s3)

184 ly

N1940

196 ly

PP

OX (s)

κ

Ru 77

132 ly

W Car (c1)

2899

N

IC 2488

CARINA

V377 (e1)

g

130 ly

−51°

−52°

−53°

−54°

−55°

−56°

−57°

9h 30m   9h 24m   9h 18m   9h 12m   9h 06m   9h 00m

Bright and Dark
Nebulae   To scale   <10'

Open Star
Clusters

Galaxies

Quasars

Planetary
Nebulae   >100" 100"−30" <30'

Globular
Clusters   To scale   <5'

10' x 5'   6' x 1'   3' x 2'   5' x 5'   4' x 2'   2' x 1'

Plotted to scale if the major axis >2', and circular
when face on or the position angle is uncertain

Galaxy
Clusters

980

994

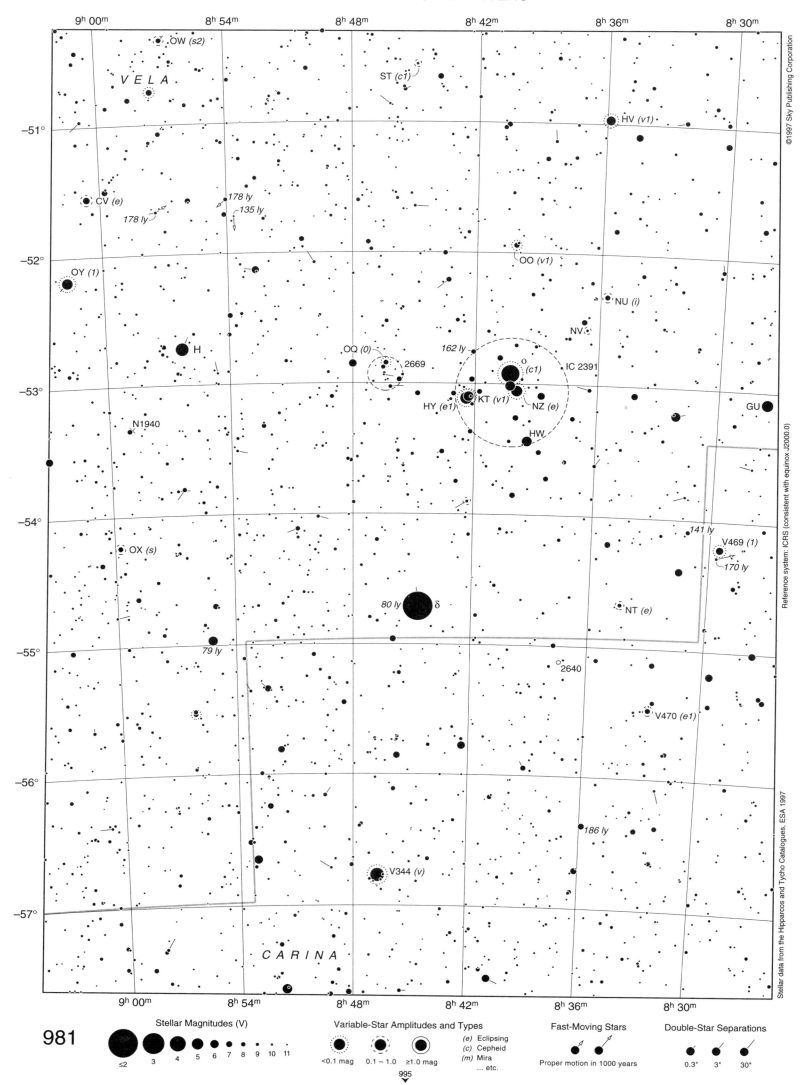

Stellar Magnitudes (V)

≤2   3   4   5   6   7   8   9   10   11

Variable-Star Amplitudes and Types

<0.1 mag   0.1 − 1.0   ≥1.0 mag

(e) Eclipsing
(c) Cepheid
(m) Mira
... etc.

Fast-Moving Stars

Proper motion in 1000 years

Double-Star Separations

0.3"   3"   30"

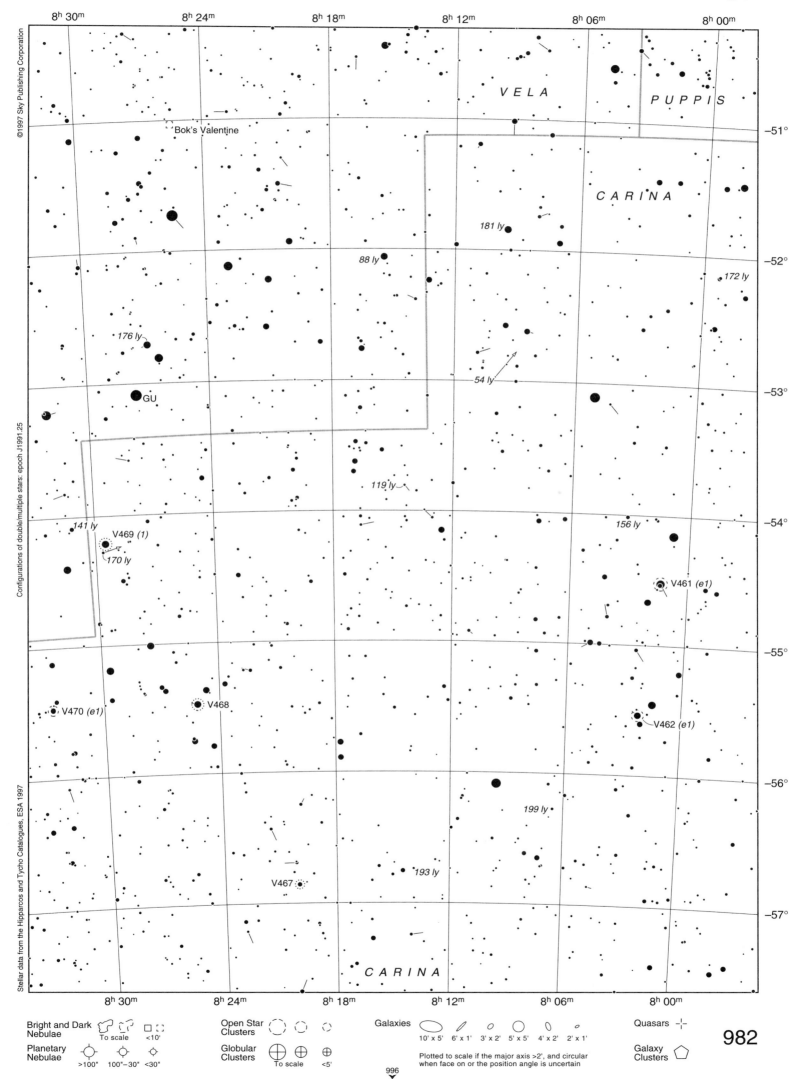

Bright and Dark Nebulae	Open Star Clusters	Galaxies
Planetary Nebulae	Globular Clusters	
		Quasars
		Galaxy Clusters

Bright and Dark Nebulae   To scale   <10'
Planetary Nebulae   >100"   100"−30"   <30"
Open Star Clusters
Globular Clusters   To scale   <5'
Galaxies   10' x 5'   6' x 1'   3' x 2'   5' x 5'   4' x 2'   2' x 1'
Plotted to scale if the major axis >2', and circular when face on or the position angle is uncertain
Quasars
Galaxy Clusters

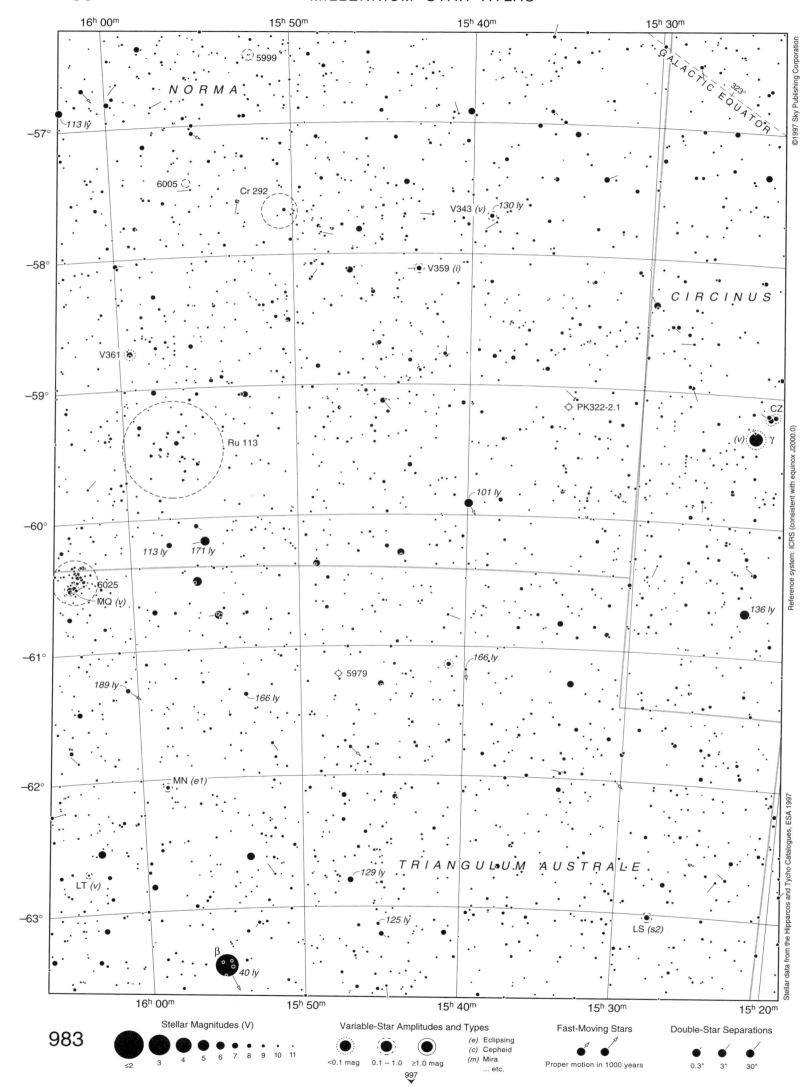

983

Stellar Magnitudes (V)

≤2 3 4 5 6 7 8 9 10 11

Variable-Star Amplitudes and Types

<0.1 mag   0.1 – 1.0   ≥1.0 mag

(e) Eclipsing
(c) Cepheid
(m) Mira
... etc.

Fast-Moving Stars

Proper motion in 1000 years

Double-Star Separations

0.3"   3"   30"

MILLENNIUM STAR ATLAS

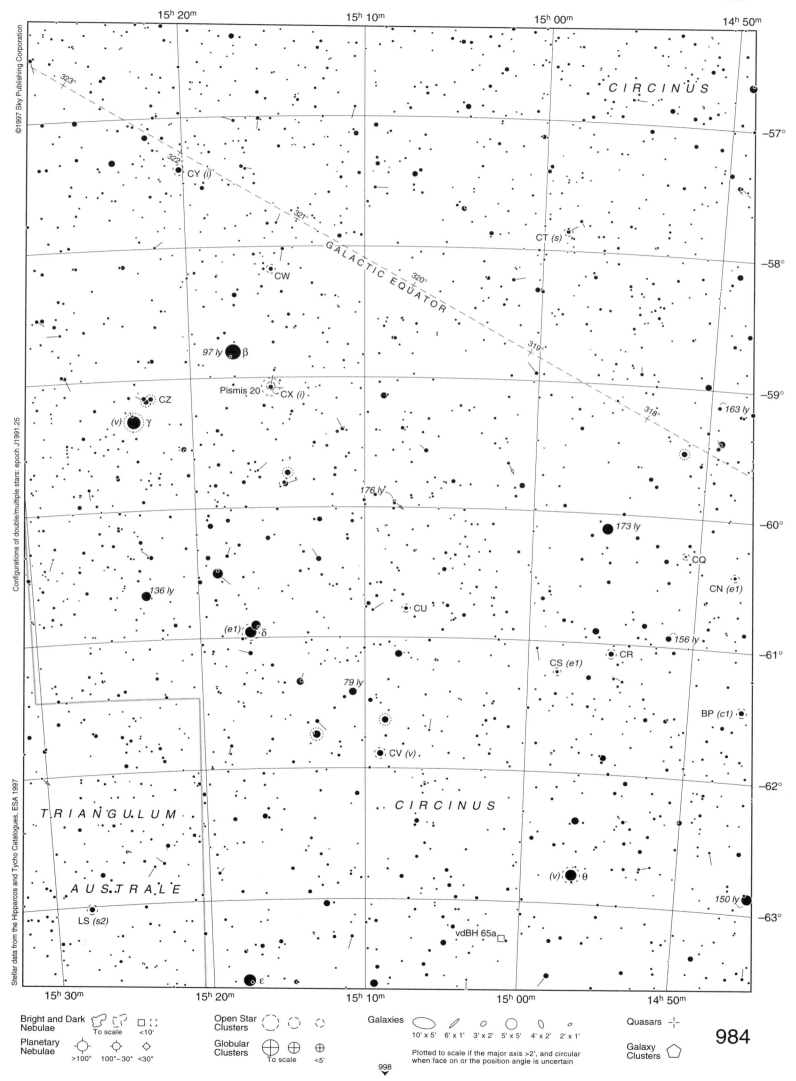

©1997 Sky Publishing Corporation

Configurations of double/multiple stars: epoch J1991.25

Stellar data from the Hipparcos and Tycho Catalogues, ESA 1997

15ʰ 20ᵐ   15ʰ 10ᵐ   15ʰ 00ᵐ   14ʰ 50ᵐ

−57°
−58°
−59°
−60°
−61°
−62°
−63°

CIRCINUS

323°
322°
CY (i)
321°
CW
GALACTIC EQUATOR
320°
CT (s)
319°
318°

97 ly β
Pismis 20   CX (i)
CZ
(v) γ

163 ly

176 ly

173 ly

CQ

CN (e1)

136 ly

156 ly

(e1) δ

CU

CR

CS (e1)

79 ly

BP (c1)

CV (v)

TRIANGULUM

CIRCINUS

(v) θ

AUSTRALE

150 ly

LS (s2)

vdBH 65a

ε

15ʰ 30ᵐ   15ʰ 20ᵐ   15ʰ 10ᵐ   15ʰ 00ᵐ   14ʰ 50ᵐ

| Bright and Dark Nebulae | To scale | <10' |
| Planetary Nebulae | >100" 100"−30" <30" |

| Open Star Clusters | | |
| Globular Clusters | To scale <5' |

| Galaxies | 10' x 5' 6' x 1' 3' x 2' 5' x 5' 4' x 2' 2' x 1' |

Plotted to scale if the major axis >2', and circular when face on or the position angle is uncertain

Quasars

Galaxy Clusters

984

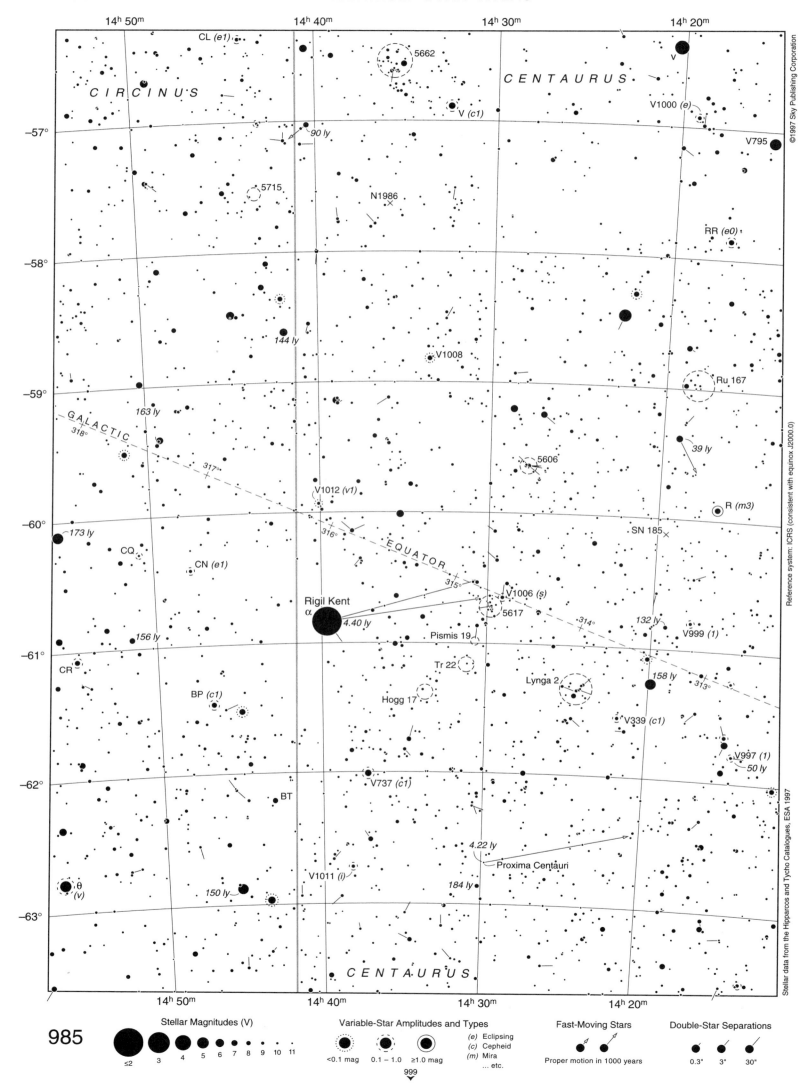

CL (e1)

5662

CENTAURUS

V

V1000 (e)

V795

CIRCINUS

90 ly

V (c1)

−57°

5715

N1986

RR (e0)

144 ly

V1008

Ru 167

−58°

GALACTIC

163 ly

318°

39 ly

−59°

317°

5606

316°

V1012 (v1)

R (m3)

173 ly

SN 185

−60°

CQ

EQUATOR

CN (e1)

315°

V1006 (s)

132 ly

Rigil Kent

5617

α

314°

V999 (1)

156 ly

4.40 ly

Pismis 19

CR

158 ly

Tr 22

313°

BP (c1)

Lynga 2

Hogg 17

−61°

V339 (c1)

V997 (1)

50 ly

V737 (c1)

−62°

BT

4.22 ly

Proxima Centauri

θ

V1011 (i)

184 ly

(v)

150 ly

−63°

CENTAURUS

14h 50m   14h 40m   14h 30m   14h 20m

985

Stellar Magnitudes (V)

≤2 3 4 5 6 7 8 9 10 11

Variable-Star Amplitudes and Types

<0.1 mag   0.1 – 1.0   ≥1.0 mag

(e) Eclipsing
(c) Cepheid
(m) Mira
… etc.

Fast-Moving Stars

Proper motion in 1000 years

Double-Star Separations

0.3"   3"   30"

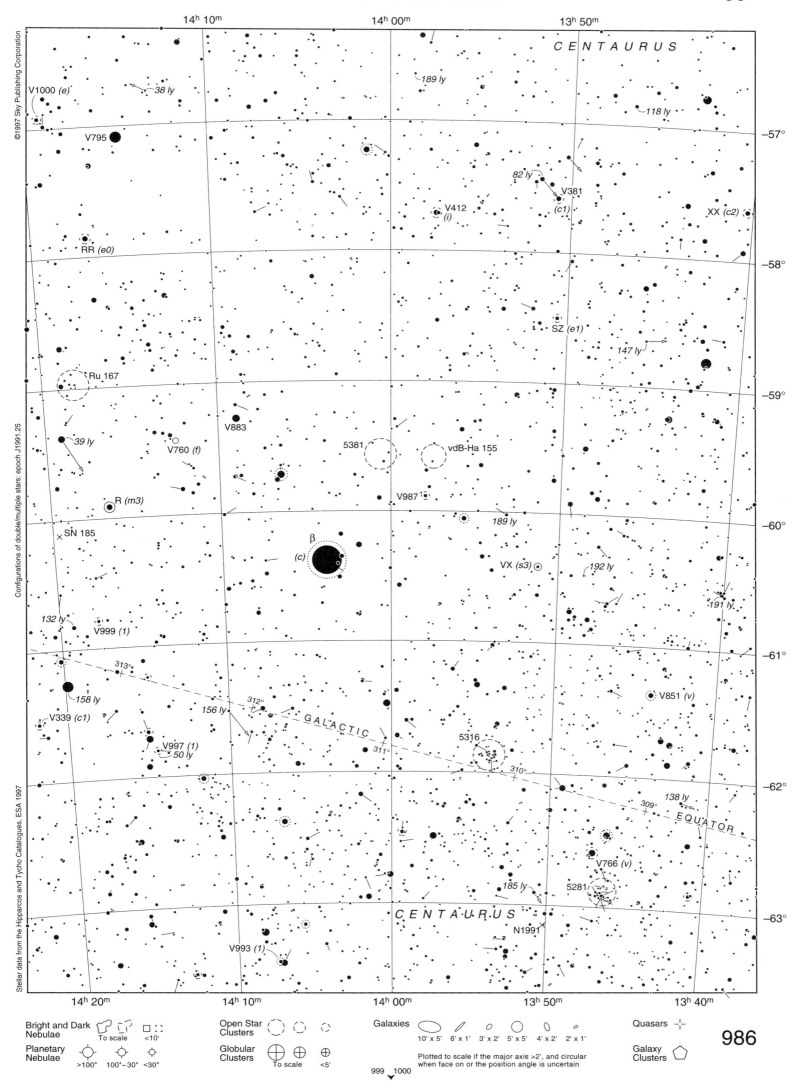

CENTAURUS

14h 10m
14h 00m
13h 50m

189 ly

118 ly

−57°

V1000 (e)
38 ly

V795

82 ly
V381
(c1)

V412
(i)

XX (c2)

RR (e0)

−58°

SZ (e1)
147 ly

Ru 167

−59°

V883

39 ly
V760 (f)
5381
vdB-Ha 155

R (m3)
V987

189 ly

β
(c)

−60°

SN 185
VX (s3)
192 ly

191 ly

132 ly
V999 (1)

−61°

313°
158 ly
312°
V851 (v)

V339 (c1)
156 ly
GALACTIC
311°
5316
310°

V997 (1)
50 ly

138 ly
309°
EQUATOR

V766 (v)

185 ly
5281

CENTAURUS

N1991

V993 (1)

14h 20m
14h 10m
14h 00m
13h 50m
13h 40m

−62°

−63°

Bright and Dark Nebulae   To scale   <10'
Planetary Nebulae   >100" 100"−30" <30"

Open Star Clusters
Globular Clusters   To scale   <5'

Galaxies
10' x 5' 6' x 1' 3' x 2' 5' x 5' 4' x 2' 2' x 1'

Plotted to scale if the major axis >2', and circular when face on or the position angle is uncertain

Quasars

Galaxy Clusters

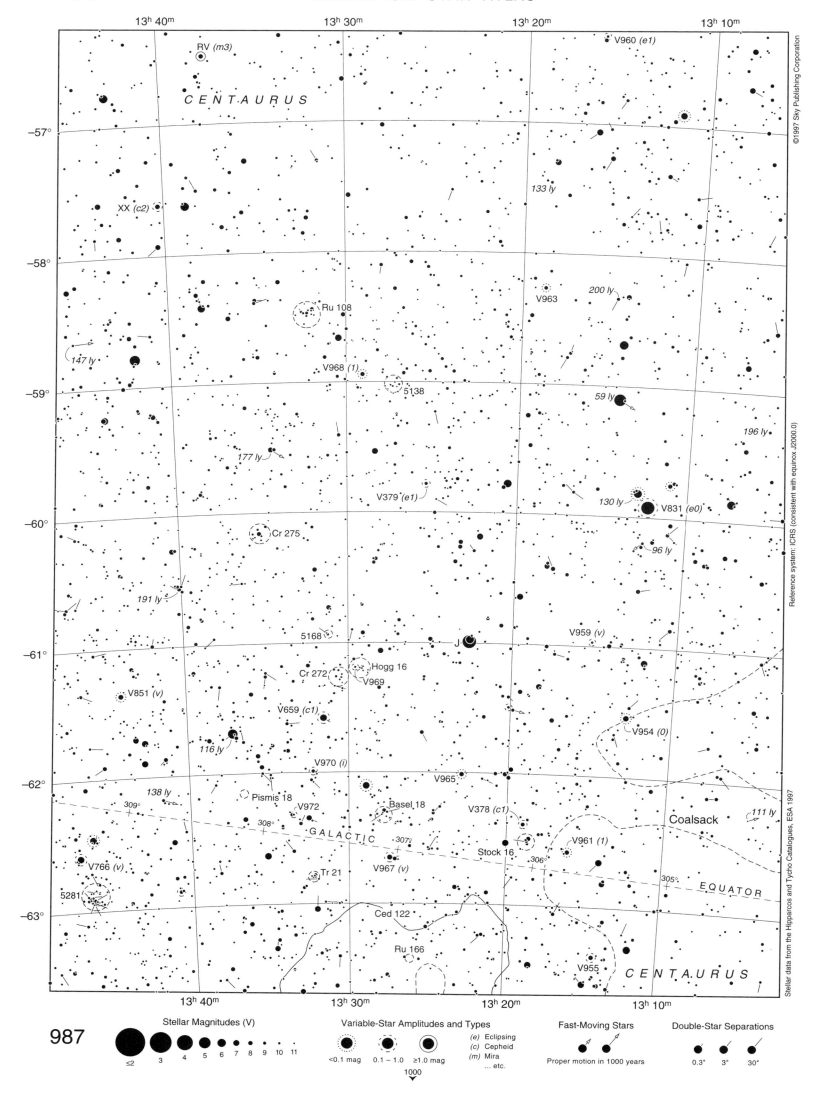

Reference system: ICRS (consistent with equinox J2000.0)

Stellar data from the Hipparcos and Tycho Catalogues, ESA 1997

987

Stellar Magnitudes (V)	Variable-Star Amplitudes and Types	Fast-Moving Stars	Double-Star Separations

Stellar Magnitudes (V)
≤2 3 4 5 6 7 8 9 10 11

Variable-Star Amplitudes and Types
<0.1 mag   0.1 − 1.0   ≥1.0 mag

(e) Eclipsing
(c) Cepheid
(m) Mira
... etc.

1000

Fast-Moving Stars
Proper motion in 1000 years

Double-Star Separations
0.3"   3"   30"

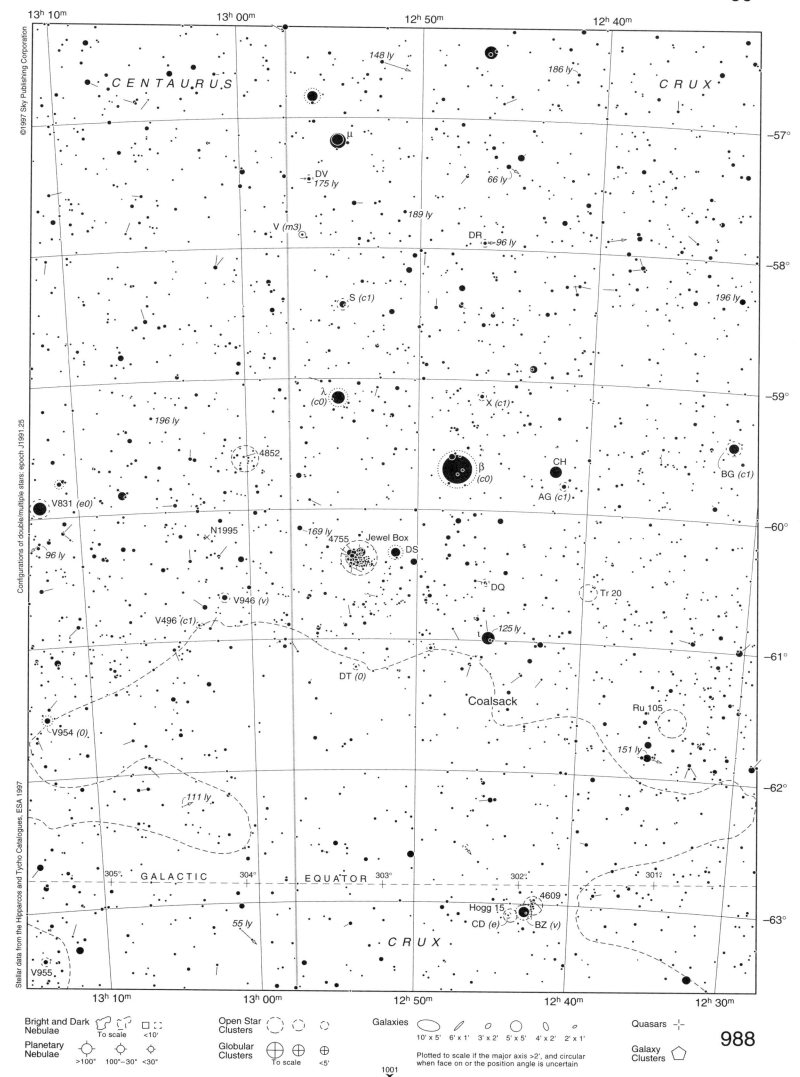

C E N T A U R U S

C R U X

148 ly

186 ly

μ

DV
175 ly

66 ly

189 ly

V (m3)

DR ▸ 96 ly

S (c1)

196 ly

λ
(c0)

X (c1)

196 ly

4852

CH

BG (c1)

β
(c0)

AG (c1)

V831 (e0)

N1995

169 ly
4755   Jewel Box

DS

96 ly

DQ

Tr 20

V946 (v)

V496 (c1)

ι   125 ly

DT (0)

Coalsack

Ru 105

V954 (0)

151 ly

111 ly

GALACTIC   EQUATOR

305°   304°   303°   302°   301°

55 ly

4609
Hogg 15
CD (e)   BZ (v)

C R U X

V955

13ʰ 10ᵐ   13ʰ 00ᵐ   12ʰ 50ᵐ   12ʰ 40ᵐ   12ʰ 30ᵐ

−57°

−58°

−59°

−60°

−61°

−62°

−63°

Bright and Dark
Nebulae   To scale   <10'

Planetary
Nebulae
          >100" 100"–30" <30"

Open Star
Clusters

Globular
Clusters
          To scale   <5'

Galaxies

10' x 5'   6' x 1'   3' x 2'   5' x 5'   4' x 2'   2' x 1'

Plotted to scale if the major axis >2', and circular
when face on or the position angle is uncertain

Quasars

Galaxy
Clusters

988

1001

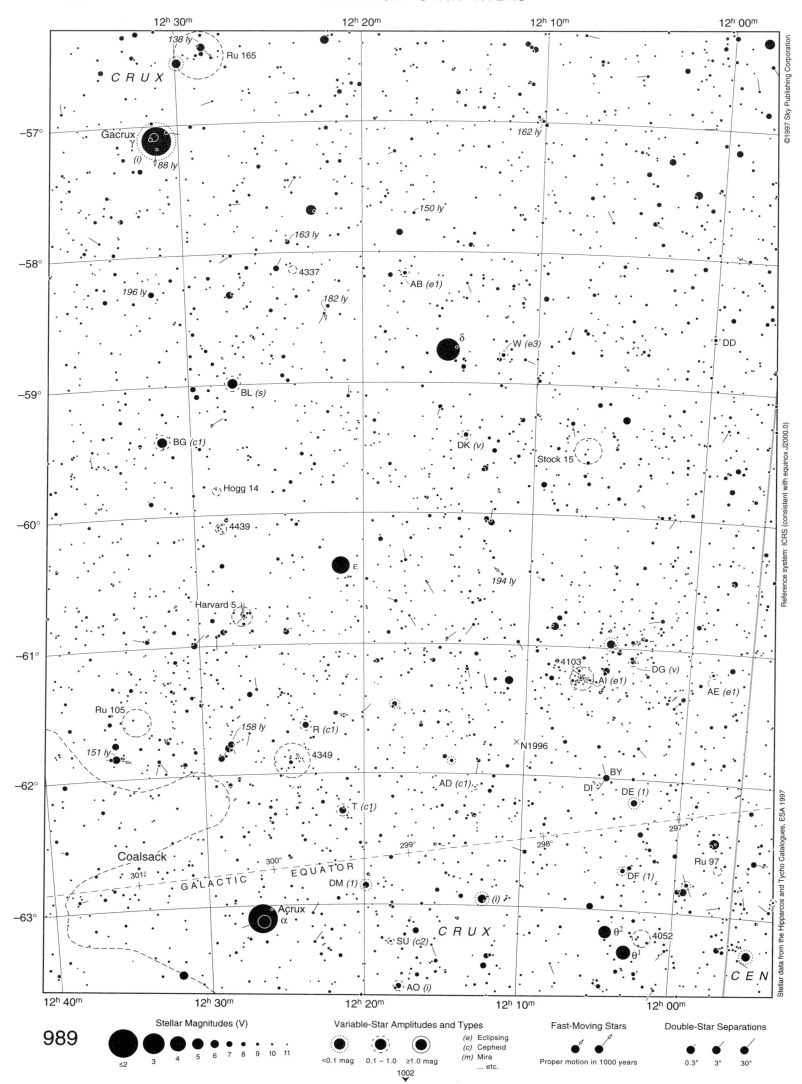

©1997 Sky Publishing Corporation

Reference system: ICRS (consistent with equinox J2000.0)

Stellar data from the Hipparcos and Tycho Catalogues, ESA 1997

C R U X

Ru 165

138 ly

Gacrux
γ
(i)
88 ly

162 ly

150 ly

163 ly

4337

AB (e1)

196 ly

182 ly

δ

W (e3)

DD

BL (s)

BG (c1)

DK (v)

Stock 15

Hogg 14

4439

ε

194 ly

Harvard 5

4103

AI (e1)

DG (v)

AE (e1)

Ru 105

R (c1)

158 ly

4349

N1996

151 ly

AD (c1)

BY

DI

DE (1)

T (c1)

297°

Coalsack

299°

298°

DF (1)

Ru 97

300°

301°

G A L A C T I C   E Q U A T O R

DM (1)

(i)

Acrux
α

θ²

4052

C R U X

SU (c2)

θ¹

C E N

AO (i)

Stellar Magnitudes (V)

≤2   3   4   5 6 7 8 9 10 11

Variable-Star Amplitudes and Types

<0.1 mag   0.1 – 1.0   ≥1.0 mag

(e) Eclipsing
(c) Cepheid
(m) Mira
... etc.

Fast-Moving Stars

Proper motion in 1000 years

Double-Star Separations

0.3"   3"   30"

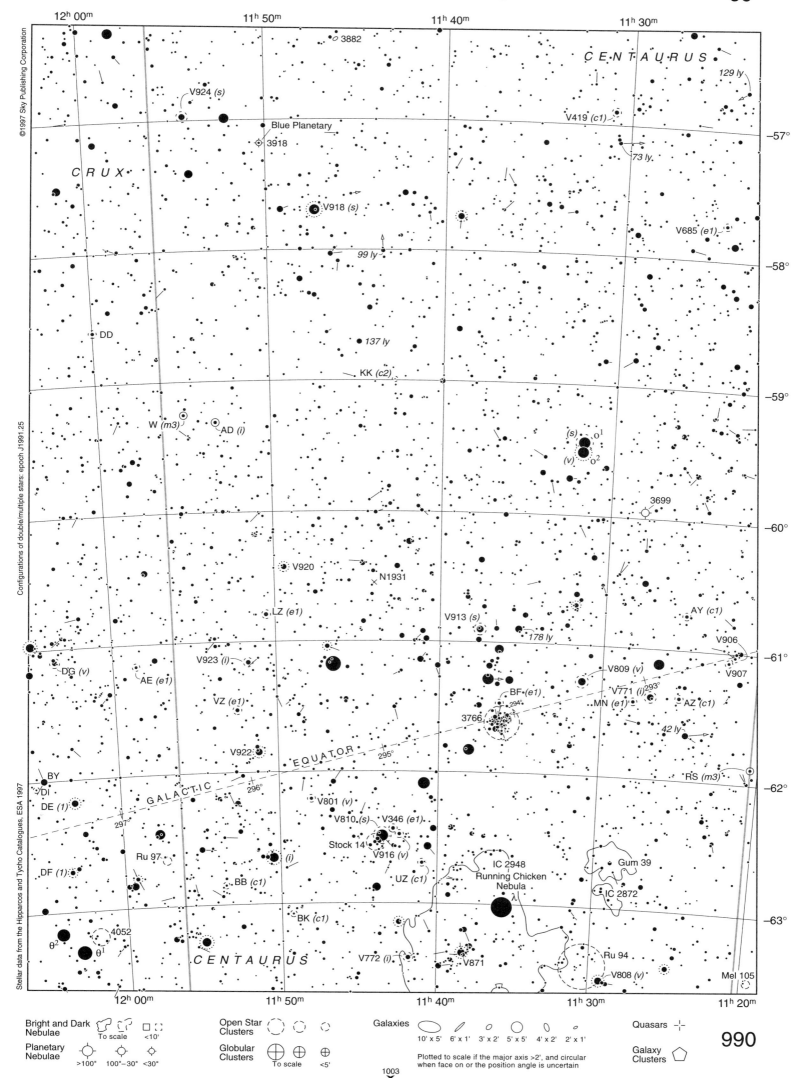

CENTAURUS

129 ly

V419 (c1)

73 ly

V685 (e1)

o 3882

V924 (s)

Blue Planetary
3918

CRUX

V918 (s)

99 ly

137 ly

KK (c2)

DD

W (m3)   AD (i)

(s)   o¹
(v)   o²

3699

V920

N1931

LZ (e1)

V913 (s)

178 ly

AY (c1)

V906

V923 (i)

V809 (v)

V907

DG (v)

AE (e1)

BF (e1)
294°

V771 (i) 293°

MN (e1)

AZ (c1)

VZ (e1)

3766
295°

42 ly

V922

EQUATOR

RS (m3)

BY

296°

DI

GALACTIC

V801 (v)

DE (1)

297°

V810 (s)   V346 (e1)

Ru 97

Stock 14

DF (1)

(i)

V916 (v)

IC 2948
Running Chicken
Nebula

Gum 39

BB (c1)

UZ (c1)

λ

IC 2872

BK (c1)

Ru 94

4052

θ²

V772 (i)

V808 (v)

θ¹

CENTAURUS

V871

Mel 105

−57°

−58°

−59°

−60°

−61°

−62°

−63°

12ʰ 00ᵐ   11ʰ 50ᵐ   11ʰ 40ᵐ   11ʰ 30ᵐ   11ʰ 20ᵐ

Bright and Dark Nebulae			
To scale	<10'		

Planetary Nebulae
>100" 100"–30" <30"

Open Star Clusters
To scale

Globular Clusters
To scale   <5'

Galaxies
10' x 5'   6' x 1'   3' x 2'   5' x 5'   4' x 2'   2' x 1'

Plotted to scale if the major axis >2', and circular
when face on or the position angle is uncertain

Quasars

Galaxy Clusters

990

1003

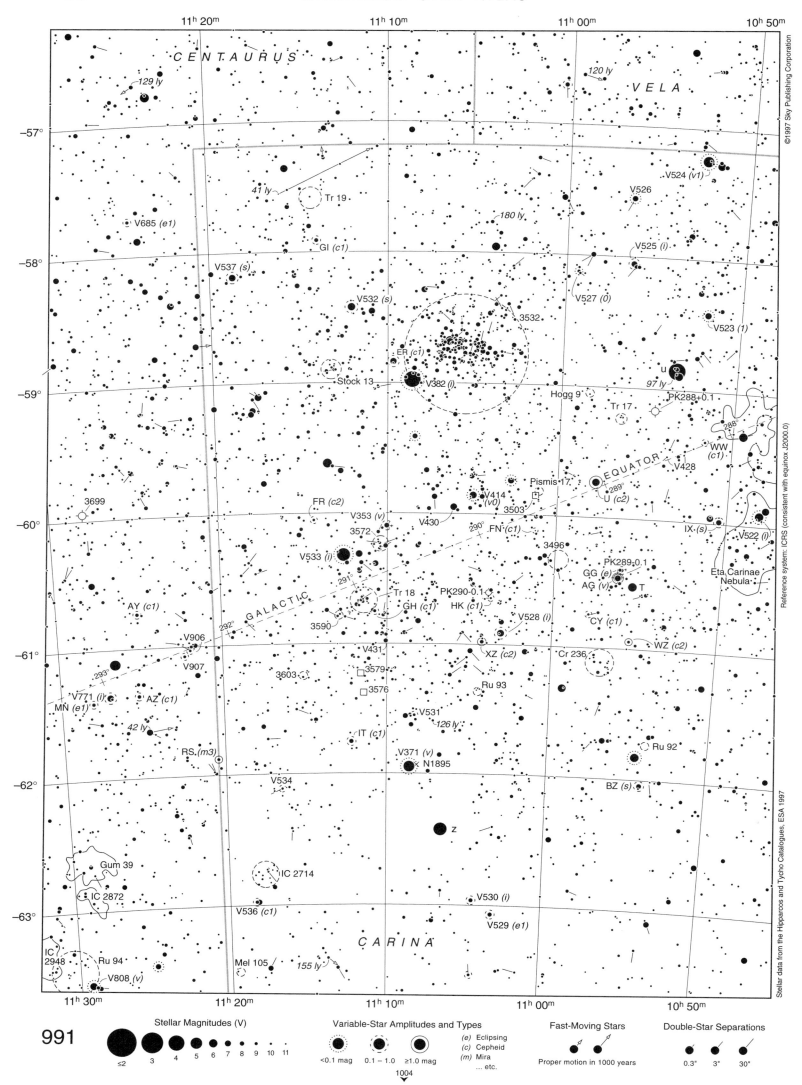

© 1997 Sky Publishing Corporation

Reference system: ICRS (consistent with equinox J2000.0)

Stellar data from the Hipparcos and Tycho Catalogues, ESA 1997

991

Stellar Magnitudes (V)

≤2 3 4 5 6 7 8 9 10 11

Variable-Star Amplitudes and Types

<0.1 mag   0.1 – 1.0   ≥1.0 mag

(e) Eclipsing
(c) Cepheid
(m) Mira
... etc.

1004

Fast-Moving Stars

Proper motion in 1000 years

Double-Star Separations

0.3"   3"   30"

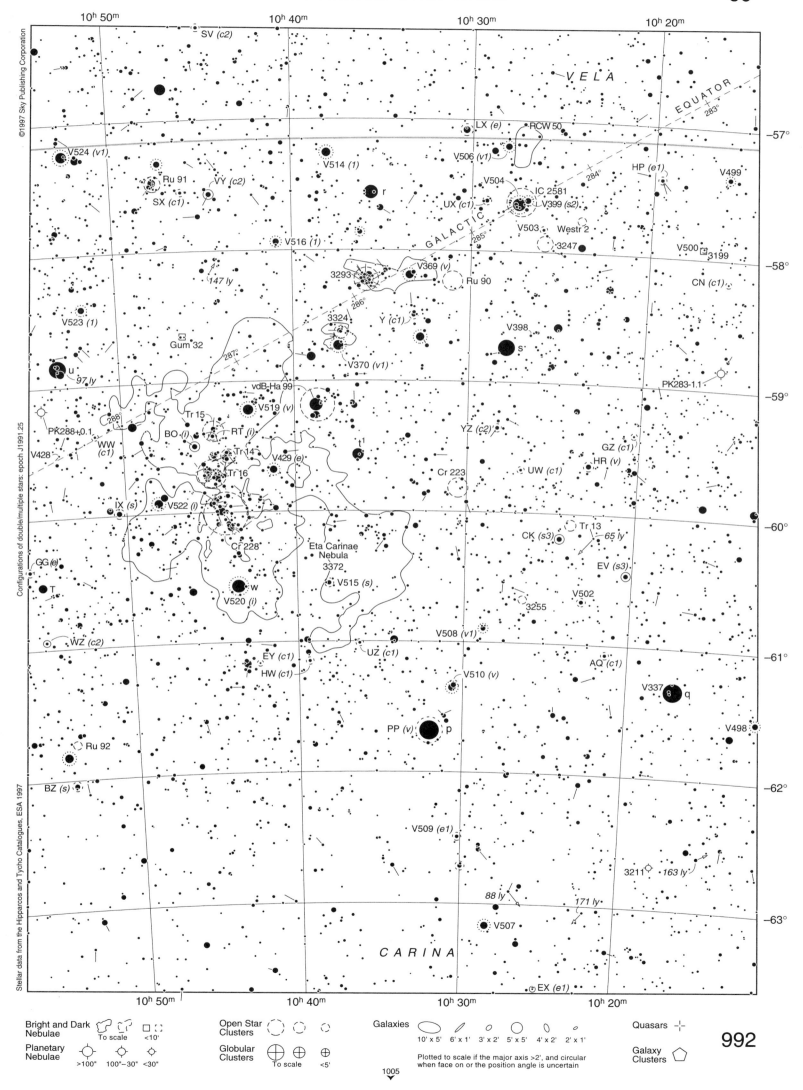

10ʰ 50ᵐ 10ʰ 40ᵐ 10ʰ 30ᵐ 10ʰ 20ᵐ

SV (c2)

VELA

EQUATOR
283°

−57°
LX (e) RCW 50
V506 (v1)
V504
IC 2581
HP (e1)
V499
V524 (v1)
Ru 91 VY (c2)
SX (c1) V514 (1)
r UX (c1) V399 (s2)
284°
V503 Westr 2
V516 (1) 285° 3247 V500 3199
CN (c1)
147 ly V369 (v)
3293 Ru 90 −58°
V523 (1) 286°
3324 Y (c1)
Gum 32 V398
287° V370 (v1) s
u PK283-1.1
97 ly vdB-Ha 99
288° V519 (v) −59°
Tr 15
PK288+0.1 BO (i) RT (i)
WW (c1) Tr 14 YZ (c2)
V428 V429 (e) t¹ GZ (c1)
Tr 16 HR (v)
Cr 223 UW (c1)
IX (s) V522 (i) Tr 13 −60°
Cr 228 CK (s3) 65 ly
Eta Carinae EV (s3)
GG (e) Nebula V502
T 3372 V515 (s) 3255
w
V520 (i)
WZ (c2) V508 (v1)
EY (c1) UZ (c1) AQ (c1) −61°
HW (c1) V510 (v)
V337 q
PP (v) p V498
Ru 92
V509 (e1)
BZ (s) −62°
3211 163 ly
88 ly 171 ly
−63°
V507
CARINA
EX (e1)

10ʰ 50ᵐ 10ʰ 40ᵐ 10ʰ 30ᵐ 10ʰ 20ᵐ

| Bright and Dark Nebulae | Open Star Clusters | Galaxies | Quasars |
| To scale <10' | To scale <5' | 10' x 5' 6' x 1' 3' x 2' 5' x 5' 4' x 2' 2' x 1' | |

Planetary Nebulae
>100" 100"−30" <30"

Globular Clusters
To scale <5'

Plotted to scale if the major axis >2', and circular when face on or the position angle is uncertain

Galaxy Clusters

992

1005

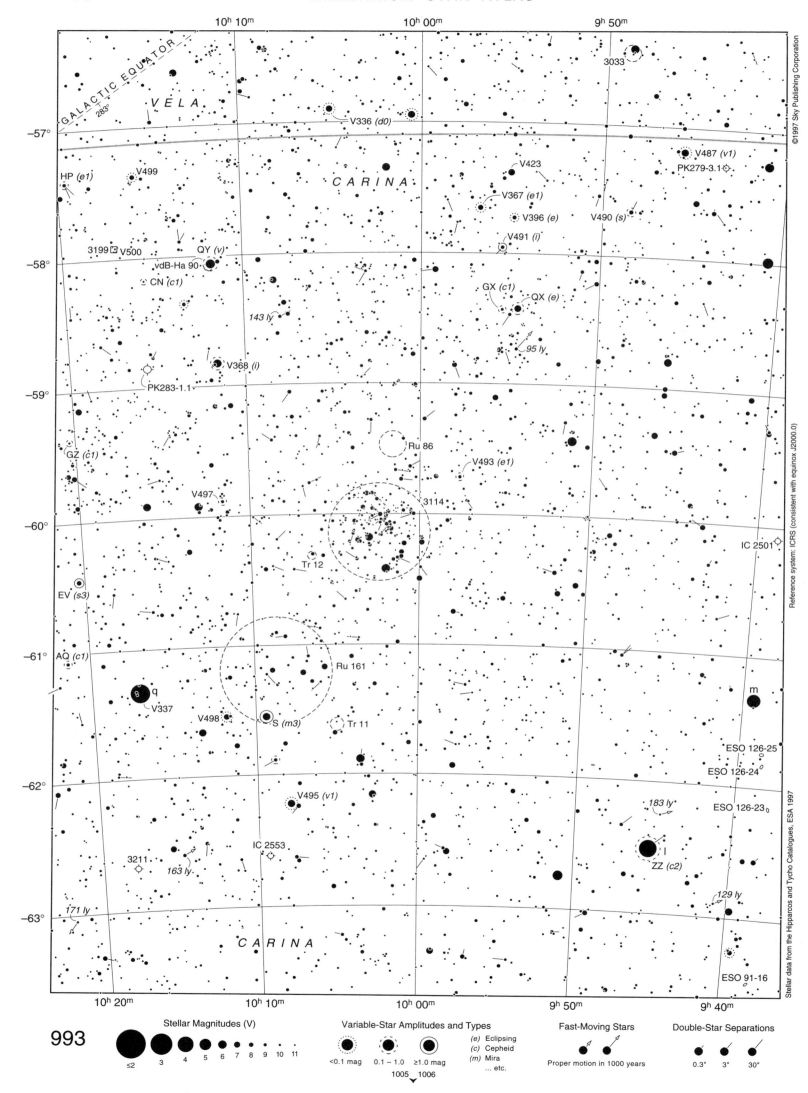

993

Stellar Magnitudes (V)

≤2　3　4　5　6　7　8　9　10　11

Variable-Star Amplitudes and Types

<0.1 mag　0.1 − 1.0　≥1.0 mag

1005ᐁ1006

(e) Eclipsing
(c) Cepheid
(m) Mira
... etc.

Fast-Moving Stars

Proper motion in 1000 years

Double-Star Separations

0.3"　3"　30"

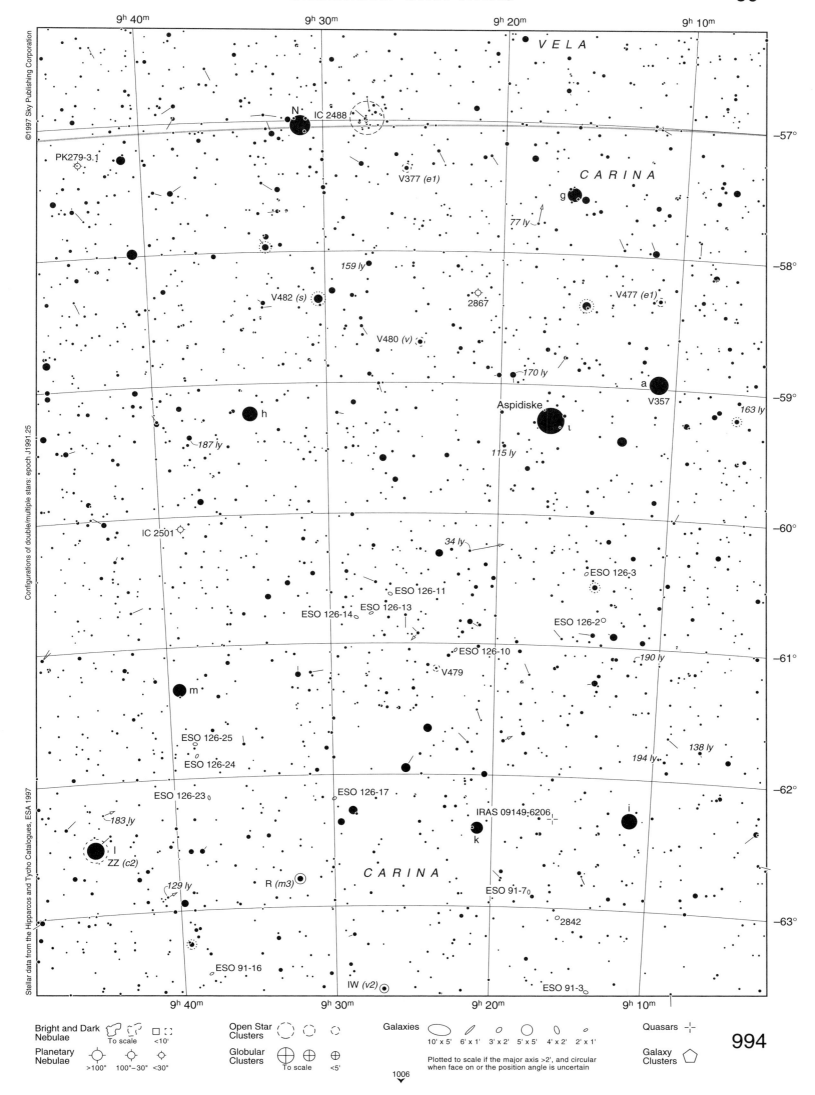

VELA

CARINA

CARINA

PK279-3.1

IC 2488

N

V377 (e1)

g

77 ly

159 ly

V482 (s)

2867

V477 (e1)

V480 (v)

170 ly

a

V357

Aspidiske

ι

163 ly

h

187 ly

115 ly

IC 2501

34 ly

ESO 126-3

ESO 126-11

ESO 126-14

ESO 126-13

ESO 126-2

ESO 126-10

190 ly

m

V479

ESO 126-25

138 ly

ESO 126-24

194 ly

ESO 126-23

ESO 126-17

183 ly

IRAS 09149-6206

i

l

k

ZZ (c2)

129 ly

R (m3)

ESO 91-7

ESO 91-16

2842

IW (v2)

ESO 91-3

Bright and Dark
Nebulae
To scale   <10'

Planetary
Nebulae
>100" 100"–30" <30"

Open Star
Clusters

Globular
Clusters
To scale   <5'

Galaxies
10' x 5' 6' x 1' 3' x 2' 5' x 5' 4' x 2' 2' x 1'

Plotted to scale if the major axis >2', and circular
when face on or the position angle is uncertain

Quasars

Galaxy
Clusters

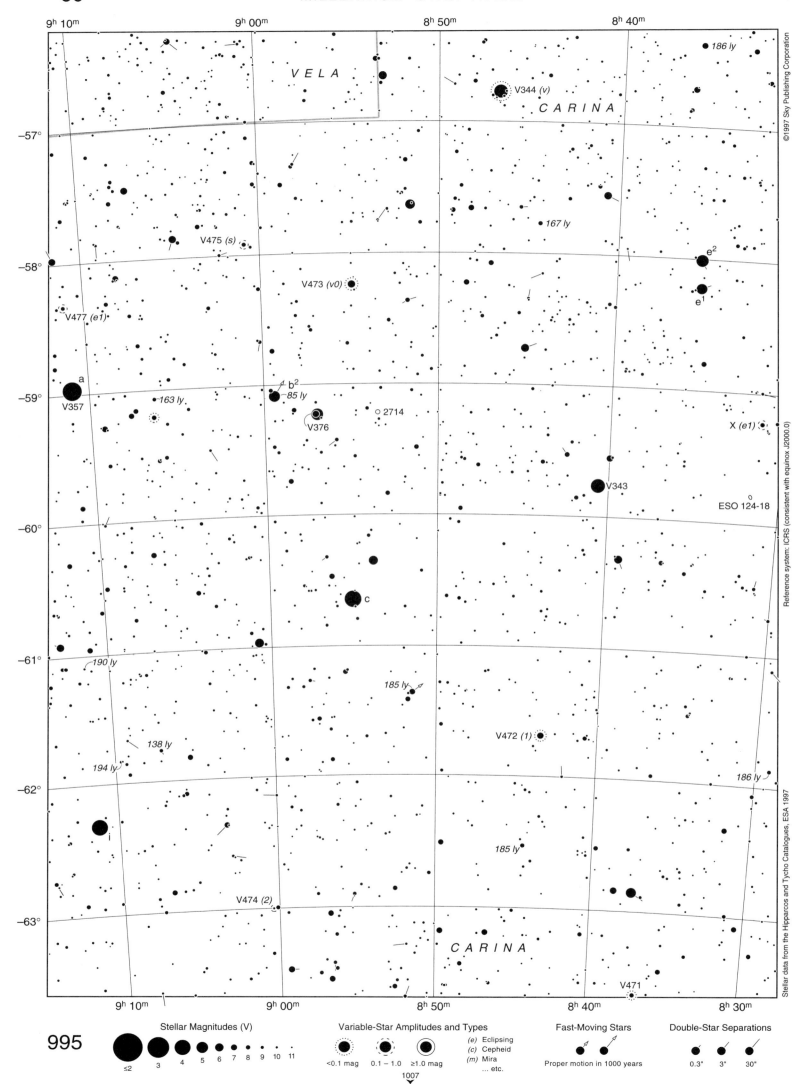

©1997 Sky Publishing Corporation

Reference system: ICRS (consistent with equinox J2000.0)

Stellar data from the Hipparcos and Tycho Catalogues, ESA 1997

995

Stellar Magnitudes (V)

≤2   3   4   5   6   7   8   9   10   11

Variable-Star Amplitudes and Types

<0.1 mag   0.1 − 1.0   ≥1.0 mag

(e) Eclipsing
(c) Cepheid
(m) Mira
... etc.

Fast-Moving Stars

Proper motion in 1000 years

Double-Star Separations

0.3"   3"   30"

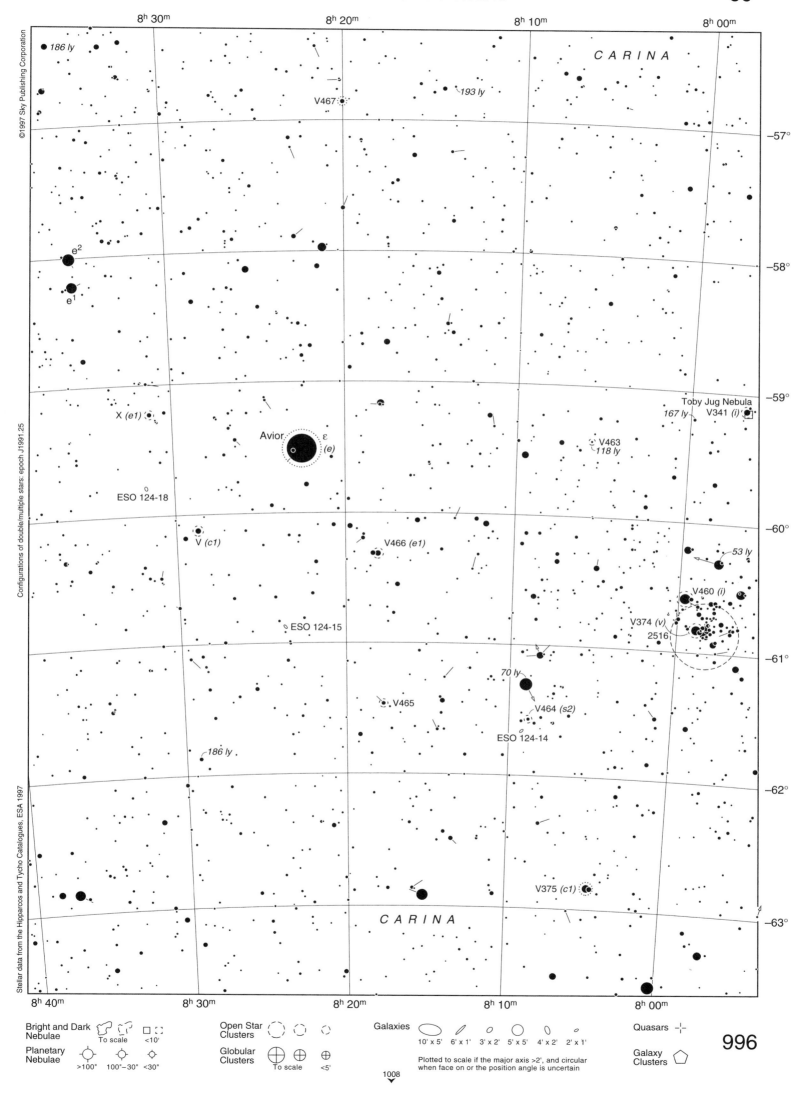

8ʰ 30ᵐ

8ʰ 20ᵐ

8ʰ 10ᵐ

8ʰ 00ᵐ

C A R I N A

186 ly

193 ly

V467

−57°

e²

e¹

−58°

Toby Jug Nebula

V341 (i)

167 ly

−59°

X (e1)

Avior   ε
         (e)

V463
118 ly

ESO 124-18

−60°

V (c1)

V466 (e1)

53 ly

V460 (i)

V374 (v)
2516

ESO 124-15

−61°

70 ly

V465

V464 (s2)

ESO 124-14

186 ly

−62°

V375 (c1)

C A R I N A

−63°

8ʰ 40ᵐ

8ʰ 30ᵐ

8ʰ 20ᵐ

8ʰ 10ᵐ

8ʰ 00ᵐ

Bright and Dark Nebulae					
To scale		<10'			

Open Star Clusters

ε

Galaxies

10' x 5'   6' x 1'   3' x 2'   5' x 5'   4' x 2'   2' x 1'

Quasars

Planetary Nebulae

>100"   100"–30"   <30"

Globular Clusters

To scale   <5'

Plotted to scale if the major axis >2', and circular when face on or the position angle is uncertain

Galaxy Clusters

996

1008

MILLENNIUM STAR ATLAS

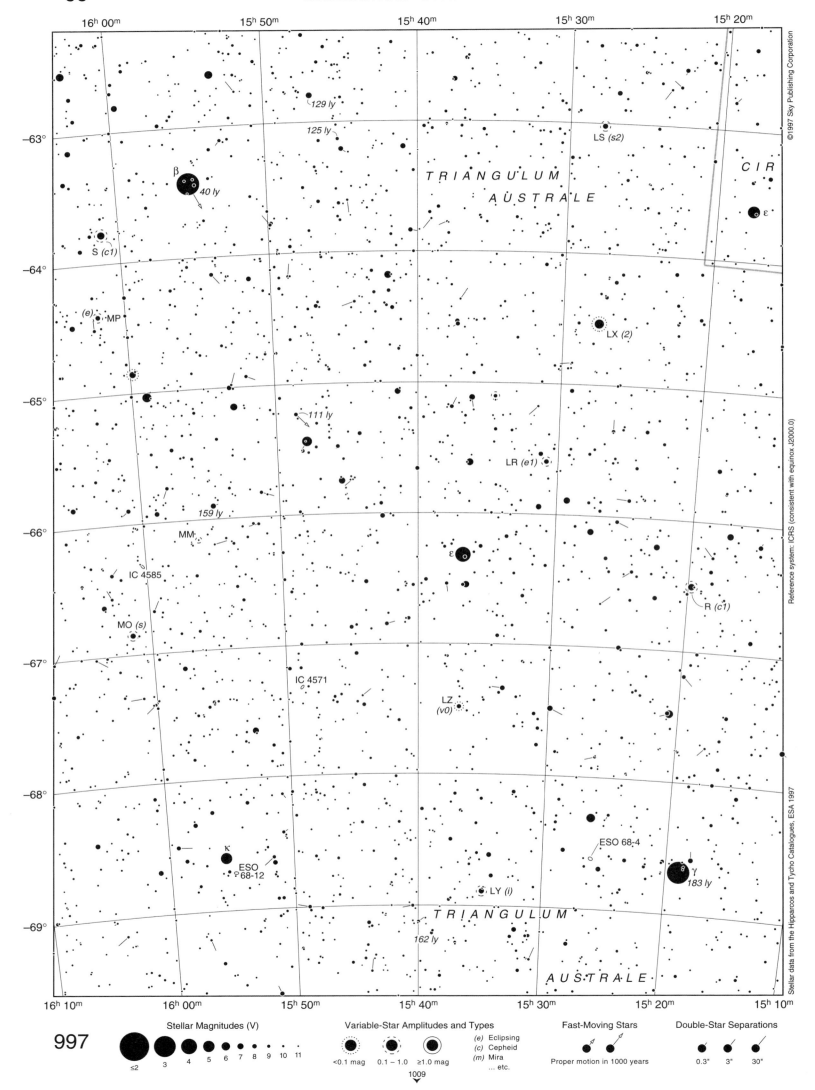

Reference system: ICRS (consistent with equinox J2000.0)

Stellar data from the Hipparcos and Tycho Catalogues, ESA 1997

997

Stellar Magnitudes (V)

≤2   3   4   5   6   7   8   9   10   11

Variable-Star Amplitudes and Types

<0.1 mag   0.1 − 1.0 mag   ≥1.0 mag

(e) Eclipsing
(c) Cepheid
(m) Mira
... etc.

Fast-Moving Stars

Proper motion in 1000 years

Double-Star Separations

0.3"   3"   30"

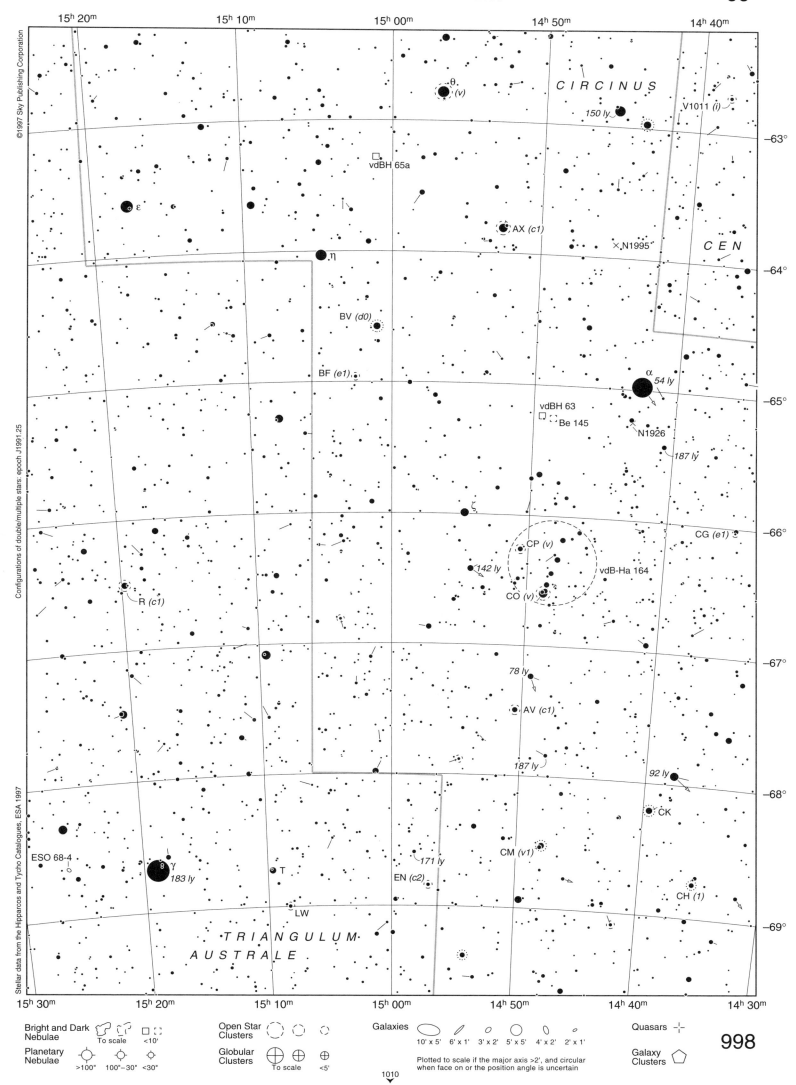

15ʰ 20ᵐ 15ʰ 10ᵐ 15ʰ 00ᵐ 14ʰ 50ᵐ 14ʰ 40ᵐ

−63°
−64°
−65°
−66°
−67°
−68°
−69°

C I R C I N U S

θ *(v)*

150 ly

V1011 *(i)*

vdBH 65a

AX *(c1)*

×N1995

C E N

η

BV *(d0)*

BF *(e1)*

α

54 ly

vdBH 63

Be 145

N1926

187 ly

ζ

CG *(e1)*

CP *(v)*

142 ly

vdB-Ha 164

CO *(v)*

R *(c1)*

78 ly

AV *(c1)*

187 ly

92 ly

CK

92 ly

CM *(v1)*

CH *(1)*

ESO 68-4

γ

183 ly

T

171 ly

EN *(c2)*

LW

T R I A N G U L U M

A U S T R A L E

15ʰ 30ᵐ 15ʰ 20ᵐ 15ʰ 10ᵐ 15ʰ 00ᵐ 14ʰ 50ᵐ 14ʰ 40ᵐ 14ʰ 30ᵐ

Bright and Dark Nebulae   To scale   <10'

Planetary Nebulae   >100"   100"−30"   <30"

Open Star Clusters

Globular Clusters   To scale   <5'

Galaxies   10' x 5'   6' x 1'   3' x 2'   5' x 5'   4' x 2'   2' x 1'

Plotted to scale if the major axis >2', and circular when face on or the position angle is uncertain

Quasars

Galaxy Clusters

998

1010

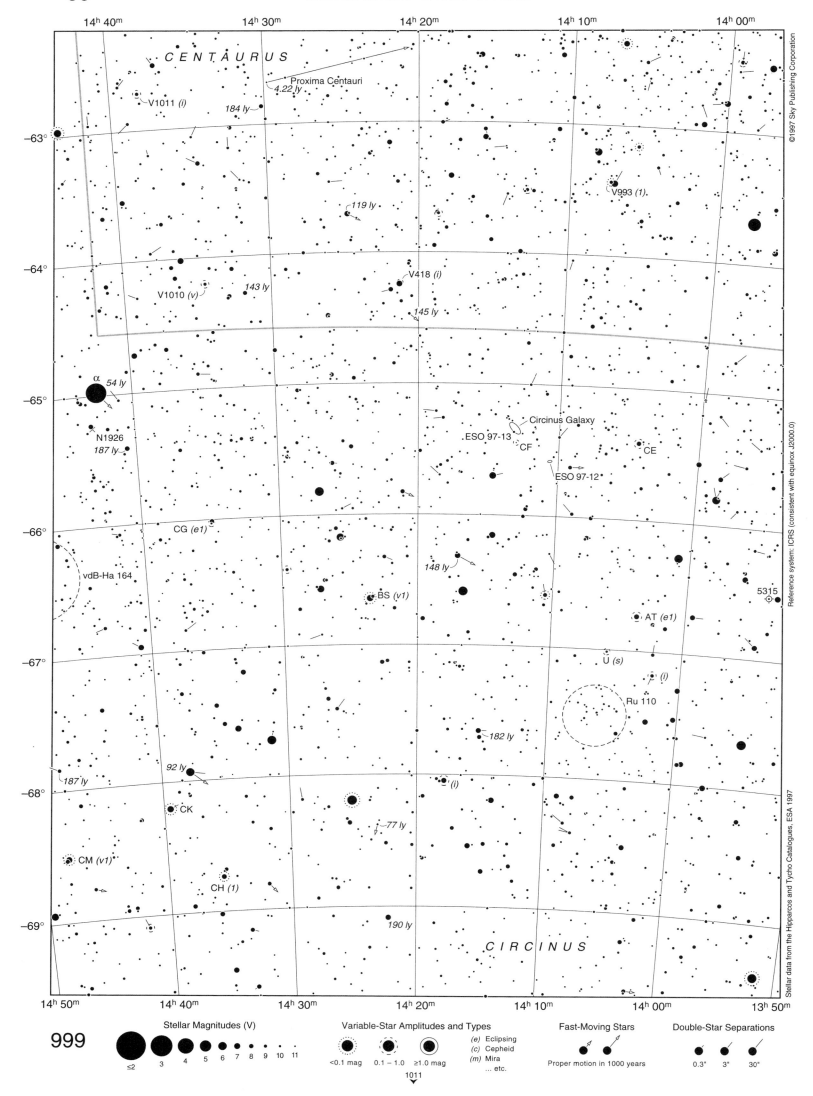

©1997 Sky Publishing Corporation

Reference system: ICRS (consistent with equinox J2000.0)

Stellar data from the Hipparcos and Tycho Catalogues, ESA 1997

CENTAURUS

Proxima Centauri
4.22 ly

V1011 (i)

184 ly

V993 (1)

119 ly

V418 (i)

V1010 (v)

143 ly

145 ly

α 54 ly

Circinus Galaxy

ESO 97-13

N1926

CF

CE

187 ly

ESO 97-12

CG (e1)

148 ly

vdB-Ha 164

5315

BS (v1)

AT (e1)

U (s)

(i)

Ru 110

182 ly

92 ly

187 ly

(i)

CK

77 ly

CM (v1)

CH (1)

190 ly

CIRCINUS

999

Stellar Magnitudes (V)

≤2   3   4   5   6   7 8 9 10 11

Variable-Star Amplitudes and Types

<0.1 mag   0.1 − 1.0   ≥1.0 mag

(e) Eclipsing
(c) Cepheid
(m) Mira
... etc.

Fast-Moving Stars

Proper motion in 1000 years

Double-Star Separations

0.3"   3"   30"

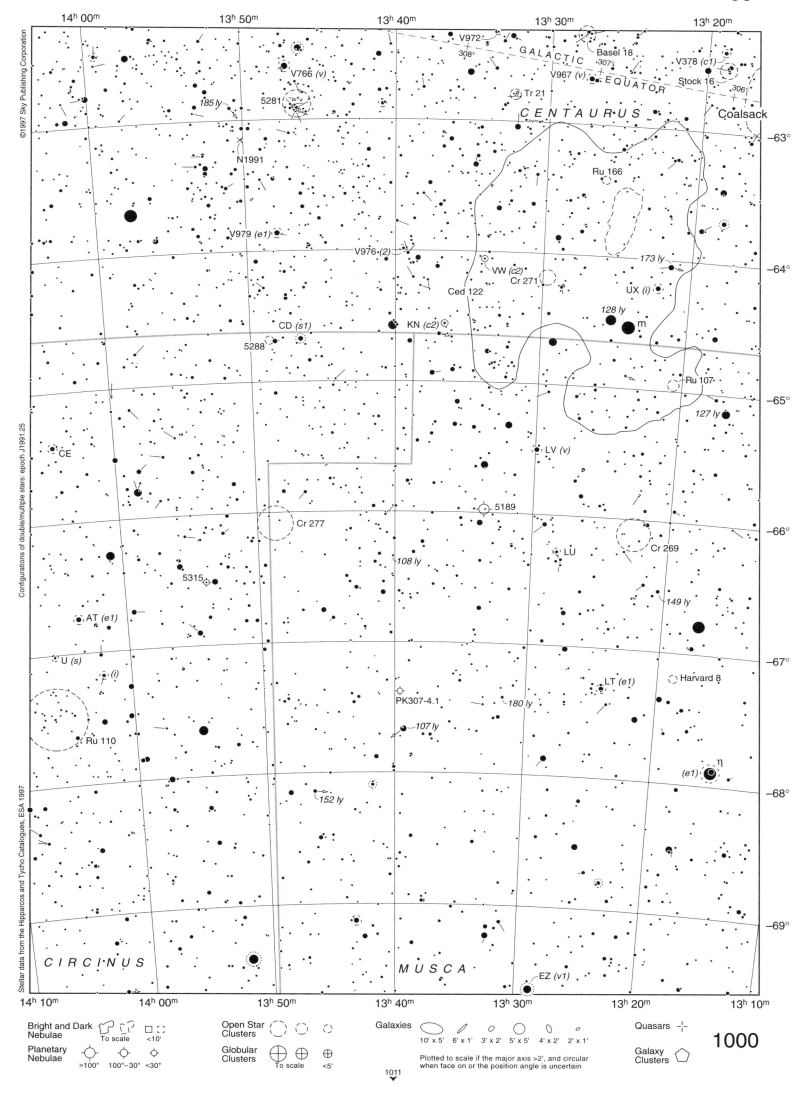

V972
308°
Basel 18
307°
V378 (c1)
V967 (v)
Stock 16
306°
Tr 21
Coalsack

C E N T A U R U S

V766 (v)
5281
185 ly
N1991
Ru 166

−63°

V979 (e1)
V976 (2)
173 ly
VW (c2)
Cr 271
Ced 122
UX (i)

−64°

CD (s1)
5288
KN (c2)
128 ly
m

Ru 107
127 ly

−65°

CE
LV (v)

−66°

Cr 277
5189
LU
Cr 269
108 ly
5315
149 ly

AT (e1)
LT (e1)
Harvard 8

−67°

U (s)
(i)
PK307-4.1
180 ly
Ru 110
107 ly
η
(e1)

−68°

152 ly

−69°

C I R C I N U S   M U S C A
EZ (v1)

Bright and Dark Nebulae
To scale   <10'
Planetary Nebulae
>100"   100"–30"   <30"

Open Star Clusters
Globular Clusters
To scale   <5'

Galaxies
10' x 5'   6' x 1'   3' x 2'   5' x 5'   4' x 2'   2' x 1'

Plotted to scale if the major axis >2', and circular when face on or the position angle is uncertain

Quasars

Galaxy Clusters

1000

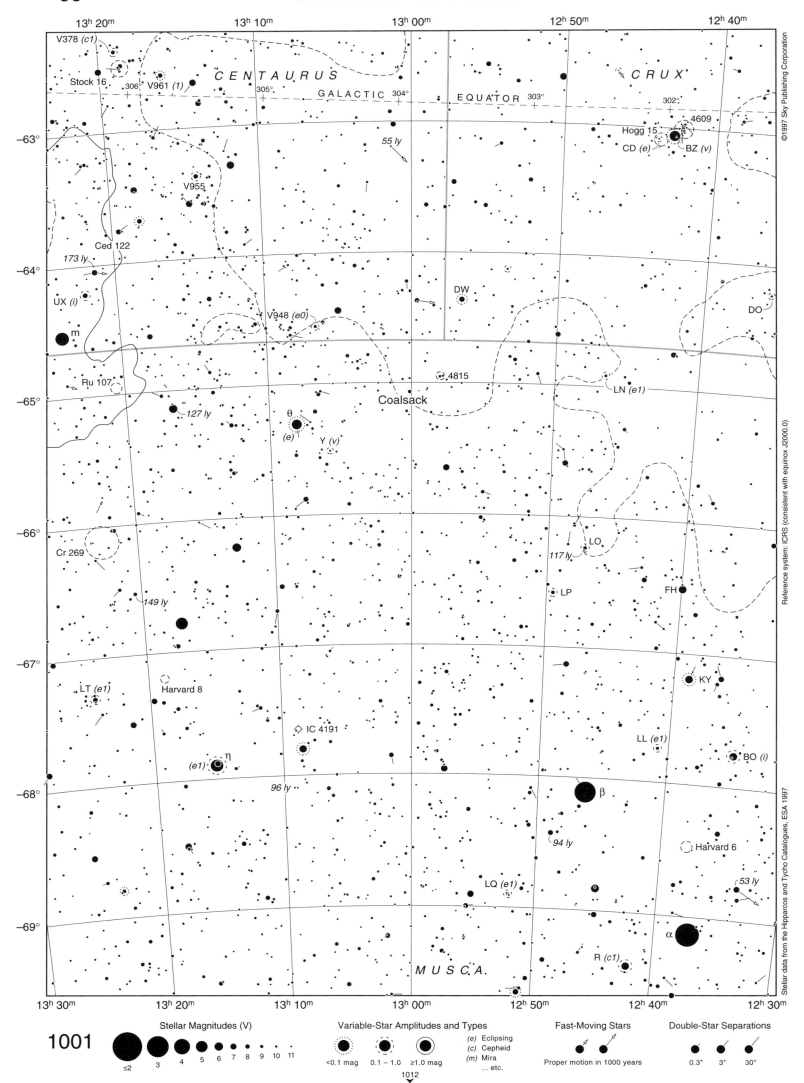

1001

Stellar Magnitudes (V)

≤2 3 4 5 6 7 8 9 10 11

Variable-Star Amplitudes and Types

<0.1 mag   0.1 – 1.0 mag   ≥1.0 mag

(e) Eclipsing
(c) Cepheid
(m) Mira
... etc.

Fast-Moving Stars

Proper motion in 1000 years

Double-Star Separations

0.3"   3"   30"

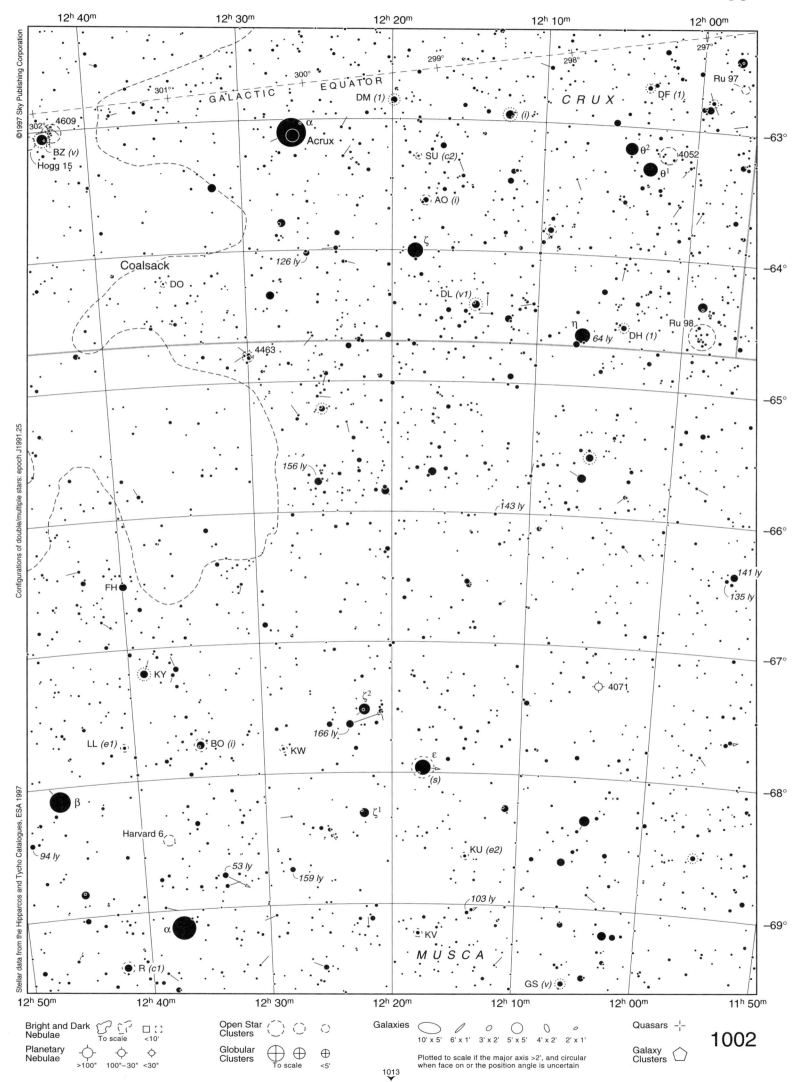

© 1997 Sky Publishing Corporation

Configurations of double/multiple stars: epoch J1991.25

Stellar data from the Hipparcos and Tycho Catalogues, ESA 1997

12ʰ 40ᵐ

12ʰ 30ᵐ

12ʰ 20ᵐ

12ʰ 10ᵐ

12ʰ 00ᵐ

GALACTIC EQUATOR

301°

300°

299°

298°

297°

302°

4609

BZ (v)

Hogg 15

Coalsack

DO

4463

DM (1)

α

Acrux

SU (c2)

AO (i)

ζ

126 ly

DL (v1)

η

64 ly

(i)

CRUX

DF (1)

Ru 97

θ²

4052

θ¹

DH (1)

Ru 98

−63°

−64°

−65°

156 ly

143 ly

141 ly

135 ly

FH

KY

LL (e1)

BO (i)

KW

ζ²

166 ly

ε

(s)

4071

−66°

−67°

−68°

β

Harvard 6

94 ly

53 ly

159 ly

α

R (c1)

ζ¹

KU (e2)

103 ly

KV

MUSCA

GS (v)

−69°

12ʰ 50ᵐ

12ʰ 40ᵐ

12ʰ 30ᵐ

12ʰ 20ᵐ

12ʰ 10ᵐ

12ʰ 00ᵐ

11ʰ 50ᵐ

Bright and Dark
Nebulae

To scale   <10'

Planetary
Nebulae

>100" 100"–30" <30"

Open Star
Clusters

Globular
Clusters

To scale   <5'

Galaxies

10' x 5' 6' x 1' 3' x 2' 5' x 5' 4' x 2' 2' x 1'

Plotted to scale if the major axis >2', and circular
when face on or the position angle is uncertain

Quasars

Galaxy
Clusters

1002

1013

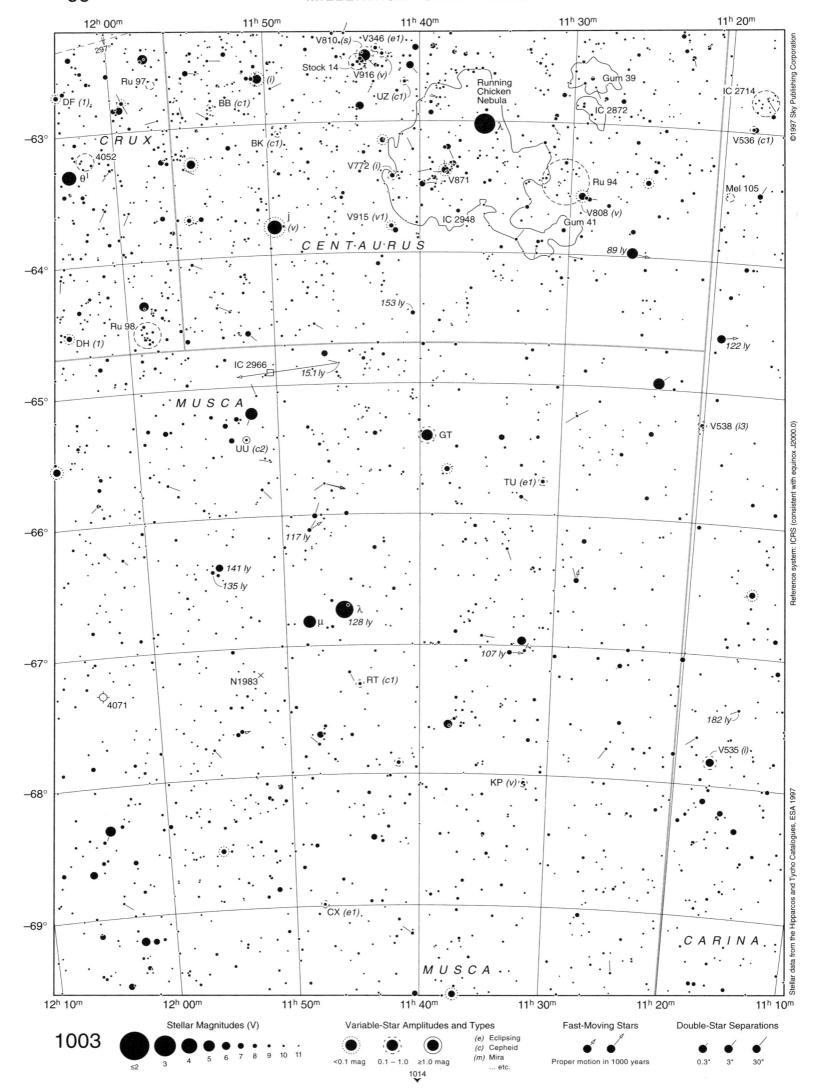

©1997 Sky Publishing Corporation

Reference system: ICRS (consistent with equinox J2000.0)

Stellar data from the Hipparcos and Tycho Catalogues, ESA 1997

1003

Stellar Magnitudes (V)

≤2   3   4   5   6   7   8   9 10 11

Variable-Star Amplitudes and Types

<0.1 mag   0.1 – 1.0   ≥1.0 mag

(e) Eclipsing
(c) Cepheid
(m) Mira
... etc.

1014

Fast-Moving Stars

Proper motion in 1000 years

Double-Star Separations

0.3"   3"   30"

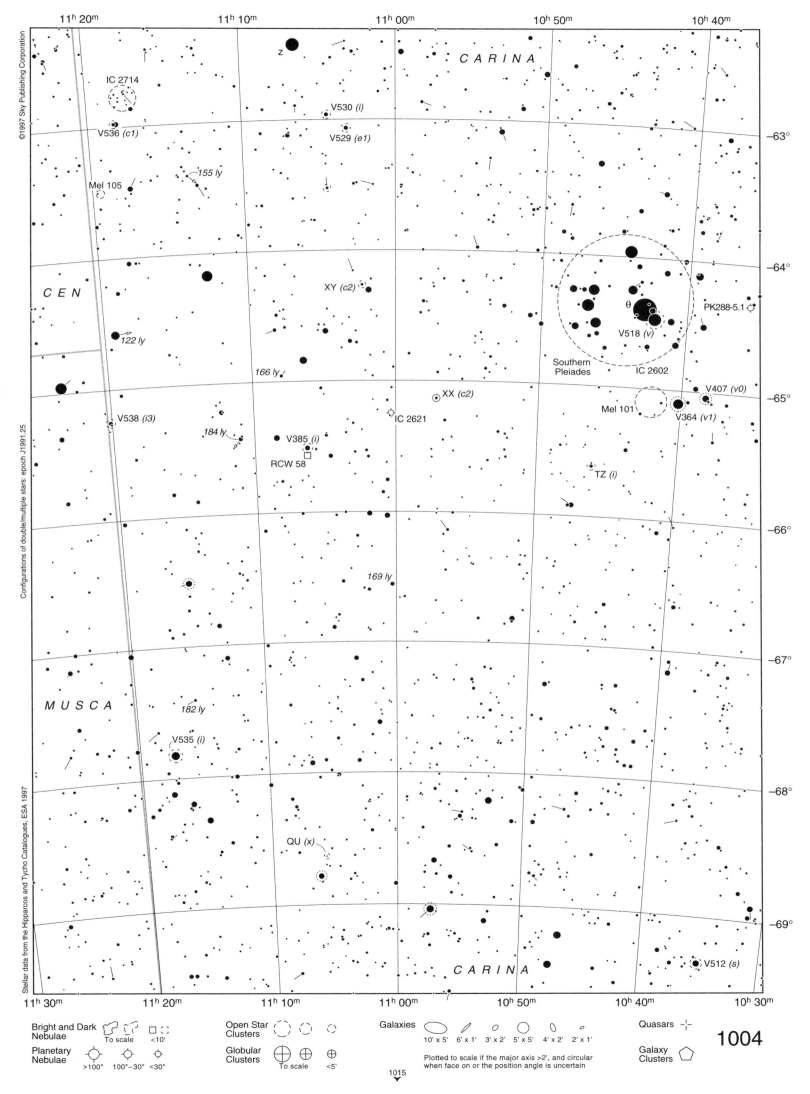

CARINA

IC 2714

V530 (i)

V536 (c1)

V529 (e1)

155 ly

Mel 105

CEN

XY (c2)

θ

PK288-5.1

V518 (v)

Southern
Pleiades

IC 2602

122 ly

166 ly

XX (c2)

V407 (v0)

Mel 101

V538 (i3)

IC 2621

V364 (v1)

184 ly

V385 (i)

RCW 58

TZ (i)

169 ly

MUSCA

182 ly

V535 (i)

QU (x)

CARINA

V512 (s)

−63°

−64°

−65°

−66°

−67°

−68°

−69°

11h 20m   11h 10m   11h 00m   10h 50m   10h 40m

11h 30m   11h 20m   11h 10m   11h 00m   10h 50m   10h 40m   10h 30m

z

Bright and Dark
Nebulae   To scale   <10'

Planetary
Nebulae   >100" 100"−30" <30"

Open Star
Clusters

Globular
Clusters   To scale   <5'

Galaxies
10' x 5' 6' x 1' 3' x 2' 5' x 5' 4' x 2' 2' x 1'

Plotted to scale if the major axis >2', and circular
when face on or the position angle is uncertain

Quasars

Galaxy
Clusters

1004

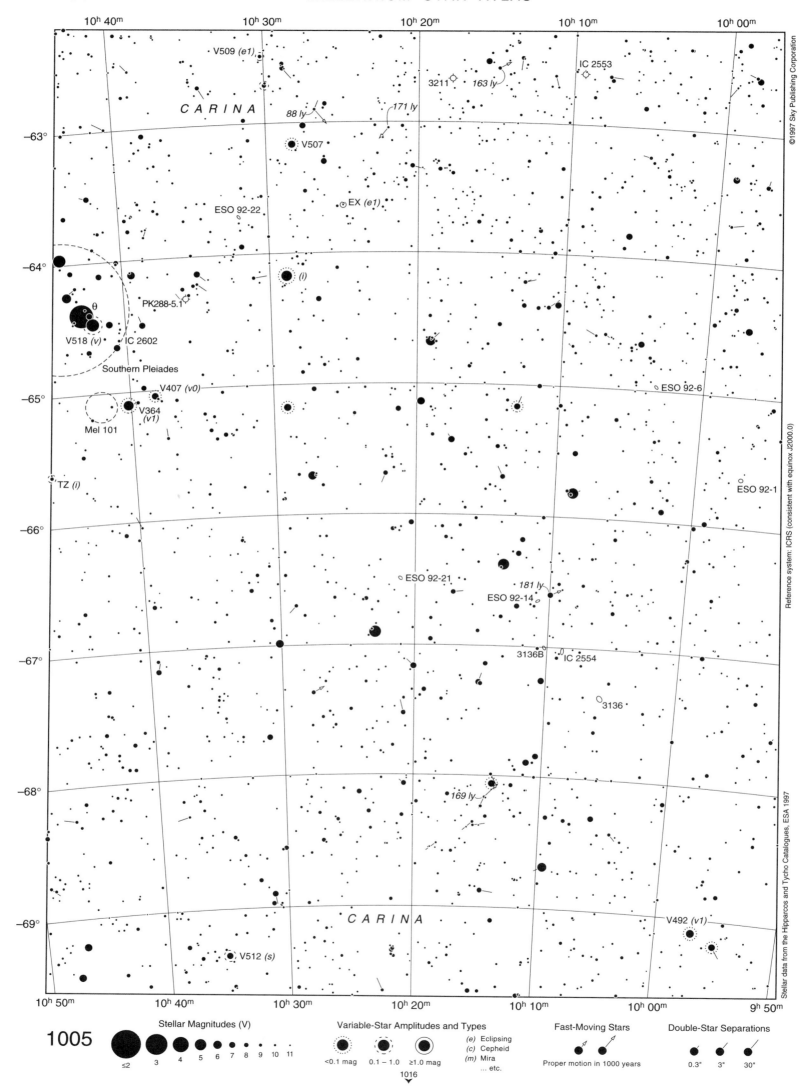

©1997 Sky Publishing Corporation

Reference system: ICRS (consistent with equinox J2000.0)

Stellar data from the Hipparcos and Tycho Catalogues, ESA 1997

1005

Stellar Magnitudes (V)

≤2   3   4   5   6   7 8 9 10 11

Variable-Star Amplitudes and Types

<0.1 mag   0.1 − 1.0   ≥1.0 mag

(e) Eclipsing
(c) Cepheid
(m) Mira
... etc.

1016

Fast-Moving Stars

Proper motion in 1000 years

Double-Star Separations

0.3″   3″   30″

MILLENNIUM STAR ATLAS

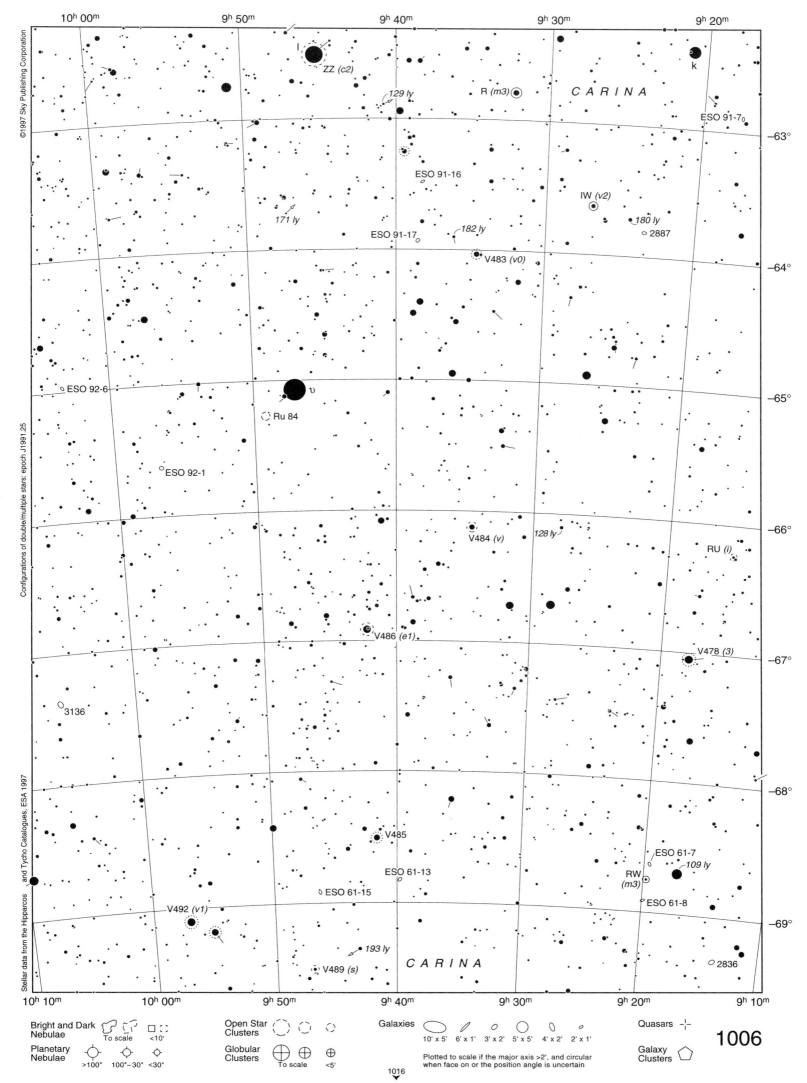

Configurations of double/multiple stars: epoch J1991.25

Stellar data from the Hipparcos and Tycho Catalogues, ESA 1997

CARINA

ZZ (c2)

129 ly

R (m3)

ESO 91-7

IW (v2)

180 ly

2887

ESO 91-16

171 ly

182 ly

ESO 91-17

V483 (v0)

ESO 92-6

υ

V484 (v)

128 ly

RU (i)

Ru 84

ESO 92-1

V486 (e1)

V478 (3)

3136

V485

ESO 61-7

109 ly

ESO 61-13

RW (m3)

ESO 61-15

ESO 61-8

V492 (v1)

193 ly

CARINA

2836

V489 (s)

k

Bright and Dark Nebulae
To scale   <10'

Open Star Clusters

Galaxies
10' x 5'   6' x 1'   3' x 2'   5' x 5'   4' x 2'   2' x 1'

Quasars

Planetary Nebulae
>100"   100"−30"   <30"

Globular Clusters
To scale   <5'

Plotted to scale if the major axis >2', and circular when face on or the position angle is uncertain

Galaxy Clusters

1006

1016

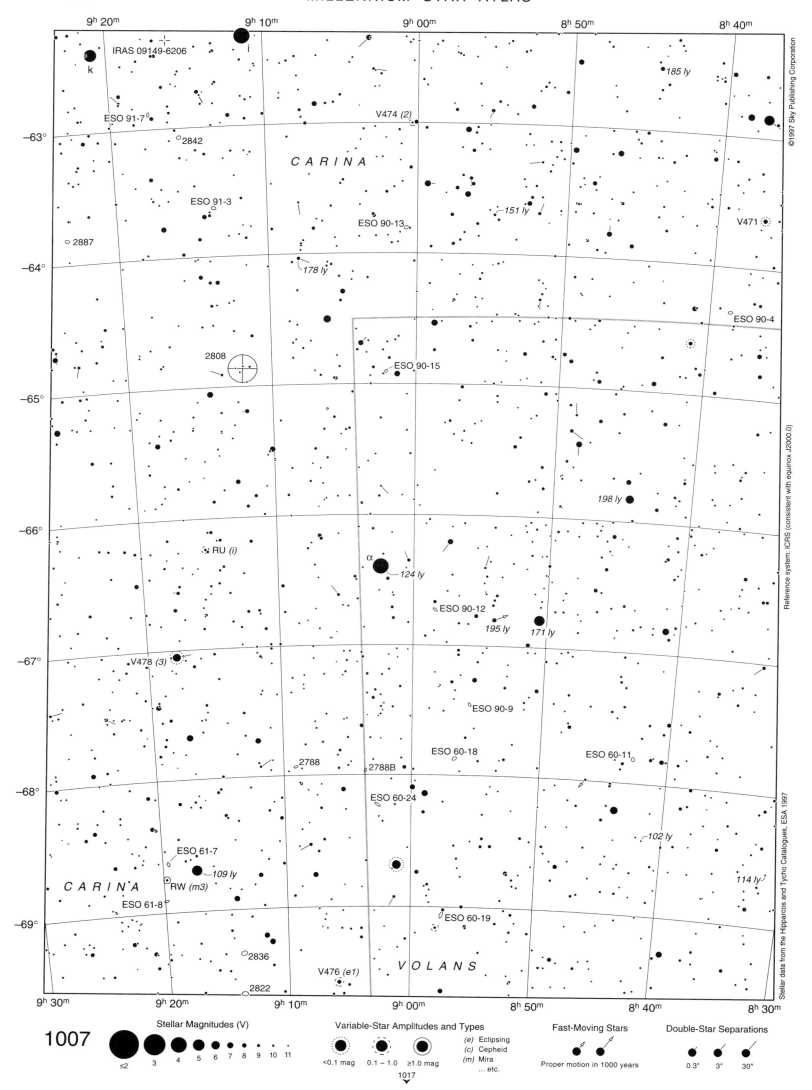

©1997 Sky Publishing Corporation

Reference system: ICRS (consistent with equinox J2000.0)

Stellar data from the Hipparcos and Tycho Catalogues, ESA 1997

Map labels (within chart):

IRAS 09149-6206
k
i
ESO 91-7
2842
CARINA
ESO 91-3
ESO 90-13
V474 (2)
185 ly
151 ly
V471
2887
178 ly
ESO 90-4
2808
ESO 90-15
RU (i)
198 ly
α
124 ly
ESO 90-12
195 ly
171 ly
V478 (3)
ESO 90-9
ESO 60-18
ESO 60-11
2788
2788B
ESO 60-24
102 ly
ESO 61-7
109 ly
RW (m3)
ESO 61-8
114 ly
CARINA
ESO 60-19
2836
VOLANS
V476 (e1)
2822

Stellar Magnitudes (V)

≤2 3 4 5 6 7 8 9 10 11

Variable-Star Amplitudes and Types

<0.1 mag   0.1 – 1.0   ≥1.0 mag

(e) Eclipsing
(c) Cepheid
(m) Mira
... etc.

1017

Fast-Moving Stars

Proper motion in 1000 years

Double-Star Separations

0.3"   3"   30"

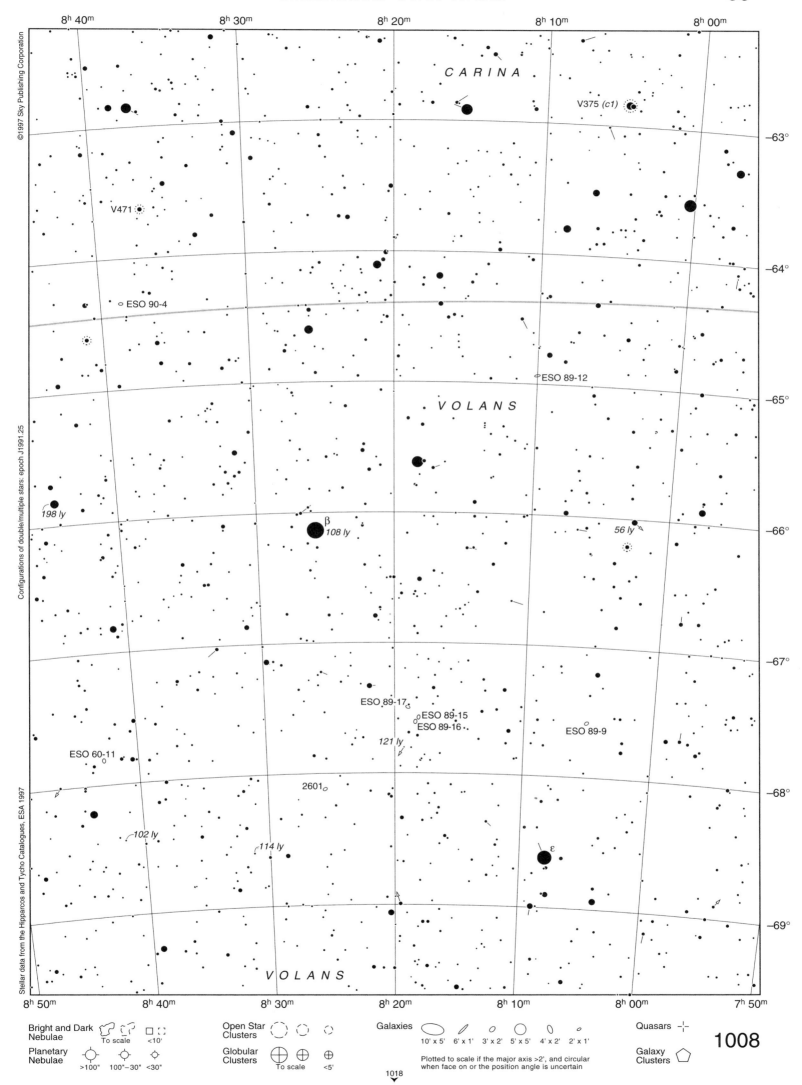

© 1997 Sky Publishing Corporation

Configurations of double/multiple stars: epoch J1991.25

Stellar data from the Hipparcos and Tycho Catalogues, ESA 1997

CARINA

V375 (c1)

V471

ESO 90-4

ESO 89-12

VOLANS

198 ly

β
108 ly

56 ly

ESO 89-17

ESO 89-15
ESO 89-16

ESO 89-9

ESO 60-11

121 ly

2601

102 ly

114 ly

ε

VOLANS

Bright and Dark Nebulae		Open Star Clusters	Galaxies	Quasars

Bright and Dark Nebulae
To scale   <10'

Open Star Clusters

Globular Clusters
To scale   <5'

Galaxies
10' x 5'   6' x 1'   3' x 2'   5' x 5'   4' x 2'   2' x 1'

Planetary Nebulae
>100"   100"–30"   <30"

Quasars

Galaxy Clusters

Plotted to scale if the major axis >2', and circular when face on or the position angle is uncertain

1008

1018

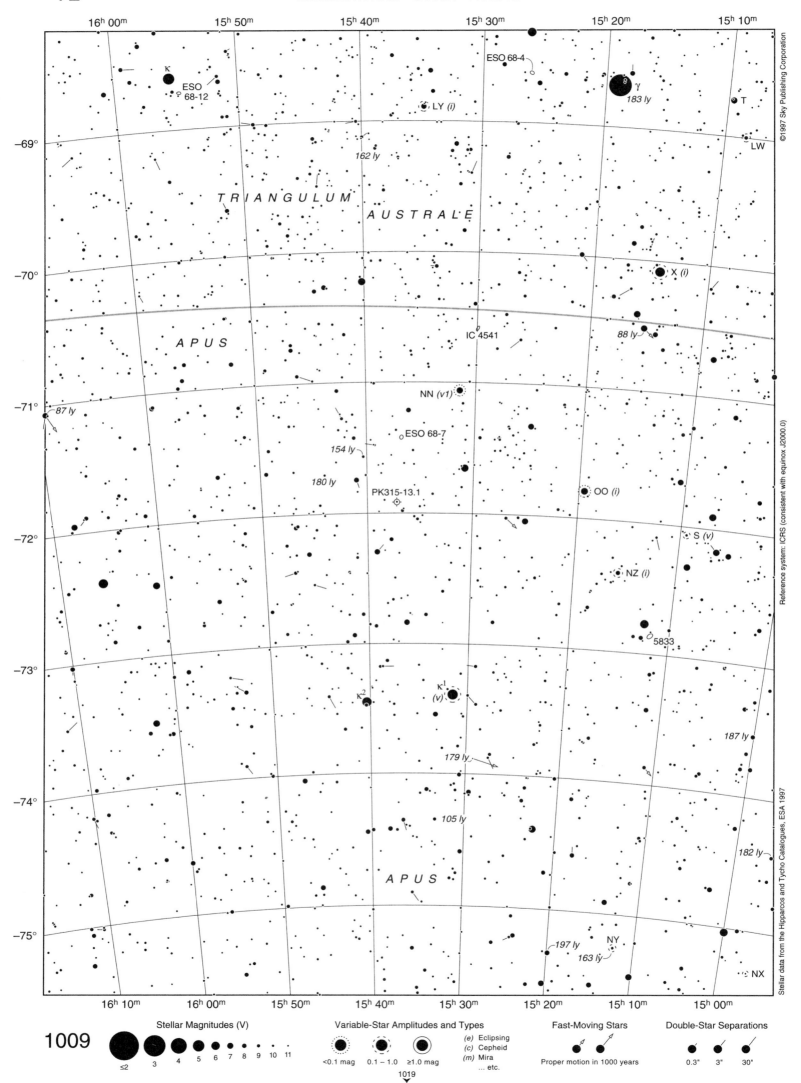

TRIANGULUM

AUSTRALE

APUS

APUS

κ

ESO 68-12

ESO 68-4

LY (i)

162 ly

γ
183 ly

δ

T

LW

X (i)

IC 4541

88 ly

NN (v1)

ESO 68-7

154 ly

180 ly

PK315-13.1

OO (i)

S (v)

NZ (i)

5833

187 ly

κ²

κ¹
(v)

179 ly

105 ly

182 ly

197 ly

NY

163 ly

NX

87 ly

1009

Stellar Magnitudes (V)	Variable-Star Amplitudes and Types	Fast-Moving Stars	Double-Star Separations

≤2   3   4   5   6   7   8   9   10   11

<0.1 mag   0.1 – 1.0   ≥1.0 mag

(e) Eclipsing
(c) Cepheid
(m) Mira
... etc.

Proper motion in 1000 years

0.3"   3"   30"

1019

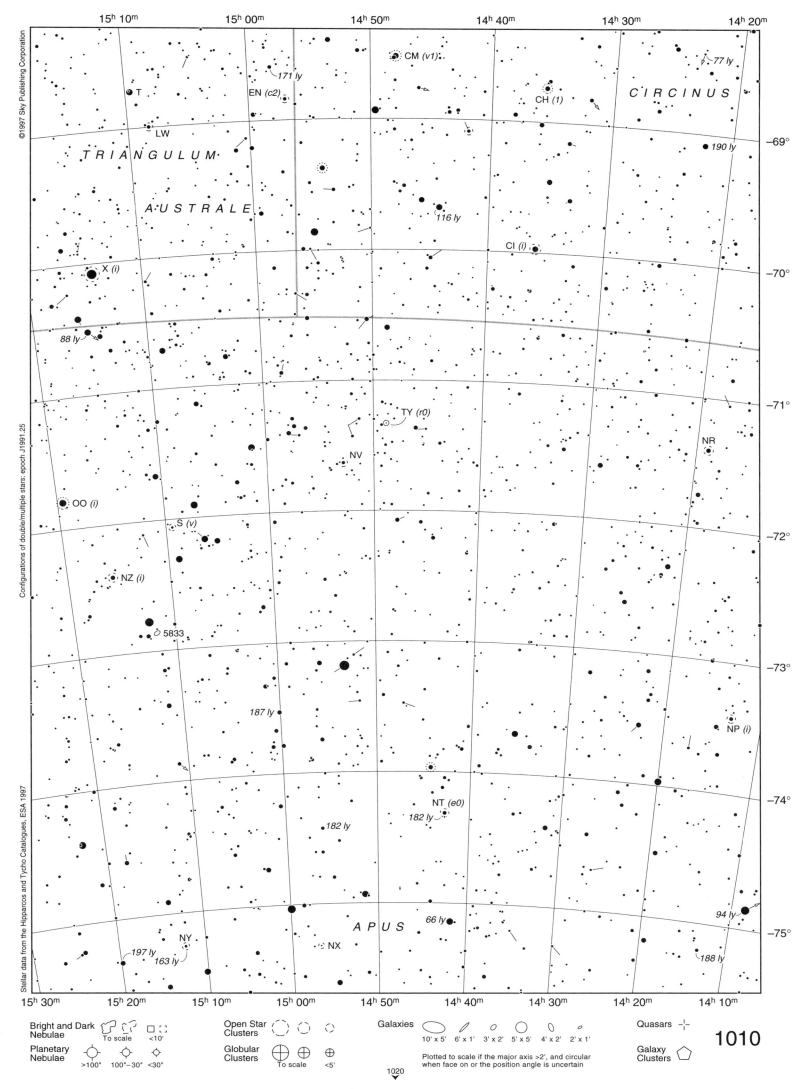

Configurations of double/multiple stars: epoch J1991.25

Stellar data from the Hipparcos and Tycho Catalogues, ESA 1997

CIRCINUS

TRIANGULUM

AUSTRALE

APUS

CM (v1)
CH (1)
171 ly
EN (c2)
T
LW
77 ly
190 ly
116 ly
CI (i)
X (i)
88 ly
TY (r0)
NR
NV
OO (i)
S (v)
NZ (i)
5833
187 ly
NP (i)
NT (e0)
182 ly
182 ly
94 ly
66 ly
NY
NX
197 ly
163 ly
188 ly

Bright and Dark Nebulae			Open Star Clusters			Galaxies							Quasars
	To scale	<10'				10' x 5'	6' x 1'	3' x 2'	5' x 5'	4' x 2'	2' x 1'		
Planetary Nebulae			Globular Clusters										Galaxy Clusters
>100"	100"−30"	<30"	To scale		<5'	Plotted to scale if the major axis >2', and circular when face on or the position angle is uncertain							

−72°

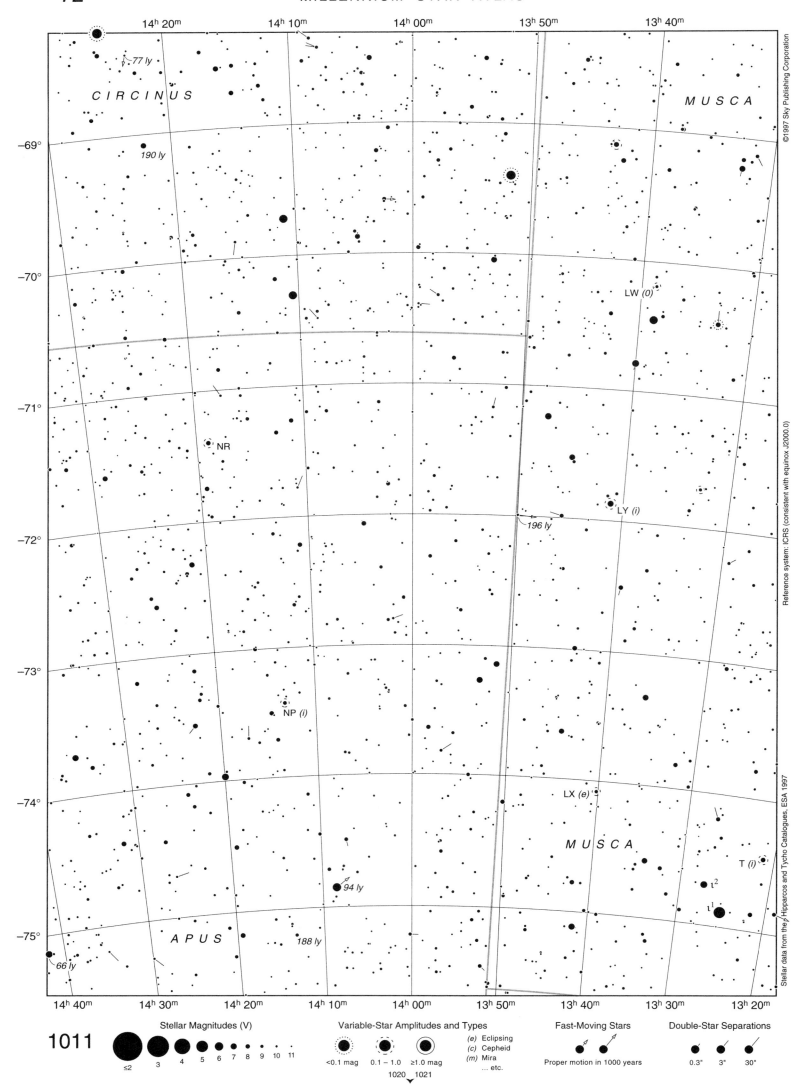

14ʰ 20ᵐ 14ʰ 10ᵐ 14ʰ 00ᵐ 13ʰ 50ᵐ 13ʰ 40ᵐ

CIRCINUS

MUSCA

77 ly

190 ly

−69°

LW (0)

−70°

NR

LY (i)

196 ly

−71°

NP (i)

−72°

−73°

LX (e)

−74°

MUSCA

T (i)

ι²

94 ly

ι¹

APUS

188 ly

−75°

66 ly

14ʰ 40ᵐ 14ʰ 30ᵐ 14ʰ 20ᵐ 14ʰ 10ᵐ 14ʰ 00ᵐ 13ʰ 50ᵐ 13ʰ 40ᵐ 13ʰ 30ᵐ 13ʰ 20ᵐ

Reference system: ICRS (consistent with equinox J2000.0)

Stellar data from the Hipparcos and Tycho Catalogues, ESA 1997

©1997 Sky Publishing Corporation

1011

Stellar Magnitudes (V)

≤2 3 4 5 6 7 8 9 10 11

Variable-Star Amplitudes and Types

<0.1 mag   0.1 – 1.0   ≥1.0 mag

(e) Eclipsing
(c) Cepheid
(m) Mira
... etc.

1020 1021

Fast-Moving Stars

Proper motion in 1000 years

Double-Star Separations

0.3" 3" 30"

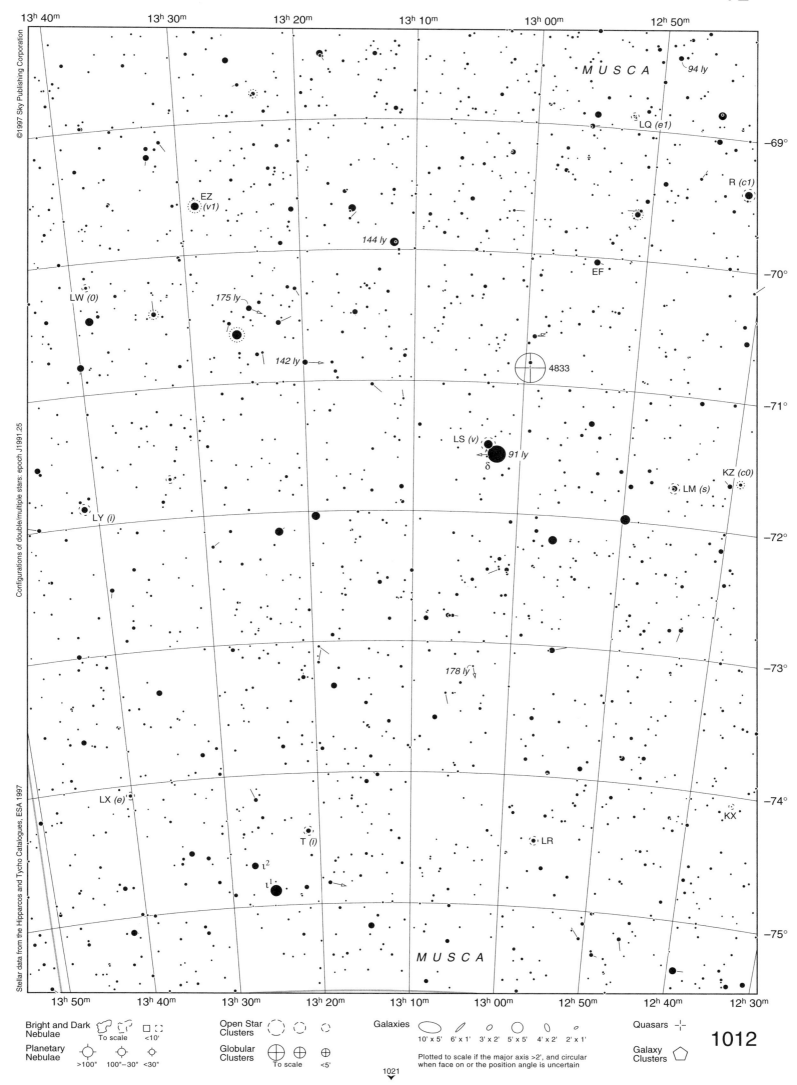

M U S C A

94 ly

LQ (e1)

R (c1)

−69°

EZ (v1)

144 ly

EF

−70°

LW (0)

175 ly

142 ly

4833

−71°

LS (v)

91 ly

δ

KZ (c0)

LM (s)

LY (i)

−72°

−73°

178 ly

LX (e)

−74°

KX

T (i)

LR

ι²

ι¹

−75°

M U S C A

13ʰ 50ᵐ   13ʰ 40ᵐ   13ʰ 30ᵐ   13ʰ 20ᵐ   13ʰ 10ᵐ   13ʰ 00ᵐ   12ʰ 50ᵐ   12ʰ 40ᵐ   12ʰ 30ᵐ

Bright and Dark Nebulae		
To scale	<10'	

Planetary Nebulae
>100" 100"–30" <30"

Open Star Clusters

Globular Clusters
To scale <5'

Galaxies
10' x 5'   6' x 1'   3' x 2'   5' x 5'   4' x 2'   2' x 1'

Plotted to scale if the major axis >2', and circular when face on or the position angle is uncertain

Quasars

Galaxy Clusters

1012

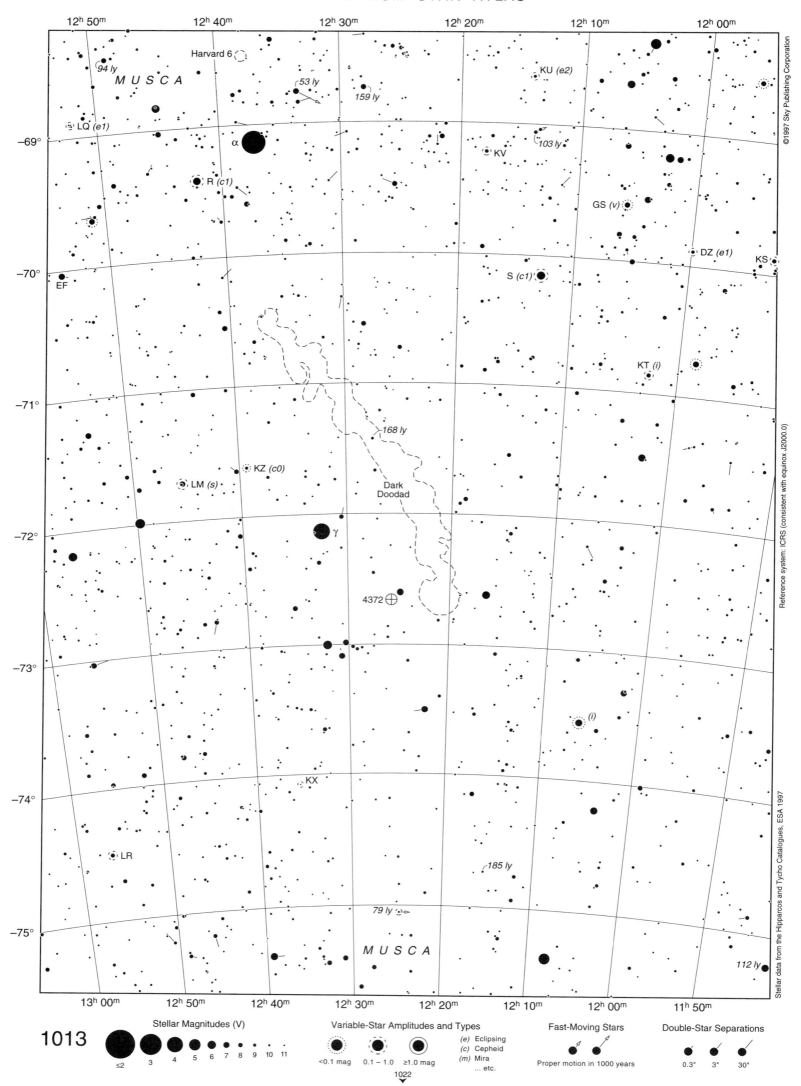

Reference system: ICRS (consistent with equinox J2000.0)

Stellar data from the Hipparcos and Tycho Catalogues, ESA 1997

94 ly

MUSCA

Harvard 6

53 ly

159 ly

KU (e2)

LQ (e1)

−69°

α

KV

103 ly

R (c1)

GS (v)

DZ (e1)

KS

EF

−70°

S (c1)

KT (i)

168 ly

KZ (c0)

LM (s)

Dark
Doodad

−72°

γ

4372

(i)

−73°

KX

−74°

LR

185 ly

79 ly

−75°

MUSCA

112 ly

13h 00m   12h 50m   12h 40m   12h 30m   12h 20m   12h 10m   12h 00m   11h 50m

1013

Stellar Magnitudes (V)

≤2   3   4   5   6   7   8   9   10   11

Variable-Star Amplitudes and Types

<0.1 mag   0.1 – 1.0   ≥1.0 mag

(e) Eclipsing
(c) Cepheid
(m) Mira
... etc.

Fast-Moving Stars

Proper motion in 1000 years

Double-Star Separations

0.3"   3"   30"

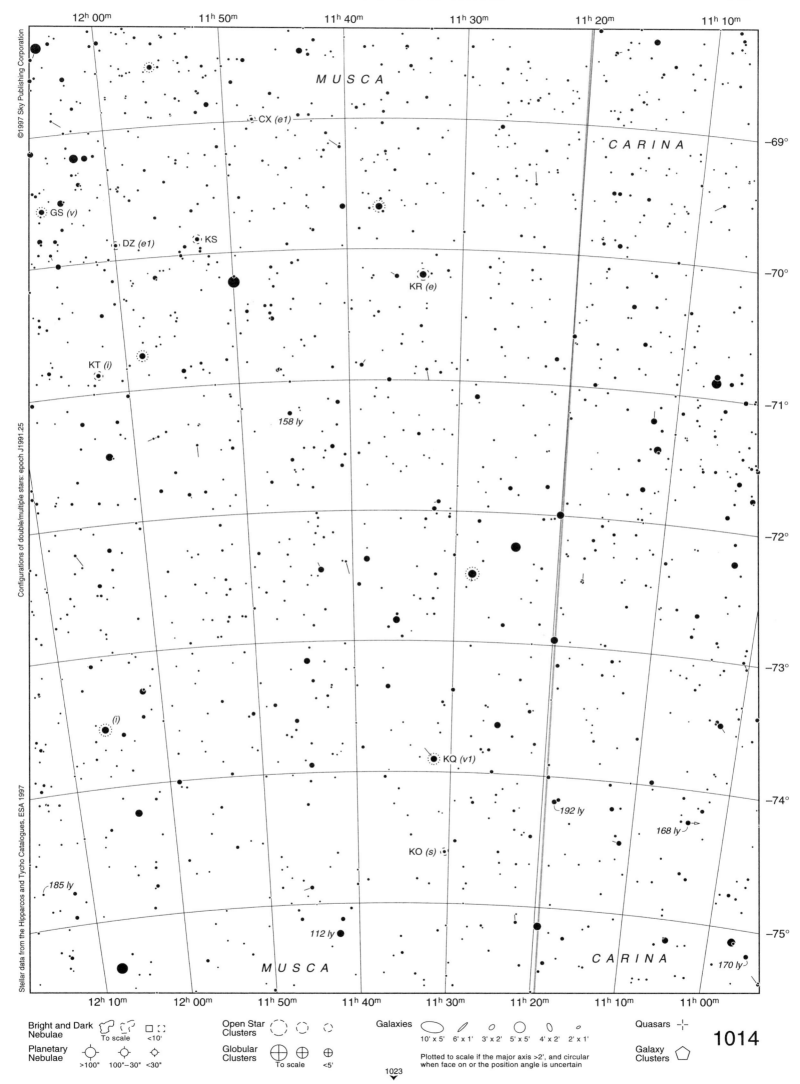

12ʰ 00ᵐ · 11ʰ 50ᵐ · 11ʰ 40ᵐ · 11ʰ 30ᵐ · 11ʰ 20ᵐ · 11ʰ 10ᵐ

M U S C A

C A R I N A

CX (e1)

GS (v)

DZ (e1)   KS

KR (e)

KT (i)

158 ly

KQ (v1)

192 ly

168 ly

KO (s)

185 ly

112 ly

M U S C A

C A R I N A

170 ly

−69°
−70°
−71°
−72°
−73°
−74°
−75°

12ʰ 10ᵐ · 12ʰ 00ᵐ · 11ʰ 50ᵐ · 11ʰ 40ᵐ · 11ʰ 30ᵐ · 11ʰ 20ᵐ · 11ʰ 10ᵐ · 11ʰ 00ᵐ

Bright and Dark
Nebulae   To scale   <10'
Planetary
Nebulae   >100" 100"–30" <30'

Open Star
Clusters   To scale
Globular
Clusters   To scale   <5'

Galaxies
10' x 5' 6' x 1' 3' x 2' 5' x 5' 4' x 2' 2' x 1'
Plotted to scale if the major axis >2', and circular
when face on or the position angle is uncertain

Quasars

Galaxy
Clusters

1014

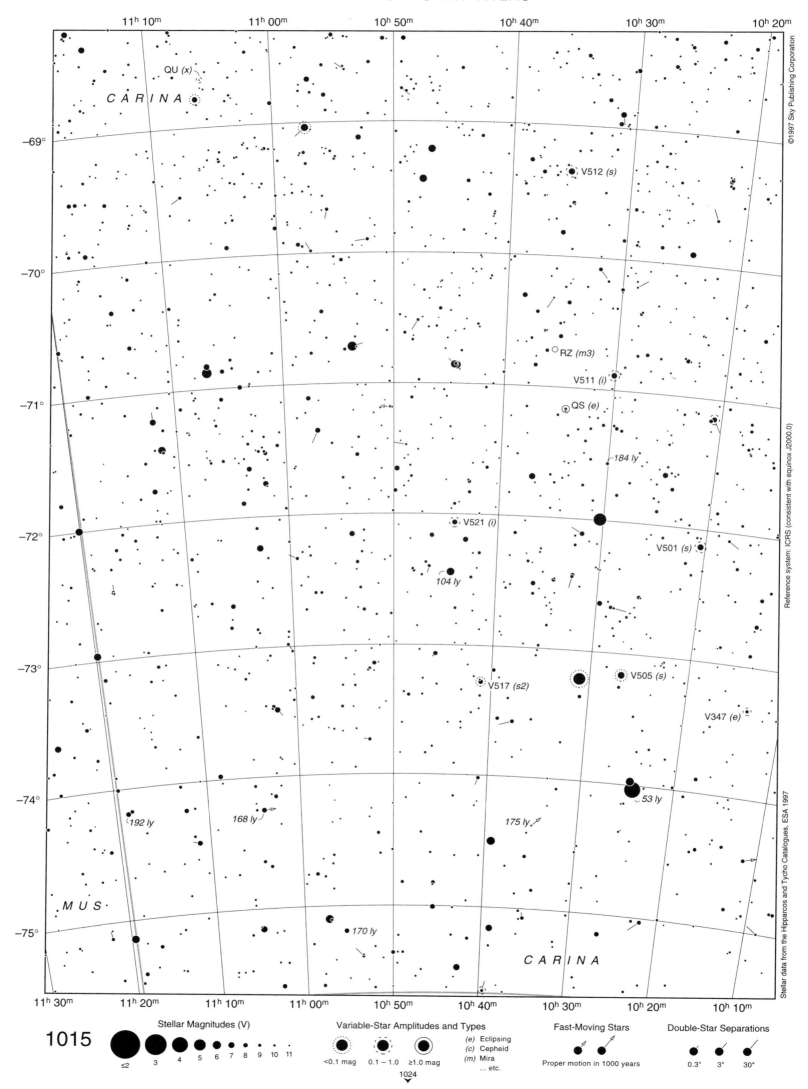

1015

Stellar Magnitudes (V)

≤2   3   4   5   6   7   8   9   10   11

Variable-Star Amplitudes and Types

<0.1 mag   0.1 − 1.0   ≥1.0 mag

(e) Eclipsing
(c) Cepheid
(m) Mira
... etc.

Fast-Moving Stars

Proper motion in 1000 years

Double-Star Separations

0.3"   3"   30"

^
1024
v

MILLENNIUM STAR ATLAS

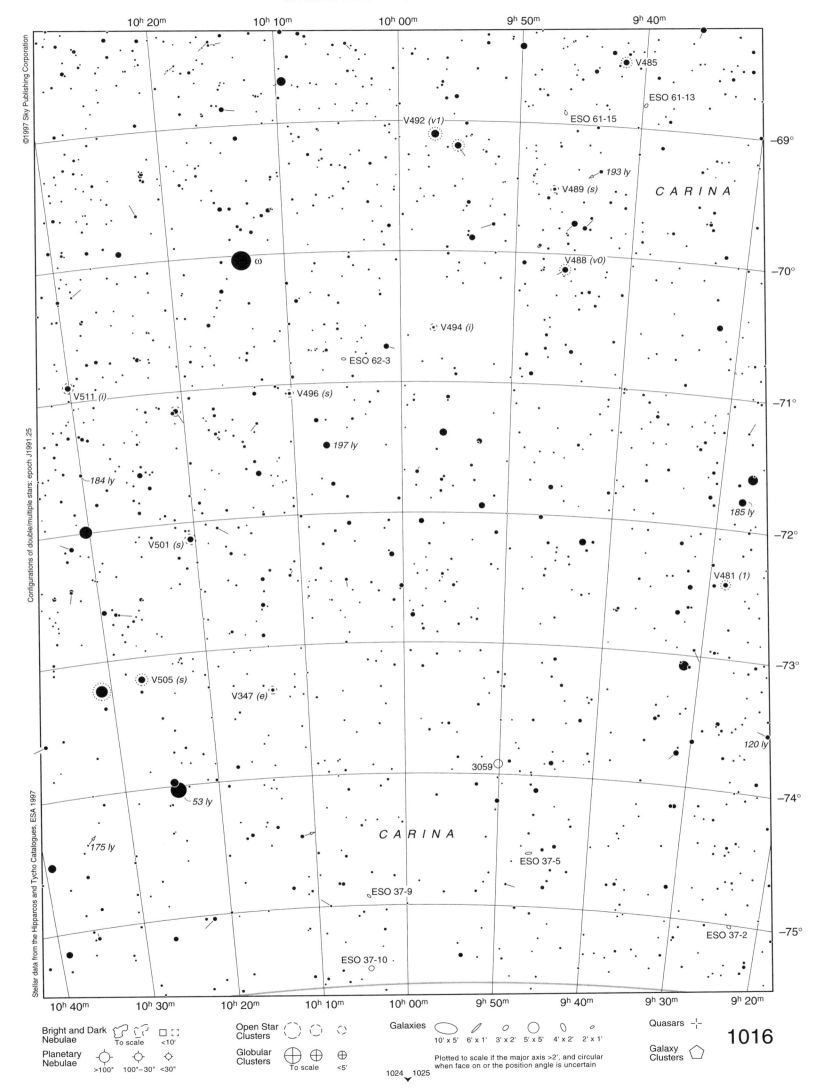

Configurations of double/multiple stars: epoch J1991.25

Stellar data from the Hipparcos and Tycho Catalogues, ESA 1997

10ʰ 20ᵐ 10ʰ 10ᵐ 10ʰ 00ᵐ 9ʰ 50ᵐ 9ʰ 40ᵐ

V485

ESO 61-13

V492 *(v1)* ESO 61-15

−69°

193 ly

CARINA

V489 *(s)*

ω V488 *(v0)*

−70°

V494 *(i)*

ESO 62-3

V511 *(i)* V496 *(s)*

−71°

197 ly

184 ly

185 ly

V501 *(s)*

−72°

V481 *(1)*

V505 *(s)*

V347 *(e)*

−73°

120 ly

3059

53 ly

−74°

175 ly

CARINA

ESO 37-5

ESO 37-9

−75°

ESO 37-2

ESO 37-10

10ʰ 40ᵐ 10ʰ 30ᵐ 10ʰ 20ᵐ 10ʰ 10ᵐ 10ʰ 00ᵐ 9ʰ 50ᵐ 9ʰ 40ᵐ 9ʰ 30ᵐ 9ʰ 20ᵐ

Bright and Dark Nebulae To scale <10'

Planetary Nebulae >100" 100"−30" <30"

Open Star Clusters

Globular Clusters To scale <5'

Galaxies 10' x 5' 6' x 1' 3' x 2' 5' x 5' 4' x 2' 2' x 1'

Plotted to scale if the major axis >2', and circular when face on or the position angle is uncertain

Quasars

Galaxy Clusters

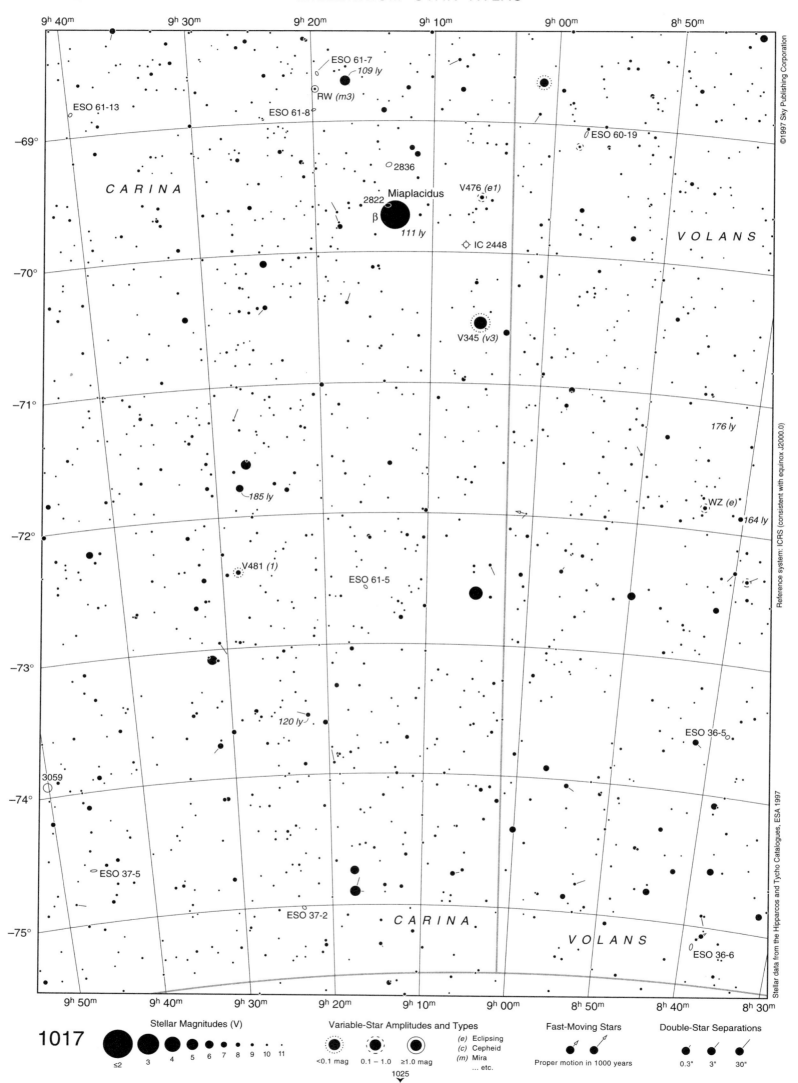

©1997 Sky Publishing Corporation

Reference system: ICRS (consistent with equinox J2000.0)

Stellar data from the Hipparcos and Tycho Catalogues, ESA 1997

1017

Stellar Magnitudes (V)

≤2   3   4   5   6   7   8   9   10   11

Variable-Star Amplitudes and Types

<0.1 mag   0.1 – 1.0   ≥1.0 mag

(e) Eclipsing
(c) Cepheid
(m) Mira
... etc.

Fast-Moving Stars

Proper motion in 1000 years

Double-Star Separations

0.3"   3"   30"

1025

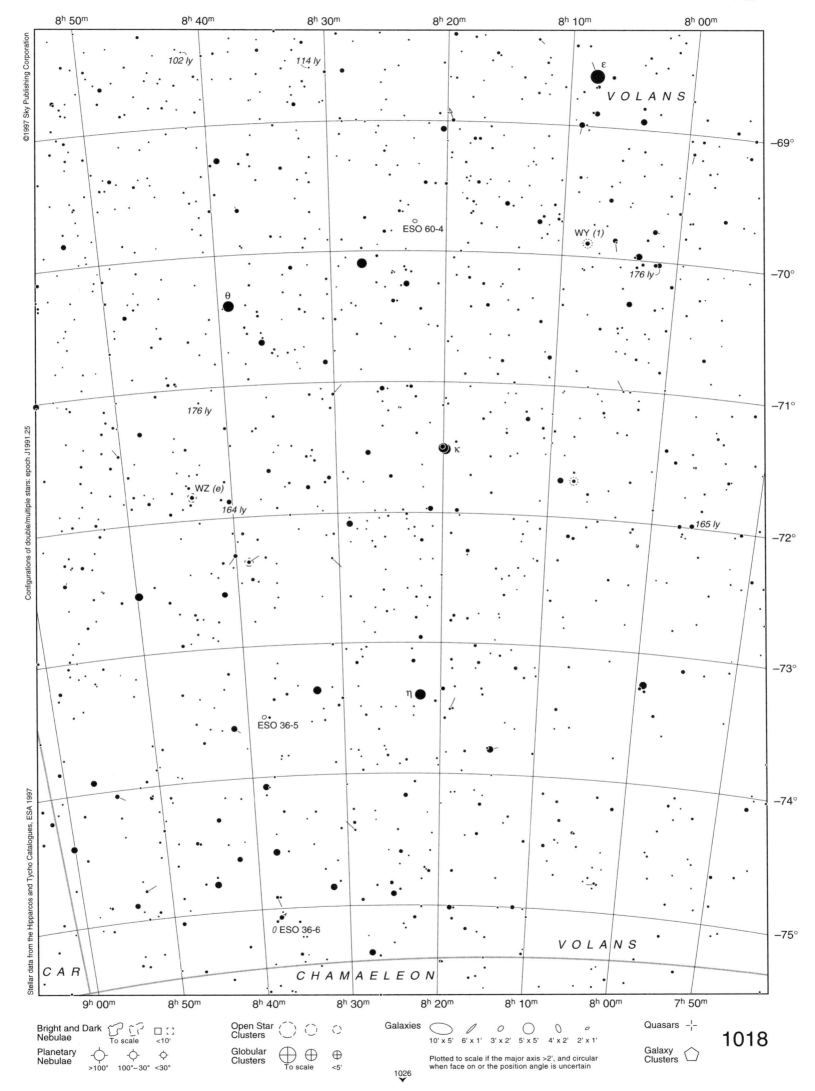

Configurations of double/multiple stars: epoch J1991.25

Stellar data from the Hipparcos and Tycho Catalogues, ESA 1997

| Bright and Dark Nebulae | Open Star Clusters | Globular Clusters | Galaxies | Quasars | Galaxy Clusters |

Bright and Dark Nebulae — To scale — <10'

Planetary Nebulae — >100" — 100"–30" — <30'

Open Star Clusters

Globular Clusters — To scale — <5'

Galaxies — 10' x 5' — 6' x 1' — 3' x 2' — 5' x 5' — 4' x 2' — 2' x 1'

Plotted to scale if the major axis >2', and circular when face on or the position angle is uncertain

Quasars

Galaxy Clusters

1018

1026

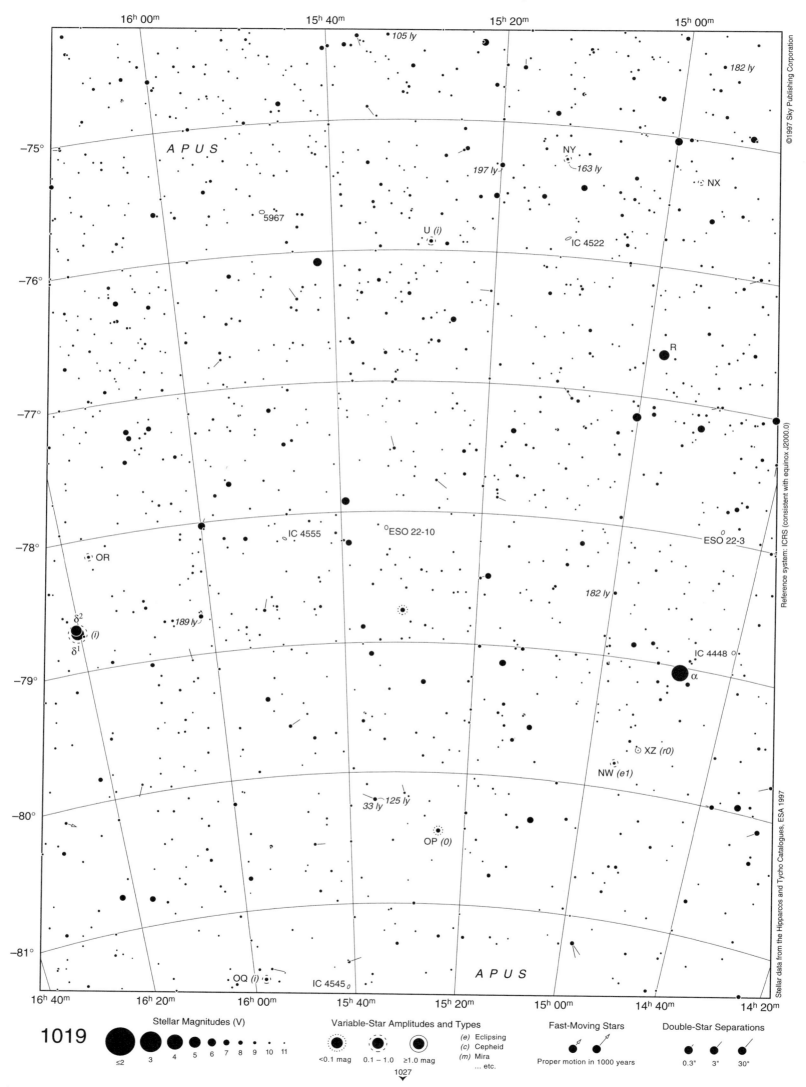

Reference system: ICRS (consistent with equinox J2000.0)

Stellar data from the Hipparcos and Tycho Catalogues, ESA 1997

APUS

105 ly

182 ly

-75°   NY   163 ly   NX

5967   197 ly

U (i)   IC 4522

R

-76°

ESO 22-10   ESO 22-3

-77°

IC 4555

-78°   OR   182 ly

189 ly   IC 4448

δ²   (i)   α

δ¹

XZ (r0)

-79°   NW (e1)

33 ly   125 ly

-80°   OP (0)

APUS

-81°   OQ (i)   IC 4545

16ʰ 40ᵐ   16ʰ 20ᵐ   16ʰ 00ᵐ   15ʰ 40ᵐ   15ʰ 20ᵐ   15ʰ 00ᵐ   14ʰ 40ᵐ   14ʰ 20ᵐ

16ʰ 00ᵐ   15ʰ 40ᵐ   15ʰ 20ᵐ   15ʰ 00ᵐ

1019

Stellar Magnitudes (V)

≤2   3   4   5   6   7   8   9   10   11

Variable-Star Amplitudes and Types

<0.1 mag   0.1 – 1.0   ≥1.0 mag

(e) Eclipsing
(c) Cepheid
(m) Mira
... etc.

1027

Fast-Moving Stars

Proper motion in 1000 years

Double-Star Separations

0.3"   3"   30"

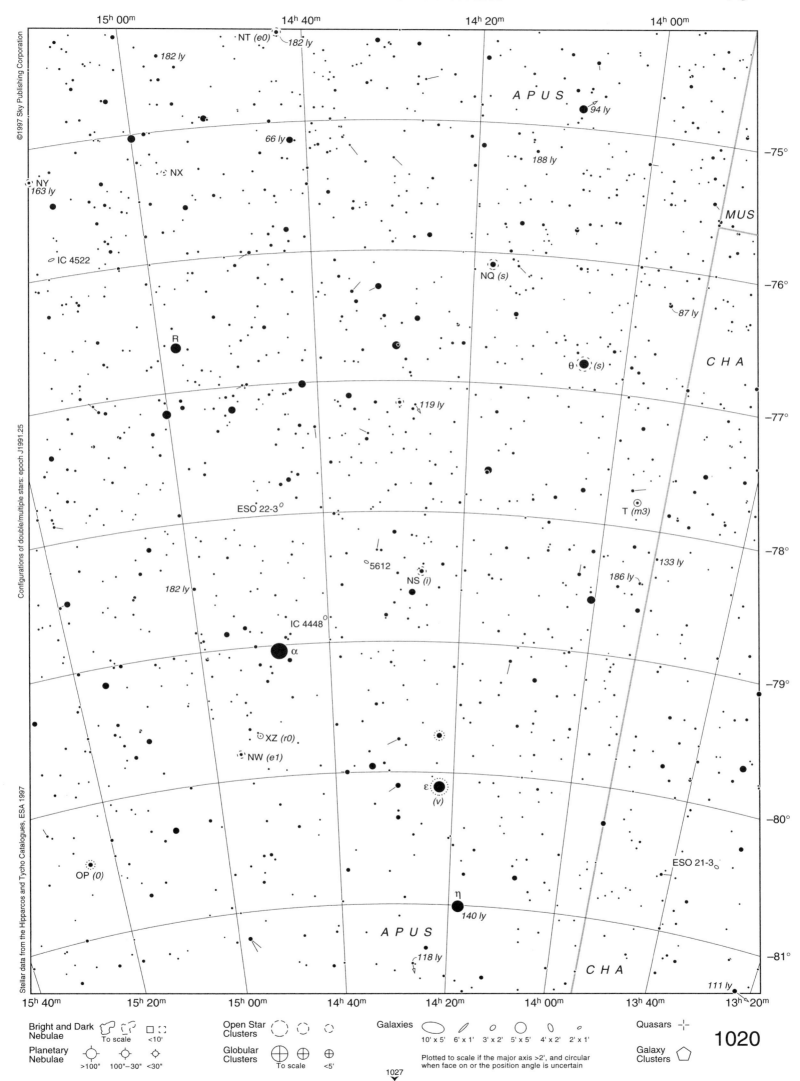

15h 00m   14h 40m   14h 20m   14h 00m

APUS

NT (e0)   182 ly
182 ly

94 ly

66 ly   188 ly
−75°

NX   MUS

NY
163 ly

87 ly
−76°

IC 4522   NQ (s)   CHA

R
θ (s)

119 ly
−77°

ESO 22-3
T (m3)

5612
133 ly

182 ly   NS (i)   186 ly
−78°

IC 4448
α

XZ (r0)
−79°

NW (e1)

ε

OP (0)   (v)
−80°

ESO 21-3

η
140 ly

APUS   ESO 21-3
−81°

118 ly   CHA

111 ly

15h 40m   15h 20m   15h 00m   14h 40m   14h 20m   14h 00m   13h 40m   13h 20m

Bright and Dark Nebulae
To scale   <10'

Open Star Clusters

Galaxies
10' x 5'   6' x 1'   3' x 2'   5' x 5'   4' x 2'   2' x 1'

Quasars

1020

Planetary Nebulae
>100"   100"−30"   <30"

Globular Clusters
To scale   <5'

Plotted to scale if the major axis >2', and circular when face on or the position angle is uncertain

Galaxy Clusters

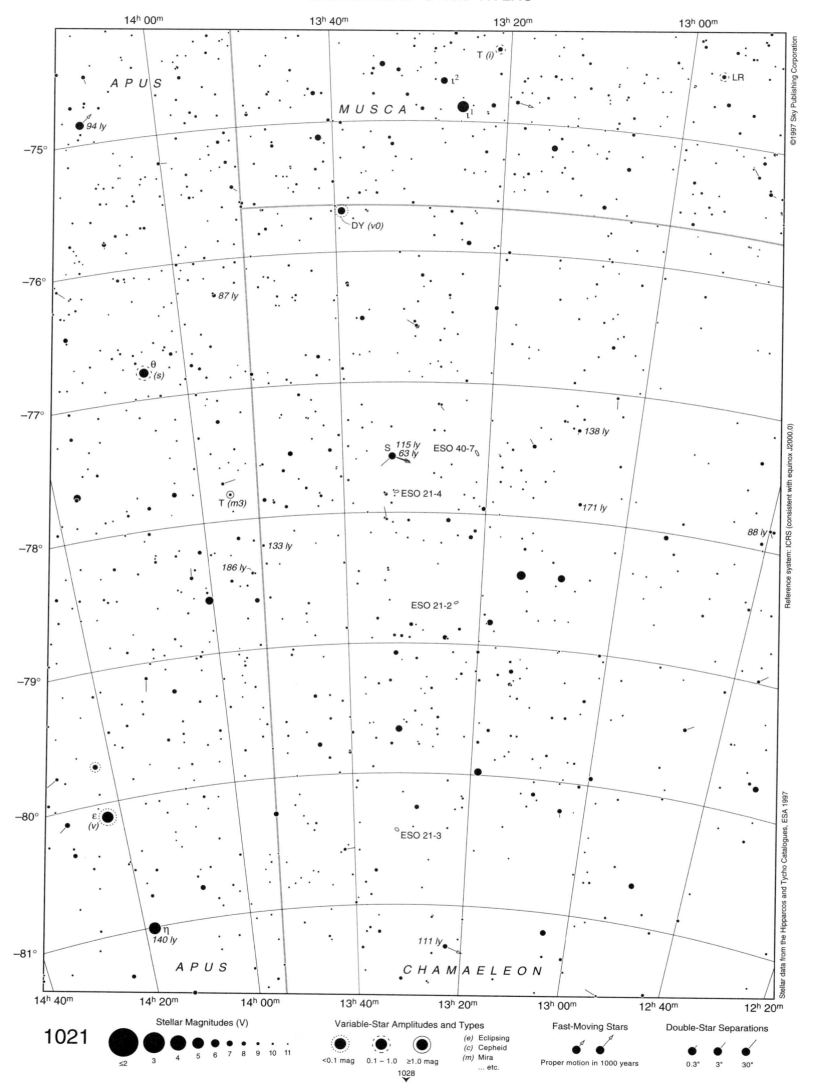

APUS

MUSCA

T (i)

ι²

ι¹

LR

94 ly

DY (v0)

87 ly

θ (s)

S 115 ly
63 ly   ESO 40-7

138 ly

ESO 21-4

171 ly

T (m3)

133 ly

186 ly

88 ly

ESO 21-2

ESO 21-3

ε (v)

η
140 ly

111 ly

APUS

CHAMAELEON

1021

Stellar Magnitudes (V)

≤2   3   4   5   6   7   8   9   10   11

Variable-Star Amplitudes and Types

<0.1 mag   0.1 – 1.0   ≥1.0 mag

(e) Eclipsing
(c) Cepheid
(m) Mira
... etc.

1028

Fast-Moving Stars

Proper motion in 1000 years

Double-Star Separations

0.3"   3"   30"

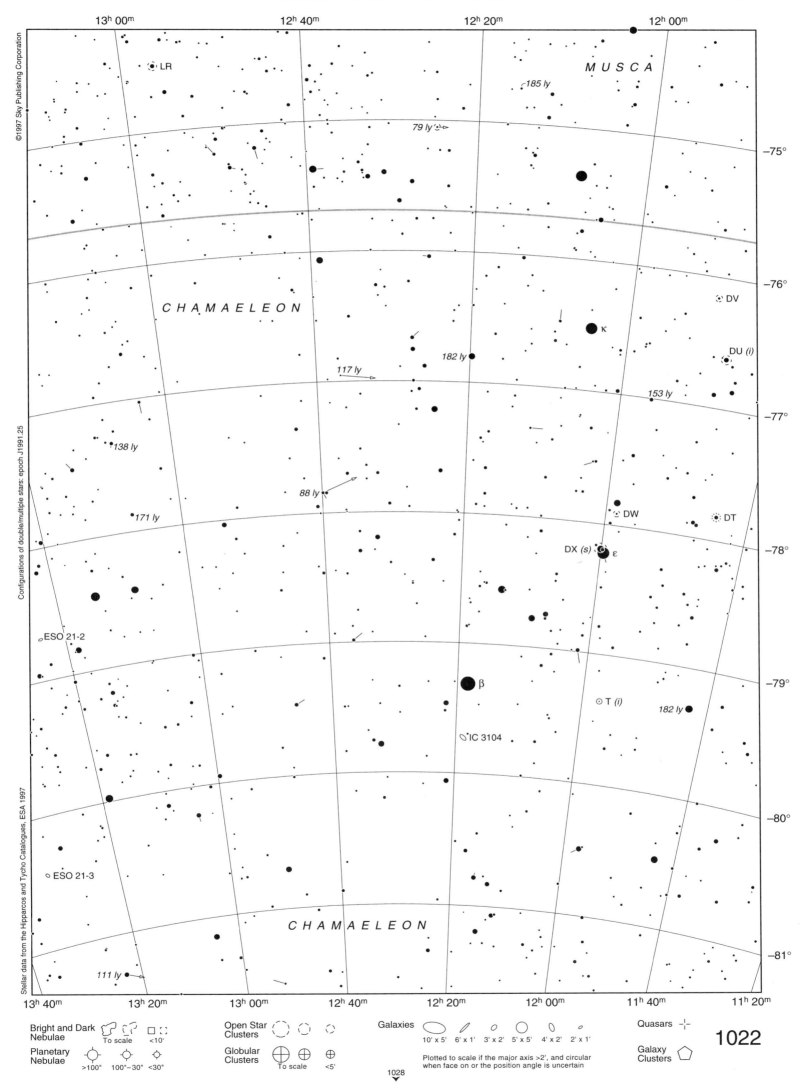

M U S C A

⌐185 ly

79 ly ⊙⊶

−75°

C H A M A E L E O N

−76°

DV

κ

DU (i)

182 ly ●

117 ly →

153 ly

−77°

138 ly

88 ly →

171 ly

DW

DT

DX (s) ⊙ ε

−78°

ESO 21-2

β

T (i)

182 ly ●

IC 3104

−79°

ESO 21-3

−80°

C H A M A E L E O N

−81°

111 ly

LR

13ʰ 40ᵐ   13ʰ 20ᵐ   13ʰ 00ᵐ   12ʰ 40ᵐ   12ʰ 20ᵐ   12ʰ 00ᵐ   11ʰ 40ᵐ   11ʰ 20ᵐ

Bright and Dark Nebulae			Open Star Clusters			Galaxies							Quasars
	To scale	<10'				10' x 5'	6' x 1'	3' x 2'	5' x 5'	4' x 2'	2' x 1'		
Planetary Nebulae			Globular Clusters										Galaxy Clusters
>100"	100"−30"	<30"		To scale	<5'								

Plotted to scale if the major axis >2', and circular
when face on or the position angle is uncertain

1022

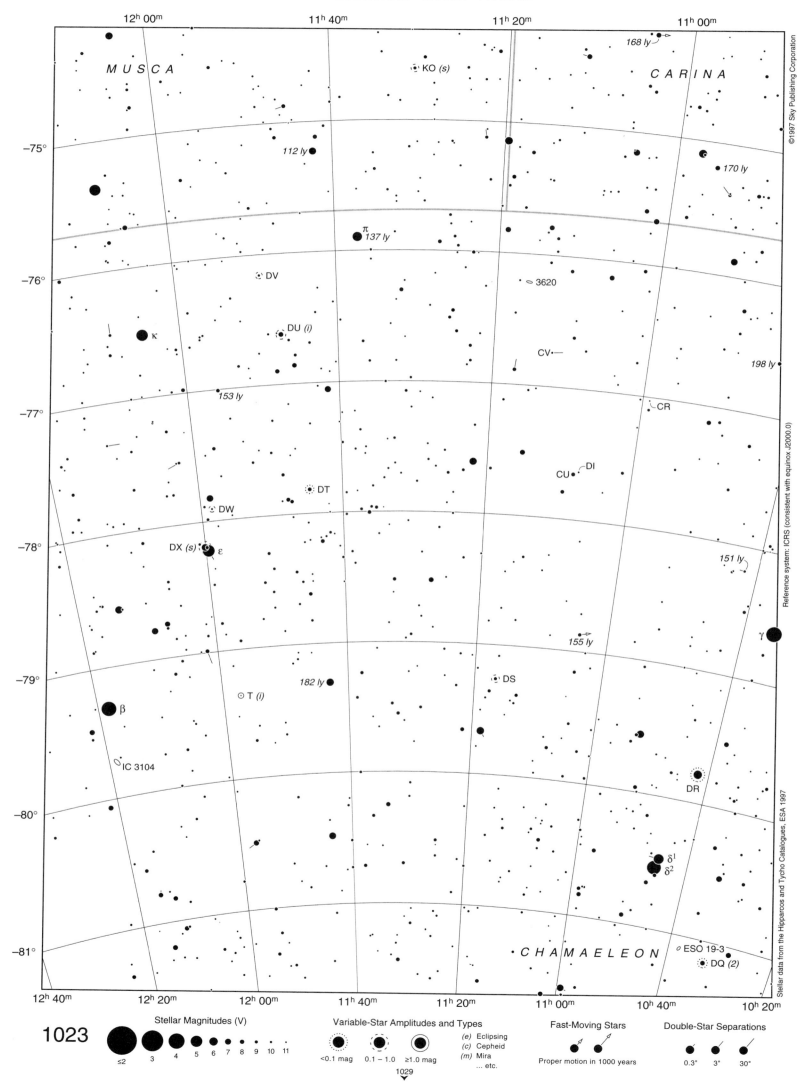

MUSCA

CARINA

168 ly

KO (s)

112 ly

170 ly

π 137 ly

DV

3620

DU (i)

CV

198 ly

κ

153 ly

CR

DI

CU

DT

DW

151 ly

DX (s) ε

155 ly

γ

DS

182 ly

T (i)

β

IC 3104

DR

δ¹

δ²

CHAMAELEON

ESO 19-3

DQ (2)

Stellar Magnitudes (V)

≤2   3   4   5   6   7   8   9   10   11

Variable-Star Amplitudes and Types

<0.1 mag   0.1 – 1.0   ≥1.0 mag

(e) Eclipsing
(c) Cepheid
(m) Mira
... etc.

1029

Fast-Moving Stars

Proper motion in 1000 years

Double-Star Separations

0.3"   3"   30"

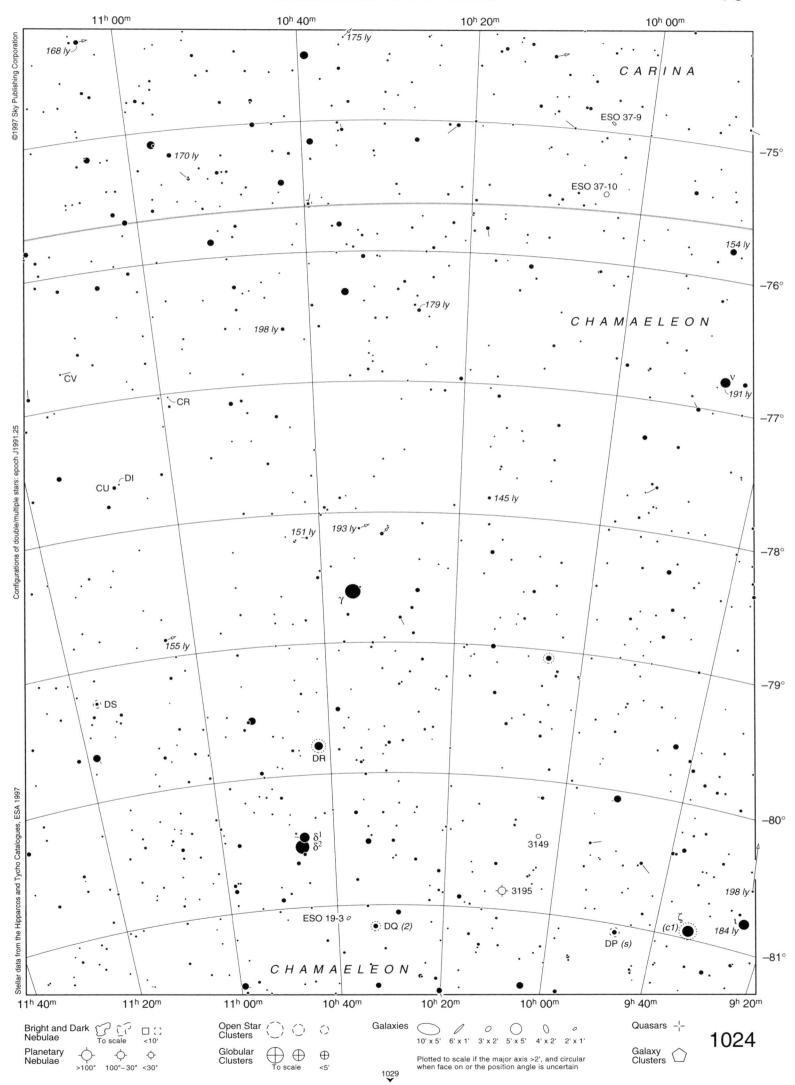

© 1997 Sky Publishing Corporation

Configurations of double/multiple stars: epoch J1991.25

Stellar data from the Hipparcos and Tycho Catalogues, ESA 1997

11ʰ 00ᵐ   10ʰ 40ᵐ   10ʰ 20ᵐ   10ʰ 00ᵐ

168 ly
175 ly
CARINA
ESO 37-9
170 ly
ESO 37-10
154 ly
179 ly
CHAMAELEON
198 ly
ν
CV
191 ly
CR
CU DI
145 ly
151 ly 193 ly
γ
155 ly
DS
3149
DR
3195
δ¹
δ²
ESO 19-3
DQ (2)
198 ly
ζ
(c1)
ESO 19-3
DP (s)
184 ly
ι
CHAMAELEON

−75°
−76°
−77°
−78°
−79°
−80°
−81°

11ʰ 40ᵐ   11ʰ 20ᵐ   11ʰ 00ᵐ   10ʰ 40ᵐ   10ʰ 20ᵐ   10ʰ 00ᵐ   9ʰ 40ᵐ   9ʰ 20ᵐ

Bright and Dark Nebulae
To scale   <10'
Planetary Nebulae
>100"   100"–30"   <30"

Open Star Clusters
Globular Clusters
To scale   <5'

Galaxies
10' x 5' 6' x 1' 3' x 2' 5' x 5' 4' x 2' 2' x 1'
Plotted to scale if the major axis >2', and circular when face on or the position angle is uncertain

Quasars

Galaxy Clusters

1024

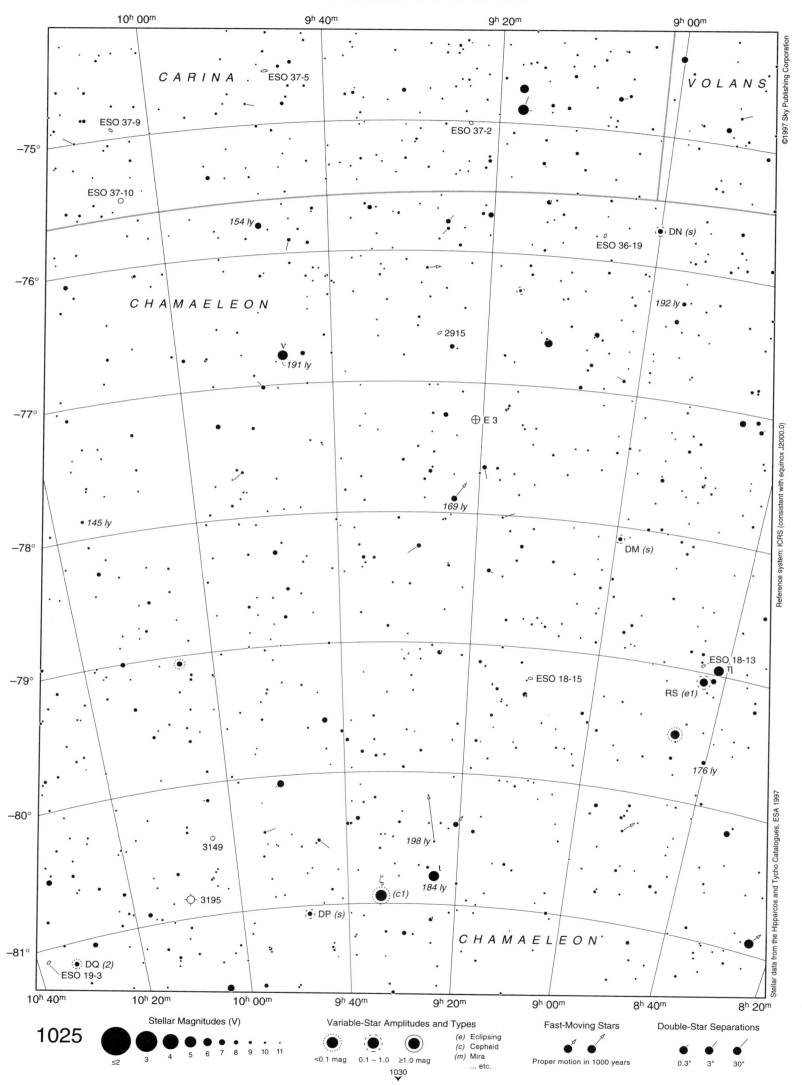

©1997 Sky Publishing Corporation

Reference system: ICRS (consistent with equinox J2000.0)

Stellar data from the Hipparcos and Tycho Catalogues, ESA 1997

CARINA

VOLANS

ESO 37-5

ESO 37-9

ESO 37-2

ESO 37-10

154 ly

ESO 36-19

DN (s)

CHAMAELEON

192 ly

2915

v

191 ly

⊕ E 3

169 ly

DM (s)

145 ly

ESO 18-13
η

ESO 18-15

RS (e1)

176 ly

3149

198 ly

ι

ζ

184 ly

3195

(c1)

DP (s)

CHAMAELEON

DQ (2)

ESO 19-3

Stellar Magnitudes (V)

≤2   3   4   5   6   7 8 9 10 11

Variable-Star Amplitudes and Types

<0.1 mag   0.1 − 1.0   ≥1.0 mag

(e) Eclipsing
(c) Cepheid
(m) Mira
... etc.

1030

Fast-Moving Stars

Proper motion in 1000 years

Double-Star Separations

0.3"   3"   30"

MILLENNIUM STAR ATLAS

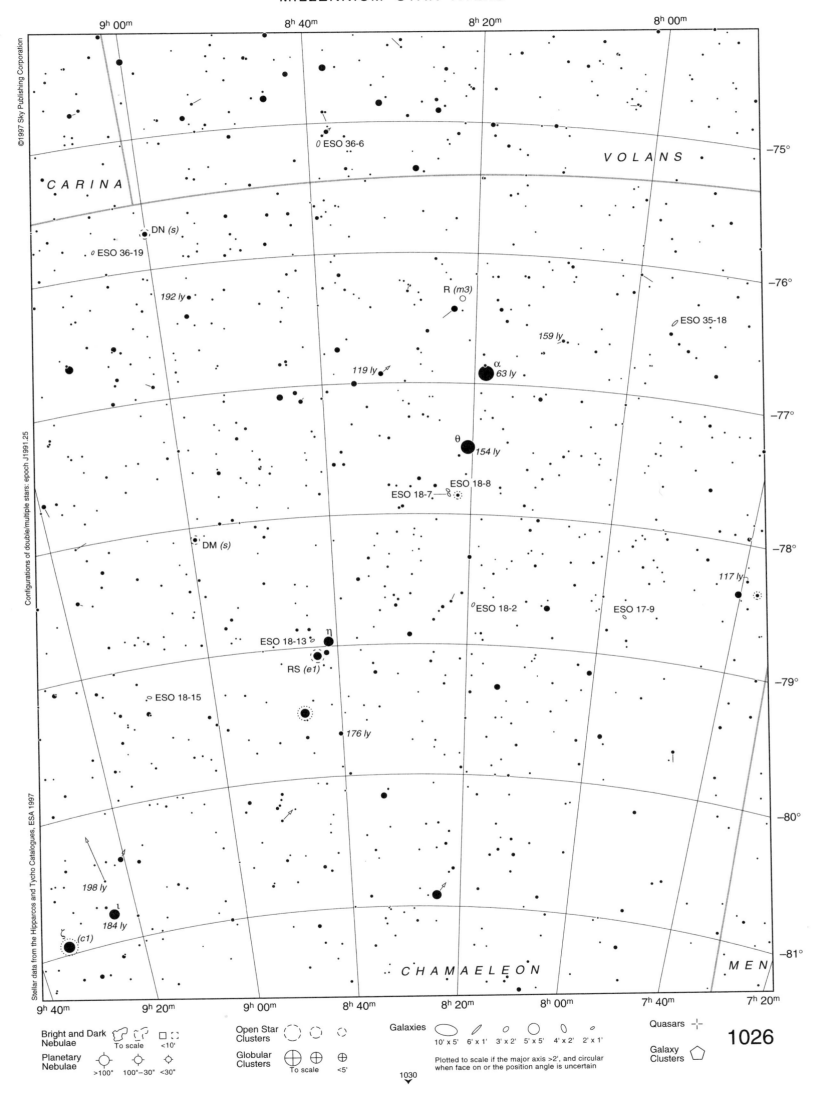

Configurations of double/multiple stars: epoch J1991.25

Stellar data from the Hipparcos and Tycho Catalogues, ESA 1997

9h 00m   8h 40m   8h 20m   8h 00m

−75°

V O L A N S

C A R I N A

DN (s)
 θ ESO 36-19

0 ESO 36-6

192 ly

R (m3)

ESO 35-18

159 ly

119 ly

α
63 ly

−76°

θ
154 ly

−77°

ESO 18-8
ESO 18-7

DM (s)

117 ly

0 ESO 18-2

ESO 17-9

−78°

η
ESO 18-13

RS (e1)

ESO 18-15

176 ly

−79°

−80°

198 ly

ι
184 ly

ζ (c1)

C H A M A E L E O N

M E N

−81°

9h 40m   9h 20m   9h 00m   8h 40m   8h 20m   8h 00m   7h 40m   7h 20m

Bright and Dark Nebulae
To scale   <10'

Planetary Nebulae
>100"   100"–30"   <30"

Open Star Clusters

Globular Clusters
To scale   <5'

Galaxies
10' x 5'   6' x 1'   3' x 2'   5' x 5'   4' x 2'   2' x 1'

Plotted to scale if the major axis >2', and circular when face on or the position angle is uncertain

Quasars

Galaxy Clusters

1026

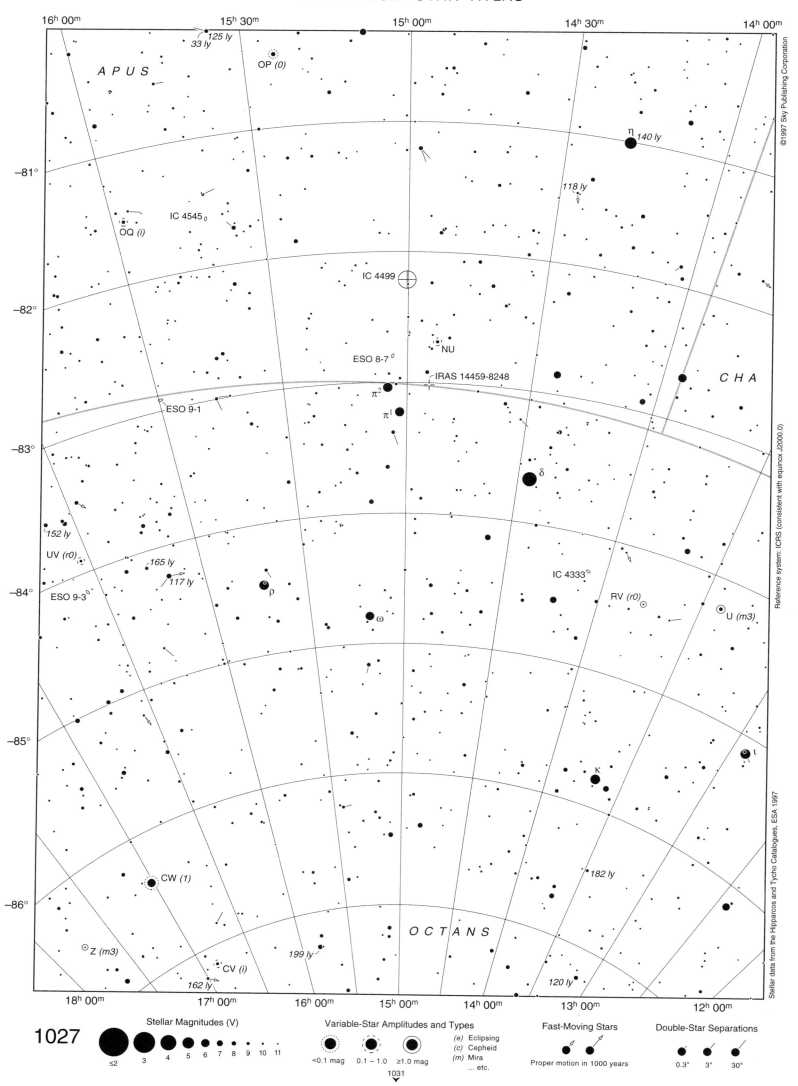

−84°

MILLENNIUM STAR ATLAS

©1997 Sky Publishing Corporation

Reference system: ICRS (consistent with equinox J2000.0)

Stellar data from the Hipparcos and Tycho Catalogues, ESA 1997

16ʰ 00ᵐ   15ʰ 30ᵐ   15ʰ 00ᵐ   14ʰ 30ᵐ   14ʰ 00ᵐ

33 ly   125 ly

OP (0)

A P U S

−81°

118 ly

η 140 ly

IC 4545₀

OQ (i)

C H A

IC 4499

−82°

NU

ESO 8-7₀

IRAS 14459-8248

π²

ESO 9-1

π¹

−83°

δ

152 ly

UV (r0)

165 ly

IC 4333₀

117 ly

ρ

RV (r0)

U (m3)

ESO 9-3₀

−84°

ω

κ

ι

−85°

182 ly

CW (1)

−86°

O C T A N S

Z (m3)

199 ly

120 ly

CV (i)

162 ly

18ʰ 00ᵐ   17ʰ 00ᵐ   16ʰ 00ᵐ   15ʰ 00ᵐ   14ʰ 00ᵐ   13ʰ 00ᵐ   12ʰ 00ᵐ

1027

Stellar Magnitudes (V)

≤2   3   4   5   6   7   8   9   10   11

Variable-Star Amplitudes and Types

<0.1 mag   0.1 – 1.0   ≥1.0 mag

(e) Eclipsing
(c) Cepheid
(m) Mira
... etc.

Fast-Moving Stars

Proper motion in 1000 years

Double-Star Separations

0.3"   3"   30"

1031

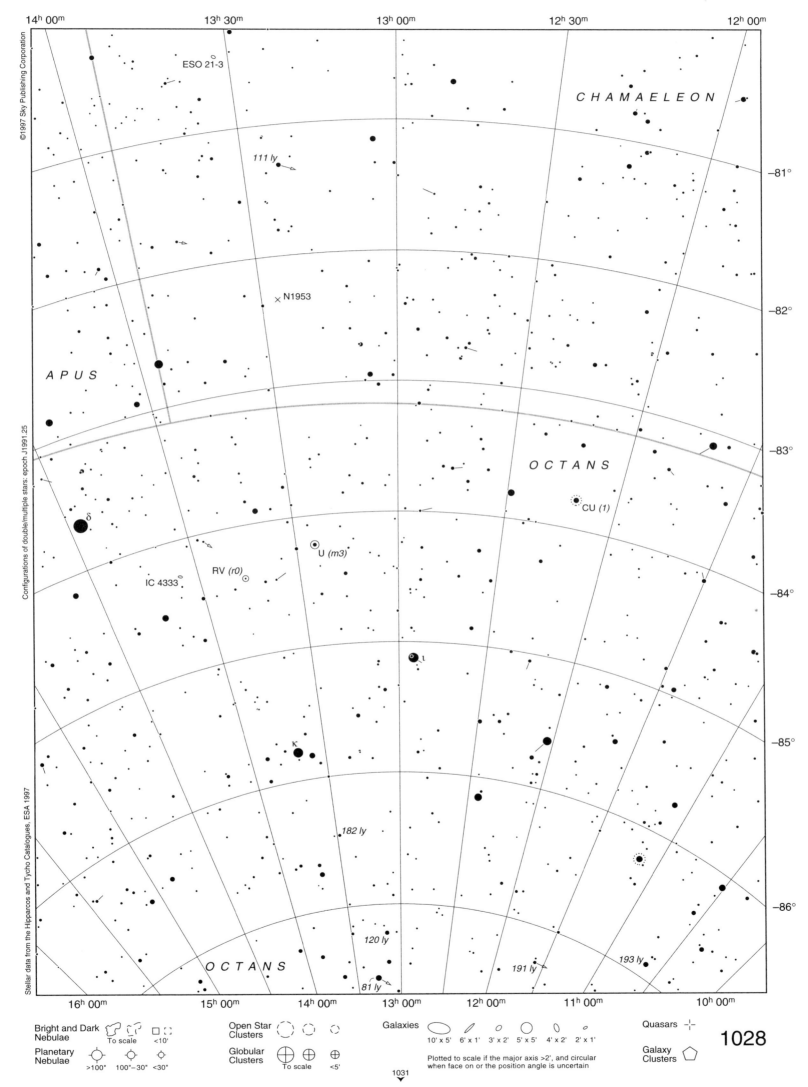

14h 00m   13h 30m   13h 00m   12h 30m   12h 00m

CHAMAELEON

ESO 21-3

111 ly

−81°

N1953

−82°

APUS

OCTANS

−83°

CU *(1)*

δ

U *(m3)*

RV *(r0)*

IC 4333

−84°

ι

−85°

κ

182 ly

OCTANS

−86°

120 ly

191 ly   *193 ly*

81 ly

16h 00m   15h 00m   14h 00m   13h 00m   12h 00m   11h 00m   10h 00m

Bright and Dark Nebulae — To scale, <10'

Planetary Nebulae — >100", 100"–30", <30"

Open Star Clusters

Globular Clusters — To scale, <5'

Galaxies — 10' x 5' 6' x 1' 3' x 2' 5' x 5' 4' x 2' 2' x 1'

Plotted to scale if the major axis >2', and circular when face on or the position angle is uncertain

Quasars

Galaxy Clusters

1028

−84°

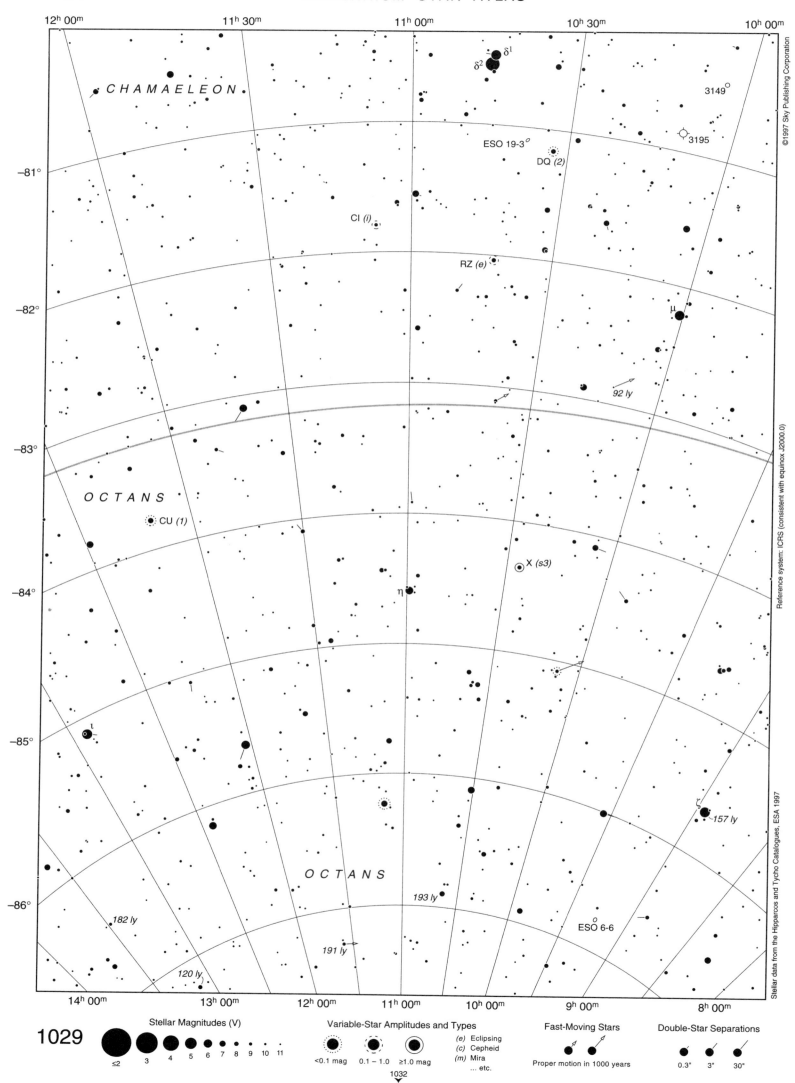

Reference system: ICRS (consistent with equinox J2000.0)

Stellar data from the Hipparcos and Tycho Catalogues, ESA 1997

CHAMAELEON

3149

3195

ESO 19-3

DQ (2)

CI (i)

RZ (e)

μ

92 ly

OCTANS

CU (1)

X (s3)

η

ι

ζ

157 ly

OCTANS

193 ly

182 ly

ESO 6-6

191 ly

120 ly

1029

Stellar Magnitudes (V)

≤2 3 4 5 6 7 8 9 10 11

Variable-Star Amplitudes and Types

<0.1 mag   0.1 – 1.0   ≥1.0 mag

1032

(e) Eclipsing
(c) Cepheid
(m) Mira
... etc.

Fast-Moving Stars

Proper motion in 1000 years

Double-Star Separations

0.3"   3"   30"

MILLENNIUM STAR ATLAS

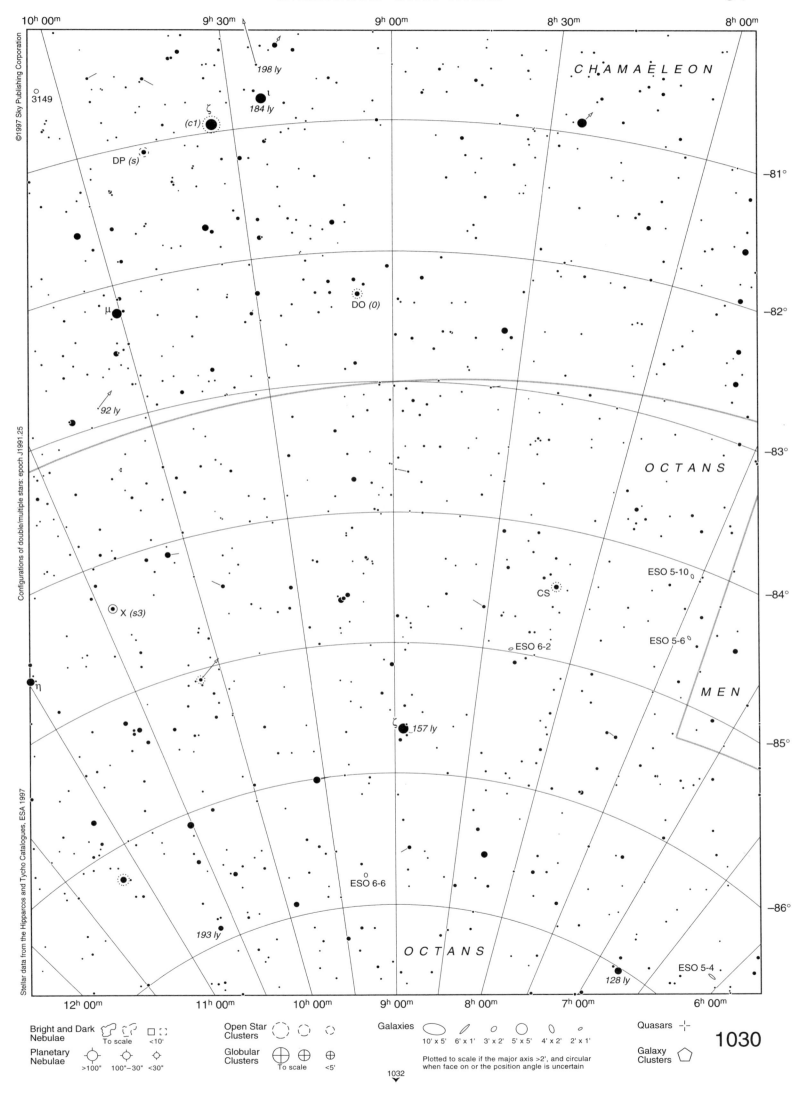

CHAMAELEON

3149

198 ly

ι
184 ly

ζ
(c1)

DP (s)

−81°

μ

DO (0)

−82°

92 ly

OCTANS

−83°

ESO 5-10

CS

−84°

X (s3)

ESO 6-2

ESO 5-6

η

MEN

ζ 157 ly

−85°

ESO 6-6

193 ly

ESO 5-4

128 ly

OCTANS

−86°

12ʰ 00ᵐ   11ʰ 00ᵐ   10ʰ 00ᵐ   9ʰ 00ᵐ   8ʰ 00ᵐ   7ʰ 00ᵐ   6ʰ 00ᵐ

Bright and Dark Nebulae	To scale <10'	
Planetary Nebulae	>100" 100"–30" <30"	
Open Star Clusters		
Globular Clusters	To scale <5'	

Galaxies
10' x 5'   6' x 1'   3' x 2'   5' x 5'   4' x 2'   2' x 1'

Plotted to scale if the major axis >2', and circular when face on or the position angle is uncertain

Quasars -|-

Galaxy Clusters

1030

10ʰ 00ᵐ   9ʰ 30ᵐ   9ʰ 00ᵐ   8ʰ 30ᵐ   8ʰ 00ᵐ

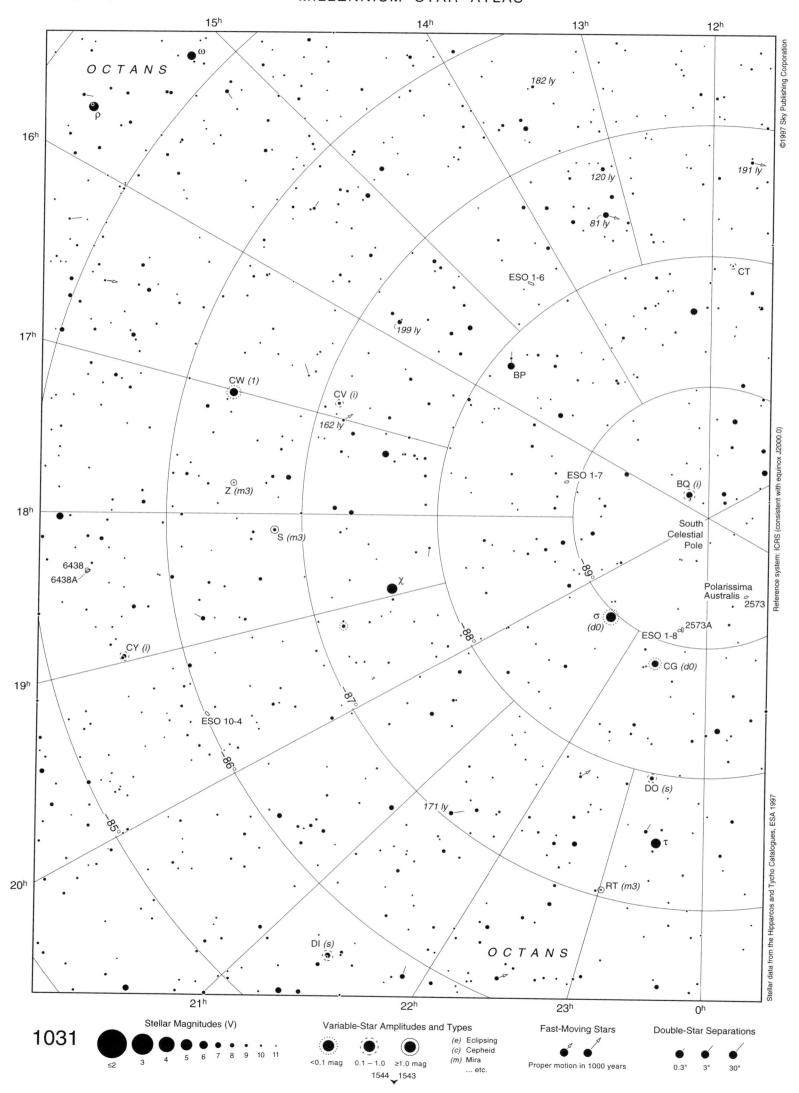

OCTANS

ω

ρ

15ʰ

14ʰ

13ʰ

12ʰ

182 ly

191 ly

120 ly

81 ly

ESO 1-6

CT

199 ly

CW (1)

BP

CV (i)

162 ly

ESO 1-7

BQ (i)

Z (m3)

S (m3)

South
Celestial
Pole

6438
6438A

χ

Polarissima
Australis
2573

89°

σ
(d0)

2573A

ESO 1-8

CY (i)

CG (d0)

88°

87°

ESO 10-4

DO (s)

86°

171 ly

85°

τ

RT (m3)

DI (s)

OCTANS

21ʰ

22ʰ

23ʰ

0ʰ

©1997 Sky Publishing Corporation

Reference system: ICRS (consistent with equinox J2000.0)

Stellar data from the Hipparcos and Tycho Catalogues, ESA 1997

1031

Stellar Magnitudes (V)

≤2   3   4   5   6   7   8   9   10   11

Variable-Star Amplitudes and Types

<0.1 mag   0.1 − 1.0   ≥1.0 mag

1544 ▾ 1543

(e) Eclipsing
(c) Cepheid
(m) Mira
... etc.

Fast-Moving Stars

Proper motion in 1000 years

Double-Star Separations

0.3"   3"   30"

MILLENNIUM STAR ATLAS

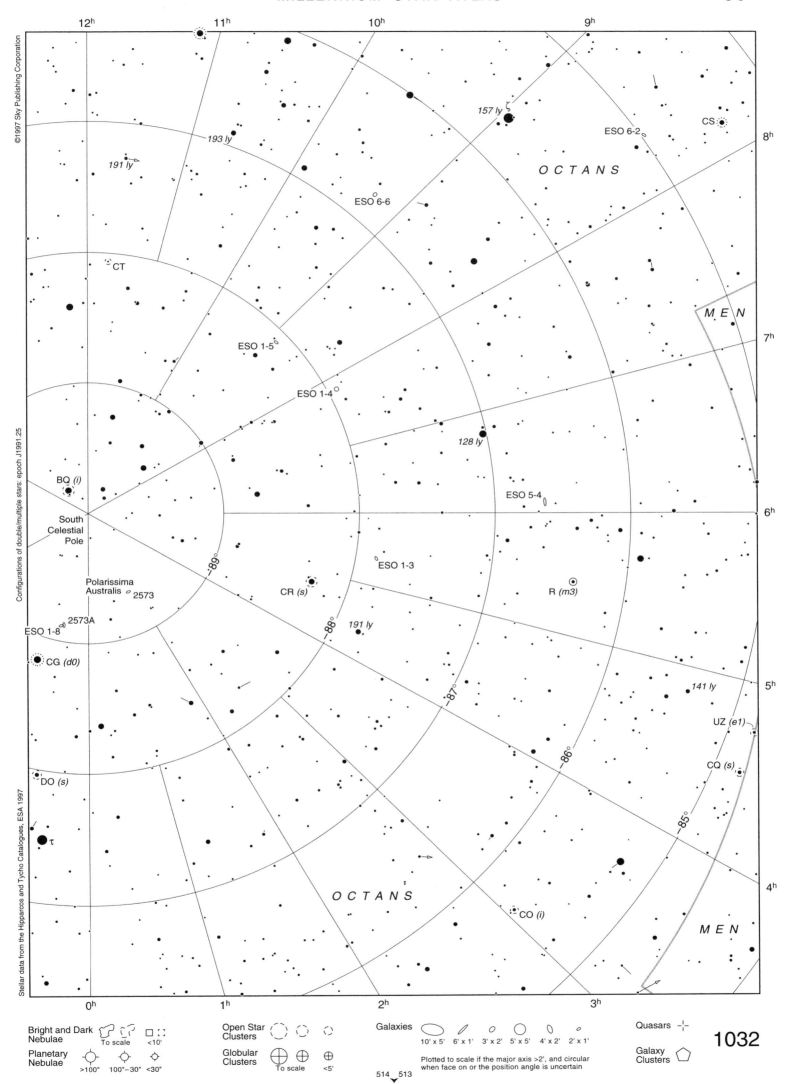

12ʰ   11ʰ   10ʰ   9ʰ   8ʰ

193 ly

191 ly

CS

ESO 6-2

157 ly

OCTANS

ESO 6-6

CT

MEN

7ʰ

ESO 1-5

ESO 1-4

128 ly

BQ *(i)*

ESO 5-4

6ʰ

South
Celestial
Pole

ESO 1-3

Polarissima
Australis   2573

CR *(s)*

R *(m3)*

2573A

ESO 1-8

191 ly

88°

CG *(d0)*

87°

141 ly

5ʰ

UZ *(e1)*

86°

CQ *(s)*

DO *(s)*

85°

τ

OCTANS

4ʰ

CO *(i)*

MEN

0ʰ   1ʰ   2ʰ   3ʰ

Bright and Dark Nebulae	Open Star Clusters	Galaxies	Quasars
To scale <10'		10' x 5' 6' x 1' 3' x 2' 5' x 5' 4' x 2' 2' x 1'	
Planetary Nebulae	Globular Clusters		Galaxy Clusters
>100" 100"–30" <30"	To scale <5'	Plotted to scale if the major axis >2', and circular when face on or the position angle is uncertain	

1032

INDEX TO SELECTED OBJECTS

THESE LISTINGS PROVIDE quick pointers to those charts that contain stars and nonstellar objects with popular names and many other benchmarks in the sky. Generally just a single chart number is given, indicating the chart on which the object is most nearly centered. Any star or object near a chart's edge can be found on at least one adjacent chart as well. Multiple chart numbers are given for a few large nebulae that extend across several charts.

Charts 1–516 are found in Volume I, which includes a more extensive index of bright stars by constellation and Bayer (Greek) letter. Charts 517–1032 are in Volume II, and charts 1033–1548 in Volume III.

SPECIAL ASTRONOMICAL NAMES

COMMON NAMES OF BRIGHT STARS

THE MESSIER CATALOGUE

CHART KEYS

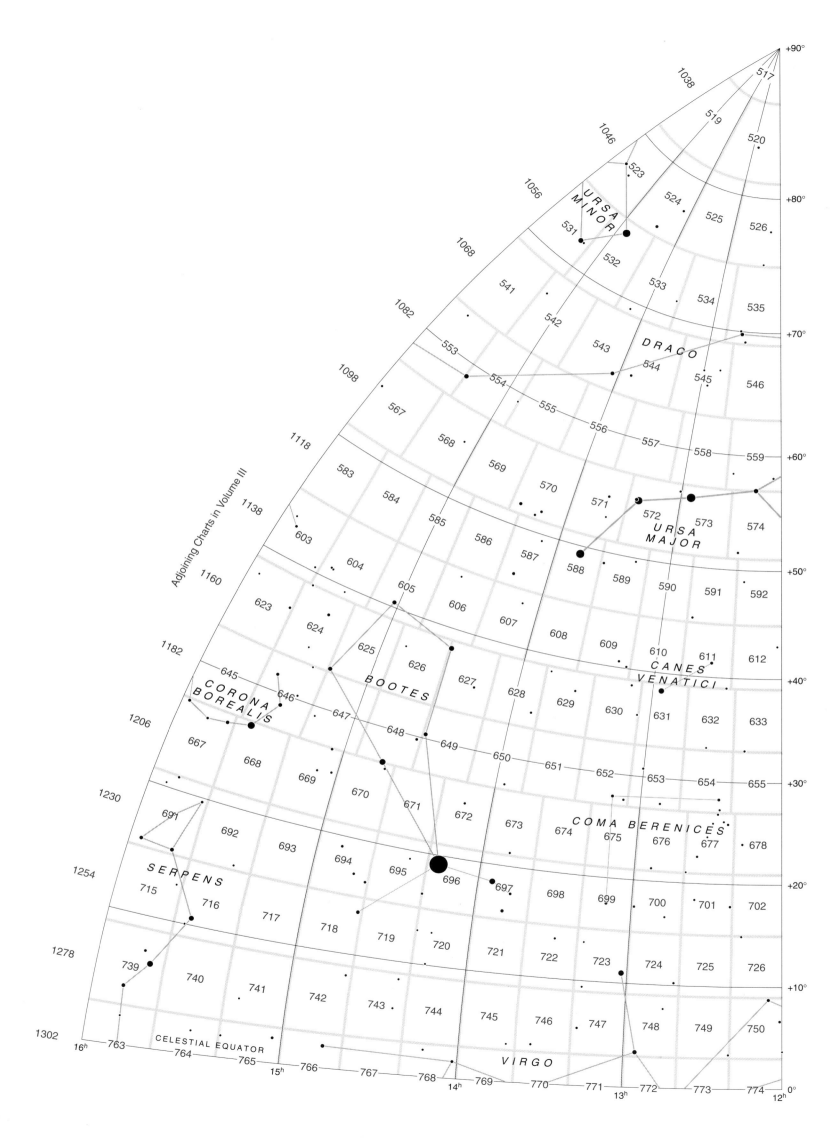

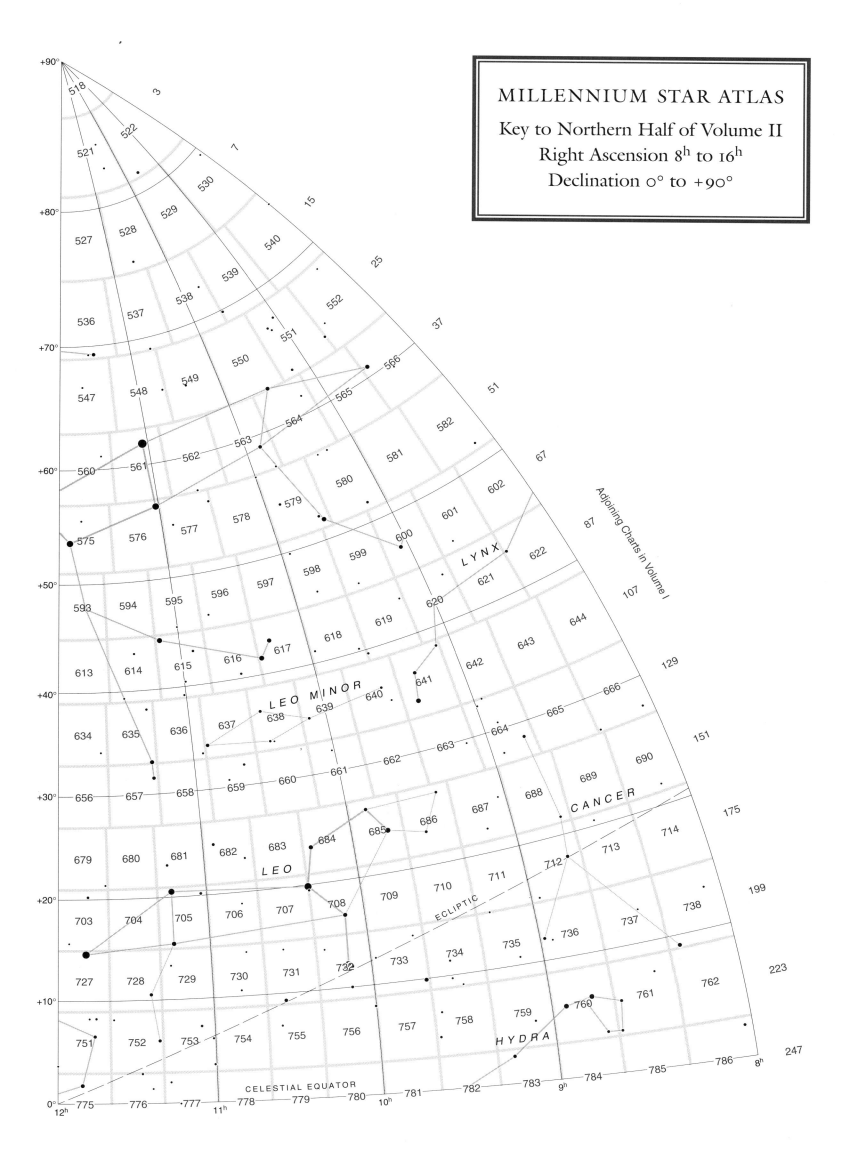

MILLENNIUM STAR ATLAS

Key to Northern Half of Volume II
Right Ascension 8^h to 16^h
Declination 0° to +90°

Adjoining Charts in Volume I

LYNX

LEO MINOR

CANCER

LEO

ECLIPTIC

HYDRA

CELESTIAL EQUATOR

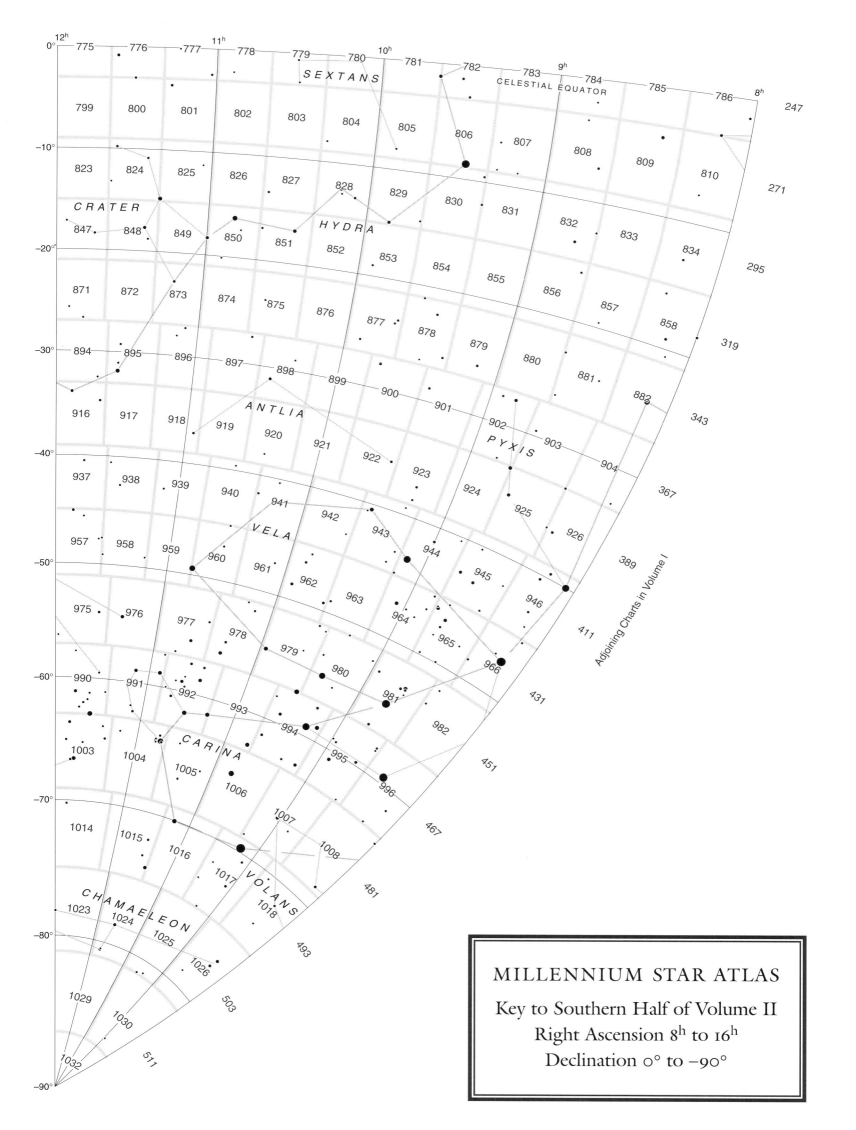

775 776 777 778 779 780 781 782 783 784 785 786

SEXTANS

CELESTIAL EQUATOR

247

799 800 801 802 803 804 805 806 807 808 809 810

-10°

271

823 824 825 826 827 828 829 830 831 832 833 834

CRATER

847 848 849 850 851 HYDRA 852 853 854 855 856 857 858

-20°

295

871 872 873 874 875 876 877 878 879 880 881 882

-30°

319

894 895 896 897 898 899 900 901 902 903 904

916 917 918 919 ANTLIA 920 921 922 923 924 925 926 PYXIS

343

-40°

937 938 939 940 941 942 943 944 945 946

367

957 958 959 960 VELA 961 962 963 964 965 966

-50°

389

975 976 977 978 979 980 981 982

411

Adjoining Charts in Volume I

990 991 992 993 994 995 996

-60°

431

1003 1004 1005 1006 CARINA 451

1014 1015 1016 1017 1007 1008

-70°

467

1023 1024 1025 1026 VOLANS 1018

CHAMAELEON 481

-80°

1029 1030 1032 VOLANS 493

503

511

-90°

MILLENNIUM STAR ATLAS

Key to Southern Half of Volume II
Right Ascension 8h to 16h
Declination 0° to −90°

CARTOGRAPHY *The charts for this atlas were prepared electronically on a Sigma Tech Pentium System using Borland Turbo Basic. Final adjustments were made in Adobe Illustrator and the book was composed in QuarkXPress on a Power Macintosh computer system.*

PREPRESS *Electronic preparation was carried out by Dartmouth Publishing, Inc., Watertown, Massachusetts, and World Color Book Services, Taunton, Massachusetts.*

PRINTING *The atlas was printed at World Color Book Services on a Cottrell web press, using direct-to-plate technology.*

PAPER *The book paper is Finch Fine 70# text stock, manufactured by Finch, Pruyn, & Co., Glens Falls, New York, and supplied by Pratt Paper Company, Boston, Massachusetts. The endleaf stock is Multicolor Slate Blue from Permalin Products, New York, New York.*

BINDING *Binding and slipcase manufacture were handled by World Color Book Services. The material is Skivertex Ubonga.*

TYPEFACES *The typefaces used are Galliard text with Mantinia display, designed by Matthew Carter. Helvetica, designed by M. Miedinger, is used in the charts, diagrams, and graphs.*

BOOK DESIGN *Typography, binding, and slipcase design are by Christopher Kuntze.*